Black's 1997 WING & CLAY

is really three easy-to-use directories in one.

Go right to the directory you want or turn the page to find detailed information about each.

PUBLISHING STAFF

James F. Black	*Publisher*
Raymond Goydon	*Sr. Associate Publisher*
Lois Ré	*Editor*
Amanda Santos	*Associate Publisher*
Ann N. Edmonds	*Associate Publisher*
David G. Hanson	*Copywriter*
Glenn J.J. Davidson	*Database Support*
Cover Design:	Guerry Associates Middletown, NJ

EQUIPMENT

Easy-access information about companies and individuals providing shotgun related products & services worldwide.

1,292 company profiles in 53 sections.

Begins on page 84

INSTRUCTION

A reference guide to shotgun shooting schools, and clinics across the U.S.

64 schools and hundreds of clinics

Begins on page 202

DESTINATIONS

An easy-to-use guide to hunting and shooting destinations. Wingshooting travel & booking agents, too.

1,279 hunting destinations and 1,694 sporting clays, trap & skeet clubs, state-by-state

Begins on page 268

CONTENTS

CHARTS & DIAGRAMS

O FF

THE BEATEN TRACK

OUR REPUTATION IS FOUNDED UPON UNSTINTING DEVOTION TO INNOVATION AND OUTSTANDING CRAFTSMANSHIP. SINCE 1835, THIS PROUD HERITAGE HAS NURTURED THE ENTIRE WORLD OF HOLLAND & HOLLAND — INSPIRING US TO CREATE ITEMS OF UNSURPASSED REFINEMENT. THE FINEST TRADITIONAL MATERIALS, THE WORKMANSHIP OF SKILLED HANDS AND AN EXACTING ATTENTION TO DETAIL AND DESIGN FIND EXPRESSION IN A UNIQUE COLLECTION FOR THE OUTDOOR WAY OF LIFE — ALL CELEBRATING THE DISTINGUISHED LINEAGE OF HOLLAND & HOLLAND. FOR MORE INFORMATION PLEASE CALL 212-752-7755.

HOLLAND & HOLLAND

Established London 1835

50 EAST 57TH STREET, NEW YORK, N.Y. 10022

IN THE COUNTRY, REFINEMENT STILL COMES WITH A DOUBLE-BARRELLED NAME

EQUIPMENT

A Word of Thanks The publication of Wing & Clay would not be possible without the support of hundreds of companies and individuals. Though it would be impossible to thank each and every one in this limited space, the publisher would be remiss in not singling out Al Anglace, CTSCA; David Bopp, ATA; Larry Cero, Hunters Pointe; Fred Collins, SCA; Alan Kelly, Orvis Endorsed Wingshooting Lodge Program; Charles P. Kallfelz, NESCA; Mike Hampton, NSCA and NSSA; Sue King, WSSF; Bill Kinsala, Americase; Dave Lyon, Buick; Peggy Mullin-Boehmer & John Mullin, Wildlife Harvest; Doug Painter, NSSF; Gary Rogers, UST; Dick Welch, Griffin & Howe. To all, a sincere thank you. And a special thanks to Susan Bernard, Bernard & Associates.

3,644 WAYS TO PREPARE STUFFED SHELLS.

To get your free copy of the latest *Reloaders' Guide,* stop by your local dealer or write: Alliant Techsystems, Inc., Smokeless Powder Group, 200 Valley Road, Suite 305, Mt. Arlington, NJ 07856-1320. Or call us at 1-800-276-9337.

ALLIANT POWDER®
(FORMERLY HERCULES POWDER)

INSTRUCTION

DESTINATIONS

Simply the best!

Diamond J, MT★   ★Eagle Nest, MT   ★Woodmoor, MI
Big Bend, SD★   • Mille Lacs, MN
• Forester Ranches, SD
★The Huntsman, MI
Falcon's Ledge, UT •   • Upland Hunts, NE
Rock Springs, CA★   Jayhawk Outfitting, KS★   Primland, VA ★
Grassy Lake Lodge, KY★
★Six Runs, NC
Rancho El Palomar, Mexico •   Live Oak, GA★ ★The Lodge at Cabin Bluff, GA
★Shirahland, GA
★Bienville, FL
★Argentina Estancias, Argentina
• Herradura Ranch, TX

ORVIS® ENDORSED WINGSHOOTING LODGES

The Wingshooting Destinations

When you're looking for wingshooting that's truly outstanding, depend on an Orvis Endorsed Lodge. Only 21 lodges in the entire world meet our rigid criteria for all-around excellence. . . your best guarantee of a memorable sporting experience.

An Orvis Endorsed Lodge has been evaluated for bird quality and habitat, guide and dog-handler skills, dog quality, processing and packaging of birds taken by hunters, and the total bird-hunting experience. Equally important, an Orvis Endorsed Lodge has met the most demanding standards for comfort, dining, social amenities and personal service.

Orvis is proud to endorse the following wing-shooting lodges. When you want the finest that wingshooting offers, they're destinations well worth special efforts to visit.

For more information about these lodges, see their listings and advertisements in the WINGS or Travel destination section of this book:

Argentina Estancias, *see ad in Travel*
Bienville Plantation, *see ad in Florida*
Big Bend, *see ads in South Dakota*
Diamond J Ranch, *see ad in Montana*
Eagle Nest Lodge, *see ad in Montana*
Forester Ranches Lodge, *see listing in So. Dakota*
Herradura Ranch, *see listing in Texas*
Falcon's Ledge, *see listing in Utah*
Grassy Lake Lodge, *see ad in Kentucky*
The Huntsman Hunt Club, *see ad in Michigan*
Jayhawk Outfitting, *see ad in Kansas*
Live Oak Plantation, *see ad in Georgia*
The Lodge At Cabin Bluff, *see ad in Georgia*
Mille Lacs Hunting Lodge, *see listings in Minn.*
Primland Hunting Reserve, *see ad in Virginia*
Rancho El Palomar, *see listing in Mexico*
Rock Springs Ranch, *see ads in California*
Shirahland Plantation, *see ad in Georgia*
Six Runs Plantation, *see ad in North Carolina*
Upland Hunts, *see listing in Nebraska*
Woodmoor, *see ad in Michigan*

Orvis® Endorsed Wingshooting Lodges. Simply the best.

For more information about Orvis® Endorsed Wingshooting Lodge Program call 800-778-4778

You've just smoked your 39th bird in a row. And they're staring at you. Hard. Since when did you become a marksman? Same gun. Same shells. As they scratch their heads you ask yourself, shouldn't I tell them about my Scopz™? About the Zeiss prescription lenses that eliminate glare? About the adjustable bridge that gives me a full field of view? About the recoil-resistant hinges that keep the glasses in place? They are, after all, my friends.

THE SHOTGUNNER'S SOURCE

A FEW FACTS ABOUT SHOTGUNS

Before you buy and shoot a shotgun you should understand the equipment you're shooting with: how it works, how to care for it and how to handle it safely. Today's shotgun is a high quality instrument designed to function flawlessly year after year. Understand your gun. Handle it safely. And the sport of shotgunning will offer a lifetime of enjoyment. (Note: Terms appearing in *italicized* type below may be found on the accompanying illustrations or defined in the Shotgunning Terms section.)

A Basic Distinction

Other types of firearms fire single projectiles. The shotgun, with one exception, fires a number of projectiles--from 45 to almost 1,170—called *shot* . The shot begins to spread as soon as it is discharged from the gun's *muzzle*. Obviously, the area the shot covers--the *shot pattern*--increases as the shot moves away from the gun and towards the target. This explains why the shotgun rather than the single projectile rifle is preferred for shooting a moving target.

Most shotguns have a constriction, or *choke*, at the muzzle that controls the shot pattern. The tighter the constriction, the greater the effective range of the shot. Many shotguns have changeable chokes that allow the gun's shot pattern to be customized for different situations.

The Right Gun

Choosing the right shotgun can be an intimidating experience for the new shooter. Doing a little homework can make it less so: Read as much as you can about shotgunning in general and about specific manufacturers; also, seek the advice of an experienced shooter or a shotgun professional before you make a purchase.

Here are some basics to get you started: There are three basic types of shotgun used today: the *pump*, the *hinge*--most often double-barreled guns in either a *side by side* or *over and under* configuration--and the *semiautomatic*. The *action*, or the moving parts that allow you to load, fire and unload the shotgun, are different in each type.

Shotguns are further distinguished by the length of their barrels--usually 26 to 30 inches long, and their diameter, or *bore*, which varies according to the gun's design and intended use. The size of the bore is indicated by the term *gauge*: the smaller the gauge number, the larger the bore size. Modern shotguns are available in 10, 12, 16, 20, and 28 gauge. An exception is the .410 bore shotgun, which is actually a 67 gauge.

Which gauge is right for you? Unfortunately, there's no easy answer to that question. To a great extent it depends on you and the primary type of shooting you'll be doing. In the long run, if you're like most shooters, you'll end up owning two or more shotguns of various gauges.

A Word About Fit

Much of what is said today about gun fit is highly technical and not particularly helpful to the novice. The essential point is this: Proper fit depends largely on the length of the gun's *stock*. And most manufacturers tailor their gunstocks to fit the average size adult. So, if you're more or less an average size shooter, an off the shelf shotgun will provide a more-or-less average fit. Shorter or taller shooters --especially youngsters--usually require some stock adjustments, which should be done by a competent gunsmith.

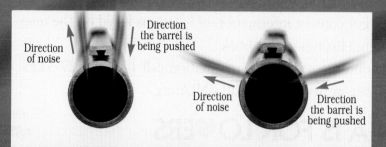

In addition to the excellent fee hunting areas in Virginia, 29 state owned Wildlife Management areas and more than 1.7 million acres of National Forest land are accessible for public hunting.

For additional information on state and national lands, contact the Virginia Department of Game & Inland Fisheries at (804)367-9369 or the George Washington and Jefferson National Forests at (540)265-5100. For contact information of locations listed on the map turn to the Virginia listings in this book.

For Virginia outdoor adventure information call 1-(800)-827-3325, or visit our web site at http://www.VIRGINIA.org.

VIRGINIA IS FOR LOVERS™

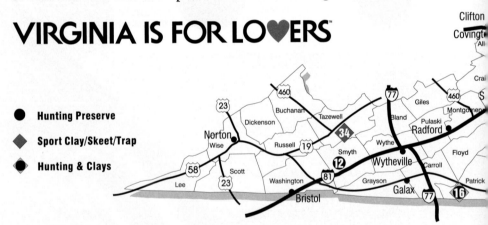

● Hunting Preserve

◆ Sport Clay/Skeet/Trap

◆ Hunting & Clays

Hunting Preserve
1 Buffalo Creek Sporting Club
2 Charles City Hunting Preserve
3 Christmas Hill Game Preserve
4 Eastern Shore Safaris
5 Falkland Farms
6 Feathers-Fur & Fin Kennels
7 Forest Green Shooting Preserve
8 Jonakin Creek Hunt Club
9 King Kennels & Shooting Preserve
10 Magnolia Shooting Preserve
11 Merrimac Farm Hunting Preserve
12 Mountain Empire Quail Ranch
13 Old Coppermine Hunting Preserve
14 Orapax Plantation
15 Plain Dealing Hunting Preserve

16 Primland
17 Red Oak Ranch-Virginia Upland Outfit
18 Sandy Point Recreational Park
19 Shady Grove Kennel & Hunting Preserve
20 Sundance Hunting Preserve, Inc.
21 Sussex Shooting Sports
22 Walnut Run Shooting Preserve
23 Windwood Farm

Sport Clay
1 Buffalo Creek Sporting Club
24 Bull Run Shooting Center
25 Cavalier Sporting Clays
2 Charles City Sporting Clays & Hunting
26 Cumberland State Forest
4 Eastern Shore Safaris

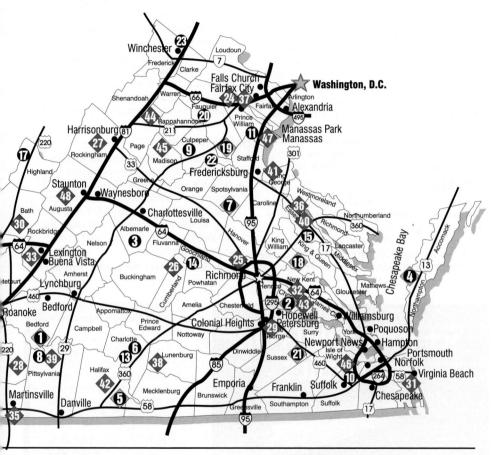

5	Falkland Farms	**Skeet/Trap**	
27	Flying Rabbit	**37**	Arlington Fairfax Izaak Walton
7	Forest Green Shooting	**38**	Arrowhead Gun Club
28	Franklin Skeet & Trap Club	**39**	Brushy Mountain Club, Inc.
29	Ft. Lee Skeet & Trap Ranges	**40**	Dunbrooke Hunt Gun Club
30	The Homestead	**41**	Fredericksburg Rod & Gun Club
31	Oceana Skeet & Trap	**42**	Halifax County Gun Club
32	Old Forge Sporting Clays	**43**	Izaak Walton S&T Club
16	Primland	**44**	Page Valley Sportsmens Club
18	Sandy Point Recreational Park	**45**	Piedmont Sportsman Club
19	Shady Grove Kennel & Hunting Preserve	**46**	Portsmouth-Norfolk Co. Izaak
33	Quail Ridge Sporting Clays	**47**	Quantico Shooting Club
21	Sussex Shooting Sports	**48**	Shenandale Gun Club
34	Thompson Valley		
35	Virginia-Carolina Shooting		
36	Walnut Hill Shooting Center		

SHOTGUN SAFETY

It's Largely Common Sense

Imagine that firearms have just been invented, and you're one of the first to be introduced to the shotgun. What precautions would you take to avoid accidental injury to humans or animals, or accidental damage to objects? What, in other words, would common sense suggest?

Because that's what safe shotgun handling and shooting largely consists of. Good old common sense, applied over and over and over again until it becomes pure instinct. And if you're an old pro to whom safety rules are second nature, why not review them anyway? Like chicken soup, if it doesn't help, it couldn't hurt. And the few minutes you spend could keep you from getting careless or falling into bad habits.

Safe Handling

In simplest terms, safe handling of your shotgun is whatever prevents you from firing accidentally, or prevents injury or damage if such a discharge does occur:

- Keep the muzzle pointed in a safe direction. Never point the muzzle at any person, animal or object you don't intend to shoot. The safest directions: upward, or toward the ground (but not toward your foot).

- Keep your finger off the trigger. Fight the natural tendency to put your finger on the trigger when you hold a shotgun. If you must curl it around something, use the trigger guard. The only time your finger should touch the trigger is when you're ready to shoot.

- Keep the gun unloaded, with the action open. Make it a reflex to open the action and check the chamber whenever you pick up a shotgun. And keep the gun empty and open until you're ready to use it.

Safe Shooting

Like safe handling, safe shooting depends on– you guessed it– common sense:

- Know your shotgun. Familiarity with your gun's basic parts and how they function is a prerequisite for safe shooting. Know how to open and close the action, for example, and how to remove ammunition.

- Don't depend on the safety. This may

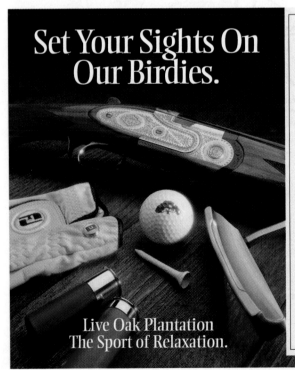

be the cardinal rule of safe shooting. Remember, the safety is a mechanical device and it can malfunction. The safety is not a replacement for safe handling and shooting practices.

- Make sure gun and ammunition match. If there is any question about compatibility between shot shell and gun, don't fire! The gauge of the shell must match the gauge of the shotgun. The gauge of the gun is likely to be stamped on the barrel. The gauge of the shell will be indicated on the box, and on each shell.

- Don't carry shells of mixed gauge. Whenever you're through shooting, immediately remove unfired shells from your clothing. It's a good way to avoid mixing ammunition. The drawings that follow illustrate the explosive—and potentially disastrous— effect of placing both a 20 and a 12 gauge shell in the same gun. Remember your fingers would have been placed directly over the blown out portion of the forearm!

Mixed Shells in Chamber

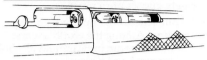

Disastrous Results!

- Be sure before you shoot. If you're not absolutely certain that you've identified your target, don't shoot! And be equally aware of what's beyond your target. If it's another person, or an object that shouldn't be hit— no matter how far—don't shoot!

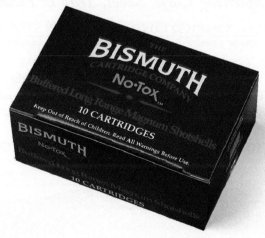

- Protect your eyes and ears. Guns make noise. Noise affects your hearing. Guns also emit debris and gases that can injure your eyes. Ear protectors and safety glasses are a must.
- If your senses are impaired, don't go shooting! Among the world's worst combinations are firearms and alcohol, and firearms and drugs.
- Don't run the risk of a clogged barrel. Barrel obstructions can cause gun bursts. If you've stumbled and jabbed the barrel into the ground, or crawled to surprise your quarry, unload and check the barrel for mud or snow.
- Don't rest your gun on your feet to keep it out of mud or snow.

Field Etiquette

Etiquette is just good manners. In shooting, etiquette also introduces another element of safety. Practice shooting etiquette in the field and you'll be a safe— and a popular— shooting companion.

- Never shoot across another shooter.
- Don't interfere with another hunter's dog. Period!
- Never put your gun off safety until game has flushed.
- Don't shoot if a dog is directly behind low flying birds.
- Make sure every member of your is wearing an article of blaze orange clothing.
- Agree prior to going into field what are the safe zones of fire.
- Always maintain a "straight line" when hunting with a partner and/or guide.
- If you don't know where your partner and guide are, don't shoot!

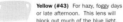

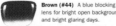

THE MAIN PARTS OF AN OVER-AND-UNDER SHOTGUN

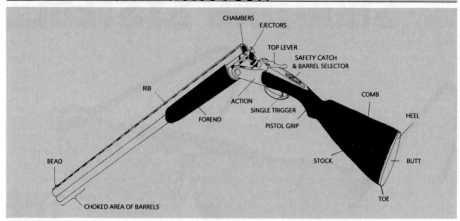

BASIC SHOTGUN STOCK GRIPS AND FOREND STYLES

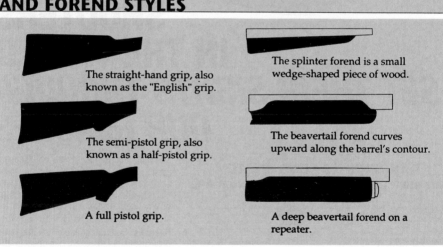

The straight-hand grip, also known as the "English" grip.

The semi-pistol grip, also known as a half-pistol grip.

A full pistol grip.

The splinter forend is a small wedge-shaped piece of wood.

The beavertail forend curves upward along the barrel's contour.

A deep beavertail forend on a repeater.

SHOTGUN RIB STYLES

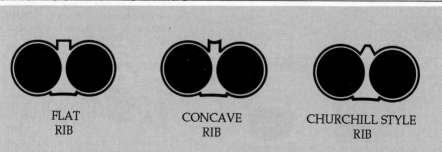

FLAT RIB

CONCAVE RIB

CHURCHILL STYLE RIB

SHOTGUN ACTIONS

BREAK ACTION, over-and-under, double barrel

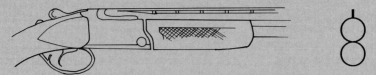

BREAK ACTION, side-by-side, double barrel

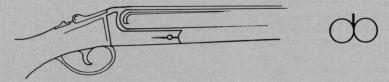

PUMP ACTION, single barrel repeater

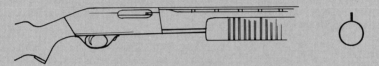

SEMI-AUTOMATIC ACTION, single barrel repeater

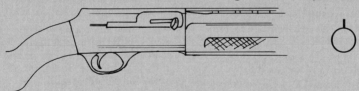

STANDARD BORE DIAMETERS

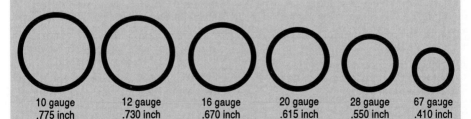

10 gauge	12 gauge	16 gauge	20 gauge	28 gauge	67 gauge
.775 inch	.730 inch	.670 inch	.615 inch	.550 inch	.410 inch

(subject to variations of a few thousandths of an inch under manufacturing tolerances)

SHOTGUN TERMS

action - the moving parts that allow you to load, fire and unload your shotgun. (See Breech, Chamber, Trigger)

barrel selector - detemines which barrel of a double barrel gun will fire first.

blacking/blueing - the blue coloration applied to protect gun barrels.

bore - in simple terms the interior diameter of a gun barrel, which will vary according to the gun's design and intended use. The size of the bore is indicated by the term gauge. Also someone who goes on interminably about shooting to the exclusion of all other subjects.

box-lock - a type of gun action, often recognizeable by its squared appearance.

breech - the end of the barrel nearest the stock.

broken gun - in a hinge type gun, where the barrels are dropped open and clear of the action, exposing the chambers to view.

butt - the rear of the shoulder end of the gun's stock.

comb - the side of the stock that fits against your cheek.

chamber - the part of the action, at the breech end of the barrel, into which the shot shell is placed.

choke - the degree of narrowing or constriction of the bore at the muzzel end of the barrel, intended to increase the effective range of the gun. (See Full, Modified, and Improved Cylinder)

ejector - the mechanism on shotguns by which spent shot cases are automatically ejected from the gun when it is opened after firing.

forearm - the part of the stock that lies under the barrel.

full choke - the tightest constriction or narrowing of the bore, producing the greatest effective range.

grip - the narrow portion of the stock held with the trigger hand.

gauge - the term used to describe the interior diameter of the bore. The smaller the gauge number, the larger the bore size. Modern shotguns are available in 10, 12, 16, 20 and 28 gauge. An exception is the .410

bore shotgun, which is actually a 67 gauge.

hinge - a type of action in which a hinge mechanism separates the barrel from the standing breech block, providing access to the chamber.

improved cylinder - Least constricted or narrowed choke causing shot pattern to widen relatively quickly.

modified choke - moderate constriction or narrowing of the bore.

muzzle - the end of the barrel from which the shot exits.

over-and-under - a two-barrelled shotgun with one barrel placed over the other. (The American version of the standard British game shooting weapon.)

pump - a type of action that loads and ejects shells by "pumping" the forearm of the stock back and forth.

recoil - force with which the gun moves backwards into the shoulder when fired.

safety - a safety device that, in the "on" position, prevents the gun from firing. In many field guns the safety is automatically engaged when the gun is opened; in other guns, particularly competition grades, the safety must be manually engaged.

semi automatic - a type of action in which gas from the burning gunpowder in the shell automatically ejects the spent shell and loads another. Semi-automatics are noted for minimal recoil.

shot - round projectiles, usually of lead or steel. Depending on shot size and load, a shell can contain from 45 to 1,170 shot.

shot pattern - The concentration of shot measured in a circle at a given range, usually 30 to 40 yards.

side-by-side - a shotgun with two barrels sitting side by side. In Great Britain, the standard game shooting weapon.

stock - The "handle" of the shotgun, the part held to the shoulder, comprising the butt, comb, grip and forearm.

shotshell or *shell* - the ammunition fired by shotguns, consisting of five components: the case, primer, powder charge, wad, and shot.

trigger - finger-pulled lever--single, double and release-- that drives the firing point forward and fires the gun.

SHOTGUN TRADE NAMES & MANUFACTURERS

Know the gun or trade name but not the company that manufactures, imports or distributes it? The index below may help. Find the name in the *Gun* column and across from it you'll find the name of the company—or companies—that can provide you with the information you need. You'll find detailed listings on each of these companies organized alphabetically in the directory section that follows.

Gun	Manufacturer/Importer	Gun	Manufacturer/Importer
AYA	Armes de Chasse	Holland & Holland	Holland & Holland, Sporting Weapons, Ltd.
Abbiatico & Salvinelli	Southwest Shooters Supply		
American Arms	American Arms, Inc.	IGA	Stoeger Industries
Armas "Azor"	Armes de Chasse	Kemen	Kemen America
Arrieta	Griffin & Howe	Kolar	Kolar Arms
	Quality Arms, Inc.	Krieghoff	Krieghoff International, Inc.
	New England Arms Co.	Charles Lancaster	Lewis Drake & Assoc.
	Orvis	Ljutic	Ljutic Industries, Inc.
	Jack. J. Jansma	Marocchi	Precision Sales Int'l., Inc.
Asprey	The Asprey Gun Room	Maverick by Mossberg	Maverick Arms, Inc.
Baikal	K.B.I., Inc.	McKay Brown	Griffin & Howe
Benelli	Heckler & Koch, Inc.	Merkel	G.S.I., Inc.
Beretta	Beretta U.S.A.	Mossberg	O.F. Mossberg & Sons
Bernardelli	Armsport, Inc.	Perazzi	Perazzi USA, Inc.
Bertuzzi	New England Arms Co.	Piotti	William L. Moore & Co.
Boss	Boss & Co., Ltd.	William Powell	William Powell & Son, Ltd.
Brno Arms	Bohemia Arms	Purdey	James Purdey & Sons, Ltd.
Browning	Browning	Remington	Remington Arms Co., Inc.
CVC Classic Sporter	Connecticut Valley Classics, Inc.	B. Rizzini	William L. Moore & Co. New England Arms Co.
Chapuis Armes	Chapuis Armes	F. lli Rizzini	William L. Moore & Co. New England Arms Co.
Churchill	E.J. Churchill Gunmakers	John Rigby	John Rigby & Co.
Cole	Cole Arms, Inc.	Rottweil Paragon	Dynamit-Nobel/RWS, Inc.
Dakota American Legend	Dakota Arms	Ruger	Sturm, Ruger & Co.
Charles Daly	Outdoor Sports Headquarters, Inc.	J&L Rutten	Labanu, Inc.
		SKB	SKB Shotguns
John Dickson	John Dickson & Son	Savage	Savage Arms, Inc.
William Evans	William Evans	Silma	Century Int'l. Arms, Inc. Keng's Firearms
Fabbri	Fabbri snc		
Ferlib	New England Arms Co.	Sky Stalker	Sile Distributors, Inc.
A.H. Fox	Connecticut Shotgun Manufacturing Co.	Symes & Wright	Symes & Wright, Ltd.
		Tikka	Stoeger Industries
Franchi	American Arms, Inc.	Tristar	Tristar Sporting Arms, Ltd.
Francotte	Armes de Chasse	Ugartechea	Bill Hanus Birdguns
A. Galazan	Connecticut Shotgun Mfg. Co.	Watson	Watson Bros.
Renato Gamba	Gamba U.S.A.	Weatherby	Weatherby
Garbi	William L. Moore & Co.	Westley Richards	Westley Richards & Co.
Harrington & Richardson	H & R 1871, Inc.	Winchester	U.S. Repeating Arms Co.
Hatfield	Hatfield Gun Co., Inc.	Winchester Model 21	Connecticut Shotgun Mfg. Co.
Hawk	DBD Enterprises, Inc.	Zoli	Antonio Zoli
		Zanotti	New England Arms Co.

SHOTGUN MANUFACTURERS/IMPORTERS

 American Arms, Inc.
"A Step Ahead"

American Arms, Inc.
715 Armour Rd.
N. Kansas City, MO 64116
(816) 474-3161
FAX: (816) 474-1225
Est.: 1982   Staff: 16
Contact: Guy Avedisian
Manufactured in: Italy & Spain
Price Range: $499 to $2,798 & custom guns to $21,000 SxS - boxlock and side lock actions, entry level to custom grades. O/U - all gauges; hunting competition, specialty 10 & 12 ga. 3 1/2", entry level to professional/competition grade. Exclusive United States importer for Franchi shotguns. Also Uberti lever action rifles, single action revolvers. New offerings include express rifle & rifle/shotgun combo.
See Our Ad Pgs. 27 & 30

ARMES DE CHASSE

Armes de Chasse
Box 86, Hartford, NC 27944
(919) 426-2245
FAX: (919) 426-1557
Est.: 1982   Staff: 3
Mktg. Mgr: Art Foley
Available: Retail & Direct
Price Range: $3,000 & Up
Auguste Francotte - Belgium;
Aguirre Y Aranzabal-Spain; Armas "Azor"-Spain
See Our Ad Below

Armsport, Inc.
3590 NW 49th St.,Miami, FL 33142
(305) 635-7850
FAX: (305) 633-2877
Est.: 1974   Staff: 8
Contact: Paul Bines
Available: Retail
Manufactured in: Italy
Price Range: $1,300 to $2,800
Importer of shotguns from Bernardelli, Rizzini and Lumar from

Italy. We also import lower priced over/unders and pump guns from Sarslimaz in Turkey. Protective snap caps from Italy.

Arrieta, S.L.
5 Barrio Ursandi
E-20870 Elgoibar, Spain
FAX: 011-34-43-74-3154
Available: Retail
Manufactured in: Spain
Importers: Griffin & Howe, New York, NY (212) 921-0980 and Bernardsville, NJ (908) 766-2287; Jack J. Jansma, Grand Rapids, MI (616) 455-7810; New England Arms Co., Kittery Point, ME (207) 439-0593; Quality Arms, Houston, TX (713) 870-8377.

The Asprey Gun Room
23 Albemarle St.
London, W1Y 0AR, England
011-44-171-493-6767 Ext. 2300
FAX: 011-44-171-917-8083
Est: 1990
Mgr: William Asprey
Available: Direct
Manufactured in: England
Side by Side shotguns available in

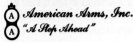

12 gauge to .410. Also double rifles and bolt rifles, in all calibers. Sporting clothing and accessories.

Beretta U.S.A.
17601 Beretta Dr.,
Accokeek, MD 20607
(301) 283-2191
Est.: 1977   Staff: 520
Exec. VP: Robert Bonaventure
Mktg: Rafael Aguirre-Sacasa
Available: Retail
O/U and Semi-Automatic Competition Shotguns and Field Guns. Pistols, knives, gun cases, Beretta Sport clothing and accessories.
See Our Ad Across

V. Bernardelli s.p.a.
Via Matteotti 125, PO Box 74
125063 Gardone V.T. (Brescia)
Italy 25063
011-39-30-891-2851
FAX: 011-39-30-891-0249
Commercial Mgr: Pino Benetti
S/S and Over/Under shotguns for hunting and sport.

Big Bear Arms & Sporting Goods
1112 Milam Way
Carrollton, TX 75006
(800) 400-2327
(214) 416-1359
FAX: (214) 416-0771
Est.: 1988   Staff: 6
President: Berg Boghossian
Gen. Mgr: Forrest William
Manufactured in: Russia
Price Range: $299 to $2,000

Bohemia Arms International
17101 Los Modelos
Fountain Valley, CA 92708
(714) 963-0809
FAX: (714) 963-0809
Available: Direct
Manufactured in: Czech Republic
Importer of the Brno Arms O/U and SxS Shotguns.

Boss & Co., Ltd.
Gun and Rifle Makers
13 Dover St.
London, W1X 3PH England
011-44-171-493-1127
Est.: 1812
Phone/Fax: 011-44-171-493-0711
Managing Dir: T.M. Robertson
Available: Direct
Manufactured in: England
Side by Side; available in 12, 20, 28 gauge and .410. Over and Under; available in 12, 20, 28 gauge & .410.

British Sporting Arms Ltd.
RR1, Box 193A
Millbrook, NY 12545
(914) 677-8303
Est.: 1988
Contact: Charles Schneible
Available: Retail & Direct
Specializing in sporting clays guns; the European Spec. B325 Browning, the Belgium made B25 Browning and fine English apparel and gifts. Retail Store.

Browning
One Browning Place
Morgan, UT 84050
(800) 333-3288 (Customer)
(801) 876-2711 (General)
Est.: 1878   Staff: 350
Available: Retail
Offers sporting clays, and skeet over/unders, new BT-100 single barrel trap and Gold Sporting Clays semi-auto. Complete line sporting firearms, gun accessories, gun safes, gun cases, knives, footwear, clothing and archery equipment for the outdoor enthusiast.
See Our Ad Pg. 31

Century International Arms, Inc.
PO Box 714, 5 Lemnah Dr.
St. Albans, VT 05478
(802) 527-1258
FAX: (802) 524-4922
Est.: 1949   Staff: 180

How Can Guns That Look So Good Be So Tough?

ntroducing Beretta's New Gold Series: Trap, Skeet & Sporting Clays Models with Our Exclusive Greystone Finish to Last a Lifetime.

Beretta's new Gold Series was named to commemorate the over 60 Gold Medals Beretta shooters have won in international competition during the past twenty years. But these guns would be standouts by any name–as your first glance will promptly confirm.

Beretta's Gold Series – Two Interpretations Of The Perfect Competition Shotgun

682 Gold Series
True competition guns, the 682's are available in over 32 models for skeet, trap and sporting clays. Each features replaceable hinge pins and barrel shoulders; neutral and RH trigger shoes and a trigger system that's adjustable for length-of-pull fit. Your choice of fixed or Mobilchoke® screw-in choke system. Stocks and fore-ends are available in left and right handed configurations with the Beretta stock removal system. Hard case included.

In place of the predictable blued finish found on most guns, the Beretta Gold Series is treated with an advanced ionic deposition process which impregnates and hardens the receiver. The result: "Greystone", a rich, lustrous finish that's as durable as the Beretta name behind it.

ASE Gold Series
All ASE Gold guns are built to the same quality standards as SO guns, but with box lock actions, Beretta's removable trigger group system, cross bolt lock-up, full 10mm competition ventilated top rib and ventilated side ribs. Available with fixed or Mobilchoke® choke system in a variety of barrel lengths. Hard case included.

Eye-pleasing in the extreme, Gold Series guns are, nevertheless, much more than merely a styling tour de force. They are the perfect blend of form and function into two disparate expressions of the gunmakers' art–each totally satisfying, each unmistakably unique.

The Gold Series retains Beretta's centuries-old tradition of nearly indestructible dependability and superior "pointability" while adding remarkably effective advances in metallurgy.

The new Competition Gold Series from Beretta: guns that look great, perform great and stay great for a lifetime. To select yours, see your Beretta dealer or contact: Beretta U.S.A. Corp, 17601 Beretta Drive, Accokeek, MD 20607, (301) 283-2191.

Beretta U.S.A.
NOBODY ELSE GIVES YOU MORE WAYS TO WIN.

When in New York, visit the Beretta Gallery at 718 Madison Avenue. For your copy of the 1996 Beretta Worldwide catalog, call 1-800-528-7453. ($3.00 shipping and handling.)

Marketing: Steve Kehaya
Available: Retail
Manufactured in: Italy
Importers of: Silma Shotgun (12 ga.)-Italy; Russian TOZ-34P (12 ga.)-Russia

Chapuis Armes
Z.I. La Gravoux, B.P. 15
St. Bonnet-le-Chateau, 42380 France
011-33-77-500696
FAX: 011-33-77-501070
Contact: Rene Chapius
Available: Direct
Price Range: Contact directly for price quote
High quality SxS and O/U shotguns. Manufactured on a limited basis.

E.J. Churchill Gunmakers, Ltd.
Ockley Rd., Beare Green,
Dorking, Surrey RH5 4PU England
011-44-1306-711435
Manufactured in: England
Side-by-side shotguns with custom features

Cole Arms, Inc.
2225 Pinehurst
McMinnville, OR 97128
(503) 472-8539
FAX: (503) 472-4600
President: Bill Cole
Manufactured in: USA

Price Range: $7,795 to $18,000
Manufacture custom single barrel trap guns. 3 basic models and custom guns available.

Connecticut Shotgun Manufacturing Co.
PO Box 1692
New Britain, CT 06051-1692
(203) 225-6581
FAX: (203) 832-8707
Contact: Dick Perrett
Available: Retail & Direct
Manufacturer of shotguns in the United States:
- A.H. Fox side by side in 4 gauges: 16, 20, 28 and .410. Five grades available. The A.H. Fox guns are priced from $9,500.
- Winchester Model 21 built to order in conjunction with US Repeating Arms. Also, factory repair and parts.
- A GALAZAN full sidelock over & under shotgun in any gauge (12, 16, 20, 28, .410), priced from $35,000.
See Our Ad Pg. 43

Connecticut Valley Classics, Inc.
650 New Ludlow Rd.
So. Hadley, MA 01075
(413) 552-3184
FAX: (413) 552-3276
Est.: 1991   Staff: 10
Contact: Dean Jendsen
Available: Retail
Price Range: $2,995 and up
High quality US made double barreled shotguns. Sporting clays and field models. Gun line available to retailers and gun club pro-shops seeking to build franchise in high grade shotguns. Manufacturing being expanded to increase availability and offer various custom features. Call or write for catalog.

DBD Enterprises, Inc.
720 Elrod Rd.,Prescott, AZ 86304
(520) 445-0100
FAX: (520) 445-4668
Est.: 1992   Staff: 4
Contact: Steve Denning
Available: Retail
Manufactured in: China
Price Range: $175-$300
The Hawk 94 is designed after the famous 870 style pump action shotgun. This style of 12 gauge pump action shotgun has proven over the

Flying Saucers Shot Down by U.S. Fighter Pilot.

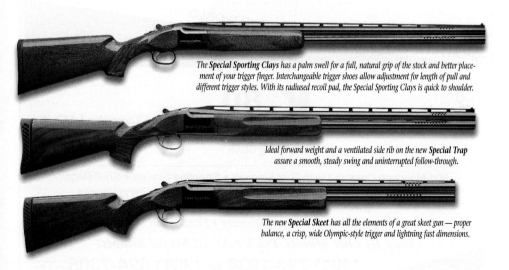

With the help of his Browning Special Sporting, U. S. Air Force Major, Bill Roy, has more "confirmed kills" than anyone in his ranks. Whether you prefer the lightning speed of skeet, the unpredictability of sporting clays, or the precision of trap, there's a "Special" Browning shotgun designed to bring out *your* best.

Browning Special shotguns give you the advantages you need to shoot and score better, like a high-post rib that puts your head high on the stock for a fast, unobstructed view of the target and keeps recoil off your face. With an optional adjustable comb you can easily customize drop, cast off and cast on. Invector-Plus™ choke tubes and back-bored barrels give you consistently uniform patterns and reduce felt recoil. Barrel porting is standard on all models.

Bill Roy, U.S. Fighter Pilot / Skeet Champion

Few can match U. S. Air Force Major, Bill Roy's shooting record.
- *1995 Captain of the All American International Skeet Team*
- *1994 National Championships Silver Medalist*
- *1994 U.S. Grand Prix Champion*
- *2-time NSSA World Champion*
- *Holder of 7 National and 3 World Records*
- *8-time U.S. Shooting Team Member*
- *1991 U.S. Shooting Team "Shotgun Shooter of the Year"*
- *10-time member of the Air Force Shooting Team*
- *Gold & Bronze medalist in Pan American Games*
- *U.S. Olympic Festival Gold medalist*

*The **Special Sporting Clays** has a palm swell for a full, natural grip of the stock and better placement of your trigger finger. Interchangeable trigger shoes allow adjustment for length of pull and different trigger styles. With its radiused recoil pad, the Special Sporting Clays is quick to shoulder.*

*Ideal forward weight and a ventilated side rib on the new **Special Trap** assure a smooth, steady swing and uninterrupted follow-through.*

*The new **Special Skeet** has all the elements of a great skeet gun — proper balance, a crisp, wide Olympic-style trigger and lightning fast dimensions.*

Visit your Browning dealer for a free 1995 Hunting & Shooting catalog *full of information on Browning firearms and accessories, clothing, boots, knives and gun safes. For $3.00 we'll send you a catalog by priority mail. Call 1-800-333-3504 to order by credit card, or send payment to Browning, Dept. C1, One Browning Place, Morgan, Utah 84050-9326. If you have questions on Browning products, please call 1-800-333-3288.*

THE BEST THERE IS.

years to be one of the most reliable and durable designs ever produced for sporting and law enforcement use. Very reasonably priced–these shotguns use the famous Winchoke style tube system.

Dakota Arms, Inc.
HC55, Box 326, Sturgis, SD 57785
(605) 347-4686
FAX: (605) 347-4459
Sales Mgr: Paulette Kok
Manufactured in: USA
Manufactures 3 grades of SxS: The American Legend (a limited edition); Premier and Classic grades. All grades weigh 6 lbs. and are offered in 20 gauge. A 12 gauge and 28/.410 gauge combination will follow.

John Dickson & Son
21 Frederick Street
Edinburgh EH2 2NE Scotland
011-44-131-225-4218
FAX: 011-44-131-225-3658
Est: 1820
Contact: Mr. Wight or Mr. Nelson
Available: Direct
Manufactured in: U.K.
Side by Side round action ejector; available in 12 and 20 gauge.

Lewis Drake & Associates
305 S. 8th St., Murray, KY 42071

(502) 436-5270
FAX: (502) 436-5257
Contact: Lewis Drake
Available: Direct
Manufactured in: England
Price Range: $30,000-$50,000
Charles Lancaster "twelve-twenty" is the lightest and strongest side by side ever made.

Dynamit Nobel

Dynamit-Nobel/RWS, Inc.
81 Ruckman Rd., PO Box 430
Closter, NJ 07624
(201) 767-1995
FAX: (201) 767-1589
Contact: Frank Turner
Available: Retail & Direct
Manufactured in: Germany
Importer of Rottweil Paragon shotgun (Germany) and Rottweil Brenneke slugs. Written inquiries welcome.

See Our Ad Across

William Evans Ltd.
67 a St. James's Street
London SW1A 1PH England
011-44-171-493-0415

Est.: 1883
Mgng. Dir: M. Gates Fleming
Available: Direct
Manufactured in: England
Side by Side; available in 12, 16, 20, 28 and .410 gauge. Over and Under; available in 12, 20, 28 and .410 gauge.

Fabbri snc
Via Dante Alighieri, 29
25062 Concesio (BS), Italy
011-39-30-275-2050
FAX: 011-39-30-275-2050
Manufactured in: Italy
Price Range: begin at $40,000

Fausti Cav. Stefano & Figlie s.n.c.
Via Martiri Dell'Indipendenza, 70 Marcheno V.T.
Italy 25060
011-39-30-8960217
011-39-30-8960220
FAX: 011-39-30-8610155
Made in: Italy
Over/under shotguns and SxS shotguns in all gauges.

G.S.I. Incorporated
108 Morrow Ave.,PO Box 129
Trussville, AL 35173
(205) 655-8299
FAX: (205) 655-7078
Est.: 1983

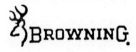

BENELLI
20 GAUGE LIMITED EDITION
LIGHTWEIGHT
FAST HANDLING
RELIABLE

An elite grade gun, the 20 gauge Limited Edition is manufactured using the finest materials available. The simple inertia operating system means dependable semi-automatic function and low recoil. The light weight nickel-plated receiver is finely etched with classic scrolling and game scenes, tastefully highlighted with gold. And its select grade walnut stock is drop adjustable for a custom fit. To put a Benelli Limited Edition shotgun in your hands, see your nearest authorized HK/Benelli dealer, or call (703) 450-1900.

HECKLER & KOCH, INC.
21480 Pacific Blvd.
Sterling, Virginia
20166 U.S.A.
Tel. (703) 450-1900

Sales Rep: Matt Bryant
Sales Rep: Ken Johnson
Sales Rep: Einar Hoff
Available: Retail
Manufactured in: Germany
US importer and service center featuring Merkel side by side and over and under shotguns, drillings and combinations guns. Traditional German quality, meticulous hand craftsmanship, exceptional value.

Gamba U.S.A.
The First National Gun Banque Corp.
PO Box 60452
Colorado Springs, CO 80960
(719) 578-1145
FAX: (719) 444-0731
Est.: 1989   Staff: 4
President: Karl C. Lippard
Available: Retail
Exclusive importer of Renato Gamba Firearm Line. O/U & SxS sporting guns in standard to highly engraved models. Factory warranty service.

Griffin & Howe

Griffin & Howe
36 W. 44th St., Suite 1011
New York, NY 10036
(212) 921-0980
Est.: 1923
Contact: Richard Welch
or
33 Claremont Rd.
Bernardsville, NJ 07924
(908) 766-2287
Contact: Joe Prather
Manufactured in: U.K.
Price Range: $5,750 & Up
The Griffin & Howe Round Body Game Gun, built by Arrieta, is a classic gun for the game shooter. Fitted to your dimensions and cased with accessories. Available in 12, 16, 20, 28 & .410 bore. Importers of McKay Brown shotguns.
See Our Ad Pg. 41

H&R 1871, Inc.
60 Industrial Rowe
Gardner, MA 01440
(508) 632-9393
FAX: (508) 632-2300
Est.: 1991   Staff: 270
VP/Sales & Mktg.: Robin Sharpless
Available: Retail
Manufactured in: USA
Price Range: $69 to $199
Single barrel single shot, shotguns including special models for deer (slug) hunting and turkey guns. From .410 to 10 ga. as well as eight distinct youth guns including

---

a 28 ga. We are the worlds largest producer of single barrel shotguns.

Bill Hanus Birdguns
PO Box 533
Newport, OR 97365
(541) 265-7433
Est.: 1988   Staff: 1
Developer and distributor of the legendary Bill Hanus Birdgun, Bill Hanus Classic and Bill Hanus Gamegun 16, 20 and 28 gauge side-by-side shotguns. Priced from about $1,500. Send stamped, self-addressed #10 envelope for complete product information.

Hatfield Gun Company, Inc.
224 North 4th St.
St. Joseph, MO 64501
(816) 279-8688
FAX: (816) 279-2716
Est.: 1981   Staff: 15
President: Ted Hatfield
C.F.O: Charles Roberts
Dir. of Mktg: Neil Oldridge
Available: Retail & Direct
Makers of Hatfield black powder rifles, uplander SxS shotguns and fine over and under shotguns.

Heckler & Koch, Inc.
21480 Pacific Blvd.
Sterling, VA 20166
(703) 450-1900
FAX: (703) 450-8160
Est.: 1976   Staff: 49
President: Steve Otway
VP: Jim Woods
Available: Retail
Heckler & Koch is the exclusive American distributor for Benelli semi-automatic shotguns, including the Super Black Eagle, the world's only 12 gauge semi-automatic that shoots 3-1/2 inch, 3 inch and 2-3/4 inch loads. HK's Benelli sales and support activities cover the full range of the Benelli shotgun line, more than forty different types, including shotguns for competition, hunting and defense.
Heckler & Koch is a significant force in the development and production of a wide range of technologically advanced firearms for sporting, defense and law enforcement use. Call or write for more information on Heckler & Koch's full range of products and services.
See Our Ads Left & Right

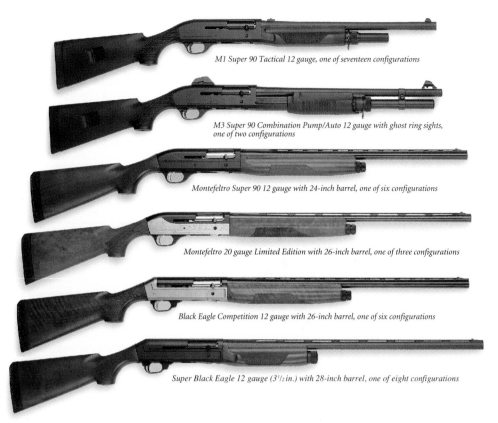

M1 Super 90 Tactical 12 gauge, one of seventeen configurations

*M3 Super 90 Combination Pump/Auto 12 gauge with ghost ring sights,
one of two configurations*

Montefeltro Super 90 12 gauge with 24-inch barrel, one of six configurations

Montefeltro 20 gauge Limited Edition with 26-inch barrel, one of three configurations

Black Eagle Competition 12 gauge with 26-inch barrel, one of six configurations

Super Black Eagle 12 gauge (3¹/₂ in.) with 28-inch barrel, one of eight configurations

The "bad" and the beautiful

With six models and more than forty different configurations, Benelli shotguns are made for *any* and *every* shooting need you have...sporting clays, trap, skeet, waterfowl, upland bird, turkey, deer, slug, and personal security.

All Benelli shotguns are based on the same field proven inertia recoil operating system—giving you the most reliable fast-firing, semiautomatic shotgun in the world.

Benelli shotguns function dependably with all standard 2¾* and 3 inch loads. And the Super Black Eagle model also fires 3½ shells, the only semi-automatic shotgun that can handle the full range of standard 3½ inch, 3 inch, and 2¾ inch 12 gauge loads.

* 1¹/₈ ounce load recommended for optimal functioning

To put a Benelli shotgun in your hands, see your authorized dealer. For more information and the location nearest you, call (703) 450-1900.

HECKLER & KOCH, INC.
21480 Pacific Boulevard
Sterling, Virginia 20166 U.S.A.

HOLLAND & HOLLAND
— *Established London 1885* —

Holland & Holland Sporting Weapons Limited
50 East 57th St.
New York, NY 10022
(212) 752-7755
FAX: (212) 752-6805
Contact: Gun Room
Makers of the famous side-by-side Royal shotguns and double rifles, as well as the new Royal Over & Under shotguns in calibers from 12 Ga. to .410 Ga. and the very successful Sporting Over & Under models in the 12 Ga. or 20 Ga. The Gun Room also has an excellent selection of second hand best London guns as well as new guns from other makers for every budget. Come visit us in the heart of New York City!

K.B.I., Inc.
3405 N. 6th St.
PO Box 5440
Harrisburg, PA 17110
(717) 540-8518
Est.: 1988   Staff: 7
VP/Sales: Steven M. Cohen
Available: Retail
Price Range: $110 to $20,000
Baikal, over/under, side by side and single barrels (Russia), Sabatti O/U's (Italy). Armscor pump action (Philippines).

Kemen America
Executive Office
2550 Hwy. 23
Wrenshall, MN 55797
(218) 384-3670
Contact: Pat LaBoone
See Ad Inside Front Cover

Keng's Firearms Specialty, Inc.
815 Wharton Dr.
Atlanta, GA 30336
(404) 691-7611
FAX: (404) 505-8445
Contact: Da Keng
Manufactured in: Italy
Price Range: $800
Importers of the Silma shotgun.

Kolar Arms
1925 Roosevelt Ave.
Racine, WI 53406
(414) 554-0800
Est.: 1968   Staff: 46
President: John Ramagli
Partner: Don Mainland
Available: Retail & Direct
Manufactured in: U.S.
Price Range: $6,400 & Up
New skeet, trap and sporting O/U

KRIEGHOFF
INTERNATIONAL

Krieghoff International, Inc.
7528 Easton Rd., PO Box 549
Ottsville, PA 18942
(610) 847-5173
Est.: 1985   Staff: 14
Chairman: Dieter Krieghoff
President: Jim Hollingsworth
Available: Retail
Manufactured in: Germany
Price Range: $3,600 & Up
Krieghoff International imports, distributes and provides factory service for K-80, KS-5 competition shotguns for trap, skeet and sporting clays.

See Our Ad Across

Labanu, Inc.
2201 F Fifth Ave.
Ronkonkoma, NY 11779
(516) 467-6197
FAX: (516) 981-4112
Est.: 1991   Staff: 6
VP: Hafiz Rahman
Available: Direct
Manufactured in: Belgium
Price Range: $1,195-$1,395
Importers of J&L Rutten of Herstal, Belgium. Available in 12 gauge-offering 2 models.

Lanber U.S.A.
Imported by ITC International
1720 Cumberland Point Dr.
Suite 5, Marietta, GA 30067
(770) 858-0048
FAX: (770) 858-0051
President: Jean Constantinides
Manufactured in: Spain
Price Range: $850 to $1,250 depending on options.
Imported by ITC International, Lanber Shotguns are manufactured by master craftsmen. Offering exceptional value, these premium quality firearms feature the exclusive Lanberchoke system to provide a consistent advantage in hunting or competitive shooting events. Both semi-automatic and over-and-under models are available. Phone or fax for a consultation.

Lebeau - Courally
Continental Firearms
Rue Saint - Gilles, 386, B-4000
Liege, Belgium   Est.: 1865
011-32-41-524843
011-32-41-520211
FAX: 011-32-41-522008
Director: Anne-Marie Moermans
Manufactured in: Belgium
Built in 12, 16, 20, 28 and .410 bore and chambered for a 2 3/4" shell.

KRIEGHOFF
A Tradition of Performance®

Gold Super Scroll

Now that you have the time, Krieghoff has the gun.

It's been a good year. You've done a good job. And now you have a little time to spend on yourself. Maybe it's time to start thinking about that new K-80.

The Gold Super Scroll is just one of several intermediate K-80 engraving styles to consider, whether it's your first Krieghoff or a well-deserved upgrade. Available for trap, skeet, or sporting clays. The premiere competition shotgun in the world today. K-80...the best you can shoot, whatever your game.

Please call or write for the new K-80/KS-5 catalogue.

KRIEGHOFF
INTERNATIONAL INC.
P.O. Box 549
7528 Easton Rd.
Ottsville, PA 18942
Ph. (610) 847-5173
Fax (610) 847-8691

Ljutic Industries, Inc.
732 N. 16th Ave., Suite 22
Yakima, WA 98902
(509) 248-0476
FAX: (509) 576-8233
Est.: 1937   Staff: 25
Gen. Mgr.: Nadine Ljutic
Available: Retail
Manufactured in: USA
Price Range: $4,795 to $21,995
12 ga. single barrel target shotguns
(only Ljutic designs) 12 ga. O/U's
for trap, skeet, live birds & international trap/skeet. The only totally
custom shotguns produced in U.S.

MagTech Recreational Products, Inc.
5030 Paradise Rd.,Suite A-104
Las Vegas, NV 89119
(702) 736-2043
Est.: 1990   Staff: 5
Contact: Joyce Petrille
Available: Retail - Importers of
ammunition, rifles & pump shotguns.

Maverick Arms, Inc.
7 Grasso Ave., PO Box 497
North Haven, CT 06473
(203) 230-5300
FAX: (203) 230-5420
Est.: 1988   Contact: Ron Fine
Available: Retail
Price Range: Under $200 - Maverick
by Mossberg pump shotguns.

William Larkin Moore & Co.
31360 Via Colinas, Suite 109
Westlake Village, CA 91362
(818) 889-4160
FAX: (818) 889-1986
Est.: 1973   Staff: 4
Contact: Don Bawcum
8227 E. Via De Commercio, Suite A
Scottsdale, AZ 85258
(602) 951-8913
FAX: (602) 951-3677
Contact: William Moore, David
Moore or Dan Moore
Available: Dealers & Importers of
F.lli Piotti, F.lli Rizzini, Rizzini B.,
Armas Garbi, Kemen, Weatherby,
Emmebi (Cases & Access.), Brady
Brothers Ltd., C.C. Filson. We spe-
cialize in fine quality and collectible
double guns, and also carry a large
selection of new and used sporting
guns. We accept consignment gun
sales. For moreinfor- mation on cur-
rent selection and pricing, please
call or write one of our locations.
See Our Ad Pg. 36

O.F. Mossberg & Sons, Inc.
7 Grasso Ave.
North Haven, CT 06473
(203) 230-5300
FAX: (203) 230-5420
Est.: 1918   Staff: 400
Mktg. Mgr: Joe Koziel
Available: Retail
Model 500, 12, 20 & .410 gauge
pump action; Model 835, pump ac-
tion 12 gauge; Model 9200, 12
gauge autoloader 3".
See Our Ad Pg. 4

New England Arms Co.
PO Box 278
Lawrence Lane
Kittery Point, ME 03905
(207) 439-0593
Est.: 1975   Staff: 6
Contact: Jim Austin or
Steve McCarthy
Available: Retail & Direct
Exclusive U.S. distributors for F.lli
BERTUZZI, Importers and dealers
for F.lli Rizzini, B. Rizzini, Tecni-Mec,
Armitalia, Cosmi, Fabbri, Ferlib,
Casartelli, Zanotti, Arrizabalaga,
Arrieta, H. Dumoulin, A.H. Fox Gun
Co.
Extensive inventory specializing in
high quality doubles. You will find
names like, Purdey, Boss, Holland &
Holland, Churchill, Westley Rich-
ards, Parker, A.H. Fox, Lefever,
Winchester, Francotte, Piotti, Ber-
etta, Perazzi, Merkel, Sauer,
Browning, and many more.
Complete gunsmithing services by
British gunsmith. Stock fitting and
bending. Complete restoration ser-
vices.
See Our Ad Across

Orvis
Historic Rt. 7A
Manchester, VT 05254
(802) 362-3622
Contact: Jack Dudley
Available: Retail & Direct
Only U.S. company offering custom
stocked Berettas offered in all configurations using the finest
exhibition grade walnut, completed
in six weeks. - Importers of Arrieta
side by side shotguns. - Professional
gun fitting by experienced fitters
using our own Beretta try guns. -
Custom stocking, alterations, and
complete gun repair. - Complete
line of used double guns. - Consignment gun sales.

Outdoor Sports Headquarters, Inc.
967 Watertower Lane
Dayton, OH 45449-2463
(800) 444-6744
FAX: (800) 488-6744
VP: Roger Vignolo
Importer of Charles Daly: Three
models in current series: Charles
Daly Field O/U - 12 & 20 gauge;
Charles Daly Deluxe Field O/U - 12
& 20 gauge; Charles Daly Sporting
Clays O/U - 12 gauge

Perazzi USA Inc.
1207 S. Shamrock Ave.
Monrovia, CA 91016
(818) 303-0068
FAX: (818) 303-2081
Est.: 1981   Staff: 6
Vice President: Lucio Sosta
Available: Through our Dealers
Manufactured in: Italy
We offer a full line of shotguns, in
all configurations for use in Sport-
ing Clays, American Trap & Skeet,
International Trap & Skeet and
Hunting. Perazzi shotguns are avail-
able from the Standard Grade
Models through Extra-Extra Gold
Grade. For a full color catalogue
and price list or the dealer nearest
you please call or write to us.
See Our Ad Pgs. 2 & 3

William Powell & Son, Ltd.
35-37 Carrs Lane
Birmingham, B4 7SX, England
011-44-121-631-3504
FAX: 011-44-121-631-3504
Est: 1802
Contact: Peter Powell
Available: Direct
Manufactured in: England
Side by Side; available in 12, 16
and 20 gauge.

Precision Sales Int'l., Inc.
Box 1776, Westfield, MA 01086
(413) 562-5055
Est.: 1978   Staff: 5
Contact: Alan Johnson
Available: Retail
Importer of Marocchi
Manufactured in: Italy
Price Range: $1,500 and up
Exclusive marketers of the new Con-
quista by Marocchi – A sporting
clays over/under with incredible per-
formance for the serious sporting
clays shooter.

James Purdey & Sons, Ltd.
57-58 S. Audley St.
London, W1Y 6ED England
011-44-171-499-1801
FAX: 011-44-171-355-3297
Est: 1814
Contact: Nigel Beaumont or
Robin Nathan
Available: Direct
Manufactured in: England
Side by Side & Over and Under
sidelock ejector available in 12, 16,
20, 28 and .410.

Remington

Remington Arms Co., Inc.
PO Box 700, 870 Remington Dr.
Madison, NC 27025-0700
(800) 243-9700 (Consumer)
(910) 548-8700 (Headquarters)
FAX: (910) 548-7770
Est.: 1816   Available: Retail
Autoloading, pump, special purpose and break-action shotguns for
the hunter. Autoloading, pump and
break-action shotguns for the trap,
skeet and sporting clays shooters.
Also, ammunition; re-loading components; clay targets; traps; gun
care and cleaning products; gun
cases; and knives.

John Rigby & Co.
66 Great Suffolk Street
Southwark, London SE1 0BU
England
011-44-171-734-7611
FAX: 011-44-171-928-9205
Contact: Paul Roberts
Available: Direct
Manufactured in: England
Side by Side sidelock ejector; avail-
able in 12 gauge to .410.

SKB Shotguns
PO Box 37669
Omaha, NE 68137
(402) 330-4492
Contact: Rob Johanson
Available: Retail
Manufactured in: Japan
Price Range: $1,000
Importer for the SKB shotgun line.

Savage Arms, Inc.
100 Springdale Rd.
PO Box 1110
Westfield, MA 01085
(413) 568-7001
FAX: (413) 562-7764
Est.: 1989   Staff: 190
Manufacturer of rifle/shotgun com-
bination guns & centerfire high
power sporting rifles.

Scattergun Technologies, Inc.
PO Box 24517
Nashville, TN 37202
(615) 254-1441
FAX: (615) 254-1449
Contact: Roger Small
Practical shotguns for the sports-
man and competitive shooter.

Sile Distributors, Inc.
998 N. Colony Rd.
Meriden, CT 06450
(203) 238-4285
FAX: (203) 237-9324
VP: Dominick Derobertis
7 Centre Market Place
New York, NY 10013
(212) 925-4111
Est: 1958
Available: Direct
Manufactured in: Italy
Price Range: $359 to $389
Over and Under shotguns; Sky
Stalker I (fixed chokes) and Sky
Stalker II (changeable chokes); avail-
able in 12, 20, 28 gauge and .410.

Southwest Shooters Supply
Box 9987
Phoenix, AZ 85068
(602) 943-8595
FAX: (602) 943-1713
Est.: 1976   Staff: 3
Contact: Alan Peck or
Bruce Kinkner

Available: Direct
Manufactured in: Italy
Price Range: begin at $7,850.
Importer of Abbiatico & Salvinelli
shotguns.

Stoeger Industries
5 Mansard Court
Wayne, NJ 07470
(201) 872-9500
FAX: (201) 872-2230
VP: David C. Perkins
Price Range: $120 to $689
Distribute IGA & TIKKA Shotguns
that include O/U, SxS, coach guns
and single barrel models including
a youth model. The TIKKA line includes sporting calys
guns–suggested retail $1,325.

Sturm, Ruger & Company
217 Lacey Place
Southport, CT 06490
(520) 778-6555
FAX: (520) 778-1217
Est.: 1949   Staff: 1700
Dir. of Mktg: Syl Wiley
Available: Retail
Price Range: $1,215 to $1,675
Ruger Red Label and Woodside
Shotguns are engineered with
American firearms know-how,
based on contemporary American
target and field experience. Pro-
duced in 12, 20 and now 28 (Red
Label only) gauge, straight stock
and pistol-grip, sporting clays (12
and 20 gauge only) and standard
models, there is a Ruger shotgun
to fit every over-and-under user.
See Our Ad Back Cover

Symes & Wright, Ltd.
8 Monmouth Place
London W2 5SA England
011-44-171-792-9698
FAX: 011-44-171-221-1424
Contact: Peter Symes
Available: Direct
Manufactured in: England
Traditional side by side, exquisite
over and under or double rifle
crafted to owners specifications. 14
month delivery.

Legendary A.H. Fox Shotguns Return to the Sporting Scene

An American classic, the legendary A.H. Fox double barreled shotgun, has returned to the American sporting scene, much to the delight of hunters, shooters and collectors throughout the country.

After a hiatus of nearly half a century, these handcrafted, customized beauties are once again available in 16, 20, 28 and .410 gauges, each in five grades. And, according to experts, the A.H. Fox shotguns represent a quality seldom encountered in the products of U.S. or European manufacturers. A clear indication of this exceptional quality is the title Shotgun of the Year awarded to the Fox 20 gauge in 1994 by the Shooting Industry Academy of Excellence.

Resurrected by the Connecticut Shotgun Manufacturing Co., New Britain, Conn., the Fox firearms reflect a heritage that dates to the halcyon days before World War I. It was then that Ansley Fox headed the A.H. Fox Gun Company, producing shotguns in three gauges and more than two dozen grades and models.

The old Foxes were considered extraordinary. Today's successors were brought to market after permission to use Fox patents and tradenames was granted by Savage Arms, which purchased the A.H. Fox Gun Company in 1929. And the modern versions demonstrate the same painstaking attention to detail that characterized the originals.

Choose Your Own Wood

Most of today's Fox shotguns are made to order. You can specify such features as weight, balance point, customized half or straight hand stock, cheekpiece or Monte Carlo comb, barrel length, chokes, single or double trigger, and numerous other options. You can also choose your own wood from an amazing supply of Turkish-grown European walnut.

The old foxes were almost entirely machine-made. The new ones are machine-made only to a point, but all parts are hand-fitted by trained gunsmiths.

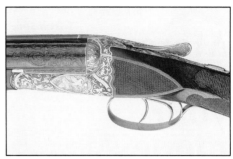

Clean, precise, and delicate engraving.

And finishing, including polishing, rust bluing, engraving and stock checkering, is also performed manually.

Engraving alone illustrates the company's scrupulous regard for quality. The Connecticut Shotgun Manufacturing Co. employs some of the nation's most prominent freelancers—James DeMunck, Tony Tuscano, Richard Roy, Jim Blair—for this step.

Clean, Precise, Delicate

Outdoor columnist Michael McIntosh, writing in Shooting Sportsman, notes that his customized Fox exhibits an oakleaf pattern cut "more cleanly, precisely and delicately than anyone in the engraving shop at (the old) Fox ever did." Gold inlay, he says, "looks more like it was done with a laser than a chisel. Only under a 10X glass does it show as free-hand work, and even then it's impressive."

Dick Perrett, president of Connecticut Shotgun, says the company's 28 and .410 gauge guns are priced slightly higher than their counterparts in 16 and 20 gauge because the smaller gauge guns require modifications to the actions. New A.H. Fox guns are priced from $9,500 for the CE grade to $18,500 for the top-of-the-line FE grade. The company is quoting 12-month delivery dates.

For additional information, including a catalog and price list, contact the Connecticut Shotgun Manufacturing Co., PO Box 1692, New Britain, CT 06051. Telephone (203) 225-6581

Tristar Sporting Arms, Ltd.
PO Box 7496
1814-16 Linn St.
N. Kansas City, MO 64116
(816) 421-1400
FAX: (816) 421-4182
Est.: 1994
President: George Woford
Vice President: Marty Fajen
Available: Wholesale & Retail
Manufactured in: Turkey
Price Range: $429-$899
TRISTAR SPORTING ARMS, LTD., a new sales & marketing company with 50 years of firearms industry experience. TRISTAR's product offering is made by the Uzumlu Factory, under the direction of the MINT Engineering Company, in the country of Turkey. Historically, their entire production has been sold to the Turkish market and bordering countries. (Turkey has the 2nd largest general hunting population in the world, after the U.S.). TRISTAR has been selected as the exclusive marketing agent, in the USA, for these fine firearms. Please see our ad for the models available. Dealer inquiries welcome.

See Our Ad, Left

Turkish Firearms Corp.
522 West Maple St.
Allentown, PA 18101
(610) 821-8660
(610) 442-6086
FAX: (610) 821-8660
Est.: 1962
President: Erbay Gonen
Manufactured in: Turkey
HHF Shotguns are handcrafted to the customer's exact specifications. Choice of gauges: 12, 16 or 20 ga; fixed chokes or 5 interchangeable choke tubes, and six grades to choose from.

U.S. Repeating Arms Co.
275 Winchester Ave.
Morgan, UT 84050
(801) 876-3440
FAX: (801) 876-3737
Est.: 1866
Available: Retail
Manufactured in: USA & Japan
Price Range: $300 & Up
Turkey, deer and field guns in RealTree camouflage patterns.

Est. 1885

Watson Bros.
39 Redcross Way
London Bridge
London SE1 1HG UK
011-44-171-403-3367
FAX: 011-44-171-403-3367
Est: 1885
Contact: Michael Louca
Manufactured in: England
Gun & rifle makers specializing in round body self-opening side x side small bore shotguns. We build only 10 guns per year.

Weatherby
3100 El Camino Real
Atascadero, CA 93422-2544
(800) 227-2023 (Cust. Svc.)
(805) 466-1767
FAX: (805) 466-2527
Est.: 1946   Staff: 65
Available: Retail
Manufactured in: Japan
Price Range: $1,289 to $2,527
Orion Grade shotguns I, II & III; Athena Grade shotguns IV, & V, High Grade Over & Under Shotguns.

Westley Richards & Co., Ltd.
40 Grange Road, Bournbrook
Birmingham B29 6AR England
FAX: 011-44-21-472-1701
Est.: 1819
Contact: Simon Clode
Available: Direct
Manufactured in: England
Side by Side: William Bishop Sidelock Ejector; 12, 16, 20 and 28 gauge. Carlton Boxlock Ejector; 12, 20, 28 gauge and .410. Connaught Boxlock Ejector; 12, 20 and 28 gauge.

Antonio Zoli
Via Zanardelli 39
25063 Gardone Val Trompia, Italy
011-39-30-891-21612
FAX: 011-39-30-891-1165
Manufactured in: Italy

SHOTGUNS/
NATIONAL DEALERS

ARMES DE CHASSE

Armes de Chasse
Box 86, Hartford, NC 27944
(919) 426-2245
FAX: (919) 426-1557
Est.: 1982   Staff: 3
Mktg. Mgr.: Art Foley

G.M. Bartelmay Guns, Inc.
911 W. Jefferson
Morton, IL 61550
(309) 263-8032
FAX: (309) 263-8271
Contact: George Bartelmay

Bedlan's Sporting Goods, Inc.
Box 244, 1318 E. Street
Fairbury, NE 68352
(402) 729-6112
Est.: 1950
Contact: Felix Bedlan

Cape Outfitters, Inc.
599 County Rd. 206
Cape Girardeau, MO 63701
(314) 335-4103
FAX: (314) 335-1555
Contact: Don Schrum

Colonial Gun Shop
143 Boone Square St.
Hillsborough, NC 27278
(919) 732-8396
(919) 732-5663
Staff: 10
President: Mark Stone
Contact: Johnny Clayton
Specializing in fine doubles & collectibles. Factory authorized Krieghoff & Perazzi dealer–call for all your shotgun needs.

David Condon, Inc.
Antique & Sporting Arms
109 E. Washington St.
Middleburg, VA 22117
(540) 687-5642
FAX: (540) 687-5649
President: David Condon
Manager: Britton Condon
Manager: Harriet Condon
David Condon Antique & Sporting Arms is in the market to buy or consign whole collections or individual items. We often do appraisals for The Smithsonian and the NRA Firearms Collection and we would pleased to lend our expertise in determining the value of your gun collection. Please call us from anywhere in the country and we'd be happy to work with you.
See Our Ad Below

du Pont/Krieghoff Gun Co.
PO Box 3528
Vero Beach, FL 32963-8007
(800) 73K-GUNS

FIELDSPORT
3313 W. South Airport Rd.
Traverse City, MI 49684
(616) 933-0767
FAX: (616) 933-0768
Contact: Bryan Bilinski
FIELDSPORT specializes in sales of fine American and European SxS and O/U for game shooting and sporting clays. Our inventory of over 100 guns includes AYA, A.H.

Fox, Belgium Browning, English-made Parker, Boss, Winchester Model 21, Beretta and many more. Call for current gun list. Trades welcome. Field Sport also appraises and purchases fine gun collections.
See Our Ad In Gunfitting

Griffin & Howe

Griffin & Howe
36 W. 44th St., Suite 1011
New York, NY 10036
(212) 921-0980
Contact: Richard Welch
or
33 Claremont Rd.
Bernardsville, NJ 07924
(908) 766-2287
Contact: Joe Prather
The Griffin & Howe Round Body Game Gun, built by Arrieta, is a classic gun for the game shooter. Fitted to your dimenions and cased with accessories. Available in 12, 16, 20, 28 & .410 bore. Importers of McKay Brown shotguns. We also stock a full line of fine used guns.
See Our Ad Pg. 41

J&J Sporting Goods
868 Derby Farms Dr.
Severn, MD 21144
(410) 551-0488

Jaqua's Fine Guns, Inc.
900 E. Bigelow Ave.
Findlay, OH 45840
(419) 422-0912
FAX: (419) 422-3575
Contact: Camille Ranzau

Mid-Maryland Outfitters, Inc.
3000 E. Ventrie Court
Myersville, MD 21773
(301) 694-7305
(301) 293-1936
FAX: (301) 293-3622
We stock a full line of Krieghoff K80's and Browning guns, along with Bob Allen clothes. Try *our own* shooting gloves, gun sleeves, & shell bags. We own and promote the "Big Pig Open". We help promote and sponsor over 5 state championships, National Ducks Unlimited, Quail Unlimited, National Wild Turkey, Ladies Charity Classics.
See Our Ad Pg. 32

William Larkin Moore & Co.
8227 E. Via De Commercio
Suite A, Scottsdale, AZ 85258
(602) 951-8913
Contact: Dan Moore
We specialize in fine quality and collectible double guns, and also carry a large selection of new and used sporting guns. We accept consignment gun sales. For more information on current selection and pricing, please call or write one of our locations.
See Our Ad Pg. 36

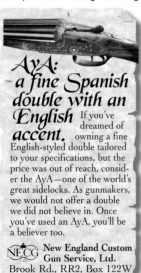

Scott Moss Gun & Tackle of Norwalk, Inc.
4 New Canaan Ave.
Norwalk, CT 06850
(203) 847-4008 Ext. 300
FAX: (203) 847-8064
Contact: Scott Moss
Your shooting sports equipment headquarters. Featuring: Browning

clothing; Le Chameau boots; Beretta sport clothing; Browning archery; Americase. Hundreds of shotguns including a full line of Beretta's and Browning's.
See Our Ad Pg. 28

Michael Murphy & Sons
6400 S.W. Hunter Rd.
Augusta, KS 67010
(316) 775-2137
FAX: (316) 775-1635
President: Michael Murphy
Krieghoff, Beretta's 682 & SO, Browning, AYA Bird Guns
See Our Ad In School Section

New England Arms Co.
PO Box 278, Lawrence Lane
Kittery Point, ME 03905
(207) 439-0593
Est.: 1975   Staff: 6
Contact: Jim Austin or Steve McCarthy
Retail showroom with over 1000 shotguns and sporting rifles. Called "The Best Gunshop in the World", by FORBES F.Y.I. Magazine. Also hailed "All That a Gun Store Should Be", by Field & Stream. Extensive inventory specializing in high quality doubles. You will find names like, Purdey, Boss, Holland & Holland, Churchill, Westley Richards, Parker, A.H. Fox, Lefever, Winchester, Francotte, Piotti, Beretta, Perazzi, Merkel, Sauer, Browning, and many more. Complete gunsmithing services by British gunsmiths. Stock fitting and bending. Complete restoration services.
See Our Ad Pg. 39

New England Custom Gun Service, Ltd.
Brook Rd., RR#2
Box 122W
W. Lebanon, NH 03784
(603) 469-3450
Contact: Dietrich Apel
If you've ever dreamed of owning a fine English-styled double tailored to your specifications, but the price was out of reach, consider the AyA–one of the world's great sidelocks. Call or write for complete literature.
See Our Ad, Left

Pachmayr Ltd.
831 N. Rosemead Blvd.
S. El Monte, CA 91733
(800) 350-7408
(818) 579-5201
FAX: (818) 358-7251
Contact: Arthur Bright
Visit our fully stocked PRO SHOP, located at the Pachmayr Shooting Sports Park, 831 N. Rosemead Blvd., S. El Monte, CA. Our PRO SHOP features Perazzi, Browning and Beretta shotguns, reloading supplies and accessories.

Paxton Arms
PO Box 150245
Dallas, TX 75226
(214) 651-9018
FAX: (214) 748-2999
Est.: 1978
Contact: Robert V. Paxton

Quality Arms, Inc.
PO Box 19477
Houston, TX 77224
(713) 870-8377
Est.: 1975   Staff: 3
Contact: John Boyd

Southwest Shooters Supply
PO Box 9987
Phoenix, AZ 85068
(602) 943-8595
FAX: (602) 943-1713

Sundog Firearms
HC82, Box 234
Kimberly, OR 97848
(888) 581-0550
FAX: (541) 934-2117
Est.: 1985   Staff: 2
Contact: Jerry Russell
Largest-volume Merkel distributor. LIve the legend and experience the quaility and durability of German craftsmanship. Best pricing anywhere.

Woods & Water Outdoor Store
Rt. 1, Box 319
Catoosa, OK 74015
(919) 266-5551
Contact: Doug Fuller
Full line of Remington, Browning, Krieghoff, and Kolar Shotguns. Call today for competitive prices.

SHOTGUN SHELLS & CHOKES

Clays, upland birds, waterfowl, big game, small game—- you can shoot or hunt them all with a shotgun. Even a single shotgun with choke tubes, thanks to the variety of specialized ammunition available.

It's the shotshell's unique design that allows individual components [see Shotshell illustration below] to be adapted for specific purposes. That means manufacturers can match the type of case, powder charge, shot size and wad to suit your needs.

Of course the shotgun has something to do with all of this. Ammunition chosen for a fixed choke model should be compatible with that choke. However, the ammunition options available for shotguns fitted with choke tubes are seemingly endless.

Chokes range from cylinder, which means no constriction or reduction of muzzle diameter, for the largest possible shot patterns, to full choke with the greatest amount of muzzle constriction and the tightest patterns. Between these extremes fall seven additional graduated choke constrictions.

Basically, the key to shooting success is matching ammunition and choke to provide a dense enough pattern for effective shooting at the ranges chosen for each species or clay target.

Ammunition selection depends on several factors: The first choice is between lead or steel shot. In the U.S., steel shot is for waterfowl hunting [see Steel Shot article]. Because it is harder than lead shot, steel shot deforms less readily and produces a denser pattern. That means for most hunting a larger shot size and a more open choke is suggested than for lead.

Standard shot sizes range from No. 9 to BB in lead, from number 6 to T in steel [see Ammo & Choke Suggestion Chart]. Buckshot, available only in lead, is yet another category of shot, used, as the name would indicate, largely for deer (buck) hunting.

Sound complicated? It's not really if you take it one step at a time. The accompanying articles and charts, while not the final word on the subtleties and nuances of shot and choke selection, should prove helpful in answering your questions.

SHOTSHELL PARTS

HULL
The outer container of a shotgun shell, typically made of plastic or paper with a metal base

WAD
Plastic or fiber separating powder and shot that forms a seal so that gasses eject shot uniformly down the barrel

PRIMER
A compound contained in the middle of the base of a shotgun shell, where the firing pin strikes

SHOT
Round projectiles, usually of lead or steel. Depending on shot size and load, a shell can contain from 45 to 1,170 shot.

POWDER
Gun powder situated above the primer where it will be ignited by flames caused by the detonation of the primer compound.

STRICTLY FOR THE BIRDS

Vihtavuori introduces SPORTING LITE (N3SL), a shotgun powder for shooters with a big appetite for clay birds. Not the typical trap and skeet fare, but a full course of those tricky clay fowl known as minis, midis, rockets, battues and rabbits.

Formulated from ribbon extrusions of pure nitrocellulose, it is produced and tested for reliability, consistency and overall performance in 12 gauge 1¹/₈ oz. and lighter loads. And SPORTING LITE gives new meaning to the words, "clean burning," light recoil

and economy.

So next time you have a craving for shooting clays, use the powder that keeps you hungry for more, Vihtavuori N3SL. Also try our new N3SM and N3SH powders for upland game and magnum field loads.

For a free Reloading Guide with recipes for all Vihtavuori Powders, contact: Kaltron-Pettibone, U.S. Importer, Dept. GW, 1241 Ellis St., Bensenville, IL 60106 (800) 683-0464.

VIHTAVUORI OY

AMMUNITION & CHOKE SUGGESTIONS

GAME	SUGGESTED SHOT SIZE	SUGGESTED CHOKES	WHAT EXPERIENCED SHOTGUNNERS SAY...
DUCKS	BB, 1, 2, 3 *	Modified--for pass shooting Improved Cylinder-- over decoys	Use BB shot for long range and pass shooting. For normal range--No. 1 or No. 2 shot while some hunters use No. 3 shot for closer range shooting over decoys.
GEESE	T, BBB, BB, 1*	Modified	Goose hunters need wallop so they use the big loads with large shot. Many hunters prefer No. 1 shot for a denser pattern at shorter ranges over decoys.
PHEASANTS	5, 6, 7½	Improved Cylinder-- for close cover Modified or Full-- for long cornfield shots	For cornfield shooting where long shots are usual - better use No. 5. On a normal rise over dogs and for all around use, No. 6 is the favorite.
GROUSE OR PARTRIDGE	5, 6, 7½, 8	Improved Cylinder or Modified--for brush work Full--for open ranges	On the smaller birds such as ruffed grouse or Hungarian Partridge, use the smaller shot. The big western grouse (sage, sooty, and blue) call for heavier loads and larger shot.
QUAIL	7½, 8, 9	Cylinder Improved Cylinder Modified	For early season shooting on bobwhites when feathers are light, some hunters use No. 9 shot. Later they switch to No. 7½ or 8. On the running or wild flushing type of quail, such as the Gambel's, larger shot is sometimes used.
DOVES AND PIGEONS	6, 7½, 8, 9	Modified Improved Cylinder	Use lighter loads and No. 7½ or No. 8 shot on mourning doves at normal ranges--for longer ranges use the heavy loads and No. 6 or No. 7½. Use the same load on band tailed pigeons and white wings.
WOODCOCK	7½, 8, 9	Improved Cylinder Modified	The choice of shot size here will depend on ranges at which the game is shot. For fast shooting in the alder thickets, No. 8 shot is a good choice.
TURKEY	BB, 2, 4, 5, 6, 7½	Full	Choice of shot size depends on the range. If you're a good caller, No. 6 or No. 7½ shot makes a clean kill. BBs, No. 2s, 4s, 5s, are best for long shots.
TRAP	7½, 8	Full or Modified	In most cases, No. 7½ is used for trap. Check the Official Rulebook.
SKEET	8, 9	Skeet Choke Improved Cylinder	In most cases, No. 9 is used for skeet, check the Official Rulebook.
SPORTING CLAYS	7½, 8, 9	Any choke (Depends on practice desired)	For targets at close range use a more open choke, at longer distances tighten the chokes.

SOURCE: NRA THE BASICS OF SHOTGUN SHOOTING

PATTERN/PELLET DENSITY & ENERGY GUIDE

*Look up distance to your game for recommended pellet. Pellets appropriate for
longer distances may also be used at shorter range. Use of pellets at distances sur-
passing their listing is not recommended*

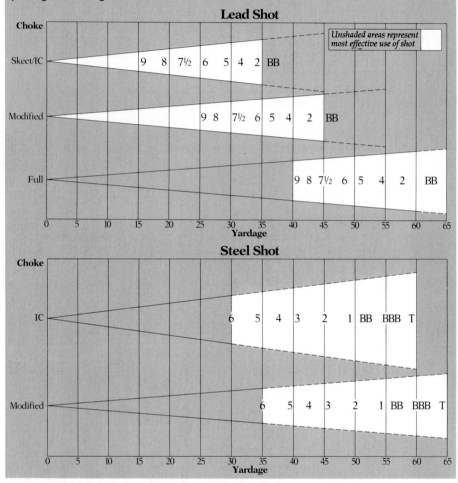

APPROXIMATE NUMBER OF SHOTS
IN VARIOUS LOADS

Shot Size	Shot Diameter	2 oz.	$1\frac{7}{8}$ oz.	$1\frac{5}{8}$ oz.	$1\frac{1}{2}$ oz.	$1\frac{3}{8}$ oz.	$1\frac{1}{4}$ oz.	$1\frac{1}{8}$ oz.	1oz.	$\frac{7}{8}$ oz.	$\frac{3}{4}$ oz.	$\frac{1}{2}$ oz.
#9	.08	1170	1097	951	877	804	731	658	585	512	439	292
#8	.09	820	769	667	615	564	513	462	410	359	308	205
#7½	.095	700	656	568	525	481	437	393	350	306	262	175
#6	.11	450	422	396	337	309	281	253	225	197	169	112
#5	.12	340	319	277	255	234	213	192	170	149	128	85
#4	.13	270	253	221	202	185	169	152	135	118	101	67
#2	.15	180	169	158	135	124	113	102	90	79	68	45

SHOTGUN SHELL MANUFACTURERS/ IMPORTERS

ACTIV Industries, Inc.
1000 Zigor Rd.
PO Box 339
Kearneysville, WV 25430
(304) 725-0451
Pres: Luis A. Perez
VP: L. Andres Perez
Customer Service Mgr: Linda
Barnhart
Plant Manager: Doug Dockeney

All Purpose Ammo
PO Box 339
Canon, GA 30520
(800) 870-2666
Est.: 1990

BISMUTH
CARTRIDGE COMPANY

Bismuth Cartridge Co.
3500 Maple Ave.
Dallas, TX 75219
(800) 759-3333
(214) 521-5880
President: W.S. Montgomery
The first real non-toxic alternative
to lead. Exclusive to the Bismuth
Cartridge Company in North America, these premium shotshells
contain patented bismuth alloy
shot, the only known non-toxic

metal with the approximate density
and hardness of lead. This shot's
ballistic qualities are similar to those
of shotshells loaded with a like
amount of lead shot and powder.
Offered in a variety of loads. Available from fine sporting goods
stores or call us direct for your nearest dealer.
See Our Ad Below

Brenneke of America, Ltd.
PO Box 2408
Sierra Vista, AZ 85636
(520) 459-7306
FAX: (520) 459-3777
Est.: 1895
Nat'l. Sales Mgr: Tom Turpin
Offering 12, 16, 20 & .410 slugs
for shotgunning.

Clever Mirage
Gene Sears Supply Co.
2003 South Shepard Dr.
El Reno, OK 73036
(800) 522-3314
Contact: Gene Sears, Jr.
Popular priced hunting loads in 12,
16, & 20 gauge.

Eley Ltd.
PO Box 705, Witton
Birmingham B6 7UT England
011-44-21-356-8899
FAX: 011-44-21-331-4173
Contact: Alan Ward
.22 rimfire cartridge manufacturers;
distributors of shotshell cartridges

Estate Cartridge Co.
2778 FM 830, Willis, TX 77078
(409) 856-7277 (Plant)
Est.: 1980   Staff: 15
Contact: Paul Butaud
(713) 980-4209: (Sales Office)
Contact: Rick Shoupe
Sales are conducted through key retailers and distributors for
commercial products and direct to
the consumer on custom items.
Commercial items include a complete line of hunting, target and
promotional shotshells. Custom
items include 2 1/2" English light
loads, competition flyer and custom requests. Estate Cartridge, Inc.
manufactures the finest shotgun
shells available today. These shells
are especially designed to give maximum power, superior long range
penetration, and extremely uniform
patterns. All of our components are
(ballistically) matched to give the
highest possible performance. We
specialize in making ammunition to
the customers specifications. We
also have the unique capability of
personalizing the shells by printing
names, initials or corporate logos directly onto the hull. "IF QUALITY IS
YOUR GOAL, ESTATE SHOULD BE
YOUR CHOICE."
See Our Ad Across

FEDERAL®
Ammunition

Federal Cartridge Co.
900 Ehlen Dr., Anoka, MN 55303
(612) 323-2300   Est.: 1922
Shoot Promotion Mgr: Mike Larsen
Federal manufactures ammunition
for all sporting uses, including Premium, Gold Medal, and Classic
brands. Federal's top of the line
Gold Medal shotshells are used by
the U.S. Shooting Team, which continues to achieve unprecedented
success in the world arena. Gold
Medal shotshells are designed for
total performance on trap, skeet or
sporting clays ranges, and known
for their superior re-loadability. Federal operates a traveling Wing &
Clay Shooting School which
teaches shotgun shooting skills to
persons at all skill levels.
See Our Ad Pg. 1

OLYMPIA CARTRIDGES

**EXPERIENCE
THE SPIRIT
OF OLYMPIA**

- **HIGH PERFORMANCE**
- **LOW RECOIL**
- **LOW COST**

OLYMPIA U.S.A

DEALER INQUIRIES INVITED

VISA, MC ACCEPTED

1720 Cumberland Point Drive, Suite 5, Marietta, GA 30067

TO ORDER:

TEL. 770-858-0048 • FAX 770-858-0051

Fiocchi of America, Inc.
5030 Fremont Rd.,
Ozark, MO 65721
(417) 725-4118
FAX: (417) 725-1039
Est.: 1983   CEO: Craig Alderman
Nat'l. Sales Mgr.: Dave Thomas
Available: Direct
Manufacturing Facilities: USA, Italy,
Greece, Hungary, New Zeal., Argen.
Small arms ammunition, shotgun
shells, primers, specialty cartridges.
See Our Ad Across

Gamebore Cartridge Co., Inc.
New England Arms Co.
Box 278, Lawrence Lane
Kittery Point, ME 03905
(207) 439-0593
FAX: (207) 439-6726
Est.: 1975   Staff: 6
Contact: Jim Austin or Steve McCarthy
Available: Retail or Mail Order, No
FFL required, UPS shipment
Gamebore Black Powder loads, 8
ga. 3 1/8", 10 ga. 2 7/8", 12, 16, &
20 ga. 2 1/2". Nitro loads in 10, 12,
16, 20, 24, 28, & .410 (2") also 12
ga. 2". NEW this year-Paper Case
12 gauge loads. Gamebore Steel
shot, and Pattern Spreaders in 12
gauge. New England Arms offers
the sportsman the widest variety of
gauges and loadings, as well as
over 1000 shotguns in stock. All
shells manufactured in Great Britain
to the highest quality standards.
Your headquarters for specialty
shotshells for older American, British and European shotguns.
Brochure available upon request.

Kent Cartridge USA
3500 Maple Ave., Dallas, TX 75219
(214) 521-5883
(800) 759-3333
Est.: 1982
Contact: W.S. Montgomery
Available: Direct
Kent Shotshells are recognized as
the finest manufactured in Europe.
In fact, George Digweed earned
three Sporting and FITASC simultaneous World Championships
shooting off-the-shelf Kent Champions exclusively. And you can shoot
them too! Kent Cartridge's outstanding line of shotshells-
Champion, Biowad, Fibre & Topm-
ark-are now available in North

America. Shoot the finest. Shoot
Kent. Call for a dealer near you.
Dealer inquires welcome.
See Our Ad Below

Lyalvale Express
Imported by D&J Supplies
PO Box 184, Vacaville, CA 95696
(707) 446-6520
Contact: Dave Collins

Olympia U.S.A.
1720 Cumberland Point Dr.
Suite 5, Marietta, GA 30067
(770) 858-0048
President: Jean Constantinides
Olympia U.S.A. is the sole importer
of Olympia Cartridges, a favorite in
Europe since 1965. Noted for quality and reliability, these outstanding
cartridges are available in 24 competition and game loads, and in all
shot sizes and varieties. Also available: "Super Premium" loads,
including high velocity, low recoil,
nickel-plated and copper-plated.
Phone or fax for additional information on these competitively priced
cartridges.
See Our Ad Pgs. 56-57

Orvis "Shot"
Historic Rt. 7A, Box 798,
Manchester, VT 05254
(800) 548-9548

Perazzi Shells
Gene Sears Supply Company
PO Box 38, El Reno, OK 73036
(800) 522-3314
Contact: Gene Sears, Jr.
Importing two grades of shells:
Competitive...12 gauge 1 & 1 1/8
oz., and light recoil...1 oz., 12
gauge Featherlite.

Polywad
Shotgun Shell
PO Box 7916, Macon, GA 31209
(912) 477-0669
Est.: 1986   Staff: 4
Contact: Jay Menefee
Excellent choice for upland
gamebird hunters. NSCA legal—our
Spred-Rs help win State and National Sporting Clays titles! Shells
now available in 12 ga. 2 3/4" in 1
1/8 oz. and 1 oz. series, and NEW—
low pressure, low recoil 2-1/2"
"ENGLISH" series—transform your
shooting of fine, lightweight double guns. 20 ga. now available.
Combining distinctive looks, with
roll crimp, high performance and
overall superior quality—Spred-Rs
take the worry out of being close.
See Our Ad Pg. 60

RST LTD.

RST, Ltd.
7 Weston Way,
Ctr. Conway, NH 03813-0127
(603) 447-6769
(603) 447-6770
FAX: (603) 447-1856
Contact: George E. Olson
Designed by shooters, for shooters,
RST Ltd. uses only the finest components from around the world and
are assembled right here in the
USA. Whether for game shooting
or a specific target discipline, RST Cartridges will give you the best
performance money can buy. Competition & game loads are available in
12, 16 & 20 gauge in both 2 3/4"
(70mm) & 2/12" (65mm) cartridges.
Custom logos may be ordered for
your club or business. Specialty loads
may also be available. Call for details.

Remington

**Remington Arms
Company, Inc.**
PO Box 700, 870 Remington Dr.
Madison, NC 27025-0700
(800) 243-9700 (Consumer)
(910) 548-8700 (Headquarters)
FAX: (910) 548-7770
Est.: 1816   Available: Retail
Remington manufactures shotshells
for upland hunting and small
game; turkey loads; steel shot waterfowl loads; rifled slugs, sabot
slugs and buckshot loads for larger
game; "duplex" layered shotshells
for hunting and target shooting;
lead and steel shot target loads for
sporting clays, trap and skeet; reloading components; and a variety
of special purpose loads.
See Our Ad Across

Sellier & Bellot, USA
PO Box 27006
Shawnee Mission, KS 66225
(913) 685-0916
FAX: (913) 685-0917
Contact: Ed Grasso
Available: Retail
Made in: Cech Republic; Shotgun
shells–all gauges–target & hunting.

Slug Group
PO Box 376, New Paris, PA 15554
(814) 839-4517
FAX: (800) 432-3236
Contact: Richard Knoster
Lightfield Hybred EXP sabot slugs
(12 ga., 2 3/4").

Top Shooters Have Discovered Gold At The 27-Yard Line.

You hear the talk everywhere you go. Around gun clubs and in big-time shoots across the country, more and more leading handicap shooters are dumping their silver and investing in gold. Our golden Nitro 27™ shotshell. That's smart. Because the Remington® Premier® Nitro 27 Handicap trap load is a shell built from the ground up to perform at the 27-yard line. With every component pushed to peak performance. The triple-tabled shot is ultra-round and cushioned by our Figure 8™ wad to produce denser, harder-hitting patterns.

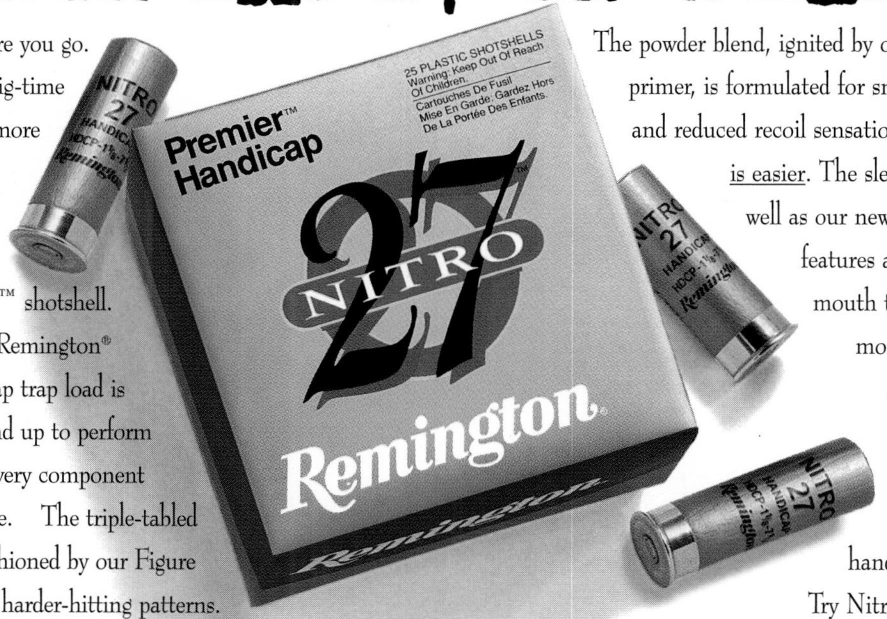

The powder blend, ignited by our consistent #209 primer, is formulated for smoother acceleration and reduced recoil sensation. Even reloading is easier. The sleek Nitro 27 hull, as well as our new STS™ target load, features a redesigned, tapered mouth that gives you easier, more consistent reloads over and over again.

Next time out, try the shotshell that's turning handicap trap on its ear. Try Nitro 27. It's pure gold.

Remember: Safe reloading is your responsibility.

LIGHTING THE WAY
TO SUCCESSFUL SHOOTING

Tru-Tracers are a revolutionary new tracer cartridge that for the first time gives a shooter an accurate assessment of where the shot has gone.

Tru-Tracers are non-phosphorous and non-incendiary, yet are clearly visible in daylight due to brand new technology. Perfect for both the beginner and expert shooter. Tru-Tracer is an invaluable training aid that will make you a better shot! Available through Kent Cartridge USA.

800-759-3333
KENT CARTRIDGE USA

Tru-Tracer

Kent Cartridge USA
3500 Maple Ave, Dallas, TX 75219
(214) 521-5883
(800) 759-3333
Contact: W.S. Montgomery
Available: Retail & Direct
Tru-Tracers are a revolutionary new tracer cartridge that for the first time give an accurate assessment of where the shot has gone. Based on an entirely new concept the trace is carried in a single projectile which stays in the centre of the pattern for over 50 yards. Clearly visible in daylight the cartridge gives the shooter immediate information on where the shot has gone. They are invaluable training aids for both teacher and shooter, beginner and expert alike. Tru-Tracers are finding major use in Police and Military training, and is non-phosphorus, safe and non-icendiary.

See Our Ad Below

U.S. Munitions Corp.
2425 Salashan Loop Rd.
Ferndale, WA 98248
(360) 366-4444
FAX: (360) 366-4445
Est.: 1990   Staff: 9
Contact: A.J. Gould

Victory Cartridge Company
PO Box 108, 100 Victory Dr.
Milford, PA 18337
(717) 296-2354
FAX: (717) 296-8639
Contact: Neil Chadwick
Choose VICTORY shells for price and performance. Victory's new TRAP & SKEET cartridges are designed specifically for the U.S.- featuring low recoil and super patterning. See our ad for the distributor in your area.
See Our Ad Pg. 53

WINCHESTER.
A M M U N I T I O N
Winchester Ammunition
Olin Corporation,
427 No. Shamrock,
East Alton, IL 62024
(618) 258-2000
Whether you shoot clay birds or upland birds, the exhilaration is the same. At Winchester®, we know just how you feel. That's why we make the most dependable ammunition in the world. Our Double A® shotshells have been the leading target load for 25 years, and the legendary Super-X® shotshells have been afield with American hunters for more than 70 years.
See Our Ad Across

APPROXIMATE NUMBER OF SHOTS IN VARIOUS LOADS

Shot Size	Shot Diameter	2 oz.	1⅞ oz.	1⅝ oz.	1½ oz.	1⅜ oz.	1¼ oz.	1⅛ oz.	1oz.	⅞ oz.	¾ oz.	½ oz.
#9	● .08	1170	1097	951	877	804	731	658	585	512	439	292
#8	● .09	820	769	667	615	564	513	462	410	359	308	205
#7½	● .095	700	656	568	525	481	437	393	350	306	262	175
#6	● .11	450	422	396	337	309	281	253	225	197	169	112
#5	● .12	340	319	277	255	234	213	192	170	149	128	85
#4	● .13	270	253	221	202	185	169	152	135	118	101	67
#2	● .15	180	169	158	135	124	113	102	90	79	68	45

TO WIN, YOUR COMPETITION HAS TO BEAT 25 STRAIGHT. OUR COMPETITION HAS TO BEAT 30.

For thirty years straight, AA® target loads have been number one in the shooting sports -- ever since we introduced them as the first shotshell with a reloadable plastic hull. As for the next thirty years, you can expect AA shotshells to keep giving you twenty-five straight.

WINCHESTER
AMMUNITION

SHOTGUN DISCIPLINES & GAMES

Layout of a trap field

Disciplines

Classifying and defining the various shotgun disciplines and clay target games is no easy task. There are almost as many out there as there are shotgunners to shoot them. And new ones spring up all the time. What follows then is not meant to be the final word on the topic--just a helpful guide to the most prominent games played and disciplines followed today.

Trap Disciplines

1. American Trap (ATA) - The most basic of all the trap disciplines. Standard targets are thrown as singles. The horizontal direction is randomized with a maximum angle of 22 degrees measured from a line from the trap to the middle station. The height at which the targets are thrown is constant. The distance is constant at 50 yards. A squad of five shooters shoot in rotation from five positions arrayed in an arc located 16 yards behind the traphouse, with five targets thrown at each station before the shooters change. A round is 25 targets with one shot allowed at each target. An English variation is called Down-The-Line, a two-barrel discipline that allows two shots at a single target with a scoring penalty for a second-barrel hit.

Handicap Trap - The same as ATA singles, except the shooter stands further back than 16 yards -- but no longer than 27 yards. The ATA reviews handicap yardage for shooters every 1000 targets as part of their handicap system.

SHOTGUN DISCIPLINES & GAMES

TRAP/GOVERNING BODY	SKEET /GOVERNING BODY
1. American Trap/ATA	1. American Skeet/ NSSA
2. Olympic Trap/UIT, USA Shooting	2. English Skeet/ CPSA
3. Olympic Trap Doubles/UIT, USA Shooting	3. International Skeet /UIT, USA Shooting
4. Automatic Ball Trap/UIT	**SPORTING/GOVERNING BODY**
5. Universal Trench/UIT	1. English Sporting/CPSA
6. ZZ/FITASC	American Sporting /NSCA, SCA
	2. FITASC or International
	Sporting/FITASC, NSCA

GAMES	
1. Crazy Quail	14. Lasersport
2. Two-Man Flush	15. AmericanZZ
3. Trap House Sporting Clays	16. Scrap/Chinese Trap
4. 5-STAND SPORTING ®	17. Follow the Leader
5. Quail Walk	18. Riverside Skeet
6. Supersport	19. Skeet Doubles
7. Tower Shooting	20. Rabbit Run
8. Pro-Sporting	21. Annie Oakley or
9. Sub-Trap	Shooting Down the Line Shooting
10. Flushes, Flurries & Mixed Bag (Team Events)	22. Buddy Shoot or Back-Up Trap
11. Starshot	23. The Red Baron Shoot
12. Double Rise	24. Simulated Live Pigeon (SLP) or Slapshot
13. Modern Skeet ®, Modern Sporting Skeet ® and Modern Trap ®	

New Motorola Sport
7, 7x, 10x two-way radios and SportBASE

Great for hunting, fishing or any recreational outdoor use

Durable and weather resistant

Compact and lightweight

Clear FM Ultra High Frequency (UHF) operation

SPORT 7 & 7X

- 7 channels
- Up to 2 mile range*
- Internal interference eliminator to block out unwanted chatter
- Operates on 3 AA batteries

SPORT 10X

- 10 channels
- Up to 5 mile range*
- Rechargeable Ni-Cad battery pack included (also capable of operation with AA batteries)

SportBASE

- Perfect for hunting clubs, land leases, cabins, fishing and camping
- Optimal range is 2 to 3 times the talk distance from base to field (range will vary by terrain)
- Easily converted for mobile use
- Compatible with Sport 10X and Sport/Handi-Com Radio series

Note: Not compatible with Sport 7 or Sport 7x

MOTOROLA
Sport Two-way radios

SHYDA'S
SERVICES, INC.

(717) 274-8676 • Fax (717) 274-8672
— 1009 S. Lincoln Ave., Lebanon, PA 17042 —

Doubles Trap - As the name implies, two targets are launched simultaneously from one machine. Squads of five shooters rotate the five positions on the 16 yard line. Shooting events consist of 25 or 50 pairs. Like 16 yard and handicap, scoring is one point per target hit.

2. Olympic Trap/Olympic Bunker/ Olympic Trench - An international discipline that incorporates fifteen machines. Targets have a minimum height of 1.5 meters and a maximum height of 3.5 meters as measured 10 meters in front of the bunker. Targets are thrown up to 110 mph depending on the target height to get the 70 to 75 meter variable distance required. The maximum target angle is 45 degrees. There are nine set programs for the fifteen traps that are used in all countries of the world. A squad of six shooters take turns shooting from five stations. Shooters move to the next station after each target in a shoot-and-move rotation. The shooting stations are located in a straight line. On the

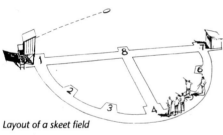

Layout of a skeet field

call "pull" (phono-pull release system is utilized to insure equitable target releases), a clay is thrown from one of three fixed traps directly in front of each of five shooters. Two shots may be used for each target with no penalty in scoring. Each shooter gets two lefts, two rights, and one straightaway target from each station. Shot charge is restricted to 24 Grams (approx. 7/8 oz.) using any safe powder charge (plated shot is allowed). Also, the Olympic target is made harder, to handle the higher target speed and is slightly smaller than the standard American trap target.

3. Olympic Trap Doubles/Olympic Bunker Doubles/Olympic Trench Doubles - Here, two targets are launched simultaneously from two traps of station three's set of three fixed traps. As in Olympic singles, squads of six shooters shoot in rotation from five stations, shooting a

round of 20 or 25 pairs (40 or 50 targets). Scoring is one point per target hit.

4. Automatic Ball Trap (ABT)/Wobble/Continental - Like ATA trap, the horizontal direction is randomized, but also the target vertical height is varied from 1.5 to 3.5 meters. The horizontal throwing angle is widened from the ATA 22 degrees to 45 degrees. The distance is set at 75 meters. Squads of six shooters shoot in rotation as in Olympic Trap. Two shots are allowed at each target with no penalty scoring. A phono-pull system may be used.

5. Universal Trench - This form of International trapshooting is also referred to as "Five Trap"; it is a variation of Olympic Trap using only five machines. Squads of six take turns shooting from each of five stations. UT is very similar to Olympic Trap in the speeds, heights and angles of targets. Trap position sequences for a round of 25, though predetermined, are unknown to the squad. Each squad member is allowed two shots at each target, with no penalty in scoring. Computer and phono-pull system for target selection are the same as in Olympic Trap.

6. ZZ/Electrocibles - A world-wide trap discipline, the target is a two or three bladed plastic propeller with a detachable (breakable) center. One of five traps in front of the shooter releases the target on call; two shots are allowed at each target. To score a "kill", the shooter must knock the center out of the target so that it lands within the confines of a circular fence.

SKEET DISCIPLINES

1. American Skeet - A round of skeet consists of 25 targets in a set sequence of singles and simultaneous doubles. Squads of five shooters take their turns from eight shooting stations. Each squad member takes two singles and one double from stations 1, 2, 6 & 7. Two singles are taken from stations 3, 4, 5 & 8. The 25th target is taken after the first target is missed, or as a final target (low house #8) after 24 kills. Targets are thrown a distance of 60 yards. Variations in the angles of the targets presented from the "high" and "low" house result from the shooter moving from station to station. American Skeet is the only discipline that has regular, specific tournament events for sub-bore shotguns: 20, 28, and .410.

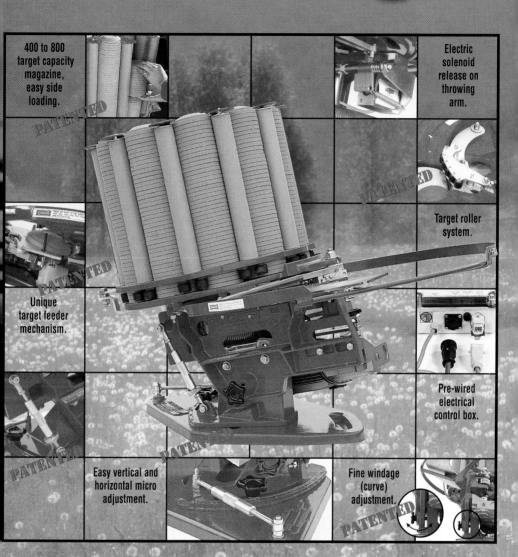

WINCHESTER® by LAPORTE®

- 400 to 800 target capacity magazine, easy side loading.
- Electric solenoid release on throwing arm.
- Target roller system.
- Unique target feeder mechanism.
- Pre-wired electrical control box.
- Easy vertical and horizontal micro adjustment.
- Fine windage (curve) adjustment.

PATENTED

185 LAPORTE SKEET
THE MOST ACCURATE MACHINE IN THE WORLD

 LAPORTE® AMERICA

Endorsed by: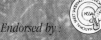

ONE TRANS-BORDER DRIVE - CHAMPLAIN - NEW YORK 12919 TEL. 1-800-335-TRAP - FAX 1-518-298-8720

Skeet Doubles - Shooters, in squads of five, start on station 1, shooting one pair of doubles each to station 7. Then they reverse, shooting one pair each from stations 7 through 1. On station 4, shooters must shoot the high house target first. On reversing, (shooting 7 through 1), they must shoot the low house target first. In tournaments, the events are on a total of 50 (or 100) targets with the last pair shot on station 1. Scoring is one point per hit target.

2. English Skeet - A seven station version of American Skeet, substituting the singles thrown on station 8 with a double on station 4.

3. International Skeet - An eight station format like that of American Skeet with faster targets thrown at 72 meters. The shooter is required to hold the butt of the gun at hip level until the target is seen, which may be delayed for up to 3.5 seconds after the "pull" request. Single and double target sequences are slightly different from American Skeet with a high single and one pair of doubles from Stations #1 & #2; high and low singles and one pair of doubles from Stations #3, #4 and #5 (on Station #4, the high bird must be attempted first in doubles); a single low and a double from Station #6; one pair of doubles from

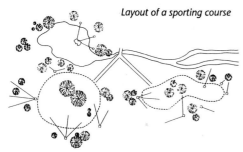

Layout of a sporting course

Station #7; a single high and a single low from Station #8. A round is 25 targets (no option shot). Like Olympic Trap, shot charge is restricted to 24 grams (approx. $7/8$ oz.), with any safe powder charge. For tournaments, all shells must be of the same type and load.

SPORTING DISCIPLINES

1. English or American Sporting - Sporting Clays, like Trap and Skeet, uses traps and clay targets to duplicate, as far as possible, conditions and presentations you would normally find while hunting. A typical sporting course is laid out over a 10, 20 or 30 acre site, ideally in rough, hilly terrain. Usually, the path the shooters follow will take a circular or horse-shoe shape enabling shooters to start and finish in roughly the same place. Along the path targets are thrown from 10 to 14 shooting stations. Courses can be laid out with either automatic or manual traps, usually set out-of-sight. Six different types of targets can be used: standard, midi, mini, battue, rocket or rabbit. Target sequence may incorporate singles, report pairs, following pairs and true (simultaneous) pairs. A round usually consists of 50 or 100 targets. The shooter's gun must be visible below the armpit and may not be mounted until the target is visible.

2. FITASC Sporting/International Sporting - The most challenging form of sporting shooting, it is the French version of practice for field shooting. Unlike the free and easy format of English or American Sporting, FITASC Sporting is shot in squads of up to six with a fixed order of stands (*parcours*, in French) that are shot in strict rotation. A competition normally consists of 200 targets shot over three days in eight rounds of 25. In each round of 25, shots are taken from at least three different stands. The shooter is required to hold the butt of the gun below armpit level until the target is seen. Great variety and lack of repetition is accomplished by use of a number of traps. Single targets are first shot by the entire squad. After the entire squad has completed the singles, combinations of the singles are presented as doubles. Here, as in English Sporting, all six types of clays are used. Generally speaking, targets tend to be at longer ranges with the added challenge of a continual variation of speeds, angles, distances and target combinations.

GAMES

1. Crazy Quail - This game simulates quail rising from cover. The trap used is hidden in a pit to prevent shooters from anticipating the flight direction of the target. Targets fly straight away, to the side, or directly toward the shooter, because the trap and the trapper's seat rotate 360 degrees. Automatic machines on special rotating bases can also be used.

2. Two-Man Flush - Using an International "Wobble" trap, the targets are launched and fly in all directions away from the trap house. Two shells are loaded

LeSabre for 1997.
The newest version of America's favorite full-size car.

There's peace of mind in knowing that others applaud your choice of a new car. And Buick LeSabre delivers that assurance: a car so satisfying, it's America's most preferred full-size sedan.* You get the power of Buick's proven 3800 Series II V6 engine, plus the benefits of an EPA-estimated 19 mpg city, 30 highway. All wrapped in an all-new interior that seats six comfortably. For more information, visit our Web site at http://www.buick.com or call 1-800-4A-BUICK.

BUICK®

LeSabre
Peace of Mind

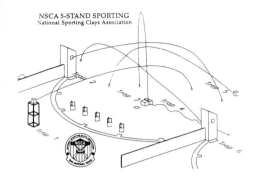

in each shotgun, and a rail holding 10 shotgun shells is set in front of each shooter to make reloading quicker. Targets (24 total) will be launched at 1.5 second intervals. Shooter one will take the first two and shooter two the next two, and so on.

3. Trap-House Sporting Clays - A self-contained transportable unit holding 15 traps presents all the angles, shots and target capabilities seen on a "traditional" sporting clays course. 13 shooting stations, separated by safety screens are positioned around the periphery of the unit. This game can be set up in the woods, in an open field or on a skeet field. [See Ad Pg. for more information.]

4. 5-STAND SPORTING® - Sometimes overlayed on a trap or skeet field this game utilizes 6-8 automatic traps. There are 3 levels of difficulty: Level I, 5 single targets with full use of the gun for scoring; Level II, 3 single and a simultaneous pair; Level III, 1 single and 2 simultaneous pairs. Shooters (squad of five) can move from station to station with a predetermined menu of shots and combinations, or in a sequence unknown to the shooters. 5-STAND SPORTING® is a registered trademark of Clay-Sport International, Inc. , Alberta, Canada. In the U.S., 5-STAND®is licensed by the NSCA.

5. Quail Walk - Another version of sporting shooting. A quail walk or walk-up involves the shooter walking down a path in a "more-or-less" straight line. Just as in "rough" shooting in the field, the shooter carries a loaded gun in anticipation of targets being presented while walking. Manual traps or automatic traps can be utilized.

6. Supersport - This game uses 15 to 30 automatic trap machines spread over 10 - 30 acres and buried in bunkers, on top of hills, placed behind trees or bushes, or up

in towers. It is the ultimate simulation of a live bird hunt. The shooter uses a controlling computer to indicate the number of targets presented and the degree of difficulty desired. As the shooter walks the course, sensors located on the course pick up signals from transmitters worn by individual shooters. These are relayed to the course control computer which adjusts the machines, angles, and the number of targets. A noise simulating the particular bird (target(s)) is generated prior to use. Less sophisticated Supersport courses attempt to achieve similar results without using the control computer, i.e. a control tower in the middle of the course. The automatic traps will present targets from all angles, heights and directions thus providing the element of surprise found in true hunting.

7. Tower Shooting - This game simulates pass shooting of dove or a driven pheasant shoot (which, depends on how the shooters are positioned around a tower equipped with one or two traps). Traps may be man-

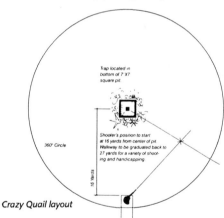

Crazy Quail layout

ual, but the best installations use automated equipment controlled from the ground.

8. Pro-Sporting - A game of 25 targets for squads of six shooters. Shooters stand in one position to attempt killing targets from five traps.

9. Sub-Trap - A game where a squad of shooters attempt targets thrown manually from a machine blocked from sight. Shooters take turns at five positioned pegs or stations. A total of 25 targets (5 at each peg) are randomly released in sequences of singles or doubles. The fun and frustration of the game is that the shooter must have his

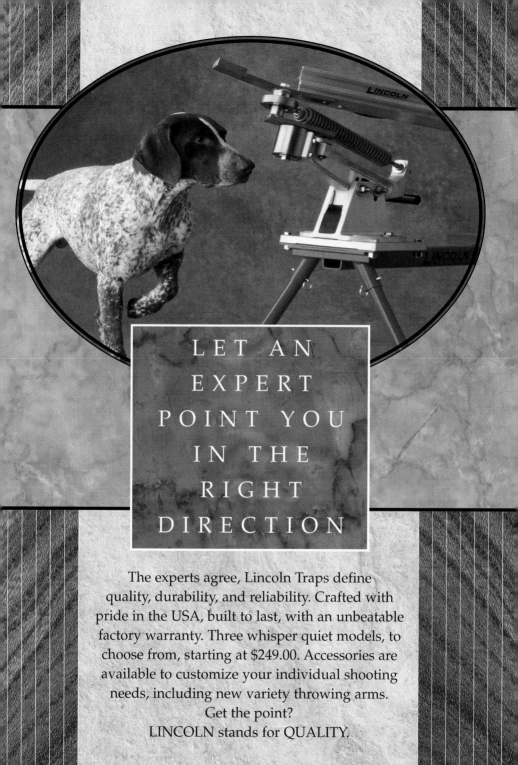

gun loaded with two cartridges at all times in anticipation of a simultaneous pair.

10. Flushes, Flurries, And Mixed Bag - A "Flush" begins at the call of "pull" and 5 clay targets are launched in crossing and going way flight patterns, with another bird in the air about every second, until 50 birds have been thrown. A "Flurry" begins the same way, but the 5 targets are all traveling towards and over the shooting stations, like a covey rise. A target is released from one of five traps until 50 birds have been launched in under one minute. In a "Mixed Bag" targets can simulate a high flying pheasant, a bouncing rabbit, a darting woodcock, a springing teal , or crossing doves, or any combination of the above. At each call of "pull", a double is shot. This scenario is repeated 8 times per shooter, with the first shooter attempting a 9th pair for a total of 50 birds. Emphasis is on the individual shooter. There is a 3 minute time limit for this event. [These games are offered as part of the "Chevy Truck Sportsman's Team Challenge" All-Around Shooting Tournament.]

11. Starshot - A game of clay pigeon shooting invented primarily for easy viewing by spectators and the television audience.The layout consists of an upright

Flush & Mixed Bag

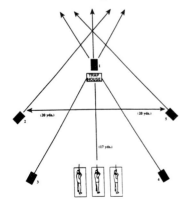

semi-circular tubular steel framework. From the shooters' and viewers' perspectives the steel framework appears to be divided into pie slices. Each "slice" is further divided by smaller semi-circular arcs that make the structure look similar to a large dart board half-sunk in the ground. The sections of the framework are numbered 1 to 12. At the base of the structure, i.e. the dart board bulls-eye, is a large pit containing four traps that release targets at different speeds across the face of the structure. The number of points scored for each target "killed" depends on the sector in which the target is broken. The highest scores come by "killing" clays within the lower, narrower sectors of the pie slices. Numerous games can be played in Starshot by teams.

12. Double Rise - Involves the shooting of two ATA targets launched simultaneously from the same trap. Squads of six shooters shoot in rotation from five stations. Competitors may only fire one shot at each bird of the pair, scoring five points for a pair killed and two points for one "kill".

13. Modern Skeet ®, Modern Sporting Skeet ®, and Modern Trap ® - Developed by Quack Sporting Clays, Inc., these new shotgun games combine the low cost of skeet (and trap) and the variable birds of sporting clays. The target's movement simulates shooting conditions (ranging from a slight breeze to gales) found on a windy day. Modern Skeet and Sporting Skeet are basically the same shotgun game. In Modern Skeet, the shooter attemps to hit 25 oscillating birds on 8 regular skeet field stations. Modern Sporting Skeet presents the shooter with a variety of close birds on the regular skeet stations and far crossing targets from 8 yards back of stations 3,4, and 5. Modern Trap uses the Quack Oscillator to present trap targets that curl rather than fly straight. [Available through Quack Sporting Clays, Cumberland, RI; (401) 723-8202.].

14. Lasersport - A true simulation of Clay Pigeon Shooting that uses deactivated shotguns to fire harmless infrared beams at plastic clay targets. 5, 10, 15 or 20 shooters, experience full sound simulation, shot pattern spread and simulation of all types and sizes of targets. Each player's progress is displayed on a large scoreboard.[Available

At home on any range.

*

Although we designed the Flyer®as a commercial grade target launching system, we find a growing number of individuals and private clubs are taking advantage of our realistic pricing. Call for a brochure and price list, because we think you will find us in your range.

Whiteside Mfg., Inc.
45408 16oth Street, West Lancaster, CA 93536
805-724-1974

WHITESIDE'S **FLYER**

At home on any range.™

through Intermark, Cedar Crest, NM, (800) 386-4861.]

15. AmericanZZ - America's version of the European "ZZ" Bird. AmericanZZ provides. an effective simulation of the zig-zagging, unpredictable flight of a live pigeon.[Available through AmericanZZ, Trumbull, CT; (203) 261-1058.]

16. Scrap/Chinese Trap - Using a skeet/trap field overlay and stations #1 through #7, squads of shooters shoot ATA trap birds. Generally, a low-gun mount is used and two shots may be taken without scoring penalty.

17. Follow the Leader - Played either on a trap or skeet field, but preferably on a field with both layouts. Shooters draw lots to determine order. Shooter #1 calls the shot to be attempted--any shot combination from any position. If he is successful, all shooters must attempt to duplicate the shot(s). Shooters who fail to match the leader's score are eliminated. The last shooter remaining wins.

18. Riverside Skeet - A game of 25 targets played on a skeet/trap overlay field. A squad of 5 shooters shoot 3 singles and 1 double from each of the arc-layout positions in ATA. The targets are launched from the skeet high and low houses with adjusted tragjectories that have been angled out. (3) singles (a left single, a right single, a "puller's option" single) are presented to each shooter before proceeding to the next shooter. After the 5th position has shot at the singles, shooter #1 is presented a simultaneous pair, and so on down the line. After completing 5 shots, all the shooters rotate.

19. Skeet Doubles - Doubles are shot at each of the regular 8 skeet stations, making a round of 16. Usually, the shooter is eliminated from the round when he misses a target.

20. Rabbit Run - Played on a trap field, the trap is set to launch targets as close to the ground as possible. The shooter stands either behind the trap house or on top of it, shooting a round of 25 "rabbits".

21. Annie Oakley or Shooting Down the Line - Shooters--as many as safety dictates is prudent--line up shoulder-to-shoulder on the 27 yard line of a ATA trap field in an order determined by lot. Shooters fire in groups of three. The first shooter calls for and fires at the target. If he misses, the second shooter fires. If he misses, then the third shooter fires. The shooter scoring the hit eliminates the pre-

Flurry

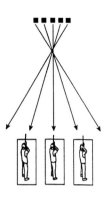

ceeding shooter (s) of the group. If all miss, none are eliminated. The first group consists of shooters 1, 2, 3. The second group becomes shooters 2, 3, and 4, and so on. The shooting continues down the line until only one winning shooter remains. When only 2 or 3 shooters remain a winner may be more quickly determined by increasing the distance from the trap and moving to the extreme stations 1 or 5.

22. Buddy Shoot or Back-up Trap - A team of two shooters stand shoulder to shoulder at the 27 yard line of a ATA trap field--the total number of teams dictated by safety considerations. When the target is launched, the shooter on the left fires; the second shooter can hit it for a score, if the first shooter misses. However, if second shooter shoots after the first shooter has hit the target, a "miss" is scored for the team. Each team member, in turn, calls for the target. The teams shoot down the line. High score wins.

23. The Red Baron Shoot - Staged primarily for fund raisers, this entertaining game challenges shooters to down a miniature remote-controlled airplane. (For additional information call: Sporting Planes, Ltd., Saratoga, CA, (408) 395-0049).

24. Simulated Live Pigeon (SLP) or Slapshot - A new and increasingly popular game from England that closely simulates the challenge of live bird shooting. In SLP, a reusable white marker is snapped to the underside of a common clay target thrown from a standard trap. To score a kill, a shooter must break the target and drop the marker inside the perimeter of a fenced in area. (For information call Jim Lee, Blakewood Sporting Estate, England, 011-44-179-887-5605.)

SPORTING, SKEET, and TRAP TARGETS
by J.E.C. Enterprises

Quality Laporte Targets have set the standard for sporting in Europe since 1927. We are proud to be the exclusive U. S. manufacturer for this premium line of targets including our standard lines for the skeet and trap enthusiasts.

Laporte Targets

CALL 1-888-8 LAPORT
1 888 852-7678 (toll free)
For Immediate Delivery
From Your Nearest Distributor!

by J. E. C. ENTERPRISES
P.O. Box 1760
Cedar Bluff, VA 24609
FAX: (540) 963-8038

RABBITS • BATTUES
STANDARDS • MINIS • ROCKETS
Also ask about our flash targets.

CALL FOR THE DISTRIBUTOR NEAREST YOU!

A Structured Approach to Shotgun Shooting

Over the years, hundreds of books and articles have been written on the fundamentals of shotgunning. Taken as a group, they tend to cover the same topics, though some do a better job than others.

The discussion of fundamentals found here breaks no new ground; nor does it offer any specific tips or techniques that will make you a super shot. What it does provide, however, is a structured approach to shotgun shooting. A way of analyzing what you are doing in a given shooting situation so you can consistently repeat hits and make the needed adjustments to correct misses.

While this article focuses on sporting clays, the approach it employs will serve you well in whatever shotgun discipline you pursue. The structured approach breaks the shooting situation into two parts: what you need to know and do before you call for the target—The Set-up—and after the target is released—The Shot.

THE STRUCTURE

Set-Up
- **Break Point**
- **Muzzle Hold Point**
- **Focal Point**

The Shot
- **Gun Mount**
- **Insertion Point**
- **Lead & Sight Picture**
- **Follow Through**

The Set-Up

Fast moving clay targets are difficult to hit. And you simply have no time for mental calculations after a target appears. Solution: Do your thinking ahead of time. Plan, and complete your set-up before you say "Pull." Because everything you do before you pull the trigger affects the outcome of the shot!

Break Point

Every target has a "break point". . .a point on its path of travel at which it is the most vulnerable. Your first task is to identify this spot.

How? Unfortunately, there is no magic formula to apply in the selection of target break points. Given the tremendous variety of shots found on today's sporting clays courses, the process is far more intuitive than scientific.

In a way, selecting a break point is a balancing act, with several—often conflicting—factors coming into play. Among them are target speed and trajectory, distance to target, target type and exposure and, of course, natural obstacles. You'll want to weigh these considerations against each other, then factor in shot and choke characteristics and your own strengths and weaknesses as a shooter, before deciding on where to take a target.

For most targets, you'll want to pick a break point that is neither too close nor too far from the trap. Too close and the target's speed will make it difficult to see and track successfully; too far out and a moment's hesitation may put it out of range.

Similarly, most instructors will tell you that you should let a target lose some of its initial speed before attempting to break it. And that's good advice—up to a point. The path of a target that has slowed too much can become erratic, making the target harder to hit. Again, a balanced appraisal is needed.

Finally, remember that the ability to read a target is an acquired skill, one that will improve with time and shooting experience.

Muzzle Hold Point

You've identified break points. Now there's another set-up step that contributes to accurate shooting. Establish a muzzle hold point, a step that will help you get on your target earlier and faster.

Here's how it's done. Point the muzzle at the break point. Then trace the target's flight path backwards, toward the trap. Stop about halfway back. Hold the muzzle still. Will the crossing target appear to fly directly over the muzzle at this point, almost touching it? Yes? Good! You're

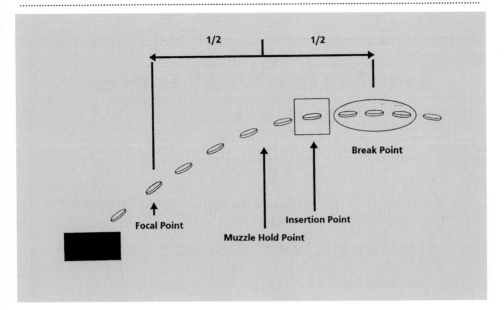

muzzle is on line and you've established the correct muzzle hold point.

Focal Point

One more step and your set-up's complete. Establish a focal point, which is the spot where the target first comes into focus, usually about half the way between the muzzle hold point and the trap. Establishing a focal point lets you see the target as soon as possible. And seeing the target clearly helps you move your gun swiftly and accurately from muzzle hold point to break point.

The Shot

You've completed your mental preparation, positioned your body and muzzle properly, and you're ready for action. Once you call "pull," the movements that follow occur in a matter of seconds, and it is only through practice and repetition that they become second nature.

Gun Mount

Before you call, "pull," remember that once the target is launched, everything will be moving: the target, your body and the gun. And the way you mount your gun contributes to your shooting success.

Ideally, your swing to target should be a quick, smooth, fluid movement that lifts your gun into firing position. Start when you first see the target. Keep focused on it. Bring the stock firmly to your cheek (don't drop your head to the stock). Place the butt against your shoulder, and lean forward slightly ("nose over toes").

Insertion Point

When the target appears, your muzzle will move from the muzzle hold point in a smoothly rising arc to intersect the target's flight path. The destination is called the insertion point. Depending upon the shooting method you employ--more on this in a moment—the insertion point will be on the target, behind it, or in front of it.

Lead & Sight Picture

Because your target is moving, in most instances you will fire in front of it. How far in front is referred to as **lead**. Don't think of lead as a precisely measured segment but in a general sense as the amount of space you'd like to see between your muzzle and target before you fire. This mental image of the relationship of muzzle to target is called the sight picture. And though this picture will vary, depending on the shooting method employed, seeing it in your mind's eye prior to saying "pull" is critical to successful shooting.

Follow-Through

Follow-through is important. Pull the trigger--crisply and quickly--while the shotgun is moving, and continue to move the gun after the shot is fired. If you stop the shotgun on touching the target, the result

TAKE A BREAK...

AND A BREAK... AND A BREAK... AND A BREAK... AND A BREAK...

The Remington Shooting School...
Where the Fun Never Stops and Break Time is All Day Long.

Come learn the basics or advanced techniques of trap, skeet, sporting clays and wingshooting at America's premier shooting school. It's a comprehensive package that offers you 3 days of instruction - including meals, lodging, targets, ammo and shuttle service between the gun club and your hotel...plus valuable gifts and accessories. Our friendly staff of NSCA certified instructors are waiting for you.

Model 11-87 Sporting Clays
12-Gauge Shotgun

SPECIAL LIMITED OFFER

Enroll in the Remington Shooting School and <u>graduate with your very own brand new 12-Gauge 11-87 Sporting Clays Shotgun (New for 1997... A retail value of over $725).</u>

Remington.
SHOOTING SCHOOL

For Locations and Schedules, Call Barbara Kerr Today at: 1 800 742-7053

INSERTION POINTS

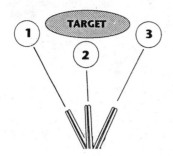

1 - Swing Through - muzzle inserted behind the target, then swept through as shot is fired.

2 - Pull Away - insert is on the target, then pulled in front as shot is fired.

3 - Sustained Lead - muzzle is inserted in front of target and lead is maintained as the shot is fired.

It's Important to Know Which Eye is Dominant

Virtually everyone has a dominant eye. And, since the ability to align your gun with a moving target is so important, it's critical that you use your dominant eye, and shoulder your gun on that side. Be aware, however, that even though you may be right-handed, it doesn't necessarily follow that your right eye is dominant. Which is your dominant eye? Here's a simple test:

1) Extend your hands in front of your face. Place them together to form a small, roughly triangular opening with your thumbs at the bottom. Using both eyes, look through the opening and focus on a distant object.

2) Maintain your focus. Now close one eye. If the object disappears from the opening, your closed eye is dominant. If it remains, your open eye is dominant.

Is your dominant eye opposite your shooting shoulder? Don't despair. If you're a beginner, consider changing hands and shooting from the other shoulder. It may be awkward at first, but it can be done. Too late to switch? Try placing a small patch on the dominant eye lens of your shooting glasses. (Use a "dot"...don't cover the entire lens.)

will be a miss. Good follow-through, on the other hand, will result in a lot more "X's."

Popular Shooting Methods

We've talked about the visual relationship between target and muzzle—the sight picture—which will vary with the shooting method you use. Similarly, the method you choose may vary with different target presentations. Here are the basic methods:

Swing Through is also widely practiced, both for clay target shooting and live birds. In this method you insert the muzzle slightly behind the target, then sweep it through the target and fire. This technique builds muzzle speed, which automatically provides lead (even though you may not always see it using this method) and helps overcome the tendency to stop the gun.

Pull Away is similar to Swing Through, but the insert is on the target and, as you pull away from the target, lead can be seen briefly. The Pull Away method also encourages good muzzle speed.

Sustained Lead is a popular method, advocated by many instructors and favored by many shooters. It consists of placing the muzzle in front of the target, and keeping it there through the shot. Lead is apparent as the stock reaches your cheek. A weakness of sustained lead is a tendency to stop the gun when you pull the trigger. But this can be overcome by not allowing the target to pass the muzzle.

The Structure—*Use It!*

Think of the structured approach developed in this article as a mental filing system for shooting tips and techniques. For example, when a shooting partner says that you are "see-sawing" your gun, he's talking about a problem that you can correct by adjusting your muzzle hold point.

Similarly, by placing the tips and techniques you pick up along the way in the context of this structured approach, you'll make it a part of a larger, organized base of shooting knowledge that you can tap to coach yourself. And the result will be more broken targets or downed birds.

BACK TO SCHOOL!
A structured approach to analyzing your shooting can be helpful, but it's no substitute for solid instruction. See the Shooting Schools section of this book for information on some of the very best schools, clinics and instructors who can help.

Body Position

Watching an accomplished shooter hit a fast moving target--clay or live bird--is exciting. And deceiving. For what seems so natural and effortless is really the result of countless hours of practice and attention to detail.

Can you reach the same level of skill? Happily, the answer is "Yes." Practice—preferably under the tutelage of a qualified instructor—pays off. And once you're comfortable with the basics the results will become apparent.

Good Stance...Good Results

Generally speaking, your break point [See Main Article] will determine your stance. And how you position your body in relationship to the expected target is critical to good shooting. Experts suggest a basic boxing position, feet about shoulder width apart and firmly planted, front knee bent slightly forward, back leg straight. (Left-handed shooters do the opposite.)

Gun-Hold and Gun-Ready Position

Maintaining your basic shooting stance, hold your shotgun in the palm of your non-trigger hand, at about the middle of the shotgun forearm, with your index finger pointing toward the end of your muzzle. Grasp one side of the forearm with your thumb. Use the other three fingers to grasp the other side. Your grip should be just firm enough to provide control. (That finger pointing toward the end of your gun will also, quite literally, point at the target when you fire. In short, you will be "pointing" at your target, not aiming at it.)

Place your trigger hand on the grip of the stock, firmly but without unnecessary strain. Position the rear of the stock along the front side of your ribs. And place the muzzle slightly below the expected flight path of the target. This gives you a clear view of the target area.

"Gun-Up" or "Gun Down" for Beginners?

If you're a beginner, you may want to follow the advice of many instructors: Even though wingshooting and sporting clays are "gun down" sports, begin your learning experience by eliminating your swing to target. In other words, start in a gun-up position. There's no need to be embarrassed. You are a beginner, and you'll work your way to gun-down soon enough. Gun-up temporarily removes a complicated step, it's faster, and it leads to fewer mistakes.

Glossary Of Shooting Terms

Regardless of whether you're coaching yourself or working with an instructor, it's important that you understand shotgunning's most commonly used terms. You'll encounter them frequently. And, like the special vocabulary of any discipline, they foster clear communication.

Break Point - The point in a target's flight path at which it's most vulnerable.

Focal Point - The point in a target's flight path at which you can first see it clearly.

Insertion Point - The point at which your gun barrel, moving smoothly in a rising arc from the muzzle hold point, first intersects the target's flight path.

Lead - A space in front of the flying target into which you direct your shot.

Muzzle Hold Point - The point in a target's flight path at which you initially point your muzzle.

Set-Up - The entire sequence of steps taken to prepare for firing at a moving target.

Sight Picture - The visual relationship, including lead, between your muzzle and the target.

Stance - The position of your body in relationship to the expected target.

BRING YOUR PUPILS TO OUR SCHOOL.

If you've got an eye on improving your shooting, look into the Federal® Wing & Clay Shooting School. We're a nation-wide, travelling school bringing top-level, NSCA certified instructors to shooters of every skill level. You'll receive three days of personalized instruction, with all ammunition and targets provided. And you'll come away a more confident hunter or shooter. For details just mail in the coupon below, or call our toll-free number: **1-800-888-WING.**

ACCESSORIES/
BAGS, POUCHES & SOFT GUN CASES

10x Products Group
2915 LBJ Freeway, Suite 133
Dallas, TX 75234
(800) WEAR10X
(214) 243-4016
FAX: (214) 243-4112
Contact: Tom Carlson
Available: Retail
Since 1934, 10x has maintained a proud American tradition of making clothes for the Great Outdoors. The 10x line of high-tech hunting apparel includes: lightweight and insulated Gore-Tex fabric garments; quiet, new Shikari Cloth insulated and non-insulated rainwear; upland hunting clothes; and coats, coveralls, bibs and pants in the most popular camouflage patterns. 10x also offers high-quality vests, jackets, shirts and accessories for shooting enthusiasts.
See Our Ad Pg. 91

Bob Allen Companies
214 S.W. Jackson St.
PO Box 477
Des Moines, IA 50315
(800) 685-7020
FAX: (515) 283-0779
Est.: 1946   Staff: 150
Ch. Board: Bob Allen
President: Matt Allen
Nat'l. Sales Mgr: Pam Bradford
Available: Retail & Direct
Bob Allen Sportswear is a premier manufacturer of shooting wear for sporting clays, trap and skeet as well as gun cases, gloves and accessories.
See Our Ad Below

Bagmaster Manufacturing, Inc.
2731 Sutton Ave.
St. Louis, MO 63143
(800) 950-8181
(314) 781-8002
FAX: (314) 781-3363
Contact: Rich Kupferer

Manufacturers of over 500 high quality nylon fabric gear items. Many of our products are made in America and carry our lifetime guarantee.
See Our Ad Across

Bianchi International
100 Calle Cortez
Temecula, CA 92590
(909) 676-5621
FAX: (909) 676-6777
Est.: 1958   Staff: 200
President: Gary French
VP/Sales: Tom Frederick
Dir. of Mktg: Hope Bianchi Sjursen
Available: Retail
Sporting Clays collection of shotgun cases, bags & pouches, constructed from fine English Bridle Leather. Handgun holsters, belts, accessories in leather & nylon. Call us for the retailer nearest you.

The Boyt Harness Co.
220 S. Main, P.O. Box 523
Osceola, IA 50213-0523
(800) 550-2698
(515) 342-6773

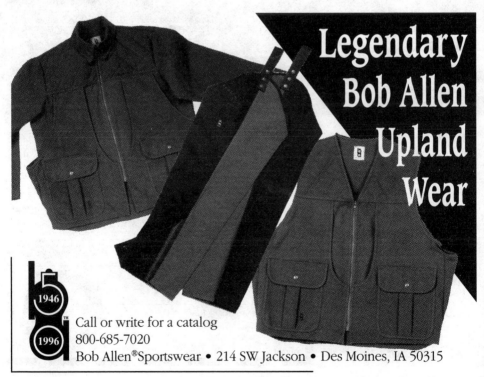

FAX: (515) 342-2703
Est.: 1901   Staff: 300
President: Tony Caligiuri
VP/Admin.: Bob Stout
Available: Retail
Nation's oldest manufacturer of quality gun cases and shooting accessories, specializing in canvas and leather breathable cases. Traditional leather & canvas gun cases and shooting accessories since 1901. "NO NONSENSE" lifetime guarantee. We specialize in durable canvas, breathable gun cases with over 30 styles available. Luggage and field bags, shell bags, new trap & tackle bag, leather slings & holsters. Dealer custom cases available. North American distributors for Brett Parsons & Sons—fine English shooting accessories.

Brauer Brothers Mfg. Co.
2020 Delmar
St. Louis, MO 63103
(314) 231-2864
FAX: (314) 241-4952
VP: Teresa E. Downs
Gun cases, gun sleeves & accessories.

CHIMERE, inc.

Chimere, Inc.
2996 Terrace Ave.
Naples, FL 34104
(941) 417-1417
FAX: (941) 417-1419
President: C.K. "Casey" Koehler
VP/Sales: Mike Boyer
Available: Retail
Competition clothing and accessories; vests, shirts, rainwear, sweaters, gloves, glasses and bags of every kind. Exclusive Remington target apparel licensee.

See Our Ad Pg. 96

Crane & Crane, Ltd.
105 N. Edison Way, Unit 6
Reno, NV 89502
(702) 856-1516
FAX: (702) 856-1616
Contact: Jim & Harriet Crane
Crane & Crane manufactures the most versatile Sporting Clays Range and Upland Game Bags on the market. Designed and constructed here in the USA for strength and durability, our bags come in several different models and a variety of

colors. Custom embroidery is available for individuals and clubs. Visa and MasterCard accepted. Dealer, pro shop and club inquiries welcome.

Fieldline
The Outdoor Recreation Group
1919 Vineburn Ave.
Los Angeles, CA 90032
(800) 438-3353 (Cust. Svc)
(213) 226-0830
FAX: (213) 226-0831
Contact: Mike Dunlap or Joel Altshule
Gen. Mgr: Algird J. Kavalauskas
Available: Retail
Pro-Guide fanny pack system. Modular fanny pack system can be customized to a hunter's specific activity and personal needs.

Galco International
2019 West Quail Ave.
Phoenix, AZ 85027
(602) 258-8295
FAX: (602) 582-6854
President: Rick Gallagher
Exec. VP: Lisa Des Camps
Galco International's Sporting Col-

lection uses only the finest materials available, from rich California latigo leather and rugged waxed canvas, right down to our solid brass hardware handmade in our in-house foundry, to create a full line of gun cases, shell bags, game bags, sporting clays pouches, trap and skeet pouches, belts, leg o'mutton cases, etc.

Holland Brothers
190 Napoleon St.
San Francisco, CA 94124
(415) 824-5995
FAX: (415) 824-0265

Est.: 1984   Staff: 180
Contact: Jay Holland or Tom Sobolewski
Available: Retail
Holland Brothers embraces the return of the by-gone era of American Craftsmanship with its fine line of products. Produced in our own factory, with meticulous attention to every detail. Holland products use prime Latigo leather, with solid brass or gold plate fixtures at the core of each basic piece. Like a well-worn saddle, our leather products improve with age.

Perazzi USA Inc.
1207 South Shamrock Ave.
Monrovia, CA 91016
(818) 303-0068
FAX: (818) 303-2081

Vice President: Lucio Sosta
Available: Through our Dealers
Perazzi offers a selection of quality bags, cases and clothing. Call for the dealer nearest you.

SHOOTING SYSTEMS GROUP INC.

Shooting Systems Group, Inc.
1075 Headquarters Park
Fenton, MO 63026-2478
(800) 325-3049
(314) 343-3575
FAX: (314) 349-3311
President: Bruce Bogue
Shooting Systems has been servicing discerning sportsmen for more than two decades. Our handsome, black ballistic nylon sporting clays bag was developed to meet your exacting needs, including quick access provided by "zipcords"; two movable, adjustable inside walls; four exterior pockets and free choke tube box. Call today to order yours! Pro shop inquiries welcome.

Sporting Bag Specialties
7300 North 101st St.
White Bear Lake, MN 55110
(612) 429-5272
(941) 495-6683 *51 (Phone/Fax)
Contact: John Ward
We have a new catalog and lots of new products. Top quality canvas and leather duffels, gun cases, shoulder bags, carry-on's, rod cases, personals.

WILD-HARE, International
PO Box 11943
Memphis, TN 38111
(800) 523-9453
Est.: 1992
Contact: Jaye Wells
Available: Retail & Direct
Get in gear this season with WILD-HARE's complete shotgunning accessory system. From our SHOT SHELL APRON to our "QUICK-SNAP" GUNBOY, WILD-HARE manufactures the best in affordable, high quality products designed by competition shooters for the sporting clay enthusiast. Available through your local dealer and catalogues.
See Our Ad Across

TAKE A SHOT ON THE WILD SIDE!

SPORT SHOOTERS EVERYWHERE ARE GOING WILD OVER **WILD·HARE'S** AFFORDABLE WORLD-CLASS SHOOTING GEAR, APPAREL, ACCESSORIES, AND CUSTOM COURSE DESIGNS. SO HEY, TAKE A SHOT AND CALL 1-800-523-WILD (9453) FOR OUR CATALOG AND MORE INFORMATION.

P.O. BOX 11943   MEMPHIS,TN 38111
1-800-523-WILD

ACCESSORIES/ GUN

B □ SQUARE

B-SQUARE
2708 St. Louis Ave.
PO Box 11281
Forth Worth, TX 76110
(800) 433-2909
(817) 923-0964
FAX: (817) 926-7012
Est.: 1957
Contact: Rudy Bechtel
Available: Retail & Direct
B-SQUARE Scope Mounts:
See Our Ad Pg. 86

B.A.T. Products, Inc.
Fischer Gunsmithing, Inc.
Box 55-8266
4235 Southwest 75 Ave.
Miami, FL 33155
(305) 261-4454
FAX: (305) 261-4491
Contact: Steve Fischer
Titainium firing pins. Lifetime warranty. Dealer inquiries invited. Call for catalog.

Barrel Button
All Sport Tech
2606 Alden Ct.
West Bloomfield, MI 48324
(810) 360-7118
FAX: (810) 360-7119
Est.: 1990   Staff: 2
Contact: Ira Place
Available: Retail & Direct

Washable long-lasting button for your shoe to rest your gun barrel on.

Beamer Line
Phase Laser Systems, Inc.
14255 N 79th St., Suite 6
Scottsdale, AZ 85260
(602) 998-4828
President: Michael J. Brubacher
Available: Direct
The Impact Laser 12/20 enables you to see precisely what your shotgun barrel "sees" without firing a round. It's compact, light and slides into the muzzle and projects a continuous pattern 100 ft.

BRILEY

Briley Manufacturing
1230 Lumpkin, Houston, TX 77043
(800) 331-5718 (Cust. Svc.)
(713) 932-6995
Contact: Chuck Webb
Available: Retail & Direct
Full line of BRILEY products made by shooters for shooters. Unique accessories include choke cases, choke and bore gauge, Turbo-choke cleaner, Speed Wrench, Unilube choke tube grease, Sportlube pump action lubricant, the best chamber brush you've ever used, and for tube sets, our Power Knockout tool for the easiest insertion or removal of any tube set. Call for brochure.
See Our Ad Pg. 45

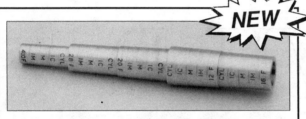
GALAZAN

GALAZAN
A Division of Connecticut Shotgun Manufacturing
PO Box 1692
New Britain, CT 06051-1692
(203) 225-6581
FAX: (203) 832-8707
Est.: 1967   Staff: 20
Contact: Dick Perrett
Available: Direct
Our catalog #2–Quality Gun Products is now available for $5.00. You can order our entire line of fine gun products directly from us. Included are many hard-to-get items including recoil pads and butt plates, gun parts (including all of the Winchester Model 21 parts), hard leather gun cases, gun case accessories, snap caps, shooting accessories, gauges, Turkish Circassian Walnut gunstock wood and tools.
See Our Ad, Left

Holland & Holland, Ltd.
50 East 57th St.
New York, NY 10022
(212) 752-7755
FAX: (212) 752-6805
1-800-SINCE 1835

HOPPE'S  ™
A DIVISION OF PENGUIN INDUSTRIES, INC.

Hoppe's — Penguin Industries, Inc.
Airport Industrial Mall
Coatesville, PA 19320
(610) 384-6000
FAX: (610) 857-5980
Contact: Patricia Lucas
Available: Retail
Shooter's screwdriver–tough light-weight set with storage chambers and spanner handle contains 2 Phillips head bits, 7 slotted head bits and 5 Allen wrenches in the most often needed sizes. May be purchased at your local gun dealer.
See Our Ad, Right

Leupold & Stevens, Inc.
PO Box 688
Beaverton, OR 97075
(503) 646-9171
FAX: (503) 526-1455
Contact: David Nicholson
Available: Retail
Shotgun scopes

MTM Molded Products Co.
PO Box 14117
Dayton, OH 45413
(513) 890-7461
FAX: (513) 890-1747
Contact: Al Minneman
MTM offers the finest in compact and durable Case-Gard™ shotshell boxes for all popular gauges. The 100-round, dust- and moisture-resistant SF-100, has two trays, heavy duty latch, fold-down handle, integral hinge, textured finish. MTM's 100-round dry box, the SD-100, features a removable lid and water-resistant O-ring design. The SF-50 model holds 50 shotshells with space for duck or goose calls, choke tubes. The Case-Gard™ Tube Box holds three long or six short 12-gauge choke tubes. Long enough for most choke tube wrenches. Foam in lid reduces rattle, protects threads. And MTM's stackable Shotshell Trays, perfect for storing reloads, hold 50 rounds, save space in your reloading area. Phone or fax for free catalog or name of nearest dealer.

Magic Dot Corporation
PO Box 513, Elm Grove, WI 53122
(414) 546-1399
FAX: (414) 546-1105
Est.: 1984   Staff: 6
President: Hugh Brown
Contact: Robert P. Ryan or Rich Stpniewksi
Available: Retail & Direct
Using Magic Dot on your shooting glasses, to correct cross dominance, double vision, and ghost image, lets you shoot with both eyes opened.

MARBLE'S ™
Poly-Choke'

Marble Arms/Poly-Choke
CRL, Inc.
PO Box 111, Gladstone, MI 49837
(906) 428-3710
FAX: (906) 428-3711
Est.: 1898   Staff: 15
President: Craig Lauerman
Available: Direct
Add a Poly-Choke® anodized, ventilated rib to your over/under, pump, auto or single shot and get on your target easier, quicker. Less than two ounces, no drilling or tapping, front and mid sights, we install, all for $79.75 plus shipping.
Or choose the high-rise International style. Complete on plain barrel $190, or $95 for top rib on existing rib, plus shipping. For a free catalog, write Marble Arms, Dept. WC, PO Box 111, Gladstone, MI 49837. Phone (906) 428-3710.
See Our Ad Pg. 202

Meadow Industries
PO Box 754, Dept. WC
Locust Grove, VA 22508
(540) 972-2175 (Phone/Fax)
Contact: Ken Vickers
Available: Retail & Direct
Accessories for your gun: "Brite-Site Crossfire"-Eliminator; Soft-Comb Shock Absorber System; Convert-A-Stock Pad; 12 Ga. Barrel-Buddy.

New England Custom Gun Service, Ltd.
Brook Rd., RR#2
Box 122W
W. Lebanon, NH 03784
(603) 469-3450
Est.: 1986   Staff: 3
Contact: Dietrich Apel
We stock an assortment of gun accessories including leather shotgun hand guards, shotgun snap caps made of chrome & aluminum, hardwood snap cap blocks, and engraved grip caps which can be personalized; true ivory beads, recoil pads, leather covered pads, spacers and buffplates, rubber finger protectors. Please request brochure.

Quality Arms, Inc.
PO Box 19477
Houston, TX 77224
(713) 870-8377
FAX: (713) 870-8524
Contact: John Boyd
Available: Direct
Fine imported accessories for the serious sportsman: European snap caps; oil bottles; English cleaning rods or complete sets; handguards; English oils and European cartridge boxes; Trunk style cases; European shotshells.

Tasco Sales, Inc.
PO Box 520080
7600 Northwest 26 St.
Miami, FL 33152-0080
(305) 591-3670 (Ext. 315)
FAX: (305) 592-5895
Contact: George Edwards
Available: Retail
Bantom scopes & PRO-point sighting device for shotguns can improve turkey hunters' performance and is excellent for other shotgun shooting applications.

ACCESSORIES/
SLINGS & CARRIERS

A A & E Leathercraft, Inc.
208 Industrial Loop
PO Box 76, Yaokum, TX 77995
(512) 293-6366
FAX: (512) 293-9127
Vice President: Emil Blaschke
Leather gun slings and hunting products for the outdoorsman.

Butt Buddy Holster
The Long Gun Holster Co.
Box 225, Olpe, KS 68865
(800) 345-2195 (Orders)
Est.: 1989
Contact: Jerry Gerleman
Available: Retail & Direct
A leather belt holster that allows the hunter to carry his gun at the ready and do away with the fatigue that sets in after carrying a shotgun/rifle for a long time.

Gun Boat
Box 381057, Birmingham, AL 35238
(800) 486-2628
FAX: (205) 995-5532
Contact: Arlie Fortner
Floating gun case

Gun Porter™
PO Box 316, Hwy. 38E
Marshfield, MO 65706
(800) 697-7491
Contact: Ed Porter
Gun Porter is 14" and attaches to your belt.

Michaels of Oregon Co.
(Uncle Mike's)
PO Box 13010
Portland, OR 97213
(503) 255-6890
FAX: (503) 255-0746
Available: Retail
Firearm/hunting accessories: sling swivels, leather and nylon slings, recoil pads, and gun cases.

The Outdoor Connnection, Inc.
PO Box 7751
201 Cotton Dr.
Waco, TX 76714
(800) 533-6076 (Sales)
(817) 772-5575
FAX: (817) 776-3553
Contact: Floyd Hightower
Super-Sling 2t, total shotgun sling system.

Palsa Outdoor Products
PO Box 81336
Lincoln, NE 68501-1336
(800) 456-9281
(402) 488-5288
FAX: (402) 488-2321
Maker of ADD-A-SLING easily and quickly slips on or off. Also ADD-A-PAD which can be built up to a thickness of one inch.

The Safety Connection Gun Cling
Hard Target, Inc.
PO Box 652
Corbin, KY 40702
(800) 887-1799 (Orders)
(606) 528-1799
FAX: (606) 528-8794
Pres: Harold W. Turner
Available: Retail & Direct
The Cling's unique design gives a hands-free carrying system and prevents the muzzle of the gun from being pointed at the head or torso if the hunter should fall or drop the gun. Dealer inquiries also welcome.

APPAREL/
CLOTHING

For related products & services see:
* *Mail Order Catalogs, Pg. 179*
* *Accessories, Pg. 84*

Every sport has its look, and hunting and shooting are no exceptions. The apparel manufacturers in the section that follows produce clothing and accessories for all tastes and budgets. If you're a retailer or a pro-shop manager, write or call them directly for information. Individuals interested in a particular company should check with that company to see if it sells direct to the consumer; or, if it doesn't, to get a list of nearby retailers that carry its product line.

10x Products Group
2915 LBJ Freeway, Suite 133
Dallas, TX 75234
(800) WEAR10X
(214) 243-4016
FAX: (214) 243-4112
Contact: Tom Carlson
Available: Retail
Since 1934, 10x has maintained a proud American tradition of making clothes for the Great Outdoors. The 10x line of high-tech hunting apparel includes: lightweight and insulated Gore-Tex fabric garments; quiet, new Shikari Cloth insulated and non-insulated rainwear; upland hunting clothes; and coats, coveralls, bibs and pants in the most popular camouflage patterns. 10x also offers high-quality vests, jackets, shirts and accessories for shooting enthusiasts.
See Our Ad Across

Bob Allen Companies
214 S.W. Jackson St.
PO Box 477
Des Moines, IA 50315
(800) 685-7020
FAX: (515) 283-0779
Est.: 1946   Staff: 150

FOLKS HAVE A BLAST WEARING 10X® SHOOTING AND HUNTING CLOTHES

Whether you're a professional, or just aiming to become one, 10x has the shooting garments and accessories that hit the mark.

Pick up a 10x vest and you'll see a range of field-tested features. You'll find international-style recoil pads. Large, expandable shell pockets. Even covered choke tube and wrench pockets. And every 10x garment is crafted with rugged construction for years of wear with very little care.

The heritage of 10x product leadership is in every garment we make. And after more than 60 years in the shooting apparel business, we aren't about to blow our reputation by building anything less than the very best.

10x
An American Tradition Since 1934 ®

2915 LBJ Freeway, Suite 133 • Dallas, Texas 75234

Call 1-800-WEAR 10X for the 10x retailer near you.
Call 1-800-433-2225 to become a 10x retailer.

Ch. Board: Bob Allen
President: Matt Allen
Nat'l. Sales Mgr: Pam Bradford
Available: Retail & Direct
Bob Allen Sportswear is a premier manufacturer of shooting wear for sporting clays, trap and skeet as well as gun cases, gloves and accessories.
See Our Ad Pg. 84

Barbour, Inc.
55 Meadowbrook Dr.
Milford, NH 03055
(800) 338-3474
FAX: (603) 673-6510
VP/Sales & Mktg: Jeammie Amos
Gen. Mgr: Tom Hooven
Available: Retail
Waxed cotton jackets, shooting vests and country clothing & accessories.

Beretta U.S.A.
c/o Beretta Gallery
New York:
718 Madison Ave.
New York, NY 10021
(212) 319-6614
Alexandria:
317 S. Washington St.
Old Town Alexandria, VA 22314
(703) 739-0596
Beretta Sport casual, travel and hunting apparel plus shooting vests and shooting accessories.

Browning
One Browning Place
Morgan, UT 84050
(800) 333-3288 (Customer)
(801) 876-2711 (General)
FAX: (801) 876-3331
Est.: 1878   Staff: 350
Available: Retail
Waterproof fleece, insultated outerwear, Dura-wax, down garments, rainwear, shirts, pants, underwear & socks.

Carhartt, Inc.
PO Box 600
Dearborn, MI 48121
(800) 833-3118 (Consumer)
(800) 358-3825 (Retail)
Est.: 1889   Staff: 2000
Contact: Customer Service
Available: Retail
All cotton rugged hunting and outerwear.

Columbia Sportswear
6600 N. Baltimore
Portland, OR 97203
(800) MABOYLE (Retail Inquiries)
(503) 286-3676
Est.: 1938   Staff: 800
Sr. Merch. Mgr: Dave Robinson

Available: Retail
Manufacturer of high quality, value-priced outdoor apparel and footwear.

Christopher Dawes Countrywear
Chapel Field Barn, 2 Old Bank
Ripponden, Sowerby Bridge, West Yorkshire HX6 4DG England
011-44-42-282-4600
FAX: 011-44-42-282-2401
Available: Retail
Contact: Christopher Dawes/Jeremy Beaumont for agents in your area.
Exclusive range of men's and ladies' country clothing for all field sports.

C.C. Filson Company
PO Box 34020
Seattle, WA 98124
(206) 624-4437
FAX: (206) 624-4539
Est.: 1897
Contact: Steve Matson
Available: Retail & Direct
C.C. Filson is a manufacturer of quality outdoor clothing, luggage and hats.

Flint River Outdoor Wear
5731 Miller Ct.
Columbus, GA 31909
(706) 562-0005
Contact: Cathy Conine

Hamilton's
PO Box 2672
S. Vineland, NJ 08360
(800) 292-3695
FAX: (609) 691-0398
Contact: Timothy D. Hamilton
Sportsman's Jacket 100% Egyptian waxed cloth, 5 pockets, two-way brass zipper, snap on hood, tartan lining, olive green. Sizes XS-XXXL.
Price: $139.00 ppd. Call for brochure.
See Our Ad Across

Hatch Gloves & Accessories
1656 Walter St.
Suite B
Ventura, CA 93003
(800) 767-1343 (Customer Svc)
(805) 642-0170
FAX: (805) 642-0224
Est.: 1964   Staff: 12
Contact: Lisa Hatch Sciuto
Pres/CEO: Robert J. Hatch
VP/Sales & Mktg: Joshua Cranford
Available: Retail
Clay target shooting and all weather hunting gloves. Distributor & dealer inquiries welcome.

Holland & Holland, Ltd.
50 East 57th St.
New York, NY 10022
(212) 752-7755
FAX: (212) 752-6805
Mail Orders: 1-800-SINCE 1835
Superb country clothing, silks and accessories.

Hunting World, Inc.
PO Box 5981
Sparks, NV 89432
(702) 331-0414
FAX: (702) 331-1130
President: Robert M. Lee
Available: Retail
Clothing & accessories of classic design.

Kobuk®, Inc.
2639 N. Grand Ave.
Suite 268
Santa Ana, CA 92705
(714) 953-6658
FAX: (714) 953-6628
Est.: 1982
Nat'l. Sales Mgr: Dan Reed
World's finest neoprene hunting and fishing outerwear and accessories.

Kool Dri® Rainwear
550 W. Rt. 897
PO Box 120
Reinholds, PA 17569
(800) 523-8025
Contact: Earl Myers
Rain protection for the sportsperson: Kool Dri™ rainsuit, 3/4 parka, waders and casual suits.

Lady Thompson Sports, Inc.

Lady Thompson Sports, Inc.
PO Box 129
Watauga, TN 37694
(800) 331-8116 (Orders)
(423) 543-4302
FAX: (423) 543-7173
President: Cindy Thompson
Shooting apparel and accessories of distinction. Our products are American-made. Custom work is welcome.
See Our Ad Pg. 97

Lewis Creek Company
1 Pine Haven Shore Rd.
Shelburne, VT 05482
(800) 336-4884
(802) 985-1099
FAX: (802) 985-1097
President: Jeff Pratt
Available: Retail

Outerwear, shooting apparel and accessories. Traditional American designs as well as classic European influence.

Marathon Apparel
150 Hollywood, PO Box 509
Childersburg, AL 35044
(205) 378-8060
FAX: (205) 378-6090
Est.: 1991   Staff: 40
Dir. of Advtg: Louise Gaither
Available: Retail
Men's sportswear-with "Country Gentleman" look.

The Martin Company
Box 502, Gold Beach, OR 97444
(800) 705-0367
FAX: (503) 247-7126
Contact: Greg Martin
The Martin Company Fly Fishing Outfitters offers a handsome, full color catalog of the finest products available for the fly fisher and up-land bird hunter. Featuring waxed cotton and other waterproof garments, Gore-Tex fleece, custom rods, leather goods, gift items, and much, much more! Call or write for free catalog.

Mossy Oak
Haas Outdoors, Inc.
200 East Main St., PO Box 757
West Point, MS 39773
(601) 494-8859
Contact: Toxey Haas
Available: Retail
Camouflage hunting apparel and accessories.

Norton & Sons, Inc.
16 Savile Row
London W1X 1AE England
011-44-171-437-0829
FAX: 011-44-171-287-4764
Managing Dir: John Granger
Available: Direct
Traditional Scottish tweeds. Savile Row designed field sports clothing enhanced with breathable Gortex for all weather protection.

PAST Sporting Goods, Inc.
PO Box 1035
Columbia, MO 65205
(573) 445-9200
Est.: 1980   Staff: 12
President: Dick Leeper
The finest in wearable recoil protection and accessories for all shooting

sports–Recoil Shields-Shooting Vests-Shooting Gloves-Gun Vise-Tumbler-Hunting Vest-Shooting Accessories-Shooting Glasses-Shooting Shirts-And More. Full line available for all ages. To purchase any of our fine products please contact your local shooting sports retailer or gun club manager. Available in both right and left handed. 100% U.S. made.

Pendleton Woolen Mills
220 N.W. Broadway
Portland, OR 97208
(503) 226-4801
FAX: (503) 273-2599
Contact: Lynnette Loop
Available: Retail
Full clothing line for men and women: shirts, pants, vests, hats.

Simmons™ Outdoor Corporation
2120 Killearney Way
Tallahassee, FL 32308-3402
(904) 878-5100
FAX: (904) 878-0300
Est.: 1995
MasterGude™ by Simmons outdoor and camouflage clothing.

Suzy Smith Outdoor Sportswear
29130 W. US Hwy. 160
South Fork, CO 81154
(719) 873-5121
FAX: (719) 873-5414
Contact: Suzy Smith

Spartan-RealTree Products, Inc.
1390 Box Circle,Columbus, GA 31907
(706) 569-9101
FAX: (706) 569-5634
Contact: Bill Jordan
Available: Retail
Hunting clothes: Bill Jordan's RealTree camouflage clothing includes clothing in the RealTree All-Purpose pattern. Fabrics include 100% cotton ripstop, 50/50 brushed twill, 100% cotton knits, Polar Tuff, several types of netting and other; products include 100% cotton tees, coats, pants, shorts, netting items, hats, sports shirts, western shirts, bib overalls, and a complete line of youth clothing.

Steinman's
Rt. 4, Box 193F, Chanute, KS 66720
(316) 431-1936
FAX: (316) 431-4660
Est.: 1995   Staff: 12

Contact: Donna Steinman
Available: Retail & Direct
Shooting shirts–100% cotton twills
and denims

Storm Shooting Apparel
320 E. 14th St., Wahoo, NE 68066
(402) 443-3720
Est.: 1990
Pres: John Storm
Available: Retail & Direct
Shooting apparel-jackets, vests and
pants.

Walls Industries, Inc.
PO Box 98
Cleburne, TX 76033
(817) 645-4366
FAX: (817) 645-7946
Est.: 1943   Staff: 1500
Contact: Jim Lowstetter
Available: Retail
Leading manufacturer of insulated
and non-insulated hunting, outdoor
and work wear apparel. Hunting
garments (in blaze orange and cam-
ouflage) include coveralls, overalls,
Water-Pruf breathable rain suits,
shirts, pants, coats and accessories.

Woolrich, Inc.
1 Mill St.
Woolrich, PA 17779
(800) 995-1299
(717) 769-6464
FAX: (717) 769-6234
Est.: 1830   Staff: 2150

VP/Merchandising: Rick Insley
Available: Retail
Manufacturers of rugged outdoor
sportswear & hunting wear. Consumer may call to find local retailer
information.

Zanika Sportswear
Outside Interests, Inc.
4315 Oliver Ave. North
Minneapolis, MN 55412
(612) 529-1785
FAX: (612) 521-4481
Contact: Veronica M. Morgan
Zanika Sportswear is a new outdoor clothing system for women
only! Now you can have function,
and great styling, all made to fit
you perfectly. And we have a
bonus feature to make your experience in the outdoors even more
comfortable. Zanika features a
unique "female fly" allowing
woman to answer nature's call without "removing it all." Invisible
zippers and pull-apart layers are dis-
creetly employed in each garment
from thermal underwear to our insulated outerwear. Available in
Realtree and Advantage.

APPAREL/
FOOTWEAR

Bottes Le Chameau
14690 Pont-D'Ouilly, Cahan France
Est.: 1927
011-33-31-698045
FAX: 011-33-31-697979
Contact: Astrid Judmaier and
Ghislain Pages
Le Chameau is the first company to
use leather and Neoprene as a lining, and as such is considered to
offer "The Ultimate Boot".

Chippewa Boot Company
PO Box 548, Fort Worth, TX 76101
(817) 332-4385
FAX: (817) 390-2566   Est.: 1901
Div. Mgr: Pete Hillier
Work sport and utility boots. We
put only the finest elements into
Chippewas. Call for the retailer
nearest you.

Danner Shoe Mfg. Co.
12722 NE Airport Way
PO Box 30148, Portland, OR 97230
(800) 345-0430
FAX: (503) 251-1119
Est.: 1932   Staff: 160
President: Eric Merk, Sr.
Ass't. Nat'l. Sales Mgr: Eric Merk, Jr.
Available: Retail & Direct
Mfg. of quality rugged footwear.
Guaranteed against defects and
leakage for 2 years.

Herman Survivors
Joseph M. Herman Shoe Corp.
200 Business Park Dr.
Suite 100, Armonk, NY 10504
(800) 962-4007
(914) 273-4499
FAX: (914) 273-6980
Est.: 1879
Vice President: Anthony DiPaolo
Available: Retail
The Herman Survivors outdoor
boot line has been designed to
meet the quality, value and innovation that today's outdoorsmen
demands. Herman Survivors waterproof collection has been expanded
to meet all the expectations of
today's consumer. For over 117
years Herman Survivors has been
dedicated to making the absolute
best product at a fair price. Call
(800) 962-4007.

See Our Ad, Left

Irish Setter Sport Boots
Red Wing Shoe Company
314 Main St.
Red Wing, MN 55066
(612) 388-8211
FAX: (612) 388-7415
Est.: 1948   Staff: 1500
Div. Mgr: Jerry Eckstrom
Available: Retail
Leading manufacturer of outdoor footwear – over 20 styles.

LaCrosse Footwear, Inc.
1319 St. Andrew St., PO Box 1328
LaCrosse, WI 54603
(800) 323-2668
FAX: (800) 658-9444
Est.: 1897   Staff: 1300
Contact: Tiffany Schilla
Available: Retail
Premium quality hand-crafted rubber footwear

Rocky Shoes & Boots, Inc.
39 E. Canal
Nelsonville, OH 45764
(800) 848-9452
(614) 753-1951
FAX: (614) 753-4024

W.C. Russell Moccasin Co.
285 S.W. Franklin
Berlin, WI 54923
(414) 361-2252
FAX: (414) 361-3274
Est.: 1889   Staff: 30
Pres: Ralph Fabricius
Available: Direct
Hand lasted custom made hunting and shooting boots and shoes. Any size, any width, color, height. Specializing in special orders and hard to fit boots. Sporting clays shoes, bird hunting boots, safari shoes & boots, big game hunting boots.
See Our Below

Timberland Company
PO Box 5050
Hampton, NH 03842
(800) 445-5545 (Customer Svc)
Available: Retail
Consumer can call 800# to find local retailers carrying apparel.

B.B. Walker Company
414 East Dixie Dr.
PO Box 1167
Asheboro, NC 27204
(800) 334-1242
(910) 625-1380
FAX: (910) 625-8125
Customer Svc. Mgr: Betty Howard
Sales Mgr: Norman Miller
Available: Retail
Golden Retriever Rugged Outdoor Footwear.

Art Carter's

Traveling Sportsman Chukka
by Russell

As Executive Editor of Sporting Classics and Traveling Sportsman, and having traveled the world for 25 years, Art Carter knows something of traveling. Art identified a need for a special multipurpose shoe... one handsome enough to be worn while traveling yet versatile enough to literally step off an airplane and be worn afield for a day of shooting. The Traveling Sportsman features built in heel counters, a comfortable cushion collar, a grippy Vibram Air-Bob sole, water resistant double vamp construction, a supportive hand molded outer sole, and an extra wide cut gusset for variable-tightness lacing. The entire shoe is fashioned from buttery-soft heirloom French Veal leather...the fine grained, long lasting leather that remains soft and supple for a lifetime. If you're a traveling sportsman...a pair of these fine shoes is a modern day necessity.

Russell Handmades...as perfect as human hands can make them

THE W.C. RUSSELL MOCCASIN CO.
285 S.W. Franklin • P.O. Box 309
Dept. BSC • Berlin, WI 54923
Phone:(414) 361-2252 • FAX (414) 361-3274

APPAREL/ VESTS

10x Products Group
2915 LBJ Freeway, Suite 133
Dallas, TX 75234
(800) WEAR10X
(214) 243-4016
FAX: (214) 243-4112
Contact: Tom Carlson
Available: Retail
Since 1934, 10x has maintained a proud American tradition of making clothes for the Great Outdoors. The 10x line of high-tech hunting apparel includes: lightweight and insulated Gore-Tex fabric garments; quiet, new Shikari Cloth insulated and non-insulated rainwear; upland hunting clothes; and coats, coveralls, bibs and pants in the most popular camouflage patterns. 10x also offers high-quality vests, jackets, shirts and accessories for shooting enthusiasts.
See Our Ad Pg. 91

A.D.S. Vest
459 Lois
Louisville, CO 80027
(303) 665-7369
FAX: (303) 666-4806
Est.: 1979   Staff: 2
Contact: Alberto DeSimone
Available: Direct
Custom made shooting vests of supreme quality.

Bob Allen Companies
214 S.W. Jackson St.
PO Box 477 ,
Des Moines, IA 50315
(800) 685-7020
FAX: (515) 283-0779
Est.: 1946   Staff: 150
Pres: Matt Allen
Nat'l. Sales Mgr: Pam Bradford
Available: Retail & Direct
Full line of vest for men & women. Premier manufacturer of shooting wear for sporting clays, trap and skeet as well as gun cases, gloves and accessories.
See Our Ad Pg. 84

B.T.P. Sports
10 Elm St., W, Valhalla, NY 10595
(914) 949-8183
Contact: Dick Thomas

Available: Direct
The ultimate shooting sweaters: Skookum and sporting clays models available.

Barbour, Inc.
55 Meadowbrook Dr.
Milford, NH 03055
(800) 338-3474
FAX: (603) 673-6510
Gen. Mgr.: Tom Hooven
VP/Sales & Mktg: Jeammie Amos
Available: Retail
Ganton vest line: all Barbour shooting vests are available in sizes 34" to 52". Functional features vary from vest to vest. Call for a brochure.

British Sporting Vest
British Sporting Arms Ltd.
RR1, Box 193A
Millbrook, NY 12545
(914) 677-8303
Contact: Margaret Schneible
Available: Retail & Direct
Customized vests available in many colors. Special features include mesh backs, left hand, and custom embroidery.

Browning
One Browning Place
Morgan, UT 84050

(800) 333-3288 (Customer)
(801) 876-2711 (General)
FAX: (801) 876-3331
Est.: 1878   Staff: 350
Available: Retail
"REACTAR" Technical shooting vests
and upland "Dura-Wax" vests

CHIMERE, inc.
Chimere, Inc.
2996 Terrace Ave.
Naples, FL 34104
(941) 417-1417
FAX: (941) 417-1419
President: C.K. "Casey" Koehler
VP/Sales: Mike Boyer
Available: Retail
Competition clothing and accessories: vests, shirts, rainwear, sweaters, gloves, glasses and bags of every kind. Exclusive Remington target apparel licensee.
See Our Ad Across, Left

C.C. Filson Company
PO Box 34020, Seattle, WA 98124
(206) 624-4437
Contact: Steve Matson
Available: Retail & Direct
Hunting vests available in oil finish tin cloth and shelter cloth.

Game Winner, Inc.
2625 Cumberland Pkwy., #220
Atlanta, GA 30339
(404) 434-9210
FAX: (404) 434-9215
Sales Mgr: Robert Ingram
Available: Direct
Upland shooting vests in a variety of fabrics. Call for information.

Lady Thompson Sports, Inc.
PO Box 129, Watauga, TN 37694
(800) 331-8116 (Orders)
(423) 543-4302
FAX: (423) 543-7173
President: Cindy Thompson
Shooting vests, apparel and accessories of distinction. Our products are American-made. Custom work is welcome.
See Our Ad Below

NICA Shooting Accessories
5334 Hillary Circle
Parker, CO 80134
(303) 840-9949
Est.: 1994   Staff: 2
Contact: Brenda Mason

PAST Sporting Goods, Inc.
PO Box 1035, Columbia, MO 65205
(573) 445-9200
Est.: 1980   Staff: 12
Pres: Dick Leeper
Available: Retail & Direct
The finest in wearable recoil protection and accessories for all shooting sports–Recoil Shields-Shooting Vests-Shooting Gloves-Gun Vise-Tumbler-Hunting Vest-Shooting Accessories- Shooting Glasses-Shooting Shirts-And More. Full Line available for all ages. To purchase any of our fine products please contact your local shooting sports retailer.

Shoot the Moon
1730 Monterey Rd., Suite 103
Colorado Springs, CO 80910
(719) 630-3825
FAX: (719) 578-9626
Est.: 1992
Contact: Susan Carter
Available: Retail & Direct

Female apparel – shooting vests, relaxed shooting shirts, quilted Bomber jackets, brush pants, anaoracks - special orders.

Vermont Vest
RR1, Box 4231
Bennington, VT 05201
(802) 442-4250
Contact: Tom Crowley
Available: Direct
A New England tradition of quality and workmanship. Men's and ladies' shooting vests for sporting clays, trap or skeet. Custom fitting.

WILD-HARE, International
PO Box 11943, Memphis, TN 38111
(800) 523-9453
Est.: 1992
Contact: Jaye Wells
Available: Retail & Direct
Our SHOOTING VEST features large double bellow pockets allowing for plenty of shell space. Our distinctive logo is embroidered into the regulation FITASC line. Button tab adjustments along the back allow for a proper fit at the waist, as well as a double brass zippered front. Made of supple cognac pigskin and a durable cotton blend, our vest cuts a stylish appearance both on and off the course. We also offer our SHOOTER'S WAISTCOAT and FIELDCOAT made to the same exacting standards as our VEST. Available through your local dealer and catalogues.
See Our Ad Pg. 87

ASSOCIATIONS

The interests of America's sportsmen and sportswomen are served by a large number of associations and organizations. You will find valuable information about the largest and most influential of these groups in the five sections that follow:

- *CONSERVATIONS GROUPS*
- *DOG CLUBS & ASSOCIATIONS*
- *GUN RIGHTS GROUPS*
- *SHOOTING ORGANIZATIONS*
- *TRADE ASSOCIATIONS*

CONSERVATION GROUPS

American Forests Assoc.
PO Box 2000
Washington, DC 20013
(202) 667-3300
Est.: 1875   Staff: 30
Members: 148,000
Exec. VP: Deborah Gangloff

The American Friends of the Game Conservancy
910 Pierremont Rd.
Suite 250
Shreveport, LA 71106
(318) 868-3631
FAX: (318) 861-4000
Est.: 1986
Exec. Dir: Don Evans

Boone and Crockett Club
250 Station Dr.
Missoula, MT 59801-2753
(406) 542-1888
Est.: 1887   Staff: 6
Members: 128
Dir. of Big Game Records: Jack Reneau

Congressional Sportsmen's Foundation
1730 K St., NW
Washington, DC 20006
(202) 785-9153
FAX: (202) 785-9155
Est.: 1989
Members: 600
Chairman: David B. Rockland, Ph.D.

President: Tom Sadler
The Congressional Sportsmen's Foundation is dedicated to "preserving and promoting our Nation's outdoor heritage, in particular sport hunting and angling." The Foundation's programs closely parallel those of the Congressional Sportsmen's Caucus which is comprised of more than 40 percent of the U.S. Congress. Referred to as "the sportsmen's link to Congress," the Foundation works to ensure that sportsmen have a strong voice in the Nation's capital. The CSF is supported through membership dues.

See Our Ad Across

Delta Waterfowl Foundation
PO Box 3128
Bismarck, ND 58502
(888) WTR-FOWL
FAX: (701) 223-4645
Est.: 1911   Staff: 12
VP: Lloyd A. Jones
Members: 12,000

Ducks Unlimited
One Waterfowl Way
Memphis, TN 38120
(901) 758-3825
Est.: 1937   Staff: 270
Members: 550,000
Exec. VP: Matthew B. Connolly, Jr.
Chrmn: Donald L. Rollins
Pres: Gene Henry
Tr: Charles H. Wright
Membership Mgr: J. William Straughan
Shoot Prog. Mgr: Gary Goodpaster
Since 1937, Ducks Unlimited has worked ceaselessly to restore, enhance and preserve North America's vanishing wetlands. In its 58-year history, DU has conserved 7 million acres of habitat which are now utilized by more than 600 wildlife species.

Foundation for North American Wild Sheep
720 Allen Ave, Cody, WY 82414
(307) 527-6261
Est.: 1981   Staff: 7
Members: 6,000
Exec. Dir: Karen Werbelow

Game Conservation International
PO Box 17444
San Antonio, TX 78217
(210) 824-7509
Est.: 1967   Staff: 2
Members: 1,000
Exec. Dir: Larry Means

Geese Unlimited
PO Box 647
Grand Rapids, MN 55744-0647
(218) 327-0774
FAX: (218) 327-1349
Est.: 1984   Staff: 1
Members: 1,000
Exec. Dir: Butch Bakken
Conservation organization dedicated to the proper management of the Canada goose functioning through relocation, habitat enhancement and legislation.

International Association of Fish & Wildlife Agencies
444 N. Capitol St., NW #544
Washington, DC 20001
(202) 624-7890
Est.: 1902   Staff: 12
Members: 450
Exec. VP: R. Max Peterson

Izaak Walton League of America
707 Conservation Lane
Gaithersburg, MD 20878-2983
(301) 548-0150
Est.: 1922   Staff: 27
Members: 55,000
Exec. Dir: Paul Hansen

National Fish and Wildlife Foundation
1120 Connecticut Ave., NW, #900
Washington, DC 20036
(202) 857-0166
Exec. Dir: Amos Eno

National Forest Foundation
1099 14th St., NW
Suite 5600 W
Washington, DC 20005-3419
(202) 501-2473
FAX: (202) 219-6585
Est.: 1993
Chairman: Grant Gregory
Exec. Dir.: J. Lamar Beasley

National Wild Turkey Federation
PO Box 530
Edgefield, SC 29824
(803) 637-3106
Est.: 1973   Staff: 55
Members: 110,000
Exec. VP: Rob Keck

National Wildlife Federation
8925 Leesburg Pike
Vienna, VA 22180
(703) 790-4000
Est.: 1936   Staff: 650
Members: Over 4 million
Pres: Mark Van Potten

Orion-The Hunters Institute

PO Box 5088
Helena, MT 59604
(406) 449-2795
Est.: 1993
Contact: Jim Posewitz
Orion-The Hunters Institute is a non-profit organization created to sustain hunting and resources essential to that purpose. National in scope, the institute works to assure ethical and responsible hunting.

Pheasants Forever

PO Box 75473
St. Paul, MN 55175
(612) 773-2000
Est.: 1982   Staff: 30
Members: 73,000
Exec. Dir: Jeffrey S. Finden
Membership Svc: Elizabeth A. Whitten
Pres. B/Directors: George A. Wilson

Pope and Young Club

Box 548
Chatfield, MN 55923
(507) 867-4144
Est.: 1961   Staff: 3
Members: 3,200
Exec. Sec: Glen E. Hisey

Putting People First

PO Box 1707
Helena, MT 59624
(406) 442-5700
FAX: (406) 442-5700
Est.: 1990   Staff: 8
Members: 45,000
Chairman: Kathleen Marquardt
Putting People First is a non-profit grassroots network of concerned citizens dedicated to human rights, animal welfare and conservation. We are ordinary people who eat meat, drink milk, support biomedical research, wear leather and wool, hunt and fish, own pets, go to zoos, circuses and rodeos, and who benefit from the wise and rational use of the earth's resources. We believe in balancing science, reason, and common sense against the deception, coersion and terrorism of the animal rights and green movements. Putting People First seeks to enhance the quality of life through the responsible use of animals and our environment.

Quail Unlimited

31 Quail Run, PO Box 610
Edgefield, SC 29824-0610
(803) 637-5731

FAX: (803) 637-0037
Est.: 1981
Members: 48,000
Exec. VP: Rocky Evans
Adm. VP: Jerry Allen
Quail Unlimited is a national non-profit conservation organization dedicated to the wise use and management of America's quail and upland game birds. Primarily a habitat management organization, the organization funds its projects through a network of chapters throughout the country.

Rocky Mountain Elk Foundation

PO Box 8249, Missoula, MT 59807
(800) CALL ELK
(406) 523-4500
FAX: (406) 523-4550
Est.: 1984   Staff: 106
Members: 100,000+
Exec. Dir: Robert W. Munson
Mission to ensure the future of elk and other wildlife by conserving, restoring, enhancing natural habitats. Publish "Bugle" Magazine.

The Ruffed Grouse Society

Dept. 110, 451 McCormick Rd.
Corapolis, PA 15108
(412) 262-4044
(888) 564-6747
Est.: 1961   Staff: 20
Members: 23,000
Exec. Dir: Samuel Pursglove, Jr.
Dir. of Com: Paul E. Carson
Membership: Roberta Sandell
Formed in 1961, the Ruffed Grouse Society uses education and leadership to enhance habitat for ruffed grouse, woodcock and other forest-dwelling animals.

Safari Club International

4800 W. Gates Pass Rd.
Tucson, AZ 86745
(602) 620-1220
Est.: 1971   Staff: 40
Members: 30,000
Exec. Dir: Philip L. DeLone
Membership Association for Hunters and Conservationists–Non-Profit

Tread Lightly!, Inc.

298 24th St.
Suite 325
Ogden, UT 84401
(801) 627-0077
FAX: (801) 621-8633
Est.: 1990   Staff: 5
Director: Lari McNeely
Members: 3,000

Waterfowl USA

Box 50, Edgefield, SC 29824
(803) 637-5767

FAX: (803) 637-6983
Est.: 1983   Staff: 10
Members: 20,000
President: Roger White
Waterfowl U.S.A. is the only national, non-profit, conservation organization, dedicated to using funds in the areas in which they are raised for local and state waterfowl projects. It was founded by biologists for the purpose of preserving and improving wintering and breeding habitat within the United States.

Whitetails Unlimited

PO Box 720
Sturgeon Bay, WI 54235
(414) 743-6777
Est.: 1982   Staff: 20
Members: 40,000
CEO: Peter J. Gerl

The Wilderness Society

900 17th St., NW
Washington, DC 20006
(202) 429-2637 (Member Services)
Est.: 1935   Staff: 108
Members: 313,000
Counselor: Gaylord Nelson
Non-profit membership organization devoted to preserving America's wilderness heritage.

Wildlife Habitat Council

1010 Wayne Ave., Suite 920
Silver Spring, MD 20910
(301) 588-8994
Est.: 1988   Staff: 11
Members: 115
Pres: Bill W. Howard
Promotes habitat enhancement on private lands.

Wildlife Management Institute

1101 14th St., NW, Suite 801
Washington, DC 20005
(202) 371-1808
Est.: 1911   Staff: 15
Pres: Rollin D. Sparrowe

The Wildlife Society

5410 Grosvenor Lane
Bethesda, MD 20814
(301) 897-9770
Est.: 1937   Staff: 12
Members: 9,500
Exec. Dir: Harry E. Hodgdon
Non-profit scientific and educational organization to enhance the ability of wildlife professionals to conserve diversity, sustain productivity and ensure responsible use of wildlife resources.

There Are People Who Think Your Business Is Just a Game. . . A Game You Can Afford To Lose.

But, your business ISN'T a game—it's your living, and now anti-gun extremists are playing with your livelihood.

Whether you are in the firearms, hunting and shooting industry or just a concerned business owner who realizes the importance of passing on our shooting sports tradition to the next generation, you can show anti-gun legislators that thousands of local businesses will not stand by and allow them to strip away our nation's heritage.

Their goal is to see the doors of shooting and hunting businesses closed for good. Through increased licensing fees, a tax increase of 300% on firearms and 1,000% on ammunition—not to mention the banning of all sporting ammunition and rationing of firearms—they are planning to tax and regulate you right out of business.

Join NRA's Business Alliance today and become part of a national network of business owners banded together to build a new front to protect the Second Amendment. List your business in NRA's Business Alliance Directory—our way of promoting member patronage of those who support us by telling our 3.4 million members which businesses are fighting to protect their rights.

As a member, you'll receive a plaque and a store-front decal, identifying your business as a solid supporter of Second Amendment rights. You'll also have access to NRA-sponsored commercial liability insurance, free and discounted NRA services and products, and much more.

It's time to protect your livelihood as well as our Second Amendment rights. You know the battle we have just to keep our firearms...imagine trying to get them back after they're gone! Join the NRA's Business Alliance Today!

For an application or more information:

CALL 1-800-672-2582

Or write:

National Rifle Association of America
Field Services, Business Alliance Program
11250 Waples Mill Road
Fairfax, VA 22030

Gun Club Operators: Are You Building? Expanding? Improving? Learn From the Experts

CONFERENCE & TRAINING PROGRAMS

Range Development Conferences—The National Rifle Association, an authority on shooting ranges, has gathered some of the country's leading experts on range design, construction, operations, environmental concerns, and more, together for the Range Development Conferences. The conferences are designed to train range owners and operators of both existing and proposed range facilities to recognize potential problems associated with engineering and/or administrative controls, environmental issues and safety. This five-day conference will teach you how to identify and solve most problems before they become insurmountable. You will learn a broader, multi-disciplinary perspective on the issues that affect range operators. In a relaxed congenial setting, you will be able to network and interact with colleagues that are involved in the same activities as you. Registration is $550.

Get Ahead on Lead—A one day workshop you cannot afford to miss. We address one of today's hottest issues facing operators and municipalities running shooting ranges, i.e., "LEAD." We cover who is affected by OSHA's Lead Standard, what constitutes an employee-employer relationship, as well as Engineering controls, administrative controls and work practices that can deliver your facility to the highest levels of care. Learn what an individual's personal hygiene has to do with their blood lead levels, and how to teach your employees about controlling the risk of over-exposure to airborne particulate lead. Understand the importance of maintaining records, schedules of clean-up, air-monitoring, and employee blood lead levels. Registration is $145.

Range Officer Training Program—The National Rifle Association has designed a Range Officer Training Program where participants are Certified as Range Officers upon completion of a 16-hour course, and passing the Post Test with 90% or better. Registration is $250.

PERSONAL HELP

Range Engineer—The National Rifle Association has a Range Engineer on staff to provide engineering support. The Range Engineer can prepare blueprints and drawings to include layout of firing and target lines, safety fans, berms, baffles and bullet catchers, for outdoor ranges. Prepare installation drawings and blueprints for the installation of ventilation and air filter systems, lighting, backstop and target mechanisms for indoor ranges. Review and prepare engineering technical documents, assist in the planning and layout of shooting facilities, serve as an expert witness.

Range Technical Team—A nation wide network of Range Development Technical Advisors who have been educated as Technical Consultants to assist those interested in Range Development and Operation. The Range Technical Team has received special training and they have the expertise to offer services in the following areas: Range Site Selection, Range Planning & Design, Evaluation of Lead Issues, Sound Studies and the evaluation of health and safety issues as related to range operation.

PUBLICATIONS

Blue Prints for American or Olympic/International Skeet & Trap—These blue prints cover trap house to include drainage and modifications for automatic trap and electricity, layout for trap field,

(Continued on page 159)

DOG CLUBS & ASSOCIATIONS

American Kennel Club
5580 Centerview Dr.
Raleigh, NC 27606
(919) 233-9767
Est.: 1884   Staff: 400
Largest association of dog clubs and registry of purebred dogs. Sanctions over 7,000 performance events each year including retriever trials and hunting tests.

Bird Dog Foundation, Inc.
PO Box 774
505 West Hwy. 57
Grand Junction, TN 38039
(901) 764-2058
Staff: 40
Pres: Gary Lockee
The National Bird Dog Museum, The National Field Trial Hall of Fame, and The Wildlife Heritage Center are under the auspices of The Bird Dog Foundation, Inc.

Hunting Retriever Club, Inc.
United Kennel Club, Inc.
100 East Kilgore Rd.
Kalamazoo, MI 49001-5592
(616) 343-9020
Est.: 1984   Staff: 35
Editorial Advisor: Michelle O'Malley-Morgan
Registering dogs, licensing their events, awarding titles dogs have earned

National Shoot-to-Retrieve Field Trial Association (NSTRA)
226 North Mill St., #2
Plainfield, IN 46168
(317) 839-4059
FAX: (317) 839-4197
Est.: 1979   Staff: 2
President: Jim Mahoney
NSTRA is a non-profit service association dedicated to promoting sportsmanship and the enjoyment of pointing breed dogs through recognized field trial competition.

North American Hunting Retriever Association (NAHRA)
PO Box 1590
Stafford, VA 22555
(540) 286-0625
FAX: (540) 286-0629
President: Jack Jagoda

North American Versatile Hunting Dog Association (NAVHDA)
PO Box 520
Arlington Heights, IL 60006
(847) 253-6487
FAX: (847) 255-1120
Est.: 1969
Members: 2,500
Merchandise Coordinator: Roberta Applegate
Educational video & correlating training book - $49.95.

GUN RIGHTS GROUPS

American Shooting Sports Council (ASSC)
1845 The Exchange, Suite 150
Atlanta, GA 30339
(770) 933-0200
FAX: (770) 953-9778
Exec. Dir: Richard Feldman
Operations Dir: Jack Adkins
Admin. Dir: Mandy K. Zamarra

Gun Owners of America
8001 Forbes Pl., Suite 102
Springfield, VA 22151
(703) 321-8585
FAX: (703) 321-8408
Est.: 1975   Staff: 10
Exec. Dir.: Larry Pratt
Pres: H.L. Richardson
The only no-compromise gun lobby in Washington. Members receive newsletters & legislative alerts.

The Hunter's Alliance
523 Main St., PO Box 188
Stevensville, MT 59870
(406) 777-2521
Exec. Dir: Dale Burk

Jews for the Preservation of Firearms Ownership
2872 S. Wentworth Ave.
Milwaukee, WI 53207
(414) 769-0760
Exec. Dir: Aaron Zelman

National Rifle Association of America
11250 Waples Mill Rd.
Fairfax, VA 22030
(703) 267-1000
Est.: 1871   Staff: 517
Exec. VP: Wayne R. LaPierre, Jr.
See Our Ad Across & Pg. 101

The Wildlife Legislative Fund of America
and The Wildlife Conservation Fund of America
801 Kingsmill Pkwy.
Columbus, OH 43229-1137
(614) 888-4868
FAX: (614) 888-0326
Est.: 1978
Members: 1,500,000
Pres/CEO: Richard B. Pierce
Sr. VP: James Goodrich
State Svcs. Dir: Robert Sexton
Comm. Dir: J.R. Absher
Companion non-profit organizations to protect the heritage of the American sportsman to hunt, fish and trap.

SHOOTING ORGANIZATIONS

Amateur Trapshooting Association (ATA)
601 W. National Rd.
Vandalia, OH 45377
(513) 898-4638
FAX: (513) 898-5472
Est.: 1923
Members: 102,360
Executive Dir: David Bopp

Canadian Sporting Clays Association (CSCA)
566 Oxford St., E.
London, Ontario
Canada N5Y 3J1
(519) 673-1664
Contact: David Stinson

Clay Pigeon Shooting Association (CPSA)
Earlstrees Court
Earlsrees Road, Corby, Northants
UK NN17 4AX
Est.: 1928
011-44-1536-443566
FAX: 011-44-1536-443438
Exec. Dir: Emilio Orduna
Members: 30,000

**Connecticut Travelers
Sporting Clays Assn. (CTSCA)**
91 Park Lane Rd.
New Milford, CT 06776
(203) 354-9351
FAX: (203) 354-1762
Est.: 1978
Members: 400
Contact: Al Anglace

**Federation Internationale
de Tir Aux Armes Sportives
de Chasse (FITASC)**
10 Rue de Lisbonne Paris
75008 France
011-33-14293-4053
Est.: 1921

**The International
Shooting Union (UIT)**
Bavariaring 21, D-80336
Munich 1, Germany
011-49-89-531012
FAX: 011-49-89-5309481
Contact: Franz Schreiber

**International Sporting
Clays Federation (ISCF)**
5 Brighton Parade
Southport 4215
Queensland, Australia
011-61-18-783515
Exec. Dir: Les Pratten

**National Skeet Shooting
Association (NSSA)**
5931 Roft Rd.
San Antonio, TX 78253
(210) 688-3371
FAX: (210) 688-3014
Est.: 1947   Staff: 29
Members: 18,000
Exec. Dir: Mike Hampton, Ext. 110
Ass't. Dir: Eric Beckmann, Ext. 106
National governing body of Ameri-
can Skeet

**National Sporting Clays
Association (NSCA)**
5931 Roft Rd.
San Antonio, TX 78253   .
(210) 688-3371
FAX: (210) 688-3014
Est.: 1989   Staff: 29
Exec. Dir.: Mike Hampton, Ext. 110
Member Services: Lois Lessing, Ext.
108; Chief Instructor: Peter
Crabtree, Ext. 123

**New England Sporting
Clays Association (NESCA)**
344 Elm St.
Milford, NH 03055
(603) 673-8466
President: Charlie Kallfelz

**Pacific International
Trapshooting Assn. (PITA)**
PO Box 9217
Brooks, OR 97305
(503) 792-3622
FAX: (503) 792-3431
Est.: 1932
Exec. Sec'y: Sue Brewer
We are an association for western
trapshooters–serving 7 states and 2
Canadian provinces.

**Sporting Clays of America
(SCA)**
9 Mott Ave., Suite 103
Norwalk, CT 06850
(203) 831-8483
FAX: (203) 831-8497
Est.: 1985
Members: 5,000
Pres: Fred G. Collins
VP/Club & Range Div: Meylert
Armstrong
VP/Nat'l Tourn. Dir: Timothy Nichols
Treas./Sec: Barbara Schaefer
See Our Ad, Right

U.S. Shooting Team
Office of Junior Development
PO Box 3207
Brentwood, TN 37024-3207
(615) 831-0485
Director: Leo R. Lujan
Established by USSTF and supported by industry to attract youth to the shooting sports and to assure that they receive competent entry level training.

USA Shooting
One Olympic Plaza
Colorado Springs, CO 80909
(719) 578-4670
FAX: (719) 635-7989
Director of Admi.: Ray Carter
USA Shooting is the national governing body for the sport of Olympic style shooting.

United States International Clay Target Association (USICTA)
PO Box 134
Lykens, PA 17048
(717) 453-7245
President: Allen Chubb, Jr.
Secretary: John Wolfington
Members: 200

Women's Shooting Sports Foundation (WSSF)
1505 Hwy. 6 South, Suite 101
Houston, TX 77077
(713) 584-9907
FAX: (713) 584-9874
Est.: 1993   Staff: 3
Exec. Dir: Sue King
Exec. VP: Glynne Moseley
Mgr/Finance: Deb Cleverdon
...to provide information, education, create opportunities, and to serve as the collective voice for women's shooting sports interests.
See Our Ad Across, Left

TRADE ASSOCIATIONS

American Custom Gunmakers Guild
PO Box 812
Burlington, IA 52601
(319) 752-6114 (Phone/Fax)
Est.: 1983
Exec. Dir: Jan Billeb

F.A.I.R. Trade Group
Firearms Importers Roundtable
PO Box 1474
Vienna, VA 22183
(703) 242-9484
FAX: (703) 242-9485
Est.: 1994   Staff: 1
Deputy Director: Craig Dowd

Firearms Engravers Guild of America
511 North Rath Ave.
Ludington, MI 49431
(616) 843-3772
FAX: (616) 845-7695
Sec: Rex Pedersen

Gun Trade Association Ltd.
PO Box 7, Evesham, Worstershire
U.K. WR11 6AN
011-44-1386-443304
FAX: 011-44-1386-443305
Contact: Brian Carter
Association representing companies that operate within the British gun trade and shooting accessories market.

Hunter Education Association

Box 490
8310 6th St., Suite 5E
Wellington, CO 80549
(970) 568-7954
FAX: (970) 568-7955
Members: 2,000
Exec. VP: David M. Knotts
To establish safe, responsible and knowledgeable hunters.

National Alliance of Stocking Gun Dealers

PO Box 187
Havelock, NC 28532
(919) 447-1313
FAX: (919) 447-0988
Exec. Dir: Bill Bridgewater

National Assoc. of Sporting Goods Wholesalers

400 E. Randolph St.
Suite 700
Chicago, IL 60601-7329
(312) 565-0233
Est.: 1954
Exec. Dir: Rebecca A. Maddy

National Hunters Association, Inc.

9312 US Hwy. 64E
PO Box 820
Knightdale, NC 27545
(919) 365-7157
Est.: 1976
President: D.V. Smith
Education: Hunting Skills; Firearm Safety; Wilderness Survival; Outdoor Ethics.

National Reloading Manufacturers Association

One Centerpointe Dr., #300
Lake Oswego, OR 97035

National Shooting Sports Foundation

Flintlock Ridge Office Center
11 Mile Hill Rd.
Newtown, CT 06470
(203) 426-1320
FAX: (203) 426-1087
Est.: 1961   Staff: 21
Members: 1,200
Pres: Robert T. Delfray
Membership: J. Mannuzza
Online: http://www.nssf.org
The NSSF is the shooting industry's trade organization. Since 1961, our mission has been to promote a better understanding of and more active participation in the shooting sports. Through positive publicity and education programs, NSSF presents the facts about recreational shooting to the non-shooting public.

National Taxidermists Association

108 Branch Dr.
Slidell, LA 70461
(504) 641-4682
FAX: (504) 641-0191
Est.: 1971
Exec. Dir: Greg Crain
Official information clearinghouse for the taxidermy industry.

North American Gamebird Association (NAGA)

PO Box 2105
Cayce-West Columbia, SC 29171
(803) 796-8163
FAX: (803) 791-0982
Est.: 1900   Staff: 2
Exec. Dir.: Walter S. Walker
Pres: Jan Toubl
The North American Gamebird Association (NAGA) is a non-profit trade organization, established in 1931. For more than 63 years, NAGA members have "led the field" in improving methods of gamebird production and hunting preserve management. JOIN TODAY! Members receive a monthly magazine, "Wildlife Harvest". Each issue (80-88 pgs.) is filled with timely information, helpful "how to" articles on cover plantings, bird dogs, gamebird production, issues and developments. Annual dues include the monthly magazine, a directory of all NAGA members; and for preserves, a free listing in NAGA's Directory of Hunting Resorts.

See Our Ad Across

Outdoor Guides Association of No. America

PO Box 12996
4500 Shannon Lakes Plaza
Tallahassee, FL 32317-2996
(904) 668-4957
Members: 2,000
Exec. Dir.: Casey Madigan

Outdoor Writers Assn. of America (OWAA)

2017 Cato Ave., #101
State College, PA 16801-2768
(814) 234-1011
Est.: 1927   Staff: 5
Members: 2,000
Exec. Dir: James W. Rainey
Pres: Mark LaBarbera
Public. Editor: C.J. Kersavage

Sporting Arms & Ammunition Manuf. Instit. (SAAMI)

11 Mile Hill Rd.
Flintlock Ridge Office Center
Newtown, CT 06470
(203) 426-4358   Est.: 1926
Exec. Dir: Robert T. Delfray
Dir. of Comm: Scott O'Mara
Represents major manufacturers of sporting firearms and ammunition.

Our Almost Perfect Staff

The staff of Black's Wing & Clay brings a wealth of directory publishing experience to this publication. Our objective: the most comprehensive, easy-to-use directory available in shotgunning. And this edition comes as close as dedicated hard work permits.

But nobody's perfect. So if you see that any of our listings are incomplete...if we've missed a company in any category...you'll be helping the entire industry if you let us know.

Our listings are free to equipment manufacturers and individual suppliers...to qualified shooting schools and to marketing oriented lodges and outfitters. But we can include only those that our research uncovers. Help us help shotgunning. And tip us off if we've overlooked some company or individual. Call: (908) 224-8700.

What Makes NAGA Preserves Special?

- NAGA Preserves abide by the Association's "Standards Of Excellence" and "Code of Ethics", making NAGA Preserves the preserves to call first.

- NAGA Preserves are serious about providing quality outdoor experiences. They are professionals continually striving to improve their establishments.

- There is a wide array of NAGA preserves to choose from. Each offers their own unique blend of style and atmosphere, making it easier to find one that suits your individual taste and budget.

WHAT IS NAGA?

The North American Gamebird Association (NAGA) is a non-profit trade organization, established in 1931.

For more than 63 years, NAGA members have "led the field" in improving methods of gamebird production and hunting preserve management.

JOIN TODAY!

Members receive a monthly magazine, "Wildlife Harvest". Each issue (80-88 pages) is filled with timely information, helpful "how to" articles on cover plantings, bird dogs, gamebird production, issues and developments.

Annual dues include, the monthly magazine, a directory of all NAGA members, and for preserves, a free listing in NAGA's Directory of Hunting Resorts.

Note: Special Liability Insurance available exclusively to NAGA preserves and sporting clays ranges.

For FREE Information contact:

NAGA (North American Gamebird Association)
PO Box 2105
Cayce, SC 29171
Phone 803/796-8163

Visa/ Mastercard Service, Phone: Wildlife Harvest Publications 319/242-3046

BOOKSELLERS

Outdoor Writer–and book lover–Tom McIntyre thinks the "serious" hunting book may well be headed the "way of the buffalo and the heath hen". To prove his point he suggests a modest experiment: Walk into your local bookshop and ask for the hunting section. Don't be surprised, McIntyre warns, if your request is met with silence–if not open hostility. Fact is, most bookstores don't have one. Why? Political correctness and anti-hunting sentiment have been suggested as possible explanations. But whatever the reason, fortunately, there is an alternative: the thriving catalog and mail-order sportsman's booksellers. Whether the title's a new one or old, a classic of its genre or a workaday handbook, if the companies listed here can't get it for you, it probably "can't be got".

Angler's & Shooter's Bookshelf
PO Box 178
Goshen, CT 06756
(860) 491-2500
Est.: 1967
Available: Direct
Catalog Available-$5.00. 4,000 hunting & fishing books; new, used, rare & collector's books.

Blacksmith Corporation
830 N. Road 1 East
Box 1752, Chino Valley, AZ 86323
(520) 636-4456
FAX: (520) 636-4457
Est.: 1975   Staff: 5
Contact: Nancy Padua
Available: Retail & Direct
Books and videos pertaining to guns, hunting & outdoors

Judith Bowman Books
Pound Ridge Rd.
Bedford, NY 10506
(914) 234-7543
Est.: 1979   Staff: 2
Contact: Judith Bowman
Mail Order Only – Hunting & Fishing Books
See Our Ad Above

Countrysport Press
1515 Cass St., Traverse City, MI 49684
(800) 367-4114
(616) 929-3320
FAX: (616) 929-9813
President: Charles Fry
Editorial Dir.: Art DeLaurier, Jr.
Available: Retail & Direct
Sold through catalog - hard cover hunting classics, historical & geographic

James Cummins Booksellers
699 Madison Ave., NY, NY 10021
(212) 688-6441
Est.: 1978   Staff: 4
Contact: James Cummins
Available: Direct — All types of antiquarian & sporting books; Old & new sporting art. Catalogues issued.

Duckett's Sporting Books and Publishing Company
1968 E. Carson Dr.,
Tempe, AZ 85282
(602) 345-2698
Est.: 1987   Staff: 2
Contact: Randy Duckett
Available: Direct
FREE search service on guns, hunting, fishing, cowboy collectibles, edge weapons and related books. In print and out-of-print—we buy one copy or a whole library.

Gary L. Estabrook Fine Sporting Books
Box 61453, Vancouver, WA 98666
(360) 699-5454
Est.: 1972   Staff: 1
Owner: Gary L. Estabrook
Available: Direct
Fine sporting books & fly fishing, salmon fishing, trout fishing, upland shooting, duck shooting, B.G. hunting, etc. Over 30,000 books in stock.
See Our Ad Across, Top

Fair Chase, Inc.
S1118 Hwy. HH
Lyndon Station,
WI 53944
(800) 762-2843
(608) 524-9677
Est.: 1982   Staff: 1
Contact: Carol Lueder
Available: Direct
Fine sporting books, new and out-of-print. We offer regular catalogs and prompt service. Also, Filson and Barbour clothing. Please call us when you are looking for:
* Big Game Hunting Books
* Wingshooting Books
* Sporting Clays and Shotgun Books
* Fine Collector's Editions
See Our Ad Across, Bottom

David Foley
76 Bonnyview Rd.
West Hartford, CT 06107
(203) 561-0783
Est.: 1987   Staff: 1
Contact: David Foley
Available: Retail & Direct
Catalog available; primarily out-of-print hunting, fishing, archery, and firearms books.

Gunnerman Books
Box 214292, Auburn Hills, MI 48321
(810) 879-2779
FAX: (810) 879-3235
Est.: 1978
Contact: Carol Barnes
Hunting, Big Game, Upland, Duck, Gun Books, In Print & Out of Print

Holland & Holland, Ltd.
50 E.57th St., New York, NY 10022
(212) 752-7755
FAX: (212) 752-6805
Mail Orders: 1-800-SINCE 1835

Hungry Horse Books
4605 Hwy. 93 South
Whitefish, MT 59937
(406) 862-7997
FAX: (406) 862-6134
Est.: 1992   Staff: 2
Books on firearms, edged weapons, gunsmithing, handloading, African safaris, hunting, competition shooting & out-of-print titles.

Inquisitive Sportsman Books
PO Box 1811
Granite Falls, WA 98252
(360) 691-7540 (Phone/Fax)
Contact: Stephen P. Gill
Available: Direct
Fine uncommon, scarce, out-of-print and rare hunting and fishing books. Wingshooting, big game, small game, fly-fishing, deep sea, etc.

Inter-Sports Book & Video
790 W. Tennessee Ave.
Denver, CO 80223
(800) 456-5842
FAX: (800) 279-9196
Marketing: Johnny J. Jones
America's largest assortment of hunting, fly-fishing and archery books, maps and videos. Please call for our 80-page catalog describing 1500 titles (retail outlets only).

Ray Riling Arms Books Co.
6844 Gorsten St.
Philadelphia, PA 19119
(215) 438-2456
Contact: Joseph Riling
Used and rare books

Sunrise Publishing Co.
481 Route 45 South
Austinburg, OH 44010
(216) 275-1310
Est.: 1992
Contact: Duke Biscotti
Available: Direct Mail Order
We specialize in unusual, rare and limited edition sporting books as well as sporting bibliographies. We are active buyers and sellers–send for free catalog.

Wilderness Adventures Sporting Books
PO Box 627
Gallatin Gateway, MT 59730-0627
(800) 925-3339
FAX: (406) 763-4911
Contact: Chuck Johnson & Darren Brown
Available: Retail & Direct
World's largest mail order dealer of fine sporting books. Publisher of Wingshooting guides to Montana, S. Dakota, Arizona, North Dakota. Call for free catalog.

CARTS

Big Shot
Shotgunner's Caddy
3227 Auburn St.
Rockford, IL 61101
(815) 962-6788
Est.: 1979
Contact: Marvin Conrad
Type: Hand
Big Shot shotgunner's caddy looks like a shotgun shell, made of impact resistant PVC with a durable high gloss acrylic finish. Lightweight with 4 compartments; fits most golf carts.

EZ-Shooter Carts
Pavo Welding Shop
100 East Harris
Pavo, GA 31778
(912) 859-2075 (Day)
(912) 859-2162 (Eve.)
Contact: Buddy Lewis
Type: Motorized
EZ-Shooter Carts are 4 wheel golf carts (gas or electric), customized for sporting shooters. Also available-custom built EZ-Load Trailers. Call for more information.

Gun/Buggy
Clay Toons
109.5 Clay St.
Suffolk, VA 23434
(800) 677-3201

(804) 934-0136
FAX: (804) 934-6151
Contact: Jennifer Beigle
Available: Direct
Type: Hand
Gun/Buggy is lightweight, holds shotguns, shells, chokes, plus a compartment for miscellaneous items. Standard, oak and walnut models available. Comes with a 3-year limited warranty. Dealer inquiries welcomed.

The Jackass
Ziegel Engineering
2108 Lomina Ave.
Long Beach, CA 90815
(310) 596-9481
FAX: (310) 598-4734
Est.: 1972   Staff: 10
Contact: Dean Ziegel
Available: Retail & Direct
Type: Hand
Heavy duty aluminum field cart for transporting rifles & shotguns. A must for the competitor. Also the largest manufacturer of aluminum gun cases. Visa and Mastercard accepted.

The Rhino

Sportscar
4340 S.E. 53rd Ave.
Ocala, FL 34472
(800) 226-3613
Est.: 1988
Contact: Janet Morales or

Joe Morales
Available: Direct
Type: Hand
The Rhino Sportscar is made of all-aluminum construction: The base is anodized aluminum in either red, blue or black with a rubber matt on the bottom where shells, a cooler or a shooting bag may be carried. Two shotguns are carried in a vertical coated gun bracket. (the Cart may be converted to carry rifles for the competitive shooter). The tires are all-terrain with zirk fittings to keep them rolling smoothly through any course. The handle is in two parts fastened with wing nuts for easy assembly and storage. The barrels rest in U-brackets with latches attached to the top of the handle. The Sportscar weighs only about 18 pounds fully assembled and pulls easily.

See Our Ad Pg. 154

Seminole Chokes & Gun Works
Mitchell Machine & Mfg., Inc.
3049 US 1
Mims, FL 32754
(407) 383-8556
FAX: (407) 383-8532
Est.: 1989   Staff: 6
Contact: Janice Mitchell or Randy Mitchell
Type: Hand
Seminole Travelcarts are made of durable aluminum tread plate, measuring 16"x24"x16". The Travelcart carries two guns and assembles in 60 seconds. In stock and ready for delivery.

The Ultimate Shooting Cart
J.M. Caldwell Co., Inc.
322 East Turner Lane
West Chester, PA 19380
(800) 890-8872
(610) 436-9997
FAX: (610) 436-9957
President: Jim Caldwell
Available: Direct
Type: Motorized
The Ultimate Shooting Cart offers you the ability to move with ease between stations, eliminating the need to carry heavy bags. Whether you enjoy sporting clays competition, claybird or range shooting, the Ultimate Shooting Cart is tailored to suit your every need and budget, ranging from $1,995 to $4,995.

Gun Club Operators

Yours is a tough business. Fortunately, Wing & Clay is here to help. No other publication contains more information about the equipment and services you need to run your operation. Turn to these sections for more information:

CHOKES

For related products & services:
• See Gunsmiths Pg. 162

Angle Porting
Ballistic Specialties
100 Industrial Dr.,
Batesville, AR 72501
(800) 276-2550
FAX: (501) 793-7933
Est.: 1991   Staff: 4
President: John Clouse
Available: Retail & Direct
Custom chokes built for your gun.

Stan Baker Barrels
10000 Lake City Way,
Seattle, WA 98125
(206) 522-4575
Contact: Stan Baker
Available: Direct
All types of shotgun barrel modification...forcing cone, lengthening,
backbore, custom re-choke and
screw-in chokes.

BRILEY

Briley Manufacturing
1230 Lumpkin
Houston, TX 77043
(800) 331-5718 (Cust. Svc.)
(713) 932-6995
FAX: (713) 932-1043
Est.: 1976   Staff: 65
Contact: Chuck Webb
Available: Retail & Direct
The only source for in-line, concen-
tric, true-to-the-bore installation of
chokes. Briley installs the world famous long choke in all makes and
gauges using special long geome-
try for improved patterns. Steel or
lead shot capability in nine true constrictions gives all shooters
maximum flexibility. For the shooter
who has a gun with factory screw-
in's, Briley has the answer in their
BRC line of factory replacement
chokes; Knurled or flush in nine constrictions they will give superior

performance at factory prices. In
stock for immediate delivery. New
choke design with the turkey
hunter in mind–for all factory guns
with screw-in chokes. Call for brochure.
See Our Ad Pg. 45

Cation
2341 Alger St., Troy, MI 48083
(810) 689-0658
FAX: (810) 689-7558
Contact: Victor Vichinksy
"Sniper" rifled choke tubes for
slugs, "Tight Shot" rifled choke
tubes for shotshells.

Clear View Products, Inc.
3021 N. Portland
Oklahoma City, OK 73107
(405) 943-9222   Est.: 1975
Contact: Larry Nailon
Available: Direct
Custom screw in chokes; Load development & Shot string
measurement.

Colonial Arms, Inc.
1109 C Singleton Dr.
PO Box 636, Selma, AL 36702
(334) 872-9455
FAX: (334) 872-9540
Est.: 1989   Staff: 10
Advtg. Dir: Traci Denson
Available: Retail
Screw-in shotgun choke tubes and
installation tooling and accessories.
Colonial Arms offers the shooting
enthusiast a full line of the world's
finest 10, 12, 16, 20, 28, and .410
gauge shotgun screw-in choke
tubes. Name your target or quarry
and Colonial has what you're looking for: sporting clays tubes,
flushmounted lead shot, extended
steel shot, turkey, rifled and car-
dshooting tubes. The knurled ends
of our sporting clays tubes extend
about 3/8" past the end of the barrel for easy changeability. Available
in cylinder, skeet 1, improved cylinder, modified and full constrictions
for the 12 gauge true size and thin
wall after market installations, Invector, Remington, Invector Plus and
Beretta Systems. Also, available for
the 20 gauge true size after market
installation, Invector and Remington systems. Contact your local
dealer or, if one is unavailable, call
or write Colonial for a list of dealers
in your area.
See Our Ad, Left

DAYSON ARMS, LTD.

Dayson Arms, Ltd.
PO Box 532, 511 Willow
Vincennes, IN 47591
(812) 882-8680
FAX: (812) 882-8446
Est.: 1993   Staff: 11
Contact: Gary Ciluffo or
Louie Dayson
Available: Retail & Direct
Patented ABS ventilated chokes will
provide a tighter shot pattern and
reduce recoil and muzzle jump by
up to 25%. Increase recoil reduction up to 60% by using our
patented muzzle break. Our tubes
fit most guns and are available in
12 & 10 gauge.

Pete Elsen, Inc.
Parabolic Chokes
1529 S. 113th St.,
West Allis, WI 53214
(414) 476-4660   Est.: 1982
Owner: Pete Elsen
Available: Direct
Screw-in chokes

Hastings
320 Court St., PO Box 224
Clay Center, KS 67432
(913) 632-3169
FAX: (913) 632-6554
Est.: 1985
President: Robert Rott
Available: Retail
One of the largest selections of
choke tubes on the market; includes standard flush mounted
chokes, Hastings Turkey Chokes; extended chokes for steel shot; and
the new QC choke line consisting
of 13 different constrictions for precise pattern control. All Hastings
chokes are available to fit most popular choke systems.

Kick's Komps
Kick's Industries, Inc.
698 Magnolia Rd.
Rt. 1, Box 71D
Statesboro, GA 30458
(912) 587-2779
FAX: (912) 587-2745
Est.: 1994   Staff: 5
Contact: Bob Bryan or
Vickie Deal

Available: Retail & Direct
Featuring angle-ported specialty
screw-in chokes for serious
shotgunning folks.
Our unique directional angled porting markedly improves patterns by
stopping wad spin and by peeling
the wad away from the shot which
allows the shot string to fly less dis-
turbed. Also, because of diffusion
of gasses through the ports the reduction of both muzzle jump and
recoil improve follow-up shots.
Your shooting buddies will appreciate our chokes because there is less
significant side blast than with
chokes that have parts of 90 degrees or less. We offer a complete
line of specialty hunting and clay
target chokes to satisfy even the
most discriminating of sportsmen.
Manufactured in true-to-bore constrictions and available for most
shotgun models.

MARBLE'S
Poly-Choke

Marble Arms/Poly-Choke
CRL, Inc.
PO Box 111
Gladstone, MI 49837
(906) 428-3710
FAX: (906) 428-3711
Est.: 1898   Staff: 15
President: Craig R. Lauerman
Available: Retail (Factory direct on
installed products)
If you want nine different choke settings and no loose choke tubes or
wrenches, yet spend under $100,
look at Poly-Choke, the original adjustable choke tube. Marble Arms
will install the Poly-Choke on any
12, 16, 20 or 28-gauge pump, auto
or single barrel shotgun. Just twist
the sleeve to select chokes from X-
Full to Open Cylinder and choose
any pattern in between. Great for
hunting or sporting clays, trap and
skeet. Standard and ventilated
styles. Marble Arms also offers a
wide selection of shotgun sights for
single or double barrel shotguns.
High quality front and mid sights
are available in bead, Bradley,
Xpert and Bev-L-Blok styles in gold,
ivory, red and sunspot colors. To improve accuracy, Marble Arms
installs anodized, ventilated shotgun ribs for all single and
over/under barrels, complete with
front and mid sights. Free catalog.
See Our Ad Across, Right

Nuline Guns, Inc.
1053 Caulks Hill Rd., Dept. 2800
Harvester, MO 63304
(314) 441-4500
FAX: (314) 447-5018
Est.: 1949   Staff: 17
Contact: B.J. Stevens
Available: Retail & Direct
Backed by over 25 years of research and development, our custom designed choke tubes greatly reduce stress on the barrel by placing the actual constriction portion outside of it. These screw-in choke tubes are made from heat-treated stainless steel, colored in "heat treat blue," and will fit most threaded barrels. Designed to provide patterns of such density and uniformity as to meet each hunter's and target shooter's demands, including:
* Duck Hunters
* Turkey Hunters
* Card Shooters
* Skeet, Trap & Sporting Clays
  Enthusiasts
Call or write today for complete details and ordering information.

Outers Choke Tubes
Blount Inc., Sporting Equipment Div.
PO Box 856, 2299 Snake River Ave.
Lewiston, ID 83501
(800) 627-3640
Contact: John Wiggert

RHINO.

Rhino Chokes
4340 S.E. 53rd Ave.
Ocala, FL 34472
(800) 226-3613
Est.: 1988
Contact: Janet Morales or
Joe Morales
The Rhino Choke is a revolutionary new design. The unique longer design has a wad stripping action yielding a 20% more effective pattern than a standard screw-in choke. It reduces muzzel jump by 15% and also reduces recoil. Made of high grade stainless steel that will not rust or corrode, no wrench needed. Call for prices and models.
See Our Ad Pg. 154

Seminole Chokes & Gun Works
Mitchell Machine & Mfg., Inc.
3049 US 1, Mims, FL 32754
(800) 980-3344
(407) 383-8556
FAX: (407) 383-8532

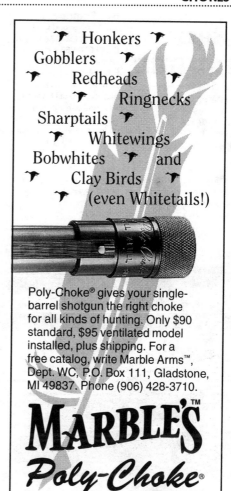
Est.: 1989   Staff: 6
Contact: Janice Mitchell or
Randy Mitchell
Available: Retail & Direct
Seminole Chokes: 9 true constrictions, each color coded for easy I.D. Tubes are designed to precisely fit barrel bore. Reasonably priced.

WRIGHT'S
(THE MODEL 12 SHOP)
Wright's
(The Model 12 Shop)
RR3, Box 414
Pinckneyville, IL 62274
(618) 357-8933
Est.: 1980   Staff: 5
Contact: Stu Wright
Available: Direct

SUPERIOR TRAP CHOKES: the permanent modification of factory chokes to improve pattern diameters and to even density, also benefits SKEET and SPORTING CLAYS. Complete repair and restoration of Winchester shotguns, Browning Competition shotguns, and Perazzis. Competition triggers installed, recoil pads installed, ribs resoldered, five different blueing techniques. Reliable service of custom handcrafted quality.

CHOKE WRENCHES

B □ SQUARE

B-SQUARE
2708 St. Louis Ave.
PO Box 11281
Forth Worth, TX 76110
(800) 433-2909
(817) 923-0964
Est.: 1957
Contact: Rudy Bechtel
Available: Retail & Direct
Texas Twister speed wrench for 12 gauge shotguns. Call for free catalog.
See Our Ad Below

K.L. Engineering
1190 Knollwood Circle
Anaheim, CA 92801
(714) 870-8629
FAX: (714) 828-6011
Est.: 1985   Staff: 3
Owner: Ray Longerot
Available: Retail & Direct
All metal wrench/container works like a screwdriver storing chokes end to end in its aluminum handle. Lifetime guarantee.

Quick-Choke
PO Box 412878
Kansas City, MO 64141
(317) 453-1024
FAX: (317) 453-1024
Est.: 1989   Staff: 1
Contact: David Dyer
Available: Retail & Direct
Patented wrench for changing choke tubes. Universally fits all guns. Wrench attaches to cordless electric screwdriver.

The Royal Choke Tube Wrench
Royal Inventions, Inc.
9921 4th Ave.
Brooklyn, NY 11209
(718) 833-6605
Est.: 1991
President: Stavros Mavraki
Available: Retail & Direct
The Royal Choke Tube Wrench securely locks into the choke tube, thus eliminating any damage to the choke tube or gun.

TUBE SETS

BRILEY

Briley Manufacturing
1230 Lumpkin
Houston, TX 77043
(800) 331-5718 (Cust. Svc.)
(713) 932-6995
Est.: 1976   Staff: 65
Contact: Chuck Webb
Available: Retail & Direct
Tube sets made for any 12 ga. or 20 ga. O/U or SxS. Order by the pair or in sets. Screw-in chokes included at no additional charge with 12, 20 & .410. Briley tube sets have a lifetime warranty and a lifetime choke exchange policy on the tube set. The exclusive Briley Ultra-Light tube set, 10 oz. the pair. This set reduces weight by 30% and improves balance and second shot recovery. Long forcing cones are a standard item in Ultra-Lights "Ultimate" as is straight rifling for wad control and reduced flyer pellets. Call for brochure. New for 1996–20-28.410 drop-in gauge conversions. No fitting required for all 12 ga. O/U or SxS. Sets for 26", 28" & 30" in stock for immediate delivery.
See Our Ad Pg. 45

Kolar Arms
1925 Roosevelt Ave.
Racine, WI 53406
(414) 554-0800
Est.: 1968   Staff: 46
Partner: Don Mainland
Partner/Pres: John Ramagli
Available: Retail & Direct
Standard or Kolarlite small gauge tubes available; All popular gauges

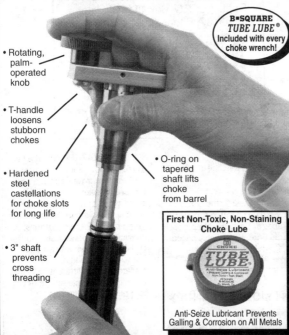

COMPUTERS/
RELATED SERVICES

ATS-SONIC
3852 20th Ave.,
Blanchard, MI 49310
(800) 247-7453 (Orders)
(517) 561-2858 (Cust. Svc.)
FAX: (517) 561-5257
Contact: Terry Dupuis
Email: sonic@nethawk.com
Visit our Website:
http://www.nethawk.com/~sonic
for dog training devices.

America Outdoors
Web Site
Operated by Outdoor Management
Network, Inc.
4607 NE Cedar Creek Rd.
Woodland, WA 98674
(360) 225-5000
FAX: (360) 225-7616
Contact: Robert R. Knopf
http://www.americaoutdoors.com
Cyberspace Sales and Marketing
for the Outdoors. Full Service Sales,
Marketing, P-R Programs. Full Ser-
vice Internet/World Wide Web
Consulting. E-mail - omni@amer-
icaoutdoors.com. America
Outdoors Site Features: Fishing,

Hunting/Shooting, Camping, General Outdoors, Photography,
Boating, Hiking/Biking, Conservation, Travel and Wildlife.
Offers listing and advertising services for game preserves, clay
ranges, outdoor manufacturers,
guides, outfitters, resorts.
Brochure Available
See Our Ad Pg. 117

DeSena Digital Design
Box 364, Bearsville, NY 12409
(800) 550-7855 (Orders)
(914) 679-2044
http://www.rivint.com/ssc
Contact: Bob DeSena

gunshop.com
2664 Cannan Rd.
East Bloomfield, NY 14469
(716) 334-9040 (Day)
(716) 657-7436 (Eve)
FAX: (716) 359-4999
Contact: David C. Weber
Email: ir001912@interramp.com
Visit our online gun store at
http://gunshop.com

Shooters' Online
Services, Inc.
One Court St.
PO Box 990
Exeter, NH 03833

(603) 778-4720
FAX: (603) 778-7265
Contact: Bert Bourgeois
email: gab@shooters.com
See Our Ad Below

Shotgun Sports
Software & Services
7912 F Harris Hill Lane
Charlotte, NC 28269
(704) 547-9798
(704) 595-6878
Contact: Steven Heyer
Users friendly computer software
for Trap and Sporting Clay Tournament accounting. ShootCompute
tracks shooter stats, prints entry
forms, scoreboard sheets, figures
purse & options, finds individual
and team winners or shoot-offs,
generates reports and much more.
Tournament accounting and training available. Call for more
information.

Sporting Adventures
47 Old Ridgefield Rd.,
Wilton, CT 06897
(203) 834-2130
FAX: (203) 834-2781
Est.: 1995   Staff: 20
President/CEO: Peter M. Cholnoky

Director/Strategic Development: Michael C. Lindsay Stewart
E-Mail Address: michael@span.com
Largest World Wide Web site for fishing, hunting and outdoor enthusiasts. www.span.com

Sporting Clays
5211 S. Washington Ave.
Titusville, FL 32780
(407) 268-5010
FAX: (407) 267-1894
Look for Sporting Clays Magazine:
http://www.webzene.com/sportingc

lays - Catch up on all the latest sporting clays news, results and notes from NSCA headquarters.

Winchester Ammunition

Division of Olin Corporation
427 North Shamrock
East Alton, IL 62024-1197
(618) 258-3595
Contact: Judy Eberhart
Visit the Winchester Ammunition World Wide Web Home Page –
http://www.winchester.com –

Here you will find: ballistic info, ammunition activities (e.g., hunting, target shooting), information for shooters (e.g., new shooters, women shooters), Winchester history, where to find a Winchester dealer, and the Winchester store (Sorry! Hats and shirts only!).
Winchester Ammunition–What America Shoots.
E-mail comments about the site to jkeberhart@corp.olin.com.
Home of Black's Wing & Clay hunting & shooting locations.

SHOTGUN RELATED WEB SITES

The shotgunning community seems no more immune to the promise of the Internet than the rest of the world. Thousands—yes, *thousands*—of shooting related sites already exist on the World Wide Web, and more are on the way. Some are great sources of information; others are a sad waste of computer memory. Key-in the Web addresses below, however, and you will be exposed to some better examples of the genre.

http://www.shootingsports.com/shtnspts/ata/home.htm - Membership and other information about The Amateur Trapshooting Association.

http://oldguns.com/ - The Antique Firearm Network, information for the firearms collector.

http://www.shooters.com/bbbooks - Sportsmans Gun & Outdoors Book Catalog. Almost 3,000 books, including shotgun-related categories.

http://www.bluebookinc.com/ - Blue Book Publications, Inc., source of firearms value information.

http://members.aol.com/usicta/bunker.html - The Bunker, on-line newsletter for the United States International Clay Target Association. Editorials, information on events, results and more.

http://dspace.dial.pipex.com/town/square/gq21/ - Information for shooters in the UK.

http://www.americaoutdoors.com - Hunting & shooting "how to," "where to go," "what to use."

http://gunshop.com/ - Information, photos for the Sportsman & Collector of fine firearms, with a focus on double guns.

http://www.gunweb.com/ - Gun Web Magazine. On-line gun publication.

http://www.nra.org/ - The National Rifle Association. The NRA home page offers political/legislative information, information on NRA programs, technical information, etc.

http://www.nssf.org - The National Shooting Sports Foundation, the organization of the shooting sports industry.

http://www.shooters.com/ponwar/index.htm - Ponsness/Warren, manufacturer of shotgun reloading equipment.

http://www.teleport.com/dputzolu/ - One of the first web sites covering firearms topics.

http://www.ccrkba.org:80/saf.org/ - Second Ammendment Foundation Home Page. Information on issues and concerns relating to the constitutional right to bear arms.

http://www.shooters.com - Information on shooting related products and services, including clubs, competitions, clubhouses, feature articles and more.

http://www.shooters.com/gunlinks - Shooters' GunLinks...the Web encyclopedia of over 700 shooting-related links.

http://www.shotgunreport.com/ - Shotgun Report, the Internet's electronic magazine dedicated to the clay target shotgun sports.

http://www.webzene.com/sportingclays/ - Sporting Clays. Official Publication of National Sporting Clays Association.

http://sportingclays.org - Sporting Clays of America (SCA) page for sporting clays shooters.

http://www.fws.gov:80/ - U.S. Fish and Wildlife Service Web site.

http://www.winchester.com - Winchester Ammunition Home Page Information on ballistics , hunting and target shooting, Winchester history, where to find a Winchester dealer. Also contains complete Black's Wing & Clay hunting and shooting location information.

Source: *Shooters' On-Line Services, Inc.*

COURSE DESIGNERS

The Key To Success

As many a failed operator will attest, the sheer popularity of sporting clays alone will not guarantee the success of any particular course. Nor will a great location and a barrel full of good intentions overcome poor course design. Thus, as a prerequisite for success, the conversion of an old course, or the establishment of a new one, calls for careful choice of a course designer.

Opinions vary about the best time to hire the designer. Some experienced sporting clays owners say that, if possible, the decision to hire a course designer should come only after you have secured--or are reasonably certain of securing--the needed approvals to open your course from local and state authorities . Others point out that in certain areas of the country, it is nearly impossible to get those approvals unless you already have a detailed plan.

What approvals are needed? And how do you make your way through the bureaucratic maze of zoning laws and environmental protection regulations? Pre-planning is critical. Obviously, you must know the local and state rules that govern the operation of a sporting clays course before you can get written approval.

When the time comes to select a designer, how do you pick a good one? The profile of a good designer might include experience, reputation and knowledge of all aspects of a club owner's business. Experience is self-explanatory--almost. At the very least your designer's credentials should include the planning and supervision of other sporting clays projects.

In addition, many course designers can help you secure funds, in many instances outright grants, that are available from federal, state and local governments for shooting fields. Finally, reputation means your designer has worked to the satisfaction of other owners. Ask for references and check them. And, if practical, visit one or two of a candidate's courses in person .

Knowledge of your business is important because a savvy designer will function not only as a course layout expert, but also as a consultant. He'll be able to advise on how to gain market share, how to achieve growth, how to purchase trap machines [see the Trap Manufacturer's Section for more information] and other equipment economically. The designer will also share his knowledge of how to organize leagues and conduct tournaments.

Finally, the more you know, the more you'll get out of your designer. Educate yourself: Read everything you can about the sport and course design [see box below]. Visit and shoot established courses as often as possible. Study their layouts. Attend shoots and tournaments regularly. And then by choosing and collaborating with a qualified designer you'll gain a course that takes full advantage of all topographical features, emphasizes safety and introduces a variety of challenges that make shooting fun for all--and profitable for you.

Books & Manuals That Can Help

Wending your way through the sporting clays course planning and approval process can be daunting. Fortunately, the publications listed below--published by some of the most prestigious organizations associated with the sport--provide much of the information you need to do a thorough job of planning and design.

Developing New Places to Shoot
Published by the National Shooting Sports Foundation, Flintlock Ridge Office Center, 11 Mile Hill Rd., Newtown, CT 06470; (203) 426-1320; Cost: $1.00.

NRA Range Manual
Published by the National Rifle Association, 11250 Waples Mill Road, Fairfax, VA 22030; (800) 336-7402; Order No.: 14840; Cost: $49.95.

Sporting Clays Course Design & Layout Package
Published by Sporting Clays magazine, 5211 S. Washington Ave., Titusville, FL 32780; (407) 268-5010; Cost: $59.95 plus shipping.

Sporting Clays Gun Club Manual
Published by the National Sporting Clays Association, P.O. Box 680007, San Antonio, TX 78268; (210) 688-3371; Cost: $25.00 plus shipping and handling.

COURSE DESIGNERS

Neil Chadwick
206 Front St.
Milford, PA 18337
(717) 296-2354
FAX: (717) 296-8639
Contact: Neil Chadwick
Neil has 15 years experience designing courses on The European Design. Course designer for the 1995 and 1996 Pan Am games.

Clay Games, Inc.
55 Lane 240 Big Otter Lake
Fremont, IN 46737
(219) 833-6645
FAX: (219) 833-6649
Est.: 1993
President: Joel Werner
See Our Ad Pg. 258

Clay-Sport International, Inc.
Box 663, Bragg Creek
28 Echlin Dr.
Alberta, Canada T0L 0K0
(403) 949-3654
Contact: Raymond Forman
The inventor of 5-STAND SPORT-ING ®, Raymond Forman, gives advice on the game that no one else can. With 24 years of international shooting and design experience, he creates a fun atmosphere to attract shooters and their families, whether for fun shoots, corporate days or world championships. The drawings from his 3-dimensional computer drawing system have proven highly successful in eliminating zoning and construction headaches. He offers advice on the best equipment, and shows you how to market and manage your range effectively. And make a profit!
See Our Ad, Right

Griffin & Howe
Griffin & Howe
33 Claremont Rd.
Bernardsville, NJ 07924
(908) 766-2287
Contact: Joe Prather
Griffin & Howe's experienced staff has designed courses in the United States and Europe. We will be pleased to discuss your requirements for a first class facility.
See Our Ad Pg. 77

Grinders Switch Club
1608 Chickering Rd.
Nashville, TN 37215
(615) 729-9732
Contact: Barry Claud
John Woolley is recognized as the world's leading course designer, having been responsible for numerous World and International Championship courses, as well many private courses.

Holland & Holland Sporting Weapons Limited
50 East 57th St.
New York, NY 10022
(212) 752-7755
FAX: (212) 752-6805

Jon Kruger
Box 213, St. Ansgar, IA 50472
(515) 736-4893
Individual design custom tailored to your specific parcel of land and personal tastes. Courses designed for the recreational shooter yet ideal for hosting tournaments. Recommendations in target and equipment selection.
See Our Ad Pg. 121

Patrick LaBoone
The Midwest Shooting School
2550 Hwy. 23
Wrenshall, MN 55797-8708
(218) 384-3670
Sporting clays course design, limited to 4 courses/year.

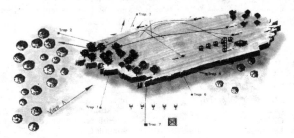

**Steve Middleditch
Course Design**
1930 Wynfield Point Dr.
Buford, GA 30519
(770) 963-5414
Contact: Steve Middleditch

**Nichols & Baldridge
Shooting Consultants**
9135 Green Tree Rd.
Philadelphia, PA 19118
(215) 247-1227
Contact: Timothy Nichols or
Ben Baldridge

Parker/Boss
Design Team
780 E. 15th St., N.
Wichita, KS 67214
(316) 265-1110
Est.: 1985   Staff: 2
Contact: Larry Leatherman
Paker/Boss as an industry leader
has recognized that many operators have design questions. These
can be answered with a 15 minute
conversation or a consultation at
your site. Parker/Boss has put together their design team which is
headed by Jon Kruger, Dan Carlisle
and Marty Fischer. Please call for
more information regarding our services and fees.

Gordon C. Philip
1701 Northwest Cookingham
Kansas City, MO 64155
(816) 734-4044
FAX: (816) 734-9650
Est.: 1987   Staff: 1
Your proposed course may be large
or small, public or private. In any
case, it should have a wide variation of targets. Challenging enough
to test the best, yet flexible enough
to encourage a beginner. Get the
experience of a designer who has
worked on 5 World Championship
and 5 National Championship
courses, who is internationally recognized throughout the industry,
and provides his clients with expertise and professionalism at all
times.

See Our Ad Below

Quack Sporting Clays, Inc.
Modern Era Clay Games-Consulting
& Course Building
4 Ann & Hope Way
PO Box 98, Cumberland, RI 02864
(401) 723-8202

FAX: (401) 722-5910
Est.: 1987
Pres/CEO: Kenneth M. Gagnon, Sr.
Quack Sporting Clays, Inc. limits its
course designing and building to established gun clubs and game
preserves. With 10 years experience in course building along with
the organization implementation of
over 200 shotgun events (6 int'l)
we're definitely the leaders in new
innovations and new support products. Always taking advantage of
the terrain, always innovative in
designing and building a Modern
Era Recreational course, our specialty. Our solid hands on skills and
honesty along with an impeccable
track record (30 years) speaks for itself. A new Modern Era
Recreational shotgun games course
and a new friendship is as close as
your telephone. We will also help
you promote your new Modern Era
Complex in our magazine "Modern
Skeet & Clays". For more information call or write.

See Our Ad Pgs. 238-239

R&R Sales and Service
9903 Geronimo Oaks
San Antonio, TX 78254
(210) 688-3165
FAX: (210) 688-9048
Est.: 1989   Staff: 3

Contact: FM "Butch" Roberson, III Course design and consultation with the owner in mind. Safety first. We are your source for single pole steel towers–available from 40 ft. to 120 ft.!

The Shooting Academy
8130 E. LaJunta Rd.
Scottsdale, AZ 85255
(602) 585-0882
Contact: Mike Davey
Michael J. Davey's course design philosophy is simple: "provide the best course possible given the restrictions and budget restraints of the customer." With over eight years experience, Michael has designed both public and private courses, but specializes in "top quality" privately owned facilities. His services include, evaluation, design, site preparation, contractor supervision, installation and training. Call today for information and references.

SHOW-ME SPORTS

Show Me Sports Corp.
8267 N. Revere, Dept. WC
Kansas City, MO 64151
(816) 587-9540
FAX: (816) 587-3906
Est.: 1978
President: Andrew Perkins •
Complete course design & consulting; Experienced on-staff consulting course designers to serve your needs worldwide. Providing full service detailed information and design. References available upon request.

See Our Ad Pg. 231

SportShooting Consultants, Ltd.
PO Box 207
Rincon, GA 31326
(912) 826-0072
Est.: 1992
Contact: Marty Fischer
Recognized across America as one of the foremost authorities on sporting clays course design and marketing and management techniques for shooting facilities and hunting preserves. Below is a list of our various services: Sporting Clays Course Design; Marketing Plans and Business Plans; Management Training and Consultation; Special Event Marketing; Hunting Preserve Consultation; Pro Shop and Retail Design; Shooting Clinics and Instructor Training. Authorized dealer for Lincoln, IBIS Auto-Sporter, and Remington, Parker/Boss traps and accessories. Call or write for a brochure describing our services.

Sporting World International
110 River Bluff
Merry Hill, NC 27957
(919) 356-2662
Contact: Barry G. Davis

Sports Marketing Group
12003 Vanilla Ct.
Orlando, FL 32837
(407) 858-0441
FAX: (407) 858-9904
Contact: Bob Edwards or Cindy Edwards
Course Design; Management; Consultation; Tournament Coordination; Shooting Instruction

Top Gun Consultants
1142 Draymore Court
Hummelstown, PA 17036
(717) 566-2900
FAX: (717) 566-1399
Contact: Dan Schindler
Experienced, flexible, on-site supervision, start to finish

Victory Shooting School and Course Design
PO Box 7148
Columbia, MO 65205
(573) 442-9189
Contact: Mark Brownlee
- Extensive sporting and FITASC design experience including 1996 SCA Championship. - Imaginative, artful presentations for new or existing courses. - Single event or long term consultation. - Excite your customers!

WILD-HARE, International
Box 11943, Memphis, TN 38111
(800) 523-9453
Contact: Jaye Wells
WILD-HARE's team of course designers includes landscape and architectural designers, as well as accomplished shooters. We can focus on every aspect of your project from parking to clubhouse to shooting stands. For FITASC parcours, English Sporting, or Five-Stand course designs that are tailored to your project requirements, yet offer flexibility, contact our design staff. We also offer the best in equipment and installation services suited to your needs.

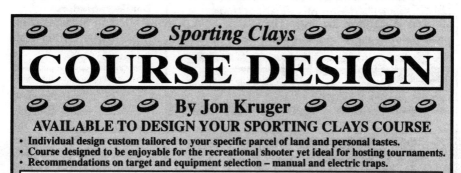

DOG TRAINERS & BREEDERS

Addieville East Farm
200 Pheasant Dr..Mapleville, RI 02839
(401) 568-3185
FAX: (401) 568-3009
Est.: 1979
Contact: Geoff Gaebe

Bay View Registered Setters
12 Upton Rd.,
LaGrangeville, NY 12540
(914) 223-5546 (Evenings)
Contact: Dan Catalano
Extensive line breeding from our own personal proven grouse/wood-cock gun dogs (champion blood lines for 39 years), has resulted in consistent, very natural pups with superior noses, style, looks and dis-positions; they are natural retrievers, point scent as early as 8-10 weeks, come to whistle, retrieve and are highly socialized. Natural close working patterns make them ideal grouse/woodcock dogs for the foot hunter. Sanitary kennels. Pups (bred from our 25 healthy dogs only!) sold by reservation year-round. Started dogs on occasion. References and brochure on request. Call (evenings) or write today.

Buckeye Kennels
5598 County Rd. 48
Waterloo, OH 45688
(614) 643-0148
Contact: Dick Geswein
English Setters & Pointers–bird dog training seminars. Full-time gun dog training.

Burchett's Bird Dogs
1758 295th St.
Argyle, IA 52619
(319) 838-2822
Contact: Bob Burchett
Classy responsive hunting dogs; Training & handling. Finishing hunt-ing companions for sale. Stud service.

Burnt Creek Setters
1 Kennel Rd., Box 123
Baldwin, ND 58521
(701) 258-6373
Contact: Jim Marti
English Setters–Brochure on re-quest.

Circle Drive Kennels
Box 50, Hill City, KS 67642
(913) 674-5723
German Shorthairs–pups, started & trained dogs.

Count Kennels
11420 Crawford Rd.
Las Cruces, NM 88005
(505) 526-6504
Breeding for amateur trainable Britts; Field bred pups.

Coyote Creek Retrievers
83574 Territorial Hwy.
Eugene, OR 97405
(541) 485-7887
Contact: Jim Fulks or
Linda Fulks
Obedience & retriever training; all levels of AKC & NAHRA hunting tests. Puppies available.

Dakota Kennels
RR1, Box 47-E, Carthage, SD 57323
(605) 772-4570
Contact: Dennis Lail
Professional training of pointing, re-trieving breeds; Pups, started & trained dogs.

Danikk Labradors
5162 Union Lake Trail
Lonsdale, MN 55046
(507) 744-2284
Contact: Fran Smith
Producing dual-purpose puppies for conformation, field and the home. Stud service. Personalized training.

Davis' Five Star Kennel
Rt. 1, Box 271
Mt. Vernon, IL 62864
(618) 242-3409
Contact: Bob E. Davis
Complete programs for pointing and retrieving breeds. Call for more information.

World Class Dog Training, Shooting Instruction, Hunting and More at Michigan's Hunters Creek Club

Metamora, MI — If you've been running a bird hunting preserve for nearly 41 years ... and if, in the process, you've become one of the best known and most popular establishments in the state ... you must be doing something right! And doing it right they are at Hunters Creek Club in southeastern Michigan, about an hour's drive from Detroit.

Founder Preston Mann and members of the Class of '98.

Hunters Creek encompasses 1,000 acres of woods, meadows, and fields of sorghum, timothy and brome grass, and boasts an impressive array of attractions and activities designed to appeal to a broad segment of sportsmen. Bird hunters, clay shooters, fishermen, and even gourmets, express constant enthusiasm for Hunters Creek.

Founded by Preston Mann in 1958, when hunting preserves in the United States were few and far between, Hunters Creek is a private club that is renowned for its attention to member needs. Certain Club services, however, are available to non-members, notably dog training and professional shooting instruction.

Dogs to Savvy Hunting Companions

With on-site kennels that can accommodate 60 dogs, Hunters Creek's widely acclaimed dog-training program converts untutored animals into obedient—and savvy—hunting companions. Charlie Mann, club owner, puts retrievers through their paces, while club manager Dale Jarvis handles pointers. Hunters Creek also sells pedigreed pups, including Brittany Spaniels and Labs.

Shooting School...The More You Know

Headed by Sporting Clays All American Pat Lieske, the shooting school offers intensive individual instruction by appointment on all aspects of gun safety, shooting etiquette and proper technique. The school is open to all levels, beginner to advanced. Quarterly stock fitting seminars, monthly group and kids' shooting clinics are also part of the program.

"Hunting and clay shooting are like any other human activity," Charlie Mann says. "The more you know about something, the

better you'll become at it. And the better you become, the more you'll enjoy yourself."

To ensure that dog and hunter are never disappointed, the club, under the guidance of Charlie Mann—a former president of the North American Gamebird Association—stocks thousands upon thousands of gamebirds. Hunters Creek Club provides a cornucopia of benefits for its members. A spacious clubhouse, for example, includes private lockers so time-pressured business people can leave the office, drive to the site, and change quickly into field gear. And a Pro Shop is generously stocked with accessories and equipment.

Catering To Clay Shooters

Clay shooters are catered to at Hunters Creek, with trap and skeet fields and a sporting clays course that entice novices and challenge old-timers. "We're never entirely satisfied with the ranges," Charlie Mann says. "Like everything else at Hunters Creek, there's not a year goes by that we don't try to improve them."

Hunters Creek also satisfied the appetite. It is a favorite location for group picnics. And folks are more than willing to drive from the city to feast on home cooked pheasant, duck in orange sauce, pan fried trout or New York strip steak.

For more information on membership, dog training and shooting instruction at Hunters Creek, where "doing things right" is a way of life, write Charlie Mann at the club, **675 Sutton Road, Metamora, MI 48455**, or phone **(810) 664-4307.**

Flushing Star Kennel
33665 Henwill Rd.
Columbia Station, OH 44028
(216) 748-1053
Contact: Debbie Karlovec
English Springer & English Cocker
Spaniels. Top Quality U.K. & U.S.
Breedings; Pups, gun dogs–training
& stud service. References & reasonable prices.

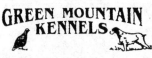

Green Mountain Kennel, Inc.
RR1, Box 438F
Center Ossipee, NH 03814
(603) 539-2106
(603) 539-6718
FAX: (603) 539-2903
Owner: David Bardzik
Green Mountain Kennel breeds
AKC Brittany Spaniels and offers
pups and started dogs. It also offers training programs that teach
the hunting dog to point and retrieve gamebirds. Training classes
for master and dog ar available on
an hourly basis. Done in the field
with live birds, this type of instruction will teach pointing, holding,
whoa command, retrieving, backing and obedience in the field. Call
today for more information.

Green Valley Kennels
15437 Derby Grange Rd.
Dubuque, IA 52001
(319) 588-3045
Contact: Bob Iler
Gun dog training, all breeds; seminars & classes.

Grouse Ridge Kennels
Preston Center Rd., Box 299
Oxford, NY 13830-3270
(607) 334-4920
Contact: Pete Flanagan or
Katie Flanagan
English Setters-Hall of fame breeding; Started & trained dogs.

Gun Dog Kennels
PO Box 38
Artesia Wells, TX 78001
(210) 676-3410
Training your started or finished
dog. Packages available upon request.

Gunsmoke Kennels
Rt. 2 Box 15
Union Springs, AL 36089
(334) 738-4642
Contact: Bill Holmes
Quality puppies & well started
young dogs; trained gun dogs;
stud service; professional training.
Call for free brochure.

High Prairie Farms
55552 WCR 23
Carr, CO 80612
(970) 897-2374
Contact: Timothy A. Degroff
Field English Springer Spaniels. Puppies, started & finished dogs.
Training, breeding & trial handling.

Hightest Retrievers
1021 Lower Honcut Rd.
Oroville, CA 95966
(916) 742-3647
FAX: (916) 742-3653
Contact: John & Debra Folsom
25 years experience-fully trained
shooting dogs available. Labrador
puppies. Stud service.

Hunter's Creek Club
675 Sutton Rd.
Metamora, MI 48455
(810) 664-4307
Contact: Charlie Mann or
Dale Jarvis
Hunter's Creek takes pride in the
quality of it's training program for
Pointers, Retrievers and Flushing
dogs. Limited numbers of Lab,
Brittany & Pointer pups available.
Call today.
See Our Ads Pgs. 122 &123

Intraset Gordons
12273 Hyfield Rd.
DeSoto, MO 63020
(314) 586-6778
Full field strain Gordons-written
guarantee.

Joshua Creek Ranch
PO Box 1946
Boerne, TX 78006
(210) 537-5090
Professional training of all pointing
& retrieving breeds. Inquire about
training, Stud service and pups.

King Llewellin Setters
27 Gapview Rd., Conway, AR 72032
(501) 329-7651
Contact: Alfred O. King, Sr.
Breeder for 31 years–references
available.

King's Kennels
238 Saunders Rd.
Riverwoods, IL 60015
(847) 945-9592
German Shorthair–Adults & Puppies
Started & Finished; Stud service;
German Imports are our specialty.

Lehmschlog Kennels
181 McDowell Lane
Selah, WA 98942
(509) 697-8879
Contact: Clay Brown
German Shorthaired & Wirehaired
Pointers. Puppies & started dogs
available.

Linden Kennels
1657 200th St.
Mt. Pleasant, IA 52641
(319) 986-5589
Contact: Hal Chaney
Field bred English Spring Spaniels–
gun dog training, all breeds

Lower Creek Kennel
Box 322, RD#1
Pedricktown, NJ 08067
(609) 351-0078
Contact: Paul Harris
English Cockers, English Springers,
Labradors

Marks-A-Lot Kennels
RR1, Box 209 D
Caddo Mills, TX 75135
(903) 527-LABS
Trainer/Handler: Dan Kielty
Full time Retriever training for field
trials, hunt tests & gun dogs. Call
or write for free brochure.

Mason Creek
126 Erin Rd,
Oconomowoc, WI 53066
(414) 474-7290
Contact: Barbara Grygiel
German Wirehaired Pointers–OFA;
Puppies; Stud service.

Mr. Ed's Brittanys
13118 McDougal Rd.
Athens, OH 45701
(614) 448-3881
Contact: David Linscott
Brittanys bred & trained for 36 yrs.

Oak Hill Kennel
Box 1605, Pinehurst, NC 28374
(910) 295-6710
Contact: John Dahl
Complete retriever training including NARHA, AKC & UKC Gun Dog
events.

Old South Pointer Farms
Rt. 1, Box 12, Rosanky, TX 78953
(210) 839-4560
Owner/Trainer: Jarrett Thompson
Pups, started and broke dogs for
sale from top bloodlines.

Pheasant Hill Sporting Dogs
709 E. Elizabethtown Rd.
Manheim, PA 17545
(717) 664-4041
FAX: (717) 664-3733
Contact: Judy & Ernie Simmons

**Pine Hill Kennels and
Sportsmen's Club**
8347 Ten Mile Rd.
Rockford, MI 49341
(616) 874-8459
Professional training of all gun dog
breeds. Breed top quality German
Shorthairs; Stud service & boarding
available.

Rainwater Kennels
3530 W. Old Hwy. 30
Grand Island, NE 68803
(308) 384-1517
Contact: Larry & Helen Heil
20 yrs. experience in all breed gun
dog training. Stud service, puppies &
started–Labs, Shorthairs, Pointers.

Rawhide Kennels
1719 Pinecrest Rd.
LaPlatte, NE 68123
(402) 291-6804
Contact: Don Paltani or Pam Paltani
Call or write for a free brochure.

Joe & Linda Regan
RR1, Box 148 J,
Sherburne, NY 13460
(607) 674-4707
Proven program for all pointing
breeds. Upland for Retrievers, Spaniels & pointing Labs. Modern kennels.

Rockhill Labradors
7119 Labrador Lane
Mechanicsville, VA 23111
(804) 781-0446
Contact: Bert Hill
Yellow, chocolate & black Labradors

Royal Flush Kennels
4914 Hwy. G
Eagle River, WI 54521
(715) 479-4188
Contact: Walter Albrecht
Specializing in field bred English
Springer Spaniels. Puppies/started
dogs; field trial prospects; professional training & handling.

Royal Hunt Kennel
Plain St., Middleboro, MA 02346
(508) 947-8141
Owner/Trainer: Joseph L. Di Santis
Professional gun dog and companion dog training for all breeds. Pups
through finished brag dogs available. English Setters, Griffons,
Drathaars, German Shorthairs,
Brittanies, English Pointers, retrievers and flushing breeds. 41 years of
experience. Outstanding pups and
gun dogs available for sale.

SSK Labradors
PO Box 55, Warner, NH 03278
(603) 456-3935
Field trial & hunting labradors. All
colors, guaranteed and committed
to excellence.

Snowy Oaks Kennels
Prior Lake, MN
(612) 440-7639
Large Munsterlanders–for the
hunter of upland game & waterfowl. Free video available.

Special K Kennels
Box 286, Riverside, IA 52327
(319) 648-5805
Contact: Mike Kellogg
German Shorthairs. Gun dog training year round. Pups & started
dogs. Satisfaction guaranteed!

Springset Kennels
2715 Skillman Lane
Petaluma, CA 94952
(707) 763-8276
Field proven & adaptable to work
in any type of cover. Call for free
brochure.

Straight Creek Kennels
Rt. 1, Box 273,
West Liberty, KY 41472
(606) 743-4765
Specializing in Llewellin gun dogs.
All phases of training from pup to
finished gun dog.

Trieven Sungold Kennels
1558 Rd. 9 1/2, Lovell, WY 82431
(307) 548-6353
Contact: Jay & Val Walker
Field bred Golden Retrievers from
the best of working bloodlines.
Pups available; working goldens at
stud.

Twin Lakes Kennel
PO Box 628, Laurel Hill, NC 28351
(910) 462-3246
Contact: Woody Thurman

Van Lee Labradors
12997 Bullis Rd.
East Aurora, NY 14052
(716) 652-8979
Contact: Carroll Lewandowski
All breeding stock OFA and CERF.
Written guarantee on hips and
eyes. Pedigrees and pictures upon
request.

LeRoy VanKrik
68437 Bellows Rd.
White Pigeon, MI 49099
(616) 641-7709
English Springer Spaniels–puppies,
started & finished dogs for hunting.

Whack-A-Quack Kennels
Rt. 5 Box 57
Blanchard, OK 73010
(405) 485-9692
Contact: Brad Smith
Professional retriever training gun
dogs; hunt test young field trial
dogs.

Whisper Oak Kennels
PO Box 2048
Hayden Lake, ID 83835
(208) 772-4504
Contact: Dan and Sandy Hosford
Professional training staff for
flushers & retrievers.

White Birch Kennels
RR1, Box 300
West Lovell Rd.
Lovell, ME 04051
(207) 925-1740
Contact: Capt. Paul R. Bois
English Setters, German
Shorthaired Pointers, Beagles.

Whitehaven Canine Center
5015 Eastern Ave.
Davenport, IA 52807
(319) 388-0004
Full service gun dog kennel. Field &
obedience training. Gun dog pups
& started dogs.

Windy Rock Kennels
RR1, Box 438
Rockwell, IA 50469
(515) 822-4905
Contact: Ralph and Cindy Marsh
Gun dog training–all breeds. AKC
Field bred English Springer Spaniels
and Brittanies. Champion blood-
lines. Puppies & started dogs on
occasion.

Von Zinshof Kennel
4900 Bridle Lane
Lincoln, NE 68516
(402) 421-6003
Contact: Bill Zins
German Shorthairs-top quality
pups, started and trained dogs. Satisfaction guaranteed!

DOG EQUIPMENT/ KENNELS/ TRAILERS/ PENS/PET DOORS

Ainley Kennels & Fabrication
1945 Washington St.
Dubuque, IA 52001-3664
(319) 583-7615
Contact: Jane Ainley
Custom dog trucks, trailers, bird
boxes & dog crates

Aluma Sport by Dee Zee
PO Box 3090
Des Moines, IA 50316
(800) 798-9899 (Cust. Service)
(515) 265-7331
FAX: (515) 265-7926

Est.: 1978   Staff: 400
Contact: Chuck Long
Cruise around in the best looking vehicle. From a complete series of Running Boards to Roof Racks, Dee Zee offers you quality products designed to enhance your vehicle's appearance. Style enhancers.

Jim Bainbridge & Co.
Uplander Doghouses
2794 96th Ave.
Marcellus, MI 49067
(708) 755-7051
Contact: Brian Niksch
Year round shelter ensuring comfort and protection equally in summer as well as winter.

Canine Enclosures
Priefert Mfg.
PO Box 1540
Mt. Pleasant, TX 75455
(800) 527-8616
(903) 572-1741
FAX: (903) 572-2798
Sales Mgr: David Bynum
Durable, safe, versatile welded wire dog kennels.

Creative Sports Supply
PO Box 765, Attalla, AL 35954
(205) 442-5244
Est.: 1968
Contact: Jerry Collett
Available: Direct

Aluminum dog crates–designed to last. Custom service available. Write for a free catalog.

Crow River Fabricating
229 County Rd. 5 SW
Cokato, MN 55321
(800) 230-4023
(612) 286-5422
Contact: Russ Scherping
Specializing in stainless steel and aluminum dog trailers, portable dog boxes, truck bodies, topper models.

Dan's D-Lux Dog Boxes
Dan's Fence Company
R.1, Box 218, Hwy. 57 South
Oakland City, IN 47660
(800) 467-5111
(812) 749-5111
Contact: Dan McKinney
Dog box trailers, insulated aluminum truck dog boxes–custom built with many available options.

Dog Equipment, Inc.
1205 East Logan,
Moberly, MO 65270
(816) 263-5533
Contact: Rob Cater

Dog Guard
Sunward American
318 Delaware Ave, Main Square Pl.
Delmar, NY 12054
(800) 865-0495
FAX: (516) 439-0495

President: Bernie Watkin
Mktg: Jill Crammond
Dog guard fencing

Dog Trailers USA
PO Box 1450
Hughes Springs, TX 75656
(903) 639-7544
FAX: (903) 639-7113
Contact: Chris Graham
Stainless steel, full insulated dog trailers. Call for free brochure.

Dole Manufacturing
1420 Higgs Rd.
Lewisburg, TN 37091
(800) 251-8990
(615) 359-6211
Est.: 1937
Contact: John Cook, Jr.
The ultimate dog box by Dole; standard features include: coated lifting handles, aluminum tread plate, 2-year warranty. Free brochure available.

Doskocil
PO Box 1246, Arlington, TX 76004
(817) 467-5116
FAX: (817) 472-9810
Contact: Pat Hoffman
Doskocil is the leading brand of portable hard-shell animal transport cages, including Vari Kennel. Also available: kennel cart, several doghouse styles.

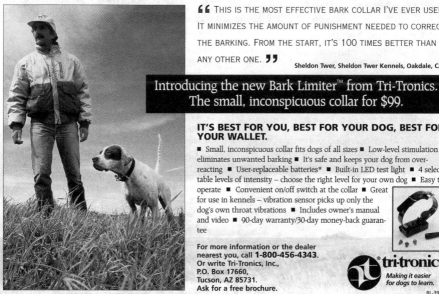

Gun Dog House Door® Co.
RR1, Sabin, MN 56580
(218) 789-7128
FAX: (701) 235-6706
Contact: Carl H. Altenbemd
Easy Dog Door™ allows a dog easy 2-way access to a building or dog house. Call for free brochure.

HME Enterprises
1632 Bald Hill Loop
Madison, NC 27025
(800) 296-6024
Mktg: Gene Hopper
Huntin-Cruiser™ transport kennels. Washable, ventilated and insulated. Call for more information and a brochure.

Hawl-EM-Rite Dog Box Co.
3503 Dan Ave.
Bono, AR 72416
(800) 931-8663
(501) 931-7663
Contact: Bruce Carr

Horst Company
Modular Concepts Corporation
101 East 18th St.
Greely, CO 80631
(800) 221-4724
FAX: (970) 353-7774
Marketing: Bruce Wegner

Jones Trailer Company
PO Box 288
Woodson, TX 76491
(800) 336-0360
(817) 345-6759
FAX: (817) 345-6505
Contact: Patsy Jones
Manufacturer of dog trailers and dog boxes.

K-9 Kondo, Inc.
HC1, Box 104
Stapleton, NE 69163
(800) 779-3546
FAX: (308) 532-4551
President: Joe Showm
Dog houses and doors.

Lifetime Products
PO Box 442, Fairfax, OK 74637
(918) 642-5509
Contact: Ron Thompson
Lifetime dog products include custom trailers, diamond-plate dog boxes, pick-up topper, dog houses, feeders.

The Mason Company
260 Depot St.
PO Box 365
Leesburg, OH 45135
(800) 543-5567
FAX: (513) 780-6336
Est.: 1892
President: Bruce Rowe

On-Point Pet Carrier Products
87 East 300 North
Logan, UT 84321
(801) 755-6913
Contact: Frank Liddiard
Protect-A-Pet provides your pet with a warm, dry, dust-free environment while being transported.

Quality Dog Box
Rt. 1, Box 97A
Weleetka, OK 74880
(918) 652-9891
Sales: Jim Winkle
Quality dog boxes and dog trailers. Call for factory direct prices and brochures.

Yellow Rose Kennels
Glover Aluminum Works
Rt. 2, Box 17
Honey Grove, TX 75446
(903) 378-2359
Contact: Rick Glover or Marcus Glover
Custom-made diamond plate aluminum boxes and trailers built to individual specifications.

DOG EQUIPMENT/ TRAINING/ ELECTRONIC FENCES

ATS SONIC

ATS-SONIC
3852 20th Ave.
Blanchard, MI 49310
(800) 247-7453 (Orders)
(517) 561-2858 (Cust. Svc.)
FAX: (517) 561-5257
Partner: Terry Dupuis
Internet:
http://www.nethawk.com/~sonic
ATTENTION BIRDHUNTERS! Find
your bird dog quickly in the heaviest cover! Easily heard "BEEP-BEEP"
tells all. Seven Models in stock from
$49.95. ATS-SONIC has built the
most popular bird dog beepers on
the market for over a decade. Ask
for our FREE BROCHURE to find out
more! Credit Cards Welcome. Online Brochure.
See Our Ad Pg. 130

Collar Clinic
3189 Logan Valley Rd.
PO Box 907
Traverse City, MI 49685
(616) 947-2010
FAX: (616) 947-6566
Est.: 1988
President: F. Jeff Gunda
Sales/Service: Rick Gamelin
Electronic training collars. We buy,
sell trade and repair.

D.T. Systems, Inc.
4872 Walnut Hill Lane
Dallas, TX 75229
(214) 350-9446
FAX: (214) 350-7847
Contact: Mrs. Choi
77-DT remote training collar with 6
intensity levels and the 125-DT mini
no-bark trainer.

Day's End Dog Training Accessories
1559 E. Taylor Ave.
East Point, GA 30344
(800) 863-3647
FAX: (404) 767-2228
President: Jerry Day
Training collars, training pistols,
whistles, slip leads, and more.

INNOTEK
SPORTING DOG DIVISION

Innotek Sporting Dog Division
One Innoway, Garrett, IN 46738
(800) 826-5527
FAX: (219) 357-3160
Marketing Dir: Jim Schlender
Manufactures remote training collars, anti-bark collars, hidden fence
containment systems and the NEW
Retriever Trainer. Innotek Command Series include the Track N
Train collar, Flush N Train collar, remote bird launchers and·
Auto-Backer. Call or write for free
product information.
See Our Ad Across

Lovett's Electronics
840 E. Pinckley St., Brazil, IN 47834
(800) 446-1093 (Orders)
(812) 446-1093
FAX: (812) 448-8742
Contact: Henry Lovett
"Six in One" Beeper programmable
for 6 or more functions: regular;
grouse; point only; run only; plus
other combinations. Free brochure.

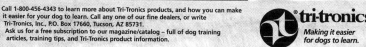

Lucky Dog Equipment, Inc.
14522 NE North Woodinville Way
Suite 103B, Woodinville, WA 98072
(206) 402-8833
FAX: (206) 402-1420
Contact: Dan Albrecht or
Philip Hart
Full line of professional dog training
equipment.

Making it easier
for dogs to learn.

Tri-Tronics, Inc.
PO Box 17660, Tucson, AZ 85731
(520) 290-6000
Est.: 1968   Staff: 200
Dir. of Mktg: Chad James
Available: Retail & Direct
Manufacture electronic dog train-
ing equipment–remote trainers
such as the Sportsman and 200
Lite; as well as other products such
as the New Bark Limiter; Beeper
Collar, Bird Releasers and educa-
tional materials related to our
products.
See Our Ads Pgs. 125-129

DOG/
MISCELLANEOUS

Angell Pedigree Service
167 Quail Ridge Ln.
Mocksville, NC 27028
(800) 468-0882 (Orders)
(704) 634-0889
FAX: (800) 468-0882
All AKC breeds researched–pedigrees include AKC titles, coat
colors, national titles. Parchtex certificates professionally prepared.
Please call for more information.

J. Bazzano Co.
Rt. 181
Pleasant Valley, CT 06063
(203) 379-0088
Owner: Joe Bazzano
Automatic red cedar ribbon dog
bedding

Burr Boots
6410 N. 23rd St.
Ozark, MO 65721
(800) 545-1218
(417) 581-4097
Contact: Mr. Kern

EZ-DIP
Rt. 1, Box 27D
Anderson, MO 64831
(417) 845-3442
Contact: Don Minkler
Completely self-contained and por-
table to make dipping your dog for
fleas easier & simpler.

The Flag
PO Box 141
Owatonna, MN 55060
The Flag will not rust, corrode or
rot. Put the harness on the dog at
the beginning of the day. The flag
mast detaches in seconds for easy
loading between hunting spots.

Hatchbag, Inc.
4475 G Morris Park Dr.
Charlotte, NC 28227
(800) 869-9091
FAX: (704) 573-2230
Dir/Mktg: Dave Morrison
Hatchbag is a tough flexible, waterproof liner that keeps the cargo
area of your vehicle "show-room"
new.

Intercoastal Technologies, Inc.
465 Jay St.
Coldwater, MI 49036
(517) 278-4578
FAX: (517) 278-8239
Controller: Wendy Wassa
"Dog Dummy"

Linear Rubber Products, Inc.
5525 19th Ave.
Kenosha, WI 53140
(800) 558-4040
FAX: (414) 652-3912
Dir. of Advtg: Jack Lane
"Kennel Komfort" dog mats increases dog health, safety &
comfort.

Osborne Industries, Inc.
Box 388
Osborne, KS 67473
(800) 255-0316
Sales & Mktg. Rep: Kail Schoen
The Canine Cantine has a 2.5 gal.
capacity with a 50 watt moisture
sealed heater, keeping water at 45
degrees throughout the winter.
See Our Ad Pg. 124

HEARING PROTECTION

A"Must" For The Shotgunner

There's no way to sugar-coat the message: If you're a shooter who pursues the pastime without adequate ear protection, there's little doubt that you'll lose, to a greater or a lesser degree, your ability to hear.

The reason? Well, the healthy ear is a finely calibrated instrument capable of registering an amazing range of sounds. And every sound, from a soft sigh to a crack of thunder, is transmitted as vibrations to the brain by some 30,000 nerve endings. Damage them and you diminish your ability to hear.

Unfortunately hearing loss can be insidious because it's so often gradual. By the time you're aware of symptoms the damage has been done. Perhaps sounds begin to seem muffled. Or you may have diffi-culty distinguishing consonant sounds in conversation. Or the warning sign may be tinnitus, a constant ringing or buzzing. Any symptom is a call to immediate action.

Louder Than A Jet

A decibel (dB) is a unit for measuring the relative level or intensity of sounds. A jet engine at full power generates 130 dB. Each blast of a 12-ga. shotgun generates 150 dB—ten times louder than the level at which most experts suggest ear protectors be worn.

So, although common sense suggests the need for hearing protection when you shoot, it's not uncommon for sportsmen to resist the use of protectors. "Uncomfortable." "Bulky." "It interferes with my shooting." You've heard these objections yourself.

For the most part, however, such objections are less valid than they once were. The variety of hearing protection available today runs from low cost one-size-fits-all plugs to devices that are marvels of electronic sophistication. The type you use will depend on 1) the shooting situation; 2) the degree to which you are willing to sacrifice comfort for protection; and 3) how much you're willing to spend.

Universal Plugs - available at many pro shops for about $2.00 a pair or less. Similar to the ear plugs that swimmers wear, they muffle sound and protect hearing. If there's a drawback to these inexpensive—often disposable—plugs, it's the fact that fit and, therefore, protection may not be perfect.

Custom Molded Plugs - The ultimate plug type protector resembles a hearing aid. The simplest type is made of a sound dampening material that is custom-fitted to your ear and sells for up to $60 a pair. A more sophisticated version of the custom molded plug, incorporates electronic circuitry that allows all normal sounds through, but shuts off very loud noises—say, a shotgun blast. The cost of this modern technology can be high—up to $675 a pair.

Ear Muffs - Many shooters and more than a few shooting instructors, opt for ear muffs. They come in a broad range of styles and models, and offer a variety of features, including cups and foam- or liquid-filled ear cushions. Prices here range from less than $50 to $200.

Plug or muff, plain or fancy, the choice is yours. Protect your hearing now, or most assuredly, pay the price later.

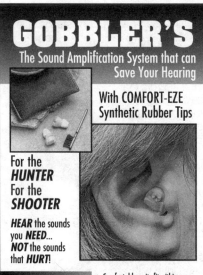

EAR PROTECTION

Action Ear-Bionic Ear
Silver Creek Industries
PO Box 1988
Manitowoc, WI 54221
(800) 533-3277
(414) 684-1225
FAX: (414) 684-6267
Est.: 1959
Contact: Kevin Edgar
Available: Retail
Hear it. See it. Shoot it. Hit more targets! The Action Ear Sport stereo amplifier allows you to hear traps and locate targets faster than single in-the-ear devices. Electronic limiter protects your hearing. FREE Brochure!

The Bilsom Group
c/o Wilson Safety
PO Box 622
Reading, PA 19603
(610) 371-7865
Est.: 1976
Mktg: Elizabeth A. Antry
Available: Retail
Hearing protection, voice amplification, GPT Eye Safety Lenses.

Cabot Safety Corporation
90 Mechanic St.
Southbridge, MA 01550
(800) 327-3431
FAX: (800) 488-8007
Marketing Dir: Joann Waite
Available: Retail
Wide selection of earmuffs, banded hearing protection and earplugs, including the E-A-R Classic foam earplug, which gradually expands and conforms to the size and shape of any ear canal to form a custom fit seal against harmful noise.

E.A.R., Inc.
Insta-Mold Division
PO Box 18888, Boulder, CO 80308
(800) 525-2690
(303) 447-2619
FAX: (303) 447-2637
Nat'l. Sales Mgr.: Garry G. Gordon
Available: Retail
Electronic & non-electronic customized ear protection
Presenting E.A.R., Inc.'s SoundScopes Magnum Ear. Electronic ear plugs that allow shooters the flexibility to enjoy hunting and shooting more than ever. With the Magnum Ear, a shooter can switch from lower output for repetitive target get shooting to higher output for enhanced hearing while hunting. Available in custom in-the-ear and behind-the-ear models. Custom fitted Magnum Ear ITEs can be made from acrylics for bowhunters or from softer materials for shooters. The behind-the-ear model comes with tubing attached to a disposable foam ear plug but can be attached to a custom ear mold. Call today for more information.
See Our Ad Below

E.S.P.
Electronic Shooters Protection, Inc.
11997 West 85th Pl.
Arvada, CO 80005
(800) 767-7791
(303) 456-8964
FAX: (303) 456-7179
Est.: 1992
Contact: Jack Hume
Available: Retail & Direct
In the field or on the course, the shooter who appreciates quality will appreciate the E.S.P. Competition Series Electronic Earplug. This all-in-the-ear hearing protection amplifies environmental and speech sounds...while simultaneously protecting you from loud noises like gun fire.
See Our Ad Across, Right

Ear Gear™ for Shooters
Westone Laboratories
PO Box 15100
Colorado Springs, CO 80935
(800) 736-9576

Gobbler Hearing Amplification System
Bracklynn Products
4400 Stillman Blvd., Suite C
Tuscaloosa, AL 35401
(205) 345-2697
(800) 247-2955 (Dealers Only)
FAX: (205) 349-2113
Est.: 1989   Staff: 7
Owner/Pres: Kenneth Lynn
Gobblers are comfortable, battery operated units that fit into the ear canal. Separate volume control enables use to adjust volume. Comes with 2 units, batteries, extra ear sleeves, cleaning brush and carrying case.
See Our Ad Pg. 132

E.S.P.
ELECTRONIC SHOOTERS PROTECTION

THE SHOOTER'S CHOICE FOR QUALITY HEARING PROTECTION

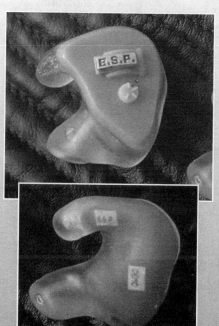

COMPARE THESE FEATURES

■ **Triple-layer construction** gives better noise reduction, resists wear and aging.

■ **Single Automatic Gain Control** provides more dependable hearing protection and better speech amplification than dual control brands.

■ **Advanced circuitry** provides better speech clarity, less distortion.

For a product brochure and information on new E.S.P. products, write to:

Electronic Shooters Protection
11997 West 85th Place, Arvada, CO 80005-5138
303-456-8964 / Fax 303-456-7179
http://www.americaoutdoors.com/esp

1-800-767-7791

© 1996 E.S.P.

DEALER INQUIRIES WELCOME

HOPPE'S ⑨™
A DIVISION OF PENGUIN INDUSTRIES, INC.

Hoppe's — Penguin Industries, Inc.
Airport Industrial Mall
Coatesville, PA 19320
(610) 384-6000
FAX: (610) 857-5980
Contact: Patricia Lucas
Available: Retail
Hoppe's Benchrest Sound Mufflers are compact, fully adjustable and may be worn over or behind the head or under the chin. Excellent noise reduction properties make Hoppe's Sound Muffler ideal for the rifle range, shotgun shooting or any other situation where noise protection is advised.
See Our Ad Below

Howard Leight Industries
1330 Colorado Ave.
Santa Monica, CA 90404
(800) 327-1110
(310) 396-3838
FAX: (310) 314-3860
Est.: 1978
Contact: Chris Leight
Available: Retail
Howard Leight Industries offers the widest selection of hearing protection products available...disposable ear plugs, re-usable earplugs, banded hearing protectors, and quality ear muffs. By following the leader in hearing protection, you can listen to the future. Call now for more information on how you can offer the fastest growing line of hearing protection in the industry.

North Safety Products
Specialty Products Division
2664 B Saturn St.
Brea, CA 92621
(714) 524-1655
FAX: (714) 524-7944
Est.: 1953   Staff: 30
Contact: Katherine Michalowicz
Available: Retail & Direct
The Sonic II Hearing Protector; The Noise Husher; Foam Ear Plug; The Gun Muffler Ear Muffs; The Com-Fit Multi-Purpose Earplug; Hearing Protectors for Youths.

PELTOR

Peltor Inc.
41 Commercial Way
E. Providence, RI 02914
(401) 438-4800
FAX: (401) 434-1708
Est.: 1952   Staff: 250
Dir. Sales/Mktg.: Frank A. D'Isidoro
Available: Retail
PELTOR offers a complete line of hearing protection that includes ear muffs, ear plugs, and electronic hearing protectors. Recently PELTOR introduced three new products; the Range Partner and the Bull's-Eye Ultimate 10 and the Tatical 6-S. The Range Partner is a combo pack containing the PELTOR shotgunner hearing protector and model 2500 amber shooting glasses. The Ultimate 10 has the highest noise reduction rating on the market (29dB) for any ear muff that has been tested in an accredited lab. The Tactical 6-S is a brand new stereophonic hearing protector, designed for anyone that uses a

shotgun or any long gun. It has been developed to facilitate ease of speech and communication, yet provide hearing protection at the same time. It is light weight and compact, folds for safe storage and easy transportation. Other popular PELTOR products include the Tactical 7 electronic hearing protector. The Tactical 7 suppresses sound above 82 dB, yet still amplifies normal sound such as speech.
See Our Ad Pg. 133

Pro-Ears Hearing Protectors
Ridgeline Products
PO Box 30410, 15429 N. 9th Pl.
Phoenix, AZ 85046-0410
(800) 888-EARS (Orders)
(800) 891-3660 (Cust. Svc.)
Est.: 1992   Staff: 12
Owner/Pres: Dan Nigro
Available: Retail & Direct
Makers of Pro-Ears Hearing Protectors/Enhancers. Features lightweight, modular, mufflers with Independent Volume Control, Superior Active Sound Control Circuitry, Surface Mount Technology, No Connective Wires–Comes with 5 year warranty–400 hr. min. batteries. Models include Pro-Slim, Pro-Mag, Pro-Hunter, Pro-Tac and new sporting clays "Soft Side" model. Also non-electronic Pro-Slim NE–since 1993–worn by more pro shooters.
See Our Ad Across, Right

Silencio/Safety Direct, Inc.
56 Coney Island Dr.
Sparks, NV 89431
(800) 648-1812
(702) 359-4451
FAX: (702) 359-1074
Contact: Gordon Kramer
Available: Retail
At Team Silencio, customer service and satisfaction are the number one goal. Earmuffs available in six models; private branding available in certain styles. Electronic earmuff hearing protection - 4 models from which to choose. Earplugs - sound baffler, economy and disposable models available. Call for catalog, (800) 648-1812.
See Our Ad Pg. 140

Sound Scopes
E.A.R., Inc.
PO Box 2146
Boulder, CO 80306
(800) 525-2690
(303) 447-2619
FAX: (303) 447-2637
Nat'l. Sales Mgr.: Garry G. Gordon
Available: Retail
Electronic & non-electronic customized ear protection
See Our Ad Pg. 134

Tico Industries, Inc.
1650 Hymer
Sparks, NV 89431
(702) 358-1611
FAX: (702) 331-8117
President: Lee Hugdal
"Quiet Please" hearing protectors.

Walker's "Game Ear", Inc.
PO Box 1069
Media, PA 19063
(610) 565-8952
FAX: (610) 566-7488
Est.: 1990
President: Bob Walker
Available: Retail & Direct
Using modern hearing aid technology, these products were designed and developed to enhance the user's hearing and offer hearing protection when needed. The "Game Ear"– designed for the hunter with maximum amplification, (49 dB) and hearing protection, (NRR 29 dB). The "Target Ear"– designed for the range with reduced amplification, (23 dB) and maximum hearing protection, (NRR 29 dB). The "Nature Ear"–designed for outdoor enthusiasts and general hearing enhancement with medium amplification (39 dB) and (NRR 27 dB). New for 1996–Tact'L Ear designed for law enforcement and military.

EYE PROTECTION

Shotgunners Should See To It

Think, for a moment, of how much your vision means to you. Then consider the effect on your life if it were impaired. How many activities that you take for granted—like driving—would you have to curtail? How many pleasures—like field hunting or sporting clays—would you have to forsake? As a shotgunner, you owe it to yourself to protect your eyes on every shooting occasion. (If sporting clays are your thing you have little choice in the matter: No reputable course will allow you to shoot without adequate eye protection.)

Why are all sporting clays courses so vision conscious? Because even a partial hit on a target directly overhead will spray shooter and spectator alike with shards of clay. Because pellets ricochet off trees and other objects. Because shooting cages don't entirely prevent the occasional stretch shot that rains pellets on those nearby.

But field hunting also involves hazards that make eye protection a matter of concern. Twigs, saplings, vines and whipping branches can scratch your eye, resulting in temporary discomfort or serious injury.

Eyeglasses Fill The Bill

Do you wear eyeglasses regularly? Then here's the good news. You're ready to shoot. But consider purchasing a large pair of sport glasses that will cover your eyes more for protection and give you better optics when you're mounting your gun. Most prescription lenses are made with optical CR-39 plastic lenses which are less than half the weight of glass. If your vision is 20/20 perfect, protect your precious eyes with some good sport glasses. Consider light to medium shade lenses to keep your pupil small. Why? Your depth of field is improved. . . just like a camera. Lenses are coated with a multitude of colors to romance the target color besides fading out the background picture. Be sure the shooting glasses ride moderately high on your face, but not so high they deprive you of protection from below. Also recommended:

- Get a lens that increases visual sharpness by filtering out light's blue wave lengths. Yellow lenses are good for this purpose, although they may be uncomfortable in bright sunlight. Also consider purple lenses. They darken the sky, flatten the green background and illuminate the oranges, green & black targets.

- Select the lightest colored lenses that will do the job. Dark lenses cause your pupils to dilate, diminishing visual acuity.

- Silicone nose pads will prevent annoying slippage when you sweat.

You may even want to consider shooting glasses with interchangeable lenses. Different colors alter contrast, depending on the light, background color and target color. (Many targets stand out distinctly from a green background when seen through vermilion lenses, for example.) And if interchangeable is your choice, why not include clear lenses? They're great for low light levels!

EYE PROTECTION

The Bilsom Group
c/o Wilson Safety
PO Box 622, Reading, PA 19603
(610) 371-7865
Est.: 1939
Mktg: Elizabeth A. Antry
Available: Retail
GPT Safety Glasses, hearing protection

Cabot Safety Corp.
90 Mechanic St.
Southbridge, MA 01550
(800) 327-3431
FAX: (800) 488-8007
Marketing Dir: Joann Waite
Available: Retail
Contemporary wraparound styling and tough polycarbonate lenses provide protection against debris from discharged powder and spent shell/cartridge particles; clear, gray and yellow.

Costa Del Mar
123 North Orchard, Bldg. #1
Ormand Beach, FL 32174
(800) 447-3700
FAX: (904) 677-3737
Pres: Ray Ferguson
VP/Mktg: Bill Darby
Available: Retail
Polarized shooting glasses.

Decot Hy-Wyd
Sport Glasses, Inc.
PO Box 15830
Phoenix, AZ 85060
(800) 528-1901
(602) 955-7625
FAX: (602) 955-7151
Est.: 1949   Staff: 11
Contact: Bud Decot
Available: Retail & Direct
Decot Hy-Wyd Sport Glasses-the original since 1949. Many times copied but never duplicated. Our Hy-Wyd frames, both the classic gold II and the satin black teflon Hy-Wyd III, have been the shooters favorite for many years. Our custom coated lenses of various shades bring out the target color like there's nothing else in sight. Our international sport glasses have also been acclaimed to

be the "Finest Under the Sun." Champions prefer the best. Dealer Inquiries Welcome. Call us for more information.

See Our Ad Across, Left

Foggles, Inc.
7700 Rivers Edge Dr.
Columbus, OH 43235
(800) 521-3001
FAX: (614) 436-0057
VP: Mary Betz
Available: Retail & Direct
Foggles eyewear prevents the scattering of glare generated light across the retina of the eye. Our unique and PATENTED design improves visual acuity...targets appear sharper and clearer. We offer the discriminating sportsman the ultimate in quality, target and environmental enhancement and sunlight protection.

HOPPE'S ⑨™
A DIVISION OF PENGUIN INDUSTRIES, INC.

Hoppe's — Penguin Industries, Inc.
Airport Industrial Mall
Coatesville, PA 19320
(610) 384-6000
FAX: (610) 857-5980
Contact: Patricia Lucas
Available: Retail

Melibrad Polarized Lens Specialist
PO Box 19689
1555 E. Flamingo, #435
Las Vegas, NV 89132
(800) 634-6786
FAX: (702) 732-0579
Est.: 1965
Contact: Larry Elton
Available: Retail & Direct

Melibrad specializes in polarized sunglasses–amber or grey. Prescription sunglasses available. Call or write for information.

Oakley, Inc.
10 Holland
Irvine, CA 92718
(800) 733-6255
(714) 951-0991
Advtg. Dir: Kris Bowers
Available: Retail

Olympic Optical
3975 Vantech, Suite 2
Memphis, TN 38115
(800) 238-7120 (Cust. Svc.)
(901) 794-3890
FAX: (800) 748-1669
Est.: 1975   Staff: 50
Contact: Danny Holmes
Available: Retail & Direct
Exclusive licensee of: Remington shooting and sport eyewear; Smith & Wesson shooting and sport eyewear; Smith & Wesson hearing protection products; Stren fishing eyewear.

Opti-Sport, Inc.
2090 Old Union Rd.
Buffalo, NY 14227
(800) 443-7981
FAX: (716) 656-0323
All Opti-Sport lenses come with

free UV light filter and scratch coating. Plano & prescription–27 specialized lens colors.

Outdoor Shades, Div. of QT
680 Fargo Ave.
Elk Grove, IL 60007
(800) 262-1180
(708) 228-1180
Est.: 1991   Staff: 15
Contact: Liz Ciprian
Available: Retail & Direct
Protective eyewear and binoculars; cameras for the outdoors.

Peltor Inc.
41 Commercial Way
E. Providence, RI 02914
(401) 438-4800
FAX: (401) 434-1708
Est.: 1952   Staff: 250
Available: Retail
Bull's-Eye Model 2500 shooting glasses

Protective Optics, Inc.
1320 W. Winton Ave.
Hayward, CA 94545
(800) 776-7842
(510) 887-2401
FAX: (510) 732-6134
Contact: Dan Freeman
Shatterproof polycarbonate lens – shooting wrap, wire, clip-on. Dealer Inquiries Welcome.

Randolph Engineering, Inc.
26 Thomas Patten Dr.
Randolph, MA 02368-3902
(800) 541-1405
(617) 961-6070
FAX: (617) 986-0337
Est.: 1973
Contact: Richard Waszkiewicz
Nat'l. Sales Mgr: Bob Bouchard
Available: Retail & Direct
Manufacturer of the Ranger Shooting Glass. Interchangable polycarbonate lenses, ophthalmic frames with spring hinges, made in the USA. Official sponsors of the U.S. Shooting Team and The Shooting Federation of Canada.
See Our Ad Pg. 21

Rocky Mountain High Sports Glasses
8121 N. Central Park Ave.
Skokie, IL 60007
(800) 323-1418
(847) 679-1012
FAX: (847) 679-0184
VP: Tibor Gross
Div. Mgr: Eric L. Esson
Available: Retail
Polycarbonate shooting glasses. Several styles including TED NUGENT BOWHUNTING GLASS, PATRIOT, CLIP-ONS, also offer polarized fishing glasses. Dealer inquiries welcome.

SCOPZ Shooting Glasses
by Carl Zeiss Optical
1015 Commerce St.
Petersburg, VA 23803
(800) 338-2984 (Ext. 382)
Available: Retail & Direct
The only shooting lenses that feature famous Zeiss lenses, specially coated to eliminate glare and distracting reflections. Custom Comfort Fitting System assures snug, comfortably fit. See the target more clearly, more sharply, more quickly. Five Zeiss tints available. May be fitted with prescription lenses. Guaranteed against scratching for two years.
See Our Ad Pg. 12 & Across

Serengeti Eyewear

Corning Optics, 203 Colonial Dr.,
Horsehead, NY 14845
(800) 525-4001 (Cust. Svc.)
(800) 831-8100 (Retail Inquiries)
Contact: Georgie Taylor
Available: Retail & Direct
High contrast rose and orange (previously the Ventor). Three frames
available.

Silencio/Safety Direct, Inc.

56 Coney Island Dr.Sparks, NV 89431
(800) 648-1812
(702) 359-4451
FAX: (702) 359-1074
Est.: 1972   Staff: 75
Contact: Gordon Kramer
Available: Retail
From economical shooting glasses
to specialized glasses, Silencio offers real value for shooters. SVS
Shooting glasses - designed to fit
over prescription eyewear, comfort

in an economical one-piece model.
AVI Shooting glasses - popular aviator style offers 99.9% U.V. blocking
with high-impact polycarbonate
lens. TRI-LENS glasses - 3 interchangeable polycarbonate lens sets.
WRAPPS Glasses - deluxe, high impact, 99.9% U.V. blocking wraparound lense. Also available in mirrored finishes. Call for catalog,
1-800-648-1812.
See Our Ad Across, Left

Simmons Outdoor Corp.

2120 Killearney Way
Tallahassee, FL 32308
(904) 878-5100
FAX: (904) 878-0300
Advtg. Dir: Jerry Cliff
Available: Retail
Wrap-around shooting glasses

Tasco Sales, Inc.

PO Box 520080
7600 Northwest 26 St.
Miami, FL 33152-0080
(305) 591-3670 (Ext. 315)
Contact: Pam Levine
Available: Retail
Shooting glasses, binoculars

OPTICIANS/ OPTOMETRISTS/ OPTHALMOLOGISTS

Cobblestone Opticians

PO Box 27532
315 N. Spence Ave.
Goldsboro, NC 27532
(800) 353-1511
(919) 778-1511
Optician: Bobby Raynor
Available: Direct
Looking to pick up an extra target
or two out on the course? Cobblestones shooting glasses might be
the answer. Our innovative lenses
are individually dyed and ground
for maximum precision. Available in
a variety of colors and tints including "watermelon", a color that
mutes green backgrounds and enhances orange targets to an
astonishing degree. Non-prescrip-

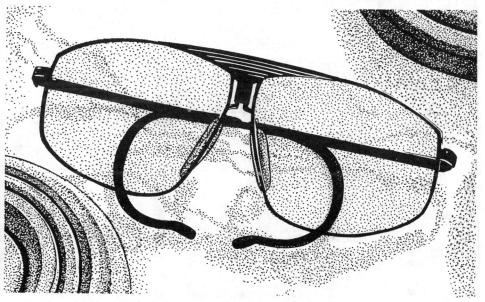

tion, single-vision and bifocal pre-· scription lenses available. Extremely reasonable prices. Most orders filled in 3 days or less. Call for information.

Decot Hy-Wyd Sport Glasses, Inc.

PO Box 15830, Phoenix, AZ 85060
(800) 528-1901
(602) 955-7625
FAX: (602) 955-7151
President: Bud Decot
Full staff of licensed opticians: Colleen Jones, Sam Cherry (both certified ABO), CeCe Deem and Sharon Alati.

See Our Ad Pg. 138

Dr. Gilchrist
402 Airport Rd.
Tappahannock, VA 22560
(800) 969-1778
FAX: (804) 443-5389
Staff: 4
Contact: Dr. Gilchrist
Available: Direct

Allan Lehman Optical
1018 E. Indian School Rd.
Phoenix, AZ 85014
(800) 255-0205
(602) 279-6100
FAX: (602) 279-6161
Est.: 1975   Staff: 5
President/Owner: Allan Lehman
Available: Retail & Direct
Manufacturer of plano and prescription sports glasses. We offer quality frames and custom lenses for your frames or ours.

Morgan Optical
912 W. State, PO Box 770
Olean, NY 14760
(800) 803-6117
FAX: (716) 373-1275
Est.: 1962   Staff: 12
Available: Direct
Plano & prescription sport glasses. An experienced shotgunner with over 30 years in the optical business, Harold Morgan knows from personal experience that eyewear can improve shooting performance. He specializes in making prescription glasses for all types of shooters. Call him today with questions about your eyewear needs and problems.

See Our Ad Below

Dr. Frank Rively - Optometrist
100 Northern Blvd.
Clarks Summit, PA 18411
(717) 586-2020
Est.: 1972
Contact: Frank Rively or Doris Pilling
Available: Direct
Vision consultation and shooting glasses. Ranger and Decot Hy-Wyd frames.

Dr. Jack Wills, O.D.
1823 Charles St.
Fredericksburg, VA 22401
(800) 544-9191
FAX: (703) 373-0017
Contact: Jack Wills, O.D.
Available: Direct
Ranger shooting glasses in stock for immediate delivery.

GAMEBIRD BREEDERS

Addieville East Farm

200 Pheasant Dr.
Mapleville, RI 02839
(401) 568-3185
FAX: (401) 568-3009
Est.: 1979
Contact: Geoff Gaebe
Type of Bird(s) Bred: Pheasant
Member of NAGA

Alwerdt's Pheasant Farm

RR1, Box 152
Altamont, IL 62411
(618) 483-6310
Est.: 1953   Staff: 2
Contact: Steve Alwerdt
At Alwerdt's Pheasant Farm we specialize only in hard-flying pheasants for the hunting preserves; we deliver in a 7-800 mile radius of south central Ilinois to make sure our pheasants get to our customers in excellent condition; we sell 12-15,000 mature pheasants yearly.

B&D Game Farm

Rt. 1, Box 812
Harrah, OK 73045
(405) 964-5235
FAX: (405) 964-5860
Contact: Diane Tumey
Type of Bird(s) Bred: Bobwhite, Pharoah and Tibetan Quail, Pheasant; Chukar

David Brandenburg

3450 E. Kinderhook Rd.
Underwood, IN 47177
(812) 889-2914
Est.: 1992
Contact: David Brandenburg
Type of Birds: Bobwhite Quail and Pheasants
Specializing in flight birds that are ground-raised. Some flight pens over an acre. Occassionally have extra eggs and chicks.

C&F Game Bird Farm

17087 Hwy. 64 East
Tyler, TX 75707
(903) 566-3526
(903) 566-8632
Est.: 1972   Staff: 2
Contact: Steve & Debbie Penett
Flight birds: Quail, Pheasant, Chukar. We deliver to several states: Arkansas; Louisiana; Oklahoma; Kansas and of course Texas. Call for bookings.

Canaan Farms, Inc.

6016 S. 121st Ave.
Tolleson, AZ 85353
(602) 925-0359
Est.: 1992   Staff: 3
Contact: R. Kent Wickware or Phyllis Wickware
E-Mail: wkrbirds@AOL.com
Type of Bird(s) Bred: Bobwhite Quail, Chukar. Flight conditioned and chicks. Year-round delivery in the U.S.

FLIGHT CONDITIONED QUAIL

Cook's Game Bird Farm

6575 Baxley Rd., Milton, FL 32570
(904) 623-9003
Est.: 1992
Contact: Steve Cook or Beverly Cook
Type of Bird(s) Bred: Bobwhite Quail, Pheasant
We offer flight conditioned birds. Our birds are very wild. Our customers have been very satisfied. We deliver in the southeast.

Cottonwood Springs Pheasant Farm

393 467th Ave., Miles, IA 52064
(319) 682-7405
Est.: 1993
Contact: Tracy Frahm

Type of Bird(s) Bred: Ringneck flight pheasant and Bobwhite Quail. It is our goal to provide our clientele with quality gamebirds bred and raised for superior appearance and flight. Let us know if we can be of assistance.

Dodge Town Quail Farm

R#1, Box 194-A
Madison, NC 27025
(910) 871-3222
Contact: Wayne H. Bullins
Full feathered flight conditioned quail for sale. Shipped anywhere in U.S.

Dogwood Hollow Gamebirds

Rt. 3, Box 2357
Claremore, OK 74017
(918) 341-6918
FAX: (918) 341-6918
Est.: 1993   Staff: 3
Owner: Tom Varner or Carolyn Varner
We sell eggs, day-old chicks, started and mature flight birds. We also operate a shooting preserve 30 miles from Tulsa. Our birds are as wild as they come–second to none.

Evans' Game Farm
1816 18th Rd.
Clay Center, KS 67432-7409
(913) 632-2541
Est.: 1992   Staff: 3
Contact: John Evans
Pheasants–flight conditioned pheasants available to preserve operators, wholesale and consumers. We deliver in the midwest or call for pick-up.

Harmony Game Farm

Harmony Game Farm
21303 Harmony Rd.
Marengo, IL 60152
(815) 568-8595
Est.: 1990   Staff: 5
Contact: Richard Gundelach
We raise 6,000 Ringneck Pheasants, 2,000 Bobwhite Quail & 1,000 Chukar. All are flight conditioned & sold to preserves in Northwestern Illinois.

J&L Game Bird Farms
1176 US Hwy. 180 W.
Rotan, TX 79546
(915) 776-2852
Contact: Jackie W. Etheredge
Type of Bird(s) Bred: Bobwhite Quail; Blue Scale Quail; Cross Pheasant and Chukar. All birds flight and weather conditioned. We are a family operated breeding and hunting operation. We know what the hunters want.

Kennedy Game Farm

4623 N.C. Highway 705
Robbins, NC 27325
(910) 464-3444
Est.: 1959
Contact: Arnold Kennedy
Types of Bird(s) Bred: Bobwhite Quail
See Our Ad Below

King Gamebird Farm
Rt. 3, Princeton, MO 64673
(816) 748-3065
Contact: K. King
The King Gamebird Farm has been specializing in raising hard-flying ringneck pheasants and chukars for 25 years. We're geared to servicing the commerical and private preserve operators. Call today–you'll be pleased with our hard-flying birds!

M&M Shooting Preserve
Hook & Winslow Rd.
Pennsville, NJ 08070
(609) 935-1230
Contact: Donna Matarese
Type of Bird(s) Bred: Mallards
M&M Hunting Preserve is a major breeder of Mallard Ducks, raising over 140,000 annually. Our ducks are strickly bred for hunting. They are strong, fast flyers, true to size and color. We guarantee top quality ducks and prompt efficient service. Being in the hunting business for over 25 years, we know what you expect in a mallard Duck– and we deliver it.

Mac Farlane Pheasant Farm, Inc.

Mac Farlane Pheasant Farm, Inc.
2821 South US Hwy. 51
Janesville, WI 53546
(800) 345-8348
FAX: (608) 757-7884
e-mail: macfar@pheasant.com
Internet: www.pheasant.com
Contact: Bill Mac Farlane
Mac Farlane's has the most modern game hatching facility in the U.S. and is the supplier of choice of the preserve operator interested in premium quality chicks or mature birds. Quick and reliable delivery guaranteed–across the U.S. and to many foreign countries.
See Our Ad Across, Right

Mahantongo Game Farms

Mahantongo Game Farms
RR01, Box 70
Dalmatia, PA 17017-9633
(800) 982-9913
FAX: (717) 758-6284
Est.: 1935   Staff: 16
Owner: Lynn A. Laudenslager
Type of Bird(s) Bred: Pheasants (Mongolian & Blueback), Chukar. Located in central Pennsylvania–maintain over 11,000 breeder birds. We sell eggs, chicks, started and mature birds throughout the United States and foreign countries.

Martz's Game Farm
RD1 Box 85
Dalmatia, PA 17017
(800) 326-8442
FAX: (717) 758-3166
Est.: 1955   Staff: 19
Contact: Don E. Martz
Type of Bird(s) Bred: Pheasants,
Chukar, Huns
We hatch over 175,000 gamebirds
annually. We sell eggs, day old
chicks, started & mature birds. We
are located in central PA & ship
eggs & day old chicks throughout
the continental U.S.

Morning STAR Game Bird Farm

**Morning Star
Game Bird Farm, Inc.**
14425 CR 392 E
Henderson, TX 75652
(903) 889-2891
Est.: 1992
President: Brent A. Tucker
Morning Star produces and sells
90,000+ Bobwhite Quail, Tennessee Reds and Chukar. Fully grown
for hunting preserves. Proven flight
ability.

Pine Acres Game Birds, Inc.
,105 South 200 East
Rupert, ID 83350
(208) 436-4241
Est.: 1958   Staff: 2
President: Leonard Huber
We raise from 12,000 to 15,000
ringneck pheasants. We specialize
in mature, flight-conditioned birds.

Quailco
Game Bird Farm

Quailco Game Bird Farm
Box 245, Dora, NM 88115
(800) 315-0016
Contact: Mikel Hays
Type of Bird(s) Bred: Northern Bob-
white, Chukar
At Quailco we specialize in day old
chicks. We can ship to all 50 states.
See Our Ad Below

**Mike Raahauge's
Shooting Enterprises**
5800 Bluff St.
Norco, CA 91760
(909) 735-2361
FAX: (909) 371-6853
Contact: Mike Raahauge
Type of Bird(s) Bred: Pheasant

Hatchery & Gamebirds

Rocky Mountain Hatchery
PO Box 1086, Hamilton, MT 59840
(800) 219-4285
FAX: (406) 642-3253 Est.: 1991
Contact: Eileen Jackson
Birds Bred: Ringneck Pheasant, Chukar, Bobwhite Quail
MONTANA HARDY Pheasant, Chukar and Quail are raised at our NPIP
and SPF facility. We offer eggs, day-
old, started and flight conditioned
birds nationwide. A FREE Equipment catalog including incubators,
brooders, a unique automatic wa-
tering system and nettings is also
available upon request with discounts given to our bird customers.

Rose Gamebird Hatcheries
PO Box 166, Rose, NY 14542-0166
(315) 923-5191
Contact: Dave F. Fox
We hatch, and deliver throughout
the USA, pheasant, duck, quail, partridge and wild turkey. They can be
delivered as day old chix, adults or
dressed (frozen). Our flyers are
sporty and hard flying, great for your
restocking program. Member NPIP.

**Dwayne Sargeant's
Gamebirds**
R.R. 3, Box 220, Auburn, IL 62615
(217) 438-6582 or (217) 438-3114
Contact: Dwayne Sargeant
Type of Bird(s) Bred: Quail, Pheasant, Chukar
We have flight conditioned and
meat birds available. We sell to preserves, wholesalers, consumers. We
cover the whole U.S.A.

Sharon Pheasant Farm
145 Gay St., Sharon, CT 06069
(203) 364-5833
Contact: Bob Wilbur
Bird(s) Bred: Pheasant, Chukar
We sell eggs, chicks, started and
mature birds. We ship day-old
chicks throughout the U.S.

**Texas Hill Country
Quail Farm**
1380 Serenity Dr., Fischer, TX 78623
(210) 933-2200
FAX: (210) 935-4327
Est.: 1995   Staff: 2
Owner: John Vallone
Available: Retail & Direct
Type of Bird(s) Bred: Bobwhite
Quail. We offer wild weather &
flight conditioned birds.

C.D. Wheeler
29519 West Hawthorne Dr.
Spring, TX 77386
(800) 333-9344 (Orders)
(713) 367-1232 (Phone)
Contact: C.D. Wheeler, Sr.
Type of Bird(s) Bred: Pheasant, Chukar, Quail
Producing over 1 million eggs yearly. Beat the rush–order in January, February, March. Shipping April to November. All breeds and ages not available at all times.

Whistling Wings, Inc.
113 Washington St.
Hanover, IL 61041
(815) 591-3512
FAX: (815) 591-3424
Est.: 1954   Staff: 10
President: Marianne Murphy
Contact: Mark or Monica Klippert
Whistling Wings offers 42 years and 3 generations of experience in raising and shooting Mallard Ducks. Over this time, we have hatched and sold over 4 million Mallards. Whether you are in the market for Day Old Mallards or Mature Flyers, our experience in shipping is invaluable. Contact Whistling Wings today to make your duck hunting dreams a reality.
See Our Ad Pg. 143

GUN CARE

B□SQUARE

B-SQUARE
2708 St. Louis Ave.
PO Box 11281
Forth Worth, TX 76110
(800) 433-2909
(817) 923-0964
Est.: 1957
Contact: Rudy Bechtel
Available: Retail & Direct
"Tube Lube" lubricant for choke tubes. First non-toxic, non-staining tube lubricant that prevents galling, seizing and corrosion. Call for free catalog.
See Our Ad Pg. 114

Beretta U.S.A.
c/o Beretta Gallery
New York:
718 Madison Ave.
New York, NY 10021
(212) 319-6614
Alexandria
317 S. Washington St.
Old Town Alexandria, VA 22314

(703) 739-0596
Est: 1977
Available: Retail
Beretta gun cleaning kits, gun oil.

Birchwood Casey
7900 Fuller Rd.
Eden Prairie, MN 55344
(800) 328-6156 (#7933)
FAX: (612) 937-7979
Est.: 1950
Contact: Mike Wenner
Available: Retail
A complete line of high quality gun care products to clean, protect and refinish your guns. Prevent stuck choke tubes caused by erosion, high stress of shot and extreme temperatures and pressure from repeated trap, skeet and sporting clays shooting. Write or call for a free catalog.

Break-Free, Inc.
1035 South Linwood Ave.
Santa Ana, CA 92705-4396
(714) 953-1900
FAX: (714) 953-0402
Est.: 1976   Staff: 20
Contact: Customer Service
VP/Gen. Mgr: Dwight B. Woodruff
Available: Retail
Gun cleaning/lubrication/preserving oils; gun cleaning kits. Powder Blast is a highly effective gun cleaner. This environmentally and user friendlier product cleans without disassembly. Completely. Metal to metal. Powder Blast is quicker, easier and safer. It leaves the metal completely dry and with a pleasant orange scent. Use Powder Blast with Break-Free CLP for complete gun maintenance.

Browning
One Browning Place
Morgan, UT 84050
(800) 333-3288 (Customer)
(801) 876-3331 (General)
Est.: 1878   Staff: 350
Available: Retail
Browning Ultra-Fine Gun Oil and Barrier Cloth™ Gun Shield.

chem-pak, Inc.
11 Oates Ave.
PO Box 1685
Winchester, VA 22604
(800) 336-9828
(703) 667-1341
FAX: (703) 722-3993
Est.: 1966
Pres.: George P. "Pete" Duane, Jr.

VP/Sales: Randy Duane
Available: Retail
Gun Sav'r gunstock finishes and firearm lubricants.

DSX, Inc.
Box 1372, Sterling, VA 20167-1372
(800) 822-0258
FAX: (703) 860-0286
Contact: Mike Mueller or Bill Orr
"DSX" firearms maintenance products. Superior cleaners, lubricants and surface treatments. Call for free brochure. Dealer inquiries welcome.

J. Dewey Mfg. Co.
PO Box 2104, Southbury, CT 06488
(203) 264-3064
FAX: (203) 262-6907
Est.: 1975   Staff: 6
Contact: George Dewey
Available: Retail & Direct
Gun cleaning equipment; Nylon coated gun cleaning rod; "No-Harm" brass core brush

Du-Lite Corp.
171 River Rd., Middletown, CT 06457
(203) 347-2505
FAX: (203) 347-9404
Contact: Walt Smith
Lubricants and rust preventative oils.

EZ Oil
Lakos Enterprises, Inc.
PO Box 2930, Cody, WY 82414
(800) 735-9266
(307) 527-7591
FAX: (307) 587-4973
Contact: Bob Zatkos

EEZOX, Inc.
PO Box 772, Waterford, CT 06385
(800) 462-3331
(860) 447-8282
FAX: (860) 447-3484
Est.: 1986
Contact: Tom Nasca
Available: Retail
Synthetic EEZOX Premium Gun Care is a TOTAL GUN CARE SYSTEM with only ONE PRODUCT for all types of guns, including Black Powder and Bow Cams. EEZOX Cleans, lubricates, prevents rust and finger printing, eliminates stiff actions, jamming and all types of residue build-up. NON-FLAMMABLE! Functions from 450 Degrees to 95 Degrees Below 0. EEZOX dries to the touch on guns in use or in storage and your guns are always protected with EEZOX.

Flitz International, Ltd.
821 Mohr Ave.
Waterford, WI 53185
(800) 558-8611
(414) 534-5898
FAX: (414) 534-2991
President: Peter Jentzsch
Available: Retail
Flitz metal polish, Polier natural wax
protectant, FZ liquid metal polish.

Free-Gunn Cleaner
Frigon Guns
Box 281
627 W. Crawford
Clay Center, KS 67432
(913) 632-5607
FAX: (913) 632-5609
Contact: A.J. Bloom
Available: Direct
Cleaner for removing lead and plastic wad build-up in chokes &
barrels; "Traveler" cleaning rod;
cleaning kits.

G96 Products Co., Inc.
PO Box 1684
River Street Station
Paterson, NJ 07544
(201) 684-4050
FAX: (201) 684-3848
Contact: Alan Goldman
Available: Retail
Gun care chemicals

HOPPE'S ⑨™
A DIVISION OF PENGUIN INDUSTRIES, INC.

**Hoppe's -- Penguin
Industries, Inc.**
Airport Industrial Mall
Coatesville, PA 19320
(610) 384-6000
FAX: (610) 857-5980
Contact: Patricia Lucas
Available: Retail
Hoppe's No. 9 Nitro Powder Solvent is the most universally used
solvent for removing primer, powder, lead and metal fouling.
Hoppe's solvent has proven itself
over the years and has been the
choice of gun owners for over
ninety years.

See Our Ad Below

Hornady Mfg. Co.
Box 1848, Dept. WS1086
Grand Island, NE 68802
(308) 382-1390
FAX: (308) 382-5761
Contact: Tom McGovern
Available: Retail
"One Shot" - gun cleaner and dry
lube.

Iosso Products
1485 Lively Boulevard
Elk Grove, IL 60007
(847) 437-8400
FAX: (847) 437-8478
President: Richard Iosso

VP/Sales: Marianne Iosso
Available: Retail
"Gunbrite" gun polish; Iosso bore
cleaner; Iosso case cleaner - a liquid
immersion cleaner for bullet casings; Iosso case polish - additive to
media for cleaning & polishing bullet casings.

KIC Distribution Co.
PO Box 14173
St. Paul, MN 55114
(612) 731-3206
FAX: (612) 730-6690
Contact: Carol Johnson
New line of products include RB-17
Gun Cleaner, Quick Action Spray,
Blue, Blue Remover, Finishing Oil,
Wood Treatment and Gun Wax.

KP Industries
10232 Black Mountain
San Diego, CA 92126
(619) 693-4460
Contact: Peter Holm
Silver-Bore™ cleans shotgun bores
without solvents. Removes lead
streaks, light corrosion and plastic
fowling. Dealers welcome.

See Our Ad Across, Right

Kleen-Bore, Inc.
16 Industrial Pkwy.
Easthampton, MA 01027
(800) 445-0301
(413) 527-0300
FAX: (413) 527-2522
Contact: Paul Judd
Quality gun care products and accessories; deluxe cleaning set.
Write for our free fully-illustrated,
color brochure.

Krieghoff International, Inc.
7528 Easton Rd.
PO Box 549, Ottsville, PA 18942
(610) 847-5173
Chairman: Dieter Krieghoff
President: Jim Hollingsworth
Available: Retail
Gun Care products: Gun Glide and
Gun Pro Lubricants. K-80 & KS-5 factory service.

MP-7 Gun Cleaner
Windfalls Distributing, Inc.
225 W. Deer Valley Rd., #4
PO Box 54988, Phoenix, AZ 85078
(800) YES-4MP7
(602) 780-2888
FAX: (602) 516-0414
President: Marten J. Niner
VP: Kelly J. Moulton
VP: Laura E. Roberts
A firearms cleaner that is odorless,
non-toxic and guaranteed to be the
best cleaner available.

MTM Molded Products Co.

Gunsmith's Maintenance Center
PO Box 14117
Dayton, OH 45414
(513) 890-7461
FAX: (513) 890-1747
Contact: Al Minneman
At home or away, count on MTM for products that make weapon maintenance easy and convenient. The new Gunsmith's Maintenance Center lets you clean shotgun or rifle quickly. Ideal for mounting scopes, swivels. Holds all tools, cleaning supplies. Compartments for bore solvent, rust preventer, patches, screwdrivers. Removable rubber-padded forks protect firearm, adjust for height, gun position. Cost: $28.48 + $3 S/H. MTM's portable maintenance center, the Case-Gard™ RMC-1, is the perfect companion at the range or on hunts. Puts all cleaning supplies at your fingertips. Includes molded dust covers for added protection. Constructed of chemical-resistant polypropylene. Cost: $30.84, free S/H. Phone or fax for free catalog, or to order.

OilRag Industries

537 Louis Dr.,
Newbury Park, CA 91320
(805) 498-0034
FAX: (805) 499-4372
Est.: 1994
Available: Retail
Gun cleaning mats; solvent resistant, oil absorbent.

Olympia U.S.A.

1720 Cumberland Point Dr., Suite 5
Marietta, GA 30067
(770) 858-0048
FAX: (770) 858-0051
President: Jean Constantinides
The unique Olympia U.S.A. Gun Care Kit meets all your firearms maintenance needs. Included are Choke Shine, an all-natural solvent that removes plastic build-up from ported choke tubes; Premium Liquid Lube, a highly refined non-chlorinated oil for lubrication and rust prevention; and Wear Resistant Grease, a non-chlorinated lubricant for all moving parts. Only $19.95 plus S&H. Phone or fax to order direct.

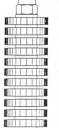
Otis Products, Inc.

Cheese Factory Rd.
RR1, Box 84
Boonville, NY 13309
(800) OTI-SGUN
Contact: Jerry Williams

Outers Gunslick

Blount, Inc., Sporting Equip. Div.
PO Box 856
2299 Snake River Ave.
Lewiston, ID 83501
(800) 635-7656
Available: Retail
Solvents, lubricants and protectors, cleaning brushes, tips and patches. For over half a century, collectors, shooters and hunters have trusted the care of their prized firearms to Outers, because they know Outers invests countless hours of research in developing the finest solvents, lubricants and protectors.

Ox-Yoke Originals

34 West Main St., Milo, ME 04463
(207) 943-7351
FAX: (207) 943-2416
Est.: 1970   Staff: 40
President: C.E. Bottomley
Plant Mgr: Robert Lee
Nat'l. Sales Mgr.: Stan Simonian
Quality shotgun rifle & black powder shooting & gun care accessories. Ox-Yoke Products are exclusively used by the U.S. Shooting Team.

PRO-SHOT™

Pro-Shot Products, Inc.

PO Box 763
Taylorville, IL 62568
(217) 824-9133
FAX: (217) 824-8861
Contact: John E. Damarin, Sr.
The finest shotgun maintenance begins with Pro-Shot products. Pro-Shot gun cleaning patches are 100% cotton flannel, finished both sides. Our extremely durable 30" and 36" shotgun cleaning rods (with patch holder) are micro-polished hardened stainless steel. Pro-Shot Lead and Powder Solvent removes plastic wad fouling with ease. Bore mops for all popular gauges are 100% cotton with brass core. Also available: Shotgun kit containing rod, solvent and patches; and shotgun brushes, jags, patch holders, chamber tools and 12 gauge gas cylinder brush. Phone or fax for detailed information, prices.

III-TECH

Prolix-Division of ProChemCo
PO Box 1348
Victorville, CA 92393-1348
(800) 248-LUBE
(619) 243-3129
FAX: (619) 241-0148
Est.: 1984
Sales/Tech: Philip Levy
Available: Retail & Direct
Most cleaning solvents and oils leave too much lubrication behind, gumming up actions, causing misfires and jams. Dry lubricating PrOlix® addresses this problem by "floating away powder and residue" and leaving behind the optimum amount of lubrication that won't wipe away during firing and handling. With PrOlix®, successive cleanings are easier and easier. Biodegradable and ozone-safe. Call today to order or for more information.

Remington

Remington Arms Company, Inc.
PO Box 700
870 Remington Dr.
Madison, NC 27025-0700
(800) 243-9700 (Consumer)
(910) 548-0700 (Headquarters)
FAX: (910) 548-7770
Est.: 1816
Available: Retail
Remington provides complete shotgun firearm care kits; oils and lubricants; cleaning fluids and supplies; gun parts and accessories.

Rig Products
87 Coney Island Dr.
Sparks, NV 89431
(702) 331-5666
FAX: (702) 331-5669
Contact: Al Selleck
Available: Retail

Rusteprufe Laboratories
1319 Jefferson Ave.
Sparta, WI 54656
(608) 269-4144
President: Robert Munger
Rust preventing oil; applicator/wiper

Sentry Solutions, Ltd.
111 Sugar Mill Rd., PO Box 130
Contoocook, NH 03229
(800) 546-8049
(603) 746-5687
FAX: (603) 746-5847
Est.: 1991
Available: Retail & Direct
Manufacturer of high tech dry film lubricants and corrosion inhibitors for all types of firearms and equipment.

SHOOTER'S CHOICE

Shooter's Choice Gun Care
Venco Industries, Inc.
16770 Hilltop Park Pl.
Chagrin Hills, OH 44023
(216) 543-8808
FAX: (216) 543-8811
Est.: 1983   Staff: 10
Contact: Joseph Ventimiglia
Available: Retail
Constantly searching for a higher standard in firearm care, Shooter's Choice offers a full line of products–cleaners, lubricants and preventatives–backed by the best guarantee in the the business: Complete satisfaction in our products ability to out perform the competition or your money back! Available at your firearms dealer.

Silencio/Safety Direct, Inc.
56 Coney Island Dr.
Sparks, NV 89431
(800) 648-1812
FAX: (702) 359-1074
President: Gordon Kramer
Marketing Mgr: Howard Levine
Available: Retail
"Bore Runner" shotgun cleaning tool.

TDP Industries
606 Airport Blvd.
Doylestown, PA 18901
(215) 345-8687
Contact: Charles Magee
SS-1 cleaner/solvent; SS2 gun lubricant; Stock Slick: wood & leather cleaner & conditioner; Absolute gun wash

Tetra Gun Products
Division of FTI, Inc.
PO Box 955, Vreeland Rd.
Florham Park, NJ 07932
(201) 443-0004
Contact: Connie McBride
Available: Retail
Lubricants and cleaning materials.

Buying a shotgun?

That's great! But with over 70 companies manufacturing and importing shotguns for the U.S. market, how do you go about finding the right one for you? The perfect place to start the buying process is in Black's Wing & Clay. Just turn to the following sections to begin:

SHOTGUN MANUFACTURERS & IMPORTERS   Pg. 26

You'll find detailed information on over 70 different shotgun manufacturing companies and importers currently serving the U.S. market. Company and individual contact names, addresses, telephone and fax numbers. Brand names, models, price ranges, and other valuable information about materials, designs models available. Write or call for catalogs, brochures and dealers.

SHOTGUNS/NATIONAL DEALERS   Pg. 46

Can't find the shotgun you're looking for near home? Or at the right price? No problem. This section lists 23 of the best national dealers. Who they are. Where they are. What they offer. How to contact them. And, yes, you can order by phone or mail.

GUN CASES

For Soft Gun Cases See:
* *Accessories/Bags, Pouches & Soft Gun Cases, Pg. 84*

Aluma Sport by Dee Zee
PO Box 3090
Des Moines, IA 50316
(800) 798-9899 (Cust. Svc.)
(515) 265-7331
FAX: (515) 265-7926
Est.: 1978   Staff: 400
Contact: Chuck Long
Available: Retail
Extruded aluminum panels provide strong construction. Airline approved.

Americase
1610 E. Main
PO Box 271
Waxahachie, TX 75165
(800) 972-2737
(214) 937-3629
FAX: (214) 937-8373
Est.: 1985   Staff: 30
Contact: Bill Kinsala
Available: Retail & Direct
Want to know more about Americase – our catalog is all you need; it contains complete details and illustrations on our entire line of standard and custom made cases. Americase engineered products combine high strength to weight ratios and classic good looks to suit your every travel need. Approved for air travel. Send for our catalog. You won't be disappointed! Americase also manufactures ATA Spec 300 products.
See Our Ad Below

Beretta U.S.A.
c/o Beretta Gallery
New York:
718 Madison Ave.
New York, NY 10021
(212) 319-6614
Alexandria:
317 S. Washington St.
Old Town Alexandria, VA 22314
(703) 739-0596
Available: Retail
For transporting and protecting your fine Beretta firearms and accessories, we offer a complete line of cases. There are custom-designed Beretta gun cases from simple soft to molded and aluminum cases. Call for catalog.

Browning
One Browning Place
Morgan, UT 84050
(800) 333-3288 (Customer)
(801) 876-2711 (General)

Est.: 1878   Staff: 350
Available: Retail
Waterproof, Travel Vault hard cases, fitted luggage case models, floating cases and a full line of flexible gun cases.

Contico International Inc.
1101 Warson Rd.
St. Louis, MO 63132
(314) 997-5900
Est.: 1985   Staff: 2000
Nat'l. Sales Coord.: Jack Berman
Available: Retail
Plastic gun cases, bow cases, ammo boxes, storage bins.

Elk River
PO Box 7321
1225 Paonia St.
Colorado Springs, CO 80933
(719) 574-4407
President: Les Turner
Available: Retail & Direct
Luggage-style gun cases.

Flambeau Products Corporation
15981 Valplast, Box 97
Middlefield, OH 44062
(216) 632-1631
FAX: (216) 632-1581
Est.: 1994   Staff: 250
Contact: Chris Paradise
Available: Retail
Full line of shotgun, rifle and pistol cases.

TRAVELING WITH YOUR SHOTGUN

Flying With Your Shotgun Is Legal And Easy

Flying within the United States on a commercial airliner with your unloaded shotgun is easy and legal. All airlines require a hard-shell, crush proof, lockable gun case (priced from $150 to $700). And just to be safe, you should allow an additional 15 minutes at check-in.

Each airline has its own rules governing firearms, but they are basically similar. If you follow these steps, you'll breeze through the process and wonder why you ever left your shotgun at home:

Going on a wingshooting adventure?

That't great! But to get the most out of your trip, you'll want to go fully outfitted. A new travel gun case might be called for. New clothes? Boots? Perhaps, a brand new shotgun. Fortunately, you're in the right place. Turn to the following sections to begin. And enjoy your trip!

- **Step 1:** *Declare Your Firearm* When you check your other luggage, tell the curbside sky-cap or customer service agent at the check-in counter that you are traveling with an *unloaded firearm* and would like to know what you need to do to check it in.

- **Step 2:** *Inspect & Tag* Very often you will be directed to a "semi-private area" at the counter or curb area and asked by an airline employee to unlock the travel case and display the unloaded firearm. After a brief inspection, you will be asked to sign a 3" by 5" *declaration tag*, which attests that you understand that traveling with a loaded firearm violates Federal law and that the firearm you are checking-in is, indeed, unloaded. The tag will then be placed in or on the case.

- **Step 3:** *Lock & Send* The customer service representative will ask you to close and lock your case—the airlines *require* that you alone hold the key or combination— and it will then be checked through to your final destination.

- **Step 4:** *Pick Up* Very often your gun case will arrive on the luggage carousel along with your other luggage. At some airports, however, the case will be taken to a special pickup area. Just ask one of the sky-caps or customer service reps when you arrive.

A Word About Ammo

Your gun is "one-of-a-kind" and well worth the extra effort to bring it along on business or vacation. But shotgun shells are readily available in most areas of the U.S. And unless you think you're going to have trouble buying the particular type of shell you like to shoot at your destination, you're better off traveling without them. If you must bring ammo with you, be aware that the airlines generally limit you to 5 pounds of ammo per firearm checked (a maximum of 10 lbs. on some airlines) and require that the ammo be factory boxed and securely packaged.

Another alternative to carrying shells is pre-shipping them to your locations via a common carrier, such as United Parcel Service. Call the carrier you are thinking of using for information.

GALAZAN

GALAZAN
A Division of Connecticut Shotgun
Manufacturing
Box 1692, New Britain, CT 06051
(203) 225-6581
FAX: (203) 832-8707
Est.: 1967   Staff: 20
Contact: Dick Perrett
- Cases built for double shotguns
and rifles. The finest quality tradi-
tional leather trunk cases and best
oak & leather cases as well as oak
& leather ammo boxes.
- Gun case accessories. The same
high quality snap caps and case ac-
cessories furnished by the best
English gun companies.
- English style gunmaker trade labels.

Gun Guard/Doskocil
PO Box 1246, Arlington, TX 76004
(817) 467-5116
Contact: Pat Hoffman
Available: Retail
Gun Guard is the largest brand of
premium, hard-side gun cases, in-
cluding Gun Guard Aluminum, All
Weather, Deluxe and Wildlife cases.
Doskocil is the largest brand of mid-
range and economy gun and
accessory case models, including
XLT, Special Edition, and Field
Locker series. Doskocil also offers
Bow Guard brand archery equip-
ment cases.

Hastings/John Hall Gun Cases
320 Court St., PO Box 224
Clay Center, KS 67432
(913) 632-3169
FAX: (913) 632-6554
Est.: 1985
President: Robert Rott
Designed by All-American Shooting
Champion John Hall to be the ultimate gun case. Ultra high impact
polycarbonate for extra strength
and rigidity makes the Has-
tings/John Hall gun case so strong
it's nearly indestructible. Available
in three configurations to accommodate any gun.

Hill Case Co.
806 Brookwood Dr.,
Landrum, SC 29356
(803) 457-2694
Est.: 1988
Contact: Lenny Hill
Available: Retail & Direct
Custom made cases for most any-
thing in shooting.
- ATA approved, hand-fitted hard
cases

- Airline approved true flight case,
won't dent
- Interior made with super high density foam for maximum protection
- Custom cut-outs for proper fit
- Constructed of 5-ply plywood, laminated with ABS sheets and milled
countersink screws, not rivets, for
maximum durability.
- Industrial level, fully recessed but-
terfly catches

Holland & Holland, Ltd.
50 East 57th St.
New York, NY 10022
(212) 752-7755
FAX: (212) 752-6805
Mail Orders: 1-800-SINCE 1835

Hoppe's -- Penguin Industries, Inc.
Airport Industrial Mall
Coatesville, PA 19320
(610) 384-6000
FAX: (610) 857-5980
Contact: Patricia Lucas
Available: Retail
Hoppe's Protecto Cases are de-
signed to carry virtually any rifle or
shotgun.

Huey Handbuilt Gun Case
Box 22456, Kansas City, MO 64113
(816) 444-1637
Est.: 1976   Staff: 2
Contact: Marvin Huey
Available: Direct

Deluxe oak & leather trunk cases,
custom fitted, no two alike.

ICC
Impact Case Co.

ICC, Impact Case Company
PO Box 9912, Spokane, WA 99209
(800) 262-3322
FAX: (509) 326-5436
Est.: 1985
Contact: Bob Knouff or
Brad Knouff
Available: Retail & Direct
ICC, Impact Case Company Protective Metal Firearms Transport/
Shipping Cases are constructed of
either .063 or .080 aluminum, with
heli-arc welded corners, full-length
staked hinge, Stainless Steel Lock-
ing Rod, plus numerous other
"toughness" features making it the
best Firearms and Archery Trans-
port/Shipping Case available. When
the success of your trip depends on
your firearms and equipment arriv-
ing intact, don't settle for anything
less than an ICC transport case.
Please call for specifications, test information and easy ordering
procedures.
See Our Ad Below

KK AIR
INTERNATIONAL

KK Air, International
PO Box 9912, Spokane, WA 99209
(800) 262-3322
(509) 467-3303
FAX: (509) 326-5436
Est.: 1985
Contact: Bob Knouff or
Brad Knouff
Available: Retail & Direct
We introduced the KK AIR International Case Products in 1991, resulting in a full-range of case designs. In addition to the ICC .063 wall standard size "flat" cases, KK AIR offers "3 piece" and "trunk" style cases, .080 wall "flat" cases, "specials" of numerous designs, plus archery cases with removable arrow panels and rifle conversion sets.

Kalispel Case Line Products
c/o Arrow Distributing
PO Box 218
Winchester, ID 83555
(800) 200-7333
FAX: (208) 924-7335
Contact: Phyllis Nash

Kolpin Manufacturing, Inc.
PO Box 107
205 Depot St.
Fox Lake, WI 53933
(800) 556-5746
FAX: (414) 928-3687
Customer Service: Mike Bentz
VP/Mktg: Cole Braun
Available: Retail & Direct
Kolpin Gun Boot III, airline approved; made of HD polyethylen shell.

Kratz Custom Cases
709 S. Adams St.
Arlington, VA 22204-2114
(703) 521-4588
Contact: David A. Kratz
Available: Direct

Mike*s Case Company
3901 Nome St., Unit #7
Denver, CO 80239
(800) 847-4002 (Cust. Svc.)
(303) 371-5659
FAX: (303) 371-5915
Est.: 1994
Contact: Mike Bryant
Available: Retail & Direct
Mike*s Case Company is a small company dedicated to designing and manufacturing the finest in flight style cases.

Nasco Aluminum
14232 McCallum Ave., NE
Alliance, OH 44601
(330) 821-4621
Contact: Otis Lee

Nizzoli of Italy Gun Cases
New England Arms Co. - Sole
Distributor
Box 278
Lawrence Lane
Kittery Point, ME 03905
(207) 439-0593
FAX: (207) 439-6726
Est.: 1975   Staff: 6
Contact: Jim Austin or
Steve McCarthy
Available: Retail & Direct
Hundreds of cases in stock for all
sizes and shapes including cases for
matched pairs. Precision leather fab-
rication. Custom cases made to
order.

Outers Silverline Gun Case
Blount Inc., Sporting Equipment Div.
PO Box 856, 2299 Snake River Ave.
Lewiston, ID 83501
(800) 627-3640
Contact: John Wiggert
Available: Retail
Every Silverline gun case carries an
airline-approved rating. Silverline
cases have a formed body of extra-
thick high-grade aluminum that's
both very strong and very light.
Soft honey-combed padding cra-
dles your firearm against shock. For
added protection, each latch has a
key lock. How much does quality
like this cost? About 25 to 50 percent less than comparable cases.
The Silverline Rifle/Shotgun case
measures 52 1/2" x 13"x4 1/4",
plenty of room for two scoped rifles or shotguns.

Plano Molding Company
431 E. South St., Plano, IL 60545
(630) 552-9435
FAX: (630) 552-9737
Est.: 1932   Staff: 500
Mktg. Mgr.: Tom Hurt
Air Glide guns case (shotgun &
scoped rifle); multi purpose storage
cases; field boxes and gun safes.

Pointer Specialties
PO Box 152
Wellsville, PA 17365
(717) 292-4776
FAX: (717) 292-0440
Contact: Jim Dickey
Available: Retail & Direct
Makers and distributors of deluxe
cherry hardwood gun cases, protec-
tive vests for dogs and shooting
bench rests.

Quality Arms, Inc.
PO Box 19477
Houston, TX 77224
(713) 870-8377
Est.: 1975   Staff: 3
Contact: John Boyd
Available: Retail & Direct
One of the largest suppliers of
trunk style cases in the U.S. Our
cases are made of aluminum, ABS,
canvas or leather. We can provide
a case for just about every situation. In addition, we can do custom
cases.

Remington Arms Company, Inc.
PO Box 700
870 Remington Dr.
Madison, NC 27025-0700
(800) 243-9700 (Consumer)
(910) 548-8700 (Headquarters)
FAX: (910) 548-7770
Est.: 1816
Available: Retail
Remington provides a full line of
soft gun cases, as well as airline-ap-
proved cases and gun stocks.

RHINO.
GUN CASES, INC.

Rhino Gun Case, Inc.
4340 S.E. 53rd Ave.
Ocala, FL 34472
(800) 226-3613
Est.: 1988
Contact: Janet Morales or
Joe Morales
Available: Retail & Direct
Retail Outlets: Dealers Worldwide.
Rhino Cases are hand crafted, custom quality manufactured for
airline travel. Exterior material is
.080 marine grade aluminum
welded at the corners for increased
strength. Water tight and dust
tight with 1/2" interior to gasket-
ing. Interior protection enhanced
with plush padded compartments,
closed cell foam with soft fabrics in
a choice of colors. No cardboard,
plastic or wood used. Custom work
available. Call for sizes & prices.
See Our Ad Across, Left

SKB Corporation
434 W. Levers Pl.
Orange, CA 92667
(800) 654-5992
(714) 637-1250
FAX: (714) 637-0491
Est.: 1974   Staff: 500
Contact: Steve Madison

TUFFPAK™ Multi Gun Case

Our Patented TUFFPAK is so "TUFF", We Offer A

LIFETIME GUARANTEE!

TUFFPAK is Virtually Unbreakable!
Hi-tech materials resist shock and damage.

TUFFPAK is Extremely Lightweight!
The lightest multiple gun case on the market.

TUFFPAK is Secure & Airline Approved!
It's unique design is not recognized by theives or vandals.
Sturdy tubular key lock keeps it secure.

TUFFPAK has Room for All Your Stuff!
Holds up to 5 long guns in their soft cases
or take fewer guns and more of your gear.

Call now for more information

NALPAK

Phone
(619) 258-1200

Fax
(800) 4-NALPAK

Also makes a GREAT shipping case for your favorite golf clubs

WARRIOR
Luggage by BRILEY®

1-800-331-5718

Available: Retail
ATA-rated rifle, shotgun, pistol &
archery cases

The Securecase Company
1904 14th St., Suite 110
Santa Monica, CA 90404
(310) 392-5438
FAX: (310) 392-5538
Contact: Jason Wall
Securecase's Enforcer™ series cases
are designed to meet the rigorous
demands of hunter's and sports
shooters. With dual Ace® locks,
anti-pry bar, o-ring seal and optional mounting system these cases
are the ultimate for your firearms
storage or transportation needs.
Also Airline approved. Call for catalog. 800-922-7656.
See Our Ad Pg. 155

TUFFPAK™

Tuffpak
Nalpak Sales, Inc.
1937 C Friendship Dr.
El Cajon, CA 92020
(619) 258-1200
FAX: (800) 462-5725
Contact: David Northup
Transport your guns in the ultradur-
able, airline-approved TUFFPAK.
Virtually indestructbile, the
TUFFPAK gun case is constructed
of lightweight, high-tech materials.
It holds four long guns or three
long guns and six handguns.
TUFFPAK features built-in rolling
casters, twin handles for balance,
removable end lid for easy access,
anti-roll octagonal design for stabil-
ity, individually keyed locks.
Designed for serious sportsmen
and competitive shooters, TUFFPAK
delivers years of security and service. Phone today for complete
information.
See Our Ad Above, Left

Vault Cases, Inc.
Box 684
O'Fallon, IL 62269
(800) 297-1198
FAX: (618) 644-9567
Contact: Frank Gordon
Available: Retail & Direct

Vermont Custom Cases
Rt. 5, Main St., Box 33
Westminster, VT 05158
(800) 952-1215
(802) 722-9019
Est.: 1989   Staff: 4
Contact: Robert L. Byington
Available: Retail & Direct
Premium quality gun cases; complete line of gun cases. Breakdown shotgun, rifle, handgun. Full upholstery with velour, built-in dividers, interior and ext. color choices.

BRILEY

Warrior Luggage by Briley
1230 Lumpkin
Houston, TX 77043
(800) 331-5718 (Cust. Svc.)
(713) 932-6995
Contact: Chuck Webb
Available: Retail & Direct
The only lightweight stainless steel case on the market. With full welded seams, automotive fabric interior, and coffered corners that defy mistreatment by baggage handlers, this case is built with modern materials to English trunk case quality standards. Also available is an aluminum traditional tube set case for those on a budget; strong, light with all the "right stuff"–in stock for immediate shipment. Call for a brochure.

See Our Ad Left, Below

Warwick Custom Cases
578 Ace St.
Belleville, WI 53508
(608) 424-3300
Est.: 1992
Contact: Paul Sedwick

Zero Halliburton
500 West 200 North
North Salt Lake, UT 84054
(801) 299-7355
FAX: (801) 299-7350
Contact: Evon Young
Available: Direct
Aluminum gun case

Ziegel Engineering
2108 Lomina Ave.
Long Beach, CA 90815
(310) 596-9481
FAX: (310) 590-4734
Est.: 1972   Staff: 10
Contact: Dean Ziegel
Available: Retail & Direct
Heavy duty aluminum travel gun cases. Visa and Mastercard accepted.

GUN CLUB SERVICES

For related products & services see:
- *Carts, Pg. 110*
- *Course Designers, Pg. 119*
- *Insurance, Pg. 176*
- *Trap Manufacturers, Pg. 227*
- *Trap Accessories, Pg. 236*

Operating a gun club–hunting preserve, sporting clay, trap or skeet location–is a complex undertaking. Fortunately, in recent years, a growing number of companies have emerged to offer professional assistance to gun clubs. Those listed in the following sections are among them. Call or write each directly for more information.

CLUB SERVICES/ LEAD SHOT ISSUES

B.E.C. Productions
398 Gary Lee Dr.,
Gahanna, OH 43230
(614) 475-7122   Est.: 1977
Contact: Fred Bichsel
Consulting in lead reclamation: (vacuuming or rotovating).

EA Engineering, Science & Technology, Inc.
11019 McCormick Rd.
Hunt Valley, MD 21031
(410) 527-2445
FAX: (410) 785-2309
Contact: Dick Peddicord, Ph.D.
EA is the most experienced U.S. firm providing advice about all aspects of lead in the environment. Our objective is to help your range with proactive and cost-effective compliance with whatever environmental requirements you may face. As the shooting sports face increasing environmental regulation, EA can support you with everything from preliminary evaluation through initial field investigation to full site assessments if warranted, including strategic consultation on the best ways to protect your interests. Offices throughout the United States and Internationally.

See Our Ad Pg. 158

Eagle Industrial Hygiene Associates
359 Dresher, Horsham, PA 19044
(215) 672-6088
Contact: Keith Crawford
Laboratory testing.

"Get The Lead Out", Inc.
P.O. Box 2029
Red Bank, NJ 07701
(908) 224-8700
Contact: Louis Edmonds
Full service consultants on leadrekated issues for shotgun clubs, including testing, monitoring, removal, and related legal matters.

Karl & Associates, Inc.
Remediation Contractor
PO Box 1790, Mohnton, PA 11540
(610) 856-7700
Director: David Shirey
Range clean-up, de-commissioning and lead reclamation.

Lead Reclamation
Division of Hardcast Enterprises, Inc.
23128 Wildwood Rd.
Newhall, CA 91321
(805) 259-4796
Est.: 1980
President: Fred W. Wooldridge

MARCOR
Box 1043, Hunt Valley, MD 21030
(800) 547-0128
(410) 785-0001
FAX: (410) 771-0348
Contact: Paul Redding

Property Solutions, Inc.
501 Delran Pkwy., Unit C
Delran, NJ 08075
(609) 764-6000
Contact: Edward M. Gallagher
Consulting, testing and design work for ranges.

Gene Sears Supply Company
PO Box 38, El Reno, OK 73036
(800) 522-3314
FAX: (405) 262-2811
Contact: Garland Sears

CLUB SERVICES/ MANAGEMENT

Comlease, Inc.
5114 E. Clinton Way, #101
Fresno, CA 93727
(800) 767-0001
Contact: Suzette Wiggs
See Our Ad Pg. 248

Connor Appraisal Company
510 North Phelps Ave.
Winter Park, FL 32789
(407) 629-5000
FAX: (407) 645-2143
Est.: 1979   Staff: 5
Contact: J. Hal "Jack" Connor, III
We are skilled at analyzing and evaluating clay shooting facilities and businesses. Formal real estate appraisal approach is used along with years of practical shooting experience. Feasibility analysis is available. We work nationally. Please call and see if we can help you with your project.

Eagle Recreational Consultants
PO Box 926, Lincoln, MT 59639
(406) 362-4270
Owner: Alan Kelly
Consulting services for hunting and fishing lodges.
See Our Ad Pg. 289

Field Sport Concepts, Ltd.
Queen Charlotte Square
256 East High St.
Charlottesville, VA 22902
(804) 979-7522
FAX: (804) 977-1194
Contact: Raymond G. Woolfe, Jr.
Land use planning services.

Marty Fischer
dba SportShooting Consultants, Ltd.
PO Box 207, Rincon, GA 31326
(912) 826-0072   Est.: 1992
Contact: Marty Fischer
Services Provided: Marketing Consultation, Management Consultation & Training, Pro Shop Set Up, Business Plans, Feasibility Studies, Clay Course Design, Clay Course Equipment Sales, Special Event marketing, Hunting Preserve Consultation, NSCA Level III Instruction

Forestry & Wildlife Management Services
Box 710, Thomaston, GA 30286
(706) 665-8285
Contact: Jim Buckner

Gun Club Computer Services
7912 F Hill Lane, Charlotte, NC 28269
(704) 547-9798 Attn: Steve

Inter-Fluve, Inc.
25 N. Wilson Ave., Suite 5
Bozeman, MT 59715
(406) 586-6926
FAX: (406) 586-8445
Est.: 1983
Principal/Hydrologist: Dale E. Miller
Inter-Fluve, Inc. is a professional consulting firm that specializes in aquatic resources. Our team of experts pioneered the integration of biology, hydrology, engineering, and landscape architecture, to become the leader in innovative aquatic resource enhancement.

The Haaland Company
PO Box 2085, Auburn, AL 36830
(334) 887-9340
FAX: (334) 821-6209
Est.: 1979   Staff: 5
Contact: Ron Haaland
The Haaland Company specializes in wildlife habitat management programs for sporting properties nationwide.

Hathaway Evans, Inc.
Box 900, Fort valley, GA 31030
(912) 822-9339
Contact: Samuel E. Anderson or Stuart H. Brown
Wildlife habitat consulting & services; hunting land improvements & management. Call for more information.

(Continued from page 102)

combination HI-LOW house to include foundation and upper floor plans, shotfall zone for both skeet & trap, combination field layout, protection fence, handicap walkway accessibility, wiring diagram for night firing. Cost is $100 plus $12.75 S&H.

NRA Range Manual—The National Rifle Association has published a 39-chapter manual separated into four sections: Section 1 has 7 Chapters containing General Range Information; Section 2 has 18 Chapters which cover Outdoor Ranges; Section 3 has Chapters dealing with Indoor Ranges; and Section 4 contains a list of Products & Services, References and Drawings. These are not actual blue prints, just drawings which you can show your architect or engineer so they can prepare the blueprints for your specific range. Cost is $49.95 plus tax and S&H.

Range Business Journal—The National Rifle Association has published this journal to assist range owners and operators in finding manufacturers and/or suppliers of range related products and services. Cost is $5 plus tax and S&H.

Range Business Journal—The National Rifle Association has published this journal to assist range owners and operators in finding manufacturers and/or suppliers of range related products and services. Cost is $5 plus tax and S&H.

RANGE ITEMS FOR SALE

Range Perimeter Signs—The signs read "CAUTION FIREARMS IN USE KEEP OUT". These signs were designed to post around the perimeter of your shooting facility to inform trespassers that they are about to enter a Firearms In Use Area. The signs measure 12" x 16", are black on high visible yellow plastic caution signs, the accepted colors for caution signs. Cost is 10 signs for $20 plus tax and S&H.

Range Rules Poster—The poster lists the NRA's Safe Gun Handling Rules. These posters were designed to post in and around the shooting facility to inform users that they are responsible for Safe Gun Handling at all times and especially while on your shooting range. The poster measures 2' x 3', are on high visible white signs. Cost is $4.95 plus tax and S&H.

Range Safety Flag—The Red Warning Flag is used for outdoor shooting ranges to indicate the range is HOT! The Red Warning Flag measures 3' x 4', are on high visible red nylon. Cost is $23.50 plus tax and S&H.

For additional information contact: Russ Friedline, Manager, Range Development Department, National Rifle Association of America; 11250 Waples Mill Road, Fairfax, VA 22030, (703) 267-1432; FAX (703) 267-3999

Interstate Graphics
7817 Burden Rd.,
Rockford, IL 61111
(815) 877-6777
Contact: Jim Norwood
Product: Signage

National Range Development Corporation
PO Box 1110
Front Royal, VA 22630-1110
(540) 635-1645
FAX: (540) 635-9984
Est.: 1994
Pres: Dick Whiting
NRD Corp's vision is based on the certainty that quality and environmentally safe ranges are needed throughout the world. Its mission is to accomplish the end result, by assembling a team of the foremost experts who possess the knowledge, skills and abilities, and link them to essential resources and technologies necessary to provide those who are involved with the best services and products available anywhere in the world.

National Rifle Association of America
11250 Waples Mill Rd.
Fairfax, VA 22030
(703) 267-1414
FAX: (703) 267-3999
Est.: 1871
Director: Bill Poole
The nation's premier organization for gun owners, the National Rifle Association, offers programs, publications and technical assistance designed specifically to meet the needs of gun clubs. Programs include five-day Range Development Conferences on design, construction and operations, and Range Officer Training, a 16-hour program and examination leading to certification as a range officer. Technical assistance includes the services of a range engineer who can help in the planning of shooting facilities, and a Range Technical Team that provides advice on range development and operation. Publications include

BluePrints for American or Olympic/International Skeet and Trap; an NRA Range Manual with drawings to assist architects in the preparation of blueprints; and Range Business Journal, a directory of manufacturers and suppliers. The NRA also offers range perimeter signs, rules posters and safety flags. For complete information and prices, phone or fax the National Rifle Association.
See Our Ad Across, Right

Quality Wildlife Services, Inc.
PO Box 6867, Aiken, SC 29804
(803) 643-0990
Est.: 1995
Contact: Neill Holloway
Specializing in Quail Management and the use of the Anchor Covey Release System. Offers Consulting Services through its National Network for bird growers, preserve development, sporting clays ranges, freshwater fisheries, deer, waterfowl, and turkey.

Southeastern Illinois College
3575 College Rd., Harrisburg, IL 62946
(618) 252-6376
Contact: Bruce Hering
The only program in the U.S. training hunting preserve managers. Associate Degree Program. Practical technical training. Hands-on, in-the-field internships. Job placement assistance.
See Our Ads Pgs. 285 & 287

Southern Sporting Clays
Box 730, Corsicana, TX 75151
(903) 872-5663
FAX: (903) 872-5660
Est.: 1987   Staff: 2
Contact: Steve Stroube
Available: Retail & Direct
Consulting & design of sporting clays courses & hunting preserves.

Jimmy Vaughan
PO Box 593
Panacea, FL 32346-0593
(904) 225-7616
Contact: Jimmy Vaughan
Consulting on all phases of hunting operations.

Wildlife Harvest Magazine
PO Box 96, Goose Lake, IA 52750
(319) 242-3046
FAX: (319) 242-7793
Contact: John Mullin and Peggy Mullin-Boehmer
Specialized consulting for preserves: planning, developing, marketing & promotion.

CLUB SERVICES/ MARKETING

Nichols Boyesen & Zino
194 Valley View Rd.
New Hartford, NY 13413
(315) 797-0700
FAX: (315) 738-0224
Est.: 1987   Staff: 30
Contact: Hans Boyesen
Creative advertising and marketing services for the outdoor industry.

Outdoor Management Network
4607 NE Cedar Creek Rd.
Woodland, WA 98674
(360) 225-5000
FAX: (360) 225-7616
President: Robert R. Knopf
Specializing in outdoor and travel marketing

Woodland Advertising
5100 Presbyterian Dr.
Conway, SC 29526
(803) 347-6862
Creative Director: Paul A. Olsen
A full service advertising agency dedicated to serving outdoor oriented businesses. We offer a full line of creative services including corporate identity programs, advertising campaigns, media planning, photography, Interent advertising and marketing. No matter what your business needs, turn to Woodland Advertising for the solution.

CLUB SERVICES/ REFEREES

Sandy Hudson
11120 Augustine Herman Hwy.
Chestertown, MD 21620
(410) 348-2148
Certified FITASC referees

National Sporting Clays Association (NSCA)
5931 Roft Rd.
San Antonio, TX 78253
(210) 688-3371
FAX: (210) 688-3014
Contact: Peter Crabtree (Ext. 123)
or 210-688-3769

Sporting Clays of America (SCA)
9 Mott Ave., Suite 103
Norwalk, CT 06850
(203) 831-8453
FAX: (203) 831-8497
Contact: Timothy Nichols

NRA's Range Development Department
We're here to meet your shooting range needs.

Building? Expanding? Improving?
Learn From The Experts

Range Development Conference
Five comprehensive days of orientation on:

- ♦ **Master Planning** ♦ **Site Selection**
- ♦ **Risk Assessment** ♦ **Construction Materials**
- ♦ **Preparing for a Public Hearing**
- ♦ **Environmental Assessments**
- ♦ **OSHA Lead Standard** ♦ **Environmental Sound**
- ♦ **Marketing** ♦ **Management**
- ♦ **Financial Opportunities** ♦ **Range Security**

Guidance from architects, engineers, certified ground water professionals, security specialists, health & safety professionals, financiers, and experienced range operators. Visit local indoor and outdoor shooting ranges and hear from actual practitioners. The registration fee also includes The Range Manual, a conference workbook, a Lead Compliance Program, a vendor list and more.

RECEIVE A 10% DISCOUNT ON THE RANGE DEVELOPMENT CONFERENCE WHEN YOU MENTION YOU SAW THIS AD IN BLACK'S WING & CLAY. OFFER GOOD UNTIL 9/1/97

NRA's Range Development Department
The first step, before the first shot!
For more information please call us at
1 (800) NRA-3888, Extension 1417.

To join the NRA, please call 1(800) NRA-3888

GUNSMITHING

That favorite shotgun of yours may need a simple repair or some maintenance work. Or perhaps you've decided the time has arrived for elaborate customizing that will improve your trap, skeet or sporting clays scores, or help you bag more birds in the field. In either case, the person to turn to is the gunsmith, a highly skilled craftsman who specializes in the repair and modification of firearms. How do you find a good one? Ask your fellow shooting enthusiasts for suggestions, inquire at a reputable gun store, or consult the list of top-rated gunsmiths that follows this article.

The following are among the modifications that can boost accuracy -- and scores:

The Barrel

- **Choke Modification:** Replacing or altering your shotgun's fixed choke changes the gun's shot pattern. The option preferred by most sportsmen is an interchangeable choke tube system. Easily removed and replaced, interchangeable chokes let you fine-tune the level of restriction and pellet distribution for particular sporting clays stations or field hunting. The alternative to interchangeable chokes is a fixed choke alteration. Describe the pattern characteristics you want and your gunsmith will recommend the appropriate fixed choke modification .

- **Porting:** Creating small "ports" near the muzzle end of the barrel bleeds off powder gases when the gun is fired, which helps control muzzle jump. Although this does little to reduce rearward thrust, it does lessen felt recoil. And, by keeping the muzzle from jumping upwards, porting permits a faster second shot. On single-barreled pumps and autos the ports are placed on top of the barrel, on either side of the rib. On over-unders it is common to port only the bottom barrel (normally fired first), although some shooters port both.

- **Backboring:** This process enlarges the diameter of the entire barrel, reducing shot pressure, felt recoil & shot deformation.

- **Lengthening The Forcing Cone:** Your factory-supplied forcing cone is an abrupt constriction where the front of the chamber meets the rear portion of the main bore. When it is lengthened (say, from 3/8" to as much as 4"), shot is forced into the barrel more easily, and shot deformation and recoil are reduced. Recoil sharpness is also reduced.

The Trigger

- **Fine-Tuning/Replacement:** A soft, hard or spongy trigger mechanism is bound to adversely affect accuracy. A crisp trigger, with no "creep," is very likely to improve it. Fine-tuning your trigger mechanism is simply polishing and fitting the action parts for smoother, more consistent action. Trigger replacement, on the other hand, is far more costly and it is much more difficult to find a gunsmith willing to do it. Ask your gunsmith for advice.

The Stock

- **Gunfitting:** For shooting efficiency— especially in field hunting or low gun games—your shotgun should fit as comfortably as an old pair of shoes. If the stock is too long you'll shoot high and perceive more recoil; too short and you'll shoot low. The gunsmith can alter the stock or create one that's customized. Other options include alterations or replacement of the forend, and changes to the buttstock to provide a better grip.

- **Recoil Pads:** Many shooters opt to have recoil pads added to the end of the butt to reduce felt recoil.

YES! YOU CAN SHIP YOUR SHOTGUN

You may have heard otherwise, but there are no laws that prohibit you from shipping your shotgun to a gunsmith. The original styrofoam-lined box the gun was sold in will work. But a safer alternative is to use a high quality hardcase and enclose it in a heavy cardboard box. (No brown paper wrapping if you ship by United Parcel Service, which considers it a distinct no-no.)

If possible, the barrel should be broken down from the action and no ammunition should be packed in the same box. Affix a packing slip pouch on the outside and insert a statement of contents, your name and address, and a description of the work you want done. Always insure the package.

GUNSMITHS

For related products & services see:
- Chokes, Pg. 111
- Gunfitting, Pg. 170
- Gunsmithing Tools, Pg. 170
- Gunstocks, Pg. 170
- Recoil Products, Pg. 173

Allem's Gun Craft
7937 Sigmund Rd.
Zionsville, PA 18092
(215) 679-9016
FAX: (215) 679-8016
Est.: 1968
Contact: Nancy Allem
Available: Direct
Factory authorized repair center for Krieghoff and Perazzi. Shotgunners. . . improve your scores by reducing recoil and increasing pattern percentages with our Grand Slam Package. For only $209 per barrel, we'll backbore it, put in custom chokes and lengthen your forcing cone. Call today with your questions – we'll be happy to help!

Angle Porting
Ballistic Specialites
100 Industrial Dr.
Batesville, AR 72501
(800) 276-2550
Est.: 1991   Staff: 4
President: John Clouse

Our specialty is angle-porting, which reduces muzzle-jump and felt recoil. These are the cleanest ports you'll ever shoot!

Art's Gun & Sport, Inc.
6008 Hwy. Y
Hillsboro, MO 63050
(314) 944-3630
FAX: (314) 452-3631
Est.: 1972   Staff: 4
President: Art Isaacson
Available: Direct
30 years of experience and factory trained-we specialize in rebuilding Brownings-Superposed, Citori, and BT-99.

Stan Baker Barrels
10000 Lake City Way
Seattle, WA 98125
(206) 522-4575
Contact: Stan Baker
Available: Direct
All types of shotgun barrel modification...forcing cone, lengthening, backbore, custom re-choke and screw-in chokes.

Bansner's
Gunsmithing Specialties
261 East Main St.
PO Box 839
Adamstown, PA 19501
(800) 368-2379
Est.: 1983   Staff: 3
Contact: Mark Bansner

Blue Arms Gun Shop
4570 West State
Boise, ID 83703
(208) 336-1661
Owner: Tony Fanelli
Owner: John Person
Shotgun specialists. Repairs of all types. Custom fitting. Chokes, alterations, forcing cones lengthened, stock bending, porting, etc. Professional gunsmithing.

BRILEY

Briley Manufacturing
1230 Lumpkin
Houston, TX 77043
(800) 331-5718 (Cust. Svc.)
(713) 932-6995
Est.: 1976   Staff: 65
Contact: Chuck Webb
Full gunsmithing services include barrel rebuilding, metal refinishing, part fabrications and basic gun services. Full pistol division makes competitive action sport pistols, 10-22 conversions and has a full line of proprietary accessories such as barrels, bushings, comps and scope mounts. Back-boring and long forcing cones are a specialty and can be combined with screw-in choke installation. Briley Ultraport now available. Call for brochure.

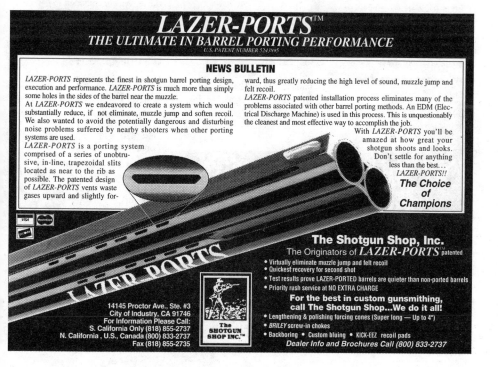

Burgin's Gun Shop
RD1, Box 66,Sidney Center, NY 13839
(607) 829-8668
Est.: 1960   Staff: 3
Owner/Gunsmith: Bryan B. Burgin
Barrel sleeving, barrel regulating, leather pads, stock bending, custom stocking and fitting, checkering, restorations, blueing, colorcase, chokes permanent and screw-in, brochure available.

Clay Target Sports, Inc.
339 Cold Soil Rd.,
Princeton, NJ 08540
(609) 921-9358
FAX: (609) 921-3282
President: Chris Maest

Jack Concannon
155 Kings Rd.
Mt. Holly, NJ 08060
(609) 267-8287
Contact: Jack Concannon
Jack Concannon, Gunsmith - Shooting Instructor. Try-gun for gun fitting. Instruction in trap & sporting clays. Custom barrel work, porting, long cones, microhoning, rechoking, fixed chokes & choke tubes, Briley & Rhino dealer. Adj. combs & L.O.P. Adj. pads, all brands; dealer in Terminator, KICK EEZ & Pachmayr pads. One Day Turnaround on most work, (609) 267-8287.
See Our Ad, Left

Custom Shooting Products
PO Box 6148
Omaha, NE 68106
(402) 551-7024
FAX: (402) 551-7024
Contact: Bruce Bowen
Release triggers; adjustable combs

Dixie Gunworks
1203 East Sandy Ridge Rd.
Monroe, NC 28112
(704) 764-3799
Gunsmith: David Stevens
Our shop offers quality polishing and blueing. We handle a list of other services–please call for details.

Fischer Gunsmithing, Inc.
Box 55-8266
4235 Southwest 75 Ave.
Miami, FL 33155
(305) 261-4454
FAX: (305) 261-4491
Contact: Steve Fischer
Master gunsmithing specializing in shotgun repairs and alterations.

James Flynn Gunsmithing
1932 Viborg Rd.
Solvang, CA 93463
(805) 688-3158
Est.: 1985   Staff: 2
Owner: James Flynn
Repair Tec: Ron Fuakamula
Complete Beretta & Browning repair. Adjustable comb stocks; trap, skeet & sporting clays.

Glen Cove Sports Shop, Inc.
189 Forest Ave.
Glen Cove, NY 11542
(516) 676-7120
Est.: 1971   Staff: 4
Contact: John Cacciola
Custom stock work; barrel work. Specializing in repairing fine double guns.

Griffin & Howe

Griffin & Howe
36 W. 44th St., Suite 1011
New York, NY 10036
(212) 921-0980
Contact: Dick Welch
or
33 Claremont Road
Bernardsville, NJ 07924
(908) 766-2287
Contact: Paul Chapman
Griffin & Howe is dedicated to the legacy of craftmanship begun in 1923 by Seymour Griffin and James Howe. We are equipped to handle stock alterations, engraving, strip cleaning, trigger adjustments, and other custom gunsmithing in our workrooms.
See Our Ad Pg. 166

Gunsite Training Center
PO Box 700
Paulden, AZ 86334
(800) 504-7571
(520) 636-4565
FAX: (520) 636-1236
Contact: Tim Beghtol

Holland & Holland Sporting Weapons Limited
50 East 57th St.
New York, NY 10022
(212) 752-7755
FAX: (212) 752-6805

Paul Jaeger, Inc.
1 Madison Ave.
Grand Junction, TN 38039
(901) 764-6909
Est.: 1935   Staff: 6
Contact: Melissa Quinn (Ext. 247)
Custom gunsmithing

LaBarge-Harkness & Company

617 E. Broadway
Alton, IL 62002
(800) 562-7980
(618) 465-7247
Est.: 1984
Contact: Paul Fuchs
Complete professional gunsmithing service, offering thirty years in caring for fine firearms. Custom wood fitting, specializing in special dimension stocks, fore arms, fine checkering, and your choice of several finishes. Our metal finishing is mostly hand polished, featuring rust blueing, salt blueing, niter blueing, metal greying and colour case hardening.

See Our Ad Below, Left

Laib's Gunsmithing

North Hwy. 23
Spicer, MN 56288
(612) 796-2686
Contact: Pat Laib
Restore & refurbish firing pin areas for all makes. Make a custom adjustable stock. Inventor of raised plastic rib. Remington warranty station.

LAZER-PORTS™

Lazer-Ports
The Shotgun Shop, Inc.
14145 Proctor Ave., #3
Industry, CA 91746
(800) 833-2737
FAX: (818) 855-2735
Contact: Bill Houston
Lazer Ports * The Ultimate in barrel porting performance. U.S. Patent Number 5243895
- Virtually eliminate muzzle jump and felt recoil
- Quickest recovery for second shot
- Test results prove LAZER-PORTED barrels are quieter than non-ported barrels - Priority rush service at NO EXTRA CHARGE The Shotgun Shop, Inc. . .We Do It All:
- Lengthening & polishing forcing cones (Super long – up to 4")
- BRILEY screw-in chokes
- Custom bluing
- Backboring
- Stock bending
- Custom Stock making
- KICK-EEZ Recoil Pad

See Our Ad Pg. 163

The Lefever Arms Co.

6234 Stokes-Lee Center Rd.
Lee Center, NY 13363
(315) 337-6722
FAX: (315) 337-1543
Owner/Pres: Giacomo Arrighini
General gunsmithing & repair for long guns.

Murray's Gun Shop

208 Madison St.
The Dalles, OR 97058
(541) 298-1220
FAX: (541) 298-1220
Est.: 1969   Staff: 4
Contact: Randy Murray
Available: Direct
Custom fit gunstocks of all types; barrel porting; gunsmithing; antique restorations; gunstock duplicating machine work; blueing; over 25 years experience.

See Our Ad Pg. 174

New England Custom Gun Service, Ltd.

Brook Rd., RR#2
Box 122W
W. Lebanon, NH 03784
(603) 469-3450
Est.: 1986   Staff: 3

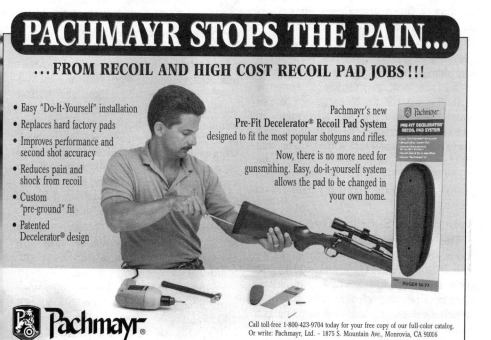

Griffin & Howe . . . Keeping the Legend Alive

New and used classic double barreled shotguns—American, British and European—are merely one of the lures used by Griffin & Howe to attract knowledgeable shooters. Because this venerable establishment, situated in midtown Manhattan and Bernardsville, N.J., is also renowned for its expert gunsmithing, a shooting school, driven bird hunts in Britain and big game safaris in Africa.

Part of a Legend

Founded in New York City in 1923, Griffin & Howe long functioned as the gunsmithing and gun sales department of the legendary sporting goods purveyor Abercrombie & Fitch. And Griffin & Howe continued as a separate shop, retailing and working on fine sporting guns, after Abercrombie & Fitch went out of business in 1976.

Griffin & Howe

Since 1923

formerly of

ABERCROMBIE & FITCH Co.

Although the company maintains a full complement of all types of shotguns at both of its locations, Griffin & Howe is particularly noted for its extensive line of double guns, still preferred by many in this day of pumps and automatics. The stores' racks are stacked with doubles, and the firm is an American agent for John Rigby & Co., and other premier London gunmakers, and for Scottish maker David McKay Brown.

Round Body Sporting Gun

The company also imports its own "house brand" gun, The Griffin & Howe Round Body Game Gun, a classic British style made by the Spanish gunmakers Arrieta. Featuring ejectors and hand-detachable sidelocks, the standard game gun has a straight buttstock with "splinter" forend and double triggers. Options include upgraded wood and single trigger.

Describing the firearm as "an heirloom gun," Griffin & Howe says it includes a fitted luggage case and accessories, including snap caps and cleaning equipment. The company's gunsmith hand fits the dimensions of each standard game gun to meet a customer's requirements. The gun is available in 12, 16, 20 and 28 gauge models, and .410 bore. The larger gauge models are $5,750; the 28 and .410 are $5,950.

Griffin & Howe is not focused exclusively on shotguns, however. Among its other products available to sporting enthusiasts are new and used rifles, antique firearms, gun accessories, hunting books and magazines, Barbour field clothing, and ammunition, including hard-to-get 2" and 2 1/2" British shotgun shells.

Individualized Instruction

The company also maintains a shooting school staffed by British-trained instructors Rex Gage and Paul Smith. Rex and Paul provide individualized instruction and use a "try gun" to help customers determine the stock dimensions that fit them best. Once measurements are determined, the gunsmithing department can restock a shooter's own gun or modify it by bending and altering for cast, drop and length of pull. The department is widely acclaimed for the quality of its repairs and modifications.

Griffin & Howe also books overseas hunts, including highly popular safaris in Botswania, Tanzania, Zimbabwe and South Africa.

Griffin and Howe is situated at 36 West 44th St., Suite 1011, New York, NY 10036 and at 33 Claremont Rd., Bernardsville, NJ 07924. For additional information phone (212) 921-0980; fax (212) 921-2327; or (908) 766-2287; fax (908) 766-1088.

Contact: Dietrich Apel
Contact: Mark Cromwell
The combined experience in gunmaking, gunsmithing and modern manufacturing enables us to provide you with a wide variety of services in a professional manner. We have a thorough knowledge of the finest European shotguns, double rifles, drillings and combination guns. We will work on most well made sporting Long Guns, be they foreign or domestic. Our shop is well equiupped to handle both wood and metal work. Tooling and methods are constantly improved and we're open to any suggestions. For the shotgun shooter we offer: stock fitting, stock and alterations, recoil pads, patterning, long forcing cones, choke alterations, screw-in chokes, and porting.

Nuline Guns, Inc.
1053 Caulks Hill Rd.
Dept. 2800
Harvester, MO 63304
(314) 441-4500
FAX: (314) 447-5018
Est.: 1949   Staff: 17
Contact: B.J. Stevens
Our outstanding reputation as a complete and quality gunsmithing service is built on 45 years of experience repairing, rebuilding and refurbishing:
* Winchester Model 12
* Super X
* Winchester 42
* Winchester 101
From trigger to barrels, we do it all; repair and sell parts. Call for information on our estimating policy and how to ship and insure your gun. For the "do-it-yourselfers", we offer a gunsmithing video for Winchester M/12 and Super X-1 shooter.... only $29.95, plus $5 S/H.

Oakland Custom Arms
4690 West Walton Blvd.
Waterford, MI 48329
(810) 674-8261
Contact: Mike Stitt
Complete bluing and gunsmithing services. Call for our price sheet.

Orvis
Historic Rt. 7A
Manchester, VT 05254
(802) 362-3622
Complete gunsmithing services on all makes; leather covered recoil pads.

P&P Gunsmithing
9324 State Ave., #318
Marysville, WA 98270
(206) 356-7708
Est.: 1987   Staff: 2
Partner: Patrick Gottberg
Custom gunsmiths specializing in competition shotguns.

Precision Porting by Len Evans, III
c/o Evans Tool & Die
157 N. Salem Rd.
Conyers, GA 30208
(770) 922-3480
(770) 922-0680 (Eve)
Gunsmithing services include porting, forcing cone work and chokes.

Pro-Port Limited
41302 Executive Dr.
Harrison Twp., MI 48045
(810) 469-7323
FAX: (810) 469-0425
The company providing porting services utilizing EDM (Electrical Discharge Machining) also offers custom shotgun services. Combined with the world famous porting process services such as lengthening & polishing forcing cones, back-boring, and rechoking. Shotgun shooters can expect nothing but quality services.
See Our Ad Below

Pylinski Arms
Rt. 2, Box 169,
Cumberland, VA 23040
(804) 492-4082
Contact: Laurence Pylinski
Specializing in clay target shotguns.
Parts and service for Beretta, Browning, Krieghoff, Perazzi, Remington, Rottweil, Silver Seitz, SKB and Winchester. Call for information.

R&D Custom Barrel
8423 Terradell St.
Pico Rivera, CA 90660
(310) 923-3608
Contact: Bob Day
Specializing in screw-in chokes for 12, 20, 28 ga. and .410 bore. Custom choke work and "Point of Impact" adjustments. Barrel porting and custom stock fitting featuring Airecoil Eliminator pads.

Rhino Gun Case, Inc.
4340 S.E. 53rd Ave,Ocala, FL 34472
(800) 226-3613
Contact: Janet or Joe Morales
Our gunsmithing services include custom choke installation and forcing cones. We can tap and thread your barrels for standard or thin wall systems.
See Our Ad Pg. 154

**Seminole Chokes &
Gun Works**
Mitchell Machine & Mfg., Inc.
3049 US 1
Mims, FL 32754
(800) 980-3344
FAX: (407) 383-8532
Est.: 1989   Staff: 6
Contact: Janice Mitchell or Randy Mitchell
Available: Retail & Direct
Forcing cones lengthened & polished; barrel porting; barrel boring & threading for screw-in chokes; backboring "Honing"; stock bending; triggers adjusted; custom work on request.

**The Shotgun Shop, Inc.
Lazer-Ports**
14145 Proctor Ave., #3
Industry, CA 91746
(800) 833-2737
FAX: (818) 855-2735
Contact: Bill Houston
Lazer Ports * The Ultimate in barrel porting performance. U.S. Patent

Number 5243895
- Virtually eliminate muzzle jump and felt recoil
- Quickest recovery for second shot
- Test results prove LAZER-PORTED barrels are quieter than non-ported barrels - Priority rush service at NO EXTRA CHARGE The Shotgun Shop, Inc. . .We Do It All:
- Lengthening & polishing forcing cones (Super long – up to 4")
- BRILEY screw-in chokes
- Custom bluing
- Backboring
- Stock bending
- Custom Stock making
- KICK-EEZ Recoil Pad
See Our Ad Pg. 15

Sportsman's Haven, Inc.
14695 E. Pike Rd.
Cambridge, OH 43725
(614) 432-7243
FAX: (614) 432-3204
Est.: 1960   Staff: 7
Pres: Brent Umberger
Available: Direct
Complete gunsmithing service-Armorer-specializing in high grade guns-most factory warranty service.

Allen Timney Gunsmith
13524 Edgefield St.
Cerritos, CA 90703
(310) 865-0181
FAX: (909) 877-4713
Contact: Allen Timney
Improve your accuracy, add to your comfort with Timney Pad Adjusters. These recoil pads allow adjustments up and down, left and right, and rotation in both directions. The Ultra Thin requires no stock cutting. The Standard and the Heavy Duty (with thicker aluminum plates) offer the choice of length-of-pull ($69.50) or length-of-pull with pitch adjustment ($95). Installation: $45 (pad not included). Additional charge when very short stock is wanted on some models. Also available: adjustable combs, barrel porting, forcing cones. Please phone or fax for additional information, and other services.

Top Line Porting
12745 Ottawa Ave., S.
Savage, MN 55378
(612) 895-0037
Est.: 1970   Staff: 1
Contact: Leigh Edwards
Custom shotgun boring. European method complete barrel bore system. Re-choking, bore restoration, machine porting. Entire system performed by custom crafted machinery. Custom 4-way adjustable stockwork done.

Doug Turnbull Restoration
6426 County Rd. 30
PO Box 471, Bloomfield, NY 14469
(716) 657-6338
Est.: 1982   Staff: 3
Contact: Doug Turnbull
Factory quality restoration on pre-1940 shotguns. Bonecharcoal color case hardening; Blueing services include rust, nitro and charcoal blue.

Wessel Gun Service, Inc.
4000 E. 9 Mile Rd.
Warren, MI 48091
(810) 756-2660
Est.: 1946   Staff: 6
Contact: Richard A. Cote
Buy, sell & trade guns; Gunsmithing; Browning warranty repair.

Westchester Gun Works
39 N. Water St.
Greenwich, CT 06830

(203) 532-9466
Contact: Nicola DiGualielmo
Master Gunsmith. Trained to work on all types of guns–English guns, Trap guns, Skeet guns.

Tom Wilkinson
5690 Bob Daniel Rd.
Oxford, NC 27565
(919) 603-0167
Contact: Tom Wilkinson
Specializing in barrel conversions for competition shotguns.

Woodcock Hill
Thomas Bland & Sons Gunmakers, Ltd.
RD#1, Box 147
Benton, PA 17814
(717) 864-3242
FAX: (717) 864-3232
Contact: Christa Baker or Glenn Baker

WRIGHT'S
(THE MODEL 12 SHOP)

**Wright's
(The Model 12 Shop)**
RR3, Box 414
Pinckneyville, IL 62274
(618) 357-8933   Est.: 1980
Contact: Stu Wright
SUPERIOR TRAP CHOKES: the permanent modification of factory chokes to improve pattern diameters and to even density, also benefits SKEET and SPORTING CLAYS. Complete repair and restoration of Winchester shotguns, Browning Competition shotguns, and Perazzis. Competition triggers installed, Recoil pads installed, Ribs resoldered, Five different blueing techniques. Reliable service of custom handcrafted quality.
See Our Ad Below

GUNSMITHING/ TOOLS & SERVICES

B-SQUARE
2708 St. Louis Ave.
PO Box 11281
Forth Worth, TX 76110
(800) 433-2909
(817) 923-0964
Est.: 1957
Contact: Rudy Bechtel
Available: Retail & Direct
One of the largest sources of shot-gun tools. Shooter's Tools: Universal Shotgun Spud-centers all bores and chokes; Recoil Pad Jig-installs recoil pads perfectly; Barrel Press-straightens any shotgun or rifle barrel; Forend Wrench-removes or installs forend slide tube recessed nuts; Rib Center Drill Jig-locates and guides drills on exact center of any rib for sight and mount installation; hammers; punches; screwdrivers; stock wrenches; shell latch; staking tools; & tube dent raiser. Call for free catalog.
See Our Ad Below

Cryo-Accurizing
1160 South Monroe
Decatur, IL 62521
(217) 423-3070
FAX: (217) 423-2756
Contact: Robert W. Brunson

Gun Parts Corporation
PO Box WC97
West Hurley, NY 12491
(914) 679-2417
FAX: (914) 679-5849
Sales Mgr.: Robert Lippman
Marketing Mgr: Linda Munro
Acquisition Mgr: Phil Hunter
World's largest suppliers of gun parts.
See Our Ad Pg. 168

Heckman Specialties
223 South B St.
Livingston, MT 59047
(406) 222-8618
FAX: (406) 222-8618
Est.: 1988
Owner: Bill Heckman
Barrel sleeving, barrel repair, bore restoration, general repair of double guns. Manufacturer of gunsmithing tools for the professional.

Spradlin's
113 Arthur
Pueblo, CO 81004
(719) 543-9462
FAX: (719) 543-9465
Owner: James R. Spradlin, Sr.
Specializing in "custom gun metal refinishing"

GUNSTOCKS & GUNFITTING

For related information see:
• *Shooting Schools, Pg. 202*

Bell & Carlson, Inc.
101 Allen Rd.
Dodge City Industrial Park
Dodge City, KS 67801
(800) 634-8586 (Orders)
(316) 225-6688
Est.: 1985   Staff: 60
Sales Mgr: Vince Carlson
Cust. Svc./Orders: Lynn Hogg
Available: Retail
Hand laminated synthetic gun stocks and custom fitting services.

Boyd's Gunstocks Industries
PO Box 305
Geddes, SD 57342
(605) 337-2125
FAX: (605) 337-3363
Est.: 1983   Staff: 25

Owner: Randy Boyd
Available: Direct
Production hardwood gunstocks
and sole distributor of Bold trigger
assemblies-an adjustable trigger for
more common bolt action rifles.

Cali'Co Hardwoods, Inc.
1648 Airport Blvd.
Windsor, CA 95492
(707) 546-4045
FAX: (707) 546-4027
Est.: 1960
Contact: Ted Smalley
Available: Retail & Direct

Clove Valley Sports Corp.
Hidden Brook Farm
RR1, Box 110 A
Salt Point, NY 12578
(914) 266-5954
Est.: 1980   Staff: 4
Contact: Charles Conger
Custom stock fitting, alterations,
bending, and leather covered recoil
pads. Shooting instruction in British
C.P.S.A. method.

Dakota Arms, Inc.
HC55, Box 326
Sturgis, SD 57785
(605) 347-4686
FAX: (605) 347-4459
Est.: 1960   Staff: 30
Contact: Norma Allen
Available: Retail & Direct
English, Ciaro & Bastogne Walnut
in 2 piece sets or rifle blanks. Stock
duplicating machine available.

J.L. Dockwiller Co.
2125 N. Orange St.
PO Box 2028
Redlands, CA 92373
(909) 793-7665
Est.: 1950
Contact: Jack or Lee Dockwiller

Custom exhibition grade stocks on
all high grade guns

Don's Carey Comb
11430 Payette Heights Rd.
Payette, ID 83661
(208) 642-1884
Contact: Don Carey

FIELDSPORT
Purveyor to the Wingshooter & Angler

FIELDSPORT
3313 W. South Airport Rd.
Traverse City, MI 49684
(616) 933-0767
FAX: (616) 933-0768
Contact: Bryan Bilinski
FIELDSPORT is an authorized stock
fitting agent for AYA, A.H. Fox and
will custom fit for any shotgun.
See Our Ad Pg. 216

John R. Frederickson
3934 Carter Mountain Dr.
Cody, WY 82414
(307) 527-4445
Est.: 1970   Staff: 1
Contact: Jack Frederickson
Specializing in custom gunstock
work. . .including chasing (re-check-
ering), checkering, refinishing &
stock bending. (Ponsness/Warren
sales & repair also offered)

GALAZAN
A Division of Connecticut Shotgun
Manufacturing
PO Box 1692
New Britain, CT 06051-1692
(203) 225-6581
FAX: (203) 832-8707
Est.: 1967   Staff: 20
Contact: Dick Perrett
America's largest selection of Turk-
ish Circassian Walnut gunstock
blanks.

Jim Greenwood
Stockmaker

Jim Greenwood
Custom Stockmaker
PO Box 183
6400 S.W. Hunter Rd.
Augusta, KS 67010
(316) 775-0161
Est.: 1986   Staff: 1
Owner: Jim Greenwood
Custom stocks, stock bending, refin-
ishing, leather pads, checkering.
See Our Ad Below

Jim Holian Stockworks
134 Collingwood Ct.
Florence, KY 41042
(606) 282-1744
Est.: 1992
Contact: Jim Holian
Over 30 years of stock work experience. Fast turn-around with very
good pricing. Repairs & refinishing.

Holland & Holland
Sporting Weapons Limited
50 East 57th St.
New York, NY 10022
(212) 752-7755
FAX: (212) 752-6805

Lee Meadows
Custom Gunstocks
6688 Belinda Dr.
PO Box 4264
Riverside, CA 92504
(909) 781-7148
Est.: 1974   Staff: 2
Contact: Lee Meadows or
Ray Randel
Custom made stocks. Personal fit-
ting. Stock duplicating, refinishing,
checkering, restorations.

Michael Murphy & Sons

6400 S.W. Hunter Rd.
Augusta, KS 67010
(316) 775-2137
Staff: 10
Pres.: Michael Murphy
Custom gun fittings.
See Our Ads Pgs. 217-219

Murray's Gun Shop

208 Madison St.
The Dalles, OR 97058
(541) 298-1220
FAX: (541) 298-1220
Est.: 1969   Staff: 3
Contact: Randy Murray
Available: Direct
Custom gunstocks for O/U, doubles, pumps and semi-automatics.
Call us for: gunsmithing, stock refinishing, checkering, stock bending, bluing, and antique restorations.
See Our Ad Pg. 174

NEW ENGLAND CUSTOM GUN FITTERS

**New England
Custom Gun Fitters**
Boyadjian Gun Works
250 County St., Seekonk, MA 02771
(508) 336-9347
Est.: 1987
Contact: Hagop "Jack" Boyadjian or Gassia Boyadjian
For more than 50 years sportsmen have depended on New England Custom Gun Fitters for the finest in shotgun customization, restoration and repair. Specialists in adjustments and alterations of length, drop, pitch and cast. Also available: hand crafted custom stocks of exhibition grade English

walnut blanks, and color case hardening and reblueing. Get the most from your shotgun by contacting New England Custom Gun Fitters.
See Our Ad Below & Pg. 20

SHOOTING SCHOOL

Pawling Mountain Club Shooting School

PO Box 573, Pawling, NY 12564
(914) 855-3825
Contact: Keith Lupton
Trained in the U.K., Keith Lupton has been a custom gunfitter for over 15 years. He uses both over-and-under and side-by-side try guns in his work. Keith does custom gunfitting for several renowned gun makers, including Holland & Holland and Krieghoff. Call Keith today for additional information at (914) 855-3825.
See Our Ad Pg. 223

Ram-Line, Inc.

545 Thirty-One Road, Suite 31
Grand Junction, CO 81504
(800) 648-9624
(303) 434-4500
FAX: (303) 434-4004
Ram-Line's new Shot-Tech and Trail-Tech stocks offer the same tough weather-proof features as our classic Syn-Tech stocks. Call for complete information or send $1.00 for catalog.

Reinhart Fajen, Inc.

1000 Red Bud Dr., PO Box 338
Warsaw, MO 65355
(816) 438-5111

FAX: (816) 438-5175
Est.: 1951   Staff: 115
Mktg. VP: Krista Kellner
Available: Retail & Direct
"Setting the Standard" in drop-in, semi-finished and custom gunstocks.

Shooter's Emporium

606 S.E. 162,Portland, OR 97233
(503) 257-0524
Makers of customized stocks

Speedfeed, Inc.

3820 Industrial Way, Suite N
Benicia, CA 94510
(707) 746-1221
Est.: 1985   Staff: 3
President: Gil Davis
Manufacturer of synthetic shotgun stock sets for OEM & wholesale.

Turkish Firearms Corp.

522 West Maple St.
Allentown, PA 18101
(610) 821-8660
FAX: (610) 821-8660   Est.: 1962
President: Erbay Gonen
Rough gun stock blanks. Circassian walnut.

STOCKS BY UMBERGER

Stocks by Umberger

14695 E. Pike Rd.
Cambridge, OH 43725
(614) 432-1100
(800) 490-5554
FAX: (614) 432-3204
Est.: 1962   Staff: 6
Pres: Brent Umberger
Available: Direct
Stocks by Umberger offer hand crafted, custom fitted, shotgun stocks primarily for the clay target shooter. Customer dimensions are determined by Brent Umberger,

Master Stockmaker, who has been fitting customers with his try gun for over 35 years. A selection of over 250 American, Claro, English, and Turkish walnut blanks are available for selection.

See Our Ad Below

Wenig Custom Gunstocks
103 N. Market St., PO Box 249
Lincoln, MO 65338
(816) 547-3334
FAX: (816) 547-2881
Est.: 1993　Staff: 12
President: Fred Wenig
Available: Direct　Custom stock fitting (by appointment), custom checkering, machine inletted "do-it-yourself" stocks, large selection of shotgun blanks of all grades:

GUNSMITHS/
RECOIL REDUCTION

Angle-Ease
Oregon Gun Works
1015 Molalla Ave.
Oregon City, OR 97045
(800) 398-5839
FAX: (503) 657-5529
Est.: 1992　Staff: 3
Contact: Al Peck
Available: Retail & Direct
Hydraulic piston activated recoil reduction system for stocks.

BreakO
Graco Corp.
PO Box 936
Gravette, AR 72736
(501) 787-6520
Contact: Jean Phipps
BreakO Recoil Reduction System;
Graco Adjustable Comb Hardware.

Counter Coil
Danuser Machine Co., Inc.
550 E. Third St.
Fulton, MO 65251
(573) 642-2246
FAX: (573) 642-2240
Est.: 1982　Staff: 65
Pres: Jerry Danuser
Contact: Mike Mitchell or Emery Smola
Available: Retail & Direct
Fully adjustable hydraulic recoil reduction device.

Edwards Recoil Reducer
1300 Seabright Dr.
Annapolis, MD 21401
(410) 349-1878
Contact: Kevin Sheff
Available: Retail & Direct
Adjustable to control barrel bounce and rearward motion. Lifetime warranty. Call for nearest dealer.

**G-Squared
Air Cushion System**
Schroll Shooting Supplies
434 Pearl St.
Upland, CA 91786
(909) 985-7147
FAX: (909) 981-0436
Pres: Wendell Schroll
Installed in "Stockmaster Stock System".

GALAZAN
A Division of Connecticut Shotgun Manufacturing
PO Box 1692
New Britain, CT 06051-1692
(203) 225-6581
FAX: (203) 832-8707
Est.: 1967　Staff: 20
Contact: Dick Perrett
Available: Direct
Hand finished recoil pads: The original Winchester Patent Date Style,

The pre-war Silvers Pad for high grade guns, The HAWKINS Pad, Our Technically Superior Recoil Pad and several other styles.

Griggs Recoil Redirector
Griggs Products
Factory:
640 N. Main St.
North Salt Lake, UT 84054
(801) 295-9696
FAX: (801) 299-1815
Est.: 1970　Staff: 2
Pres: Jay P. Griggs
Ass't: George Abrams
Available: Retail & Direct
There is nothing in this world that treats recoil the same as the Griggs Recoil Redirector, and no phony claims either. Shooters report after using one that it takes all the kick from the face and from 50% to 80% of the kick from the shoulder. Also the Griggs Adjustable system, so great it's patented. Records have been set and are being set, shoots are being won with the Griggs system.

JS Air Cushion Stocks
850 W. Foothill Blvd., #21
Azusa, CA 91702
(818) 334-2563
Est.: 1986　Staff: 1
Contact: Joe Shiozaki
Attention Skeet Shooters: Feel the ultimate in shooting comfort with your different gauge shotguns. New guns shipped direct from manufacturer or send your gun direct.

KICK-EEZ
PO Box 12767
Wichita, KS 67277-2767
(316) 721-9570
FAX: (316) 721-5260

Contact: Robert Pearce or Star Pearce

The Sorbothane® visco-elastic material in KICK-EEZ recoil pads reduces recoil. Less recoil reduces flinching, eases sore shoulders or cheeks. Eliminating the rebound effect of the first shot, second shots are quicker and more accurate. Independent lab tests available on request.

MGS M-10029
McClelland Gun Shop
1533 Centerville Rd.
Dallas, TX 75228
(214) 321-0231
Est.: 1972
Contact: Joe Ketchum
Available: Retail & Direct
Recoil Reducer; Firearm & accessory sales.

Mercury Inertia Recoil Control
Staub Gun Specialties
261 Herbert
Alton, IL 62002
(618) 465-6286
Contact: Bill Staub

Mercury Recoil Suppressor
C & H Research
115 Sunnyside Dr.
Lewis, KS 67552
(316) 324-5445
Est.: 1978
Contact: Frank O'Brien
Available: Retail & Direct
Mercury Recoil Reducer
Your best buy in recoil reduction!
The Mercury Recoil Suppressor overcomes the practical limitations of

competing spring-weight systems by using liquid mercury to slow down and partially offset apparent recoil. Simple, reliable, easy to install and remove. Complete satisfaction, or your money back! Call or write for free brochure.

Pachmayr, Ltd.
1875 South Mountain Ave.
Monrovia, CA 91016
(800) 423-9704
(818) 357-7771
FAX: (818) 358-7251
Contact: Les Whitney
Available: Retail
Eliminate the expense of gunsmithing with Pachmayr's new Pre-Fit Decelerator® Recoil Pad System. Replace hard factory pads at home. Easy, do-it-yourself installation. Patented Decelerator design improves performance and second shot accuracy, reduces recoil shock. Fits most popular shotguns, rifles. Phone for complete information. And visit our Pro Shop at 831 N. Rosemead Blvd., S. El Monte, CA: Perazzi, Browning and Beretta Shotguns, reloading supplies, accessories.

See Our Ad Pg. 165

Palsa Outdoor Products
PO Box 81336
Lincoln, NE 68501-1336
(800) 456-9281
(402) 488-5288
FAX: (402) 488-2321
The Palsa Add-A-Pad is made from

a shock absorbent, blended neoprene with a specially formulated adhesive backing.

Poorman's Magtube Recoil Reducer
Tom Morton & Company
19309 Gristmill Lane
Knoxville, MD 21758
(800) 382-9691
FAX: (301) 620-1622
Est.: 1975   Staff: 2
Contact: Tom Morton
Available: Direct
Manufacturers of shotgun shooting accessories. Call for free catalog.

Pro-Port Limited
41302 Executive Dr.
Harrison Twp., MI 48045
(810) 469-7323
FAX: (810) 469-0425
Est.: 1980   Staff: 12
Available: Retail & Direct
The one company that has spent years developing a porting process specifically for use on shotguns. Shotgun shooters have benefited from the reduced recoil and muzzle jump provided by the Pro-Port process. The originators of barrel porting used EDM (electrical discharge machining) offering a style of porting suited for all types of shotgun shooters.

See Our Ad Pg. 167

Recoil-Less Engineering
9 Fox Oaks Court
Sacramento, CA 95831
(916) 391-1242
Contact: Steven J. Jones
Produce the Deal Mule Recoil Reducer, Jones Stock Adjuster, Gun Nut System, and the Terminator Recoil Pad.

Soft Touch
Shooter's Emporium
606 S.E. 162nd
Portland, OR 97233
(503) 257-0524
Est.: 1985   Staff: 4
Owner: Moe Bragg
Available: Retail & Direct
Customize your stock to reduce recoil

Stagecoach, Inc.
AiRecoil Shooting Products
PO Box 339
Pahrump, NV 89041
(702) 727-7993
FAX: (702) 727-7994
Contact: Jim Jensen
The recoil pads, from .410 to 10-gauge, have a web weave solid, butt plate and can absorb up to 55% of the recoil.

YES! YOU CAN SHIP YOUR SHOTGUN

You may have heard otherwise, but there are no laws that prohibit you from shipping your shotgun to a gunsmith. The original styrofoam-lined box the gun was sold in will work. But a safer alternative is to use a high quality hardcase and enclose it in a heavy cardboard box. (No brown paper wrapping if you ship by United Parcel Service, which considers it a distinct no-no.)

If possible, the barrel should be broken down from the action and no ammunition should be packed in the same box. Affix a packing slip pouch on the outside and insert a statement of contents, your name and address, and a description of the work you want done. Always insure the package. For additional information about shipping a shotgun, contact a customer service representative at the common carrier of your choice.

GUNFITTING MEASUREMENTS

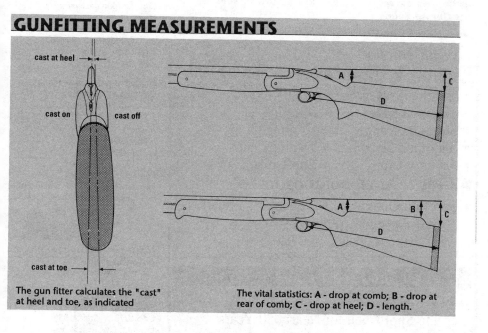

The gun fitter calculates the "cast" at heel and toe, as indicated

The vital statistics: **A** - drop at comb; **B** - drop at rear of comb; **C** - drop at heel; **D** - length.

INSURANCE

**Carpenter
Insurance Service**
Friendly service for almost 50 years
134 Holiday Court, Suite 300
Annapolis, MD 21401-7059
(800) 472-7771 (Voice Phone)
FAX: (410) 266-9154
Contact: Fred Mann
Liability insurance for hunting preserves...sporting clays.. .trap and skeet...shooting ranges...shooting clubs...hunting clubs...plus archery, fishing and sportsmen clubs. Amounts of club liability insurance range from $100,000 to $1,000,000. Choice of broad or limited coverage. Extensions for landowners and sponsors. There is no deductible. All- Risk 3-Year fire, flood, theft, explosion and other accidental damage insurance for sporting guns. Reduced rate Personal All-Risk 3-Year loss or damage insurance for firearm collections used solely for exhibit or personal display. FREE INFORMATION with no obligation. Prompt, accurate attention to requests and claims.
See Our Ad Below

Joseph Chiarello & Co., Inc.
31 Parker Rd., Elizabeth, NJ 07208-2118
(908) 352-4444
FAX: (908) 352-8512
Contact: Tina Hegyes or Bob Chiarello
Providing insurance for the firearms industry since 1979. Placed with A++ 15 insurance company licensed in all states. Coverage is comprehensive general liability including products and property including burglary and theft. Additional insureds can be included for vendors and landlords. $1,000,000 limit of liability for firearm retailers and wholesalers; ammo manufac-turers; reloaders; gunsmiths; trap, skeet, sporting clays; rifle and pistol ranges. General liability coverage for firearms (shooting) instructors with limits of $250,000, $500,000, or $1,000,000. Umbrella coverage with limits to $15,000,000 is available through the same insurer.
See Our Ad Across

Ferguson & McGuire, Inc.
PO Box 189
Durham, CT 06422
(203) 349-1215
FAX: (203) 349-7799
Est.: 1975
Contact: Gary D'Amico, CIC. CEFS. Gun club/gun dealers/preserves/range insurance programs for Connecticut, Mass. & Rhode Island. Both NRA and CT state certified firearms instructor.
See Our Ad Above

Hilb, Rogal & Hamilton Company of Amarillo
1800 Washington, Suite 400
PO Box 1149
Amarillo, TX 79105
(806) 376-4761
FAX: (806) 376-5136
Est.: 1916   Staff: 48
Contact: Judy Hartsock
Specialty markets–trap, skeet, outfit-ters, guides, guest ranches. Call us.

INSURANCE
MANAGEMENT
ASSOCIATES
INC **IMA**

Insurance Management Associates
250 North Water, #600
Wichita, KS 67202
(800) 333-8913
FAX: (316) 266-6254
Est.: 1973   Staff: 135
Contact: Jay Chapple or Kim Rogers

Specialty designed insurance programs. With 15 years experience insuring outdoor sports facilities, IMA provides tailor-made Public Liability and Property insurance programs. Specialties for the outdoorsman include Sporting Clays, Trap-Skeet, Hunting Clubs & Preserves.

International Special Events & Recreation Assn.
(ISERA)
PO Box 526 148
Salt Lake City, UT 84152-6148
(800) 321-1493
(801) 942-3000
FAX: (801) 942-8095
Est.: 1986   Staff: 4
Program Manager: Rick Lindsey
Non-profit industry trade association specifically set up to provide insurance.

K&K Insurance Group, Inc.
1712 Magnavox Way
PO Box 2338
Ft. Wayne, IN 46801
(219) 459-5000
Contact: Steve Hendricks

Kirke-Van Orsdel, Inc.
99 Canal Center Plaza/Suite 400
Alexandria, VA 22314
(703) 706-9600

Contact: Harry Palmer
Available: Retail & Direct
Insurance coverage provided to NRA members.

Mike Kohout Agency
PO Box 55453
Seattle, WA 98155-0953
(800) 800-4413
FAX: (206) 365-0107
Contact: Mike Kohout
Recreation insurance coverages

**George O'Keefe,
Insurance Broker**
5516 Northwest Flint Ridge Rd.
Kansas City, MO 64151
(800) 741-2845
Est.: 1980   Staff: 3
Contact: George M. O'Keefe
The "pioneer" in shotgun sports operators "tailored" insurance programs. First offered in 1989 and since that time NO changes in rates, insurance underwriters, or coverages. "A" rated company. Annual policies with installment payment plans available. Comprehensive General Liability Policy format with NO deductible. Land owners (Lessor's) and Members as additional insureds at NO additional premium. Available limits of $300,000; $500,000; $1,000,000

and up to $10,000,000. Excess if needed. Policy on "occurence" basis. Your trap/skeet/sporting clays machines insured under separate policy for physical damage. All Risks and on a REPLACEMENT VALUE basis. Reasonable rates. We offer "QUALITY" insurance products and give prompt, professional and courteous service. Inquiries welcomed.

See Our Ad Across

The Outdoorsman Agency
126 E. Church St.,PO Box 151
Bishopville, SC 29010
(800) 849-9288
Contact: Steve Murray or
Andrew Woodham, Jr.
Specialized commercial insurance programs for hunting preserves and clubs, plantations, lodges, sporting clays, outfitters and guides, and hunting dog field trial clubs.

See Our Ad Below

Sportsman's Insurance Agency, Inc.

555 W. Granada Blvd., Suite E-11
Ormond Beach, FL 32174
(800) 925-7767
(904) 677-2588
FAX: (904) 677-3292
Contact: Hollis E. Boss
Specializing in insurance programs for the shooting sports. Commercial General Liability Programs specifically for and endorsed by the following: National Skeet Shooting Association; National Sporting Clays Association; North American Gamebird Association; New York State Conservation Council, Inc., and Outdoor Writers Association of America, Inc. Additional insured landowners can be included at no additional cost.
Gun insurance on a replacement value basis.
General liability insurance for firearms instructors.
Excess limits and umbrella coverage with limits to $10,000,000 available.

Woodward Long & Rieger, Inc.

821 Main St.
PO Box 99
Niagara Falls, NY 14302
(716) 285-8441
FAX: (716) 285-8445
Est.: 1916   Staff: 7
Pres: John Long, Sr.
Liability insurance for game preserves and hunting clubs/ NAGA affiliated.

MAIL ORDER CATALOGS

For related products & services see:
• *Accessories, Pg. 84*
• *Apparel, Pg. 90*
• *Vests, Pg. 96*

Mail order shopping is a time-honored shotgunning tradition. Indeed, the oldest mail order company in the country began serving the hunter five years before Abe Lincoln moved into the White House. Today catalog/mail order houses offer the upland hunter, waterfowler and sporting clays shooter a vast array of functional and reliable products. Before you begin your mail order shopping spree, remember: Safety, Comfort & Personal Style– in that order–should be be your prime considerations when choosing your hunting clothing and related items. The companies listed below offer the wingshooting enthusiast a wide range of apparel, accessories, dog training, hunting gear, and gun related equipment.

Atlantic British Ltd.

Box 110, Rover Ridge Dr.
Mechanicville, NY 12118
(800) 533-2210
Contact: Al Budde
We sell the complete line of Barbour sportswear and accessories.

Ballistic Products, Inc.

20015 75th Ave., N.
Corcoran, MN 55340
(612) 494-9237
Est.: 1975
Contact: Grant Fackle or Kurt Fackler
At Ballistic Products handloading is more than a simple money saving diversion. Our customer is the serious sportsman who wants the right ammunition for the right game. Call or write today for our FREE catalog.

Bass Pro Shops

1935 S. Campbell,
Springfield, MO 65898-0400
(800) 227-7776
(417) 887-1915

L.L. Bean, Inc.

Casco St.,Freeport, ME 04033-0001
(800) 221-4221
(207) 865-4761
Est.: 1912   Staff: 3500
Pres.: Leon A. Gorman
Tr. Sec./Sr. VP: Norman Poole

Beretta Gallery

718 Madison Ave.
New York, NY 10021
(212) 319-6614
Sports and casual wear, hand-tooled luggage, gifts, shooting accouterments, fine art and prints, sportsman's library.

Brownells, Inc.

200 S. Front St., Rt. 2, Box 1
Montezuma, IA 50171
(515) 623-5401
FAX: (515) 623-3896
Est.: 1939   Staff: 98
Available: Retail & Direct
Gunsmithing tools and custom accessories for shotguns, handguns, rifles; choke tubes and tooling, long forcing cone reamers, sights, recoil pads.

Foster & Smith, Inc.
2253 Air Park Rd., PO Box 100
Rhinelander, WI 54501-0100
(800) 826-7206
Pet supply company owned and operated by veterinarians.

Fox Ridge Outfitters
400 N. Main St., PO Box 1700
Rochester, NH 03867
(800) 243-4570
Contact: Bob Gustafson

Gamaliel Shooting Supply,
1525 Fountain Run Rd.
Box 156, Gamaliel, KY 42140
(800) 356-6230 (Orders)
(502) 457-2825 (Customer Service)
FAX: (502) 457-3974
Contact: Garon Pare or Geoff Pare

Graf & Sons, Inc.
Rt. 3, Hwy. 54 South
Mexico, MO 65265
(800) 531-2666 (Orders Only)
(314) 581-2266
FAX: (314) 581-2875
Reloading supplies are our specialty.

Gun Parts Corporation
PO Box WC97
West Hurley, NY 12491
(914) 679-2417
FAX: (914) 679-5849
Sales Mgr: Robert Lippman
Marketing Mgr: Linda Munro
Acquisition Mgr: Phil Hunter
World's largest suppliers of gun parts.
See Our Ad Pg. 168

Hamilton's
PO Box 2672, S. Vineland, NJ 08360
(800) 292-3695
FAX: (609) 691-0398
Contact: Timothy D. Hamilton
Sportsman's Jacket 100% Egyptian
waxed cloth, 5 pockets, two-way
brass zipper, snap on hood, tartan
lining, olive green. Sizes XS-XXXL.
Price: $139.00 ppd. Call for brochure.
See Our Ad Above

Happy Jack
PO Box 475, Snow Hill, NC 28580
(800) 326-5225
FAX: (919) 747-4111
Est.: 1946
Contact: Ashe Exum, Sr.
Available: Retail & Direct
Dog care products, hunting apparel, hunting art.

Cabela's
812 13th Ave., Sidney, NE 69160
(800) 237-4444
(308) 254-5505
FAX: (308) 254-2200
Est.: 1961   Staff: 1000
Contact: James W. Cabela

Countrysport
1515 Cass St.,
Traverse City, MI 49684
(800) 367-4114
(616) 929-3320
FAX: (616)929-9813
Editorial Director: Art DeLaurier, Jr.
Enjoy exciting shopping for quality
sporting books, wildlife art, wax cotton outerwear, unique products
and gifts designed exclusively for
sportsmen by sportsmen. Call for
your free catalog.

Crow's Nest Trading Co.
208 N. Tarboro St.
PO Box 3975, Wilson, NC 27895
(800) 900-8558 (Orders)
(919) 291-5577

Dogs Unlimited
Box 1844, Chillicothe, OH 45601
(800) 338-DOGS (3647)
FAX: (614) 772-2150
Owner: John Ingram

Dunn's
One Madison Ave.
Grand Junction, TN 38039
(800) 223-8667
FAX: (901) 764-6503
Est.: 1950   Staff: 75
America's best selection of clothing
and equipment for wing and clay
shooters. Call for free catalog.

FIELDSPORT
3313 W. South Airport Rd.
Traverse City, MI 49684
(616) 933-0767
FAX: (616) 933-0768
Contact: Bryan Bilinski
FIELDSPORT specializes in fine clothing, equipment and giftware for
the wingshooter and angler.
See Our Ad Pg. 216

C.C. Filson Company
PO Box 34020, Seattle, WA 98124
(206) 624-4437
FAX: (206) 624-4539
Est.: 1897
Contact: Steve Matson
Available: Retail & Direct
C.C. Filson is a manufacturer of
quality outdoor clothing, luggage
and hats.

Hawks
322 East Main, PO Box 207
Blytheville, AR 72315-0207
(800) 333-8288 (Orders)
FAX: (501) 763-0473
Est.: 1952
Owner: Brad Hawks

Herter's
Waterfowling & Outdoor Specialists
PO Box 1819
Burnsville, MN 55337-0499
(800) 654-3825
(612) 894-9510
The authentic world source for hunters, fishermen, guides, gun smiths, forest rangers, trappers and explorers.

Kevin's Guns & Sporting Goods, Inc.
3350 Capital Circle, Northeast
Tallahassee, FL 32308
(800) 953-8467 (Orders)
FAX: (904) 422-1512
Kevin's caters to the outdoorsman's demands for high quality sporting equipment.. Call for our free brochure.

Mack's Prairie Wings
210 E. Michigan, PO Box 391
Stuttgart, AR 72160
(800) 229-0296
FAX: (501) 673-3687
Owner: Marion McCollum
Mack's Sport Shop now offers a waterfowl oriented catalog to service the duck and goose hunter.

New England Arms Co.
PO Box 278, Lawrence Lane
Kittery Point, ME 03905
(207) 439-0593
Contact: Jim Austin
Call for our catalog of fine sporting arms and accessories.
See Our Ad Pg. 39

NICA Shooting Accessories
5334 Hillary Circle, Parker, CO 80134
(303) 840-9949
Est.: 1994
Contact: Brenda Mason

Orvis Company
Historic Rt. 7A
Manchester, VT 05254
(800) 548-9548 (Orders)
(802) 362-3622
Est.: 1865   Staff: 400
CEO: Leigh H. Perkins
VP/Fin.: Thomas Vaccaro
VP/Mktg.: Howard Steere

PAST Sporting Goods, Inc.
PO Box 1035,Columbia, MO 65205
(573) 445-9200

Est.: 1980   Staff: 12
Pres: Dick Leeper
Available: Retail & Direct
The finest in wearable recoil protection and accessories for all shooting sports–Recoil Shields-Shooting Vests-Shooting Gloves-Gun Vise-Tumbler-Hunting Vest-Shooting Accessories- Shooting Glasses-Shooting Shirts-And More. Full Line available for all ages. To purchase any of our fine products please contact your local shooting sports retailer or gun club manager. Available in both right and left handed. 100% U.S. made.

Ponsness/Warren
S. 763 Highway 41, PO Box 8
Rathdrum, ID 83858
(800) 732-0706 (Orders)
(208) 687-2231
FAX: (208) 687-2233

E-MAIL: bsteele@reloaders.com
Internet: www.reloaders.com
Contact: Brian Steele

William Powell Catalogue
22 Circle Dr., Bellmore, NY 11710
(516) 679-1158
FAX: (516) 679-1598
Contact: Mike Patton
Featuring the finest in English guns; specialists in all shooting accessories and country clothing.

Precision Reloading, Inc.
161 Crooked S Rd., PO Box 122
Stafford Springs, CT 06076
(800) 223-0900
Est.: 1978
Contact: Peter C. Maffei
Precision Reloading, Inc. was established in 1978 and has quickly grown into a Worldwide Mail Order Company.

Quality Arms, Inc.
PO Box 19477, Houston, TX 77224
(713) 870-8377
FAX: (713) 870-8524
Contact: John Boyd
We have many accessory items for the serious sportsman: trunk style cases, European shooting items, European cartridge boxes and European shotshells.

W.C. Russell
Moccasin Co.
285 S.W. Franklin
Berlin, WI 54923
(414) 361-2252
FAX: (414) 361-3274
Est.: 1898
Pres.: Ralph Fabricius
Custom fitted handcrafted moccasin boots and shoes for avid sportsman and women. Dozens of custom options-Thinsulate, Air-Bob Soles, Snake Proof. Fine made-to-measure any size, width or height. Call or write for free color brochure.
See Our Ad Pg. 95

Scott's Dog Supply, Inc.
9252 Crawfordsville Rd.
Indianapolis, IN 46234
(800) 966-3647
(317) 293-9850
Specializing in hunting & training equipment for sporting dogs.

Shyda's Shoe & Clothing Barn
1635 S. Lincoln Ave.,
Lebanon, PA 17042
(717) 274-2551
Est.: 1966   Staff: 8
Complete line of trap & skeet, sporting clays, hunting and fishing outerwear.
See Our Ad Pg. 181

The Sportsman's Closet
365 W. 19th St.
Houston, TX 77008
(800) 841-0851
(713) 802-1840
FAX: (713) 880-5660
Contact: Tim and Martha Holt
Call for our color brochure featuring Mac-Jac and Springing Teal Leather products and accessories.

The Sportsman's Guide
411 Farwell Ave.
South Saint Paul, MN 55075-0239
(800) 888-3006 (Orders)
(612) 451-3030
FAX: (612) 450-6130
Est.: 1970
Contact: Gary Olen
"The fun to read catalog"

Stafford's
715 Smith St., PO Box 2055
Thomasville, GA 31799-2055
(800) 826-0948
Est.: 1945
Contact: Warren Stafford
A 51 year tradition of providing a unique selection of merchandise relating to hunting dogs and being outdoors.

R.C. Steele
1989 Transit Way, Box 910
Brockport, NY 14420
(800) 872-3773 (Orders)
(800) 872-4506 (Questions)
Wholesale gun dog & kennel supplies

Tidewater Specialties
US Rt. 50, Box 158
Wye Mills, MD 21679
(800) 433-5277 (Orders)
(410) 820-2076
FAX: (410) 364-5215
Est.: 1974
Unique selection of gifts and gear, clothing and home accessories for everyone interested in shotgunning, wildfowl, field dogs, golf and more.

Tiemann's
PO Box 130, Priddy, TX 76870
(800) 410-3006
Tiemann's specializes in custom fitted, fine quality hunting, riding and safari clothing for men and women. Whether you are XXS or 4XL, we guarantee to fit. Our products are made to order in our shop in Priddy, TX. Call today for a free catalog. Visa, Mastercard and American Express accepted.

Tri-Tronics, Inc.
PO Box 17660
1650 S. Research Loop
Tuscon, AZ 85731
(800) 456-9494 (Orders)
FAX: (602) 722-9000
Tri-Tronics catalog provides a number of training aids and educational materials to help you better understand the principals of electronic dog training.
See Our Ads Pgs. 126- 128

Willis & Geiger Outfitters
1902 Explorers Trail
Reedsburg, WI 53959
(800) 223-1408 (Orders)
FAX: (800) 566-2329
Est.: 1902
Contact: Burt Avedon

Wing Supply
PO Box 367, Greenville, KY 42345
(800) 388-9464 (Orders)
(502) 338-2808
FAX: (502) 338-0057

Wings & Clays, Inc.
24852 Harper Ave.
St. Clair Shores, MI 48080
(800) 746-8486
FAX: (810) 814-9194
Est.: 1993
Contact: Larry Woo
Available: Retail & Direct
Michigan's exclusive dealer for K-80, Perazzi, Premium Beretta and Parker Reproductions. Dealer for Lewis Creek, Barbour and Beretta Sport clothing. Also dealer for Wild-Hare Products, Holland Brothers, Briley & Kolar products. New Wings & Clays Pro-Shop supply catalog available.
See Our Ad Pg. 42

Wingset
RR2, Box 800
718 Gabert Rd.
Woodstock, VT 05091
(800) 356-4953
Quality clothing & equipment for waterfowlers & upland hunters.

Question or problem? Give Wing & Clay a call 9 am - 5 pm E.S.T. and we'll try to help. Our number is: (908) 224-8700.

PUBLICATIONS

The American Field
The American Field Publishing Co.
542 South Dearborn St.
Chicago, IL 60605-1528
(312) 663-9797
FAX: (312) 663-5557
Est.: 1874
Managing Editor: Bernard J. Matthys
Advtg. Mgr: Ronald Betley
Circulation: 11,000
Frequency: Weekly

American Firearms Industry
2245 E. Sunrise Blvd., #916
Fort Lauderdale, FL 33304
(954) 561-3505
FAX: (954) 561-4129
Est.: 1973   Staff: 14
Publisher: Andrew Molchan
Mgng. Editor: Robert Lesmeister
Advtg: Danny J. Vincent
Trade publication for the firearms industry.

American Hunter
National Rifle Association
11250 Waples Mill Rd.
Fairfax, VA 22030
(703) 267-1300
FAX: (703) 267-3971
Est.: 1973

Exec. Dir: E.G. "Red" Bell, Jr.
Editor: Tom Fulgham
Advertising: Diane Senesac
Circulation: 1,632,900
Frequency: Monthly

Bird Dog News
563 17th Ave., NW
New Brighton, MN 55112
(612) 636-8045
FAX: (612) 636-8045
Est.: 1992
Publisher: Dennis Goldan
Circulation: 2,500
Frequency: 6 Times Per Year plus August & October newsletters
Hunter's guide to hunting upland waterfowl including seasons, trial dates & training tips.

The Bird Hunting Report
Pasha Publications, Inc.
1616 N. Fort Myers Dr.
Suite 1000,
Arlington, VA 22209
(800) 424-2908
(703) 528-1244
FAX: (703) 351-9771
Est.: 1989   Staff: 6

Publisher/Editor: Todd Sedgwick
Adm. Asst.: Christina Muntaneu
Circulation: 2,000
Frequency: 12 Times Per Year
See Our Ad Below

Blue Book Publications, Inc.
8009 34th Ave. So., Dept. WC
Minneapolis, MN 55425
(800) 877-4867 (Orders only)
(612) 854-5229
FAX: (612) 853-1486
Est.: 1981   Staff: 13
E-Mail: bluebook@bluebookinc.com
Web: http://www.bluebookinc.com
Publisher: S.P. Fjestad
Publisher with the following titles in print: *Blue Book of Gun Values*, by S.P. Fjestad, 17th Edition, soft cover, annual firearms pricing guide; *Blue Book of Guitars*, editor S.P. Fjestad, 3rd Edition, soft cover; *Blue Book of Pool Cues* by B. Simpson, 1st Edition, soft cover; *The Billiard Encyclopedia* by V. Stein and P. Rubino, 2nd Edition, hardcover, *Tee Time Guide* by NADA Sports Inc., lists most U.S. golf courses, soft cover; *The Book of Colt Firearms* by R.L. Wilson, hardcover, the bible on Colt firearms manufactured 1836-1870; *Gun Journal*, monthly firearm magazine; *Mossberg: More Gun for the Money* by Victor & Cheryl Havlin, soft cover.

Clay Shooting Magazine/UK
c/o Vilardi Publications, Ltd.
43 Main St.
Avon-By-The-Sea, NJ 07717
(908) 502-0500
FAX: (908) 502-9606
President: Tom Vilardi
U.S. Agent: Tom Vilardi
Circulation: 16,000
Frequency: Monthly
See Our Ad Below

Ducks Unlimited
One Waterfowl Way
Memphis, TN 38120
(901) 758-3825
Est.: 1937
Publisher: Matthew B. Connolly, Jr.
Editor: Lee D. Salber

Advertising: Beth Bryan
Circulation: 515,000
Frequency: Bimonthly
Ducks Unlimited is a magazine for
active outdoor sportsmen and con-
servationists.

Field & Stream
Times Mirror Magazines, Inc.
2 Park Ave.
New York, NY 10016
(212) 779-5000
FAX: (212) 686-6877
Est.: 1895
Publisher: Michael Rooney
Editor: Duncan Barnes
Circulation: 2,000,000
Frequency: Monthly

Fur-Fish-Game
A.R. Harding Publishing Co.
2878 E. Main St.

Columbus, OH 43209
(614) 231-9585
Est.: 1925
Editor: Mitch Cox
Advertising: Eric R. Schweinhagen
Circulation: 107,114
Frequency: Monthly

Gray's Sporting Journal
North American Publications, Inc.
735 Broad St.
PO Box 2123
Augusta, GA 30901
(706) 722-6060
Est.: 1975
Publisher: William S. Morris, III
Editor: David C. Foster
Advertising: Lea Cockerham
Circulation: 35,000
Frequency: Bimonthly
Literature and Art edited for the
advanced angler, hunter, shooter
and conservationist.

Gun Dog
The Stover Publishing Co., Inc.
1901 Bell Avenue
Des Moines, IA 50315
(515) 243-2472
Est.: 1981
Publisher: Carrell Bunn
Editor: Bob Wilbanks
Advertising: Mary Stearns
Circulation: 55,718
Frequency: Bimonthly
GUN DOG is edited for sportsmen
who own and hunt with upland
bird dogs and waterfowl dogs.

Gun List
Krause Publications
700 E. State St.
Iola, WI 54990
(715) 445-2214
FAX: (715) 445-4087
Est.: 1952   Staff: 368
Publisher: David Kowalski
Advtr. Mgr: John Kronschnabl
Promotional Mgr: Tom Luba
Circulation: 72,641
Frequency: Bi-Weekly

Hunting
Petersen's Publishing Company
6420 Wilshire Blvd.
Los Angeles, CA 90048
(213) 782-2184
Est.: 1973
VP & Exec. Publisher: Ken Elliot
Editor: Todd Smith
Circulation: 325,000
Frequency: Monthly

Modern Skeet & Clays Magazine
Quack Sporting Clays, Inc.
4 Ann & Hope Way
PO Box 98
Cumberland, RI 02864
(401) 723-8202
FAX: (401) 722-5910
Est.: 1991
Publisher/Editor: Kenneth M.
Gagnon, Sr.
Ass't. Editor: Joan Mandeville
Frequency: Bi-Monthly
Modern Skeet & Clays Magazine,
established in 1991, is published bi-
monthly, promotes and reports
news on all the clubs who have en-
tered the Modern Era of
Recreational shotgun shooting and
Modern Era games.

North American Hunter
North American Outdoor Group, Inc.
12301 Whitewater Dr.
Suite 260
Minnetonka, MN 55343
(612) 988-7100
FAX: (612) 936-9169
Est.: 1978
Publisher: Russ Nolan
Editor: Bill Miller
Advertising: Tom Perrier
Circulation: 695,000
Frequency: 7 Times Per Year
Official publication of the North
American Hunting Club–not avail-
able on newsstands.

Outdoor Life
Times Mirror Magazines, Inc.
2 Park Ave., New York, NY 10016
(212) 779-5000
FAX: (212) 686-6877
Est.: 1898
Publisher: Michael Rooney
Editor: Vin Sparano
Circulation: 1,350,000
Frequency: Monthly

Pheasants Forever
PO Box 75473
St. Paul, MN 55175
(612) 773-2000
Est.: 1982
Exec. Dir: Jeffrey S. Finden
Editor: Dennis Anderson
Advertising: Dill & Associates
Circulation: 73,000
Frequency: 5 Times Per Year

The Pointing Dog Journal
Box 968, Traverse City, MI 49685
(616) 946-3712
Est.: 1992
Publisher: David G. Meisner
Editor: David G. Meisner
Advertising: John Shoemaker
Circulation: 30,000
Frequency: Bimonthly
The only full- color magazine in the
world devoted totally to pointing
dogs.

Quail Unlimited
31 Quail Run, PO Box 610
Edgefield, SC 29824-0610
(803) 637-5731
FAX: (803) 637-0037
Est.: 1981   Staff: 25
Publisher: Jerry W. Allen
Editor: Diana J. Kogon
Advertising: Cathleen M. Vetter
Circulation: 48,000
Frequency: Bimonthly

RGS-The Ruffed Grouse Society Magazine
451 McCormick Rd.
Coraopolis, PA 15108
(412) 262-4044
Est.: 1961
Exec. Dir. & VP: Samuel R.
Pursglove, Jr.
Editor: Paul E. Carson
Advertising: Paul E. Carson
Circulation: 23,000
Frequency: 5 Times Per Year

The Retriever Journal
Box 968, Traverse City, MI 49685
(616) 946-3712
FAX: (616) 946-3289
Est.: 1995
Publisher: David G. Meisner
Editor: Steve Smith
Advertising: John Shoemaker
Circulation: 20,000
Frequency: Bi-monthly
The only full-color magazine in the
world devoted totally to the re-
triever breed.

RIFLE & SHOTGUN
SportShooting·

Rifle & Shotgun SportShooting
NatCom, Inc., 5300 CityPlex Tower
2448 E. 81st Street
Tulsa, OK 74137-4207
(918) 491-6100
FAX: (918) 491-9424
Est.: 1994
Publisher: Gerald W. Pope
Exec. Editor: Mark Chesnut
Advertising: Ellie Shimer

Circulation: 100,000
Frequency: Bi-Monthly
RIFLE & SHOTGUN SportShooting
delivers valuable tips and information on the shooting sports from
trap to sporting clays, and hunting
from waterfowl to plantation quail.
The magazine provides innovative
and entertaining stories on shooting
activities for youth, beginners and experienced shooters. This high-quality
magazine also covers big- game hunting and other long gun issues.
See Our Ad Pg. 185

Shooting Sports Retailer
130 W. 42nd St., Suite 1804
New York, NY 10036
(212) 840-0660
FAX: (212) 944-1884
Publisher: Bruce Karaban
Editor: Bob Rogers
Advtg: Gina Domanico
Circulation: 16,560
Frequency: 6 Times Per Year

SHOOTING SPORTSMAN
The Magazine of Wingshooting & Fine Guns

Shooting Sportsman
Down East Enterprise, Inc.
PO Box 1357, Camden, ME 04843
(800) 666-4955 (Subscription)
(207) 594-9544
FAX: (207) 594-5144
Est.: 1988
Publisher: Silvio Calabi
Editor: Ralph P. Stuart
Advertising: Bill Anderson
Circulation: 20,000
Frequency: Bimonthly
Shooting Sportsman brings readers
the best in wingshooting and fine
shotguns. From upland gunning
and waterfowling to sporting clays,
the magazine celebrates our sports,
their traditions and the people who
keep them; the birds and the dogs;
and the exciting places we visit - be
they around the corner or around
the world.
See Our Ad Across

Shot Business
11 Mile Hill Rd.
Flintlock Ridge Office Center
Newtown, CT 06470
(203) 426-1320
FAX: (203) 426-1087
Assoc. Editor: Tim Gorel
Advertising: C. Kenneth Ramage
Circulation: 20,000+
Frequency: Monthly
Official publication of the National
Shooting Sports Foundation.

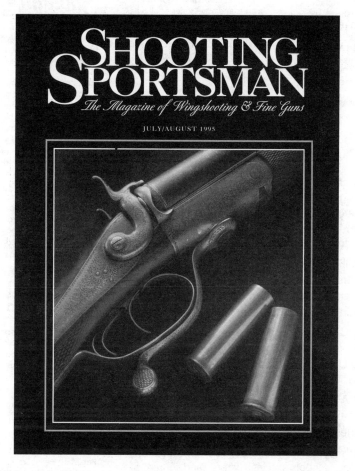

Shotgun News
Snell Publishing Company
PO Box 669, Hastings, NE 68902
(800) 345-6923 (Subscriptions)
(402) 463-4589   Est.: 1948
Publisher: Robert M. Snell
Advertising: Mary Kriger
Circulation: 142,000
Frequency: 3 Times a Month

It's the leading publication for the sale, purchase and trade of firearms and accessories of all types. Shotgun News has aided thousands of gun enthusiasts to locate firearms, both modern and antique - rifles, shotguns, pistols, revolvers, scopes, mounts...all at money-saving prices.

Shotgun Sports MAGAZINE

Shotgun Sports
Box 6810, Auburn, CA 95604
(800) 676-8920
FAX: (916) 889-9106
Est.: 1979
Publisher: Frank Kodl
Editor: Frank Kodl
Advertising: Lynn Berger
Circulation: 103,153
Frequency: 11 Times Per Year
Shotgun Sports. . .the magazine for informed shotgunners. Name your game, trapshooting, sporting clays, skeet. . .are you into reloading, patterning or shotgun testing? Do you live for hunting waterfowl & upland birds or all of the above! Whatever your choice, Shotgun Sports magazine is the nation's only magazine that delivers it all.
See Our Ad Across

Skeet Shooting Review
5931 Roft Rd.
San Antonio, TX 78253
(210) 688-3371
FAX: (210) 688-3014
Est.: 1947
Publisher: Mike Hampton, Ext. 110
Editor: Susie Fluckiger, Ext. 105
Advertising: Jennifer Bittle, Ext. 118
Circulation: 18,000
Frequency: Monthly

Southern Outdoors
5845 Carmichael Rd.
Montgomery, AL 36117
(334) 277-3940
Est.: 1968
Publisher: Helen Sevier
Editor: Larry Teague
Advertising: Ken Woodard
Circulation: 249,937
Frequency: 9 Times Per Year

Sporting Classics
PO Box 23707
9330 A Two Notch Rd.
Columbia, SC 29224
(800) 849-1004
(803) 736-2424
Est.: 1981
Publisher: Art Carter
Editor: Chuck Wechsler
Advertising: Bernard & Associates
(702) 323-6828
Circulation: 35,000
Frequency: Bimonthly

Sporting Clays
Patch Communications
5211 S. Washington Ave.
Titusville, FL 32780
(800) 677-5212 (Subscription)
(407) 268-5010
FAX: (407) 269-2025
Est.: 1989
Publisher: Christi Ashby
Editor: George Conrad
Advertising: Jackie Miller
Circulation: 22,500
Frequency: 12 Times Per Year
Sporting Clays reports on shooting
activities with instructional columns, equipment reviews and
range listings. Each issue features
top tournament coverage as well
as National Sporting Clays Association news, shooter profiles and
hunting and shooting adventure
stories. Special sections on shooting gear, clothing, accessories, and
sporting vehicles are also part of
the Sporting Clays package.
See Our Ad Across

Sports Afield
250 W. 55th St.,
New York, NY 10019
(212) 649-4302
Est.: 1887
Exec. Editor/Publ.: Terry McDonell
Assoc. Publisher: Michael P. Wade
Circulation: 450,000
Frequency: 10 Times Per Year
Sportsman's magazine covering:
hunting, fishing, shooting sports,
boating, nature conservation.

Thicket's Hunting and Fishing Journal
2100 Riverchase Center
Suite 118, Birmingham, AL 35244
(800) 329-4868
FAX: (205) 987-2882
Circulation: 125,000
Frequency: Bi-Monthly

Trap & Field
Curtis Magazine Group
1200 Waterway Blvd.
Indianapolis, IN 46202
(317) 633-8802
Est.: 1890
Publisher/Editor: Bonnie Nash
Advertising: Tracy Price
Circulation: 16,284
Frequency: Monthly
Official publication of the Amateur
Trapshooting Association

Turkey & Turkey Hunting
Krause Publications, Inc.
700 E. State St., Iola, WI 54990
(715) 445-2214
FAX: (715) 445-4087
Est.: 1983   Staff: 24
Publisher: Debbie Knauer
Circulation: 98,800
Frequency: Bimonthly
Practical and comprehensive hunting
information for turkey hunters.

Waterfowl Magazine
Waterfowl U.S.A.
National Headquarters
PO Box 50, Edgefield, SC 29824
(803) 637-5767
Est.: 1983
Publisher: Roger L. White
Circulation: 20,000
Frequency: Bimonthly
Grass roots waterfowl conservation
organization funding local water-
fowl habitat projects

Western Outdoors
3197 E. Airport Dr.
Costa Mesa, CA 92626
(714) 546-4370
Est.: 1960
Publisher: Bob Twilegar
Editor: Jack Brown
Advertising: Joe Higgins
Circulation: 86,083
Frequency: 9 Times Per Year

Wildfowl
The Stover Publishing Co., Inc.
1901 Bell Ave., Suite 4
Des Moines, IA 50315
(515) 243-2472
Est.: 1985
Publisher: Carrell Bunn
Editor: Roger Sparks
Advertising: Mary Stearns
Circulation: 34,444
Frequency: Bimonthly
WILDFOWL is edited for and de-
voted to serious duck and goose
hunters.

Wildlife Harvest Magazine
NAGA, Inc.
PO Box 96
Goose Lake, IA 52750
(319) 242-3046
Pub/Editor: John Mullin
Assoc. Editor: Peggy
Mullin-Boehmer
Circulation: 2,500
Frequency: Monthly
The magazine for gamebird produc-
tion and improved hunting.

Black's WING & CLAY

Wing & Clay
43 West Front St., Suite 11
Box 2029, Red Bank, NJ 07701
(800) 224-WING (9464)
(908) 224-8700
FAX: (908) 741-2827
Est.: 1991   Staff: 5
Publisher: James F. Black, Jr.
Editor: Lois Re'
Assoc.Publisher: Raymond Goydon
Associate Publisher: Amanda Santos
Circulation: 60,000
Frequency: Annual

Wing & Shot
Stover Publications, Inc.
1901 Bell Ave., Suite 4
Des Moines, IA 50315
(515) 243-2472
Est.: 1986
Publisher: Carrell Bunn
Editor: Bob Wilbanks
Advertising: Mary Stearns
Circulation: 17,879
Frequency: Bimonthly
WING & SHOT is for outdoorsmen
interested in upland hunting. Each
issue covers pheasant, grouse,
quail, dove and turkey hunting.

WINGSHOOTING
THE TRADE PAPER OF THE SHOTGUNNING INDUSTRY

Wingshooting Dealer
The Outdoor Group
Down East Enterprise, Inc.
PO Box 1357, Camden, ME 04843
(800) 766-1670 (Subscription)
(207) 594-9544
FAX: (207) 594-5144
Est.: 1996
Publisher: H. Allen Fernald
Editor: Ralph P. Stuart
Advertising: Bill Anderson
Circulation: 15,000
Frequency: Bimonthly
Wingshooting Dealer is the only
trade periodical devoted exclusively
to the shotgunning industry. Edito-
rial emphasis in on wingshooting
(both hunting and target shooting)
retail and mail-order management;
profiles of businesses and industry
leaders; news and new products.
WSD offers market penetration unavailable through any other
publication.
See Our Ad Pg. 187

Get Your <u>FREE</u> Copy of

 **SPORTING CLAYS**™

The Shotgun Hunter's OWN Magazine...
The Official Publication of the
National Sporting Clays Association

"Missing an issue of Sporting Clays is like being without my gun"—A Satisfied Reader

• **Super Shooting Features:** Fully illustrated articles in each issue.

• **Sporting Emporium:** Up-to-the-minute look at what's new.

• **Sporting Shot:** No-nonsense commentary by Richard Owen.

• **Shotshells:** Reviews of equipment and ammo.

• **Wingshooting:** Great instruction and helpful tips.

• **Ballistics:** How to get more from your gun.

PLUS: A comprehensive calendar of tournaments and events • The sport's biggest bazaar of items for sale • A shooting club and course directory

How to get your FREE "I'll take a look" issue:

We'll send you a sample issue of *Sporting Clays*—and if you like what you see, you can get a whole year (12 big issues) for just $23.95. You'll save a whopping $23.45 off the newsstand price. If you aren't delighted or if *Sporting Clays* isn't what you thought it would be, your free copy is yours to keep regardless.

Call 1-800-677-5212 TODAY!

Sporting Clays Magazine • 5211 S. Washington Ave.• Titusville, FL 32780

RELOADING

Why Reload Your Own Shells?

For individuals who love shotgunning, shotshell reloading is a rewarding hobby. It's not surprising then to learn that each year the number of reloads nearly equals the number of new shells manufactured!

Why's reloading so popular? First, you save money. And the more you shoot, the more money you save. The chart [right >] compares the approximate cost of new shells with the cost of reloads. Second, reloading is truly enjoyable hobby, done alone or with a shooting buddy.

Third, for the person who loves shotgun shooting, there's nothing like the satisfaction of breaking a clay target or downing a game bird with your own reloads. Inter-

Type of Shotshell (Box of 25)	Average Store Price	Handloaded Price (Average price on components)	Savings Per Box
10-ga. 3½" Mag., 2 oz. shot	$19.50	$4.31	$15.19
12-ga. 3" Mag., 1⅞ oz. shot	$12.75	$3.89	$ 8.86
12-ga. 2¾" Mag., 1½ oz. shot	$11.00	$3.47	$ 7.53
12-ga. Target load, 1⅛ oz. shot	$ 5.75	$2.27	$ 3.48
20-ga. 3" Mag., 1¼ oz. shot	$10.50	$3.05	$ 7.45

The price you pay may be more or less depending on your component purchases.

ested? Here's what you need to know to get started.

Selecting Components

A shotshell comprises several components--primer, powder, wad, and shot—in various combinations depending on the particular use [see diagram pg. 22]. Each combination has been carefully tested by ballistics experts for maximum effectiveness and safety. Never experiment with combinations of your own. It can be wasteful at best, and very possibly dangerous.

The Hull: An Important Choice

When just getting started as a reloader, it's best to keep things as simple as possible. Not all shells have the same capacity or crimp and you must use a different set of components to reload each. That's why most experts suggest that you begin by choosing your area's most popular low brass or skeet hull and stick with it until you have enough experience to move on to other types of hulls. Consistent use of the same hull permits consistent use of the same components for all your loads. Less chance for confusion. Less chance of error.

A Word About Shot

Both lead and steel shot are easy to reload. But it's imperative that instructions for each type are followed to the letter. Never substitute steel shot for lead. The result could be chamber pressure high enough to burst the gun, causing death or injury to the shooter or bystanders.

Wads that work fine with lead shot will not work with steel shot. If you're using steel shot, employ steel shot components only, and follow the manufacturer's directions religiously.

As shot size increases, fewer pellets can be loaded into the hull. Smaller sizes are used for trap, skeet, sporting clays and small game birds. Larger sizes are suitable for heavier game, such as ducks, geese, and turkeys.

Selecting The Right Wad

The wad is that part of the shotshell between the powder and the shot. A tight seal permits expanding gas from the burning powder to push the shot column from the barrel with maximum velocity. Easy to reload, modern "wad columns" combine cup and wad in a single piece. Use only the specific wad column recommended for the other components you are using.

Powder Precautions

Powders have different burning speeds. The heavier the shot load, the slower the powder must burn, because it takes longer to accelerate such a load than a light one. A fast-burning powder ignited behind a heavy load can cause excessive breech pressure, resulting in gun damage and personal injury. Conversely, a slow-burning powder will not propel a light load effectively. Without proper pressure buildup many powders will fail to burn uniformly, diminishing shot velocity.

When you purchase powder, get—and read— a Sporting Arms and Manufacturers Association (SAAMI) pamphlet on the properties and proper storage of smokeless powder.

Always store powder in its original container (designed to burst without causing an explosion if the powder is accidentally ignited.) Don't store powder in a glass jar or bottle, or any container that will allow pressure to buildup. Store powder in a cool, dry, child-safe place where there is no chance of sparks or flame reaching it.

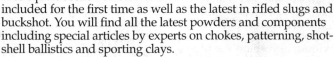

Use The Proper Primer

When you pull the trigger on your shotgun, the hammer falls on the firing pin denting the primer cup. This detonates the primer, which ignites the main powder charge. Primer characteristics vary, depending on their purpose. Always use a primer that is compatible with your other components. Never remove it from its container until you're ready to use it. And store it away from your powder, exercising the same precautions.

Choosing The Right Tool

There are three basic types of reloading tools--manual, semi-automatic/single-stage, and semi-automatic/progressive. The type you choose will depend on cost, convenience and speed.

Manual Reloaders

If low price is your overriding consideration, you can make do with a manual reloader, although speed will be sacrificed and accuracy and uniformity may be somewhat inconsistent. With a manual reloader, care is called for because deviations from the recommended quantities can produce a shell that fails to perform as expected.

Semi-automatic

When the handle of a typical semi-automatic reloader is pulled the tool performs all the reloading steps—depriming, priming, resizing the metal base, measuring the powder, seating the wad column, measuring the shot, and crimping--automatically.

In a single-stage, semi-automatic reloader you manually move the hull from one station to the next. Each shell is processed singly and finished before starting a new one. Completion of eight to ten boxes per hour is not unusual with this type of device. Recommended for the shooter who doesn't require high volume and maximum speed.

Progressive, semi-automatic reloaders process more than one shell simultaneously, and complete a finished shell with each pull of the handle. Skeet and trap enthusiasts, who may run through eight or more boxes of shells in an afternoon, generally prefer progressive reloaders. Hydraulically-operated models eliminate the need to pull a handle.

RELOADING EQUIPMENT

Hornady

Hornady Mfg. Co.
Box 1848, Dept. WS1086
Grand Island, NE 68802
(308) 382-1390
FAX: (308) 382-5761
Contact: Tom McGovern
The Hornady APEX Auto comes loaded with automatic time-saving features. And no shot or powder will drop without hulls present. Hornady Manufacturing offers shotshell and metallic reloading equipment and accessories with lifetime warranties, as well as rifle, pistol and muzzleloading bullets, ammunition, and shooter accessories.

See Our Ad Pg. 198

Lee Precision, Inc.
4275 Highway "U"
Hartford, WI 53027
(414) 673-3075
FAX: (414) 673-9273
Available: Retail & Direct
Load -all II (12, 16 & 20 ga.)
Send $1 for complete catalog.

MEC
Mayville Engineering Co.
715 South St.
Mayville, WI 53050
(414) 387-4500
FAX: (414) 387-5802
Sales & Mktg: Dave Kern
Single stage and progressive shotshell reloaders. Also accessory items.

Ponsness/Warren
S. 763 Highway 41
PO Box 8
Rathdrum, ID 83858
(208) 687-2231
FAX: (208) 687-2233
Marketing Mgr: Brian Steele
Available: Retail
Each Ponsness/Warren machine is hand assembled, thoroughly inspected, fully adjusted and put through the reloading process, producing factory looking shells right out of the box. 4 models of shotshell reloaders: LS1000; 950 Elite; 900 Elite; Du-O-Matic 375 and hydraulic units.

See Our Ad Below

Spolar Power Load, Inc.
17376 Filbert, Fontana, CA 92335
(800) 227-9667
(909) 350-9667
FAX: (909) 350-4276
Est.: 1990
President: Carter Spolar
VP: Dicksie Spolar
Available: Direct
Go for the Gold in '96. Spolar Gold Premier Reloader, manual or hydraulic. The world's best! Superbly crafted, beautiful, user friendly. Sizing dies can be removed and replaced any time, at any position. Change gauges in 5 minutes or less. Custom assembled with parts machined to aircraft quality standards from 6061-T6 aluminum and steel. Sealed ball bearing movement. No castings, stampings or plastic parts. At Spolar quality and customer service is not our goal, it's our obsession! Selling direct to assure superior quality at fair prices. All products carry a 100% satisfaction warranty.

See Our Ad Pg. 199

RELOADING ACCESSORIES

Hydra-Load, Inc.
3018 D Wildwood Ave.
Jackson, MI 49202
(800) 241-0155
Hydraulic system for progressive shotshell reloaders.

K&T Company
1027 Skyview Dr.
West Carollton, OH 45449
(513) 859-8414
President: F. Keith Tomlinson
Shell organizing systems, rust inhibiting snap caps, gun lubricants

Kennedy Mfg. Co.
520 E. Sycamore St.
Van Wert, OH 45891-0151
(800) 413-8665
(419) 238-2442
FAX: (419) 238-5644
Est.: 1911
Mktg. Mgr: John Aycock
Reloading benches. Compact and deluxe models of industrial grade steel construction with "butcher block" maple tops.

Multi-Scale Charge Ltd.
PO Box 101, LPO
Niagara Falls, NY 14304
(905) 566-1255
President: Peter Trnkoczy
All metal, fully adjustable charge bars. Models available for lead and steel shot for MEC reloaders.

The Rock
Production Industries, Inc.
240 Teller St.
Corona, CA 91719
(909) 272-0555
Contact: Bill Burns or Greg Burns
Available: Direct
"The Rock" reloading bench with an adjustable height of 36" to 42" and a 60" x 30" work surface; lockable cabinet and drawer. Shipped within 48 hrs. Dealer inquiries also welcomed.

Spolar Power Load, Inc.
17376 Filbert
Fontana, CA 92335-5901
(800) 227-9667
(909) 350-9667
FAX: (909) 350-4276
Est.: 1990   Staff: 2
President: Carter Spolar
VP: Dicksie Spolar
Available: Direct
Manufacturers of the superbly designed and precision manufactured Power Load Hydraulic; the industry's first, best and most imitated hydraulic for the Ponsness/Warren and now the New Spolar Gold Premier progressive reloader. Spolar Power Load considers their customers to be their friends and treats them accordingly. At Spolar quality and customer service is not our goal, it's our obesssion!
Selling direct to assure superior quality at fair prices. All products carry a 100% satisfaction warranty.
See Our Ad Across

RELOADING POWDERS & COMPONENTS

Accurate
Scot Powders,
5891 Highway 230 West
McEwen, TN 37101
(800) 416-3006 (Cust. Svc.)
(615) 729-4207
FAX: (615) 729-4211
For years, shooters have trusted Scot™ Powders—now a division of Accurate Arms—to meet their reloading needs. Representing a tradition of quality, these clean-burning propellants are ideal for applications that call for precise pattern control. Scot Powders excel in 20, 28, .410 and other small gauge shooting. And all Scot Powders, from our Scott 4100 for .410 bore to our Nitro 100 in 12 gauge loads, are backed by our toll-free technical support line. Send for our free brochure of shotshell reloading data.

All Star Lead Shot
c/o Estate Cartridge, Inc.
Box 3702, Conroe, TX 77305
(409) 856-7277
Contact: Paul Butaud
Our lead shot strictly keeps the quality standards of the hunting and shooting sports for the lead shot market. 2 types of shot available: "Chilled" (medium hard); "Magnum" (hard).

Alliant Techsystems, Inc.
(formerly Hercules Powder)
New River Energetics
State Rt. 114, PO Box 6
Radford, VA 24141-0096
(800) 276-9337
FAX: (540) 639-7189
Dir. of Mktg: John Schrader
Tech Info Rep: Harry Pascoe
Tech Info Rep: Ben Amonette
Shooter's have achieved more "100 straights" at 27 yards with Alliant Red Dot® than with any other powder. That kind of consistency is just one of the reasons to load with Red Dot. The fact is that it's one of the cleanest burning powders on the market, and one of the cleanest handling. Ask your dealer for American-made Red Dot. Or write to us for information.
See Our Ad Pg. 9

Black Magic Wads
KTA Gun Club
3432 E. 1017th North
Sedgwick, KS 67135
(316) 755-2933
Est.: 1994   Staff: 6
Available: Retail & Direct
Quality replacement 1 1/8 oz. wads for Winchester AA or Remington hulls. 1 oz. wads and Federal gold medal replacement wads.

Blount, Inc.
Sporting Equipment Division
PO Box 856, Lewiston, ID 83501
(800) 627-3640
Available: Retail
Primers

Cheddite France
99, Route de Lyon
Bourg-les-Valence
France 26500
011-33-75-56-4545
FAX: 011-33-75-56-3587
Contact: Jean-Claude Blais
Primed empty shells; hunting and sporting cartridges.

Claybuster Wads
Division of C&D Special Products
309 Sequoya Dr.
Hopkinsville, KY 42240
(502) 885-8088
FAX: (502) 885-1951
Est.: 1988   Staff: 7
President: William MacTavish
Vice President: Dirk MacTavish
Available: Retail
Claybuster is a line of replacement shotgun wads designed for economical reloading in the sport of clay target shooting.

Duster Wads
by Micro Technologies
PO Box 105, Lodi, WI 53555
(888) 438-7837
(608) 635-4205
FAX: (608) 635-4251
Est.: 1991   Staff: 3
President: Mike Busser
Duster Wads by Micro Technologies help you turn clay targets into nothing but dust! Noted for producing better patterns, superior powder seal, lower pressures and less recoil, Duster Wads are manufactured with 100% prime certified virgin plastic, assuring reloaders of premier quality. Available in one ounce (BlueDuster WAA12) and 1 1/8 ounce (GreenDuster WAA12SL) loads. Contact Mike Busser for the location of your nearest distributor. Dealer inquiries welcome.

Federal Cartridge Company
Sporting Ammunition & Components
900 Ehlen Dr.
Anoka, MN 55303-7503
(612) 323-2300
Est.: 1922
Available: Retail
Primers (shotshell & centerfire) and wads

Fiocchi of America, Inc.
5030 Fremont Rd.,
Ozark, MO 65721
(417) 725-4118
FAX: (417) 725-1039
CEO: Craig Alderman
Nat'l. Sales Mgr: Dave Thomas
Available: Direct

Hodgdon Powder Co., Inc.
6231 Robinson
PO Box 2932-Dept. WC
Shawnee Mission, KS 66201
(913) 362-9455
FAX: (913) 362-1307
Est.: 1946   Staff: 50
Chairman: J.B. Hodgdon
President: R.E. Hodgdon
VP/Sales & Mktg: Tom Shepherd
Available: Retail
Hodgdon Powder Company represents the "Visible Improvement". . .Clays! This powder was developed especially for 12 gauge clay target shooters. Clays is an EXTRA CLEEN burning propellant perfect for trap, skeet and sporting clays 1-ounce to 11/8th loads! Try clays. . .it's the "Visible Improvement!"

IMR

IMR Powder Company
1080 Military Tpke., Suite 2
Plattsburgh, NY 12901
(804) 363-2094
Est.: 1987
Mktg. Mgr: Larry Werner
Available: Retail
We sell a complete line of smokeless powders through master distributors to the handloading market. As the oldest and most experienced powder manufacturer in North America, IMR Powder Company offers shooters the broadest and best-known line of smokeless powders available. Among these are "Hi-Skor" 700-X, an exceptionally clean- burning powder for both field and target loads, as well as a wide range of proven powders for shotshell, rifle and handgun reloading.

Littleton's Shotmaker
275 Pinedale Ave.
Oroville, CA 95966
(916) 533-6084
Contact: J.F. Littleton
Making shot is easier than reloading. 2 models available to make any one of the following sizes: 6, 7 1/2, 8, 8 1/2, or 9. Call or write for more information.

Pattern Control Shotshell Wads and Accessories
Triple G Plastics, Inc.
327 Main St., Gamaliel, KY 42140
(502) 457-4023
FAX: (502) 457-4050
Manufacturers of PC wads, magnetic gun rests, powder baffle, shotshell box, reloading organizer and shell holster kit.

Polywad Spred-R
PO Box 7916, Macon, GA 31209
(912) 477-0669
Est.: 1986   Staff: 4
Contact: Jay Menefee
POLYWAD, "Spred-Rs" are the easiest loading, most effective component you can use to improve your close range gunning. Acclaimed by writers and shooters for nearly 10 years, you will always want to have some for upland game and Sporting Clays. Now available in 4 types for handloaders, 12 ga. "3-hole" for all around use, 12 ga. Solid Disc for tight chokes, 16 ga. and 20/28 ga.
See Our Ad Pg. 60

Reloading Specialties, Inc.
Box 1130, Pine Island, MN 55963
(507) 356-8500
FAX: (507) 356-8800
Est.: 1985   Staff: 15
VP: Mark R. Braaten
CEO: Jon T. Samuelson
Available: Retail
Manufacturers of steel shot and steel shot wads.

Remington Arms Company, Inc.
PO Box 700, 870 Remington Dr.
Madison, NC 27025-0700
(800) 243-9700 (Consumer)
(910) 548-8700 (Headquarters)
FAX: (910) 548-7770
Est.: 1816
Available: Retail
Shotshell primers and wads are available from Remington for reloading.

Super Hawk™ Wads

Hawk International
PO Box 219, Gary, SD 57237
(605) 272-5501
FAX: (605) 272-5502
Contact: Glen Gust
Serious shooters rely on Super Hawk™ Wads for superior quality and proven performance. Available in one ounce and 1 1/8 ounce loads, Super Hawk Wads are highly praised for consistency, superior lab results and reloading benefits. Look for loading data specs in powder companies' reloading manuals. Major credit cards welcome. For your nearest distributor contact Dan (612) 891-4444, or Glen (507) 283-4429.

Taracorp Industries

1200 16th St.
Granite City, IL 62040-4495
(618) 451-4400
FAX: (618) 451-9310
Est.: 1870   Staff: 100
Contact: Bill Schulze
Available: Retail & Direct
Lawrence Brand Shot–an accepted brand for over 100 years, and made in the USA! Made by Taracorp Industries, Inc., the only company to offer factory shotshell specifications and quality in component shot for hunters and target shooters. Highly polished, consistently round and accurately weighted to provide excellent pattern, desirable shot string and effective impact. Graphite coated and manufactured to American standards by the largest maker of shot in the world–and made from alloys compounded to the highest standards in the industry. Available in easily identifiable bags. Packaged in 25 lb. quantities for maximum convenience.

Top Gun Tournament Shot

Gene Sears Supply Company
PO Box 38, El Reno, OK 73036
(800) 522-3314
FAX: (405) 262-2811
Contact: Gene Sears, Jr.
High quality chilled shot

U.S. Munitions Corp.

2425 Salashan Loop Rd.
Ferndale, WA 98248
(360) 366-4444
FAX: (360) 366-4445
Est.: 1990   Staff: 9
Contact: A.J. Gould
Loaded ammunition & reloading components

VIHTAVUORI OY

Vihtavuori

Kaltron-Pettibone
1241 Ellis St.
Bensenville, IL 60106
(800) 683-0464
(708) 350-1116
FAX: (708) 350-1606
Contact: Bob Trownsell
Kaltron-Pettibone, importers of Vihtavuori Oy shotgun powders: "Sporting Lite", N3SL, is ideal for 12 ga. 1 oz. and 1 1/8 oz. loads for clay shooters. Two other shotshell powders, N3SM and N3SH, are being introduced for medium and heavy loads for upland game and magnum field loads. All are available in 4 lb. plastic bottles. Load and bushing data is available from Kaltron-Pettibone, 1-800-683-0464.
See Our Ad Above & Pg. 49

W.T.W., Inc.

770 W. Hampden Ave., Suite 170
Englewood, CO 80110
(303) 781-6329
FAX: (303) 781-1386
Est.: 1979   Staff: 2
Owners: Dick Loveland and Bill Jackson
Available: Retail
Windjammer tournament wads, 12 ga. & 20 ga. only. Universal wads, 1 oz., 1 1/8 oz. & 1 1/4 oz. loads.

WINCHESTER.
A M M U N I T I O N

Winchester Ammunition

Olin Corporation
427 North Shamrock
East Alton, IL 62024
(618) 258-2000
Available: Retail
Primers, wads, "Ball Powder" smokeless propellants and shot.

SHOOTING SCHOOLS

Sharpen Your Skills

So you're a natural shooter, eh? Good technique is just sort of instinctive with you? Could be. But consider, if you will, the concert pianist who repeats scales for hours a day; the top-flight golf pro who practices the same shot, ball after ball after ball.

You get the point. No matter how good you are, there's always room for improvement. And this is just as true of hunting and clay shooting as it is of countless other disciplines. Fact is, every shooter, from enthusiastic beginner to seasoned veteran, can benefit from instruction and plenty of practice.

Add a Poly-Choke® anodized, ventilated rib to your over/under, pump, auto or single shot and get on your target easier, quicker. Less than two ounces, no drilling or tapping, front and mid sights, we install, all for $79.75 plus shipping.

Or choose the high-rise International style. Complete on plain barrel $190, or $95 for top rib on existing rib, plus shipping. For a free catalog, write Marble Arms™, Dept. WC, P.O. Box 111, Gladstone, MI 49837. Phone (906) 428-3710.

Fortunately, there is no shortage of professionally run schools, clinics and instructors that can help you hone your skills and break bad shooting habits. The trick is to find the instruction that meets your needs.

Start your search here.

You can start your search right here, with Wing & Clay's detailed listing of shooting schools and instructors. Before you choose, however, a few preliminaries are called for. First, determine the type of shooting that most interests you. Is it trap or skeet? Sporting clays? Upland or driven pheasant hunting? Consider, too, the shooting style you find most compatible: sustained lead, swing-through, pull-away or instinctive. Next, read ads and articles, and talk to other shooters. Now you can start to zero in. Write or call the shooting schools that appeal to you and ask for more information. Determine if you'll be in a small class with others of similar ability. And don't be shy about discussing costs. Does tuition cover meals and accommodations? Ammunition and clay birds? Are hearing protectors, recoil protectors and shooting glasses provided? Ask for references. Contact them. Finally, select a school that you can return to as your skills improve.

What will you learn?

What you will learn depends to a large degree on the length of the course. A two-hour clinic will differ— in style and content— from that of an intensive three-day shooting course. Many schools begin a session with gun-fitting, including pattern board testing. Most precede shooting with a lecture on gun handling and safety. A discussion of shooting concepts and theories is not uncommon. And the fun part— actual shooting— may take place on a skeet field or, in some instances, on a specially designed sporting clays course. You can expect instructors to critique your shooting stance and posture, mounting, swing and follow-through, mostly on the spot, sometimes while reviewing videotape playbacks. Be prepared to be critiqued and corrected. And be prepared to advance toward a new level of skill in your favorite sport!

• Proper gun fit is critical to shooting success. For more information, see Gunstocks & Gunfitting, page 170.

First and Finest
The Orvis Shooting Schools

When you make the decision to invest time and money in improving your shooting, plan to attend the oldest and finest shooting school in the country. Now entering our third decade, the Orvis Shooting Schools, under the direction of 15 year veteran Rick Rishell, use a modified American version of the famed Churchill method of instinctive shooting. This method is based on the combined elements of proper stance, concentration on the target, proper gun mounting, and the acquisition of a properly fitted shotgun. It's an ideal course of instruction for both field shooting and sporting clays.

Locations in Vermont, Florida and New York

•July - October — Two and three day programs in the Green Mountains, Manchester, Vermont, July and August in this 19th century resort town are filled with activities from golf and fine dining, to antiquing and hiking. From September through October, the foliage season and upland game season combine to offer an unparalleled experience for the wing shooter.

• November and December - 2-day sessions at private Mays Pond Plantation (near Tallahasee) in northern Florida's finest quail hunting country. Full and half day private lessons available.

• Year-round - One and two day sessions at Orvis Sandanona, located in Millbrook, New York, just 60 miles north of New York City.

Who Can Benefit

The Orvis Schools are designed to benefit beginners and veteran wing shooters.
•Easy, non-intimidating style
•Professional instructors with years of wing shooting experience.
•Group sizes limited for maximum personal attention.
•Women-only school in August.

The Course of Instruction

•Essential instruction on shotgun safety and etiquette.
•Selection of proper ammunition and patterning.
•Crossing shots, low incomers, high incomers, and pass shooting at our tower station, quail walk, and singles and doubles on the legendary Orvis course which was the precursor to sporting clays courses now showing up all over the country.

What's Included

Students receive comprehensive instruction and will fire hundreds of rounds with an instructor at their side. All clay birds and ammunition are included, as well as the use of an Orvis Custom Shotgun if desired, a complete custom gun fitting, use of hearing protectors, shooting glasses, and recoil pads, daily lunches and a copy of *The Orvis Wing Shooting Handbook.*

How to Register

To register for the Orvis Shooting Schools, or to receive information and a brochure call director Rick Rishell at **1-800-235-9763** or by FAX at **1-802-362-3525**.

SCHOOLS

For related information, see:
- Article, A Structured Approach to Shooting, Pg. 76
- Gunfitting, Pg. 170

Addieville East Farm

200 Pheasant Dr. Mapleville, RI 02839
(401) 568-3185
FAX: (401) 568-3009
Est.: 1979   Staff: 8
Contact: Geoff Gaebe
Instructors: Jack Mitchell/Russ Jette
Students/yr: 700+
School Location: 35 mi. south of Boston; 20 mi. north of Providence
Sessions: By appt./1-6 hrs.
Loaner Guns Available
Method Taught: Instinctive; Pass-through; Pull away
Shooting Taught: SC, WS
Brochure Available
World renowned British shooting coach Jack Mitchell teaches proven techniques modified to best suit each individual.

Arnold's Custom Shooting Sports

Custom Shooting Sports
6970 Somers-Gratis Rd.
Camden, OH 45311
(513) 787-3352
FAX:
Est.: 1984
Contact: Jim Arnold, NSCA Level III
School Location: Mad River Shooting School, Bellefontaine, Ohio and will travel to your club
Sessions: 1/2, full & multi-day
Group Size: Group and Private
Instruction Available
Method Taught: All Methods specific to students' needs
Shooting Taught: SC, WS, FITASC, TR, SK
Brochure Available
Jim Arnold has over 23 years of teaching experience and has been described by Sporting Clays Magazine as "one of the country's most polished and resourceful instructors." His students vary widely in experience from new shooters to competitive shooters including the 1996 Michigan State Champion, Dennis Fuller and the 1996 Illinois State Champion, Dr. Ralph Everson.

He also trains Level I & II instructors for the NSCA. His specialty is enhancing, not changing, your shooting style.
See Our Ad Pg. 206

L.L. Bean Shooting School

Casco St., Freeport, ME 04033
(800) 341-4341 Ext. 6666
(207) 865-4761
FAX: (207) 865-0766
Est.: 1990
Contact: Tom Ackerman
School Location: Durham Rod & Gun Club, Durham, Main
Sessions: 1 Day Courses available in Wingshooting and 5-Stand Sporting Clays
Loaner Guns Available
Shooting Taught: WS, SC
Brochure Available

Bender Shima Shooting Clinics

217 Linden Ave.
Oak Park, IL 60302
(800) 438-7340
FAX: (708) 386-6418
Est.: 1991
Contact: John Shima
Instructors: John Shima & Todd Bender
Students/Yr: 800
School Location: Entire U.S.
Group Size: Limited-5 students per instructor
Loaner Guns Available
Method Taught: All methods depending on student's needs
Shooting Taught: SC, SK, Int'l. Skeet
Brochure Available

Bill Yeatts Instinct Shooting Clinic

7066 Hardisty St.
Ft. Worth, TX 76118
(817) 589-2666
Est.: 1962
Contact: Bill Yeatts
Instructor: Bill Yeatts
Students/yr: 25
Sessions: 3 days
Student Rounds Fired: 75
Shooting Taught: WS
In his 35 years of teaching shotgunning skills, Bill Yeatts has successfully instructed over 4,500 individuals. Most of his students, after his 3-day course, will hit 90% of targets using only a 1/2 oz. load, fired from a .410 shotgun. Bill Yeatts will teach you one-on-one to ensure success! And he invites all of his students back for a refresher. . .free of charge.
See Our Ad, Left

"Your basis for success as a shotgunner is understanding..."

Instructor Patrick LaBoone

The Instructor

My name is Patrick LaBoone. I learned the instructor's trade at the side of Cornwall's master shotgunning coach, Jack Mitchell. It was with Mitchell's urging that I began instructing in 1987. While I consider myself a wing-shooting or downgun coach, I have taught effectively on a variety of shotgunning formats ... game shooting, sporting clays, live pigeon, trap, skeet, Olympic Trap and International Skeet. References available.

The Method

This method is based on the belief that your hands, body and eyes should move as simply and as naturally as possible ... as if there were no gun involved.

For want of another name, some of my shooters have been calling what I teach, The Method. Elegantly simple, and incredibly effective, The Method is not magic, even though many shooters have described it as such. Quickly learned, it works well for the vast majority of people.

You'll love the look and feel of shooting this way, and the success that comes with it. After all, this is the way you were born to shoot!

As a student, you'll leave The Midwest Shooting School with a solid foundation in an elegantly natural wing-shooting method. With experience, you can learn to apply it effectively to every shot you take, no matter what the distance, height, speed or angle. You'll leave with an understanding of some fundamental theories about what you should see, and how you should move a shotgun. Just as importantly, you'll understand the reasons why.

The Course

The course is at Clear Creek Outdoors, Inc., our hunting club. In a beautiful setting, it offers an incredible array of target presentations, with unmatched flexibility. There are appropriate targets here for the new shooter to learn on, as well as a myriad of targets for the world-class competitor. For a student of wingshooting or sporting clays, this may be the finest teaching venue in the country.

- Hourly Instruction or half day, single day and multiday schools are available.
- Patrick LaBoone instructs regularly at public clubs across the United States.

Call or write for schedules, price guide and information: 218-384-3670.

2550 Hwy 23
Wrenshall, MN 55797

Bull Run Shooting Center
7700 Bull Run Dr.
Centerville, VA 22020
(703) 569-9085
FAX: (703) 569-3696
Contact: Warren Jones
Instructors: 5 on Staff & Guest Instructors/Clinics
NSCA Certified Level I, II
Students/yr: 150+
Sessions: By Appt., Hrly, 1/2- 1 Day
Groups: 1-20 w/ multiple instructors
Method Taught: All
Shooting Taught: SC, SK, WS
Loaner Guns Available
Ammo & Accessories on Site
Handicap Access
Women & Beginners Very Welcome
Live Bird Hunts (Preserve) OFF SITE During Season
- 30 miles from Washington, D.C., just off of Rt. 66
- Excellent Location for Corporate Events!
- Women Shooters Welcome– Individuals or Groups
- On-Site Camping, Swimming Pool and Nature Trails
- Say You Saw Us in Wing & Clay for a Discount on lessons!

Broxton Bridge Plantation Shooting School
PO Box 97, Hwy. 601
Ehrhardt, SC 29081
(800) 437-4868
Contact: Jerry Varn, Jr. (7am-9pm)
School Location: 25 miles West I-95 (Walterboro Exit); 60 miles West of Charleston
Sessions: 1st Sat. of Every Month
Loaner Guns Available
Brochure Available

Buz Fawcett's Wingshooting Workshop
2090 S. Meridian Rd.
Meridian, ID 83642
(208) 888-3415
Est.: 1986
Contact: Buz or Barbara Fawcett
Instructor: Buz Fawcett
Students/yr: 100+
School Location: The Shooting Grounds, Sporting Clays course in Boise, Idaho
Sessions: M/T/W; Th/ F/S/3 days
Group Size: 1 or 2 only
School side-by-sides only available
Student Rounds Fired: Case +\-
Method Taught: Buz Fawcett's method of Instinctive shooting
Shooting Taught: SC, WS
Money Back Guarantee
Brochure Available - This past Associate Editor of Sports Afield, Editor of Guns & Ammo and military shooting instructor, brings to you 50 years of side-by-side experience, coupled with a unique way to succeed in shotgun shooting. What's more, it's guaranteed!

See Our Ad Across, Below

Casa de Campo Shooting Center
PO Box 140, La Romana
Dominican Republic
(809) 523-3333 Ext. 2145
Est.: 1988
Shooting Director: Michael W. Rose
Instructors: Hermogenes Guerrero
and 4 other instructors
Students/yr: 3,000
Sessions: Everyday/1-5 hrs
Group Size: 1 to 25
Loaner Guns Available
English Competition Shooting
Special Packages
Private Parties and Corporate Days
Also Live Pigeon Shooting Available

Neil Chadwick Shooting Clinics
206 Front St., Milford, PA 18337
(717) 296-2354
FAX: (717) 296-8639
Instructor: Neil Chadwick
School Location: Will travel to your club
Sessions: Hourly rates, group sessions, corporate days
Group Size: 1-6
Loaner Guns Available
Shooting Taught: SC, WS, FITASC

Deborah Cleverdon Shooting Clinic
15306 Bonita Springs
Houston, TX 77083
(713) 530-3754
FAX: (713) 530-0851
Est.: 1995
Instructor: Deb Cleverdon
Students/Yr: 100
School Location: Available to travel to your club by appt.
Sessions: Hourly, 1/2 day, full day
Group Size: 1-10
Loaner Guns Available
Method Taught: Instinctive
Shooting Taught: SC, WS
Handgun for personal protection
Brochure Available

Clove Valley Sports Corp.
Hidden Brook Farm
RR1, Box 110 A
Salt Point, NY 12578
(914) 266-5954
Est.: 1980   Staff: 4
Instructor: Charles Conger
Students/yr: 200
School Location: Several
Sessions: Hourly
Group Size: Individual
Loaner Guns Available
Method Taught: C.P.S.A.
Shooting Taught: SC, WS

See Our Ad Above, Right

Don't forget to say "I saw it in Black's Wing & Clay" when responding to advertisements.

Competitive Edge Shooting Schools
PO Box 293913
Lewisville, TX 75029-3913
(214) 914-8496
(800) 216-5776 (Dan-Pager)
(800) 381-5067 (Scott-Pager)
Est.: 1995
Instructors: Dan Carlisle and Scott Robertson
School Location: Available by appointment to travel to your club
Sessions: By appt.
Method Taught: Competitive Edge Method
See Our Ad Across, Right

Deep River Shooting School
3420 Cletus Hall Rd.
Sanford, NC 27330
(919) 774-7080
FAX: (919) 708-5052
Est.: 1989
Contact: Bill Kempffer
Instructors: 4 certified on staff
Location: 35 min. SW of Raleigh, NC
Sessions: Hourly by app't., Packages available; Group Size: 1 to 5;
Loaner Guns Available
Method Taught: All Methods
Shooting Taught: SC, WS
See Our Ad Below

Andy Duffy Shooting Clinics
10 Bartlett Dr.,Middletown, NY 10940
(914) 692-2868
Contact: Marty Famiglietti
School Location: Available to travel to your gun club
Sessions: By Appt.
Method Taught: Swing through, pull away, sustained
Shooting Taught: SC, WS, Specializing in FITASC
Holds 8 National Titles in both sporting clays and FITASC
See Our Ad Pg. 221

Dunn's Shooting School
Rt. 3, Box 39D4
Holly Springs, MS 38635
(800) 564-1396
Est.: 1993
Contact: Jim Cassidy
School Location: Dunn's Shooting Grounds
Sessions: Call for schedule
Loaner Guns Available
Shooting Taught: SC, WS
Brochure Available
Our expert and personal instruction can sharpen the skill of an experienced gunner or provide a perfect start for novices. The three day course of instruction includes classroom, 10 station sporting clays course, and gun fitting. Among the nationally recognized coaches at the shooting school are Gil Ash, Jerry Meyer and many others. Shooting schools run Fall, Winter and Spring. Nestled on 1,000 acres of beautiful, rolling countryside, Dunn's Shooting Grounds includes a 6,000 sq. ft. lodge and 8 bedroom motel. Airport pickup from nearby Memphis International Airport available. Call for information and latest schedule.

Shooting Taught Key:
SC:	Sporting Clays
WS:	Wingshooting
TR:	Trap
SK:	Skeet

Federal Wing & Clay Shooting School

Operated by Federal Cartridge Co.
900 Ehlen Dr.
Anoka, MN 55303
(800) 888-WING (9464)
Contact: Steve Schultz
Instructors: All instructors are NSCA Level II or Level III
Chief Instructor: Steve Schultz, NSCA Level III
Students/yr: Non-restrictive
School Location: Travels Nationwide; Also at specific locations (call for current listing)
Group Size: 6 students/instructor
Sessions: 3 day comprehensive school; one day clinics nationwide
Loaner Guns & Accessories Available
Student Rounds Fired: 200+ per day
Method Taught: All
Shooting Taught: All
Brochure Available
Ammunition Provided
See Our Ad Pg. 83

FIELDSPORT Shooting School

3313 W. South Airport Rd.
Traverse City, MI 49684
(616) 933-0767
FAX: (616) 933-0768
Est.: 1994
Contact: Bryan Bilinski
Instructor: Bryan Bilinski
School Location: Traverse City, MI
Sessions: 1/2 day to 2 days
Loaner Guns Available
Method Taught: Churchill/Instinctive
Shooting Taught: SC, WS
Brochure Available
Bryan is the founder of Sporting Clays in the U.S. while managing Orvis/Houston. Bryan is a qualified gunfitter and fitting agent for AYA and A.H. Fox shotguns.
See Our Ad Pg. 216

Friar Tuck Wing & Clay Shooting School

Friar Tuck Inn
4858 Rt. 32, Catskill, NY 12414
(800) 832-7600 Ext. 447
(518) 678-2271 Ext. 447
FAX: (518) 678-2214
Est.: 1994
Contact: Ross Caridi
Instructor: Mick Howells

- 96 US Open Champion
- 96 SCI Sporting Champion
- 94 World Sporting Clays Champion
School Location: One premise of hotel grounds
Sessions: Day time, year round
Group Size: 1 to 5
Loaner Guns Available
Method Taught: All methods
Shooting Taught: SC, WS, FITASC
Brochure Available
20 Stations, under cover 5-Stand, auto & manual traps, 500 room hotel on premises, clubhouse & pro shop.
See Our Ad Pg. 210

Grassy Lake Lodge
Gun & Hunt Club
PO Box 319, Wickliffe, KY 42087
(800) 526-0095
(502) 462-3595
FAX: (502) 334-3644
Contact: Greg Joles
Instructors: Jon Kruger, Pat Lieske, John Wooley
Location: In the heart of the Mississippi Flyway, Wickliffe, KY–30 miles from Paducah's commerical airport.
Group Size: 8-12
Shooting Taught: WS, SC
The first and only Orvis-Endorsed lodge specializing exclusively in waterfowl.
See Our Ad Pg. 225

Griffin & Howe

Griffin & Howe
36 W. 44th St., Suite 1011
New York, NY 10036
(212) 921-0980
Contact: Richard Welch
or
33 Claremont Rd.,
Bernardsville, NJ 07924
(908) 766-2287
Contact: Joe Prather
Instructors: Rex Gage, Paul Smith
School Locations: New York and New Jersey, each 1 hour from NYC
Students/yr: 450
Sessions: Year round, Hourly, 1/2 day, full day
Individual Hourly Instruction
Method Taught: Instinctive
Gun Fitting: with Over & Under and Side-by-Side Try-Guns
Loaner Guns Available
Shooting Taught: SC, WS, TR, SK
In operation since 1936, when Griffin & Howe was part of the former Abercrombie & Fitch Co. The school originally operated in cooperation with Boss & Co. and later Holland & Holland. Rex Gage, the lead instructor is complemented by Paul Smith, who has completed succcessfully in Sporting Clay and FITASC events in his home country of England.Stocking, stock bending and alteration are available from our own workrooms. Whether you are new to shooting, or an experience shooter, give us a call to book lessons (908) 766-2287.
See Our Ad Pg. 77

Grinders Switch Club
1608 Chickering Rd.
Nashville, TN 37215
(615) 729-9732
Contact: Barry Claud
Location: 50 mi. W. of Nashville
Sessions: Individual & Group
Group Size: 1-3
Loaner Guns Available
Shooting Taught: SC, WS & FITASC
Brochure Available
John Wooley, is one of the world's leading wingshooting and sporting clays instructors. John is available at Grinders Switch and also to host clinics at your facility.

Gunsite Training Center
PO Box 700, Paulden, AZ 86334
(800) 504-7571
Contact: Richard Jee
Firearms and other training courses. Specialized firearms and accessories offered by the Gunsite custom shop, including the Accuracy International rifle. Varied related merchandise offered through our pro shop.

Jo Hanley
Shooting Instruction
3208 N. Flagler Dr.
West Palm Beach, FL 33407
(407) 881-8323 (Oct. thru May)
(412) 238-4901 (June thru Sept.)
FAX: (407) 844-1997
Instructor: Jo Hanley
Sessions: Private Individual Lessons; Corporate-Group Clinics Available
Method Taught: All
Shooting Taught: SC, WS, TR, SK
NSCA All American and Level III Instructor

Jon Kruger: World Champion Turns Shooting Instructor

The key to success is eliminating the "frustration factor"

Kruger, left, helping a student "simplify the game".

Photo: L. Ré

"What sets Jon Kruger apart from the rest of the top sporting clays shooters," said one of his fiercest competitors on the tournament circuit, "is that he's so consistent. He never has a really bad day. And he *NEVER* seems to get frustrated!"

I spoke to Jon about it later. "It's not true that I don't have bad days," he said with a smile. "Everyone who shoots does. But it is true that I don't get frustrated. Frustration is self-defeating, and only feeds on itself to make things even more difficult. Beyond technique and visualization and everything else, it's the key point I try to teach to all of the shooters I instruct. Don't beat yourself by getting frustrated!"

Jon Kruger's name has become almost synonymous with sporting clays in America since he started in the game back in 1987. His list of titles would fill half this page. But, unbeknownst to many, equally important to him has been the success he's had instructing both new and experienced Sporting shooters.

KISS: Keep It Simple Shooter

"My objective," says Jon, "is to simplify the game of shooting. Everybody seems to make the game harder than it really is. My objective is to teach the student what to think about before attempting any target. When they understand both the physical AND mental mechanics of the process, it takes the frustration out of any target presentation."

Too many American shooters have an inherent disdain for instruction, and psychologists would have a field day ferreting out the reasons. But the fact of the matter is instruction makes common sense. Like any sport that requires physical dexterity (shooting a shotgun at a clay target is the classic example of hand/eye coordination; no other game requires that you coordi-

nate three moving objects to be successful: target, gun, shot charge), it takes input from someone who's been through the long learning process to make logical and practical sense out of it. If you were to take up any other sport (golf, tennis, etc.) you'd go to an instructor or coach to help you get off the ground. Maybe not the minute you pick up the racket or club for the first time, but soon after you've lost a couple dozen golf balls, or have chased down a wheelbarrow full of tennis balls sprayed all over adjacent courts. Shooting should be no different because improvement, and satisfaction, accelerate when you learn the "right" things you're doing as well as the "wrong".

Asking the wrong question

"In most cases," says Jon, "shooters only want to know why they've missed a target, never why they've hit one. Until they understand the necessity of that part of the game, they can only progress so far. It's when you know why you've broken a clay that you begin to generate the memory, both physical and mental, that allows you to repeat the same thing over and over again."

Kruger's instruction process starts off on a patterning board or plate in order to determine gun fit. If necessary, minor adjustments to the gun can be made. (Major changes are another story, and he's wise enough to know you don't achieve anything but frustration--there's that word again--if the shooter's gun doesn't point where he looks.)

The next step is the actual shooting at

clays. If you're at his training center in Iowa, it'll initially be on the 5-Stand field equipped with American made traps from Parker-Boss, one of several of Jon's major industry sponsors.You'll start off with basic singles so Jon can get a feel for your ability and temperament. And so you can ease into the comfortable, relaxed atmosphere that his typically Midwest, laid-back personality generates. Being relaxed is important. Few people learn well if they're confronted with an instructor (in any sport except maybe aerobics), who's hyper or artificially over enthusiastic. And, generally, an instructor that isn't too full of his own ego can better analyze and deal differently with each personality depending on their wants and needs.

Personal attention

There's not enough space here to describe Jon's entire instructional process. Justice couldn't be done to it, because it's such a uniquely personal experience. Suffice it to say that it includes all manner of target presentations. (The Iowa facility can provide everything from floppy pairs in your face to long going-away or crossing birds off a 100 foot tower. At other gun clubs around the country where he does clinics, target presentations are carefully selected or specifically set-up to be equally suitable.) And the level of instruction and shooting method taught have been fine-tuned by experience to accommodate the rank novice all the way up to the advanced shooter looking for those few extra targets that mean the difference between High Overall and also-ran in tournament competition. For example, Jon focuses on his own, obviously successful method with novices. For the more advanced shooter, on the other hand, he offers alternative methods for any specific target; something you can keep in reserve if circumstances demand a change from your normal technique.

To illustrate the importance of that final point, California's Medardo Canales invested in a couple of days with Jon in 1990, and another in '93. One week later, Medardo shot the very first 100 straight registered Sporting Score in the United States.

There's more. . . . .

In addition to instruction, Jon has also built a national reputation for course design. Everywhere you go around the country, you'll see clubs unabashedly proclaim their successful layout as a "Jon Kruger Signature Course". He also performs exhibitions for charities and special events--something you almost never hear about in the black and white, "who won what" world of Sporting.

As Jon freely admits, much of what he continues to accomplish in sporting clays wouldn't be possible without the support of the best companies in the industry. *Krieghoff, Remington, Parker-Boss, Kolar, Ballistic Specialties, ESP and Lube Shot* (guns, cartridges, traps, small-gauge tubes, chokes, ear protection and lubricants, respectively) would be expected to support a winner. But they also support the person. And that alone says all you need to know about the "quality" on both sides of the equation.

"Jon helps you truly understand all the simple things one normally takes for granted," said Canales. "Focus and mindset for any type of competitor are the biggest hurdles they must overcome."

Eliminating the "frustration factor" is a major step in learning how to shoot sporting clays well. And who better to teach you the process than the most successful Sporting shooter in the U.S.? A full day of private instruction, which includes targets, costs $400. Group instruction (five shooters maximum so everyone gets ample personal attention) is $175 per person for a 4 1/2 hour session. Scheduling can be arranged at the Iowa training center, or at any number of clubs around the country. **[For more information, simply call Jon Kruger at 515-736-4893.]**

Holland & Holland Sporting Weapons Limited
50 East 57th St.
New York, NY 10022
(212) 752-7755
FAX: (212) 752-6805

HOMESTEAD.
1766
The Homestead Shooting School
Box 2000, Hot Springs, VA 24445
(540) 839-7787
Contact: David Judah, Club Mgr.
Instructors: 5 Certified NSCA Instructors on staff
School Location: The Homestead, Hot Springs, VA
Sessions: Hourly, 1/2 day or full day clinics
Loaner Guns Available
Shooting Taught: SC, TR, SK
Shooting packages available (2 and 3 day) which include accommodations, shells, targets and instruction. Packages can be arranged to suit individual preferences. Please call for details.
See Our Ad Pg. 220

Hunter's Creek
Club Shooting School
675 Sutton Rd.
Metamora, MI 48455
(810) 664-4307
Contact: Charlie Mann
Chief Instructor: Pat Lieske
School Location: Hunter's Creek Club, Michigan
Sessions: Group & Private Lessons
Beginners to Advanced Level
Stock fittings & Corporate Shooting Days Available
See Our Ad, Right

Instructional Shooting Associates, Ltd.
PO Box 764, Bethel Park, PA 15102
(412) 835-5749
Est.: 1989
Master Instructor: Connie L. Fournier (SCA & NSCA Certified)
15 Certified Staff Instructors
School Location: At facilities across the country
Group Size: 1-5
Sessions: By Appt.
Loaner Guns Available
Method Taught: All Methods
Shooting Taught: SC, WS, TR, SK, Int'l. TR & SK, FITASC, Personal Protection
Brochure Available

READY ON THE FIRING LINE

Instructional Shooting, Inc.
164 Andover St.
Lowell, MA 01852
(800) 984-GUNS (Mass only)
(508) 452-8450
Est.: 1989   Staff: 6
Contact: Greg A. Danas
Instructors: Greg, George, Peter Danas, NSSA, NSCA Cert.
Students/Yr: 1,000+
School Location: 27 mi. N/NW of Boston
Group Size: Max. 24 students/class
Sessions: Regularly scheduled classes, by app't., also year 'round
Loaner Guns Available

Shooting Taught: Basic, Combat and Advanced Handgun/Shotgun
Cert. 14 courses, 4 Colleges/Universities, Skeet, Trap
Method Taught: All methods per student need
Brochure Available
Massachusetts' full-time, privately owned shooting school. Courses taught to law enforcement, general public, and through four colleges/universities in Eastern Mass. Law enforcement instructors constantly training at advanced academies throughout the U.S. Classroom and individual instruction. NRA affiliated club. In association with A.G. Guns and Ammo, Inc., fully stocked Trap and Skeet supplies, over 500 firearms in stock.

Jon Kruger

Box 213, St. Ansgar, IA 50472
(515) 736-4893
Instructor: Jon Kruger
Students/yr: 200
School Location: Kruger's Clay
World, St. Ansgar, Iowa; available
to travel to your club or facility.
Sessions: Hourly; 1/2 day; full day
Group Size: 1 to 5
Loaner Guns Available
Student Rounds Fired: Varies
Shooting Taught: SC, WS, TR
See Our Ad Pgs. 211-212

Shooting Taught **Key:**
SC: Sporting Clays
WS: Wingshooting
TR: Trap
SK: Skeet

At Callaway Gardens

Llewellin's Point Shooting School

at Callaway Gardens
4897 Salem Rd.
Pine Mountain, GA 31822
(800) 636-9819
Contact: Floyd Clements
Instructors: Floyd Clements, Ernie
Wilkins
Guest Instructors: Andy Duffy, Jerry
Meyer
School Location: Callaway Gardens
Sessions: Hourly; 1/2 day or full
day; 2 or 4 day clinics
Group Size: 1-6
Loaner Guns Available
Method Taught: All Methods
Shooting Taught: SC, WS, TR, SK
Brochure Available
Corporate Clinics can be arranged.

Mad River Sportsman's Club Shooting School

1055 County Rd. 25
Bellefontaine, OH 43311
(513) 593-8245
FAX: (513) 592-5625
Est.: 1991
Contact: Tony Stratton, Mgr. (8-5)
Club Pro & Instructor: Jim Arnold,
NSCA Level III
Students/yr: 300+
School Location: Mad River
Sportsman's Club, Ohio (45 miles
NW of Columbus)
Sessions: 1, 2 & 3 Day Clinics
Loaner Guns Available
Shooting Taught: SC,WS,TR,SK
Brochure Available
Wingshooting Instruction;
Corporate Entertainment
See Our Ad Below, Left

Middleditch Shooting School

1930 Wynfield Point Dr.
Buford, GA 30519
(770) 963-5414
Instructor: Steve Middleditch
School Location: Wolf Creek Sport
Shooting, Atlanta, GA and available
to travel to your club.
Sessions: Hrly, 1/2 day, full , 3 day
Group Size: 1-4
Loaner Guns Available
Method Taught: The Natural Way
Shooting Taught: SC, WS, FITASC,
TR, SK
Brochure Available
See Our Ad Across, Right

The Midwest Shooting School
2550 Hwy. 23,
Wrenshall, MN 55797
(218) 384-3670
Est.: 1988

Contact: Patrick LaBoone
Instructor: Patrick LaBoone
Students/yr: 200
School Location: 6.5 miles south of Duluth, MN at Clear Creek Outdoors, Inc. Also available to travel to your club or facility.
Sessions: 10/year/1/2 to 3 days
Group Size: 1 to 6
Loaner Guns Available
Student Rounds Fired: Varies
Method Taught: English- Mitchell
Shooting Taught: SC, WS
Brochure Available
See Our Ad Pg. 205

Millbrook Shooting School & Preserve Ltd.
RR1, Box 193A, Millbrook, NY 12545
(914) 677-5756   Est.: 1993
Contact: Margaret Schneible
Instructor: Charles Schneible
Location: 70 mi. North of NYC
Sessions: Anytime by appt/ hourly, 1/2 day, 2 day schools
Group Size: 1 to 20
Loaner Guns Available
Student Rounds Fired: 75-100/hr
Method Taught: The best method for the target & student
Shooting Taught: SC, WS, FITASC
Brochure Available

Dan Moseley Recreational Shooting Sports Service
16115 Alta Mesa Dr.
Houston, TX 77083-1105
(713) 530-1620   Est.: 1970
Instructors: Dan & Glynne Moseley
Location: Houston or your club
Group Size: 1 to 20
Loaner Guns Available
Method Taught: "Instinctive" Relaxed Method
Shooting Taught: SC, WS
Brochure Available
Level III & Level II Certifications held by USSCA, SCA, WSSF, FITASC & NRA. Assistance in the setup and management of shooting events. Gunfitting and custom gunsmithing.

Michael Murphy & Sons
6400 S.W. Hunter Rd.
Augusta, KS 67010
(800) 843-4513 (Order Line)
(316) 775-2137
FAX: (316) 775-1635
Chief Instructor: Michael Murphy
Instructors: Daryl Banmister; Gary Phillips
Students/yr: 400
Location: 15 miles E. of Wichita
Sessions: Formal 2 day schools; 12x/year; 4 students max. per instructor. Private lessons by appt. Summer classes at The Broadmoor, CO & The Homestead, VA; Winter classes,Palm Springs, CA & Orlando, FL
Loaner Guns Available
Method Taught: Swing through & pull away
Shooting Taught: SC, WS
Brochure Available
Stock Fitting Available
See Our Across & Pg. 219

World-Class, Complete Shooting Establishment in the Heartland

by Michael Pearce

Most American shooters equate a trip to a world-class shooting establishment with a lengthy journey to England, or maybe Italy. But such a long quest for excellence isn't necessary.

There is a special place in our heartland, just off a tree-shrouded country road not far from friendly little Augusta, Kansas where those who love all the aspects of fine gunning can find all they could ever hope for at one location. Once you drive past the simple sign that says "Michael Murphy & Sons," you enter what many think is the most complete shotgunning service in the nation, maybe the world.

A true full service shop, Michael Murphy & Sons offers a large selection of fine firearms.

Quality Gun Lover's Heaven

The short driveway leads you directly to a relatively plain building of native stone that houses a quality gun lover's heaven. Past the waiting room, in a long, well-lighted vault, lies a selection that must be seen to be believed, where gun after glorious gun neatly line the walls and shelves. Word has it some have tried to count the selection only to have their tallying stopped when their eyes fall upon a fine piece that's just waiting to be handled. Murphy estimates the number of firearms on hand to be "several hundred." Asked to value the inventory, he just slowly shakes his head and says, "I'm not sure I want to know."

Scanning the selection shows shotguns of all actions and quality—from new three-digit semi-autos all the way up to $50,000 vintage arms that have collectors checking in on a regular basis. But a simple study of the guns in stock shows that Michael Murphy & Sons caters largely to serious shooters who demand maximum performance from fine shotguns.

One of their top distributors in the nation, Murphy carries a great selection of upper-end Berettas, ranging from popular 682s up through the legendary SO grades. Fine Krieghoffs are readily available as is a full selection of classy Browning sporting clays guns. Dedicated wingshooters will find a vast variety of quality upland guns.

Clients needn't worry that the vast assortment of fine shotguns could get them confused. Michael Murphy and his small staff pride themselves in being able to help a gunner find the gun that fits their particular need. A man whose love of guns lead him away from a more lucrative business career to his country shop, Michael Murphy is a walking, talking encyclopedia of fine gun knowledge. As one family friend noted, "Hey, when Murphy starts talking shotguns even his teen-agers listen."

Full Range of Services

But selecting and buying a gun is just the first step in the full range of services offered at the estate. One of the most sought after stock-fitters in the world, Murphy's expertise has gained him exposure in publications from *The Wall Street Journal* and *The Robb Report* on down. A considerable percentage of his clients opt to have their just purchased gun custom-fitted and altered on the premises, something that currently can't be done at any other U.S. facility.

A veteran of over 4,000 custom fittings, Murphy has all but perfected the process of tailoring a stock to fit a shooter's

Murphy works with a student.

unique dimensions and needs. For beginners he'll start with lessons on gun mount and stance. For more experienced shooters he'll go right to work on such variables as cast, length of pull, drop and pitch.

Murphy's Fit

Though he once relied heavily on adjustable tryguns that helped take him to national prominence, Murphy now mainly just utilizes the adjustable guns for those ordering a new gun with a custom-fitted stock. For most clients, however, he prefers to work directly with the shotgun the client requests to have fitted.

Murphy uses an assortment of shims, pads, tape, tools and a broad sampling of spare stocks and a good mixture of knowledge, to gradually come up with an arrangement that has the shooter putting pattern after pattern right where he or she is looking. Some minor fitting adjustments can be made on the spot. Should the stock require more detailed alterations, that, too, can be done on the grounds.

Above Murphy's gun shop visitors will find master stock maker Jim Greenwood on hand. Gunners can leave an existing stock for a hot oil bend or have it trimmed to perfection. Or, they can pick a beautiful piece of wood and have Greenwood sculpt it to their specific needs.

See How It Works

At Murphy's complex, you don't have to wait till you get home to see how it works. Once a new gun is purchased or altered, shooters are within easy walking distance of four clay target games.

Those who simply want a little test of their gun and gunning can step up to a double-wobble set-up across from the shop. Not far away shooters can enjoy a fine five-stand sporting clays arrangement. Those with more time, can take advantage of the establishment's traditional sporting clays course.

Guests who want to try a unique challenge can try a trip through Murphy's "quail walk", which greatly simulates the kind of bobwhite hunting the area is noted for. True hunters and target shooters who relish the challenge of unannounced flushes and unknown angles will love the game. Traditional clay target shooters who are use to regimented circumstances may well have a very different opinion.

Master Instruction—One-on-one

But for those who desire to improve their clay target shooting, lessons, too, can be arranged. Michael Murphy, a master shotgunning instructor, has helped everyone from rank amateurs through Olympic caliber shooters. His amiable personality allows him to ease students through private lessons. And his experience with gun fitting helps students better understand their need for specialized equipment.

One student commented: "It seemed like we were just a couple of friends out having a ball, but when it was over I'd shot a better score than I'd ever dreamed!"

Schools & Clinics

Michael Murphy & Sons also offers a number of limited-entry one- and two-day shooting schools which are perfect for new or experienced shooters. Co-taught by legendary National and World sporting clays champion Gary Phillips, the shooting schools feature a laid-back atmosphere, plenty of personal attention from the professionals and hundreds of rounds of shooting at one of the finest sporting clays courses in the region.

Those who can't make it to one of the Kansas schools will be glad to know that Murphy and Phillips take their lessons on the road, with schools taught in California and Florida during the winter months.

For more information on the many services offered, contact Michael Murphy & Sons, 6400 SW Hunter Road, Augusta, KS 67010; (316) 775-2137 (phone) or (316) 775-1635 (fax).

NSCA Instructors School

5931 Roft Rd.
San Antonio, TX 78253
(210) 688-3371, Ext. 123
FAX: (210) 688-3014
Chief Instructor: Peter Crabtree
Students/yr: 150
School Location: All over the U.S. by appt. at your club. Call for application forms.
Group Size: 6
Sessions: 2-3 times per month at different locations
Shooting Taught: SC, SK
Flyer Available
NSCA Instructors School certifies 3 levels of instructors: Level I, II, III.

NSCA Shooting School

5931 Roft Rd.
San Antonio, TX 78253
(210) 688-3769
Est.: 1992   Staff: 3
Chief Instructor: Peter Crabtree
Phone (210) 688-3371, Ext. 123
School Location: National Gun Club
Sessions: By appointment-Lessons, Clinics, Corporate
Method Taught: NSCA Shooting
Shooting Taught: SC
Flyer Available

National Shooting School

Operated by Outdoor Management Network
4607 NE Cedar Creek Rd.
Woodland, WA 98674
(360) 225-5000
FAX: (360) 225-7616
Contact: Bob Knopf
Chief Instructor: Steve Schultz, NSCA Level III
Instructors: All NSCA Certified
Students/yr: Unlimited
School Location: Travels Nationwide
Scheduled Schools Nationwide (call/write for current listing)
Sessions: Half day, one day and multiple day clinics & schools
Group Size: 6 students/instructor
Loaner Guns & All Equipment Items Available
Student Rounds Fired: Variable
Method Taught: All
Shooting Taught: All

Northwest Wing & Clay Shooting School

An Affiliate of National Shooting School, Inc.
Operated by Outdoor Management Network
4607 NE Cedar Creek Rd.
Woodland, WA 98674

(360) 225-5000
FAX: (360) 225-7616
Contact: Bob Knopf
Instructors: All NSCA Certified
Chief Instructor: Bob Knopf
Students/yr: Unlimited
School Location: Travels Across Northwest (call to schedule school)
Sessions: Half day, one day & multiple day clnics & schools
Group Size: 4-6 students/instructor
Loaner Guns & All Accessories Available
Student Rounds Fired: Variable
Method Taught: All
Shooting Taught: All
Brochure Available

OSP/Optimum Shotgun Performance Shooting School

15020 Cutten Rd.
Houston, TX 77070
(713) 897-0800
FAX: (713) 469-2450
Est.: 1994
Contact: Gil Ash
Instructors: Jerry Meyer, Gil Ash and Vicky Ash
School Location: All major gun clubs throughout the U.S.
Sessions: 2 1/2 days

Group Size: 4-6
Loaner Guns Available
Method Taught: Instinctive
Shooting Taught: SC, WS, SK
Brochure Available

On Target
19702 Larkridge,
Yorba Linda, CA 92886
(714) 970-8072
Est.: 1986
Contact/ Instructor: Jay Braccini
Students/yr: 100
School Location: Raahaughes Shoot-
ing Grounds, 5800 Bluff St.,
Corona, CA
Sessions: By hour/up to 2 days
Loaner Guns Available
Rounds Fired: 1 case/day
Method: "Dan Carlisle" Method
Shooting Taught: SC, WS, TR, SK
Flyer Available

**Orlando World
Shooting Center
Wingshooting School**
Box 721412, Orlando, FL 32872
(407) 240-9444 (Blackjack)
FAX: (407) 240-5103
(800) 742-7053 (Remington Shoot-
ing School)
General Mgr: Steven A. Smith
Chief Instructor: Steve Middledtich

Touring Instructors: Gil Ash, Marty
Fischer, Dan Carlisle, Andy Duffy
Novice Instruction by: Steve Smith
& Virgil & Carol Minshew
Students/yr: 500
School Location: Blackjack Sporting
Clays, Orlando, FL
Sessions: By Appt. Group Size: 1-6
Loaner Guns Available
Method Taught: Sustained Lead,
Swing Through, Pull-Away, Positive
Shooting Method
Special Services: Gunsmith & stock
fit; Remington & Beretta loaner guns
Southern home of The Remington
Shooting School
See Ad In FL Clays Section

**Orvis Shooting
Schools**
Historic Rt. 7A,
Manchester, VT 05254
(800) 548-9548   Est.: 1973
Contact: Rick Rishell, Director
Students/yr: 350-400
School Location & Sessions:
Manchester, VT–Mid- July through
Mid-October; Mays Pond Planta-
tion, Monticello, FL–Nov./Dec; Orvis
Sandanona, Millbrook, NY- Yr.- round
Group Size: 4 to 16
Loaner Guns Available
Student Rounds Fired: 500 Average
Method Taught: Instinctive
Shooting Taught: SC, WS
Brochure Available
See Our Ad Pg. 203

SHOOTING SCHOOL

**Pawling Mountain Club
Shooting School**
PO Box 573
Pawling, NY 12564
(914) 855-3825
Contact: Keith Lupton
Instructor: Keith Lupton
Students/yr: 1,000
School Location: Pawling, NY and
other locations by request
Sessions: By appt., hourly, 1/2 day
and full day
Group Size: 1 to 5
Loaner Guns Available
Method Taught: English style
Shooting Taught: SC, WS, FITASC
Brochure Available
Keith Lupton has 15 years
experience teaching & coaching in
the U.K. and the U.S.A., offering ex-
pert gunfitting with the use of "Try
Guns" in both side by side and over
and under.
See Our Ad Pg. 223

**Gary Phillips
Shooting Instruction**
1210 Shallcross Ave.
Wilmington, DE 19806
(302) 655-7113
Est.: 1985

Instructor: Gary Phillips
Students/yr: 250+
School Location: Available to travel to clubs across U.S.; Group Size: 1-5
Sessions: 2 hours, 1/2 day; full days
Loaner Guns Available
Method Taught: All Methods Used
Shooting Taught: SC; WS; FITASC; SK & TR available upon request
Brochure Available

The Remington Shooting School

Remington Arms Company, Inc.
14 Hoefler Ave., Ilion, NY 13357
(800) 742-7053
(315) 896-3574
FAX: (315) 895-3665
Contact: Barbara Kerr
Director: Dale Christie
School Location: Ilion Fish & Game Club, NY, May - Oct.; Orlando, FL, Oct. - April
Sessions: 2 1/2 Days, twice weekly
Loaner Guns Available
Method Taught: Most
Shooting Taught: SC, WS, TR, SK
Brochure Available
See Our Ad Pg. 79

River Road Sporting Clays

32562 River Rd.
PO Box 3016
Gonzales, CA 93926
(408) 675-2473
FAX: (408) 675-3495
Contact: Bruce Barsotti
Instructors: 8 Certified NSCA Level I & II instructors on staff
Students/yr: 200+
School Location: River Road Sporting Clays
Sessions: By appointment
Group Size: Individual or Group
Loaner Guns Available in all gauges
Rounds Fired: Varies
Method Taught: All Methods
Shooting Taught: SC, WS, FITASC
Also available: Gunfitting, stock bending, gunsmithing and custom gun building by Dale Tate, formally of James Purdey & Son, London, England. We have a wide range of shooting available: Sporting Clays (40 stations), 5-Stand, Duck Tower (10 stations), FITASC, Trap, & Skeet (American & International). Modern guest-rooms; fishing ponds.

Royal Berkshire Shooting School at Timberdoodle

The Timberdoodle Shooting Club
One Webster Hwy.
Temple, NH 03084
(603) 654-9510
Est.: 1967
Contact: Randall Martin
Instructors: George Digweed/Robert Cross
Location: U.S., 1 hr. N of Boston; U.K., 3/4 hr. W of London Loaner Guns Available
Method: Stanbury
Shooting Taught: SC, WS
See Our Ad Below, Left

SCA Shooting School

9 Mott Ave.
Norwalk, CT 06850
(203) 831-8483
FAX: (203) 831-8497
Contact: Gil Faircloth, Chief Certifying Instructor at (419) 994-4592
SCA is now offering a 3-day school in shooting methods and styles: Sporting Clays, Wingshooting, S.C.I. and International 5-Stand.
School Location: Available to travel to your location. Classes established by appointment with Gil Faircloth (419) 994-4592
Method Taught: Swing through, Pull away, Sustained lead, Spot and Instinctive
Course of Instruction: Safety, gun fit and the method you need to get those targets that have eluded your gun. Also offer help on the proper ammunition and the gun that best suits your needs.
Cost for three day session: $750.
See Our Ad Pg. 224

GUN FIT
A Sure Way To Improve Your Shooting

by Hans Boye Boyesen

It is a simple analogy. When you prepare to drive a car, there are adjustments that enhance your ability to drive...the mirror, the seat, and the steering wheel must fit your personal needs. So is the case in shotgunning.

Keith Lupton, chief instructor of the Pawling Mountain Shooting School in Pawling, New York, is the country's foremost expert in the field of gun fitting.

"It is a proven fact, that proper gunfit definitely improves the ability of the shooter," states the British born Lupton. "Our system of assisting the shotgunner is a basic one." Keith begins by observing the person shooting. The next step takes place at the *Pattern Board*. This allows the shooter to see the shot pattern after mounting and shooting the gun at a stationery target. An evaluation of where the gun shoots (i.e., left and low) is then made.

Enter now, the "TRY GUN", a specially engineered shotgun which is fully adjustable to the shooters anatomy. Arm length, neck height and facial structure all come into play. Once the gun is adjusted to fit at the pattern board, the shooter will then graduate to the excersise of moving

targets thrown in a variety of angles and speeds replicating realistic shooting situations. Careful observation by Keith will then facilitate the *fine adjustments* which will result in a perfect match between the shooter and the shotgun.

Keith showing a client the left target depicting poor gun fit.(insufficient cast-off) Right target indicates corrected fit with the try gun.

The Pawling Mountain Shooting School offers expert gunsmithing services for correcting gunfit.

With the increasing popularity of shotgunning, more shooters are finding gunfit essential to improve both target and wingshooting skills.

The Pawling Mountain Shooting School welcomes both individuals and groups for gunfit and instruction. Keith is also available for corporate clinics and off-premises instruction.

For further information call **914 855-3825**

PAWLING MOUNTAIN CLUB
SHOOTING SCHOOL

P.O.Box 573 Pawling, NY 12564
Gary Hall- General Manager

SCA Instructors Course

9 Mott Ave., Norwalk, CT 06850
(203) 831-8483
FAX: (203) 831-8497
Contact: Gil Faircloth, Chief Certifying Instructor (419) 994-4592
SCA has established this 3 day Instructor's Course to teach you how to instruct. This is not a course to teach you how to shoot, however, your shooting will improve as a result of taking this course.
School Location: Available to travel to your club
Group Size: Minimum of 5 students
Method Taught: All methods taught
Level 1 Instructor's Course = $400
Level 2 Instructor's Course = $400
Master Level Instructor's Course - $400

Sea Island Shooting School

PO Box 30351
Sea Island, GA 31561
(800) SEA-ISLA nd (732-4752)
(912) 638-5839
FAX: (912) 638-5163
Est.: 1945
Contact: Justin Jones
Skeet and five-stand sporting and introductory sporting clay layout.

"Shoot Where You Look"

Exemplary Instruction
408 Fair St.
Livingston, TX 77351
(800) 201-5535
(713) 457-1250
FAX: (713) 457-1255
Contact: Leon Measures
Want to learn to shoot a shot-gun...like an expert? Want to teach your kid how to hit those fascinating targets? Leon Measures has designed a comprehenisve self-help instructional program and kit, complete with: An adult-size BB gun (without sights), 1500 BB's, "The Shoot Where You Look" book, a one hr., 20 min. training video, two pairs of safety glasses, and a shoulder patch. For only $165, we'll UPS ship these items in a convenient shipping/carrying case anywhere in the continental U.S. This will be the best $165 you ever spent...to teach or improve your shotgunning skills! Call today!

Shooting Sports Unlimited

1500 Oliver Rd., #K
Suite 231
Fairfield, CA 94533
(800) 731-7277
FAX: (707) 255-5095
Est.: 1990
Contact: Dennis Rapp
Instructor: Dennis Rapp
Students/yr: 125
School Location: Northern California; Also available to travel to your location.
Sessions: By appointment
Group Size: 1-4
Method Taught: Instinctive/ Wingshooting
Shooting Taught: SC, WS
For six years my mentor Jack Mitchell, World Renowned Shooting Instructor has been teaching me the finer points of shooting instruction. With this knowledge and the NSCA Level I, II & III Certification behind me, I can provide you with the skills necessary to become a better shooter.

SKAT Shooting School

PO Box 137
New Ipswich, NH 03071
(603) 878-1257
Est.: 1988
Contact:
Cynthia Haigh
Instructors:
Tony Haigh &
Cynthia Haigh
Students/Yr: 1,000
Group Size: 1-20
Sessions: By Appointment
Loaner Guns Available
Method Taught: Modified Churchill
Shooting Taught: SC, WS, TR, SK
Brochure Available

Opta Praestarae

Victory Shooting School

PO Box 7148
Columbia, MO 65205
(573) 442-9189
Est.: 1990
Contact: Mark Brownlee
Instructor: Mark Brownlee
School Location: Columbia, MO;
and other locations
Sessions: Hourly & 1-5 days by
appt./individualized
Group Size: 1-6
Method Taught: Instinctive, CPSA,
Maintained
Shooting Taught: SC, WS, SK
Brochure Available
Certified: SCA Master, NSCA, NRA
Two time All American Team. Sport
Psychology/Human Performance
consultant providing professional
guidance in physical, visual and psy-
chological shooting skills
development. Victory Shooting
School provides a truly unique learning experience by offering a total
commitment to teaching excellence
combined with knowledge from
eastern and western sport sciences
to maximize your success and enjoyment.
- Instruction for beginning, intermediate and advanced individuals.
- Ladies and youth schools.
- Complete coaching for the competitor.
- Advanced mental skills training
seminars.
Victory Shooting School is your
guide to a new enhanced level of
thought and performance. Choose
to excel and begin to realize your in-
finite potential.

Westervelt Turkey School
PO Box 2362
Tuscaloosa, AL 35403
(205) 373-8212
Est.: 1977
Website:
http://www.westervelt.com
Instructor: Tom Kelly
Sessions: Once in Spring/3 days
Group Size: 1 to 20
Shooting Taught: WS
Brochure Available

White Oak Farm Turkey School
2098 Hwy. 36 W.,
Jackson, GA 30233
(800) 666-2619
(770) 775-2619
Est.: 1983
Contact: Bob Boan
Students/yr: 25
Sessions: Once a year/3 days
Location: White Oak Farm, GA
Group Size: 1 to 3
Loaner Guns Available
Shooting Taught: WS
Brochure Available

**White Oak Plantation
Shooting Schools**
5215 B County Road 10
Tuskegee, AL 36083
(334) 727-9258
FAX: (334) 727-3411
Contact: Matthew or Robert Pitman
Chief Instructor: Steve
Schultz/Federal Wing & Clay School
http://www.americaoutdoors.com/
woak
School Location: White Oak Planta-
tion, 20 mi. SW of Auburn
Group Size: 1-6
Shooting Taught: SC, WS

Certified: NSCA Level III, Level I, NRA
Brochure Available
Shooting schools are held from
Feb.-May with either Steve Schultz
or Jerry Meyer, two of the most outstanding shooting instructors in the
nation. Each has helped hundreds
of students to become better shooters in a fun and non-intimidating
manner. Beginners, intermediate,
advanced, ladies & youth will all
benefit from their instruction.
"HAVE A BLAST!"
YOUTH SHOOTING CAMPS
5215 B County Rd. 10
Tuskegee, AL 36083
(334) 727-9258
http://www.americaoutdoors.
com/woak
Sessions: 3x/yr., 6 days, July
Group Size: 12 Ages: 10-14, Coed
Taught: shooting, safety, conservation

**Wings & Clays
Shooting School**
at Bald Mountain Gun Range
2500 Kern Rd.
Lake Orion, MI 48360
(810) 814-9193
Est.: 1993
Contact: Larry Woo
Instructor: Pat Lieske
Student/Yr: 100
School Location: Bald Mountain
Gun Range
Group Size: Max. of 5
Sessions: 1/2 to full day
Loaner Guns Available
Shooting Taught: SC, WS, TR, SK
Brochure Available
Guest instructors throughout the
year

**Wise Wingshooting
Academy**
7829 Sandy Bottom Rd.
Chestertown, MD 21620
(410) 778-4950
Est.: 1989
Contact: Ben E. Wise
Instructor: Ben E. Wise
Students/yr: 40-50
School Location: Pintail Point,
Queenstown, MD
Group Size: 1 to 10
Sessions: Feb-Oct (per day) week or
weekends
Loaner Guns Available
Method Taught: Instinctive
Shooting Taught: SC, WS, TR,
Flyers Shooting
Brochure Available

Woodcock Hill
Thomas Bland & Sons Gunmakers, Ltd.
RD#1, Box 147, Benton, PA 17814
(717) 864-3242
FAX: (717) 864-3232
Est.: 1989
Contact: Christa Baker or
Glenn Baker

**Woods and Water
Shooting School**
Rt. 1, Box 319
Catoosa, OK 74015
(919) 266-5551
Contact: Doug Fuller
Instructor: Doug Fuller
Sessions: 1/2 to 2 day programs
Loaner Guns Available
Shooting Taught: SC, WS, TR, Flyers

TARGETS

AmericanZZ, Inc.
171 Spring Hill Rd.,
Trumbull, CT 06611
(203) 261-1058
FAX: (203) 452-9359
Contact: Millo Bertini
Available: Direct
American "ZZ" Bird, AmericanZZ
Trap line simulates box-bird live pigeon shooting. The targets are plastic discs fitted onto stamped-metal propellers. A "bird" is counted as "dead" when the shot separates the disc from the prop. Launchers include the Sport Wing, with a non-oscillating, or fixed head, designed for sporting clays ranges, where more consistent target presentation are often needed. The Flush Bird is an oscillating unit that's capable of throwing pigeons in almost any direction. Five or nine of these units with a computer controller are all that is needed for a simulated box-bird ring. The targets are susceptible to wind currents and speed. The discs are reusable if they are not hit, and the props are good for about eight throws. "ZZ" targets are approved in the NSCA rule book.
See Our Ad Pg. 236

CCI International
Clark Clay Industries, Ltd.
Priors Haw Road, Corby
Northamptonshire, NN17, 5JG
England
011-44-1536-260933
Est.: 1982   Staff: 40
FAX: 011-44-1536-401138
Chairman: Jonathan Cridland
Full range of sporting clay pigeons and automatic traps

CHAMPION TARGET COMPANY

Champion Targets
232 Industrial Pkwy.
Richmond, IN 47374
(317) 966-7745
FAX: (317) 966-7747
Est.: 1975
The only USA target manufacturer who produces the complete line of targets needed for trap, skeet, international and sporting clay shooting.

Two new clays in 1996 include a multi-purpose standard target for all shooting applications and a tournament grade standard for trap. Two locations: Indiana and Minnesota. For your nearest distributor call (317) 966-7745.

LaPorte Targets
Manufactured by JEC Enterprises of VA
PO Box 1760
Cedar Bluff, VA 24609
(540) 963-7932
Contact: Jim Cooper

Now Made in the U.S. – Quality Laporte Targets have set the standard for sporting in Europe since 1927. We are proud to be the exclusive U.S. manufacturer for this premium line of targets including our standard lines for the skeet and trap enthusiasts.
See Our Ads Below & Pg. 75

Lawry Shooting Sports, Inc.
27 Industrial Dr.
Caledonia, Ontario
Canada N3W 2G6
(905) 765-3343
Est.: 1984   Staff: 10
Contact: Bob or Richard Lawry
Clay targets for trap & skeet shooting.

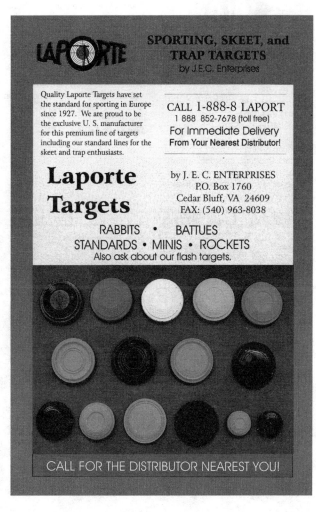

Midwest Target Co.
1103 S. State St.
Litchfield, IL 62056
(217) 324-4895
Est.: 1980   Staff: 15
Gen. Mgr: Jon Sutton
Available: Retail & Direct
Manufacturer of clay targets.

Northwest Targets
278 78th St., NE
Salem, OR 97302
(503) 399-7879
Est.: 1979   Staff: 3
Contact: Tim Elliott
Available: Retail & Direct
Manufacturer of regulation trap &
skeet targets.

Quack Sporting Clays, Inc.
Modern Era Shotgun Targets
4 Ann & Hope Way
PO Box 98
Cumberland, RI 02864
(401) 723-8202
FAX: (401) 722-5910
Est.: 1987
Available: Retail & Direct
Quack Sporting Clays, Inc., a multi-
faceted manufacturer, also makes
a series of tough almost unbreak-

able plastic targets and target inserts (QUACK-VAC'S™) which fly
exactly like the real clays for fun
and games, which when hit pull
apart and separate. Each plastic target and insert can be used over
and over. Our new "QUACK-VAC"™
inserts are also available for standard clay birds for use in our
Modern Era Recreational Clays
games. If you like to shoot a shotgun and would like to learn more
about our Modern Era shotgun philosophy and direction, then send
for more information and subscribe
to our Modern Skeet & Clays magazine. Plastic birds are available in
standard, midi, mini and rabbit and
can be used many times. Black,
white and colors are available.
QUACK-VAC™ a thin plastic circular
insert that fits underneath a clay
bird or Quack plastic target which
"DROPS OUT" once the target is hit.
Developed by Quack Sporting
Clays, Inc. for "FUN" and Modern
Era Recreational games. Each
QUACK-VAC™ can be used ofer
and over again is used as per our instructions. Call or write for
information.
See Our Ad Pg. 238 - 239

**Remington Arms
Company, Inc.**
PO Box 700
870 Remington Dr.
Madison, NC 27025-0700
(800) 243-9700 (Consumer)
(910) 548-8700 (Headquarters)
FAX: (910) 548-7770
Est.: 1816
Available: Retail

White Flyer Targets
124 River Rd.
Middlesex, NJ 08846
For the name of your nearest dis-
tributor please call:
East - 800/423-6077
Central - 800/647-2898
West - 800/872-7888
Manufacturing quality targets from
three modern plants. The shooters
choice for over one hundred years.
Full and complete line of Trap,
Skeet, International and Sporting
Clays targets in the widest variety
of colors. Knowledgeable distribu-
tors throughout the country.
See Our Ad Across

CLAY TARGETS

STANDARD
4 ¼ inches in diameter, 1 ⅛
inches thick; dome shaped;
standard in trap and skeet.

ROCKET
4 ¼ inches in diameter; ⅝ inch
thick; deceptive in flight;
appears to float, but retains
more velocity than the
standard.

RABBIT
4 ¼ inches in diameter; ½ inch
thick; rolls and bounces on the
ground; thick rim, density
prevent shattering on impact
with ground.

BATTUE
4 ¼ inches in diameter; ⅜ inch
thick; "flying razor blade,"
difficult to pick up edge-on;
does rolls and wingovers.

MIDI
3 ½ inches in diameter, ⅞ inch
thick; smaller size make it
appear farther away than it
actually is; retains initial
velocity longer than other
targets.

MINI
2 ⅜ inches in diameter, ⅝ inch
thick; deceptive because small
size makes it appear to be
moving faster than it actually is;
slows quickly because it's light.

TRAPS

Buying A Trap:
What To Look For

Knowing what you want when you're buying a trap is easier said than done. And the problem compounds when you try to match your needs with the growing number of clay target throwers—made in the U.S. and abroad—now available on the market.

As always, knowledge is your best ally. So whether you are an individual shooter looking for a portable trap or a gun club manager putting in a tournament quality sporting clays course, here are some tips on getting the best value for your dollar.

First the basics: Clay target throwers fall into two broad categories: manual and automatic.

Manual Traps

Very basic, and less-expensive manual machines usually allow only minimal adjustment for the height or speed and distance the target travels. The durability of these models depends on design and construction, but, generally speaking, those made with solid metal frames are more durable than the light sheet metal variety.

Greater durability comes at greater cost, as does a variety of desirable features such as a double throwing arm (for launching two targets simultaneously); target height, angle and speed adjustment; teal clips (for throwing targets vertically); electric release; a semi-cocking device that makes it easier for the machine to be cocked; a feature that allows different size sporting targets to be thrown by the same machine (including rabbit targets that bounce along the ground); a seat attached to the base; and finally, extra safety features.

Automatic Traps

Automatic traps range in complexity from relatively simple, no nonsense designs to feats of engineering wizardry. But remember, the greater the automation, the higher the price. Before buying, consider the following: Was the machine you are considering designed for the use you have planned? Many machines do a fabulous job at skeet, for example, but don't perform as well when put out on a sporting clays course, and vice versa.

Key Concerns

Maintenance: If you're all thumbs around any thing mechanical, you'll want a machine that you can deal with easily and quickly in the event of breakdown. Key questions to ask when you are shopping: What are the machine's annual maintenance requirements and costs? Are replacement parts readily available? What about service technicians, when you can't make the necessary repairs. [cont'd>]

Durability And Dependability: How many targets will the trap throw before breaking down? How many in its lifetime? Also, experts agree that a good trap will usually break less than 3% of the targets it throws. How does the model you're considering compare to this standard?

Versatility: What else can this trap do? Certain shooting disciplines, American Trap (ATA) and Skeet, for example, do not require much versatility from a trap. They do require a high degree of target flight consistency, though. Models destined for use as a sporting clays thrower, on the other hand, should be more versitile. Additional features to look for include:

- Portability--light weight construction

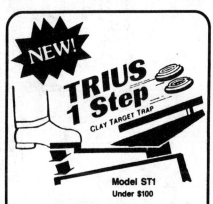

Model ST1
Under $100

ONE EASY STEP COCKS & RELEASES TARGET

Almost Effortless To Use

- **One person can throw & shoot!**
- **Singles/Doubles**
- **High Angle Clip Included**
- **American Made - Guaranteed**

See your dealer today.

For Catalog Contact **TRIUS**
P.O. Box 25, Cleves, OH 45002

Phone: (513) 941-5682
FAX: (513) 941-7970

Sporting Clay Traps Available.

(to make it easier to move around the course)

- Adjustable elevation -- ideally to the teal position (the ultimate in height adjustment!)
- Fast recocking time (good for "following pairs")
- Battery power option (see Power Source)
- Tiltability-- can be the model be tilted over on its side to throw curving targets (increasingly popular with shooters).

Target Capacity: How many targets should a machine hold? The consensus among experts is that 300 to 400 is the most efficient number. Remember, the more targets the machine holds, the longer it takes to fill it--but you won't have to fill as often!

Power Source: Plug-in or battery power? The installation costs for plug-in power (110v AC) can be high. Power cables have to be buried and this generally confines the size and "changeability" of your layout. With battery power, you can install a machine practically anywhere, and move it as often as you want.

Release Sytems: Ask about the different ways targets can be released--manually, electrically, by radio, and even by voice. Also, ask about the back-up systems that can be used if the primary release system fails.

A Final Word

Finally, as with many products, trap prices are often more a measure of mechanical complexity than quality. The type of trap and the make you buy should be determined by the your needs and budget. To avoid being trapped with the wrong trap, do your homework. Contact as many of the manufacturers and distributors listed on the following pages as you can. Check references. Call gun club and clay target operators for personal recommendations, before you write that check.

[For information about the cost and acreage requirements of shotgun shooting games and disciplines, see following chart on page 234.]

WINCHESTER® by LAPORTE®

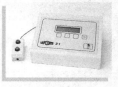

COST & ACREAGE REQUIREMENTS OF SHOTGUN SHOOTING DISCIPLINES & GAMES

	ACREAGE & COST ESTIMATES				THROUGHPUT OF SHOOTERS			
DISCIPLINE/ GAME	**ACRES** Construction	**ACRES** Fallout *	**COST** Machine (in thousands of dollars)	**COST** Construction	**CONSTRUCTION COMMENTS**	**SHOOTERS PER HOUR**	**TIME PER SHOOTER/ SQUAD**	**NO. OF TARGETS**
TRAP ** (ATA, ABT, DT)	.25	52	7-9	2.5-8	Layout, trap pit, walkways, electr.,floodlights	18-25	13-16 min./ 5 shooters	
OLYMPIC TRAP	.38	52	42-65	12-28	Large pit for traps, walkways,electr., floodlights	18-24	15-18 min./ 6 man squad	
UNIVERSAL TRENCH	.32	52	14-22	8-16	5 trap pit, walkways, electr., floodlights	18-24	15-18 min./ 6 man squad	
ZZ BIRD	.38	52	.5-9	.2-1	Layout & small fence	6-12	6-8 min./ shooter	
SKEET (NSSA/UIT)	.34	58	8-9	8-12	Layout, buildings, walkways, elect., floodlights	10-12	25 min./ 5 shooters	
SPORTING ***	20-30	100/ 200	M: 12-16	4-23	Stands, trap mounts, gun racks, shelters, walkways	50	1 hr./5 man squad	50
			A: 73-92	12-45	As above + trap houses & electr.			
FITASC	15-30	100/ 200	M: 18-32	8-30	Stands, trap mounts,racks, shelters, walkways	20	2 hrs./5 man squad	200
			A: 90-150	18-68	As above + trap houses & electr.			
CRAZY QUAIL	1	58	M: 1 A: 5-9	1	Trap pit	12-15	5 min./ shooter	25
TWO-MAN FLUSH	.20	48	A: 5-9	1-1.8	Trap house/ shooting platform	60-80	34 sec./ 2 shooters	24
TRAP HOUSE	6	100	7	0	Trailer with 10-20 M traps	10-40	25-35 min./ 5 man squad	50
5-STAND SPORTING®	.80	58	A: 18-30	0	Skeet or empty field	10-15	20-25 min./ 5 man squad	25
QUAIL WALK	0.5-2	50-60	M: 3-9	1-4				
			A:18-40	3-15	Including electr.	4-10	15 min./ shooter	25
SUPERSPORT	10-30	150/ 200	A: 80-140	15-25	12-25 traps & electrics	4-10	15-25 min./ shooter	50
TOWER SHOOTING	.2	160	A: 7-10	2.5-15	Tower	10-20	6-10 min.	25
PRO-SPORTING	1	58	A: 15-18	1.5-5	5 traps	360	36-50 sec./ 6 man squad	25/ squad
SUB-TRAP	1	58	.6 - .8	.1-1.5		18-25	10-25 min./ 5 man squad	25
FLUSH AND FLURRIES	0.5-2	50/ 110	M: 1.2-2 A: 4.8-6.6	.1-1.5 .6-2		100-300	36 sec./ 4,5 or 6 man squad	25/ squad
STARSHOT	.34	58	48	3-25		15-30	3 min./shooter	25
DOUBLE RISE	.25	52	7.6-9.2	2.5-8		18-25	16-22 min./ 6 man squad	25

* No shot larger than 7 1/2.   ** For a Skeet/Trap overlay field, the combined construction costs would be $10,000-$17,000.

*** Quality of landscaping varies price.   M = Manual   A = Automatic   Source: The Shooting Academy

WINCHESTER® by LAPORTE®

TRAP TECHNOLOGY AT ITS' ULTIMATE...

THE LAPORTE TRAP MODEL 185 TA -TAH
Fully automatic
American & International Shooting
400 clay magazine
185 TA horizontal oscillation
Conforms to A.T.A regulations
185 TAH horizontal & vertical "Wobble"
Simple design & adjustments.
Easy installation:
Fits directly onto Western 1524 base

185 TA-TAH

TWINLAP - LAPORTE HAS REDEFINED THE MEANING OF DOUBLE TRAP SHOOTING!

285 TWINLAP

THE LAPORTE TRAP MODEL 285 TWINLAP
The <u>only</u> doubles machine to conform precisely to A.T.A regulations, 900 target capacity
Fine adjustment for each trajectory - horizontal, vertical, windage (curve)
Changes from single to double by the flick of a switch
A.T.A. singles - computerized random controlled oscillation
Easy installation and maintenance.

LAPORTE AMERICA : ONE TRANS-BORDER DRIVE - CHAMPLAIN - NEW YORK 12919
TEL. 1-800-335-TRAP - FAX 1-518-298-8720

TRAP MANUFACTURERS & IMPORTERS

AmericanZZ, Inc.
171 Spring Hill Rd.
Trumbull, CT 06611
(203) 261-1058
FAX: (203) 452-9359
Contact: Millo Bertini
Available: Retail & Direct
AMERICANZZ provides an effective simulation of the zig-zagging, unpredictable flight of a live pigeon at reasonable cost. Five or nine computer controlled launching machines placed in a pigeon ring release targets at controllable speed from 25 to 40 mph. Birds randomly selected by computer. Machines oscillate 130-degrees. Adjustable launch angles, and an innovative head design provides unpredictable height variations when bird is released. FLUSHBIRD is a single launcher designed to provide wing shooters with a training target that simulates the erratic flight of wild game such as snipe, quail, dove, woodcock and pheasant. A perfect low-cost alternative for small clubs, hunting preserves and private installations. SPORT WING model for Sporting Clays applications. DEALER INQUIRIES WELCOME!
See Our Ad Below

Auto-Arm Rabbit
Clay-Tech Industries, Inc.
1003 M-55 Ave., NE
Calgary, Alberta
Canada T2E 6W1
(800) 940-2529
FAX: (403) 295-2531
Contact: Harry Isaac
Manufactured in: Canada/USA
Available: Direct
A portable throwing arm style rabbit, featuring instant release. Battery powered or 115V AC. Adjustable to throw "Looper" Targets. Simple, quiet, reliable operation; the most affordable arm rabbit in its class.

Auto-Sporter

Clay-Tech Industries, Inc.
1003 M-55 Ave., NE
Calgary, Alberta
Canada T2E 6W1
(800) 940-2529
FAX: (403) 295-2531
Contact: Harry Isaac
Manufactured in: Canada/USA
Available: Direct
Type: Automatic
Commercial duty, portable automatic sporting clay trap machine, battery powered or AC/DC. Over 4000 throws per charge. Fast recocking for following pairs, adjustable to springing teal position. Quick installation *midi* conversion kit. Solid state electrical control system. Extremely simple design for easy servicing. Available with oscillating base for ATA, "Crazy Quail" targets, or remote angle adjustment in towers. The "Wobble" version provides both vertical and horizontal unpredictable (interrupted) movement for an entire sporting clays course in one machine. The ideal 5-Stand machine.
See Our Ad Below

Auto-Sporter Vertical/Teal

Clay-Tech Industries, Inc.
1003 M-55 Ave., NE
Calgary, Alberta
Canada T2E 6W1
(800) 940-2529
FAX: (403) 295-2531
Contact: Harry Isaac
The only trap on the market to throw a true vertical full faced target. The vertical/teal provides a left to right adjustment of 45 degrees and features, the same, simple design featured in the entire Auto-Sporter line. This unique trap does not tilt when loading a target. Recocking time is a fast two seconds.

AutoClay Traps

Acorn Systems
2726 134th Ave., Hopkins, MI 49328
(616) 793-7400
Contact: Jim Spray
Available: Direct
Manufactured in: England
Type: Automatic
The AutoClay is a portable, reliable automatic trap with a 50 clay capacity hopper. It operates on a 12V battery and a full charge launches 3,500 targets 90-100 meters. Target presentation ranges from horizontal to 70 degrees. Optional extras include foot operated switch, 50 metre extension cable, electronic upgrade module, "Midi" size mechanism and auto angling base.

BEOMAT
500 SERIES MACHINES

Beomat of America, Inc.

300 Railway Ave., Campbell, CA 95008
(408) 379-4829
Contact: Sten Nilsson
Manufactured in: Sweden
Type: Automatic
The 500 Series machines will be available for all disciplines of clay target shooting: Skeet, Trap, Double Trap, Wobble Trap/Ball Trap, Olympic Trap, Sporting Clays, 110V AC or 12V DC. Any of the machines load 530 targets standard (except Olympic trap with 350 targets per machine– for a total of 5250 targets loaded in the bunker) 900 target magazine optional for all except the wobble trap. MJDT500 and the MTD500 throw single targets as well as American Trap doubles, utilizing any standard American target, and can with a simple magazine conversion throw 90 mm targets in both single and double mode. The machines are

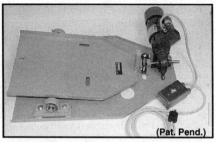

using any standard American trap or skeet target (108 mm) and all International (110 mm) trap or skeet targets without any changes. The weight of the trap machines has been reduced substantially as compared to our 400 series machines, and all trap machines are now equipped with adapter brackets to fit the existing (standard) trap house pier. Improved power distribution internally, includes so called motor saver device, or if you will, an electric power saving feature; i.e., the machine shuts itself down into a "sleep mode" after 5 minutes of no activity, and re-activates itself automatically. Any of the 500 series machines can be equipped with 12V DC motors. Simplified target loading, magazine release, allows all targets to be loaded from the most convenient position.

Bowman
Clay-Sport International, Inc.
Box 663, Bragg Creek, Alberta, Canada T0L 0K0
(403) 949-3654
Contact: Raymond Foreman
Manufactured in: England
Type: Manual
A versatile and sturdy range of manual throwers, with a model to meet every sporting clays needs. The best selling manual thrower in Great Britain.

CCI International
Clark Clay Industries, Ltd.
Priors Haw Road, Corby
Northants, NN17 5JG, England
Est.: 1982
011-44-1536-260933
FAX: 011-44-1536-401138
Chairman: Jonathan Cridland
Type: Automatic

Chucker Clay Thrower Traps
R.L. Torresdal Co., Inc.
Hwy. 52 East, Ossian, IA 52161
(319) 532-9884
FAX: (319) 532-9387
Contact: Ray Torresdal
Manufactured in: Iowa, US
Type: Manual
Durability and ease of use characterize the new lever-operated flush/flurry machine from the R.L. Torresdal Co. Throws birds as fast as an operator can pull the lever. Interchangeable magazines hold 30 standard, midi or mini clay birds. Throws following pairs, report pairs, flurries. Also available: manual and rabbit traps, each with a stand with removable legs, bolt-down base and truck-mountable swivel base; and a new 360-degree rotation Crazy Quail stand. Please phone for details.

CLAYMASTER
UPGRADABLE TRAP MACHINES ™

Clay Master
11 Spinnaker Way
Chico, CA 95926
(916) 345-1613
FAX: (916) 345-1613
Contact: Tom Hampton
Type: Full line   Automatics & 3/4 Manuals
A new concept in trap design...total upgradeability. Both our full line of quality automatics can throw all sizes of targets and our manual 3/4 cock line can be upgraded. Now a club or individual can begin with our low cost commerical quality traps such as our 3/4 cock or one of our automatics, and as their needs change, upgrade at fantastic savings! Full automatics in the past have been a dream for most, but now an easy reality for everyone. No longer do you need to lose thousands of dollars on manual machines when you decide to go automatic! You can upgrade our manuals to automatic for a lot less than you might think! All our American made traps are built on high quality aluminum on our super strong box beam design. Parts are precision made on CNC milling machine so that all upgrades bolt on in a snap! In the automatic line of traps, the sky's the limit with interchangeable high boy and low boy carousel models, vertical oscillator and/or random horizontal rotating bases are just a few of the options available that can be added with one of our upgrade kits. Solid state low power all weather electronics for maximum field are used on all 12 volt models. Great versatility on rotating and oscillating models with A/B and total random mode that are non readable by shooters. All automatics come standard with our exclusive auto puller mode that allows you to shoot by yourself, no puller required! Hard wire and radio control available. Affordable pricing standard! Call or fax for more information or check us out on the Internet! http://www.claymaster.com

See Our Ad Across, Left

Clay-Sport Sporting Traps
Unit II, Whitehall Ind. Estate
Walkern Rd., Watton-at-Stone,
Hartfordshire SG1 43RP England
011-44-92-083-0070
FAX: 011-44-92-830-989
Manufactured in: England
Type: Manual & Automatic

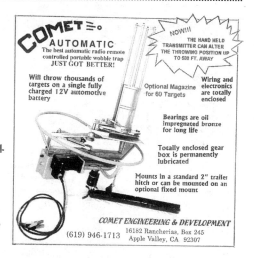
Clubmaster Traps
Rota-Trap
537 A Mt. Pleasant Rd.
Toronto Canada M4S 2M5
(416) 487-9133
Est.: 1985   Staff: 5
Contact: Jeff Beallor
Available: Retail & Direct
Manufactured in: New Zealand
Type: Manual

Comet Automatic
Comet Engineering & Development
16182 Rancherias
Box 245
Apple Valley, CA 92307
(619) 946-1713
Contact: Tom Hunt
Manufactured in: USA
Type: Automatic
The Comet Automatic radio remote-controlled wobble trap throws thousands of targets on a single fully charged 12V auto battery. Hand-held transmitter alters throwing position at distances up to 500 feet. Optional magazine for 60 targets. Totally enclosed wiring and electronics. Totally enclosed, permanently lubricated gear box. Bronze bearings are oil impregnated for long life. Mounts in standard 2" trailer hitch. Optional fixed mount available.

See Our Ad Above

Dayson Arms, Ltd.
PO Box 532, Vincennes, IN 47591
(812) 882-8680
FAX: (812) 882-8446
Est.: 1993   Staff: 11
Contact: Gary Ciluffo

Due/Matic Traps

Golden West Industries
750 Arroyo Ave., San Fernando, CA 91340
(800) 548-5444
(818) 365-3946
FAX: (818) 365-8725
Contact: Chuck Elton
Manufactured in: Denmark
Type: Automatic & Manual
Automatic versions of these smoothly functioning traps are available in skeet, ISU, ATA, bunker and sporting configurations. Features include ease of access to elevation changes and target directions, 200-target magazine capacity (expandable to 400 on skeet and sporting models), minimal vibration, safety guards. Problem-free feeding with all brands of targets. Sporting model has interchangeable magazines for 110mm and 90mm targets. Also available: manual version for mini, midi, standard, battue or rabbit targets. Call for information.

G.M.V. Super-Star Traps

G.H. Enterprises
Box 939, Okotoks
Alberta, Canada T0L 1T0
(403) 938-6070
FAX: (403) 938-3206
Contact: Gert Holmqvist
Manufactured in: Sweden
Type: Automatic
This full range of automatic traps features a special elevator that lower targets gently onto the throwing table, thus reducing target breakage. The large throwing table and long throwing arm puts a fast spin on the target for a consistent flypath. The lineup of these Swedish-built traps include G.M.V. 285T which throws DOUBLES and SINGLE targets. The G.M.V. 274T singles trap, G.M.V. 296T Wobble trap all with a 400 target capacity. The G.M.V. 455S Skeet and G.M.V. 466S Sporting trap feature a vertical angle adjustment up to 60 degrees on accessory spring for throwing targets up to 90 yards. The sporting comes with a 24-volt release and the skeet with Winchester compatibility or 24-volt release. The G.M.V. 477S are 12 Volt ma-

chines with a target capacity ranging from 250 to 700. New to the lineup of excellent machines are the G.M.V. 800ST Teal with horizontal and vertical adjustments and hold 250 targets. The G.M.V. 840R Rabbit is a wheel operated rabbit with a 400 target magazine. The target speed and distance is easily changed with a five speed selector lever. The machine has two carrying handles for easy handling. The G.M.V. 380T Olympic Trench is also available. Accessories includes: acoustic releases, remote releases and magazine inserts that makes these machines versatile for even midi and mini targets.

See Our Ad Across, Left

HOPPE'S ⑨™
A DIVISION OF PENGUIN INDUSTRIES, INC.

Hoppe's — Penguin Industries, Inc.
Airport Industrial Mall
Coatesville, PA 19320
(610) 384-6000
FAX: (610) 857-5980
Contact: Patricia Lucas
Available: Retail
The new Hoppe's Clayking™ combines durability, versatility and safety to give shotgunners a sporting clays target thrower that's excellent for teaching fundamentals and ideal for sharpening reflexes and improving aim. A heavy-duty welded steel frame with weather-resistant polymer coating can be pressed easily into the ground or mounted on a spare tire (all hardware is included). Dimples on the Clayking's throwing arm prevent targets from slipping. Flight angle and height are fully adjustable. Throws left, right or center according to place-

ment of targets. Singles and doubles can be thrown in virtually any flight pattern. Pull-cord release makes the Clayking safer to operate. One-person operation. Ask for the Clayking, Item No. 4004.

See Our Ad Pg. 230

IBIS Traps - IBIS Clay Target Products
Div. of Show Me Sports Corp.
8267 N. Revere
Kansas City, MO 64151
(816) 587-9540
FAX: (816) 587-3906
Est.: 1978
Contact: Andy Perkins
Manufactured in: USA & Australia
Type: Automatic & Manual
Traps for Trap, Skeet, Sporting Clays & private use. IBIS Target Products manufactures clay target traps which are ideally suited to all possible requirements. The traps are affordable enough for small and private ranges, yet they are of World Class standard, suitable for the largest sporting events. The IBIS Hand Traps and Autos have set the standards for quality in the shooting industry. Call for free quote before making your purchase. Hand Traps starting @ $350; Autos starting @ $2750. References available upon request. IBIS Traps are rated #1 by top course designers among all major brands for overall customer satisfaction.

See Our Ad Pg. 231

WINCHESTER® by

LAPORTE®

LAPORTE AMERICA
One Trans-Border Drive
Champlain, NY 12919
(800) 335-TRAP
(800) TRAP-185
FAX: (518) 298-8720
Est.: 1927
Available: Retail
Manufactured in: France
Semi-Automatic, Automatic & Manual
Established since 1927, the LAPORTE strength
and success lies in it's commitment to service
and quality. The company prides itself on producing machines that are reliable and always at
the forefront of the market in their technological developments and revolutionary ideas: This
quality is recognized worldwide.
All Winchester by LAPORTE traps are of a simple
design and virtually maintenance free. The
LAPORTE Skeet machine is endorsed by the
NSSA and is the most accurate machine on the
market, with its uncomplicated design and user
friendly adjustment mechanisms. The LAPORTE
range of Sporting automatic traps is available in

both 12V & 110V and of a technical excellence
that is recognized worldwide. Whilst our automatic trap range for American & International
style shooting, including the new revolutionary
285 LAPORTE TWIN LAP is the finest and most
technically advanced available on the market.
When you purchase a WINCHESTER BY
LAPORTE trap you can rest assured that the service and technical support you receive will live
up to the highest standards of the American
sportsman.
See Our Ad Pgs. 67, 233 & 235

Lincoln Traps
1009 S. Lincoln Ave.
Lebanon, PA 17042
(717) 274-8676
FAX: (717) 274-8672
Manufactured in: USA, a division of Shyda's Services, Inc.
Type: Manual & Automatic
Lincoln Traps are known for their whisper quiet
performance, durable cast design and an UN-
BEATABLE WRITTEN WARRANTY. Models are
available to accommodate shooters from beginner to expert. The "SC-90E" is a 3/4 cock worthy

WE'RE ABOUT TO UNCRATE PERFECTION.

LINCOLN'S AMERICAN TRAP MACHINE (ATM)

The Bright New Choice for Automatic DOUBLES or Singles.

SHYDA'S
HOME OF THE LINCOLN

1009 South Lincoln Ave. • Lebanon, PA 17042-7166 • Tel: 717-274-8676 • Fax: 717-274-8672

of a commercial grade rating and has a 5 year warranty. The "Falcon" is a personal grade 3/4 cock machine, and the "Junior" is a manual cock machine. Prices begin at $249. All three models will throw single or doubles, standards, midis, minis and battues. Rabbit and Variety arms, as well as many accessories are available to meet your needs. The two newest Lincoln machines will be available in early 1997. The first, is a new 3/4 cock to throw rabbits, teal and chondel targets, at the same time, from a triple arm. The second is our new automatic "ATM" (American trap machine) which will throw automatic doubles or singles, and will bolt onto a V1524 Western platform, into existing trap houses. "Discover the Lincoln Difference."

See Our Ad Pg. 245

MIDAS GOLD

The Midas Gold
Rhodeside, Inc.
1704 Commerce Dr., Piqua, OH 45356
(513) 773-5781   Est.: 1991
Pres: Jim Printz
Available: Direct
Manufactured in: U.S.
Type: Manual
The Midas Gold is a 3/4 cocking manual trap.

Heavy duty zinc plated steel construction for years of dependable service. Easily recocked, very quiet release, and all traps have a two year warranty. One mainspring adjusts to throw any size or quantity of targets the desired distance. The two piece extruded aluminum carrier arms can be unbolted to use only one carrier arm, thereby throwing the target(s) a greater distance. All carrier arms throw singles or doubles, standards, minis, midis, and battues. Heavy duty bearings are installed on mainshaft and roller release. Trap base easily mounts to any flat surface or trap stand. Trap base has slots to adjust elevation and windage. Trap weighs less than 30 pounds for UPS shipments. All this for less than $400.

See Our Ad Below

Nasta Traps
Nasta Division, Rexxell Corporation
1300 W. Belmont, Suite 207
Chicago, IL 60657
(312) 880-8825
FAX: (312) 880-2233
Mngng. Dir: Arto Saariner
Manufactured in: Finland
Type: Automatic
Technically superior NASTA Automatic Clay Target Launching Machines have delivered peak performance at clubs and competitions for

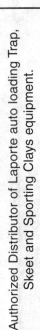

NASTA
Automatic Clay Target Launching Machines

TRAP SKEET NASTA O-MATIC

NASTA machine's and involvement has been present at many competitions where world shooting records have been achieved. The list of records is extensive and impressive. Nasta Division of Rexxell Corporation has now made these technically superior machines available here in America. Nasta machines have proved their reliability and accuracy in both clubs and competitions for more than 20 years.

- Nasta has a complete range of machines for all shotgun sports including Olympic Trap, American Trap, Skeet and Sporting Clays.

- With years of research and development, Nasta has been able to minimize the throwing shock and eliminate the delay making the machines consistent and quick. It's these type of refinements that have allowed so many shotgun sportsmen to achieve their best results and even set world records.

- Nasta has the most advanced Phon-O-Matic control system available. This system applies the latest technology in computerized acoustic systems for Olympic trapshooting. No manual operators or complicated programming is needed with its automatic operation.

- Nasta also manufactures competition quality clay targets. Nasta's clay pigeons are known for their tight weight dimensions which virtually eliminate machine adjustments and gives the target straight flight. Nasta's clay pigeons also burst ideally when hit.

NASTA Traps Improve the Operation of Any Range

more than 20 years. Complete range of models to accommodate all shotgun sports. Advanced Phon-O-Matic control system provides automatic operation without complicated programming. NASTA advanced design assures quick, consistent throws. NASTA is also the preferred source for competition quality clay targets, noted for straight flight and ideal bursts. Phone or fax for complete information.
See Our Ad Pg. 247

Outers Traps
Blount, Inc., Sporting Equipment Division
PO Box 856
2299 Snake River Ave.
Lewiston, ID 83501
(800) 627-3640
Contact: Dick Stawarz
Manufactured in: U.S.A.
Type: Manual
American Sporter, Flightmaster, Flightmaster Jr. & Birdmaster

Parker Traps International, Inc.
624 W. McNair St.
Chandler, AZ 85224
(602) 345-2911
FAX: (602) 345-2772
Contact: John Lockwood
Type: Automatic
Parker Traps from England has now added new features that have improved an already great trap. Built to last and virtually maintenance free. Together with the longest Warranty in the industry.

Machines are available for every discipline. All machines (except the Battue) will throw multiple target sizes (Standard, Midi, etc). Even our Arm Rabbit machine is designed to throw Rabbit and Standard targets. All Sporting traps will throw Teal presentations. Skeet layouts are configured to American Skeet. However, they are supplied standard with an ISU loom. A special adapter allows a quick change from a Skeet trap to a Sporting trap (for limited area sporting games). Our Wobble trap is another machine that has benefited from a special high lift adapter. That allows you to throw and extra high target while oscillating. Accessories include inserts and radio release systems (also, available for multiple trap release with counter). All machines are available in 12 volt DC and 110 volt AC. All traps are now fitted with an enhanced lift plate to handle softer targets.
See Our Ad Across, Right

Parker/BOSS
780 E. 15th St., N.
Wichita, KS 67214
(316) 265-1110
Contact: Larry Leatherman
Manufactured in: USA
Type: Automatic & Manual
This line of automatic traps is now manufactured in Wichita, Kansas. The automatic traps originated in England, but were redesigned for the American market by Graham Parker, so that they are capable of throwing any make of target. All traps have sealed-for-life

heavy duty gearboxes and oilite bushes. Maintenance is low and the machines are warranted for two years parts and labor (extended warranty available) the main bearing has a five year warranty. The automatic product line includes: Skeet traps - 110 volt or 12 volt DC with or without ISU timer. 400 or 500 magazine capacity; ATA traps - double or single 110 volt with timer. 400 or 500 magazine capacity. Wobble - double or single 110 volt with timer. 400 or 500 magazine capacity; Sporting - double or single 110 volt or 12 volt. 400 or 500 magazine capacity. All sporting traps can be fitted with midi and mini inserts. A quick adjustment converts the sporting trap to a springing teal. The single sporter can be adapted to throw single or double battues. Sporting Rabbit - 110 volt only. 400 or 500 magazine capacity. Double Arm Rabbit - 110 volt or 12 volt 400 or 500 magazine capacity. This machine is not only capable of throwing double rabbits, but can throw double chandelle or a mix chandelle and rabbit at the same time. The manual product line includes: 3/4 cock machines in sporting, rabbit and teal. A special teal stand is available as is a rabbit adapter for the basic stand. A new bearing (same as the automatic traps) has been fitted to the manual traps and carries a FIVE YEAR warranty. 6 GOOD REASONS TO BUY PARKER/BOSS: (1) EXPERIENCE - Our design engineer, Graham Parker, is one of the most knowledgeable design engineers in the world and is constantly looking for new ideas. (2) WARRANTY - We give the best in the industry, a TWO year (NO NONSENSE) parts and labor and a FIVE year warranty on our sprag bearing. (3) MAINTENANCE - Virtually no maintenance. The design of our traps is simple and efficient and if the need ever arose you could do it yourself. No need to pay a high price for a factory-trained repairman. (4) PRICE - The highest quality at competitive prices! Why pay more for a trap of lessor quality when you can buy the best? (5) SUPPORT - Our goal is to give the best support and service in the industry. Whether you need advice on course design, update or information on the best traps for your course, we will be there before, during and after the sale. (6) MADE IN USA - Everything is on your doorstep. No need to worry about the supply of anything!

See Our Ad Across, Right

Make the Best Better

Black's Wing & Clay is the most comprehensive, well organized and easy-to-use
directory available to shotgunning enthusiasts and the companies that serve them.
Help us make it even better. If we've made
an error or an omission, let us know. Call:
(908) 224-8700. Thanks.

Pat-Trap
Henniker Pallet Co. Inc.
16 Colby Hill Rd.
Henniker, NH 03242
(603) 428-3396
Contact: Amy Patenaude
Manufactured in: U.S.A.
Type: Automatic
The automatic PAT-TRAP throws doubles and single targets too! The patented PAT-TRAP
Automatic Doubles machine is made in the USA
and with its no nonsense design is simple to operate and easy to load. It holds four full cases of
clay targets with a side-loader magazine available. The PAT-TRAP fits ATA regulation trap
houses and is able to throw doubles while oscillating for Sporting Clays. The vibration-free
PAT-TRAP features commercial grade heavy
duty steel construction, sealed ball and roller
bearings and oilite bushings. It is fully adjustable
for windage and elevation. The hydraulic mode
of operation means no gear boxes. With today's
ever increasing array of State and insurance regulations, the PAT-TRAP will pay for itself in no
time. No personnel in the trap house means
safety and savings. The PAT-TRAP can be
equipped for voice release eliminating the need
for pullers. Double scores can increase due to
the ease and convenience of changing from singles to doubles in seconds allowing more
practice time. The PAT-TRAP will make shooting
more enjoyable and save money too.
See Our Ad Left

Pro-Matic (U.K.)
1 City Farm, Barsham City, Beccles, Suffolk
NR34 8JT England
011-44-50-271-7261
Contact: Ian Peatrie

Quack Traps Division
Quack Sporting Clays, Inc.
4 Ann & Hope Way, PO Box 98
Cumberland, RI 02864
(401) 723-8202
FAX: (401) 722-5910
Est.: 1987
Pres/CEO: Kenneth Gagnon, Sr.
Available: Retail & Direct
Manufactured in: Rhode Island, USA
Type: Manual
Quack 3/4 cock traps are the safest, fastest,
easiest to operate and set-up, most universal,

quietest, most durable (all weather), most dependable (lifetime warranty on clutch) most innovative and reasonably priced machine made in the United States today. Throws ALL birds, springing teal and rabbit, 110, 90, 60, battue, rocket–available in portable or permanent set-up. Manufactured in Rhode Island, USA since 1987. For more information contact us. New for 1996 our LEFT handed 3/4 cock machine with up to 4 throwing arms & 3 assorted spring tensions: Light (34-40 yds); Medium (70-80 yds); Heavy (100 yds+). New for 1996 is our Modern Pigeon Quick Change Rotary Base. Now ranges can change from, rabbit to springing teal in 5 seconds without the use of tools. Over two dozen different variable combinations can now be offered shooters and it only takes 5 seconds to change. Another original innovative idea from Quack Sporting Clays, Inc.

See Our Ad Pgs. 238 - 239

Quality Model '92
Quality Replacement Parts
1015 North 195 Ave, Buckeye, AZ 85326
(800) 742-0425   (602) 278-9556
Est.: 1982
Contact: Roger Coveleskie
Available: Retail & Direct
Type: Electric handset trap.

Quikfire Traps
Hunters Pointe Mfg. Corp.
Rt. 1, Box 166, Augusta, KS 67010
(316) 778-1122
FAX: (316) 778-1115   Est.: 1983
Contact: Larry Cero
Available: Direct
Manufactured in: Kansas, USA
Type: Automatic & Manual
Superior performance traps engineered to last. Quikfire II-60: Redesigned to accommodate newly released oscillating and wobble base. Quikfire II for '97 weighs just 39 pounds, very fast cocking and less battery drain than any other trap. The only trap to use two independent clutches for virtually trouble free performance. Our own industrial quality ball bearing, Dura Clutch™ is made from heat treated solid steel billet. No stamped or broached parts. 24 hardened steel engagements rollers. The longest clutch warranty in the industry. All load points feature ball bearing construction. New skelitized steel tube frame makes this a very compact, heavy duty machine. Wireless remote is also available. 3/4 cock manual extruded dual arm. Available soon: 200 target automatic. Total weight 50 lbs. Fast cocking, heavy duty. Also, 200 target, arm rabbit. Call for delivery date.

See Our Ad Below

Serena Fabbrica Lanciapiatelli
Northwest Ohio International
mailing: 2923 Plumbrook
Maumee, OH 43547
(419) 867-8884
FAX: (419) 867-8884
Contact: Joseph Rusin
Manufactured in: Brescia, Italy
Type: Automatic & Manual
Trap machines for: sporting clays (manual &
automatic, including specialty traps) for rabbit,
teal sparrow (mini), pheasant (chandelle); Amer
can trap machines; continental or wobble trap
machines; complete line of Int'l. Bunker in manual and automatic; International & American
skeet machines; specialty machines can be set
up for 12V, 115, 220, 240 or 360V. Also available is a full line of electric selectors and
phono-pull (voice release) systems.

Sportrap
Sportrap Clay Target Products
PO Box 708, Millville, NJ 08332
(609) 327-2030
FAX: (609) 825-3986
Est.: 1989   Staff: 8
Contact: Brian Keen
Available: Retail & Direct
Type: Manual & Automatic
3/4 cocking, counter balanced, quiet operation
fast and easy recocking for on-report or following pairs. Trap with dual arms and choice of
launch spring–$395. 3 leg portable stand with
swivel trap mount–$135. With our specialty
launch arms you can throw many different target presentations such as: 1) Hi-Low
Arm–throws vertically split pairs; 2) Fur and
Feather Arm–throws rabbit & chandelle;
3) Rabbit Arm-throws one or two rabbits, just
drop in to load; 4) Following Pair Arm–throws
one slow one fast target; 5) Jersey Devil Arm–
throws rising targets; 6) Battue Arm– throws
one or two battue targets; 7) 3 or 4 Bird Flush
Arms–throws multiple targets. Quantity discounts, call for further information and
brochure price list. UPS Delivery. Visa-
Mastercard Accepted.
See Our Ad Right

Model 1001
Automatic Trap

3/4 Cocking
FAST 1.33 SEC.
RECYCLE TIME
Up To 4 Targets
In The Air At Once
For Fast
Following Pairs
500 Target Capacity

Counter Balanced Arm
Vertical Adjustment 5 to 50 Degrees
Low Maintenance, Simple Design
No Microswitches, Belts Or Elevators To Service
Aluminum & Stainless Steel Construction
No Castings! All Machined Parts!
Heavy Duty Sprag Type Clutch

Model 1001 Automatic Trap $2,750.00
Includes 1 wired hand trigger with 100 ft. cord
With long range wireless release system $2,950.00
Hand trigger release system with 100. cord $45.00
100 ft. extension for wired hand trigger $35.00

Same Price for 12 VDC or 110VAC or 220VAC

Model 101
Manual Trap

3/4 Cocking - Counter Balanced Arm
Heavy Duty Sprag Type Clutch
Rated for 10 million cycles
Quiet Operation - Quantity Discounts

Model 101 Manual Trap (With Dual Arm) $395
Also Available: Custom Arms, Stands &
Mounts - Custom Left Handed Traps

Call or write today for information:

609-327-2030
P.O. Box 708
Millville, NJ 08332

Trius Traps

Trius Products, Inc., 221 S. Miami Ave.
PO Box 25, Cleves, OH 45002
(513) 941-5682
FAX: (513) 941-7970
Est.: 1955   Staff: 10
Contact: Hart Luebkeman
Manufactured in: Ohio, U.S.A.; Manual
TRIUS, manufacturing clay target traps since
1955 has progressed from its first trap Model
E56 to 8 models in 1993. These models consist
of 5 traps for the recreational shooter and 5
models for Hunter Clays/Sporting Clays. The 5
recreational models, TRIUS TRAP, BIRDSHOO-
TER, TRAPMASTER, 1 STEP TRAP and EZ
TRIPPER are available through finer retailers and
catalog mail order firms nationwide. Prices
range from $59 to $299. TRIUS for 41 years has
been known for the quality of the thrown target and minimum of maintenance. For brochure
or dealer information, please call today.
See Our Ad Pg. 232

Western Traps

by H-S Precision, Inc.
1301 Turbine Dr., Rapid City, SD 57701
(605) 341-3006
FAX: (605) 342-8964
Manufactured in: South Dakota, USA
Tyoe: Automatic & Manual
For regulation, international and skeet shooting,
Western Traps have long been the machine of
choice by trap shooting enthusiasts the world
over. During the past several decades, Western
Trap machines have been the only equipment
used at the Grand American Trap Shoot. For
more information on Western Traps, parts or
our network of distributors, contact H-S Precision, Inc.
See Our Ad Below

Whiteside's Mfg. Co., Inc.
45408 160th St. West, Lancaster, CA 93536
(805) 724-1974
FAX: (805) 724-1905
Contact: David Whiteside
Automatic
The Whiteside Model 300 is an automatic 12-Volt sporting clay thrower that is known for three things:
* Simplicity in design
* Reliability
* Rough construction
Mike Raahauge. . .a range operator from southern California said,"It's a good, simple, reliable machine that's priced right. From day one, it has worked flawlessly." Please call for our free brochure, accessories and optional information, (805) 724-1974.
See Our Ad, Right

Winchester by LAPORTE
One Trans-Border Drive
Champlain, NY 12919
(800) 335-TRAP
(800) TRAP185   FAX: (518) 298-8720
Est.: 1927   Available: Retail
Manufactured in: France
Semi-Automatic, Automatic & Manual
Established since 1927, the LAPORTE strength and success lies in it's commitment to service and quality. The company prides itself on producing machines that are reliable and always at the forefront of the market in their technological developments and revolutionary ideas: This quality is recognized worldwide.
All Winchester by LAPORTE traps are of a simple design and virtually maintenance free. The LAPORTE Skeet machine is endorsed by the NSSA and is the most accurate machine on the market, with its uncomplicated design and user friendly adjustment mechanisms. The LAPORTE range of Sporting automatic traps is available in both 12V & 110V and of a technical excellence that is recognized worldwide. Whilst our automatic trap range for American & International style shooting, including the new revolutionary 285 LAPORTE TWIN LAP is the finest and most technically advanced available on the market. When you purchase a WINCHESTER BY LAPORTE trap you can rest assured that the service and technical support you receive will live up to the highest standards of the American sportsman.
See Our Ad Pg. 67, 233 & 235

TRAP ACCESSORIES

Auto-Counter
Clay-Tech Industries, Inc.
1003 M-55 Ave., NE
Calgary, Alberta
Canada T2E 6W1
(800) 940-2529
FAX: (403) 295-2531
Contact: Harry Isaac
Hand held automatic counter ideal for unsupervised sporting clays courses. Simply plug into trap release cable and the Auto-Counter records all targets fired for easy tabulation at the clubhouse. Entirely self-contained, nothing left out in the field. Affordably priced.

Auto Pilot
11551 Douglas Rd.
Rancho Cordova, CA 95742
(916) 351-0538
Est.: 1994   Staff: 3
Contact: Pat Glaze
Programmable microprocessor controls up to 25 custom launch sequences.

the BIRDBRAIN. system

Bird Brain
Clay-Sport International, Inc.
Box 663, Bragg Creek
Alberta, Canada T0L 0K0
(403) 949-3654
Contact: Raymond Foreman
An innovative trap control system, featuring our own invention - 5-Stand Sporting - includes other original games designed to attract hunters and competitors. Automatic "hands free" function.
See Our Ad Pg. 119

Claymaster ATA & OLY Voice Release Systems
Clay Target Enterprises
300 Railway Ave.
Campbell, CA 95008
(408) 379-4829
Contact: Sten Nilsson
Imported from Norway, the Claymaster Voice Release System is available for ATA and Olympic Trap.

Claymate Voice Activated Trap Release
Claymate, Inc., PO Box 903
Concord, NH 03302-0903
(800) 603-2286
Contact: Bill Anzaldi
Radio Controlled voice release system with many applications including trap, sporting clays and games.

Coastal Industries Products
4082 N. South Bank, Suite C
Oxnard, CA 93030
(805) 988-5845
FAX: (805) 988-5847
Contact: Ron Whitney
Coastal Industries manufactures 4 different trap accessories: (1) Limited Area Sporting Clays which is an electronic controller and the base unit costs $1,100. (2) A Voice Release System which costs $750. (3) A Radio Release System for eight traps which costs $2,400. (4) A Trap Counter which costs $220 per station and $125 for the carrying unit.

Course Control Bird Counter
The Shooting Academy
8130 E. LaJunta Rd.
Scottsdale, AZ 85255
(602) 585-0882
Contact: Mike Davey
System that allows a shooter or group of shooters to go around a course or shooting field on their own, pulling as many targets as they wish. This system allows to keep check on targets released and eliminates trapper help.

Crazy Quail Base
Whiteside's Mfg. Co., Inc.
45408 160th St. West
Lancaster, CA 93536
(805) 724-1974
Contact: David Whiteside
A flat platform that can rotate 360 degrees. The user can mount any standard skeet type of machine on it. Can be used in continuous or positional mode.

EAGLE - i_{TM}

EAGLE-i™
Manufactured by Interactive Innovations, Inc.
11009 Jordan Lane
Austin, TX 78758
(888) 469-3817
(512) 873-7136
Contact: Bo Hazard
The patented EAGLE-i™ wireless target presentation system is the best engineered, most reliable product of its type available. This hand-held, multi-function control system features user programmed or pre-stored target presentation se-

quences for: 5 Stand, "Flush" formats, FITASC, and Target Counting. Additional programming capability allows users to assign fields for skeet, trap or various sporting clay configurations. Eagle-i will operate with all automatic trap machines currently on the market. Extremely users-friendly and reasonably priced! Call today for more information.

See Our Ad Pg. 244

The Hunters Pointe Wireless Release
Rt. 1, Box 166
Augusta, KS 67010
(316) 778-1122
FAX: (316) 778-1115
Est.: 1983
Contact: Larry Cero
Available: Direct
Wireless release, oscillating base, full wobble base, trap stands and controls.

InteliTrap
DNK, Inc.
5809 S.W. 5th St.
Oklahoma City, OK 73128
(800) 730-6656
(405) 947-6656
FAX: (405) 947-7014
Est.: 1994   Staff: 6
Contact: David Park
Available: Retail

Long Range
Systems
10840 Switzer, #110
Dallas, TX 75238
(800) 987-6749
FAX: (214) 349-6027
Contact: Ken Lovegreen
Wireless release systems for 5-Stand & skeet. Also manufacture a target counter.

See Our Ads Pgs. 243 - 263

SSI
9836 S. 219th E. Ave.
Broken Arrow, OK 74014
(800) 348-1111
FAX: (918) 455-9321
Contact: Randy Buchman
Revolutionary new launching technology for traps! Less breakage, quieter, quicker & smoother.
See Our Ad, Right

SHYDA'S
S E R V I C E S , I N C.

Shyda's Services, Inc.
1009 S. Lincoln Ave.
Lebanon, PA 17042
(717) 274-8676
FAX: (717) 274-8672
Distributor for wireless release systems, voice activated release systems, 5-Stand controllers, foot pedal releases, and programmable counter systems for all types of clay target machinery. We can also solve your communications needs with the new Motorola Sport 2-way radios and base station. Many accessories available.

See Ads Pgs. 65, 71 & 245

Tail Gunner
Throw-Rite Inc.
913 Baltimore
Kansas City, MO 64105
(800) 624-9083
Contact: Laurence R. (Brud) Jones, III
Available: Retail & Direct
Tail Gunner - portable trap platform. Mounts on any vehicle using a 1 7/8" ball.

Trap-House Sporting Clays
EZ Trap, 13575 SW 72nd Ave.
Miami, FL 33156
(800) 671-8121
Contact: Mickey Moore

Trapper's Buddy
Clay-Tech Industries, Inc.
1003 M-55 Ave., NE
Calgary, Alberta
Canada T2E 6W1
(800) 940-2529
FAX: (403) 295-2531
Contact: Harry Isaac
Budget priced manually operated eight (8) trap controller. Fires up to 8 traps simultaneously or individually. Great for training purposes, creating your own games or back-up for your electronic controller. Optional remote release. Ideal as teaching aid. Fully portable, self-contained and requires no external power source.

THE **V**ENTRILOQUIST

The Ventriloquist
The Computer Learning Works, Inc.
Box 866, Starkville, MS 39760-0866
(800) 445-3038
FAX: (601) 324-1189
Call: Gary Brunner/Michael Goines
http://www.netdoor.com/com/clw
email: clw@netdoor.com
The premier voice release system for trap or skeet offers radio or hardwired configurations. This sys-

tem has proven dependability and provides the consistency and reliability that other systems are trying to achieve. The VENTRILOQUIST offers, switchable delay options, custom programming for sporting clays applications, and compatiblity with all types of target machines backed by delivers prompt and professional customer service. CLW's sporting clays products range from a three-machine flush box to a fully computerized 5-stand controller. All products have a one year warranty covering parts and labor. CLW has applied the skills and technology developed over 12 years as a national educational software manufacturer to make its shooting products versatile and adaptable to most shooting situations. MC/VISA.

TRAP DISTRIBUTORS

Auto-Sporter USA
411 Northtrail
San Antonio, TX 78216
(210) 342-2118
FAX: (210) 342-2118
Contact: Dave Armstrong

B&B Trap Services Company, Inc.
PO Box 8312
Alton, IL 62002
(618) 467-6419
FAX: (618) 467-6351
Contact: Forrest G. Booth, Sr.
Winchester by LAPORTE Distributor

Clay Games, Inc.
55 Lane 240 Big Otter Lake
Fremont, IN 46737
(219) 833-6645
FAX: (219) 833-6649
Est.: 1993
President: Joel Werner
Available: Direct
Exclusive manufacturer of "Upland Clays" and distributors of NRA-Clays, Lincoln Traps and Target Pigeon.
See Our Ad Across, Right

Clay-Sport International, Inc.
Box 663, Bragg Creek
28 Echlin Dr.
Alberta, Canada T0L 0K0
(403) 949-3654
Contact: Raymond Forman
Distributor of Auto-Sporter, Bowman, IBIS, G.M.V. Super Star and Cock Pheasant Traps.

Deep River Sporting Clays and Shooting School
3420 Cletus Hall Rd
Sanford, NC 27330
(919) 774-7080
FAX: (919) 708-5052
Contact: Bill Kempffer
LAPORTE AMERICA, Pro-Matic & Lincoln Traps Distributor

Marty Fischer
SportShooting Consultants, Inc.
PO Box 207
Rincon, GA 31326
(912) 826-0072
Est.: 1992
Contact: Marty Fischer
Available: Direct
Lincoln, IBIS Auto-Sporter & Remington, Parker/Boss traps and accessories.

Doug Fuller
c/o Woods & Water
Rt. 1, Box 319
Catoosa, OK 74105
(918) 266-5551
Parker/Boss & Lincoln Distributor

G.H. Enterprises
Box 939
Okotoks, Alberta
Canada T0L 1T0
(403) 938-6070
FAX: (403) 938-3206
Contact: Gert Holmqvist

Golden West Industries
750 Arroyo Ave.
San Fernando, CA 91340
(818) 365-3946
Contact: Chuck Elton
Due/Matic Traps Importer

Howell Shooting Supplies
Rt. 3, Box 346A
Enterprise, AL 36330
(334) 393-2843
FAX: (334) 393-9274
Est.: 1985   Staff: 3
Sales & Repair Tech: Harrell Howell
Winchester by Laporte & Western Trap distributor. The South Eastern factory authorized trap, sales, service, parts and repair station. Same day parts shipping. Service at your place or mine by factory trained technician since 1985.

The Hunters Pointe
Rt. 1, Box 166, Augusta, KS 67010
(316) 778-1122
FAX: (316) 778-1115
Est.: 1983
Contact: Larry Cero
Available: Direct
Sales, parts, service, accessories for QUIKFIRE and other traps.

J&S Wholesale, Inc.
PO Box 638
13200 Jackson Gate Rd.
Jackson, CA 95642
(8000 445-4867 (ext. 231)
(800) 441-8484 (CA)
(209) 223-3094
FAX: (209) 223-3778
Pres: Jerry Jones
Available: Retail
LAPORTE AMERICA Distributor.
Wholesaler of ammunition, targets, reloading supplies, gun cases, gun safes, chokes and accessories.
See Our Ad Pg. 250

Jon Kruger
Box 213
St. Ansgar, IA 50472
(515) 736-4893
Parker/Boss Distributor

Michael Murphy & Sons
6400 S.W. Hunter Rd.
Augusta, KS 67010
(316) 775-2137
Est.: 1976   Staff: 2
Pres: Michael Murphy
Distributor of Kromson, Lincoln and Quikfire Traps

Gordon C. Philip
1701 Northwest Cookingham
Kansas City, MO 64155
(816) 734-4044

R&R Sales and Service
9903 Geronimo Oaks
San Antonio, TX 78254
(210) 688-3165
Est.: 1989   Staff: 3
Contact: FM "Butch" Roberson, III
Lincoln, Beomat, Winchester by LAPORTE, Parker/Boss and Hunters Pointe trap distributor. Ask about our single pole steel towers–available from 40 ft. to 120 ft. tall!

Rhodeside, Inc.
1704 Commerce Dr.
Piqua, OH 45356
(513) 773-5781
FAX: (513) 778-9056
Contact: Jim Printz
LAPORTE AMERICA Distributor

Shooters Network
450 Briscoe Blvd.
Lawrenceville, GA 32045
(404) 338-1405
FAX: (404) 338-0732
Contact: Steve Middleditch
LAPORTE AMERICA Distributor

SHOW-ME SPORTS

Show-Me Sports Corp.
Headquarters for IBIS Clay Target Products
8267 N. Revere
Kansas City, MO 64151
(816) 587-9540
FAX: (816) 587-3906
Est.: 1978
Contact: Andy Perkins
Headquarters for IBIS Clay Target Products & Distributors for Promatic, Remington, Sportrap and other major quality brands of traps and trap accessories for all shooting disciplines. Call for competitive quotes before making your purchase. Extended warranty and service contracts available.
See Our Ad Pg. 231

SHYDA'S
S E R V I C E S , I N C.

Shyda's Services, Inc.
Home of Lincoln Traps
1009 S. Lincoln Ave.
Lebanon, PA 17042
(717) 274-8676
FAX: (717) 274-8672
Trap sales, parts, service and repair. Automatic and manual machines and accessories for Trap, Skeet,

Sporting Clays, 5-Stand and FITASC. We carry a full line of repair parts for many brands of clay target machines and specialize in Winchester Western rebuilding. Trade-ins accepted. Quality service of the clay target industry since 1985.
See Ads Pgs. 65, 71 & 245

R.L. Torresdal Co., Inc.
Hwy. 52 East
Ossian, IA 52161
(319) 532-9884
FAX: (315) 532-9387
Contact: Ray Torresdal

Trap Services Company
333 West 6160 South
Murray, UT 84107
(801) 288-9056
FAX: (801) 261-4149
Contact: Bruce Tofft
LAPORTE AMERICA Distributor

Tyler Trap Repair Center
4839 Justin Dr.
Dryden, MI 48428
(810) 796-2625
FAX: (810) 796-2625
Contact: Tyler Stewart
LAPORTE AMERICA Distributor

Robert W. Zeller
45 W 660 Plank Rd.
Hampshire, IL 60140
(708) 683-2039
Chucker Clay Thrower Trap Distributor

HAND TRAPS

Clark ProThrow
C. Richard Co., Inc.
2218 Taggert St.
Erie, PA 16510
(814) 899-7533
Est.: 1993   Staff: 3
Contact: Mick Clark
Available: Direct
Hand held clay target thrower made of high quality wood & metal. Only $19.97 from your local supplier or call us direct. The Pro-Thrower throws every time without breakage. Satisfaction guaranteed–call today!

Crazie Covie
2929 West Seventh St.
Fort Worth, TX 76107
(817) 332-7332
FAX: (817) 332-3666
Est.: 1986
Contact: Christopher K. Ryan
Crazie Covie is a TrueHand* Trap that has the capability of throwing up to four targets at a time. Available in Standard, Midi, Mini or Battue. Order individually or save and order the complete set for $199.00 Dealers Welcome!

The Hurler
PO Box 702861
Tulsa, OK 74170
(918) 631-1264
Contact: Bill Herring
Throws doubles or singles.

MTM Molded Products Co.
PO Box 14117
Dayton, OH 45413
(513) 890-7461
FAX: (513) 890-1747
Contact: Al Minneman
Sporting clay shoots with hand-held throwers? Yes, when they're from MTM! Our EZ-THROW-IT™, the original hand-held thrower, propels clays faster and farther than most mechanical devices. Jump birds, curves, ground-skimmers. Throws right and left handed. $4.96 + S/H. The EZ-DOUBLE-THROW™ lofts doubles or singles up to 60 yards. Adjustable horizontal and vertical separation of clays. $11.95 + S/H. The EZ-THROW-MR™ medium range thrower hurls a single clay up to 95 yards. Designed for high flyover practice. $13.45 + S/H. Phone or fax for free catalog or name of nearest dealer.

TRAPS FOR HIRE/ MOBILE UNITS

Clay Games, Inc.
55 Lane 240 Big Otter Lake
Fremont, IN 46737
(219) 833-6645
FAX: (219) 833-6649
Est.: 1993
President: Joel Werner
Portable unit with compact design fits on a single trap or skeet field. Throws standard trap & skeet, midis, minis, rabbits, battues, & AmericanZZ. Please call for more information.
See Our Ad Pg. 261

MID-CAL Trap
Sales & Service
7728 West McKinley
Fresno, CA 93722
(209) 275-1775
Contact: Al Milla or Ron Doris
Completely mobile and automatic sporting clays and 5-station unit. Target Pigeon/ZZ also available. Set-ups at your club events or private property.
See Our Ad Below

John Meitzen
Outdoors Unlimited
Box 515, Eagle Lake, TX 77434
(409) 234-5750
Contact: John Meitzen
Our mobile unit specializes in specialty targets. All equipment is battery (12V) operated. Certified instruction available.

NSCA 5-Stand Sporting
5931 Roft Rd.
San Antonio, TX 78253
(210) 688-3371 (Ext. 109)
FAX: (210) 688-3014
Staff: 4
NSCA 5-Stand Sporting Scheduler: Don Snyder, Ext. 109
Thanks to the sponsorships of Ducks Unlimited, Winchester and The Texas Parks & Wildlife Department, the NSCA has 3 single game NSCA 5-Stand units available. We also have, thanks to Briley, Browning, Jeep, Laporte, National Sports Shooting Foundation, Winchester and White Flyer, an NSCA Sporting Clays demonstration unit with all the equipment necessary to set up multiple NSCA 5-Stand Sporting fields or sporting clays courses.

Quack Mobile Modern Era Recreational Shotgun Game Fair & Tour-Division
Quack Sporting Clays, Inc.
4 Ann & Hope Way
PO Box 98
Cumberland, RI 02864
(401) 723-8202
FAX: (401) 722-5910
Est.: 1987
Pres/CEO: Kenneth Gagnon, Sr.
Now "On the Road", our instructional mobile tour for the Modern Era Recreational Shotgun Games Fair & Tour. Our shotgun games include: Modern Skeet, Modern Action Clays (MARC-5) where only semi-auto's and pump shotguns are allowed to shoot 3-4 or 5 birds in the air or on the ground by a single hunter. Some of our other Modern Era games; Modern Pigeon, Lone Goose, Ring-My-Chimes, Covey Rise, Blackjack, "Rapid Fire", English Sporting Clays, and more.
See Our Ad Pgs. 238 - 239

R&R Sales and Service
9903 Geronimo Oaks
San Antonio, TX 78254
(210) 688-3165
FAX: (210) 688-9048
Est.: 1989   Staff: 3
Contact: F.M. "Butch" Roberson, III
We sell and service Lincoln, Beomat, Winchester by Laporte, Remington Parker/BOSS and Hunters Pointe machines. We offer a traveling mobile NSCA 5-Stand, as well as design and install NSCA 5-Stand, Sporting Clays, Skeet and Trap fields. Quint Roberson is our Level I Skeet and Sporting Clays instructor and NSCA 5-Stand operator. Bobby Head is our chief technician. Please do not hesitate to contact Bobby for technical assistance. My Place or Yours!

Retriever Sporting Clays/Targets to Go
2929 West Seventh St.
Fort Worth, TX 76107
(817) 332-7332
FAX: (817) 332-3666
Contact: Christopher K. Ryan
Our mobile demonstration unit can provide: full sporting clays, flush 5-stand sporting clays, crazy quail, trap or skeet. We cover the Southwest region including: TX, NM, CO, OK, KS, AR, LA MS and Mexico. We bring our fun to you.

SHOW-ME SPORTS

Show Me Clays
8267 N. Revere
Kansas City, MO 64151
(816) 587-9540
FAX: (816) 587-3906
Est.: 1978
Contact: Andy Perkins
Centrally located in Kansas City. Specializing in major shoot support. Tournaments, fund raisers, company outings, private parties, organizations and club events. Custom design to suit your needs for trap, skeet, wobble, 5-Stand,

FITASC and sporting. We can assist in making your event a success. Call for booking: Andy (816) 587-9540.
See Our Ad Pg. 231

South Jersey Sporting Clays
404 S. White Horse Pike
Berlin, NJ 08009
(609) 768-8149
FAX: (609) 768-0372
Contact: Bill Barrett
We will bring our Fun Unit to your shooting facility– serving NJ, DE, Eastern PA and Southern NY.

Super Sporting Clays
PO Box 433
Detroit Lakes, MN 56502-0433
(218) 849-5376
FAX: (218) 847-0941
Contact: Duane Gjesvold
The Very Best Mobile Sporting Clays Unit Available! Super Clays uses top of the line throwers to provide consistent presentation on all sporting targets–standards, midis, minis & battues. We can set up to 20 shooting stations in less than 30 minutes. Available anywhere in the

U.S. Perfect for tournaments, shooting seminars, fund raisers, corporate/private parties and fun shoots. Call today for fee schedule and booking information. "We bring the fun to you!"

Top Gun Shooting Sports
800 3rd Ave., NE
Waseca, MN 56093
(507) 835-8245
Contact: Ed Prechel or Brian Breck

Trap-House
Sporting Clays
Next Generation, Inc.
13575 SW 72nd Ave.
Miami, FL 33156
(800) 671-8121
Contact: Mickey Moore
A self-contained transportable unit holding 15 traps to present all the angles, shots and target capabilities seen on a "traditional" sporting clays course. 13 shooting stations, separated by safety screens are positioned around the periphery of the unit. This game can be set up in the woods, in an open field or on a skeet field. Call 1-800-671-8121 to schedule your shoot.
See Our Ad Pg. 253

TROPHIES, AWARDS & PROMOTIONS

If there's anything a shotgunner likes more than winning his gun club's annual sporting clays tournament, it's showing off the trophy at work the next day. Fact is, shotgunners in general just can't seem to get their fill of shooting related pins, plaques, buckles, medals, trophies and awards. When used correctly by gun club operators, these items can be powerful tools in promoting business. Best of all, the immense selection of products in this category includes something in every price range. So if you're planning a tournament or fun-shoot, an organized hunt or a fund raiser—or just looking for something to promote your business day-to-day—call or write the suppliers in this section for more information.

Great Gift Idea!

Black's Wing & Clay makes a great gift for your favorite shotgunner! Why not order one now? Call: 800-224-9464 (9am-5pm EST)

Champion Awards

Champion Awards
3116 E. Shea Blvd., #153
Phoenix, AZ 85028
(602) 493-3064
FAX: (602) 956-7763
Est.: 1978   Staff: 6
Owner: D.W. "Nick" Nichols
Owner: Joyce M. Nichols
Available: Direct
Gun Club award specialists. Distinctive awards of the highest quality. Custom designed for your needs and budget. Specializing in buckles, money clips, bracelets, pendants, custom logos. Extensive line of awards: Wildlife Collectibles, Stained Glass, Framed Wildlife Scenes, Etched Glass, Clocks, Steins, Decanters, Collectors Plates, Sports Glassware. Call for quote.

Crown Trophy
1 Odell Plaza, Yonkers, NY 10701
(914) 963-0005
FAX: (914) 963-0181
Customer Svc. Mgr: Elyse Weisenfeld
Custom event medals; trophies and plaques.

Kapan-Kent Co., Inc.
701 E. 60th St.,
Los Angeles, CA 90001
(800) 845-1097 (Factory)
(213) 233-6162
FAX: (213) 233-6635
Est.: 1958
Contact: Kipp K. Anders
Custom glass & ceramic decorating–promotional, events & gift items.

Linden Awards
6201 Miller Rd., Suite C
Swartz Creek, MI 48473
(800) 253-9579
FAX: (810) 635-9112
Contact: Ronnie Alle
Long time supplier of trophies for sporting clays, trap and skeet clubs nationwide. Call today and request our 38-page color brochure and Tips on How to Run a Successful Shoot.

M-T Shell
1874 E. Old Lincoln Hwy.
Langhorne, PA 19047
(215) 757-0260
Contact: Mark R. Suder, Jr.
M-T Shell's new eight-inch diameter, 24-inch tall plastic containers are ideal for the shooting range. Made of durable polyethylene, they will hold more than 400 empty shells. They attach easily to sporting clays stands and can be labeled with any club or company name or logo. Available in red or green. Call for more information.

Mains Enterprises, Inc.
1770 B Industrial
Las Vegas, NV 89102-2620
(702) 474-9200
FAX: (702) 474-9897
CEO: Brandon T. Blackwell
Extensive line of trophy buckles, money clips, jewelry items and pins. Gun accessories - bird scene and monogram grip caps, gold bird scene & initial trigger guards, and custom side plates. Please call today for our free brochure.
See Our Ad Below

nördik

Nordik of America, Ltd.
3739 Douglas Ave.
Racine, WI 53402
(800) 972-5905
FAX: (414) 681-9545
Contact: Robert Lovdahl
Custom Laser Engravers specializing in awards & giftware for the sportsmen market. Catalogs available for $5.00, refundable with first order.
See Our Ad, Right

O.C. Monogram Co.
PO Box 250
Ocean City, MD 21842
(410) 213-7707
(800) 845-8306
Contact: Cathy Ritchie
Custom embroidery and garments. Hats, jackets, ties, sportshirts, towels and more.

Quack Sporting Clays, Inc.
K.G. Mfg. Co.-Awards Division
4 Ann & Hope Way
PO Box 98
Cumberland, RI 02864
(401) 723-8202
FAX: (401) 722-5910
Est.: 1968
Available: Retail & Direct
Quack Sporting Clays sister company K.G. Mfg. Co. has been manufacturing skeet, trap and sporting clays (shotgun) awards and prizes since 1968. Our custom participant pins, corporate emblematic logo pins, and stock shotgun merit pins are worn by shotgun shooters worldwide. We can accommodate small (100 pcs) or larger orders. Many items in stock; pins, buckles, silver bowls, decorative decoys etc. Custom in house engraving, quality workmanship, quick delivery, affordable prices, are the reasons why we have celebrated over 25 years in business. For more information call (401) 723-8202. (Manufacturer representatives wanted)
See Ads Pgs. 238-39 & 266

Shamrock Leathers, Inc.
9722 320th St.
St. Joseph, MN 56374
(800) 728-5184
(612) 363-7441

Don't forget to say "I saw it in Black's Wing & Clay" when responding to advertisements.

President: Edward Brophy
Available: Direct
We produce a great leather plaque as a shooting award as well as other leather products that can be either gifts or awards. Call today.

Shooting Awards
PO Box 596
Lafayette Hill, PA 19444
(800) 554-9742
FAX: (610) 828-0885
Est.: 1990
President: Terry O'Donnell
Exact replica of the AA White Flyer in bronze and aluminum.

Silver State Silver
1469 Greg St.
Sparks, NV 89431
(702) 358-1320

FAX: (702) 358-1328
Contact: Phil Nielsen or Karlin Paul
We manufacture trophy belt buckles, gold and silver items, awards including bronze statues, prints, decoys, clocks and more.

Tilden & Bonser, Inc.
1175 Spring Centre S.
Altamonte Springs, FL 32714
(407) 682-2646
FAX: (407) 884-9399
Contact: Jim Beasley
Available: Direct
Serving gun clubs nationwide, Tilden & Bonser offers a broad variety of premium quality trophies of every description, including belt buckles, money clips, precious met-

als, jewelry items and rare coins. Complete trophy packages from $59. Specialists in customizing. Quality craftsmanship. All orders–small or large–delivered promptly. Also available: wildlife prints, duck stamps. Call for our new brochure or a quote on your club's trophy needs. Our products and service will delight you. Satisfaction guaranteed!
See Our Ad Pg. 265

The Wildlife Den
6401 Schantz
Allentown, PA 18104
(610) 395-0140
FAX: (610) 395-0140
Est.: 1985   Staff: 3
Contact: Freeman or Barbara Kline
Nationwide suppliers of fine quality prizes, trophies and awards for Trap, Skeet and Sporting Clays clubs and associations. Extensive line of wildlife-themed sculptures, bronze statues, afgans, decoys, pewter steins and plates, custom-made buckles, engravings, art, limited edition prints, leather items, keepsake boxes, wall clocks, lamps, marble pictures and coasters, weather stations watches, jewelry and scrimshaw. Engraving available on all orders. In business ten years. Supplier of prizes to numerous State and Zone Shoots, smaller shoots, and leagues. Large inventory on hand for last minute orders. Request our 24-page catalogue and check out our affordable prices.

K.G. MFG. COMPANY

KG Manufacturing Company is a leader in the production of awards, participant pins and corporate promotional pins for the shooting sports since 1968.

Let us reproduce your club emblem or corporate logo in a unique handcrafted collectible. Send for free catalog.

4 Ann & Hope Way P.O. Box 98
Cumberland, RI 02864
(401) 723-8202; Fax (401) 722-5910

DESTINATIONS

It all starts here: a round of clays at a new gun club, a day-hunt at a nearby preserve, or an annual dream getaway to Georgia or Texas for quail, South Dakota for pheasant or Argentina for dove.

Black's DESTINATIONS directory puts information on thousands of shooting locations right at your fingertips. And dozens of experts who will help you plan, book your wingshooting trips abroad.

Turn to one of the following sections or pages and let the shooting and hunting adventures begin:

Wingshooting Travel & Booking Agents 268

Today there are wonderful opportunities to shoot abroad. The problem, of course, is taking advantage of them. Fortunately, there are many knowledgeable and experienced professional travel and booking agents who can help. You'll find 24 of the best on the pages that follow.

Hunting Preserves 283
Sportsmen think they're *Fantastic!* Here's why.

How to Use the WINGS Directory 286

Typical WINGS Listing 287

WINGS - Hunting Preserves, Lodges, & Outfitters 290
1,292 of them. State-by-state, alphabetically. State/page. . .

International Wingshooting Destinations 441

How to Use the CLAYS Directory 443

Typical CLAYS Listing 444

CLAYS - Sporting Clays, 5-Stand, Trap & Skeet 445
1,694 clubs. State-by-state, alphabetically. State/page. . .

WINGSHOOTING TRAVEL & BOOKING AGENTS

Let An Expert Show You The Way

Today there are wonderful opportunities to shoot abroad—whitewinged dove in Mexico, driven grouse in Scotland, waterfowl in Argentina, and others. The problem, of course, is taking advantage of them.

Even when expense is not an issue, the myriad arrangements necessary to make a wingshooting trip abroad can seem daunting to the average sportsman. Each country has its own laws concerning the movement of firearms; game licenses; shotgun and firearm certificates; carrying and purchasing ammunition (Mexico, for example, allows only 100 cartridges to be brought in by each person entering the country).

Why not have your fun the easy way? Let an expert show you the way. For want of a better designation, we'll call them wingshooting travel agents. In point of fact, many also serve big game hunters, fishing fanatics, and photo enthusiasts. Most of them are top-flight, highly experienced sportsmen themselves. Very often, the names of the companies they run are suggestive of the services offered. Some specialists restrict their services to North America. Others can place you or a group—fully escorted—-virtually any place in the world.

Services are extensive, customized to fit your time, schedule and budget, and designed to assure a carefree experience. Beginning with the basics, like a list of gear to bring, they include travel arrangements, reservations at lodges or resorts, professional guides, and more.

Additionally, these well traveled entrepreneurs handle all the details involved in reaching foreign destinations. And their knowledge of local customs and requirements—from Austria to Argentina, from New Zealand to Nairobi—makes shooting, not coping, the most memorable part of your trip.

TRAVEL AGENTS

Joe Abbott Tours
2613 Country Valley Rd.
Garland, TX 75043
(800) 233-8211
(214) 840-1935
FAX: (214) 278-5760
Est.: 1986
Contact: Joe Abbott
Destinations: Argentina
Birds Hunted: Dove, Duck, Geese & Perdiz over dogs

Addieville Adventures
200 Pheasant Dr.
Mapleville, RI 02839
(401) 568-3185
FAX: (401) 568-3009
Est.: 1979   Staff: 8
Contact: Geoff Gaebe
Destinations: England & Nova Scotia
Birds Hunted: Dove, Pigeon, Geese
Partridge, Driven Pheasant, Woodcock
Packages/Comments: Not your typical booking agent - personal attention before, during and after trips; booking from 1-8.
• Nova Scotia - the ultimate rod and gun combination of Atlantic Salmon and grouse and woodcock -

October only for the combination of the Salmon run and grouse and woodcock. We are now offering pheasant hunting trips in Nova Scotia.
• Classic English Driven Pheasant while residing on centuries old estates and accompanied by world renowned shooting coach JACK MITCHELL.

Argentina Estancias
(800) 778-4778 (Orvis)
011-54-972-27391
FAX: 011-54-972-27111
Argentina Estancias, an Orvis Endorsed Wingshooting Lodge, offers "never-to-be-forgotten" hunting and shooting in Argentina. English speaking guides and superb accommodations. Call today!

See Our Ad Across

Argentina Wings
20780 Temelec Dr.,
Sonoma, CA 95476
(800) 946-4486
FAX: (707) 938-0937

Est.: 1980
Contact: Carlos A. Brouard
Wingshooting and fishing with first class lodging at exclusively private country estates (Estancias). Excellent options for non-shooting guests. With many years of experience in the European market, Argentina Wings is now offering their services to hunters in the United States. Argentina Wings S.A. offers different duck, partridge and dove shooting locations in Argentina from the most popular "Los Laureles in Entire Rios" to the most exclusive "La Sistina" in Buenos Aires or Santa Rita in Cordoba. Twelve locations in all for shooting and fishing throughout the country. Our programs are custom tailored to meet each individual group's preferences. Discover the amazing wonders of Argentina's wildlife. Please call for our brochure and more information.

See Our Ad Pg. 270

Carolina Outdoor Consultants
PO Box 481, Bethune, SC 29009
(803) 334-6620   Est.: 1985
Contact: John Boulware
Destinations: Alaska, Mexico, Costa Rica (Worldwide)

The Detail Co., Inc.
3220 Audley, Houston, TX 77098
(800) 292-2213
FAX: (713) 524-7244   Est.: 1980
Contact: Jeri Booth or
Shawna Van Ness
Destinations: Mexico, Central America, South America, U.S., Scotland,
S. Africa, Spain
Birds Hunted: Dove, Duck, Goose
Perdiz, Pheasant, Quail, Partridge
Fishing: Bass, Marlin Tarpon,
Peacock, Snook, Salmon, Sail, Trout
Packages: The Detail Company specializes in individual or groups and
will personally oversee the planning
of your itinerary. Let us worry
about all the details. Just enjoy the
hunt of a lifetime. Call today.

Dunn's Adventure Travel
One Madison Ave.
Grand Junction, TN 38039
(800) 228-3006
FAX: (901) 764-2658
Est.: 1950   Staff: 75
VP: Jeff Sellers
Destinations: Worldwide
Birds Hunted: Upland, Waterfowl

**Escorted Adventures for
Disabled Adults**
PO Box 87, R.R. 25A
Orford, NH 03777
(603) 353-9826
Contact: Frank Lepore
Destinations: Worldwide, individually-tailored, one-on-one, hunting,
fishing and sporting trips.

Esplanade Tours
581 Boylston St.
Boston, MA 02116
(800) 628-4893
FAX: (617) 262-9829
Contact: Bill Keith

Fishing International
PO Box 2132
Santa Rosa, CA 95405
(800) 950-4242
FAX: (707) 539-3366
Contact: Bob Norman
Destinations: Argentina, Mexico
Birds Hunted: Duck, Dove

Frontiers Intern'l Travel
PO Box 959
Wexford, PA 15090
(800) 245-1950
FAX: (412) 935-5388
Est.: 1969   Staff: 44
Contact: Mike Fitzgerald, Jr.
Destinations: Worldwide, Including
Mexico, Argentina, Africa & Europe

Gage Outdoor Expeditions
608 2nd Ave., So., Suite 166
Minneapolis, MN 55402
(800) 888-1601
FAX: (612) 339-0964
Contact: Baird Pittman
Destinations: Argentina, Mexico,
South Dakota
Birds Hunted: Dove, Duck, Goose,
Quail, Pheasants
We offer destinations that are
plentiful in game and partner with
outfitters who have years of experience hosting guests from around
the world. We have brochures and
FREE videos on all of our programs.
We also have a wide variety of fishing programs. Corporate and
individual references available.
See Our Ad Across, Right

Griffin & Howe
Griffin & Howe
36 W. 44th St., Suite 1011
New York, NY 10036
(212) 921-0980
Est.: 1923   Staff: 15
or
33 Claremont Rd.
Bernardsville, NJ 07924
(908) 766-2287
Contact: Joe Prather
Destinations: African & North American big game and wingshooting.
England, Scotland & Europe for
wingshooting.
See Our Ads Pg. 77 & 166

High Adventure Company
2941 Little River Rd.
Madison, GA 30650
(800) 847-0834
Contact: Chuck Humphrey
Destinations: South America, Africa, North America
Birds Hunted: Dove, Duck, Geese, Quail, Perdiz, Francolin; Also Big Game & Sportfishing Packages.
Packages/Comments: The High Adventure team has been in the hunting and fishing business 23 years, and we have personally visited all of our destinations. We understand that timing as well as location can make or break a trip. Let us put our experience to work for you. ARGENTINA: The world's best high volume dove and duck hunting as well as perdiz over pointing dogs. A minimum group size of four shooters is required and we will assist you in putting your group together. Private ranch accommodations, great food and wine, and a superb staff make for an outstanding trip! Hunts start at $2,595 from Miami. Non-shooters are also welcome. SOUTH AFRICA: Great duck and goose hunting, along with fantastic upland birds. Included is a big game photo safari, superb food and accommodations. 8 day packages $3,980.
Let the High Adventure Company take you there so you can say "Been There - Done That".
See Our Ad Pg. 273

Holland & Holland Limited
32 Bruton Street
London W1X 8JS England
011-44-171-499-4411
Est.: 1835
Chairman: Alain Drach
Contact: John Ormiston/Piers Vaux
Driven partridge and pheasant at our own Devon estate. Also Scotland, Africa and Argentina.

The Hollek Company, Ltd.
117 East Louisa St., Box 144
Seattle, WA 98102
(206) 621-0846
FAX: (206) 621-0756   Est.: 1993
Owner: Harvey Hollek
Destinations: Russia, New Guinea, South America
Birds Hunted: Waterfowl & Upland Game "We don't send you, we take you."

Wingshooting The World

Argentina - Dove, Duck, Goose
Mexico - Dove, Duck, Goose, Quail
South Dakota - Pheasants

*E*njoy hunting like it was in the "good old days." Experience fields full of quail, a never-ending stream of fast flying doves, a sky filled with ducks and geese, and the sound of flushing pheasants. The choice is yours!

*G*age Outdoor Expeditions offers only those destinations that are plentiful in game and partners with outfitters who have years of experience hosting guests from around the world. We provide both individual and corporate clients with outdoor experiences custom tailored to their specific requirements.

*A*im for the finest hunting and fishing experiences, call Gage today for brochures and free videos of these and other outdoor destinations.

Call today for
more information:
1·800·888·1601

We're going great guns!

Sheila Horne Associates
PO Box 474, Salem, SC 29676
(800) 213-0303
FAX: (864) 944-0300
Contact: Johanna Reader
Luxury hunting, fishing in British Isles. Royal Estates, or Lodges. Commission/Free Place for escort. Partners programmes. Falconry, Gun dog displays, skeets, etc.

J/B Adventures & Safaris
2275 E. Arapahoe Rd., #109
Littleton, CO 80122
(303) 794-4485
FAX: (303) 794-4486
Contact: Beverley Wunderlich
Destinations: Worldwide, Africa, North America, Pacific Rim, South

America, Mexico & Argentina

Laguna Vista International
PO Box 44, Combes, TX 78535
(800) 274-4401
FAX: (210) 421-4402
Contact: Roger Gerdes
Destinations: Northern Mexico, Tampico, Vera Cruz
Birds Hunted: Whitewing Dove, Wild Quail, Duck, Geese, Sandhill Crane

LandsEnd Expeditions
5878 Springwood Dr.
Mentor, OH 44060
(216) 257-9403
FAX: (216) 257-9403
Est.: 1988   Staff: 3
Contact: Larry King

Destinations: Canada, Alaska, South America, Europe, Russia
Birds Hunted: Geese, Ducks, Sea Ducks, Pheasant, Grouse, Dove
Packages/Comments: We offer packages for groups of 2 to 20. Our wingshooting packages offer the client the best shooting available anywhere.

Las Palomas de Loma Colorada
PO Box 202, Linn, TX 78563
(800) 375-4868
FAX: (210) 380-3723
Est.: 1986   Staff: 35
Owners: Don Turner/Phillip Veale
Location: San Fernando, Mexico–85 miles South of McAllen, Texas
Capacity: 44 (Dove Season), 20 (Quail/Duck/Goose Season)
Car/Van from McAllen, TX
Airstrip
Agent: Outdoor Adventures (owner/operator)
See Our Ad Below

Los Patos
PO Box 202, Linn, TX 78563
(800) 375-4868
FAX: (210) 380-3723
Est.: 1992   Staff: 12
Owners: Don Turner/Phillip Veale
Location: 30 mi . E. of San Fernando
Capacity: 12
Birds: Duck, Geese
Car/van from McAllen, TX
Airstrip
Agent: Outdoor Adventures (owner/operator)
See Our Ad Below

Jim McCarthy Adventures
4906 Creek Dr.
Harrisburg, PA 17112
(717) 652-4374
FAX: (717) 652-5888
Est.: 1979   Staff: 11
Contact: Jim McCarthy
Destinations: Africa, Texas, Mexico, Argentina, Canada
Birds Hunted: Dove, Geese, Ducks, Francolin, Sand Grouse

ARGENTINA
ADVENTURES
William Larkin Moore & Co.
8227 E. Via De Commercio
Suite A, Scottsdale, AZ 85258
(602) 951-8913
FAX: (602) 951-3677
Est.: 1990   Staff: 4
Contact: Dan Moore
Destinations: Argentina, Uruguay
Birds Hunted: Dove, Pigeon, Partridge, Ducks, Geese (Big Game and Trout Fishing Combination Trips Also Available with Wingshooting Packages)
Packages/Comments: We specialize in full service wingshooting packages starting at $2,495 our trips include: friendly English speaking guides and assistance, all necessary permits & licenses, transfers, deluxe accommodations and International airfare on Aerolineas Argentinas. Price based on double occupancy and a minimum group size of four. Customized itineraries are available for all destinations. Groups sized from 1-12 persons.

HIGH ADVENTURE, CO....
They really have "Been There, Done That"

By Bret Barger

The High Adventure Company is a relatively new booking agency, but an experienced player in the outdoor recreation market. The company owns Burnt Pine Plantation, an up-scale shooting preserve, located near Madison, Georgia. And one of High Adventure's two owners is a partner in Game & Fish Publications, publisher of 30 monthly state hunting and fishing magazines.

Needless to say, when it comes to hunting and fishing, High Adventure knows what's going on. That's why, after hearing their guests at Burnt Pine complain about poorly organized or botched trips, the owners of High Adventure decided to share their experience and expertise with the rest of us. I'm glad they did, since it has taken much of the worry out of my outdoor travel!

Successful Trips

I have taken several of the trips offered by High Adventure and on each, they have consistently delivered more than they promised. And I am not alone in that assessment: The same good report comes back from friends who traveled with High Adventure. When "HA" says you will catch a bill fish, *you will*—probably several. When they say you will shoot at least a case of shells a day, they really mean two, or more, each day. If they send you to Africa for leopard, alert your taxidermist!

Best of all, when you travel with High Adventure, there is a good chance one of the owners will accompany you on your trip. They say they go to monitor quaility and to learn how to improve the overall experience. This practice is one very few booking agents follow and it may account for High Adventure's success.

Attention to Detail

I have a pet peeve with booking agents that won't let you in on the "real cost" of a trip—those little "extras" not quoted in the package price. That's not the case with High Adventure. With them, you will know what your trip will cost before you go. And whether you are a seasoned pro and know what questions to ask, or novice, you will be provided with the necessary detailed information to ensure a successful trip.

High Adventure may not have a lot of fancy brochures, but they do provide quality outdoor experiences. Most importantly, they can be trusted. On a recent mule deer hunt they booked for me I know they didn't make a dime of commission. When I asked about it, I was told: "It's the best place to go for a 'big mulie'." Now how many agents do you know that put a client's success above profitability?

Recommended Destinations

Here's a quick run-down of the High Adventure trips I have been on and can highly recommend: Argentina for dove, duck and perdiz; Africa for leopard and plain's game; Costa Rica, Guatemala, Baja and Canada for fishing. Friends of mine have had equally great success with trips booked for whitetail deer in Mississippi, exotics in Texas, bird shooting in Africa, and elk and antelope in New Mexico. If it's high sporting adventure you're after, my advice is to call High Adventure. Then you too can say, "Been There—Done That". Call or write: High Adventure, 2941 Little River Rd., Madison, GA; (800) 847-0834.

Outdoor Adventures, Inc.
PO Box 608, McAllen, TX 78505
(800) 375-4868
FAX: (210) 618-1037
Est.: 1987   Staff: 7
Contact: Don Turner
Destinations: Mexico, Costa Rica,
Canada, Alaska, Argentina, Africa
Birds Hunted: Whitewing Dove,
Quail, Duck, Geese
- Outdoor Adventures is a professional travel company with a FULL TIME dedication to consistently providing our clients with the finest adventure travel.
- Outdoor Adventures' staff personally previews each destination to assure our standards are maintained. "Follow-up" trips are regularly scheduled.
- Outdoor Adventures provides an important service to our outfitters-CLIENTS! As a result, our clients

often receive preferential treatment and preferred dates.
- Outdoor Adventures services are provided AT NO COST to our clients. All fees are incurred by the outfitter at the same cost as if you would have booke direct.
- Outdoor Adventures often provides a personal host for your group at no charge.
- Outdoor Adventures has in excess of 85% repeat clientele.
See Our Ad Pg. 272

Outdoor Travel, Inc.
Box 131687, Houston, TX 77219
(800) 533-7299
FAX: (713) 526-4302
Est.: 1984
Contact: J. David Settles
Destinations: La Loma, Mexico
Birds Hunted: Whitewing Dove,
Quail, Geese

The Outside Connection, Inc.
PO Box 288E, Sonia Lane
East Clarendon, VT 05759
(802) 775-7269   Est.: 1985
Owner: Bryce Towsley
Destinations: North America
Birds Hunted: Most species in
North America

Pathways International
449 E. Main St., PO Box 3276
Spartansburg, SC 29304
(803) 583-2435
FAX: (803) 583-7237
Est.: 1985   Staff: 8
Contact: Will Hudson
Destinations: Argentina, Uruquay,
Mexico, Kenya, Europe, Canada,
United States
Birds Hunted: Duck, Dove, Partridge, & Geese in Argentina.

Rod & Gun Resources, Inc.
Rt. 3, Box 465, Killeen, TX 76542
(800) 211-4753
FAX: (512) 556-2367
Est.: 1980   Staff: 8
Contact: David Gregory
Destinations: Mexico & Brazil, Canada, Argentina, Uruguay, Alaska, Texas and Idaho
Birds Hunted: Dove, Wild Quail, Pheasant, Perdiz, Duck & Geese, Hungarian Partridge, Chukar

Safari de Colombia Hunting & Fishing

Contact: Kjell Erland von Sneidern
(800) 684-5110 (U.S.A.)
FAX: 011-572-555-1581 (Colombia)
FAX: 011-572-555-2740
Destination: Colombia, Bolivia & Paraguay
Birds Hunted: Dove & Pigeon Year Round
See Our Ad Across, Left

Luis Sier Safaris

8168 Sierra Ventana
Buenos Aires, Argentina
FAX: 011-54-91-91-5268
Looking for the world's finest wingshooting? Contact Luis Sier Safaris for incredible hunts in Argentina. Each hunter will bag 25 to 30 birds per day during three-day goose hunts with guides and dogs. Five-day combination hunts for geese, ducks, pigeons and partridge. High volume dove hunts (six hunter minimum) September 15-February 28 include bird boys, all meals. Heavy bird population assure your satisfaction. Operating from a five-star ranch, Luis Sier Safaris has served the world's wingshooters for more than 20 years. Fax today to arrange your most unforgettable hunt.
See Our Ad, Right

Sporting Adventures

20211 Patio Dr., Suite 240
Castro Valley, CA 94546
(510) 886-5544
FAX: (510) 886-2250
Est.: 1987
Owner: Lee Bohner
Destinations: Western Mexico, Alberta, Colombia, Argentina, Botswana
Birds Hunted: Duck, Dove, Geese, Partridge, Goulds Turkey

Sporting Charters

PO Box 160818
Austin, TX 78716
(800) 448-8994
(512) 458-8900
FAX: (512) 458-6935
Est.: 1988   Staff: 3
Contact: Tosh Brown
Destinations: U.S., Mexico
Birds Hunted: Quail, Geese, Pheasant, Dove, Partridge, Duck

Sporting Holidays Internat'l

1701 Northwest Cookingham
Kansas City, MO 64155
(816) 734-4044
FAX: (816) 734-9650
Est.: 1977   Staff: 25
Contact: Gordon Philip
Destinations: Scotland, England
Birds Hunted: Black Game, Red Leg & Gray Partridge, Pheasant, Woodcock, Duck
Packages/Comments: 8 guns per party, completely guided; luxurious accomodations. No extra charge for non-shooting guests. Alaska fishing trips: June, July, Aug., Sept. All arrangements-guides, accommodations, transportation, one full week of the greatest fishing in the world.

Sporting International

15608 S. Brentwood
Channelview, TX 77530
(800) 231-6352
FAX: (713) 744-5271
Est.: 1967   Staff: 30
Contact: Tommy Morrison
Destinations: Mexico, Scotland, Botswania, Tanzania, Argentina, Colombia, Western U.S.
Birds Hunted: Whitewing Dove, Quail, Geese, Pheasant, Grouse, Duck, Francolin, Guinea Fowl, Sand Grouse.

Stafford & Stafford, Inc.

PO Box 11196
Jacksonville, FL 32239-1196
(800) 383-0245
(904) 725-9935
FAX: (904) 725-2588
Est.: 1991   Staff: 4
Contact: Ron Stafford
Destinations: Argentina, Mexico & Europe
Birds Hunted: Ducks, Geese, Whitewing & Mourning Dove, Quail, Perdiz
Packages/Comments: Stafford & Stafford is a service-oriented company, specializing in exclusive & private hunting trips, generally for 6-8 hunters, but groups of 4 welcome. A complete line of Central & South American fishing trips is also available.

Sunbelt Hunting & Fishing
3554 Boca Chica Blvd.
Brownsville, TX 78521
(800) 876-4868
FAX: (210) 544-4731
Est.: 1972   Staff: 6
Contact: Barry Batsell
Destinations: Mexico
Birds Hunted: Dove, Quail, Geese

Supreme Sporting Tours
Supreme Sporting U.K. Ltd.
Bordesley House, Birmingham
Rd., Redditch, Worcestershire
B97 6RH England
Phone/Fax: 011-44-1527-61000
Contact: Ashton D. Hall
Experience the finest in traditional
British games/shooting. Supreme
Sporting Tours guides you to the
most challenging of English sporting birds on long established
estates (many with Royal Patronage). Enjoy classic double gun days
with experienced loaders or instructors. Complete packages include
airport pickup and accommodations to make your sporting holiday
trouble free and carefree. Guaranteed testing birds, quality and
quantity to please all. Phone or fax
to make arrangements.
See Our Ad Below

The TBJ Group, Inc.
17326 W. Bluff Rd.
Lemont, IL 60439
(708) 972-1060
Est.: 1993   Staff: 3
Pres: Tom Jagielski
Destinations: Argentina; Guinea
Bissau
Birds Hunted: Dove, Pigeon, Duck,
Geese, Partridge, Guinea Fowl

Tex Mex Hunts, Inc.
PO Box 701189
Houston, TX 77270-1189
(800) 284-1286
Est.: 1987   Staff: 4
Contact: Darrell Donaldson
Destinations: Argenti. Mexico, Texas
Birds Hunted: Whitewing Dove,
Duck, Geese, Quail

The
Timberdoodle Club
One Webster Hwy.
Temple, NH 03084
(603) 654-9510
FAX: (603) 654-5964
Est.: 1967   Staff: 4
Contact: Randall Martin
Destinations: United Kingdom, Af-
rica, Central America
Packages/Comments: Small private
groups, custom itineraries.

Venture West
PO Box 7543, Missoula, MT 59807
(406) 825-6200   Est.: 1984
Contact: Cathy Ream, PhD
Destinations: Montana, Idaho,
North Dakota, Wyoming & Oregon
For a consultation fee of $10, we

will set up hunts for the following
birds: Pheasants, Huns, Blue
Grouse, Ruffed Grouse, Franklin's
Grouse, Sharptail, Sage Hen, Chukar, Turkey & Waterfowl.

**Whitehair Hunting &
Fishing Travel**
PO Box 503
Chestertown, MD 21620
(410) 778-3592
Est.: 1989   Staff: 5
President: G. Michael Whitehair
Destinations: Argentina, Canada,
U.S. & Mexico
Birds Hunted: Ducks, Geese, Quail,
Pheasant, Prairie Chicken, Grouse,
Dove, Turkey, Perdiz, Partridge, Pi-
geon

Wilderness Adventures
219 John Wise Ave.
Essex, MA 01929
(508) 768-3338
FAX: (508) 768-3239
Contact: Allan Guminski

Wilderness Expeditions, Inc.
1080 Goffle Rd.
Hawthorne, NJ 07506
(800) 852-HUNT
(201) 427-8600
FAX: (201) 427-2447
Est.: 1979   Staff: 3
Contact: Nancy Alward or
Phil Alward
Destinations: North America
We arrange trips for hunting,
fishing & birds all over N.A. and
some areas in So. America.

Wilderness Pursuits Int'l.
Box 1258, Center Harbor, NH 03226
(800) 231-1650
FAX: (603) 253-3043
Est.: 1989   Staff: 3
Pres.: Rick Davis
Destinations: Canada & Western U.S.
Birds Hunted: Grouse, Woodcock,
Wilson Snipe, Canada Geese, Black
and Sea Duck, Ptarmigan.

Wing Shooting Adventures
0-1845 West Leonard
Grand Rapids, MI 49544
(616) 677-1980
FAX: (616) 667-1986
Est.: 1982   Staff: 4
Contact: Jack J. Jansma
Destinations: Hungary & Spain
Birds Hunted: Driven Pheasant &
Driven Partridge

Wings, Inc.
403 Greene St., PO Box 743
Camden, SC 29020-0743
(803) 425-7260 (Day)
(803) 432-5877 (Eve)
FAX: (803) 425-7270
Est.: 1989   Staff: 3
Contact: Don Terrell
Destinations: Argentina, Mexico
Birds Hunted: Dove, Duck
See our ad for special 3-day pack-
ages to Argentina and Eastern
Mexico.
See Our Ad Above, Right

World Hunts, Inc.
PO Box 777, Latrobe, PA 15650
(412) 537-7668
FAX: (412) 537-5301
Est.: 1986
Contact: Peter C. Theron
Destinations: Africa, Mexico, South
Pacific & Europe
Birds Hunted: Egyptian Geese,
Guinea Fowl, Rock Pigeon, Red-Eye
Dove, Cape Turtle Dove, Rameron
Pigeon, Yellow Bill Duck, Red Bill
Teal, Cape Teal, African Shelduck,
Cape Shovelier, Pheasant, Francolin
& Partridge (grey wing).

**Worldwide Hunting
Adventures, Inc.**
Box 93687, Las Vegas, NV 89193
(702) 791-2079
FAX: (702) 791-5118
Est.: 1988   Staff: 3
Contact: Dick Krafve
Destinations: Worldwide
Birds Hunted: All types of birds.

Going on a wingshooting adventure?

That't great! But to get the most out of your trip, you'll
want to go fully outfitted. A new travel gun case might be
called for. New clothes? Boots? Perhaps, a brand new shotgun. Fortunately, you're in the right place. Turn to the
following sections to begin. And enjoy your trip!

1997 CALENDAR OF EVENTS

January

Jan. 15-18
65th Annual NAGA
Convention & Short Course
Pinnacle Hotel Four Seasons,
Albuquerque, NM
(803) 796-8163
Contact: Walter Walter
North American Gamebird Assoc.
PO Box 2105
Cayce-West Columbia, SC 29171

Jan. 23-26
11th Annual Quail Unlimited
Celebrity Hunt
Albany, GA
(803) 637-5731
Contact: Connie Greene
Quail Unlimited
PO Box 610
Edgefield, SC 29824

Jan. 24-26
13th National Firearms
Engravers & Gunmakers
Exhibition
The Sands Hotel, Reno, NV
(319) 752-6114
Contact: Jan Billeb
American Custom Gunmakers Guild
PO Box 812
Burlington, IA 52601

Jan. 24-26
Rocky Mountain Elk
Foundation Eastern Rendevous
Valley Forge Convention Ctr., PA
(800) 225-5355
Conventions Mgr: Carrie Cummings
Rocky Mountain Elk Foundation
PO Box 8249
Missoula, MT 59807

Jan. 29-Feb. 1
SCI's 25th Annual
Hunters Convention
Sands Expo Center, Las Vegas, NV
(602) 620-1220
Contact: Safari Club International
4800 West Gates Pass Rd.
Tucson, AZ 85745

Jan. 30-Feb. 2
19th Annual S.H.O.T. Show
Las Vegas Convention Center,
Las Vegas, NV
(203) 840-5600
Contact: Reed Exhibition
Companies
383 Main Ave.
Norwalk, CT 06851

JANUARY

S	M	T	W	T	F	S
			1	2	3	4
5	6	7	8	9	10	11
12	13	14	15	16	17	18
19	20	21	22	23	24	25
26	27	28	29	30	31	

FEBRUARY

S	M	T	W	T	F	S
						1
2	3	4	5	6	7	8
9	10	11	12	13	14	15
16	17	18	19	20	21	22
23	24	25	26	27	28	

MARCH

S	M	T	W	T	F	S
						1
2	3	4	5	6	7	8
9	10	11	12	13	14	15
16	17	18	19	20	21	22
23	24	25	26	27	28	29
30	31					

February

Feb. 20
Pheasants Forever West
Metro Annual Banquet
Sheraton Park Place Hotel,
St. Louis Park, MN
(612) 773-2000
Contact: Pheasants Forever
PO Box 75473
St. Paul, MN 55175

Feb. 21-23
Quail Unlimited
Championship Trial
Central Florida Hunting Grounds,
Lake Wales, FL
(317) 839-4059
Contact: National Shoot to
Retrieve Field Trial Assoc.
226 North Mill St., #2
Plainfield, IN 46168

Feb. 27-March 2
Rocky Mountain Elk
Foundation Elk Camp & Expo
Salt Palace, Salt Lake City, UT
(800) 225-5355
Conventions Mgr: Carrie Cummings
Rocky Mountain Elk Foundation
PO Box 8249
Missoula, MT 59807

Feb. 28-March 2
NAHC's 1997 Jamboree
MGM Grand Hotel, Las Vegas, NV
(612) 988-7116
Contact: Kristine Houtman, Events
Director North Amer. Outdoor Group
12301 Whitewater Dr.
Minnetonka, MN 55343

March

March 14-17
IWA-International Trade Fair
for Hunting and Sporting
Arms & Accessories
Nuremberg Fair Grounds,
Nuremberg, Germany
(508) 371-2203
Contact: Kathy Donnelly
Concord Expo Group
PO Box 677
Concord, MA 01742

March 21-23
Sportsman's Fiesta
National Gun Club, San Antonio, TX
(210) 688-3371
Contact: Dee Dee Sarff, Ext. 103
National Sporting Clays Association
5931 Roft Rd.
San Antonio, TX 78253
The Sportsman's Fiesta will be an
outdoor fair unique to any other
event ever created. Visitors will try
out different brands of firearms,
archery equipment, fishing tackle,
and test drive off-road vehicles
provided by various manufacturers.

March 22-23
National Pheasant Championship
Oakwood Sporting Resort,
Sigourney, IA
Contact: Pheasant Hunters
Unlimited
995 East County Rd. 1550
Hamilton, IL 62341

April

April 9-11
Firearms Trade Expo (FTE)
Atlantic City Convention Ctr.,
Atlantic City, NJ
(954) 561-3505
Contact: Andrew Molchan
American Firearms Industry
2245 E. Sunrise Blvd., #916
Fort Lauderdale, FL 33304
Open to the trade only.

April 10-13
11th Annual Ducks Unlimited
Continental Fun Shoot
Wolf Creek Sport Shooting,
Altanta, GA
(901) 758-3816
Contact: Gary Goodpaster
Ducks Unlimited
Special Projects Department
One Waterfowl Way
Memphis, TN 38120

April 17
Pheasants Forever Annual
Banuqet
Radisson Hotel,
St. Paul, MN
(612) 773-2000
Contact: Pheasants Forever
PO Box 75473
St. Paul, MN 55175

April 17-20
Association of College Unions -
International Clay Target
Championship
National Gun Club,
San Antonio, TX
(513) 529-3355
Contact: John Walker
Manager of Special Events
Miami University
Oxford, OH 45056

April 17-20
Triple Crown (formerly known
as Alabama Governor's Cup)
4/17 - Sub-gauge event
Rockfence Station, Alabama
4/18 - Main event
Llewellin's Point, Georgia
4/19 - Main event
White Oak Plantation, Alabama
4/20 - Main event
Rockfence Station, Alabama
(334) 864-0217
Contact: Kane Hudmon
Rockfence Station
4388 Chambers Cty. Rd. 160
Lafayette, AL 36862

April 17-20
12th Annual U.S. Open
Pheasant Championship
Minnesota Horse & Hunt Club,
Prior Lake, MN
(612) 447-2272
Contact: Terry Correll
Minnesota Horse & Hunt Club
PO Box 482
Prior Lake, MN 55372

APRIL

S	M	T	W	T	F	S
		1	2	3	4	5
6	7	8	9	10	11	12
13	14	15	16	17	18	(19)
20	21	22	23	24	25	26
27	28	29	30			

MAY

S	M	T	W	T	F	S
				1	2	3
4	5	6	7	8	9	10
11	12	13	14	15	16	17
18	19	20	21	22	(23)	24
25	26	27	28	29	30	31

JUNE

S	M	T	W	T	F	S
1	2	3	4	5	(6)	7
8	9	10	11	12	13	14
15	16	17	18	19	20	21
22	23	24	25	26	27	28
29	30					

April 19-20
WSSF Ladies Charity
Classic "Mother Shoot"
Bayou Rifles, Houston, TX
(713) 584-9907
Contact: Sue King
Women's Shooting Sports
Foundation
1505 Hwy. 6 South, Suite 101
Houston, TX 77077

April 21-27
NSTRA Champion of
Champions
Conservation Bird Dog Club,
Amo, IN
(317) 839-4059
Contact: National Shoot-to-Retrieve
Field Trial Association
226 North Mill St., #2
Plainfield, IN 46168

April 24-26
9th Annual Chevy Truck
Sportsmen's
Team Challenge National
Championships
Markham Regional Range,
Sunrise, FL
(203) 426-1320
Contact: National Shooting Sports
Foundation
Flintlock Ridge Office Center
11 Mile Hill Rd.
Newtown, CT 06470

May

May
World English Sporting Clays
National Gun Club,
San Antonio, TX
(210) 688-3371
Contact: Lois Lessing, Ext. 108
National Sporting Clays Association
5931 Roft Rd.
San Antonio, TX 78253
Annual international event that
rotates between Great Britain and
the U.S. in partnership with the
CPSA and NSCA.

May
NSCA U.S. Open
American Shooting Center,
Houston, TX
(210) 688-3371
National Sporting Clays Association
5931 Roft Rd.
San Antonio, TX 78253
This annual event is held at
different locations throughout the
U.S. each year.

May
The Ducks Unlimited Great
Outdoors Sporting
and Wildlife Festival
Agricenter International,
Memphis, TN
(213) 782-2900
Contact: Maril Baumann
Petersen Publishing
6420 Wilshire Blvd.
Los Angeles, CA 90048-5515

May
Quail Unlimited/Redman
National Sporting Clays
Tournament
Quail Unlimited
Location: T.B.A.
Macon, GA
(803) 637-5731
Contact: Connie Greene, QU
PO Box 610
Edgefield, SC 29824

May 2-6
NRA Annual Meetings & Exhibits
Seattle Convention Center,
Seattle, WA
(703) 267-1000
Contact: National Rifle Association
11250 Waples Mill Rd.
Fairfax, VA 22030

May 15-19
Ducks Unlimited National Convention
Chicago, IL
(901) 758-3716
Contact: Convention Central
Ducks Unlimited
One Waterfowl Way
Memphis, TN 38120

HOMESTEAD.
1766

May 23-25
The Homestead Cup
The Homestead, Hot Springs, VA
(800) 838-1766 or (540) 839-1766
Contact: The Shooting Club
The Homestead
PO Box 2000
Hot Springs, VA 24445
See Our Ad Across

May 31-June 1
Lew Horton's Great Eastern Sporting Clays Classic
Addieville East Farm,
Mapleville, RI
(401) 568-3185
Contact: Geoff Gaebe
Addieville East Farm
200 Pheasant Dr.
Mapleville, RI 02839

June

June 6-8
The Big Pig
Location: T.B.A.
(301) 293-1936
Contact: Mid-Maryland Outfitters, Inc.
3000 E. Ventrie Ct.
Myersville, MD 21773

June 14-15
SCI United States Championships
Orvis Sandanona,

JULY

S	M	T	W	T	F	S
		1	2	3	4	5
6	7	8	9	10	11	12
13	14	15	16	17	18	19
20	21	22	23	24	25	26
27	28	29	30	31		

AUGUST

S	M	T	W	T	F	S
					1	2
3	4	5	6	7	8	9
10	11	12	13	14	15	16
17	18	19	20	21	22	23
24	25	26	27	28	29	30
31						

SEPTEMBER

S	M	T	W	T	F	S
1	2	3	4	5	6	
7	8	9	10	11	12	13
14	15	16	17	18	19	20
21	22	23	(24)	25	26	27
28	29	30				

Millbrook, NY
(203) 831-8483
Contact: Sporting Clays of America
9 Mott Ave.
Suite 103
Norwalk, CT 06850

June 21-22
The Ohio Cup
Mad River Sportsmen's Club,
Bellefontaine, OH
(513) 593-8245
Contact: Tony Stratton
Mad River Sportsmen's Club
One Hunter Place
Bellefontaine, OH 43311

June 22-26
OWAA Annual Conference
Haines City, FL
(814) 234-1011
Contact: Eileen King
Outdoor Writers Association of
America
2017 Cato Ave., Suite 101
State College, PA 16801-2768

Question or problem?
Give Black's Wing & Clay
a call 9 am - 5 pm E.S.T.
(908) 224-8700.

July

July
Quail Unlimited National Convention & Sportsmen's Expo
Kansas City, MO
(803) 637-5731
Contact: Connie Greene
Quail Unlimited
PO Box 610
Edgefield, SC 29824

July 29-Aug. 3
SCA National Championships
Location: T.B.A.
(203) 831-8483
Contact: Sporting Clays of America
9 Mott Ave., Suite 103
Norwalk, CT 06850

August

August
98th Grand American
Amateur Trapshooting
Association, Vandalia, OH
(513) 898-4638
Contact: Amateur Trapshooting
Association 601 W. National Rd.
Vandalia, OH 45377

August
NSCA/FITASC Nationals
Location: T.B.A.
(210) 688-3371
Contact: Lois Lessing, Ext. 108
National Sporting Clays Association
5931 Roft Rd.
San Antonio, TX 78253
This annual event is held at
different locations around the
country. Watch Sporting Clays
Magazine for the 1997 location
and date of this exciting event
typically held in August.

HOMESTEAD.
1766

August
The Homestead Sporting Clays Golf Championship
The Homestead, Hot Springs, VA
(800) 838-1766 or (540) 839-1766
Contact: The Shooting Club
The Homestead
PO Box 2000
Hot Springs, VA 24445
See Our Ad Across

HOMESTEAD®
1766

AMERICA'S PREMIER MOUNTAIN RESORT

Home of

The Homestead Cup Sporting Clays Championship
–Memorial Day Weekend, May 23-May 25, 1997–

The Homestead Sporting Clays Golf Championship
–Annually in August–

And Former Host Of

- The 1992 United States Open Sporting Clays Championship
- 1992, 1993 & 1994 Land Rover Challenge for the Virginia Cup
- 8 United States Golf Association Championships
- The 1995 Merrill Lynch Senior PGA TOUR Shoot-Out Championship

Visit The Homestead and experience the ultimate sporting vacation. Located on 15,000 acres in the Allegheny Mountains of Virginia, the resort offers 521 rooms, sporting clays, skeet, trap, golf, tennis, fly fishing, horseback and carriage rides, 100 miles of hiking and mountain bike trails, complete children's program and a European style spa. Enjoy fine or casual dining and browse through 20 sport shops and boutiques.

LEVEL I and III N.S.C.A. INSTRUCTION AVAILABLE
Specializing in Corporate Meetings
Featuring Sporting Clays and Golf Outings

For More Information or Reservations Call:

The Homestead
P.O. Box 2000 • Hot Springs, VA 24445
800-838-1766 • 540-839-1766

CLUB RESORTS™
Where every guest is a Member®

Aug. 8-10 & Aug. 15-17
The 16th Annual Game Fair
Armstrong Ranch, Anoka, MN
(612) 427-0944
Contact: Charles Delaney
Game Fair, 8404 161st Ave., NW
Anoka, MN 55303

Aug. 30-Sept. 1
NSTRA Purina Hi-Pro National
Endurance Classic
Location: T.B.A.
(317) 839-4059
Contact: National Shoot-to-Retrieve
Field Trial Association
226 North Mill St., #2
Plainfield, IN 46168

September

September
NSCA National Sporting Clays
National Gun Club,
San Antonio, TX
(210) 688-3371
National Sporting Clays Association
5931 Roft Rd.,San Antonio, TX 78253
Come enjoy the world's finest in
sporting clays in Sept. at the Na-
tional Gun Club in San Antonio, TX.

Sept. 5-10
International Association of
Fish and Wildlife Agencies
Annual Meeting
Scottsdale, AZ
(202) 624-7890
Contact: International Association
of Fish and Wildlife Agencies
444 North Capitol St., NW
Suite 544
Washington, DC 20001

Sept. 24
8th Annual
Congressional
Sportsmen's
Foundation Banquet
Hyatt Regency Washington, On
Capitol Hill, Washington, DC
(202) 785-9153
Contact: Tom Sadler, President
Congressional Sportsmen's
Foundation
1730 K St., NW, Suite 1300
Washington, DC 20006

OCTOBER

S	M	T	W	T	F	S
			1	2	3	4
5	6	7	8	9	10	11
12	13	14	15	16	17	18
19	20	21	22	23	24	25
26	27	28	29	30	31	

NOVEMBER

S	M	T	W	T	F	S
						1
2	3	4	5	6	7	8
9	10	11	12	13	14	15
16	17	18	19	20	21	22
23	24	25	26	27	28	29
30						

DECEMBER

S	M	T	W	T	F	S
	1	2	3	4	5	6
7	8	9	10	11	12	13
14	15	16	17	18	19	20
21	22	23	24	25	26	27
28	29	30	31			

Sept. 26-27
4th Annual Louise Mandrell
Celebrity Shoot
Nashville Gun Club
Nashville, TN
(615) 792-1103
Contact: Sande Weiss
Louise Mandrell Celebrity Shoot
605 C North Main St.
Ashland City, TN 37015

Sept. 27
National Hunting &
Fishing Day
(203) 426-1320
Contact: National Hunting &
Fishing Day Headquarters
c/o NSSF, 11 Mile Hill Rd.
Newtown, CT 06470

October

October
NSSA World Skeet
Championship
National Gun Club,
San Antonio, TX
(210) 688-3371
National Sporting Clays Association
5931 Roft Rd.
San Antonio, TX 78253
NSSA World

Held annually at the National Gun
Club in San Antonio, TX, this event
draws shooters from around the
world for a week of shooting and
fun for everyone.

October
National All-Around Shotgun
Championships
(210) 688-3371
Contact: Mike Hampton
National Sporting Clays Association
5931 Roft Rd.
San Antonio, TX 78253
This event is a test of one's ability
to shoot a variety of different clay
target games. Each year it proves
to be more challenging. Watch
Skeet Shooting Review and
Sporting Clays Magazine for more
details on date and location.

Oct. 20-26
NSTRA Dog of the Year
Conservation Bird Dog Club,
Amo, IN
(317) 839-4059
Contact: National Shoot-to-Retrieve
Field Trial Association
226 North Mill St., #2
Plainfield, IN 46168

November

Nov. 14-16
Waterfowl Festival
Easton, MD
(410) 822-4567
Contact: Judy Price, Managing Dir.
Waterfowl Festival
PO Box 929
Easton, MD 21601

Nov. 20-22
National Association of
Sporting Goods Wholesalers
Hunting Show
Phoenix Civic Plaza, Phoenix, AZ
(312) 565-0233
Contact: Rebecca Maddy
National Association of Sporting
Goods Wholesalers
400 E. Randolf St., #700
Chicago, IL 60601

Nov. 26-29
62nd Annual World
Championship Duck Calling
Contest & Wings Over the
Prairie Festival
Stuttgart, AR
(501) 673-1602
Contact: Stuttgart Chamber of
Commerce
PO Box 932
Stuttgart, AR 72160

HUNTING PRESERVES

Hunting Preserves: Fantastic

If you've ever hunted a well run preserve, you know there's just one word for it: Fantastic!

Preserves offer longer seasons, larger bag limits and more consistent results. They're not overcrowded and are extremely safe.

More importantly, they're fun. There's no better place to train a new hunter--your spouse, son, daughter, or friend--than a hunting preserve. No better, more convenient place to enjoy a day afield.

Where else but a preserve can you begin the day with a big cup of coffee in front of the clubhouse pot-belly stove followed by shooting 25 rounds at the wobble trap to sharpen the eye and get the heart pounding.

Then you're off on a half-day hunt for any one of a variety of flighty birds, led by an experienced guide and a well trained dog. Just at the moment your stomach lets you know it's lunchtime, it's back to the clubhouse for a bite.

What's next? Perhaps a round of sporting clays or an afternoon dove hunt, while the staff processes the morning's take.

It's hard for today's time-pressured hunter to find a more convenient and flexible way to pursue his beloved pastime. In short, preserves offer something for everyone and surely as much hunting as you want.

It all depends on where you are, what you're looking for, and, of course, what you can afford. Whatever the case, Wing & Clay can help you find it-- near home or while you're traveling on business or vacation.

What To Expect

Hunting preserves are state licensed hunting areas that offer extended season or year-round hunting for ring-necked pheasants, bobwhite quail, chukar, Hungarian partridge, mallard ducks, wild turkey, and other birds, depending on locale. They are open to the public on a daily-fee or an annual membership basis or both.

What should you expect when you hunt a preserve? For starters, a warm welcome. Preserve hunters are valued customers, not tolerated intruders, and your host should do everything he can to provide a safe, enjoyable hunt.

Once afield, expect the preserve grounds to look like good hunting country with a rich blend of natural and planted cover. Properly reared, the game birds will be mature, full-plumed, strong flyers-- the same color and conformation as their wild counterparts.

Almost all preserves provide experienced guides and trained hunting dogs; many preserves will allow you to hunt with your own dog, if you prefer.

At some preserves, the hunt is only half the story. Roomy, well-appointed clubhouses, quality meals, comfortable, private accommodations and a variety of services

FLIGHT SPEED OF GAMEBIRDS IN MPH

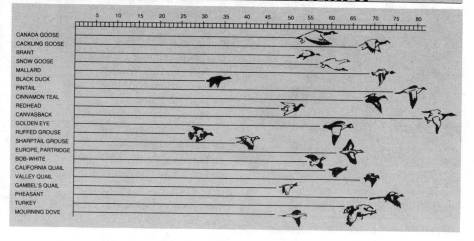

and amenities--ranging from airport pickup and shooting instruction to dog kenneling and sporting clays--await you. At other preserves, the services and amenities are more modest, or unavailable.

But one type is not necessarily better than the other. It all depends on you. Whether you're a new or seasoned hunter looking for a red-letter day of good dog work and flighty birds or a corporate executive looking for a place to entertain clients, there's a preserve out there to meet your needs and tastes. But remember, you may have to shop around.

Costs

How about cost? Well, again, it depends on how much hunting you want and the kind of "extras" you're looking for. Some hunting preserves charge a set-up fee for game birds released; others charge for a half- or full-day hunt (some offer longer hunt packages). All charge a minimum fee per hunter or hunting party. Some charge for dressing game birds; others do not.

In any case, fees vary. But a day on a hunting preserve doesn't have to cost more than a so-called "free hunt", and will certainly

JUDGING RANGE

40yd

30yd

50yd

60yd

20yd

TO HELP JUDGE RANGE

Prop up this page or lay it open on the floor. Select one of the birds in the chart and place the muzzle of your gun directly below it on the page itself. Look along the barrel. The bird will look the same size that it would appear at the selected distance.

take up far less of your time and probably prove more consistent and satisfying results.

Wherever you live in the U.S., there is likely to be a good hunting preserve within easy driving distance. And, if you're a typical hunter without landowner contacts, that preserve may be the most practical (and in the long run, the cheapest) way to spend a day afield with dog, gun and game birds.

Who To Contact

Inside Wing & Clay you'll find information on over 1,100 U.S. preserves open to the public on a daily-fee or a membership basis: Preserve names, addresses, and telephone numbers; the name of the person to call to ask questions or make a reservation; even information about the best time to call, not to mention details on the size and scope of the operation, the types of shoots offered, birds hunted, membership details and more. [See sample listing in the How To Use Wing & Clay section on the following page for a complete rundown on what you learn about a preserve from a Wing & Clay listing.]

Calling Checklist

Once you know what you're looking for, Wing & Clay's listings will help you identify those preserves likely to fit the bill. But it's a pretty good idea to put together a checklist of questions to ask, before you make a call. A quick question on the phone could save you a disappointing day in the field. For example: Does the preserve...

☐ Provide needed licenses?
☐ Provide airport pickup?
☐ Kennel bird dogs?
☐ Process game birds?
☐ Have a sporting clays course?
☐ Have deer hunting?
☐ Provide shooting instruction?
☐ Serve quality meals?
☐ Have special hunting jeeps?
☐ Train bird dogs?
☐ Have private bedrooms?
☐ Provide loaner guns?
☐ Sell factory ammo?
☐ Have a quality clubhouse?
☐ Offer other recreational activities?

Wing & Clay can help you explore the wide and exciting world of hunting adventures that awaits you. Enjoy. Safe hunting!

How to Use Wing & Clay's Hunting Preserve Directory

Your Prime Source Of Information

Finding a place to hunt takes time—especially when you are in parts of the country you don't know very well. Fortunately, you now have a copy of Wing & Clay to make the job easier.

The heart of the Hunting Preserve or Wings section of this book is its list of wingshooting preserves—the most comprehensive published.

An individual listing in Wing & Clay contains all the information you need to locate and contact a hunting operation that offers the kind of experience you're looking for. [See explanation of a Typical Listing found on page 288]. The advertisements that appear in the Wings section provide even more information about an operation. In short, they are an operator's way of telling you he or she is eager for your business, of saying, "Shotgunner's Welcome—stop by for a visit!"

A Note On Calling Or Writing

Contacting a hunting preserve by phone can be tricky, owing mostly to the seasonal nature of the business and that many operators work full time jobs in addition to running their hunting operations. Don't be put off if you have trouble making contact by phone. Many of the listings in the Wings section contain information on the best time to call. Look for times immediately following the contact name and call again. Or write and ask for a flyer, brochure or, when available, a video.

Say You Saw It In Wing & Clay

The publication of Wing & Clay would be impossible without the advertising support of hundreds of companies in the shotgun industry trying to reach and influence you efficiently and effectively. So whenever you contact one of these companies, tell them that you have benefitted from seeing their ad or listing. And don't forget to say that you "saw it in Wing & Clay."

HUNTING PRESERVE STATE/PAGE INDEX

Southeastern Illinois College: The Only School in the U.S. Training Preserve Managers

by Raymond Goydon

There was a time in this country when the words "commercial hunting property" described a farmer looking to squeeze an extra dollar or two from his land by making it available to hunters. Times have changed. Who says so? Bruce Hering, for one. Hering is the founder and director of an innovative program at Southeastern Illinois College designed to train the industry's first generation of professional hunting preserve managers.

"There's a growing number of hunting operations out there that exist as discrete business operations—not just agricultural sidelines," he says. And these operations make entirely different "management demands" on their operators.

Hering points out that the operator of yesteryear needed only to understand the use and care of hunting dogs, a bit about hand reared game birds, and at least a rudimentary idea of how to organize and run a hunt. "Some basic social skills never hurt either," Hering adds.

Southeastern's Shooting Preserve Commercial Wildlife Management program—the only one of its kind in the country—confers on its graduates an Associate Degree and a solid footing in disciplines ranging from game bird propagation and wildlife management to human relations and the principles of marketing.

Program participants spend three semesters in class and the field and a fourth, year-long semester interning on a working hunting preserve for what Hering describes as a "ground level view of how the industry works."

Students range from 18 to 35 years of age and come to the program from diverse backgrounds. (A recent class included an ex-coal miner, a former computer science major, and a tele-communications technician.) All have high school diplomas, and some have bachelor or graduate degrees.

"The program gives you the big picture," says a current participant just beginning his year-long internship at a prestigious southeastern plantation. "I had worked in the industry for three years before enrolling, but it wasn't until I started the program that I realized how complex a business this really is," he adds.

Hering's own research shows that the majority of successful commercial hunting operations have implemented a "professional" management plan dealing with all facets of the business. While no two plans are exactly alike, most include fairly sophisticated marketing and advertising programs, designated work assignments, and a clear sense of the importance of quality customer relations.

That last area—dealing with the public—is one of Hering's and the program's primary concerns: "When it comes right down to it, the student has to learn to make the customer comfortable or else we've failed. Knowing how to raise birds, tend cover and run hunts just isn't enough."

If industry response is any indication, Hering is clearly on the right track. The program's files are filled with glowing letters of praise for interns and graduates who have only just started to have an impact on the day-to-day operations of the industry.

"Like all businesses, commercial hunting operations will have to grow and evolve, or face the consequences," Hering says. "With a little bit of luck and a lot of hard work, our graduates will help lead the way."

INTERESTED IN LEARNING MORE? Each year the Shooting Preserve Commercial Wildlife Management program enrolls up to 16 students and places an additional 16 in intern programs across the U.S.

Operators and students interested in learning more about the program, its interns and graduates should write Bruce Hering at Southeastern Illinois College, 3575 College Rd., Harrisburg, IL 62946-4925; or call (618) 252-6376.

TYPICAL LISTING

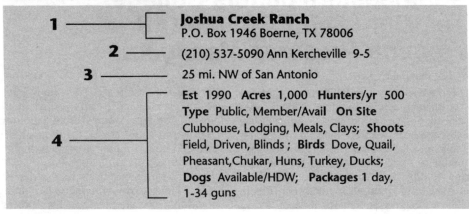

1 —————
Joshua Creek Ranch
P.O. Box 1946 Boerne, TX 78006

2 ————— (210) 537-5090 Ann Kercheville 9-5

3 ————— 25 mi. NW of San Antonio

4 —————
Est 1990 **Acres** 1,000 **Hunters/yr** 500
Type Public, Member/Avail **On Site**
Clubhouse, Lodging, Meals, Clays; **Shoots**
Field, Driven, Blinds ; **Birds** Dove, Quail,
Pheasant,Chukar, Huns, Turkey, Ducks;
Dogs Available/HDW; **Packages** 1 day,
1-34 guns

How The Directory Is Organized

Listings in Wing & Clay's Hunting Preserve Directory are organized alphabetically by state—Alabama through Wyoming—and within each state alphabetically by preserve name.

1 Preserve Name & Address Obviously helpful in finding a hunting operation's location, the address can help you gather detailed information when you are planning a hunting excursion. Write and ask for a descriptive flyer or brochure, most preserves have them.

2 Telephone Number, Contact name(s) & Best Time to Call The number and name of the person to call when you're looking for information or making a reservation. In many listings information about the best time to call follows the contact name.

3 Nearest Major Town/City Distance in miles and direction from a large city or town; intended to give you a better general idea of where the hunting operation is located.

4 Particulars Whenever possible, Wing & Clay offers detailed information—provided by the operator— about each hunting location. The categories are described below.

Est The year the preserve began operation.

Acres Number of acres owned or leased.

Hunters/yr The approximate number of hunters using the facility annually.

Type Specifically, type of membership. That is, whether the operation is open to all hunters (**Public**) or to members only–individual (**Member/Avail** or **Member/Ltd**) or corporate (**Corp**). Many membership clubs are also open to the public. Membership usually means an annual fee (ranging from $15.00 to more than $15,000) is required.

Member/Ltd. (or Limited) implies that the club's membership roster was filled at the time Wing & Clay went to press. **Member/Avail** means the club is private but new members are welcome. If you are interested in a club membership, Wing & Clay strongly urges you to write or call for information. Preserves typically respond quickly and courteously even when memberhip is currently filled.

On Site Services and amenities available at the preserve. Clubhouse, Lodging, Meals and Clays (some form of clay target shooting, not necessarily a sporting clays course). Note: Hunting preserve Lodging runs the gamut from bare-bones bunkhouses to luxurious private suites; similarly, meals might mean a hot dog and iced tea or a candle lit gourmet event.

Shoots Type of hunts or shoots offered at the preserve, including **Field Hunts, Tower Releases, Driven Shoots**, and **Blinds** and **Boats**.

Birds Type of birds hunted at the preserve. Wing & Clay currently tracks the following birds: Dove, Quail, Pheasant, Ruffed Grouse, Woodcock, Chukar, Huns (Hungarian Partridge), Wild Turkey, Prairie Chicken, Sage Grouse, Snipe, Sharp-Tail Grouse, Ducks and Geese.

Dogs Avail indicates that the preserve provides dogs and guides. /HDW means "hunter's dogs welcome" and you may hunt with your own dog if you wish.

Packages Indicates the shortest hunt package available, usually 1/2- or 1-day. The number of guns is the range of hunters the preserve will accommodate from the smallest to largest number. (Example: a preserve that will allow a single hunter to hunt, but can handle up to 4 guns per party on each of 4 separate hunting fields would include **1-16 guns** in its listing.)

Eagle Recreational Consultants Help Hunting & Fishing Lodges Achieve...

Uncompromising Quality

If there's anything Alan Kelly knows, it's how to deliver a quality wingshooting and fishing experience to today's demanding sportsman. But that's not very surprising when you consider that much of what Kelly has done in his private and professional life has prepared him for his role as expert in the field.

Expert in the making

Early experiences with bird hunting and fly fishing led Kelly to a career in wildlife management, first as a U.S. government biologist on the famous Big Horn River in Montana. In 1981 Kelly set out on his own as a consultant, advising clients around the country in fish and wildlife management. Later Kelly developed Eagle Outfitters and Eagle Nest Lodge to serve the growing hunting and fly fishing public drawn to his beloved Big Horn River.

Within a short time, Eagle Nest established itself as the premiere fishing and wingshooting lodge on the Big Horn, a reputation capped by a coveted endorsement from Orvis, Inc.

Today, the lodge's tradition of excellence continues under Kelly's direction and, he's quick to point out, with the help of his wife Wanda and sons, Keith and Matthew. (Orvis, Inc., was so impressed with the uncompromising quality of Eagle Nest that it selected Kelly to direct and manage its endorsed wingshooting lodge program. See sidebar for more.)

Consultant will travel

In addition to his work at the lodge and with Orvis, Eagle Recreational Consultants continues to advise many established and developing wingshooting and fly fishing lodges, both public and private.

Says Kelly: "I tell each of my clients that the lodge business is one of the most challenging, frustrating, educational and, ultimately, rewarding ventures an entrepreneur can undertake."

Kelly's consulting clients can tap his vast store of knowledge and experience in subjects as wide ranging as habitat development and management and customer service to lodge design and marketing strategies. Operators interested in learning more about Eagle Recreational and the Orvis Endorsement Programs should write Kelly at P.O. Box 926, Lincoln, MT 59639; or call (406) 362-4270.

ORVIS ENDORSED WINGSHOOTING LODGES

Launched in 1989, the Orvis Endorsed Wingshooting Program has one clear purpose: to identify the best bird hunting experiences available in the U.S. Of the hundreds of top-notch lodges currently in operation only 21, at the time of this writing, have earned the coveted endorsement.

To qualify, a lodge must convince program director Alan Kelly that it meets or exceeds Orvis's exacting standards. Kelly evaluates each lodge nominated for the program personally. In addition to what Orvis calls a"complete and totally uncompromising bird hunting experience", the lodge must provide professional guides and well-trained bird dogs. Equal in importance to the quality of the hunt is the lodge itself: first rate accommodations, prompt courteous service, memorable dining, and after-hunt amenities are a must.

"When you choose an Orvis Endorsed Lodge, you can be sure you're in for one of the finest hunting experiences available anywhere," says Kelly. For more information about the program contact: Alan Kelly, P.O. Box 926, Lincoln MT 59639; (406) 362-4270.

ALABAMA

Aldar Hunting Lodge
PO Box 806, Greenville, AL 36037
(334) 382-9660 Alan or Lorie Gentry
Type Public; **On Site** Clubhouse, Lodging, Meals;
Shoots Field; **Birds** Turkey; **Dogs** Avail/HDW

Arrowhead Lodge
PO Box 711, Butler, AL 36904
(205) 459-2604 David L. Ezell 8:30am-8pm
26 mi. SW of Meridian, MS
Est 1985; **Acres** 8,500; **Hunters/yr** 150; **Type**
Public; **On Site** Clubhouse, Lodging, Meals; **Shoots**
Field; **Birds** Turkey; **Dogs** Avail; **Packages** 2 Days,
1-16 guns

Bent Creek Lodge
PO Box 4267, Jachin, AL 36910
(205) 398-3437 Leo Allen
35 mi. E of Meridan
Est 1983; **Acres** 30,000; **Type** Public; **On Site**
Clubhouse, Lodging, Meals; **Shoots** Field; **Birds**
Quail, Turkey; **Dogs** Avail/HDW; **Packages** 1/2
Day, 4-12 guns

Bubber Cameron's Shooting Preserve
Rt. 1, Box 144, Aliceville, AL 35442
(205) 455-2420 Bubber Cameron/Rush Cameron
Est 1974; **Acres** 2,300; **Type** Public, Corp.; **On**
Site Clubhouse, Lodging, Meals; **Shoots** Field;
Birds Dove, Quail, Snipe; **Dogs** Avail/HDW;
Packages 1 Day, 1-15 guns o NAGA/See Pg. 107

Cedar Ridge Hunting Lodge
1137 Co. Rd. 258, Five Points, AL 36855
(334) 864-0404 Frazier Rudd/David Lowe
Type Public; **On Site** Lodging; **Shoots** Field; **Birds**
Quail, Chukar o NAGA/See Pg. 107

Dixieland Plantation
PO Box 168, Hatchechubbee, AL 36858
(334) 667-7876 Donald Dixon 8 am to 9 pm
25 mi. SW of Columbus, GA
Acres 5,000; **Type** Public; **On Site** Clubhouse,
Lodging, Meals, Clays; **Shoots** Field; **Birds** Dove,
Quail, Turkey; **Dogs** Avail/HDW; **Packages** 1/2
Day, up to 8 guns

Doublehead Resort & Lodge
145 Cty. Rd. 314, Town Creek, AL 35672
(800) 685-9267 Donny Patrick 8am-10pm
20 mi. W of Florence
Est 1996; **Acres** 950; **Type** Public; **On Site**
Lodging, Meals, Clays; **Shoots** Field, Tower; **Birds**
Quail; **Dogs** Avail/HDW; **Packages** 1/2 Day

Drakes Quail Farm
1123 Co. Rd. 771, Cullman, AL 35055
(205) 796-5857 D. Drake
Shoots Field; **Birds** Quail, Pheasant
o NAGA/See Pg. 107

Enon Plantation
Rt. 2, Box 275, Midway, AL 36053
(800) 950-1892 Diane & John Rex Gates 9-5
60 mi. SE of Montgomery
Est 1991; **Acres** 10,000; **Type** Public; **On Site**
Clubhouse, Lodging, Meals, Clays; **Shoots** Field;
Birds Quail; **Dogs** Avail; **Packages** 1 Day, 4-6 guns

Greenfield Hunting Preserve
Hwy. 4 West, PO Box 174, Pittsview, AL 36867
(334) 855-9118 Rick Cunningham
25 mi. S of Columbus, GA
Est 1987; **Acres** 2,200; **Type** Public; **On Site**
Clubhouse, Lodging, Meals, Clays; **Shoots** Field;
Birds Quail; **Dogs** Avail/HDW; **Packages** 1/2 Day,
2-12 guns

Gunsmoke Kennels
Rt. 2, Box 15, Union Springs, AL 36089
(334) 738-4642 Herb Holmes anytime
40 mi. SE of Montgomery
Est 1987; **Acres** 2,000; **Hunters/yr** 150; **Type**
Public; **On Site** Clubhouse, Lodging, Meals; **Shoots**
Field; **Birds** Quail, Pheasant, Chukar; **Dogs**
Avail/HDW; **Packages** 1/2 Day, 2-6 guns
o NAGA/See Pg. 107

Limestone Hunting Preserve
Box 227A, Ardmore, AL 35739
(205) 423-6029 Wayne Mitchell after 6pm
12 mi. N of Huntsville
Est 1990; **Acres** 500; **Type** Public; **On Site**
Clubhouse; **Shoots** Field; **Birds** Dove, Quail,
Pheasant, Chukar, Ducks; **Packages** 1/2 Day, 1-9 guns

Master Rack Lodge
Rt. 1, Box 95-A, Union Springs, AL 36089
(334) 474-3600 Tony/Becky Gibson 8-5
50 mi. SE of Montgomery
Est 1986; **Acres** 10,000; **Hunters/yr** 200; **Type**
Public; **On Site** Clubhouse, Lodging, Meals; **Shoots**
Field; **Birds** Quail, Turkey; **Dogs** Avail; **Packages** 3
Days, 5-20 guns

Portland Landing Hunting Reserve
3201 International Dr., Selma, AL 36703
(334) 875-2414 Phil Blake 7am-3:30pm, CT
40 mi. W of Montgomery
Est 1987; **Acres** 14,000; **Type** Public; **On Site**
Clubhouse, Lodging, Meals; **Shoots** Field; **Birds**
Turkey; **Packages** 3 Days, 1-8 guns

Rhodes Quail Hunting Preserve
105 N. Dobson Ave., Bay Minette, AL 36507
(334) 937-7580 Virgil V. Rhodes, Jr. Noon & 5-9pm
30 mi. NE of Mobile
Est 1984; **Acres** 140; **Hunters/yr** 150; **Type**
Public; **Shoots** Field; **Birds** Quail; **Dogs**
Avail/HDW; **Packages** 1/2 Day, 1-6 guns
o NAGA/See Pg. 107

Alabama's Westervelt Lodge: Where Business Is A Pleasure

Entertaining clients and attending meetings are facts of business life, endured or enjoyed according to circumstance. But few meetings, conferences or seminars are likely to be as memorable—or as productive—as those held at Westervelt Lodge in Alabama.

A Favored Destination

Indeed, Westervelt, with its elegant lodge, sumptuous meals and abundance of unsurpassed hunting and fishing, is a favorite among those who plan meetings, and those who attend them.

Westervelt's main lodge—the perfect place for mixing business and pleasure.

The reasons for this popularity are quickly apparent. Sprawling across 22 square miles of lush pine ridges and hardwood bottomlands, pristine lakes and fields of corn and millet, Westervelt offers all the amenities a businessperson treasures, all the excitement an avid sportsman craves.

As a meeting site/conference center, the Lodge specializes in accommodating groups of 26 or fewer overnight. But larger groups can be pampered here, too, at day meetings conducted in hotel-like comfort; or overnight with a combination of on-site and off-site lodging. Westervelt offers all the modern conveniences and equipment—including audio/visual—that contribute to a successful business gathering and its "away from it all" environment adds sharp focus to a meeting.

True Southern Style Quail Hunting

It's the lure of a wide variety of outdoor sports, however, that makes Westervelt a unique experience. But it's quail hunting, according to John Roboski, Westervelt's sales manager, that is favored by many of Westervelt's corporate guests. "Especially those eager to impress an important client or prospect," he quickly adds.

With hard-flying birds, good honest dog work, and a guide who puts you where the opportunities are, a Westervelt quail hunt begins with a plantation-style breakfast, continues in quiet, comfortable mule-drawn wagons that convey you to the action, and ends in a flurry of native wild quail and peak-quality, flight conditioned birds released throughout the year.

Wild turkeys thrive at Westervelt, too, and the Lodge's spring turkey hunts are world renowned. Accompanied by your personal guide—a certified master turkey hunter—you'll hunt the wily tom in your own assigned 1,000-acre area. The Lodge is also noted for our three-day school for turkey hunters, a concentrated course that sharpens your skills in tactics, camouflage, shooting and scouting.

Westervelt is prime habitat for quality white-tailed deer, which modern wildlife management techniques maintain at ideal population levels. So when guests apply their skills to this demanding sport—each in his own exclusive hunting area—the chances of success are high.

Other Attractions?

Westervelt abounds in activities and services. Among them: Bowhunting and bowhunting schools. Dove shoots. A rifle range. A professionally designed sporting clays course. The finest bass fishing in Alabama. Equipment rentals, licensing and game processing. And food so good it lends new fame to Southern cooking.

For business...for sport...for the happy combination of both...you're sure to be thrilled when you visit Alabama's pride, Westervelt Lodge. To find out how you can take advantage of the South's pre-eminent sporting/business entertainment location write Charles Bedwell at PO Box 2362, Tuscaloosa, AL 35403; or call him at (205) 373-8212. Visit Westervelt's Web Site: http://www.westervelt.com

Rockfence Station

4388 Chmbrs. Cty Rd. 160, Lafayette, AL 36862
(334) 864-0217 Kane Hudmon Su-S, 8am-5pm
95 mi. SW of Atlanta
Est 1986; **Acres** 7,000; **Hunters/yr** 1,000; **Type**
Public; **On Site** Clubhouse, Lodging, Meals, Clays;
Shoots Field; **Birds** Quail, Pheasant, Chukar, Turkey;
Dogs Avail/HDW; **Packages** 1/2 Day, 1-12 guns
○ NAGA/See Pg. 107

Selwood Hunting Preserve
706 Selwood Rd., Alpine, AL 35014
(800) 522-0403 O.V. Hill 8-5
35 mi. E of Birmingham
Est 1984; **Acres** 1,000; **Type** Public, Member/Avail,
Corp.; **On Site** Clubhouse, Meals, Clays; **Shoots**
Field; **Birds** Quail; **Dogs** Avail; **Packages** 1/2 Day,
2-10 guns ○ NAGA/See Pg. 107

Vick Quail Farm
5190 County Rd. 39, Oneconta, AL 35121
(205) 274-7625 Marvin Vick
Shoots Field; **Birds** Quail ○ NAGA/See Pg. 107

Westervelt Hunting Lodge
PO Box 2362, Tuscaloosa, AL 35403
(205) 373-8212 Charles Bedwell Visit Our Web Site
http://www.westervelt.com
50 mi. SW of Tuscaloosa
Acres 14,000; **Type** Public; **On Site** Clubhouse,
Lodging, Meals, Clays; **Shoots** Field; **Birds** Dove, Quail,
Turkey; **Dogs** Avail; **Packages** 1/2 Day, 2-12 guns
See Our Ad Below & Pg. 291

Wheeler Station Hunting Preserve
PO Box 594, Courtland, AL 35618
(205) 637-8770 A.G. Simmons Nights
35 mi. W of Huntsville
Est 1989; **Acres** 13,000; **Type** Public; **On Site**
Clubhouse, Lodging, Meals, Clays; **Shoots** Field;
Birds Dove, Quail, Pheasant; **Dogs** Avail/HDW;
Packages 1/2 Day, 2-25 guns

White Oak Plantation
5215 B County Road 10, Tuskegee, AL 36083
(334) 727-9258 Robert Pitman
20 mi. SW of Auburn
Est 1983; **Acres** 16,000; **Hunters/yr** 500; **Type**

Quail hunting as it was meant to be.

Public; **On Site** Clubhouse, Lodging, Meals, Clays;
Shoots Field; **Birds** Quail, Turkey; **Dogs**
Avail/HDW; **Packages** 1/2 Day, 2-8 guns
O Fishing   Brochure Available
O Shooting Instruction Available - See Ad Pg.
http://www.americaoutdoors.com/woak
Plantation style quail hunts are enjoyed from Oct.-
March. Professional guides, hard hunting dogs &
native wild birds interspersed with top quality,
flight-conditioned birds produce enough memories
to last a lifetime. Whether business or pleasure,
White Oak's renown hospitality and hunting exper-
tise will make a truly quality hunt.

Wood's Gamebird Farm
18247 US Hwy. 231, Titus, AL 36080
(334) 567-7711 Thomas E. Wood 7 to 10 pm
20 mi. N of Montgomery   **Est** 1982; **Acres** 400;
Hunters/yr 250; **Type** Public; **Shoots** Field; **Birds**
Quail, Pheasant; **Dogs** Avail/HDW; **Packages** 1/2
Day, 4-5 guns   O NAGA/See Pg. 107

ALASKA

Afognak Wilderness Lodge
Seal Bay, AK 99697
(800) 478-6442 Roy & Shannon Randall
Est 1973; **Type** Public; **On Site** Clubhouse,
Lodging, Meals; **Birds** Ducks

Alaska Trophy Hunting & Fishing
PO Box 220247, Anchorage, AK 99522
(907) 344-8589 Mel Gillis After 3pm **Est** 1983;
Acres 500,000; **Hunters/yr** 45; **Type** Public; **On
Site** Clubhouse, Lodging, Meals; **Shoots** Field; **Birds**
Ducks; **Dogs** Avail **Packages** 6 Days, 2-10 guns

Eagles' Ridge Ranch
HC62, Box 5780, Delta Junction, AK 99737
(907) 895-4329 Mike Crouch
100 mi. S of Fairbanks Est 1994; **Acres** 2,800;
Hunters/yr 100; **Type** Public; **On Site** Clubhouse,
Meals, Clays; **Shoots** Field, Blinds; **Birds** Quail,
Ruffed Grouse, Pheasant, Chukar, Turkey, Sharp Tail
Grouse, Ducks, Geese; **Dogs** Avail/HDW; **Packages**
1/2 Day, 1-10 guns   O **NAGA/See Pg. 107**
Fish for salmon and wingshoot–all on the same
trip? Yep, you can fish kings, reds & silvers one
day, hunt pheasant, quail, grouse and chukar the
next. Alaska's unusual April 1- October 31
wingshooting season makes it possible. Add Geese
& Cranes to the quarry beginning September 1. Interested? Just give us a call at Eagles' Ridge Ranch
and we'll put together a complete package specifically designed for you and your party. (Sporting
Clays shooters see our listing in the Alaska Clays
section.) Call today!

ARIZONA

Arizona Hunt Club
PO Box 1021, Mayer, AZ 86333
(520) 632-7709 Kent Henry 8am-5pm
65 mi. N of Phoenix
Est 1986; **Acres** 730; **Type** Public, Member/Avail,
Corp.; **On Site** Clubhouse, Clays; **Shoots** Field,
Driven; **Birds** Dove, Quail, Pheasant, Chukar; **Dogs**
Avail/HDW; **Packages** 1/2 Day, 1-4 guns
O NAGA/See Pg. 107

Long Meadow Preserve
HC30, Box 1030, Prescott, AZ 86301
(520) 778-9563 Jim Puntenney 8-6 daily
20 mi. NW of Prescott
Est 1982; **Acres** 6,000; **Type** Public, Member/Avail,
Corp.; **On Site** Clubhouse, Lodging, Clays; **Shoots**
Field, Blinds; **Birds** Dove, Quail, Pheasant, Chukar,
Snipe, Ducks, Geese; **Dogs** Avail/HDW; **Packages**
1/2 Day, 1-16 guns O NAGA/See Pg. 107

River's Edge Sporting Retreat
HC1, Box 742, Benson, AZ 85602
(520) 212-4868 Norm Crawford Anytime
70 mi. SE of Tucson
Est 1989; **Acres** 700; **Type** Public, Member/Avail,
Corp.; **On Site** Clubhouse, Lodging, Meals, Clays;
Shoots Field; **Birds** Dove, Quail, Pheasant, Chukar;
Dogs Avail/HDW; **Packages** 1/2 Day
O NAGA/See Pg. 107

Wingshooters Lodge
1305 N. Grand Ave., Suite 20-122, Nogales, AZ 85621
Ruben Del Castillo 011-52-641-49934 (Mexico)
from Obregon, Mexico
Est 1972; **Hunters/yr** 300; **Type** Public; **On Site**
Clubhouse, Lodging, Meals; **Shoots** Field, Blinds,
Boat; **Birds** Dove, Quail, Turkey, Ducks; **Packages** 2
Days, 2-12 guns

ARKANSAS

Casscoe Quail
Hunting Club
PO Box 215, Stuttgart, AR 72160
(501) 673-7283 Carroll Evans Daytime
or (501) 673-6664 Evenings
17 mi. E of Stuttgart
Est 1993; **Acres** 140; **Hunters/yr** 50; **Type**
Public; **On Site** Clubhouse, Lodging; **Shoots** Field;
Birds Quail; **Dogs** Avail/HDW; **Packages** 1/2 Day,
2-8 guns

Coley Game Preserve
4700 S. Hwy. 367, McRae, AR 72102
(501) 726-3239 Ken Coley 5pm-10pm
Est 1989; **Acres** 1,200; **Hunters/yr** 30; **Type**
Public; **Shoots** Field; **Birds** Dove, Quail; **Dogs**
Avail/HDW; **Packages** 1/2 Day, 1-4 guns

Drake's Landing
Rt. 1, Box 177, Tichnor, AR 72166
(800) 548-4389 Tommy or Chris Turner
Type Public; **On Site** Clubhouse, Lodging, Meals,
Clays; **Shoots** Blinds; **Birds** Ducks; **Dogs** HDW
O NAGA/See Pg. 107

Ducks and Ducks, Inc.
Rt. 1, Box 169-C, Lake City, AR 72437
(800) 822-3825 Dutch Noe Anytime
4.5 mi. S of Harrisburg
Acres 1,100; **Hunters/yr** 400; **Type** Public; **On
Site** Clubhouse, Lodging, Meals; **Shoots** Field, Blinds,
Boat; **Birds** Pheasant, Ducks; **Dogs** Avail/HDW;
Packages 2 Days, 2-24 guns O NAGA/See Pg. 107

Farelly Lake Duck Club
PO Box 629, DeWitt, AR 72042
(501) 946-3853 Lester McKinley
6 mi. S of DeWitt
Acres 10; **Hunters/yr** 300; **Type** Public; **Shoots**
Blinds; **Birds** Ducks; **Dogs** Avail

Foothills Quail Farm & Hunting Preserve
265 Water Valley Rd., Imboden, AR 72434
(501) 892-8906 Tim or Pam Miller Anytime
Est 1983; **Acres** 280; **Type** Public, Member/Avail,
Corp.; **On Site** Clubhouse, Lodging, Meals; **Shoots**
Field; **Birds** Quail; **Dogs** Avail/HDW; **Packages**
1/2 Day, 1-12 guns

Grandview Plantation
PO Box 201, Columbus, AR 71831
(501) 983-2526 Charles Butler
120 mi. SW of Little Rock
Acres 5,160; **Type** Public, Member/Avail, Corp.;
On Site Clubhouse, Lodging, Meals, Clays; **Shoots**
Field; **Birds** Dove, Quail, Pheasant, Chukar, Ducks;
Dogs Avail/HDW; **Packages** 1/2 Day

Greenhead Hunting Club
PO Box 306, Gillett, AR 72055
(501) 548-2365 Danny or Sara Sloate 8am-8pm
Est 1986; **Acres** 2,000; **Type** Public; **On Site**
Clubhouse, Lodging, Meals; **Shoots** Field, Blinds;
Birds Ducks; **Dogs** Avail/HDW

Hawk's Range Hunting Club
PO Box 589, Foreman, AR 71836
(501) 542-7350 Paul Hawkins, Jr.
30 mi. W of Texarkana
Est 1990; **Acres** 4,000; **Type** Public; **On Site**
Clubhouse, Clays; **Shoots** Field, Blinds, Boat; **Birds**
Ducks; **Dogs** Avail/HDW; **Packages** 1 Day, 2-6 guns

LaCotts' Hunting Lodge
616 E. 7th, DeWitt, AR 72042
(501) 946-3283 Don LaCotts
Est 1984; **Type** Public; **On Site** Clubhouse, Meals;
Shoots Field, Blinds, Boat; **Birds** Ducks; **Dogs**
Avail/HDW; **Packages** 1/2 Day, up to 14 guns

Mill Bayou Hunting Lodge
PO Box 885, Stuttgart, AR 72160
(501) 673-1541 Tommy Ives **Est** 1986; **Type** Public;
On Site Clubhouse, Lodging, Meals; **Shoots** Field,
Blinds; **Birds** Ducks; **Dogs** Avail; **Packages** 1 Day

Nevada Gamebirds
Rt. 1, Box 171, Buckner, AR 71827
(501) 899-2902 Karl Salb
100 mi. S of Little Rock
Est 1982; **Acres** 1,500; **Hunters/yr** 600; **Type** Public,
Corp.; **On Site** Clubhouse, Lodging, Meals, Clays;
Shoots Field, Tower; **Birds** Quail, Pheasant, Chukar;
Dogs Avail/HDW; **Packages** 1/2 Day, 1-36 guns

Old Timer Hunting Club
PO Box 628, Stuttgart, AR 72160
(501) 673-6921 Randy Lee
Est 1985; **Type** Public; **On Site** Clubhouse,
Lodging, Meals; **Shoots** Field, Blinds; **Birds** Ducks;
Dogs Avail/HDW; **Packages** 1/2 Day, up to 6 guns

Point Remove WMA, Inc.
PO Box 133, Hattieville, AR 72063
(501) 354-0136 Scott Kaufman 8-4 weekdays
Est 1982; **Acres** 3,500; **Type** Member/Avail, Corp.;
On Site Clubhouse, Lodging, Meals, Clays; **Shoots**
Field, Blinds, Boat; **Birds** Dove, Quail, Pheasant,
Turkey, Ducks; **Dogs** Avail/HDW

Quail Busters, Inc.
9432 Batesville Rd., Jacksonville, AR 72076
(501) 988-5302 Charles Venus
25 mi. NE of Little Rock
Est 1990; **Acres** 800; **Type** Public; **On Site**
Clubhouse, Lodging, Meals; **Shoots** Field; **Birds**
Dove, Quail; **Dogs** Avail/HDW; **Packages** 1/2 Day,
up to 15 guns O NAGA/See Pg. 107

Quail Mountain Enterprises
811 Hymes, Van Buren, AR 72956
(501) 474-9294 Jerry Friddle
25 mi. N of Ft. Smith
Est 1990; **Acres** 500; **Type** Public; **On Site**
Clubhouse, Lodging, Meals, Clays; **Shoots** Field;
Birds Quail, Pheasant, Chukar; **Dogs** Avail/HDW;
Packages 1/2 Day, 2-4 guns O NAGA/See Pg. 107

Dennis Seidenschwarz
PO Box 151, Ulm, AR 72170
(501) 241-3855 Dennis Seidenschwarz After 6pm
Est 1978; **Acres** 800; **Hunters/yr** 150; **Shoots**
Field, Blinds; **Birds** Ducks; **Dogs** Avail; **Packages**
1/2 Day, 1-7 guns

Sportsman's Lodge
HC77, Box 1075, Melbourne, AR 72556
(501) 368-4393
On Site Lodging, Clays; **Shoots** Field; **Birds** Quail
O NAGA/See Pg. 107

Trotter Shooting Preserve
PO Box 162, Roe, AR 72134
(501) 241-3318 Wiley L. Lawson After 6pm
60 mi. SE of Little Rock
Est 1987; **Acres** 400; **Hunters/yr** 120; **Type**
Public, Member/Avail; **Shoots** Field; **Birds** Quail;
Dogs Avail/HDW; **Packages** 1/2 Day, 2-6 guns

Waterfowl Flyway, Inc.
PO Box 323, Wynne, AR 72396
(800) 545-5944 Cecil "Shorty" Owens 7am-9pm
65 mi. W of Memphis, TN
Est 1989; **Acres** 8,000; **Type** Public, Corp.; **On
Site** Clubhouse, Lodging, Meals; **Shoots** Field,
Driven, Blinds; **Birds** Ducks, Geese; **Dogs**
Avail/HDW; **Packages** 1 Day, 1-26 guns

White Front Hunting Lodge
Rt. 2, Box 75, Stuttgart, AR 72160
(501) 673-6543 Jerry Maier after 8pm
Est 1984; **Acres** 30,000; **Hunters/yr** 200; **Type**
Public; **On Site** Clubhouse, Lodging, Meals; **Shoots**
Field, Blinds; **Birds** Ducks, Geese; **Dogs** Avail/HDW;
Packages 1/2 Day, 2-20 guns

CALIFORNIA

Antelope Valley
45408 160th St., W., Lancaster, CA 93536
(805) 724-1291 Dave Whiteside
60 mi. N of Los Angeles
Acres 3,500; **Type** Public, Member/Avail, Corp.;
On Site Clubhouse, Meals, Clays; **Birds** Dove, Quail, Pheasant,
Tower, Driven, Blinds; **Birds** Dove, Quail, Pheasant,
Turkey, Geese; **Dogs** Avail/HDW; **Packages** 1 Day,
2-35 guns
O Sporting Clays   O Camping & RV Area
O Fishing   O Western Style Barbecues
O Special Hunts: Dove & Pheasant Openers

Birds Landing Hunting Preserve
PO Box 5, Birds Landing, CA 94512
(707) 374-5092 Dan Cirillo
60 mi. NE of San Francisco
Est 1987; **Acres** 1,200; **Hunters/yr** 6,000; **Type**
Public, Member/Avail; **On Site** Clubhouse, Meals,
Clays; **Shoots** Field; **Birds** Pheasant, Chukar; **Dogs**
Avail/HDW; **Packages** 1/2 Day, 1-120 guns

Birds of a Feather
Box 3645-Parkfield, San Miguel, CA 93451
(805) 463-2335 Mel or Ruth Taylor 8pm-9:30pm
115 mi. NW of Los Angeles
Est 1990; **Acres** 320; **Type** Public, Member/Avail;
On Site Clays; **Shoots** Field; **Birds** Pheasant,
Chukar; **Dogs** Avail/HDW; **Packages** 1/2 Day, 1-8
guns O NAGA/See Pg. 107

Black Point Game Bird Club
7711 Lakeville Hwy., Petaluma, CA 94954
(707) 763-0076 Mike Sutsos
25 mi. N of San Francisco
Est 1964; **Acres** 1,000; **Type** Member/Avail; **On
Site** Clubhouse, Meals, Clays; **Shoots** Field; **Birds**
Pheasant, Chukar; **Dogs** Avail/HDW

Buckshorn House
11000 Old Hernandez Rd., Paicines, CA 95043
(800) 209-5175 Ken Range
75 mi. S of San Jose
Est 1994; **Acres** 16,000; **Type** Public; **On Site**
Clubhouse, Lodging, Meals, Clays; **Shoots** Field, Driven;
Birds Dove, Quail, Pheasant, Chukar, Huns, Turkey;
Dogs Avail/HDW; **Packages** 1 Day, 1-24 guns
See Our Ad Pg. 296

C&L Pheasant Club
1831 Road R, Willows, CA 95988
(916) 934-8805 Lisa Heuschkel
10 mi. SW of Maxwell
Acres 500; **Hunters/yr** 30; **Type** Member/Avail;
Shoots Field; **Birds** Pheasant O NAGA/See Pg. 107

C.C.F. Hunting Club
2005 Alice Ave., Palermo, CA 95968
(916) 894-5555 Peter Rouse
125 mi. N of San Francisco
Est 1952; **Acres** 800; **Type** Member/Avail, Corp.;
On Site Clubhouse; **Shoots** Field; **Birds** Pheasant;
Dogs HDW ○ NAGA/See Pg. 107

Cahoon Pheasant Club
31249 E. Combs Rd., Escalon, CA 95320
(209) 838-6233 Dave & Patti Cahoon
3 mi. N of Escalon
Est 1990; **Acres** 900; **Hunters/yr** 3,000; **Type**
Public, Member/Avail; **On Site** Clubhouse, Meals,
Clays; **Shoots** Field; **Birds** Pheasant, Chukar; **Dogs**
Avail/HDW ○ NAGA/See Pg. 107

Camanche Hills Hunting Preserve
2951 Curran Rd., Ione, CA 95640
(209) 763-5270 Larry L. Skinner
80 mi. E of San Francisco
Est 1981; **Acres** 1,500; **Type** Public, Member/Avail;
On Site Clubhouse, Lodging, Meals, Clays; **Shoots**
Field, Driven; **Birds** Pheasant, Chukar, Ducks; **Dogs**
Avail/HDW; **Packages** 1 Day

Cameron Outing, Inc.
10411 Old Placervile, #220, Sacramento, CA 95827
(916) 366-0486 Thomas Neutzling
1 mi. SE of Riooco
Acres 1,600; **Hunters/yr** 40; **Type** Member/Avail;
On Site Clubhouse; **Shoots** Blinds; **Birds** Dove,
Pheasant, Ducks, Geese

Camp 5
1230 Arbor Rd., Paso Robles, CA 93446
(805) 237-1201 Craig W. Rossier
Type Public, Member/Avail; **Shoots** Field; **Birds**
Pheasant ○ NAGA/See Pg. 107

Circle HH Hunting Preserve
HCR#1, Box 512, Nipton, CA 92364
(702) 642-9405 Fred Hymes/Jessie Hymes 5pm-10pm
**78 mi. S of Las Vegas, NV - 100 mi. E of
Barstow/20 mi N. I-40**
Est 1988; **Acres** 200; **Hunters/yr** 72; **Type**
Public, Member/Avail, Corp.; **On Site** Clubhouse,
Meals, Clays; **Shoots** Field; **Birds** Dove, Quail,
Pheasant, Chukar, Turkey; **Dogs** Avail/HDW;
Packages 1/2 Day, 1-6 guns ○ NAGA/See Pg. 107
Circle HH Hunting Preserve is located in unspoiled
country, surrounded by California's East Mojave
Natural Preserve Area just 85 miles south of Las
Vegas, 50 miles west of Laughlin, with interstate
access off I-15 and I-40. We have committed ourselves to provide excellent hunting of pheasant,
chukar and quail on a preserve that incorporates
habitat improvement. An altitude of nearly 5,000
feet presents changing temperatures throughout
the day. The Preserve is set up to accommodate six
(6) hunters per 1/2 day reservation hunt.

Clear Creek Sports Club
3971 Keefer Rd., Chico, CA 95926
(916) 343-9263 Bob or Janet Henman
45 mi. N of Sacramento
Est 1986; **Acres** 1,000; **Type** Public, Member/Avail,
Corp.; **Shoots** Field; **Birds** Pheasant, Chukar;
Dogs Avail/HDW; **Packages** 1 Day, 4-60 guns
○ NAGA/See Pg. 107

Creekside Pheasant Club
Box 3640, Parkfield Rt., San Miguel, CA 93451
(805) 463-2349 Larry Hamilton
115 mi. NW of Los Angeles
Est 1985; **Acres** 800; **Type** Member/Avail; **On
Site** Lodging, Clays; **Shoots** Field, Blinds; **Birds**
Dove, Quail, Pheasant, Chukar, Ducks; **Dogs**
Avail/HDW ○ NAGA/See Pg. 107

Rock Springs: The *Only* Orvis Endorsed Wingshooting Lodge in California

If you're looking for wingshooting adventure, look no further than California's Rock Springs Lodge—the only Orvis endorsed wingshooting lodge in the State—and you won't be disappointed. The moment you set foot on this private ranch you're a V.I.P. And Rock Springs' operators, Nola and Ken Range, wouldn't have it any other way.

Superb Wingshooting

Located in California's inner coastal mountain range, just a three hour drive from the Golden Gate Bridge, the 19,000 acre ranch is a rich and varied wildlife habitat. Oak savanna and chaparral, river bottoms and deep shaded canyons, fields planted with barley, vetch and sudangrass are the backdrop for some of the finest upland gamebird hunting available anywhere.

Full-time, experienced guides and a kennel of superbly trained Setters, Brittanys and Shorthairs assist in the pursuit of bobwhite quail, pheasants, Huns, and chukar from September to May. A generous three month season on native California Valley Quail provides even experienced wingshooters with a real challenge. Wild turkeys, introduced here about twelve years ago and thriving in the favorable environment, are also on the hunting bill. Dove shooting (two seasons) and Continental style pheasant shoots complete the upland shooting spectrum.

Amenities to Match

To earn an Orvis endorsement, a wingshooting lodge must provide lodging, dining and service every bit as good as the requisite world-class hunting. In this regard, Rock Springs is no exception. The ranch's spectacular 6,000 sq. ft. cedar lodge has four large bedrooms with baths, three stone fireplaces, a bubbling hot spa, and a deck that wraps around two sides of the building and offers scenic views in all seasons.

Fireplace in the Great Room at Rock Springs Lodge.

What about the meals? Well, more than one visitor to the ranch has been heard to say: "I came for the hunting, but I stay for the food." No wonder. Under the direction of a graduate of the prestigious Culinary Institute of America, the kitchen at Rock Springs serves up fare that can compete with the best offered in restaurants in San Francisco and L.A.

Warmin' Up or Coolin' Down

Wingshooters at Rock Springs can warm up before a hunt or cool down after one with a round or two at the ranch's NSCA 5-Stand. Six automated traps offer an array of incoming, outgoing, left and right crossing shots, along with a rabbit and tower shot. A wobble trap, housed in a bunker under a short bluff, can test the experienced shooter, or be set to throw repetitive targets perfect for training a novice.

Whether you're visiting California on business or vacation, or just looking for that wingshooting adventure of a lifetime, include Rock Springs in you plans. For great hunting, great food, and great times, it is hard to beat. Orvis says so, and so will you. Call or write, Ken or Nola today for more information or reservations: Rock Springs Lodge, 11000 Old Hernandez Rd., Paicines, CA 95043; (800) 209-5175.

The Duck Club
PO Box 323, Richvale, CA 95974
(916) 534-8401 Jack Smith
85 mi. NW of Sacramento
Acres 725; **Type** Public; **On Site** Lodging, Meals; **Shoots** Field, Blinds; **Birds** Pheasant, Ducks, Geese; **Dogs** Avail; **Packages** 1 Day, 1-24 guns

Fairlee Ranch
1740 Colusa Way, Gridley, CA 95948
(916) 392-7260 Jean Davis
115 mi. NE of San Francisco
Acres 400; **Type** Public; **Shoots** Blinds; **Birds** Ducks, Geese; **Dogs** Avail; **Packages** 1/2 Day

First in the Field Guide Service
1003 West 2nd St., Alturas, CA 96101
(916) 233-5755 Paul Siegel 5-8pm
10 mi. SE of Altunas
Est 1983; **Acres** 10,000; **Type** Public; **Shoots** Field, Blinds; **Birds** Ducks, Geese; **Dogs** Avail/HDW; **Packages** 1 Day, 4-8 guns

Flying D Ranch
Pheasant Hunting Club
PO Box 1242, Jamul, CA 91935
(619) 468-3857 Ken Davis, Owner/Mgr.
22 mi. SE of San Diego
Acres 1,200; **Hunters/yr** 200; **Type** Public, Member/Avail; **On Site** Clubhouse, Lodging, Meals, Clays; **Shoots** Field; **Birds** Quail, Pheasant, Chukar; **Dogs** Avail; **Packages** 1/2 Day, 1-30 guns

Four Winds Pheasant Club
2806 May Ave., Redondo Beach, CA 90278
(310) 370-2238 Sam Elder
75 mi. SE of Los Angeles
Est 1993; **Acres** 155; **Type** Public, Member/Avail, Corp.; **On Site** Clays; **Shoots** Field; **Birds** Quail, Pheasant, Chukar; **Dogs** Avail/HDW; **Packages** 1/2 Day, 1-36 guns   o NAGA/See Pg. 107

G & G PHEASANT SHOOT
G&G Pheasant Shoot
PO Box 116, Gazelle, CA 96034
(916) 435-2309 John or Dot Giorgi
60 mi. S of Oregon Border
Est 1980; **Acres** 750; **Type** Corp.; **On Site** Clubhouse, Meals; **Shoots** Field; **Birds** Pheasant, Chukar; **Dogs** Avail/HDW; **Packages** 1/2 Day, 1-20 guns   o NAGA/See Pg. 107

Gabilan Valley
Sportsmans Club
PO Box 1207, Gilroy, CA 95021
(800) 632-HUNT J. Harvey/E. Weis 8-4
35 mi. S of San Jose
Est 1987; **Acres** 360; **Hunters/yr** 3,500; **Type** Public, Member/Avail, Corp.; **On Site** Clubhouse; **Shoots** Field, Blinds; **Birds** Quail, Pheasant, Chukar, Huns, Ducks; **Dogs** Avail/HDW; **Packages** 1/2 Day, up to 50 guns   o NAGA/See Pg. 107

Golden Ram Sportsman Club
840 Hinckley Rd., #250, Burlingame, CA 94010
(415) 692-6670 Nick Tacito/Lou Federico 10-5, M-F
10 mi. NW of Sacramento
Est 1970; **Acres** 3,000; **Hunters/yr** 700; **Type** Public, Member/Avail, Corp.; **On Site** Clubhouse, Meals; **Shoots** Field; **Birds** Quail, Pheasant, Chukar, Huns, Ducks, Geese; **Dogs** Avail/HDW; **Packages** 1/2 Day, 25-50 guns

H&H Gun Club
3971 Keefer Rd., Chico, CA 95926
(916) 343-9263 Bob Henman
10 mi. S of Chico
Acres 1,100; **Hunters/yr** 90; **Type** Member/Avail; **On Site** Clubhouse; **Shoots** Field; **Birds** Pheasant, Chukar; **Dogs** Avail   o NAGA/See Pg. 107

Hastings Island Hunting Preserve
7758 Hastings Island Rd., Rio Vista, CA 94571
(916) 678-3325 8am-4pm
50 mi. E of San Francisco
Est 1969; **Acres** 4,700; **Type** Member/Avail, Corp.; **On Site** Clubhouse, Meals, Clays; **Birds** Pheasant, Chukar; **Dogs** Avail/HDW   o NAGA/See Pg. 107

High Desert Hunt Club
PO Box 89, Gorman, CA 93243
(888) 425-HUNT Lisa McNamee/Jeff Lee
60 mi. N of Los Angeles City Hall
Acres 8,000; **Type** Public, Member/Avail; **On Site** Clubhouse, Meals; **Shoots** Field, Tower; **Birds** Dove, Quail, Pheasant, Chukar, Ducks; **Dogs** Avail/HDW; **Packages** 1/2 Day, 1-50 guns
o Bird Processing
o Brochure Available
o Corporate Membership
o Half, Full and Multi-Day Hunts
o Experienced Guides
o Excellent Upland Game Habitat
High Desert Hunt Club is located just 60 miles from Los Angeles City Hall. We have committed ourselves to provide excellent hunting for Wild/Native Valley Quail and top quality, flight conditioned, released Pheasant, Chukar, and Bobwhite Quail. Our professional staff is trained to cater to each unique need; business entertainment or individual.

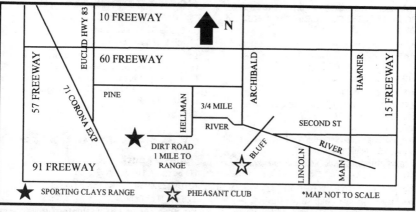

Knowles Ranch Sporting Clays
PO Box 982, Willows, CA 95988
(916) 934-5595   Clark Knowles   8am-5pm
75 mi. N of Sacramento
Est 1950;   **Acres** 1,100;   **Hunters/yr** 200;   **Type**
Public;   **On Site** Clubhouse, Clays;   **Shoots** Field,
Blinds;   **Birds** Pheasant, Chukar, Ducks, Geese;   **Dogs**
Avail/HDW;   **Packages** 1 Day, 2-16 guns

Lakeview Farms, Inc.
5490 Riosa Rd. West, Lincoln, CA 95648
(916) 633-9112   Donald Norris
20 mi. NE of Sacramento
Acres 1,000;   **Hunters/yr** 350;   **Type** Public,
Member/Avail;   **On Site** Clubhouse, Lodging;
Shoots Field, Blinds;   **Birds** Dove, Quail, Pheasant,
Chukar, Ducks, Geese;   **Dogs** Avail
O NAGA/See Pg. 107

Lone Pine Pheasant Club
430 N. Main St., Lone Pine, CA 93545
(619) 876-4595   Bruce Ivey   8am-3pm
200 mi. N of Los Angeles
Est 1988;   **Acres** 1,000;   **Hunters/yr** 500;   **Type**
Public, Member/Avail;   **On Site** Clubhouse, Meals;
Shoots Field;   **Birds** Quail, Pheasant, Chukar;   **Dogs**
Avail/HDW;   **Packages** 1 Day, 1-12 guns
O NAGA/See Pg. 107

Moffatt Road Gun Club
700 Vine St., Menlo Park, CA 94025
(415) 281-2180   Giulio Accornero
60 mi. SE of San Jose
Acres 426;   **Hunters/yr** 22;   **Type** Member/Avail;
On Site Clubhouse, Lodging, Meals;   **Shoots** Field,
Blinds;   **Birds** Pheasant, Ducks, Geese

Napa Shooting Preserve
3195 Wooden Valley Rd., Napa, CA 94558
(707) 255-5095   Dennis Rapp
Type Member/Avail;   **On Site** Clays;   **Shoots** Field;
Birds Quail, Pheasant, Chukar, Ducks   O NAGA/See
Pg. 107

Pheasant Flats
Box 311, Dayton, CA 82836
(916) 655-9638   Robert Mock
60 mi. S of Medford, OR
Est 1993;   **Type** Member/Avail;   **Shoots** Field;
Birds Pheasant   O NAGA/See Pg. 107

Potter Valley Sportsmen's Club
6950 Hwy. 20, Ukiah, CA 95482
(707) 485-5188   Jim Guntly   Morning or evening
50 mi. N of Santa Rosa
Est 1991;   **Acres** 5,500;   **Type** Public, Member/Avail;
On Site Clays;   **Shoots** Field;   **Birds** Dove, Quail,
Pheasant, Chukar, Turkey;   **Dogs** Avail/HDW
O NAGA/See Pg. 107

Mike Raahauge
Shooting Enterprises
5800 Bluff St., Norco, CA 91760
(909) 735-2361   Mike Raahauge
Sporting Clays: (909) 735-7981
35 mi. E of Los Angeles
Acres 2,000;   **Hunters/yr** 400;   **Type** Public,
Member/Avail, Corp.;   **On Site** Clubhouse, Clays;
Shoots Field, Blinds;   **Birds** Pheasant, Chukar, Ducks;
Dogs Avail/HDW;   **Packages** 1 Day, 1-50 guns
O NAGA/See Pg. 107
See Our Ad Pg. 299

Red Bank Ale & Quail Gamebird Club
PO Box 8295, Red Bluff, CA 96080
(916) 529-9435   Brian Rielly   8am-5pm
170 mi. N of San Francisco
Est 1976;   **Acres** 5,000;   **Hunters/yr** 1,500;   **Type**
Public;   **On Site** Clubhouse, Lodging, Meals, Clays;
Shoots Field, Blinds;   **Birds** Dove, Quail, Pheasant,
Turkey, Ducks, Geese;   **Dogs** Avail/HDW;   **Packages**
1/2 Day, up to 22 guns   O NAGA/See Pg. 107

Reibar Hunt Club
7480 Domingos Rd., Lompoc, CA 93436
(805) 736-5309   Grady Istre
6 mi. W of Boellton
Acres 150;   **Hunters/yr** 65;   **Type** Public,
Member/Avail;   **On Site** Clubhouse, Meals;   **Shoots**
Field;   **Birds** Dove, Pheasant, Chukar;   **Dogs** Avail

▼ ORVIS ENDORSED ▼

Rock Springs Lodge
11000 Old Hernandez Rd., Paicines, CA 95043
(800) 209-5175   Ken Range
75 mi. S of San Jose
Est 1994;   **Acres** 16,000;   **Type** Public;   **On Site**
Lodging, Meals, Clays;   **Shoots** Field, Driven;   **Birds**
Dove, Quail, Pheasant, Chukar, Huns, Turkey;   **Dogs**
Avail/HDW;   **Packages** 1 Day, 1-24 guns
O NAGA/See Pg. 107
See Our Pg. 297

▲ ORVIS ENDORSED ▲

Romero Ranch
PO Box 517, Likely, CA 96116
(916) 233-4938   Chris or Rich Hamel   10-5
125 mi. N of Reno, NV
Est 1989;   **Acres** 1,680;   **Hunters/yr** 300;   **Type**
Public;   **On Site** Clubhouse, Lodging, Meals, Clays;
Shoots Field, Tower, Blinds;   **Birds** Pheasant, Chukar,
Ducks, Geese;   **Dogs** Avail/HDW;   **Packages** 1/2
Day, 1-16 guns   O NAGA/See Pg. 107

Stillwater Sportsmen's Club
5890 Dersch Rd., Anderson, CA 96007
(916) 365-6845 Doyle & Laurel Besecker
160 mi. N of Sacramento
Acres 1,500; Type Member/Avail, Corp.; Shoots
Field, Blinds; Birds Dove, Quail, Pheasant, Chukar,
Huns, Turkey, Ducks; Dogs Avail/HDW

Timbuctoo Sporting Estate
PO Box 357, Smartville, CA 95977
(916) 639-2200 Sam Craig
50 mi. NW of Sacramento
Est 1988; Acres 6,000; Hunters/yr 500; Type
Public; On Site Clubhouse, Meals, Clays; Shoots
Field, Driven, Blinds, Boat; Birds Quail, Chukar, Huns,
Turkey, Ducks; Dogs Avail/HDW
○ NAGA/See Pg. 107

Valley Quail Hunting Club
PO Box 942, Lathrop, CA 95330
(209) 239-2576 John & Robin Herrera

West Valley Sportsmen Club
PO Box 257, Gustine, CA 95322
(209) 634-1547 Robert Kloepfer 8-5
80 mi. SE of San Francisco
Est 1987; Acres 1,875; Type Public, Member/Avail,
Corp.; On Site Clubhouse, Meals, Clays; Shoots
Field; Birds Quail, Pheasant, Chukar; Dogs
Avail/HDW ○ NAGA/See Pg. 107

Wild Wings Preserve
PO Box 572, Sutter, CA 95982
(916) 755-0524
160 mi. N of San Francisco
Acres 4,000; Type Public, Member/Avail; On Site
Clubhouse; Shoots Field; Birds Quail, Pheasant,
Chukar, Huns, Turkey; Dogs Avail/HDW; Packages
1 Day ○ NAGA/See Pg. 107

Wilderness Unlimited
20954 Corsair Blvd., Hayward, CA 94545
(510) 785-4868 Rick Copeland Anytime
Acres 200,000; Hunters/yr 1,000; Type
Member/Avail, Corp.; On Site Clubhouse; Shoots
Field, Blinds; Birds Dove, Quail, Pheasant, Ducks,
Geese; Dogs HDW

Wildlife Game Birds
2787 Pleasant Grove Rd., Pleasant Grove, CA 95668
(916) 656-2544 George Zents 8am-4pm
25 mi. NE of Sacramento
Est 1984; Acres 700; Hunters/yr 1,500; Type
Public, Member/Avail, Corp.; On Site Clubhouse,
Meals; Shoots Field; Birds Pheasant, Chukar;
Dogs Avail/HDW; Packages 1/2 Day, 1-40 guns

Willow Run Hunting Preserve
Rt. 1, Box 530, Glenn, CA 95943
(916) 934-3407 Chris Beane/Gary Alves
Type Public, Member/Avail; Shoots Field; Birds
Quail, Pheasant ○ NAGA/See Pg. 107

COLORADO

A J Gamebirds
1251 Paddock, Elizabeth, CO 80107
(303) 646-0229 Jerry William
On Site Clays; Shoots Field; Birds Quail, Pheasant,
Chukar ○ NAGA/See Pg. 107

Bang-A-Away Gun Club & Kennels
17629 Weld County Rd. 5, Berthoud, CO 80513
(970) 535-4538 Bill Voigt 8am-4pm
40 mi. N of Denver
Est 1972; Acres 300; Type Member/Ltd, Corp.;
On Site Clubhouse, Clays; Shoots Field; Birds
Pheasant, Chukar; Dogs Avail/HDW; Packages 1/2
Day, 1-4 guns ○ NAGA/See Pg. 107

Chipeta Guest Ranch
1938 Hwy. 133, Paonia, CO 81428
(800) 521-4055 Larry Mantz
70 mi. W of Aspen
Est 1991; Acres 4,000; Hunters/yr 50; Type
Public; On Site Clubhouse, Lodging, Meals, Clays;
Shoots Driven; Birds Pheasant, Turkey, Sage Grouse,
Ducks, Geese; Dogs HDW

Colorado Pheasant Association
RD53, Kiowa, CO 80117
(303) 693-1065 Clay Blyth 9-4pm
35 mi. SE of Denver
Est 1989; Acres 840; Hunters/yr 500; Type
Public, Member/Avail; On Site Clubhouse, Meals,
Clays; Shoots Field, Blinds; Birds Dove, Quail,
Pheasant, Chukar, Ducks; Dogs Avail/HDW;
Packages 1/2 Day, 3-15 guns

Four Directions
Upland Game Club
2690 O Rd., Hotchkiss, CO 81419
(970) 835-3658 Charlie & Marilee Gilman
60 mi. SW of Aspen
Est 1982; Acres 2,000; Hunters/yr 400; Type
Public, Member/Avail; On Site Clubhouse, Lodging,
Meals; Shoots Field; Birds Quail, Pheasant, Chukar;
Dogs Avail/HDW; Packages 1 Day, 2-6 guns
○ NAGA/See Pg. 107

Fox II
6085 S. Iola Way, Englewood, CO 80111
(303) 781-9007 Ron Wilson
35 mi. N of Denver
Est 1990; Acres 330; Type Member/Avail; On
Site Clubhouse; Shoots Field, Blinds; Birds Quail,
Pheasant, Chukar, Ducks, Geese; Dogs HDW;
Packages 1/2 Day, up to 30 guns

Go-Fer Broke Gun Club
19995 Myers Rd., Colorado Springs, CO 80928
(719) 683-3807 Jerry Shatley
Est 1985; **Acres** 200; **Type** Public; **Shoots** Field;
Birds Quail, Pheasant, Chukar; **Packages** 1/2 Day,
2-10 guns ○ NAGA/See Pg. 107

High Country Game Birds
33300 County Rd. 25, Elizabeth, CO 80107
(303) 646-3315 Todd Pederson 7 am - 7 pm
35 mi. SE of Denver **Est** 1985; **Acres** 200;
Hunters/yr 1,150; **Type** Public, Member/Avail,
Corp.; **On Site** Clubhouse, Lodging, Meals, Clays;
Shoots Field; **Birds** Dove, Quail, Pheasant, Chukar,
Huns, Ducks, Geese; **Dogs** Avail/HDW; **Packages**
1/2 Day, 2-5 guns
○ NAGA/See Pg. 107

Indian Bend Ranch
1619 N. Greenwood St., Pueblo, CO 81003
(719) 544-7115 Charles Bedard
28 mi. E of Pueblo **Acres** 402; **Hunters/yr** 50;
Type Public, Member/Avail; **On Site** Clubhouse;
Shoots Field, Blinds; **Birds** Dove, Quail, Pheasant,
Ducks, Geese; **Dogs** Avail ○ NAGA/See Pg. 107

Jalmor Sportsmen's Club
47939 Elbert Co. Rd. 22, Ramah, CO 80832
(719) 541-2854 Al & Jane Morse
100 mi. SE of Denver

Est 1980; **Acres** 300; **Type** Public, Member/Avail,
Corp.; **On Site** Clubhouse, Clays; **Shoots** Field;
Birds Dove, Pheasant, Chukar, Ducks; **Dogs**
Avail/HDW ○ NAGA/See Pg. 107

Kiowa Creek Sporting
46700 E. Quincy, Bennett, CO 80102
(303) 644-4627 Bill Bear/Mark Moore
On Site Clays; **Shoots** Field; **Birds** Quail, Pheasant,
Chukar ○ NAGA/See Pg. 107

Menoken Wildlife Park
60998 Jay Jay Rd., Montrose, CO 81401
(970) 249-7662 Dale Parker
60 mi. SE of Grand Junction **Acres** 2,500; **Type**
Member/Avail; **Shoots** Field; **Birds** Ducks, Geese

Mt. Blanca
Game Bird & Trout
PO Box 236, Blanca, CO 81123
(719) 379-3825 Bill Binnian 7am - 7pm
150 mi. SW of Colorado Springs
Est 1987; **Acres** 6,000; **Hunters/yr** 1,000; **Type**
Public, Member/Avail, Corp.; **On Site** Clubhouse,
Lodging, Meals, Clays; **Shoots** Field, Driven, Blinds;
Birds Dove, Quail, Pheasant, Chukar, Ducks, Geese;
Dogs Avail/HDW; **Packages** 1/2 Day, 1-16 guns
○ NAGA/See Pg. 107

See Our Ad Across

Quail Run Hunting Preserve
PO Box 693, Nucla, CO 81424
(970) 864-7985 Byron or Tandie Morgan Evenings
100 mi. S of Grand Junction
Est 1992; **Acres** 840; **Type** Public; **Shoots** Field;
Birds Pheasant, Chukar; **Dogs** Avail/HDW;
Packages 1/2 Day, 2-10 guns o NAGA/See Pg. 107

Quint Valley
Release & Shoot
55936 County Rd. 46, Strasburg, CO 80136
(303) 622-9674 Rick Wallace
40 mi. E of Denver
Est 1991; **Acres** 4,000; **Type** Public; **On Site**
Lodging; **Shoots** Field; **Birds** Quail, Pheasant, Chukar;
Dogs Avail/HDW; **Packages** 1/2 Day, 1-5 guns

R&T Gun Club
9912 Downing, Thornton, CO 80229
(303) 452-4777 Dave Redell 8-5
100 mi. NE of Denver
Est 1974; **Acres** 15,000; **Type** Public,
Member/Avail, Corp.; **On Site** Clubhouse, Lodging,
Meals, Clays; **Shoots** Field, Driven, Blinds; **Birds**
Dove, Quail, Pheasant, Chukar, Turkey, Ducks, Geese;
Dogs Avail/HDW; **Packages** 1/2 Day, up to 30 guns

Renegade Gun Club, Inc.
3570 Weld County Road #23, Fort Lupton, CO 80621
(303) 857-6000 Dick Chikuma **Type** Member/Avail;
On Site Clubhouse, Meals, Clays; **Shoots** Field,
Blinds; **Birds** Dove, Quail, Pheasant, Chukar, Turkey,
Ducks, Geese; **Dogs** Avail/HDW; **Packages** 1/2 Day

Robinson
Game Birds L.L.C.
217 E. 37th St., Durango, CO 81301
(970) 259-4673 Rob Robinson
Est 1994; **Acres** 2,000; **Type** Public; **On Site**
Clays; **Shoots** Field; **Birds** Quail, Pheasant, Chukar;
Dogs Avail/HDW; **Packages** 1/2 Day, 1-4 guns
o NAGA/See Pg. 107

ROCKY
MOUNTAIN
ROOSTERS
INC.©

Rocky Mountain Roosters
PO Box 10164, Colorado Springs, CO 80932
(719) 635-3257 Brett M. Axton 9-6
35 mi. E of Colorado Springs
Est 1985; **Acres** 5,000; **Hunters/yr** 2,000; **Type**
Public, Member/Avail, Corp.; **On Site** Clubhouse,
Meals, Clays; **Shoots** Field, Blinds; **Birds** Dove,
Quail, Pheasant, Chukar, Turkey, Ducks, Geese; **Dogs**
Avail/HDW; **Packages** 1/2 Day, 1-60 guns
o NAGA/See Pg. 107
See Our Ad Pg. 302

Rocky Mountain Training Kennel
18519 WCR3, Berthoud, CO 80513
(970) 535-4600 Bobbie Christensen Evenings
30 mi. N of Denver
Est 1960; **Acres** 160; **Type** Public; **Shoots** Field;
Birds Quail, Pheasant, Chukar; **Dogs** Avail/HDW;
Packages 1/2 Day

Rocky Ridge Hunting Club
633 Gait Circle, Ft. Collins, CO 80524
(970) 221-4868 Michael Q. Moreng 7 am - 9 pm
55 mi. N of Denver **Est** 1984; **Acres** 700;
Hunters/yr 300; **Type** Public, Member/Avail, Corp.;
On Site Clubhouse, Clays; **Shoots** Field, Tower,
Driven, Blinds; **Birds** Quail, Pheasant, Chukar, Ducks,
Geese; **Dogs** Avail/HDW; **Packages** 1/2 Day, 1-12
guns o NAGA/See Pg. 107

Rogers Country
32259 Road 13, Lamar, CO 81052
(719) 336-2124 Jim Rogers
100 mi. E of Pueblo
Acres 3,000; **Type** Public, Member/Avail; **Shoots**
Field; **Birds** Dove, Quail, Pheasant, Chukar, Ducks;
Dogs HDW; **Packages** 1 Day, up to 1 guns

Scenic Mesa Ranch
PO Box 251, Hotchkiss, CO 81419
(970) 921-6200 Pam & Mat Turnbull
100 mi. SW of Aspen
Est 1995; **Acres** 8,000; **Hunters/yr** 50; **Type**
Public, Member/Avail; **On Site** Clubhouse, Lodging,
Meals, Clays; **Shoots** Field, Blinds; **Birds** Quail,
Pheasant, Chukar, Ducks, Geese; **Dogs** Avail/HDW;
Packages 2 Days, 1-60 guns o NAGA/See Pg. 107
o New, Comfortable Lodge
o Deer Hunting
o Fly Fishing
o Packages Available
o Airport Pick-Up

Seven Lakes Lodge
738 CR 59, Meeker, CO 81641
(970) 878-4772
100 mi. NE of Grand Junction **Acres** 500; **Type**
Public; **On Site** Clubhouse, Lodging, Meals, Clays;
Shoots Field; **Birds** Pheasant, Chukar; **Dogs**
Avail/HDW; **Packages** 2 Days, 1-22 guns

SPORTHAVEN, LTD.
50500 E. 72nd Ave., Bennett, CO 80102
(303) 644-3030 David A. Lincoln, Jr. 9am-5pm
20 mi. NE of Denver
Est 1993; **Acres** 400; **Type** Public, Member/Avail;
On Site Clubhouse, Clays; **Shoots** Field, Tower;
Birds Dove, Quail, Pheasant, Chukar; **Dogs**
Avail/HDW; **Packages** 1/2 Day, 1-8 guns

Stillwater Gun Club
& Upland Game Preserve
16588 Telluride St., Brighton, CO 80601
(303) 659-8665 Mark Beam After 6pm, MST
15 mi. N of Denver
Est 1983; Acres 15,000; Type Public; Shoots
Field, Blinds; Birds Pheasant, Chukar, Ducks, Geese;
Dogs Avail/HDW; Packages 1/2 Day
Colorado is one of the hottest goose and duck
hunting areas in North America. Thousands upon
thousands of waterfowl winter here along
Colorado's front range. I invite you to join us for
some of the finest decoy gunning for waterfowl
one can experience. We're Colorado's only licensed
outfitter specializing in waterfowl hunting.

Strasburg Game Birds
5220 S. Co. Rd. 157, Strasburg, CO 80136
(303) 622-4608 Robert Porter
Shoots Field; Birds Quail, Pheasant, Chukar
O NAGA/See Pg. 107

Valhalla-Bijou Inc.
450 Co. Rd. 133, Bennett, CO 80102
(303) 644-4300 Steve Barnhardt
20 mi. E of Denver
Est 1989; Acres 2,000; Hunters/yr 900; Type
Member/Avail; On Site Clubhouse, Meals, Clays;
Shoots Field; Birds Dove, Pheasant, Chukar; Dogs
Avail/HDW; Packages 1/2 Day, 1-20 guns
O NAGA/See Pg. 107

Western
Wildlife Adventure
6255 WCR 74, Windsor, CO 80550
(970) 686-5210 Tim Brough Mornings or T/Th pm
50 mi. N of Denver
Est 1985; Acres 1,000; Hunters/yr 500; Type
Public, Member/Avail, Corp.; On Site Clubhouse,
Clays; Shoots Field; Birds Dove, Quail, Pheasant,
Chukar, Huns; Dogs Avail/HDW; Packages 1/2
Day, 1-25 guns O NAGA/See Pg. 107

White River Game Birds
703 E. Rangely Ave., Rangely, CO 81648
(970) 675-2355 Terry Smalec
Shoots Field; Birds Pheasant, Turkey
O NAGA/See Pg. 107

Windmill Farms
5885 S. Nepal Way, Aurora, CO 80015
(303) 699-5795 Phil Beckman
On Site Lodging; Shoots Field; Birds Quail,
Pheasant O NAGA/See Pg. 107

CONNECTICUT

Connecticut Woods
& Water Guide Service
6 Larson St., Waterford, CT 06385
(860) 442-6343 Capt. Dan Wood
100 mi. NE of New York
Est 1982; Acres 5,000; Hunters/yr 300; Type
Public; Shoots Blinds, Boat; Birds Ducks, Geese;
Dogs Avail/HDW; Packages 1/2 Day, 1-12 guns

Double Cluck Outfitters
PO Box 1, Chester, CT 06412
(203) 526-4002 Dick Tracy
35 mi. SE of Hartford Est 1985; Acres 5,000;
Hunters/yr 1,800; Type Public, Corp.; On Site
Clubhouse; Shoots Blinds; Birds Dove, Pheasant, Ducks,
Geese; Dogs Avail/HDW; Packages 1 Day, 3-30 guns

Markover Game Farm & Hunting Preserve
719 Cook Hill Rd., Danielson, CT 06239
(860) 774-4116 Norman Olsen
75 mi. SW of Boston, MA Est 1917; Acres 300;
Type Public; On Site Clubhouse, Meals, Clays;
Shoots Field; Birds Pheasant, Chukar, Ducks; Dogs
Avail/HDW; Packages 1/2 Day O NAGA/See Pg. 107

Millstream Preserve
130 Lake Rd., Columbia, CT 06237
(203) 228-1657 Jay Lembo 25 mi. E of Hartford
Acres 300; Type Public; Shoots Field; Birds
Pheasant; Dogs Avail/HDW; Packages 1/2 Day

Venwood Lake
Hunting Preserve
541 Rt. 148, Killingworth, CT 06419
(860) 663-3055 Donald or Diane Venuti Anytime
20 mi. E of New Haven Est 1994; Acres 350;
Type Public; Shoots Field; Birds Pheasant, Chukar,
Ducks; Dogs Avail/HDW
O NAGA/See Pg. 107
O Bird Processing   O Quality Clubhouse
O Sporting Clays   O Family Run Business
O Fishing

DELAWARE

Owens Station Sporting Clays
RD1, Box 101-C, Greenwood, DE 19950
(302) 349-4478 Bill Wolter/Ernie Bennett
75 mi. E of Washington, DC Est 1979; Acres 600;
Type Public, Member/Avail, Corp.; On Site
Clubhouse, Lodging, Meals, Clays; Shoots Field,
Tower, Blinds, Boat; Birds Dove, Quail, Pheasant,
Chukar, Huns, Ducks, Geese; Dogs Avail/HDW;
Packages 1/2 Day, 1-4 guns

FLORIDA

Adams Farms, Inc.
Pheasant Shooting Preserve
2575 County Hwy. 185, Glendale, FL 32433
(904) 837-2957 Dr. Tom Guyton or Leonard Adams
or (904) 859-2334
12 mi. N of DeFuniak Springs, 12 mi. N of I-10
Est 1996; **Acres** 1,100; **Type** Public; **On Site** Clubhouse, Meals, Clays; **Shoots** Field; **Birds** Dove, Quail, Pheasant, Chukar; **Dogs** Avail/HDW; **Packages** 1/2 Day, 1-12 guns O NAGA/See Pg. 107

▼ ORVIS ENDORSED ▼

Bienville Plantation
PO Box 241, White Springs, FL 32096
(912) 755-0705 Steve Barras
60 mi. W of Jacksonville, FL
Est 1994; **Acres** 19,000; **Type** Public, Member/Avail, Corp.; **On Site** Clubhouse; **Shoots** Field, Blinds; **Birds** Dove, Quail, Ducks; **Dogs** Avail/HDW; **Packages** 1/2 Day

See Our Ad Across

▲ ORVIS ENDORSED ▲

BIG D
• PLANTATION •

Big D Plantation
Rt. 15, Box 1760, Lake City, FL 32024
(800) 437-4441 Charlie Parnell
30 mi. N of Gainesville
Est 1988; **Acres** 1,400; **Hunters/yr** 750; **Type** Public, Member/Avail; **On Site** Clubhouse, Meals, Clays; **Shoots** Field; **Birds** Dove, Quail, Pheasant, Chukar; **Dogs** Avail/HDW; **Packages** 1/2 Day, up to 16 guns O NAGA/See Pg. 107

See Our Ad Pg. 309

Bonnette Hunting
& Fishing Club
5309 Hood Rd., Palm Beach Gardens, FL 33418
(407) 626-5180 Alix Bonnette
10 mi. N of West Palm Beach
Est 1961; **Acres** 3,200; **Hunters/yr** 500; **Type** Member/Avail; **On Site** Clubhouse, Lodging, Meals, Clays; **Shoots** Field; **Birds** Quail, Pheasant, Chukar; **Dogs** Avail/HDW; **Packages** 1/2 Day, up to 20 guns
O Kennel Bird Dogs   O Brochure Available
O Sporting Clays   O Quality Clubhouse
O Gourmet Meals   O Rifle & Pistol Range

Dixie Wildlife Safaris
5001 Hwy. 630 East, Frostproof, FL 33843
(941) 696-3300 Mike Acreman
48 mi. S of Orlando
Est 1980; **Acres** 5,000; **Type** Public; **On Site** Clubhouse, Meals; **Shoots** Field; **Birds** Quail; **Dogs** Avail/HDW; **Packages** 1/2 Day

Donna Plantation
Rt. 6, Box 61, Quincy, FL 32351
(904) 875-1615 Al Hartman
1 mi. NE of Quincy
Type Public; **On Site** Lodging; **Shoots** Field, Blinds; **Birds** Turkey, Ducks

Double WW Hunting Preserve
1200 Cassat Ave., Jacksonville, FL 32205
(904) 783-2626 Wayne Scarborough, Jr.
12 mi. SW of Jacksonville
Est 1988; **Acres** 700; **Hunters/yr** 400; **Type** Public; **On Site** Clubhouse, Meals, Clays; **Shoots** Field; **Birds** Dove, Quail; **Dogs** Avail/HDW; **Packages** 1/2 Day, 1-8 guns
O Airport Pickup   O 2 Sporting Clays Courses
O Brochure Available   O NSCA Certified Instructor
O Family Run Business   O Southern Home Cooking
O Corporate Hunts Our Specialty
O Custom Hunting Wagon
O No License Required

El Rancho Hunting Preserve
2153 Coon Hollow Trail, Chipley, FL 32428
(904) 638-1353 Rex T. Yates
65 mi. W of Tallahassee
Est 1956; **Acres** 320; **Hunters/yr** 400; **Type** Public; **On Site** Clubhouse, Lodging, Meals; **Shoots** Blinds, Boat; **Birds** Ducks; **Dogs** Avail/HDW; **Packages** 1 Day, up to 20 guns

Everglades Adventures

3280 4th Ave., NE, Naples, FL 33964
(941) 455-5910 Mark Clemons 8am-9pm
E of Naples **Est** 1989; **Acres** 4,000; **Hunters/yr**
300; **Type** Public, Member/Avail, Corp.; **On Site**
Meals; **Shoots** Field; **Birds** Dove, Quail, Turkey, Snipe;
Dogs Avail/HDW; **Packages** 1/2 Day, 2-6 guns
o **NAGA/See Pg. 107**
o Brochure Available
o Custom Vehicles
EVERGLADES ADVENTURES–Featuring bountiful
and beautiful wild Osceola turkeys native only to
Florida. Your hunt day begins at pre-dawn with
you traveling with your guide to the selected site
where he has roosted gobblers located. At first
light we call the gobbler in using various combinations of calls. We shoot only in range customer
selected trophy toms. This hunt lasts from daylight
until 1 pm and is available during the spring season
only–$400 per day, per person or $950 for a three
day hunt. You may enjoy a full day in the field at
your option, by joining the guide the evening before to assist in stalking gobblers to the roost for
the next day hunt. Our quail hunts consists of riding on custom vehicles while watching the bird dogs
working. Once they go on point we get off the vehicle
and in position to shoot. 1/2 day hunts, including
drinks, guides, vehicles and dogs–$375 for two guns,
$550 for three. Our dove shoots are over large pre-
pared fields planted with millet and cover-shot once
per week on Sunday afternoon for 3-4 hours–we can
handle 50 or more hunters at $65 per gun.

Fisheating Creek Hunting Preserve

PO Box 117, Palmdale, FL 33944
(941) 675-4117 David Austin 9 to 5 pm
100 mi. S of Orlando **Est** 1988; **Acres** 25,000;
Hunters/yr 150; **Type** Public; **On Site** Clubhouse,
Lodging; **Shoots** Field; **Birds** Quail, Turkey; **Dogs**
Avail/HDW; **Packages** 2 Days, 1-9 guns

Foxcreek Hunting Preserve

Fox Creek Plantation

PO Box 39, Monticello, FL 32344
(904) 997-8063 Jimmy Thurman 8am-5pm
32 mi. NE of Tallahassee
Est 1987; **Acres** 600; **Hunters/yr** 200; **Type**
Public; **On Site** Clubhouse, Lodging, Meals, Clays;
Shoots Field; **Birds** Quail; **Dogs** Avail/HDW;
Packages 1/2 Day, 1-6 guns

Hardy Bradford Shooting Preserve

2114 NW 15th Ave., Gainesville, FL 32601
(800) 541-1015 R.B. Davis 9 to 5
85 mi. W of Jacksonville
Est 1992; **Acres** 300; **Type** Public, Member/Avail;
Shoots Field; **Birds** Dove, Quail; **Dogs** Avail/HDW;
Packages 1/2 Day, 1-6 guns

Iron-Wood Preserve

PO Box 1949, Lake City, FL 32056
(904) 963-3508 Nickey Jackson
60 mi. W of Jacksonville
Est 1985; **Acres** 2,000; **Hunters/yr** 80; **Type**
Public, Member/Avail; **On Site** Clubhouse, Lodging,
Meals, Clays; **Birds** Quail; **Dogs** Avail/HDW;
Packages 1/2 Day, up to 5 guns

J&R Hunting Preserve

8400 S.W. Fox Brown Rd., Indiantown, FL 34956
(407) 597-4757 Joe or Liz O'Bannon 7am-9pm
30 mi. NW of West Palm Beach
Est 1984; **Acres** 5,000; **Hunters/yr** 300; **Type**
Public, Member/Avail, Corp.; **On Site** Clubhouse,
Lodging, Meals, Clays; **Shoots** Field, Tower; **Birds**
Dove, Quail, Pheasant, Chukar, Turkey, Sage Grouse,
Snipe; **Dogs** Avail/HDW; **Packages** 1/2 Day, 1-8
guns o NAGA/See Pg. 107
o Sporting Clays
o Brochure Available
o 30 Miles NW of West Palm Beach
o Axis Deer Hunting & Exotics
o Processing Available

Jennings Bluff Hunting Preserve

Jennings Bluff Hunting Preserve

Rt. 2, Box 4250, Jennings, FL 32053
(904) 938-5555 Troy Tolbert 9 to 5
65 mi. NE of Tallahassee
Est 1989; **Acres** 1,800; **Hunters/yr** 504; **Type**
Public, Member/Avail; **On Site** Clubhouse, Lodging,
Meals, Clays; **Shoots** Field, Tower; **Birds** Quail,
Pheasant; **Dogs** Avail/HDW; **Packages** 1/2 Day,
3-16 guns o NAGA/See Pg. 107
o Hunting License   o Airport Pickup
o Brochure Available   o Quality Clubhouse
o Family Run Business

Plantation Outfitters

14 N. Cone St., Quincy, FL 32351
(904) 575-1260 David A. Avant, III Evenings
35 mi. NW of Tallahassee
Est 1823; **Acres** 3,000; **Hunters/yr** 300; **Type**
Public, Member/Avail; **On Site** Clubhouse, Lodging,
Meals, Clays; **Shoots** Field, Driven, Blinds; **Birds**
Dove, Quail, Pheasant, Chukar, Turkey, Snipe, Ducks;
Dogs Avail/HDW; **Packages** 1/2 Day
o NAGA/See Pg. 107

H.D. Ryals Preserve
6600 Pinewood Lane, Punta Gorda, FL 33982
(941) 639-3656 Jim Kelly 6pm-9pm
25 mi. N of Ft. Myers
Est 1952; **Acres** 12,000; **Hunters/yr** 400; **Type**
Public, Member/Avail; **On Site** Meals; **Shoots** Field;
Birds Dove, Quail, Snipe, Ducks; **Dogs** Avail;
Packages 1 Day, 2-4 guns

TM Ranch
15600 TM Ranch Rd., Orlando, FL 32832
(407) 273-2026 Mark Holland 6pm-9pm
7 mi. SE of Orlando
Est 1996; **Acres** 5,000; **Type** Public; **On Site**
Clubhouse, Meals; **Shoots** Field; **Birds** Quail;
Dogs Avail/HDW; **Packages** 1/2 Day, 2-8 guns
O Airport Pickup   O Factory Ammunition
O Bird Processing   O Family Run Business
O Shooting Instruction   O Gun Rentals Available
O Hunting Jeeps
O No Hunting License Required!

Three Rivers Kennels
Rt. 3, Box 200, Jasper, FL 32052
(904) 938-3405 Trammel or Travis Dees 9am-9pm
85 mi. E of Tallahassee
Est 1995; **Acres** 865; **Hunters/yr** 150; **Type**
Public; **On Site** Meals; **Shoots** Field, Tower; **Birds**
Quail, Pheasant; **Dogs** Avail/HDW; **Packages** 1/2
Day, 2-4 guns

Two Rivers Ranch
40 Ranch Rd., Thonotosassa, FL 33592
(813) 986-5788 David Tarr 9-5; (813) 894-6173, after 6
10 mi. NE of Tampa
Acres 17,000; **Type** Public; **On Site** Clubhouse,
Lodging; **Shoots** Field; **Birds** Quail, Turkey; **Dogs**
Avail
O Deer & Wild Hog

Wingshooters
PO Box 980, LaBelle, FL 33935
(941) 693-2549 Don Teston
30 mi. E of Ft. Myers
Acres 4,000; **Type** Public, Member/Avail; **On Site**
Clubhouse, Lodging, Meals, Clays; **Birds** Quail,
Turkey, Snipe; **Dogs** Avail

GEORGIA

Ashburn Hill
Hunting Preserve, Inc.
PO Box 128, Moultrie, GA 31776
(912) 985-1507 F.R. Pidcock, III 8:30am-4:30pm
60 mi. NE of Tallahassee
Est 1968; **Acres** 5,000; **Hunters/yr** 400; **Type** Public; **On Site** Clubhouse, Lodging, Meals, Clays; **Shoots** Field; **Birds** Quail; **Dogs** Avail/HDW; **Packages** 1 Day, 1-24 guns

Barksdale Bobwhite Plantation
Rt.4, Longstreet Rd., Box 851, Cochran, GA 31014
(912) 934-6916 Beth Manning FAX: (912) 934-0877
35 mi. S of Macon
Est 1991; **Acres** 2,200; **Type** Public; **On Site**

Clubhouse, Lodging, Meals, Clays; **Shoots** Field; **Birds** Quail, Pheasant, Chukar; **Dogs** Avail/HDW; **Packages** 1/2 Day, 2-24 guns ○ NAGA/See Pg. 107
○ Sporting Clays, Skeet, 5-Stand
○ Shooting Instruction Available
○ Res/Non-Resident Hunting License Available
○ Gun Rental & Ammunition Available
○ Corporate Discounts
○ Hunt Your Own Dog-Half Days
○ Deer & Turkey Hunts in Season
○ Excellent Business Retreat
○ Lodging   ○ Brochure/Video Available

Bevy Burst Hunting Preserve
Rt. 2, Box 245, Edison, GA 31746
(800) 447-9389 Kathy Gray 9am-5pm
40 mi. SW of Albany
Est 1991; **Acres** 3,000; **Type** Public; **On Site** Clubhouse, Lodging, Meals, Clays; **Shoots** Field; **Birds** Dove, Quail; **Dogs** Avail/HDW; **Packages** 1/2 Day, 1-10 guns ○ NAGA/See Pg. 107

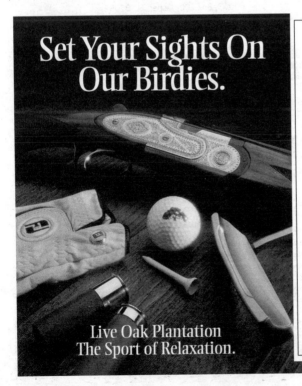

BURNT PINE PLANTATION...
New, Different, Diverse–Better!
by **Aaron Pass**

Burnt Pine Plantation, near historic Madison, Georgia, is now operating under new management, but that's not all that is new and different. Burnt Pine has been well known as the South's premier trophy whitetail hunting plantation for 20 years, but new programs have developed the bird-hunting/wing-shooting potential to that same high level. The game resource base has been deepened and the quality, quantity and variety of shooting have been greatly expanded.

In other words, there is more to shoot, more to do and more traditional sporting fun to be had at the "new" Burnt Pine than ever before.

Enhanced quail shooting in a natural and "classic" quail hunting setting.

Choose the challenge
Quail management activities and shooting areas have been increased and enlarged. Quail habitat is carefully managed, burned and planted in quail food crops, including grain and native wild food plants, to provide enhanced quail shooting in a natural and "classic" quail hunting setting. The various quail courses are classed by "difficulty factor" so that the individual bird hunter can choose just how challenging and sporty he wants his quail shooting to be. Natural production in natural cover is augmented by birds stocked early in the season to provide well-acclimated, strong-flying game birds until season's end. The plantation kennel is stocked with stylish, well-trained bird dogs assuring the high-class dog work associated with quality quail hunting. Every effort is made by the Burnt Pine staff to preserve and provide the traditional style and amenities of Old South quail hunting.

Pheasant and chukar partridge shooting also are available. When hunted over pointing dogs, these two strong-flying species provide a different and very exciting bird hunting challenge.

Continental shoots
The Continental Shoot is a new and very special wing shooting experience now offered at Burnt Pine Plantation. The "Continental" affords the unique experience and social esthetics of European driven game shooting at a fraction of the cost of trans-Atlantic air fare. Duplicating the driven pheasant shoots of Britain and the red-legged partridge shooting of Spain, gunners take high incomers from a series of shooting butts just as upper-class European sportsmen have done for decades. Ideally suited for group entertainment, the Continental Shoot is a fast-paced adventure in world-class wing shooting.

Waterfowling is Burnt Pine's newest and most ambitious venture. The focus is on decoyed ducks shot from a blind in the classic manner. Well-set decoy spreads, expert callers and trained retrievers provide high-quality waterfowling in the grand manner of old-time duck hunting with limits to match.

Of course, the Burnt Pine deer hunting program remains first rate. Two decades of trophy management have resulted in a quality deer herd significantly superior to that commonly found on over-shot public land. Private land and controlled access provide an un-crowded and safe deer hunting experience. This is fair-chase, fair-chance hunting for wild whitetails with a better than average chance for a real trophy buck.

Clays and fishing
More shotgun shooting opportunity is provided by expanded clay target facilities. The existing trap range has been aug-

The lodge is comfortable and spacious. And no, you don't have to "dress" for dinner.

mented by a unique Crazy Quail range and a 20-bird Quail Walk that no one has yet run straight on their first (or second) attempt. Great recreational shooting in themselves, the clay birds also offer "Top Gun" tie-breakers for hunting buddies who have scored equally well in the game fields.

With this much shooting potential, it is possible that a Burnt Pine guest might become temporarily burned out on burned powder. Should that occur, bass fishing offers a first-rate angling option. Eleven ponds are well stocked with big largemouth bass, feisty bluegills and tasty catfish and you have to really work at not filling your stringer. Fly fisherman take notice -- these classic shallow-water farm ponds offer the ideal environment for serious topwater bass bugging.

The Burnt Pine lodge and guest cabins have been completely renovated and expanded to luxurious standards. The main lodge now provides 5,000 square feet and includes a fully equipped game room and well-stocked bar for after-hunt relaxation. Burnt Pine's longstanding reputation for great food remains unchanged except that the traditional hearty home cooking now shares the gastronomic spotlight with gourmet dining and fine wines.

Obviously, with such a diverse resource base and variety of facilities, Burnt Pine Plantation has a lot to offer. Whether one wants to focus on one species or try a bit of everything, customized agendas are easily arranged. Special events, such as the Continental Shoot, are fast-paced and exciting. A mixed program including a morning duck shoot and an afternoon quail hunt (with a hearty lunch and maybe a siesta in

the middle) are more leisurely. The emphasis is on individual service and attention to detail. The atmosphere is low-key and relaxed. The shooting is good, the food is good and the beds are soft. Bagging a good time is the goal and rat racing is not allowed. A genteel "sporting weekend in the country" is the Burnt Pine product line.

From complimentary morning coffee served with your wake-up call to after dinner drinks and a good cigar, Burnt Pine Plantation is dedicated to providing a quality shooting, excellent food, comfortable facilities and relaxed "good old days" hunting experience to modern sportsmen.

Burnt Pine Plantation Shooting Programs

BIRD SHOOTING — Season, Oct. 1-Mar. Preserve License provided by Burnt Pine Plantation.

QUAIL — Full day (16 Birds) $339; half day (8 birds) $199. Additional birds $6.95 each.

PHEASANT/CHUKAR (w/dogs) — Half days (8 pheasant/10 chukar) $210. Additional birds, pheasant $14.99/chukar $9.75.

CONTINENTAL/DRIVEN PHEASANT SHOOT — 15 birds released per gun. Shooting from butts, European style. Including lunch and apres hunt refreshments, $235 per gun. Six public hunts per season; private parties accommodated.

DUCK — Two guns per blind, limit 10 ducks. (shooters must have a valid Federal Migratory Bird Stamp) $250 per gun.

DEER — Georgia seasons and licensing requirements apply. Numerous options and hunting packages, including archery and either sex hunting from mid-September through 1 January. High-success parent/child deer hunts are a specialty. Write for details. Also spring wild turkey and feral hog hunting, write for details.

Except as noted, prices do not include lodging/meals. Ammunition and rental firearms are available. Located just over one hour east of Atlanta, GA, limo service to Atlanta airport is available.

CONTACT:
BURNT PINE PLANTATION, 2941 Little River Road, Madison, GA 30650. Phone: (706) 342-7202. FAX (706) 342-2170.

Bienville Plantation

1158 Oakcliff Road, Macon, GA 32211
(912) 755-0705 Steve Barras
60 mi. W of Jacksonville, FL
Est 1994; **Acres** 19,000; **Type** Public,
Member/Avail, Corp.; **On Site** Clubhouse, Lodging,
Meals, Clays; **Shoots** Field, Blinds, Boat; **Birds**
Dove, Quail, Ducks; **Dogs** Avail/HDW; **Packages**
1/2 Day, 1-20 guns
See Our Ad Pg. 307

Big Red Oak Plantation

PO Box 247, Gay, GA 30218
(706) 538-6870 Arthur Estes 8am-10pm
50 mi. S of Atlanta
Est 1976; **Acres** 3,500; **Hunters/yr** 2,000; **Type**
Public, Member/Avail, Corp.; **On Site** Clubhouse,
Lodging, Meals, Clays; **Shoots** Field; **Birds** Dove,
Quail, Pheasant, Chukar, Turkey; **Dogs** Avail/HDW;
Packages 1/2 Day, 2-12 guns ○ NAGA/See Pg. 107
○ Family Run Business
○ Great Home Cooking
○ Fish for Bass & Bream
○ Professionally Trained Dogs
○ 45 min./Atlanta Airport

Bobwhite Plantation
PO Box 227, Waynesboro, GA 30830
(706) 554-6221 Tom Reynolds After 8pm
25 mi. S of Augusta
Est 1988; **Acres** 2,000; **Hunters/yr** 100; **Type**
Public, Member/Avail; **On Site** Clubhouse, Lodging,
Meals, Clays; **Shoots** Field, Blinds; **Birds** Dove,
Quail, Turkey, Ducks; **Dogs** Avail/HDW; **Packages**
1/2 Day, 2-8 guns

Boggy Pond Plantation

1084 Lanier Rd., Moultrie, GA 31768
(912) 985-5395 Mackie Dekle 9-7
55 mi. NE of Tallahassee, FL
Est 1983; **Acres** 3,000; **Hunters/yr** 250; **Type**
Public; **On Site** Clubhouse, Lodging, Meals, Clays;
Shoots Field; **Birds** Dove, Quail, Pheasant, Chukar;
Dogs Avail/HDW; **Packages** 1/2 Day, 2-14 guns

Boll Weevil Plantation
4264 Thompson Bridge Rd., Waynesboro, GA 30830
(706) 554-6227 Al McClain M-F, 9-5
35 mi. S of Augusta
Est 1987; **Acres** 6,191; **Type** Public; **On Site**
Clubhouse, Lodging, Meals, Clays; **Shoots** Field;
Birds Dove, Quail, Turkey; **Dogs** Avail; **Packages**
1/2 Day, 1-27 guns ○ NAGA/See Pg. 107

Burge Plantation
Rt. 1, Morehouse Rd., Mansfield, GA 30255
(770) 787-5152 A.G. Morehouse
45 mi. SE of Atlanta
Est 1982; **Acres** 1,000; **Type** Member/Ltd; **On**
Site Clubhouse, Lodging, Meals, Clays; **Shoots** Field,
Driven; **Birds** Dove, Quail, Pheasant, Turkey, Ducks;
Dogs Avail/HDW; **Packages** 1/2 Day
○ NAGA/See Pg. 107

Burnt Pine Plantation

2941 Little River Rd., Madison, GA 30650
(706) 342-7202 Steve Spears
60 mi. E of Atlanta
Est 1973; **Acres** 7,000; **Hunters/yr** 2,000; **Type**
Public, Member/Avail; **On Site** Clubhouse, Lodging,
Meals, Clays; **Shoots** Field, Tower, Driven; **Birds**
Dove, Quail, Pheasant, Chukar, Turkey, Ducks; **Dogs**
Avail/HDW; **Packages** 1/2 Day, 1-25 guns
○ NAGA/See Pg. 107
See Our Ad Pg. 311-312

▼ ORVIS ENDORSED ▼

The Lodge at Cabin Bluff

PO Box 30203, Sea Island, GA 31561
(912) 638-3611 Karen Cate 9am-5pm, Monday - Friday
9am-5pm, Monday - Friday
15 mi. W of Woodbine, GA
Acres 45,000; **Hunters/yr** 150; **Type** Public; **On**
Site Clubhouse, Lodging, Meals, Clays; **Shoots** Field;
Birds Dove, Quail, Turkey, Ducks; **Dogs** Avail;
Packages 3 Days, 1-16 guns
○ NAGA/See Pg. 107
○ Alternate Phone: (912) 729-5960 (Lodge)
See Our Ad Pg. 315

▲ ORVIS ENDORSED ▲

Come Away Plantation
3739 N. Elam Church Rd., NW, Norwood, GA 30821
(706) 465-3292 Jodie McWhorter 8am-6pm
100 mi. E of Atlanta
Est 1985; **Acres** 4,000; **Hunters/yr** 200; **Type**
Public; **On Site** Clubhouse, Lodging, Meals, Clays;
Shoots Field; **Birds** Quail, Turkey; **Dogs**
Avail/HDW; **Packages** 1/2 Day, 3-12 guns
○ NAGA/See Pg. 107

Copperhead Kennels
1202 Old Adgateville Rd., Hillsboro, GA 31038
(706) 468-8368 David Bentley
Shoots Field; **Birds** Quail, Pheasant
○ NAGA/See Pg. 107

Covey Rise Plantation, Inc.
Rt. 1, Box 30, Camilla, GA 31730
(912) 336-5413 Robin Singletary
60 mi. N of Tallahassee
Acres 3,500; **Type** Public; **On Site** Clubhouse, Lodging, Meals; **Shoots** Field; **Birds** Dove, Quail; **Dogs** Avail/HDW; **Packages** 1 Day, 2-6 guns

Dogwood Hunting Preserve
376 Grainey Rd., Cairo, GA 31728
(912) 872-3508 Sidney Gainey 7am-11pm
25 mi. N of Tallahassee **Type** Public, Member/Avail; **On Site** Clubhouse, Lodging, Meals, Clays; **Shoots** Field, Tower, Driven; **Birds** Dove, Quail, Pheasant, Chukar; **Dogs** Avail/HDW; **Packages** 1/2 Day, 2-9 guns

DOGWOOD PLANTATION
Dogwood Plantation Hunting Preserve
1409 Hwy. 42 South, McDonough, GA 30253
(770) 957-7005 Bill Pullin (770) 229-8284 9-5
28 mi. S of Atlanta Est 1989; **Acres** 1,000; **Type** Public; **On Site** Clubhouse, Lodging, Meals; **Shoots** Field, Tower; **Birds** Quail, Pheasant; **Dogs** Avail/HDW; **Packages** 1/2 Day, 2-10 guns
○ NAGA/See Pg. 107
○ Airport Pickup
○ Family Run Business
○ Brochure & Video Available
○ Tower Shoots Available for up to 25 Guns
○ Gun Rental Available

Flint River Hunting, Inc.
385 Killian Rd., Suite A, Lilburn, GA 30247
(770) 564-4826 J.M. Tierney
45 mi. SW of Macon **Est** 1990; **Acres** 1,500; **Type** Public, Member/Avail, Corp.; **On Site** Lodging, Meals; **Shoots** Field; **Birds** Dove, Quail, Pheasant, Chukar, Turkey; **Dogs** Avail/HDW; **Packages** 1/2 Day

Hog Liver
Quail Shooting Preserve
2863 Hog Liver Rd., Carrollton, GA 30117
(770) 834-6296 Harold Hendrix 8am-9pm
40 mi. W of Atlanta
Est 1987; **Acres** 475; **Type** Public; **On Site** Clubhouse, Lodging, Meals, Clays; **Shoots** Field; **Birds** Quail, Pheasant; **Dogs** Avail/HDW; **Packages** 1/2 Day, 2-16 guns ○ NAGA/See Pg. 107
○ Airport Pickup   ○ Bird Processing
○ Loaner Guns   ○ 45 Minutes from Atlanta
○ Umbrella Hunting License: In-state & Out-of-state

▼ ORVIS ENDORSED ▼

Live Oak Plantation
Rt. 2, Box 308, Adel, GA 31620
(800) 682-4868 Cecil S. Harrell 9am-5pm, M-F
45 mi. N of the Georgia-Florida state line
Est 1987; **Acres** 2,500; **Hunters/yr** 800; **Type** Public; **On Site** Clubhouse, Lodging, Meals, Clays; **Shoots** Field; **Birds** Quail, Pheasant; **Dogs** Avail/HDW; **Packages** 1 Day, 2-16 guns
○ Golf & Fishing
See Our Ad Pg. 310

▲ ORVIS ENDORSED ▲

A tradition for every season.

The Lodge at Cabin Bluff offers groups of up to 32 guests Orvis-endorsed wingshooting and fly fishing at its privacy-shrouded preserve overlooking famed Cumberland Island on the Georgia coast. By season, enjoy quail, turkey and whitetail deer hunting. Outstanding sporting clays and shooting instruction year round, too. Amenities are exceptional. Please call Karen Cate for information and reservations, 912-638-3611.

The Lodge at Cabin Bluff
KINGSLAND • GEORGIA
Orvis-endorsed wingshooting & fly fishing.
Operated by the Sea Island Company.

Llewellin's Point Hunting Preserve & Kennel
4897 Salem Rd., Pine Mountain, GA 31822
(800) 636-9819 Floyd Clements
70 mi. S of Atlanta
Est 1952; **Acres** 1,100; **Type** Public, Member/Avail;
On Site Clubhouse, Lodging, Meals, Clays; **Shoots**
Field; **Birds** Quail, Pheasant, Chukar; **Dogs**
Avail/HDW; **Packages** 1/2 Day, 1-35 guns
o NAGA/See Pg. 107

See Our Ad Across

Marsh Hunting Preserve
3079 Metts Rd., Statesboro, GA 30458
(912) 587-5727 Windel Marsh
50 mi. NW of Savannah
Est 1960; **Acres** 600; **Hunters/yr** 1,000; **Type**
Member/Avail, Corp.; **On Site** Clubhouse, Lodging,
Meals, Clays; **Shoots** Field; **Birds** Dove, Quail;
Dogs Avail/HDW; **Packages** 1/2 Day, up to 12 guns

Millcreek Hunting Preserve, Inc.
PO Box 131, Rincon, GA 31326
(912) 826-4968 William Exley/Jesse 9-5

Myrtlewood Hunting/Sporting Clays
PO Box 199, Thomasville, GA 31799
(912) 228-0987 Bob or John
35 mi. NE of Tallahassee
Est 1988; **Acres** 3,300; **Type** Public; **On Site**
Clubhouse, Lodging, Meals, Clays; **Shoots** Field;
Birds Quail; **Dogs** Avail

On site clubhouse, 3 lodges, meals available, 1/2
day and full day quail hunts with trained dogs and
guides, Sporting Clays. Specializing in corporate
groups. Brochure available upon request. Myrtlewood offers field Quail hunting on 1000 acres of
beautiful South Georgia high pine country, you'll
hunt with trained dogs, professional guides and
rigs. Myrtlewood also offers one of the areas most
challenging Sporting Clays courses. Trophy deer
hunting and premier bass fishing are also available.
Myrtlewood's spacious course and large clubhouse
is especially convenient to accommodate corporate
groups up to 80. Run by great ol' southern boys,
Myrtlewood is a place for every sportsman.

Ochlocknee Plantation
PO Box 423, Sylvester, GA 31791
(912) 776-1122 Todd Ford
20 mi. SE of Albany
Acres 2,500; **Hunters/yr** 700; **Type** Public,
Member/Avail; **On Site** Clubhouse, Lodging, Meals,
Clays; **Shoots** Field; **Birds** Dove, Quail; **Dogs** Avail

Partridge Point Hunt Club
PO Box 15241, Savannah, GA 31416
(912) 354-2020 Tony Calandra After 6pm
55 mi. from Savannah
Est 1987; **Acres** 944; **Hunters/yr** 700; **Type**
Public, Member/Avail, Corp.; **Shoots** Field; **Birds**
Dove, Quail, Pheasant; **Dogs** Avail/HDW; **Packages**
1/2 Day, 2-8 guns

Pear Tree Farm
6730 Seven Island Rd., Madison, GA 30650
(706) 342-3017 James Patrick 9-5
60 mi. E of Atlanta
Est 1994; **Acres** 500; **Type** Public; **On Site**
Clubhouse, Lodging, Meals; **Shoots** Field; **Birds**
Quail; **Dogs** Avail

Pinefields Plantation
Rt. 2, Box 215, Moultrie, GA 31768
(912) 985-2086 Charlie Cannon, III 8 to 8
12 mi. E of Moultrie
Est 1912; **Acres** 5,000; **Hunters/yr** 600; **Type**
Public; **On Site** Clubhouse, Lodging, Meals;
Shoots Field; **Birds** Dove, Quail; **Dogs** Avail/HDW;
Packages 1 Day, up to 8 guns

Pounderosa Plantation
Rt. 1, Box 267 K, Hwy. 15 S, White Plains, GA 30678
(800) 215-4196 Dee Lindsey M-F 8-5
75 mi. SE of Atlanta
Est 1995; **Acres** 2,200; **Type** Public; **On Site**
Clubhouse, Lodging, Meals, Clays; **Shoots** Field;
Birds Quail, Turkey, Ducks; **Dogs** Avail/HDW;
Packages 1/2 Day, 2-16 guns

Pretoria Station
Hunting Preserve
4601 Leary Rd., Albany, GA 31707
(912) 439-4132 Bob Hayes
80 mi. N of Tallahassee
Est 1989; **Acres** 1,800; **Type** Public, Member/Avail,
Corp.; **On Site** Clubhouse, Lodging, Meals, Clays;
Shoots Field; **Birds** Dove, Quail, Turkey; **Dogs**
Avail/HDW; **Packages** 1/2 Day, 2-12 guns
See Our Ad Pg. 314

Quail Country Lodge
Rt. 1, Box 690, Arlington, GA 31713
(912) 725-4645 Joy and Tom Newberry
30 mi. W of Albany
Est 1972; **Acres** 5,000; **Hunters/yr** 500; **Type**
Public, Member/Avail, Corp.; **On Site** Clubhouse,
Lodging, Meals, Clays; **Shoots** Field; **Birds** Quail;
Dogs Avail/HDW; **Packages** 1/2 Day, 2-16 guns

LLEWELLIN'S POINT
HUNTING PRESERVE & KENNELS

At Callaway Gardens

Llewellin's Point Gun Club & Sporting Clays at Callaway Gardens offers a top hunting experience in the heart of the true Bobwhite Quail country of southwestern Georgia. At Llewellin's Point you'll hunt on over 1,000 acres of open field and low brush habitat, which will challenge and please even the best veteran hunters.

Llewellin's Point staff of hunting professionals grew up hunting quail, and have put themselves and an excellent kennel of experienced Llewellin setters at your disposal. There's nothing they'd rather do than put you over an exploding covey of quail. No matter what your level of expertise, Llewellin's Point guides can outfit you, hone your technique on their super sporting clays course, 5-stand sporting clays and skeet or trap fields, then guide you to a great day's hunting.

Llewellin's Point is not just a superlative hunting preserve. Guests of the Club enjoy accommodations ranging from the 345-room inn at Callaway Gardens to 2-bedroom cottages or 4-bedroom villas, the ultimate in privacy and elegance. There are seven restaurants to choose from, all offering their unique brand of Southern fare. And there's more, including fly fishing, golf and tennis amidst some of the most beautiful gardens in the world. Easily accessible by car, only 70 miles south of Atlanta and just 2 miles off I-185. Or fly in by private plane to our 5,000 ft. paved, lighted airport.

Call Today For Information, Reservations Or A Color Brochure:

800-636-9819

4897 Salem Road • Pine Mountain, GA 31822

Quail Ridge Preserve
Rt. 3, Box 387-C, Douglas, GA 31533
(912) 384-0025 Francis Fountain
140 mi. NE of Tallahassee
Est 1990; **Acres** 900; **Type** Public; **On Site**
Clubhouse, Meals; **Shoots** Field, Blinds; **Birds** Dove,
Quail; **Dogs** Avail/HDW; **Packages** 1/2 Day, 2-10
guns O NAGA/See Pg. 107

Quailridge Plantation
PO Box 155, Norman Park, GA 31771
(912) 985-5011 Edwin Norman 8 to 5
35 mi. E of Albany
Est 1969; **Acres** 4,000; **Hunters/yr** 750; **Type**
Public; **On Site** Clubhouse, Lodging, Meals, Clays;
Shoots Field; **Birds** Quail; **Dogs** Avail/HDW;
Packages 1 Day, 2-12 guns

Redhawk Plantation
PO Box 882, Unadilla, GA 31091
(912) 783-1991 Mitch Slay
40 mi. S of Macon **Acres** 8,000; **Type** Public,
Member/Avail; **On Site** Clubhouse, Lodging, Meals;
Shoots Field; **Birds** Dove, Quail, Turkey, Ducks;
Dogs Avail; **Packages** 1/2 Day, 1-10 guns

Riverview Plantation
Rt. 2, Box 515, Camilla, GA 31730
(912) 294-4904 Cader B. Cox, III 9-5

Rocky Creek Plantation
237 Joe Harden Rd., Lyons, GA 30436
(912) 526-4868 Chuck Thompson/Sandon Wright
75 mi. W of Savannah
Est 1996; **Acres** 300; **Type** Public, Member/Avail;
On Site Meals, Clays; **Shoots** Field, Tower; **Birds**
Pheasant, Chukar, Ducks; **Dogs** Avail/HDW;
Packages 1/2 Day, 2-20 guns

Samara Plantation
PO Box 356, Norman Park, GA 31771
(912) 769-3065 Harold Ivey during noon hour
80 mi. NE of Tallahassee
Acres 5,100; **Hunters/yr** 1,100; **Type** Public; **On
Site** Clubhouse, Lodging, Meals, Clays; **Shoots** Field;
Birds Quail; **Dogs** Avail; **Packages** 1/2 Day, 1-24 guns

▼ ORVIS ENDORSED ▼

Shirahland Plantation
Rt. 1, Box 340, Camilla, GA 31730
(800) 538-8559 Tim Shirah
25 mi. S of Albany
Acres 9,000; **Type** Public; **On Site** Clubhouse,
Lodging, Meals, Clays; **Shoots** Field; **Birds** Quail;
Dogs Avail/HDW; **Packages** 1 Day, 2-6 guns
See Our Ad Across

▲ ORVIS ENDORSED ▲

Southpoint Plantation
PO Box 4309, Albany, GA 31706
(912) 888-6598 Jimmy Harris 8 to 5, M-F

Spring Creek Lodge
PO Box 38, Brooklet, GA 30415
(912) 842-2197 W.M. Sheppard
40 mi. NW of Savannah
Type Public, Member/Avail, Corp.; **On Site**
Clubhouse, Lodging, Meals; **Shoots** Field; **Birds**
Turkey; **Dogs** Avail; **Packages** 1/2 Day

Tannenwood-A Hunting Preserve
PO Box 130, Davidsboro, GA 31018
(912) 348-4931 Chad Tanner
60 mi. SW of Augusta
Est 1995; **Type** Public; **On Site** Meals, Clays; **Shoots**
Field, Blinds; **Birds** Dove, Quail, Turkey, Ducks; **Dogs**
Avail/HDW; **Packages** 1/2 Day, 2-6 guns

Three Creeks Farm
Rt. 5, Box 765, Bainbridge, GA 31717
(912) 246-2266 John M. Simmons

Wise Olde Pine Plantation
Rt. 2, Box 39, 3 Bridges Rd., Americus, GA 31709
(912) 846-5491 Jean Wise, Jr. After 6:30 pm
30 mi. N of Albany
Acres 4,000; **Hunters/yr** 200; **Type** Public; **On
Site** Clubhouse, Lodging, Meals, Clays; **Shoots** Field;
Birds Quail, Woodcock, Pheasant, Turkey; **Dogs**
Avail/HDW; **Packages** 1/2 Day, up to 6 guns

Woodland Farms/Brier Creek
1100 Woodland Academy Rd., Matthews, GA 30818
(706) 547-3712 Mary Barnes After 6pm
25 mi. S of Augusta
Est 1977; **Acres** 365; **Type** Public; **Shoots** Field;
Birds Dove, Quail, Pheasant, Chukar; **Dogs**
Avail/HDW; **Packages** 1/2 Day, 1-3 guns

Wynfield Plantation
2413 Tarva Rd., Albany, GA 31707
(912) 883-2210 Larry L. Ruis
180 mi. S of Atlanta
Est 1988; **Acres** 1,500; **Type** Public; **On Site**
Clubhouse, Lodging, Meals, Clays; **Shoots** Field; **Birds**
Quail; **Dogs** Avail/HDW; **Packages** 1 Day, 2-9 guns
O Hunting License
O Airport Pickup
O Bird Processing
O Loaner Guns
O Fishing

HAWAII

IDAHO

Ulupalakua Hunting Club
42 Alokele Pl., Pukalami, HI 96768
(808) 572-0227 Patrick Fisher Evenings
25 mi. SE of Kahului
Est 1992; **Acres** 10,500; **Hunters/yr** 400; **Type**
Public, Member/Avail; **On Site** Lodging, Meals, Clays;
Shoots Field; **Birds** Pheasant, Chukar, Turkey;
Dogs Avail/HDW; **Packages** 1/2 Day, 1-8 guns
○ NAGA/See Pg. 107

Waialua Hunt Club
PO Box 922, Waialua, HI 96791
(808) 637-9441 Steve Gelakoski
On Site Clays; **Shoots** Field; **Birds** Pheasant
○ NAGA/See Pg. 107

Flying B Ranch
PO Box 400, Grangeville, ID 83530
(208) 983-3410 9-5, M-F
65 mi. SE of Lewiston, ID
Est 1986; **Acres** 5,000; **Hunters/yr** 150; **Type**
Public; **On Site** Clubhouse, Lodging, Meals; **Shoots**
Field; **Birds** Quail, Ruffed Grouse, Pheasant, Chukar,
Huns, Sage Grouse, Ducks; **Dogs** Avail/HDW;
Packages 2 Days, 1-14 guns ○ NAGA/See Pg. 107
See Our Ad, Right

High Desert Ranch
P.O. Box 470, Weiser, ID 83672
(800) 284-2843

Idaho Gamebirds
Rt. 1, Box 1212, Homedale, ID 83628
(208) 337-4826 Jim Davenport 40 mi. W of Boise
Est 1993; **Acres** 320; **Type** Public, Member/Avail;
On Site Clubhouse, Meals, Clays; **Shoots** Field;
Birds Quail, Pheasant, Chukar; **Dogs** Avail/HDW;
Packages 1/2 Day, 1-4 guns ○ NAGA/See Pg. 107

Skyline Hunting Club & Clays
Rt. 2, Box 14A, Homedale, ID 83628
(208) 337-4443 George & Dolly Hyer
40 mi. W of Boise Est 1988; **Type** Public, Mem-
ber/Avail, Corp.; **On Site** Clubhouse, Clays; **Shoots**
Field; **Birds** Quail, Pheasant, Chukar; **Dogs**
Avail/HDW; **Packages** 2 Days ○ NAGA/See Pg. 107
See Our Ad, Left

Teton Ridge Guest Ranch
200 Valley View Rd., Tetonia, ID 83452
(208) 456-2650 Albert Tilt 40 mi. W of Jackson Hole,
WY Est 1985; **Acres** 4,000; **Type** Member/Avail;
On Site Clubhouse, Lodging, Meals, Clays; **Shoots**
Field; **Birds** Quail, Pheasant, Chukar, Huns, Sharp Tail
Grouse; **Dogs** Avail/HDW; **Packages** 1 Day

Tews Ranches
745 N. 550 W., Shoshone, ID 83352
(208) 886-2100 Rusty or Carla Tews 8pm mst
50 mi. S of Sun Valley, ID **Type** Public, Member/Avail,
Corp.; **On Site** Clubhouse, Meals, Clays; **Shoots** Field;
Birds Quail, Pheasant, Chukar; **Dogs** Avail/HDW;
Packages 1/2 Day, 1-20 guns

The Flying B, Idaho's Hunting Utopia

The 6,000 acre Flying B Ranch at Kamiah, is a short drive from the Lewiston, Idaho airport. If you fly in, you'll be picked up at the airport and driven to the ranch on a road that parallels a trout stream. The canyon walls on both sides of the stream climb toward the sky and, on certain days, disappear into the mists. You'll follow the canyon floor road until you see the first of the Flying B's outbuildings. That's when you'll soon realize that this is no ordinary ranch. How many ranch's, for example, can boast to housing more than 50 high quality pointing dogs.

Focus on top quality

But no surprise, here, since The Flying B is a year-round outfitter that has focused hard on providing top quality services to a discriminating clientele since 1986.

Enjoying Idaho's hunting utopia!

The Flying B offers some of the finest upland game hunting in North America. A typical day of wingshooting begins with a hearty breakfast and warm greeting from one of the ranch's experienced guides. Most hunts are a mixed bag affair, the kind that never allow you to relax with one specie of bird. The birds include quail, partridge, chukars and pheasants and you're never quite sure what the splendidly trained dogs are pointing.

As an aside, the Flying B has excellent big-game hunting for five species of big game including elk, cougar, bear, whitetail and mule deer. Big game hunters enjoy all the comforts of home at the ranch's lodge or in well situated back country camps.

Built entirely of native logs, the Lodge captures the essence of Northwestern friendliness and warmth and is easily as impressive as the hunting. Fifteen spacious guest rooms, elegant dining, a huge main trophy room, conference room, game and relaxation areas, gun room, sauna, and Jacuzzi are among the splendid features of this centerpiece of the Flying B experience.

In addition, the Flying B offers sporting clays, 3-D archery, pistol and rifle ranges. For more information about this spectacular facility set in some of the last pristine frontier in the U.S., call or write, The Flying B Ranch, P.O. Box 400, Grangeville, ID 83536; or call: 208-983-3410; Fax (208) 983-1516.

The new, 14-bedroom lodge at the Flying B Ranch

ILLINOIS

Ambraw Valley Outdoors
9885 1175th Ave., Newton, IL 62448
(618) 783-3160 Wade Eaton/Doug Hartke Anytime
120 mi. E of St. Louis, MO
Est 1993; Acres 400; Type Public, Member/Avail,
Corp.; On Site Clubhouse, Meals, Clays; Shoots
Field, Driven; Birds Dove, Quail, Pheasant, Chukar,
Turkey; Dogs Avail/HDW; Packages 1/2 Day, 1-20
guns ○ NAGA/See Pg. 107

BHF Preserve
Rt. 1, Box 271, Mt. Vernon, IL 62864
(618) 242-3409 Bob Davis Anytime
10 mi. E of Mt. Vernon
Est 1996; Acres 1,000; Type Member/Avail; On
Site Clubhouse, Meals; Shoots Field, Blinds, Boat;
Birds Dove, Quail, Pheasant, Chukar, Ducks, Geese;
Dogs Avail/HDW; Packages 1/2 Day, 1-5 guns

HUNTING PRESERVE

The Break Hunting Preserve
Rt. 4, Box 31, Warsaw, IL 62379
(217) 647-3355 John or Sue Caldwell After 6pm
100 mi. NW of Springfield
Est 1988; Acres 1,740; Hunters/yr 450; On Site
Clubhouse, Lodging, Meals, Clays; Shoots Field,
Blinds; Birds Quail, Pheasant, Chukar, Turkey, Ducks,
Geese; Dogs Avail/HDW ○ NAGA/See Pg. 107

Love to hunt? Then The Break is for you! Enjoy
guided pheasant, chukar and quail hunting on
700+ acres along the Mississippi in west central
Illinois. Duck, turkey and deer hunting are also available. Fishing, too! Our A-frame lodge has all the
modern conveniences you'd expect to find at an exclusive sportsmen's club. Home cooked meals and
comfortable overnight accommodations. You de-
serve a break...at The Break! Call today for
information.

Calhoun County Hunting
PO Box 369, Hardin, IL 62047
(618) 576-2221 Jerry or JoAn Corbett Daytime
60 mi. N of St. Louis Est 1990; Acres 1,000; Type
Public; On Site Lodging, Meals; Shoots Field; Birds
Dove, Quail, Turkey; Dogs HDW; Packages 1 Day

Callahan Ranch Hunting Club
RR#1, Box 7A, Montrose, IL 62445
(217) 924-4412 Tom & Dana Thull
100 mi. NE of St. Louis, MO
Est 1991; Acres 250; Hunters/yr 300; Type
Public; On Site Clubhouse, Meals, Clays; Shoots
Field; Birds Quail, Pheasant, Chukar; Dogs
Avail/HDW; Packages 1/2 Day, 1-10 guns

Covey Ridge I & II
Rt. 1, Box 256A, Geff, IL 62842
(618) 854-2269 Charles R. Hazel
110 mi. E of St. Louis
Est 1988; Acres 896; Type Public; Shoots Field;
Birds Dove, Quail, Pheasant, Chukar; Dogs
Avail/HDW; Packages 1/2 Day, 1-20 guns

Cranfill Shooting Preserve
RR2, Hillsboro, IL 62049
(217) 532-2797 Don Cranfill
50 mi. SE of Springfield
Est 1954; Acres 372; Hunters/yr 250; Type
Public, Member/Avail, Corp.; On Site Clubhouse,
Meals, Clays; Shoots Field; Birds Quail, Pheasant,
Chukar; Dogs Avail/HDW; Packages 1/2 Day,
1-12 guns

D&M Hunting Club
Rt. 5, Box 71, Marion, IL 62959
(618) 993-8914 Doc & Mark Schaede 7-10pm
Est 1980; Acres 80; Hunters/yr 900; Type
Public; On Site Clubhouse; Shoots Blinds; Birds
Geese; Dogs Avail; Packages 1/2 Day, 8-39 guns

Doctorman's Cache Core Hunting
Rt. 1, Box 69, Ulin, IL 62992
(618) 845-3367 Dean Doctorman
150 mi. SE of St. Louis
Type Public; Shoots Field; Birds Quail, Pheasant;
Dogs Avail/HDW

East Grove Game Farm, Inc.
841 Todd Rd., Ohio, IL 61349
(815) 376-4901 James Schulte anytime
Est 1990; Acres 400; Type Member/Avail; On
Site Clubhouse; Shoots Field; Birds Quail,
Pheasant, Chukar, Turkey; Dogs Avail/HDW;
Packages 1/2 Day

El-J World Class
Shooting Preserve
RR1, Box 448, Johnston City, IL 62951
(618) 983-8758 James R. Moore
80 mi. SE of St. Louis
Est 1988; Acres 228; Hunters/yr 100; Type
Public, Member/Avail; On Site Clubhouse, Lodging,
Meals; Shoots Field; Birds Quail, Pheasant; Dogs
Avail/HDW; Packages 1/2 Day, up to 2 guns

Elliot Acres Hunting Club
PO Box 783, Huntley, IL 60142
(708) 669-5564 Steve Berggreiter
Shoots Field; Birds Pheasant ○ NAGA/See Pg. 107

Elm River Shooting Preserve
RR#2, Box 188, Cisne, IL 62823
(618) 673-2372 Donald Lewis
120 mi. E of St. Louis
Est 1988; Acres 250; Type Public; On Site
Clubhouse; Shoots Field; Birds Quail; Dogs
Avail/HDW; Packages 1/2 Day, 2-6 guns

Prairie Lakes: Great Hunting in Chicagoland

Only 55 miles southwest of Chicago, the Prairie Lakes Hunt Club offers individual, private group and corporate sportsmen an impressive array of hunting opportunities rarely found so close to a major urban center. The 750-acre preserve combines covered fields, woodlands and water areas, and provides a habitat that pheasant, geese, duck, partridge, quail and turkey find congenial.

Quality Hunting

Founded in 1952, Prairie Lakes Hunt Club in Marseilles, Illinois has recently embarked on an ambitious project to make its environment even more conducive to excellent hunting. Additional fences, trees, and hedge rows have been installed to provide cover for game birds, and new planting of grain and other crops provide abundant food.

Hunting Heaven—just 55 miles from Chicago.

Professional hunt guides accompany all guests and well trained dogs are available for those who request them. While the club is available to meet the needs of single hunters, it is impressively adept at meeting the varied needs of private and corporate groups of 2 to 25 hunters.

The quality of the birds at Prairie Lakes is notable. An outdoor columnist who recently visited said, "for some reason these roosters fly like wild ones, with power and jet-assisted takeoffs, making the shooter think twice about each shot as if it were a final exam." At the conclusion of his hunt, the writer said, "game bags took on the appearance of an after-holiday shopping spree, loaded with pheasant and Hungarian partridge."

"This scene could have been mistaken for one of the great cover shots on any national outdoor magazine," he said. "It was a day for friends to come together and sample the kind of quality hunting only a few clubs are able to offer."

Quality Resort

While excellent shooting is reason enough to motivate a sportsman's visit, Prairie Lakes actually constitutes a complete resort that also boasts a full-service restaurant, banquet facilities to accommodate 200, and a sports bar, lounge and outdoor terrace overlooking the adjacent Prairie Lakes Golf Course. Modern lodging facilities assure comfort and convenience for overnight guests and the 2500 ft. grass airstrip can accommodate privately owned or corporate aircraft. These amenities supervised by resort manager Jack Knoebel, add immeasurably to the pleasure of visitors.

Prairie Lakes offers a limited number of individual, family and corporate hunt club memberships that include special rates at the lodge, restaurant and golf course. The club also conducts family events, including picnics, fishing, golf and special group outings and has attractive weekend getaway packages available to suit any need. Special events include Continental Pheasant Shoots, Dove Shoots, Turkey Shoots and year round lighted trap shooting.

Committed to maintaining hunting tradition and good sportsmanship, Prairie Lakes Hunt Club invites shotgunners to experience great shooting and first-class comfort. To arrange a visit, inquire about membership or obtain additional information, contact Prairie Lakes Hunt Club, 2550 N. 32nd Road, Marseilles, IL 61341; telephone (815) 795-5107 or visit their Internet web site at http://www.prairie-lakes.com.

Frisco Game Preserve

RR1, Ewing, IL 62836
(618) 629-2527 M. Norris Webb 6-7am
15 mi. from Benton
Est 1985; **Acres** 915; **Hunters/yr** 2,000; **Type**
Public, Member/Avail, Corp.; **On Site** Clubhouse,
Meals; **Shoots** Field, Tower; **Birds** Dove, Quail,
Pheasant, Chukar, Turkey; **Dogs** Avail/HDW;
Packages 1/2 Day, 2-8 guns O NAGA/See Pg. 107
Continental Hunt in the Round. Fast action. Frisco
Game Preserve offers 900+ acres of prime south-
ern Illinois hunting land. Varied wildlife habitat
with an abundance of native quail, deer and rab-
bit. Hunting to suit almost anyone's liking. You
won't be disappointed. Call today for details.

Garden Plain Hunt Club

7737 Long Rd., Fulton, IL 61252
(309) 887-4439 Curt Ebersohl Anytime
120 mi. W of Chicaco
Est 1991; **Acres** 1,000; **Hunters/yr** 800; **Type**
Public, Member/Avail, Corp.; **On Site** Clubhouse,
Lodging, Meals, Clays; **Shoots** Field, Driven; **Birds**
Dove, Quail, Pheasant, Chukar, Huns, Turkey; **Dogs**
Avail/HDW; **Packages** 1/2 Day, 2-50 guns

Gobbler's Knob Hunting

26471 E. Hwy. 9, Canton, IL 61520
(309) 647-3641 Don Deuel
Shoots Field; **Birds** Quail, Pheasant, Chukar
O NAGA/See Pg. 107

Grassy Lake Hunting Club

RR2, Jonesboro, IL 62952
(618) 883-7890 Collin Cain
Acres 300; **Type** Public; **On Site** Clubhouse, Meals;
Shoots Blinds; **Birds** Geese; **Dogs** Avail/HDW;
Packages 1 Day

Green Acres
Sportsman's Club, Inc.

1458 N 1700 E Rd., Roberts, IL 60962
(217) 395-2588 Randy Sellek
80 mi. SW of Chicago
Acres 700; **Type** Public, Member/Avail; **On Site**
Clubhouse, Clays; **Shoots** Field; **Birds** Dove, Quail,
Pheasant, Chukar, Ducks; **Dogs** Avail/HDW;
Packages 1/2 Day, 1-30 guns O NAGA/See Pg. 107
O Bird Processing
O Family Recreation
O Train Bird Dogs
O Fishing
O Safety Instruction

Green River Roger Conservation Area, Inc.

727 Maytown Rd., Ohio, IL 61349
(815) 379-2702 Roy or Roxie Rogers
90 mi. W of Chicago
Acres 2,300; **Type** Public; **Shoots** Field; **Birds**
Pheasant; **Dogs** Avail/HDW

Hickory Grove Hunting Club

RR1, Wyanet, IL 61379
(815) 699-2603 Leroy Wirth
115 mi. W of Chicago
Acres 1,100; **Type** Member/Avail; **Shoots** Field;
Birds Dove, Quail, Pheasant, Chukar, Turkey, Ducks;
Dogs Avail/HDW; **Packages** 1/2 Day
O NAGA/See Pg. 107

Hopewell Views
Hunting Club

Rt. 2, Box 232, Rockport, IL 62370
(217) 734-9234 Rick Wombles
85 mi. NE of St. Louis, MO
Acres 1,900; **Type** Public, Member/Avail, Corp.;
On Site Clubhouse, Lodging, Meals, Clays; **Shoots**
Field; **Birds** Dove, Quail, Pheasant, Chukar, Turkey,
Ducks, Geese; **Dogs** Avail/HDW; **Packages** 1/2 Day
O NAGA/See Pg. 107

The Hunt Club

Rt. 1, Box 204, Percy, IL 62272
(618) 497-2526 Ron Doering 8-5
50 mi. SE of St. Louis, MO
Est 1988; **Acres** 10,300; **Hunters/yr** 350; **Type**
Member/Avail, Corp.; **On Site** Clubhouse, Lodging,
Meals; **Shoots** Field, Driven, Blinds, Boat; **Birds**
Dove, Quail, Pheasant, Chukar, Turkey, Ducks, Geese;
Dogs Avail/HDW; **Packages** 1/2 Day, 2-24 guns

Hunting Sports Plus

710 Main St., Ste. E, Blue Springs, MO, Hunting in 4
States including, IL
(800) 729-1924 Dan Gasser
Est 1989; **Acres** 200,000; **Type** Public,
Member/Avail; **On Site** Clubhouse, Lodging, Meals,
Clays; **Shoots** Field, Blinds, Boat; **Birds** Quail,
Pheasant, Turkey, Prairie Chicken, Ducks, Geese;
Dogs Avail/HDW; **Packages** 1 Day, 1-24 guns
Quality hunting on over 200,000 acres of private
farm land in 7 Midwest States–AR, IA, IL, KS, MO,
NE, OK. Hunt quail, pheasant, turkey, deer, prairie
chicken, ducks and geese. Affordable Midwestern
hospitality. Large selection of low cost member-
ships, daily plans or hunting vacation package
hunts. Call today for more information.

Hunting Unlimited

RR4, Box 98, Mt. Sterling, IL 62353
(217) 289-3366 Larry Hanold 9-5
110 mi. N of St. Louis, MO
Est 1986; **Acres** 3,500; **Type** Public, Member/Avail,
Corp.; **On Site** Clubhouse, Lodging, Meals, Clays;
Shoots Field, Blinds; **Birds** Dove, Quail, Pheasant,
Chukar, Turkey, Ducks; **Dogs** Avail/HDW; **Packages**
1/2 Day, 2-16 guns

Keck's Marsh

RR2, Box 190, Vandalia, IL 62471
(618) 425-3740 Fred Keck
65 mi. NE of St. Louis

Est 1984;   Acres 3,000;   Type Public;   Shoots Field;
Birds Quail, Pheasant, Chukar, Ducks, Geese;
Packages 1/2 Day

Koeberlein's
Hunting Preserve
274 County Rd., 1400 E., Tolono, IL 61880
(217) 867-2310 Debbi Koeberlein
25 mi. S of Champaign
Acres 440;   Hunters/yr 365;   Type Public,
Member/Avail;   On Site Clubhouse, Lodging, Meals,
Clays;   Shoots Field;   Birds Dove, Quail, Pheasant,
Chukar;   Dogs Avail O NAGA/See Pg. 107

Little Wabash Shooting Preserve
610 E. 5th St., Neoga, IL 62447
(217) 895-2677 Gary Hartke 8-5
100 mi. NE of St. Louis
Est 1986;   Acres 320;   Type Public;   Shoots Field;
Birds Quail, Pheasant, Chukar;   Dogs Avail/HDW;
Packages 1/2 Day, 1-18 guns O NAGA/See Pg. 107

McCullom Lake Hunt Club
10603 Okeson Rd., PO Box 303, Hebron, IL 60034
(815) 648-2775 Skip Hauri 8-5
40 mi. E of Rockford
Est 1956;   Acres 430;   Type Member/Avail;   On
Site Clubhouse, Meals, Clays;   Shoots Field, Tower;
Birds Dove, Quail, Pheasant, Chukar;   Dogs
Avail/HDW O NAGA/See Pg. 107

Middlefork Valley Shooting Sports
PO Box 8, Paxton, IL 60957
(217) 379-4152 Mark Diedrich
110 mi. S of Chicago Type Member/Avail;   On Site
Clubhouse, Lodging;   Shoots Field;   Birds Dove,
Quail, Pheasant, Chukar, Ducks, Geese

Millbrook Hunting Club
7519 Finnie Rd., Newark, IL 60541
(708) 232-3004 David W. Withall M-F, 9-4
60 mi. SW of Chicago
Est 1949;   Acres 400;   Hunters/yr 400;   Type
Member/Avail;   On Site Clubhouse, Meals, Clays;
Shoots Field, Blinds;   Birds Dove, Quail, Pheasant,
Chukar, Ducks;   Dogs Avail/HDW;   Packages 1/2
Day, 1-8 guns O NAGA/See Pg. 107
O Bird Processing
O Deer Hunting
O Gourmet Meals
O Brochure Available
O Fishing

Nilo
7900 Highway 67-111, Brighton, IL 62012
(618) 466-0613 Roger C. Jones, Mgr.
35 mi. NE of St. Louis
Est 1953;   Acres 640;   Hunters/yr 900;   Type
Member/Avail;   On Site Clubhouse, Meals, Clays;
Shoots Field, Blinds;   Birds Quail, Pheasant, Chukar,
Ducks;   Dogs Avail;   Packages 1 Day, 8-16 guns
O NAGA/See Pg. 107

Nishkawee Preserve
21887 Pigeon Rd., Morrison, IL 61270
(815) 772-3394 Norman F. Spencer
140 mi. W of Chicago
Est 1994;   Acres 240;   Type Public, Member/Avail;
On Site Lodging, Clays;   Shoots Field;   Birds Quail,
Pheasant, Huns;   Dogs Avail/HDW;   Packages 1/2
Day, 1-30 guns O NAGA/See Pg. 107
O Dog Training Area Available

North Pike Hunting Club
RR2, Griggsville, IL 62340
(217) 236-3131 Donovan Baldwin Evenings
60 mi. W of Springfield
Est 1989;   Acres 1,500;   Hunters/yr 200;   Type
Public, Member/Avail, Corp.;   On Site Clubhouse,
Lodging, Meals, Clays;   Shoots Field;   Birds Quail,
Pheasant, Chukar, Turkey;   Dogs Avail/HDW;
Packages 1/2 Day, 2-4 guns

Oakmount Game Club
30808 N. Darrell Rd., McHenry, IL 60050
(815) 385-2144 Peter Reiland, Jr.
Est 1982;   Acres 1,200;   Type Member/Avail, Corp.;
On Site Clubhouse, Meals, Clays;   Shoots Field;
Birds Quail, Pheasant, Chukar, Turkey;   Dogs
Avail/HDW;   Packages 1/2 Day, 1-4 guns
O NAGA/See Pg. 107

Obermeier Dakota Game Farms
2122 W. Hopkins Pl., Chicago, IL 60620
(312) 445-3686 Chess Obermeier
40 mi. W of Watertown, SD
Acres 3,000;   Type Public;   On Site Lodging, Meals;
Shoots Field;   Birds Pheasant, Ducks, Geese;   Dogs
Avail/HDW;   Packages 1 Day

Otter Creek Hunting Club
Rt. 3, Box 125G, Jerseyville, IL 62052
(618) 376-7601 Mike Runge
40 mi. N of St. Louis, MO
Est 1990;   Acres 3,000;   Type Public, Member/Avail,
Corp.;   On Site Clubhouse, Lodging, Meals, Clays;
Shoots Field;   Birds Dove, Quail, Pheasant, Chukar,
Turkey;   Dogs Avail/HDW;   Packages 1/2 Day, 2-30
guns O NAGA/See Pg. 107

Pheasant Valley Hunt Club

R#1, Box 360, Bunker Hill, IL 62014

(618) 585-3956 Sharon Wilkinson

30 mi. NE of St. Louis, MO

Est 1970; **Acres** 200; **Hunters/yr** 350; **Type**
Public, Member/Avail; **On Site** Clubhouse, Clays;
Shoots Field; **Birds** Dove, Quail, Pheasant, Chukar;
Dogs Avail/HDW; **Packages** 1/2 Day, 1-16 guns

Pinewood Hunt Club

RR#1, Box 36, Beaverville, IL 60912

(815) 435-2314 Wayne DeYoung 6am-7pm

55 mi. S of Chicago

Est 1975; **Acres** 875; **Hunters/yr** 500; **Type**
Member/Avail, Corp.; **On Site** Clubhouse, Lodging,
Meals, Clays; **Shoots** Field; **Birds** Quail, Pheasant,
Chukar, Huns; **Dogs** Avail/HDW; **Packages** 1/2
Day, 2-16 guns ○ NAGA/See Pg. 107

Prairie Lakes Hunt Club

PO Box 410, 2550 N. 32nd Rd., Marseilles, IL 61341

(815) 795-5107 Jack Knoebel/Brian Carlson

55 mi. SW of Chicago

Est 1952; **Acres** 1,250; **Hunters/yr** 450; **Type**
Member/Avail; **On Site** Clubhouse, Lodging, Meals,
Clays; **Shoots** Field, Blinds; **Birds** Quail, Pheasant,
Chukar, Turkey, Ducks, Geese; **Dogs** Avail/HDW;
Packages 1/2 Day, 1-5 guns ○ NAGA/See Pg. 107

○ Bird Processing   ○ Quality Clubhouse
○ Gourmet Meals   ○ Family Recreation Activities
○ On-Site Pro Shop   ○ Private Bedrooms
○ Fishing   ○ Sporting Clays Course
○ 2 Miles N. of I-80

See Our Ad Pg. 323

The Quail Sned

RR3, Box 32, Martinsville, IL 62442

(217) 382-5230 Don Stephen

Shoots Field; **Birds** Quail, Pheasant, Chukar
○ NAGA/See Pg. 107

Rend Lakes Hunting Preserve

PO Box 907, Benton, IL 62812

(618) 629-2368 Dennis Sneed

On Site Lodging, Clays; **Shoots** Field; **Birds** Quail,
Pheasant, Chukar ○ NAGA/See Pg. 107

Richmond Hunting Club

Hwy. 173, Rt. 12, Richmond, IL 60071

(815) 678-3271 Chuck Wonderlic

Acres 800; **Hunters/yr** 1,000; **Type** Public,
Member/Avail, Corp.; **On Site** Clubhouse, Meals,
Clays; **Shoots** Field; **Birds** Quail, Pheasant, Chukar,
Huns, Turkey, Ducks; **Dogs** Avail/HDW; **Packages**
1/2 Day ○ NAGA/See Pg. 107

Riverwood Game Preserve, Ltd.

RR1, Box 68, Tennessee, IL 62374

(309) 776-4368 Sam Biswell

110 mi. N of St. Louis

Est 1990; **Acres** 1,000; **Hunters/yr** 500; **Type**
Public; **On Site** Lodging, Clays; **Shoots** Field; **Birds**
Quail, Pheasant, Chukar; **Dogs** Avail/HDW
○ NAGA/See Pg. 107

Rocky Run Hunt Club

8821 N. Greenwood Ave., Niles, IL 60714

(847) 297-1450 Sean Derrig

Shoots Field; **Birds** Quail, Pheasant, Chukar
○ NAGA/See Pg. 107

Roy Rogers
Hunting Club, Inc.

727 Maytown Rd., Ohio, IL 61349

(815) 379-2427 Roy or Roxie Rogers 6-8pm

100 mi. W of Chicago

Est 1957; **Acres** 1,300; **Hunters/yr** 1,500; **Type**
Public, Member/Avail, Corp.; **On Site** Clubhouse,
Meals, Clays; **Shoots** Field, Tower, Blinds; **Birds**
Dove, Quail, Pheasant, Chukar, Huns, Turkey; **Dogs**
Avail/HDW; **Packages** 1/2 Day, 1-36 guns
○ NAGA/See Pg. 107

○ Hunting License
○ Airport Pickup
○ Bird Processing
○ Quality Clubhouse
○ Family Run Business

Sand Prairie Farms, Inc.

185 Rogers Rd., Ohio, IL 61349

(815) 376-6641 Tom Yucus 7-9am; 8-10pm

90 mi. W of Chicago

Est 1990; **Acres** 680; **Type** Member/Avail, Corp.;
On Site Clubhouse, Lodging, Meals, Clays; **Shoots**
Field, Blinds; **Birds** Dove, Quail, Pheasant, Chukar,
Huns, Turkey, Ducks, Geese; **Dogs** Avail/HDW;
Packages 1/2 Day, 1-4 guns ○ NAGA/See Pg. 107

Seneca Hunt Club

PO Box 824, Seneca, IL 61360

(815) 357-8080 Larry Higdon 8am-4:30pm

60 mi. SW of Chicago

Est 1982; **Acres** 715; **Hunters/yr** 2,500; **Type**
Public, Member/Avail, Corp.; **On Site** Clubhouse,
Lodging, Meals, Clays; **Shoots** Field, Tower, Blinds;
Birds Dove, Quail, Pheasant, Chukar, Huns, Turkey,
Ducks, Geese; **Dogs** Avail/HDW; **Packages** 1/2
Day, up to 6 guns ○ NAGA/See Pg. 107

Smokin' Gun Hunt Club
995 E. County Rd. 1550, Hamilton, IL 62341
(217) 847-2227 Darrin Miller or Terry Phillips
100 mi. NW of Springfield
Est 1991; **Acres** 320; **Type** Public, Member/Avail,
Corp.; **On Site** Clubhouse, Meals, Clays; **Shoots**
Field; **Birds** Quail, Pheasant, Chukar; **Dogs**
Avail/HDW; **Packages** 1/2 Day, 1-20 guns

Tamarack Farm Hunt Club
7210 Keystone Rd., Richmond, IL 60071
(815) 678-4989 Dick Hendricksen 8am-2pm
40 mi. NW of Chicago
Est 1986; **Acres** 1,100; **Type** Member/Ltd; **On
Site** Clubhouse, Lodging, Meals, Clays; **Shoots** Field,
Tower; **Birds** Pheasant; **Dogs** Avail; **Packages** 1
Day, 10-32 guns

Trail of Tears Lodge & Sports Resort
1575 Fair City Rd., Jonesboro, IL 62952
(618) 833-8697 Ron & Deb Charles
15 mi. NE of Cape Girardeau
Est 1988; **Type** Public, Member/Avail, Corp.; **On
Site** Clubhouse, Lodging, Meals, Clays; **Shoots** Field;
Birds Dove, Quail, Pheasant, Chukar, Turkey, Ducks,
Geese; **Dogs** Avail/HDW; **Packages** 1/2 Day

Tri-R Hunting Preserve
408 W. Arch, Jerseyville, IL 62052
(618) 498-4666 Robert Swearingin
40 mi. N of St. Louis
Est 1988; **Acres** 380; **Type** Public, Member/Avail;
On Site Clubhouse; **Shoots** Field; **Birds** Dove,
Quail, Pheasant, Chukar; **Dogs** Avail; **Packages** 1/2
Day, 1-12 guns

Upland Bay Rod & Gun Club
PO Box 337, Spring Grove, IL 60081
(815) 678-4411 Mike Mathews
45 mi. NW of Chicago
Est 1982; **Acres** 500; **Type** Public, Member/Avail,
Corp.; **On Site** Clubhouse, Lodging, Meals, Clays;
Shoots Field, Blinds; **Birds** Dove, Quail, Woodcock,
Pheasant, Chukar, Huns, Turkey, Snipe, Ducks, Geese;
Dogs Avail/HDW; **Packages** 1/2 Day, 1-4 guns
O NAGA/See Pg. 107

Upland Hunt Club
14755 Edson Rd., Davis Junction, IL 61020
(815) 874-7444 Mike McInerney, Mgr. 8am-10pm
55 mi. NW of Chicago
Est 1987; **Acres** 250; **Hunters/yr** 1,000; **Type**
Public, Member/Avail, Corp.; **On Site** Clubhouse,
Meals, Clays; **Shoots** Field; **Birds** Dove, Quail,
Pheasant, Chukar; **Dogs** Avail/HDW; **Packages** 1/2
Day, 1-25 guns

White Oak Reserve
RR1, Box 153, Barry, IL 62312
(217) 335-2921 George Metcalf
25 mi. SE of Quincy
Est 1993; **Acres** 500; **Type** Public, Member/Avail;
On Site Clubhouse, Lodging, Meals, Clays; **Shoots**
Field; **Birds** Quail, Pheasant, Chukar; **Dogs**
Avail/HDW; **Packages** 1/2 Day, 1-4 guns
O NAGA/See Pg. 107

Fred K. Wright
Rt. 1, Box 195, Bridgeport, IL 62417
(618) 945-7409 Fred Wright After 7:30 pm
125 mi. E of St. Louis
Est 1980; **Acres** 300; **Type** Public; **Shoots** Field;
Birds Quail; **Dogs** HDW; **Packages** 1/2 Day, 1-5 guns

INDIANA

Blue Creek Game Preserve
28498 Blue Creek Rd., Sunman, IN 47041
(812) 623-3742 Earl Stenger
30 mi. W of Cincinnati
Acres 240; **Hunters/yr** 200; **Type** Public,
Member/Avail; **On Site** Clubhouse; **Shoots** Field;
Birds Quail, Pheasant, Chukar; **Dogs** Avail/HDW;
Packages 1/2 Day, 1-5 guns O NAGA/See Pg. 107

Buck Run Shooting Preserve
24 Webster St., Chesterfield, IN 46017
(317) 378-6341 Berg Bert
6 mi. NW of Anderson
Acres 244; **Type** Public; **On Site** Clubhouse,
Lodging, Meals; **Shoots** Field, Blinds; **Birds** Quail,
Pheasant, Ducks, Geese; **Dogs** Avail

County Line Farms
RR3, Box 85, Plymouth, IN 46563
(219) 935-4526 Mark Hedges
40 mi. SW of South Bend
Acres 103; **Hunters/yr** 100; **Type** Public; **On Site**

Clubhouse; **Shoots** Field; **Birds** Quail, Pheasant, Chukar, Huns; **Dogs** Avail/HDW

County Line Hunt Club
855 N. 1200 E., Plymouth, IN 46563
(219) 935-4526 Mark Hedges
40 mi. S of South Bend
Est 1991; **Acres** 155; **Hunters/yr** 50; **Type** Public; **On Site** Clubhouse, Lodging; **Shoots** Field; **Birds** Quail, Pheasant, Chukar, Huns; **Dogs** Avail/HDW; **Packages** 1/2 Day, 2-5 guns ○ NAGA/See Pg. 107

Deer Creek Outfitters
PO Box 39, Sebree, KY 42455
(502) 835-2424 Tim Stull
20 miles south of the Indiana Border
Est 1984; **Acres** 5,000; **Type** Public, Member/Avail; **On Site** Clubhouse, Lodging, Meals, Clays; **Shoots** Field, Blinds; **Birds** Dove, Quail, Pheasant, Chukar, Turkey, Ducks, Geese; **Dogs** Avail/HDW; **Packages** 1/2 Day, 1-12 guns

Flatrock Hunting Preserve
5188 W SR 244, Milroy, IN 46156
(317) 629-2354 Merrill Carrigan 6am to 10pm
40 mi. SE of Indianapolis
Est 1991; **Acres** 104; **Type** Public; **On Site** Clubhouse; **Shoots** Field; **Birds** Quail, Pheasant, Chukar; **Dogs** Avail/HDW; **Packages** 1/2 Day, 1-4 guns ○ NAGA/See Pg. 107

Horrall Hunting Preserve
PO Box 131, Petersburg, IN 47567
(812) 354-6129 Mike Horrall After 8pm
45 mi. NE of Evansville
Acres 400; **Type** Public; **Shoots** Field; **Birds** Quail, Pheasant, Chukar; **Dogs** Avail/HDW; **Packages** 1/2 Day, 2-20 guns ○ NAGA/See Pg. 107

J.E.M.P.
711 South 21st St., Chesterton, IN 46304
(219) 926-1023 Ed Lewandowski 4-9pm
40 mi. E of Chicago
Est 1988; **Acres** 100; **Hunters/yr** 30; **Type** Public, Member/Avail; **On Site** Clays; **Shoots** Field, Blinds, Boat; **Birds** Dove, Quail, Woodcock, Pheasant, Chukar, Ducks, Geese; **Dogs** Avail/HDW; **Packages** 1/2 Day, 1-4 guns ○ NAGA/See Pg. 107

King Farms
Rt. 1, Box 12, Parker, IN 47368
(317) 468-6706 Eldred King
Est 1970; **Type** Public, Corp.; **On Site** Clubhouse, Meals; **Shoots** Field; **Birds** Dove, Quail, Pheasant, Chukar; **Dogs** HDW; **Packages** 1/2 Day ○ NAGA/See Pg. 107

Maier Pheasant Farm & Hunting Area
65450 Fir Rd., Bremen, IN 46506
(219) 633-4654 Marvin Maier
80 mi. E of Chicago

Est 1955; **Type** Public; **Shoots** Field; **Birds** Quail, Pheasant; **Packages** 1/2 Day, up to 3 guns ○ NAGA/See Pg. 107

Muddy Fork Hunting Preserve
5666 E. 1000 N., Seymour, IN 47274
(812) 522-2684 Donn O. Schlehuser
4 mi. NW of Seymour
Acres 320; **Hunters/yr** 350; **Type** Public, Member/Avail; **On Site** Clubhouse, Clays; **Shoots** Field; **Birds** Dove, Quail, Pheasant, Chukar; **Dogs** Avail

P.D.Q. Hunting Preserve
64500 Elm, Bremen, IN 46506
(219) 633-4044 Jim Haines After 5pm
60 mi. E of Chicago
Est 1988; **Acres** 200; **Hunters/yr** 800; **Type** Public; **On Site** Clubhouse; **Shoots** Field; **Birds** Quail, Pheasant; **Dogs** Avail/HDW; **Packages** 1/2 Day, 2-6 guns ○ NAGA/See Pg. 107

Quail Ridge
Sportsman's Club
PO Box 148, Sunman, IN 47041
(812) 926-4999 Shawn D. Hance, Mgr.
60 mi. E of Indianapolis
Est 1990; **Acres** 850; **Hunters/yr** 1,000; **Type** Member/Avail, Corp.; **On Site** Clubhouse, Lodging, Meals, Clays; **Shoots** Field, Tower, Driven; **Birds** Dove, Quail, Pheasant, Chukar, Huns, Turkey; **Dogs** Avail/HDW; **Packages** 1/2 Day, up to 30 guns ○ NAGA/See Pg. 107

Springer Run Hunting Farm
PO Box 816, New Albany, IN 47151
(812) 739-4848 Tony Thomas
3 mi. N of Levenworth
Est 1992; **Acres** 700; **Type** Public; **On Site** Clubhouse, Clays; **Shoots** Field; **Birds** Quail, Pheasant, Chukar; **Dogs** Avail/HDW; **Packages** 1/2 Day, 1-20 guns

Sugar Creek Hunting
& Sporting Clays
RR2, Box 413, Mitchell, IN 47446
(812) 849-2296 Dale Waldbieser or (812) 849-5020
40 mi. S of Bloomington
Est 1992; **Acres** 750; **Type** Public; **On Site** Clubhouse, Meals, Clays; **Shoots** Field; **Birds** Quail, Pheasant, Chukar; **Dogs** Avail/HDW; **Packages** 1/2 Day, 1-6 guns ○ NAGA/See Pg. 107
○ Bird Processing   ○ Brochure Available
○ Sporting Clays   ○ Factory Ammunition
○ Loaner Guns   ○ Family Run Business
○ Less than 1 hour from Lousiville, KY
○ Just 35 minutes off I-65

West Creek Shooting Preserve
15547 W. 169th Ave., Cedar Lake, IN 46303
(219) 696-6101 Patty Lukasik 9am-8pm
○ NAGA/See Pg. 107

IOWA

Arrowhead Hunting Club
3529 170th St., Goose Lake, IA 52750
(319) 577-2267 Gloria or Dan Mullin 8-5
40 mi. N of Davenport
Est 1952; **Acres** 1,173; **Hunters/yr** 800; **Type**
Public, Member/Avail, Corp.; **On Site** Clubhouse,
Meals, Clays; **Shoots** Field; **Birds** Quail, Pheasant,
Chukar; **Dogs** Avail/HDW; **Packages** 1/2 Day, 1-20
guns ○ NAGA/See Pg. 107

Cedar Valley Pheasants
30332 Goose Hill Rd., Cascade, IA 52033
(319) 852-3933 Ron & Donna Miller
30 mi. SW of Dubuque
Est 1987; **Acres** 1,000; **Type** Public; **Shoots** Field;
Birds Quail, Pheasant; **Dogs** Avail/HDW; **Packages**
1/2 Day ○ NAGA/See Pg. 107

Doc's Dog Kennel & Hunt Club
2933 Prospect Circle, Adel, IA 50003
(515) 993-3711 Pat or Harold Adams 8-6, M-S
20 mi. W of Des Moines
Est 1980; **Acres** 600; **Hunters/yr** 1,000; **Type**
Public, Member/Avail, Corp.; **On Site** Clubhouse,
Meals, Clays; **Shoots** Field; **Birds** Quail, Pheasant,
Chukar; **Dogs** Avail/HDW; **Packages** 1/2 Day, 2-25
guns ○ NAGA/See Pg. 107

Flood Creek Hunting Preserve
1760 Cameo Rd., Rockford, IA 50468
(515) 756-2327 Todd A. Peterson
120 mi. N of Des Moines
Est 1989; **Acres** 640; **Type** Public, Member/Avail;
On Site Clubhouse, Meals; **Shoots** Field; **Birds**
Quail, Pheasant; **Dogs** Avail/HDW; **Packages** 1 Day

Hunting Sports Plus
710 Main St., Ste. E, Blue Springs, MO
Hunting in 4 States including, IA
(800) 729-1924 Dan Gasser
Est 1989; **Acres** 200,000; **Type** Public,
Member/Avail; **On Site** Clubhouse, Lodging, Meals,
Clays; **Shoots** Field, Blinds, Boat; **Birds** Quail,
Pheasant, Turkey, Ducks, Geese; **Dogs** Avail/HDW;
Packages 1 Day, 1-24 guns

K-Bar-C Hunting Preserve
Box 118, Davis City, IA 50065
(515) 876-2473 Arnold W. Thompson 7-10pm
80 mi. S of Des Moines
Est 1989; **Acres** 960; **Hunters/yr** 100; **Type**
Public, Member/Avail, Corp.; **On Site** Clubhouse,
Lodging, Meals, Clays; **Shoots** Field; **Birds** Quail,
Pheasant, Chukar, Turkey; **Dogs** Avail/HDW; .
Packages 1/2 Day, 2-6 guns

Bill Kuntz's Oakwood Sporting Resort
RR#2, Box 69, Sigourney, IA 52591
(800) 432-3290 Bill Kuntz 7am or pm
40 mi. SW of Iowa City
Est 1990; **Acres** 2,000; **Hunters/yr** 125; **Type**
Public, Member/Avail, Corp.; **On Site** Clubhouse,
Lodging, Meals, Clays; **Shoots** Field; **Birds** Quail,
Pheasant, Chukar; **Dogs** Avail/HDW; **Packages** 1/2
Day, 2-12 guns ○ NAGA/See Pg. 107

Lampe Shooting Preserve
1056 122nd St., Hillsboro, IA 52630
(319) 253-5421 Larry Lampe
40 mi. E of Burlington
Acres 750; **Type** Public; **On Site** Clubhouse,
Lodging, Meals; **Shoots** Field; **Birds** Quail,
Pheasant, Chukar, Turkey; **Dogs** HDW; **Packages**
1/2 Day, up to 6 guns

Lazy H Hunting Club
RR#2, Woodbine, IA 51579
(712) 647-2877 Murray Hubbard 9-5
45 mi. NE of Omaha/Co. Bluffs
Est 1988; **Acres** 360; **Hunters/yr** 350; **Type**
Public, Member/Avail, Corp.; **On Site** Clubhouse,
Lodging, Meals, Clays; **Shoots** Field, Driven; **Birds**
Quail, Pheasant, Chukar; **Dogs** Avail/HDW;
Packages 1/2 Day, 1-20 guns

206 Main St., Bedford, IA 50833
(712) 523-2177 Lanny DeMott
100 mi. SW of Des Moines
Acres 6,000; **Type** Public; **On Site** Clubhouse,
Lodging, Meals; **Shoots** Field; **Birds** Quail, Pheasant;
Dogs Avail/HDW; **Packages** 1 Day, 4-12 guns

Oak View Hunting Club
RR2, Prairie City, IA 50228
(515) 842-3576 Ronald De Bruin Evening
25 mi. E of Des Moines
Est 1963; **Acres** 1,280; **Type** Public, Member/Avail,
Corp.; **On Site** Clubhouse, Meals, Clays; **Shoots**
Field; **Birds** Quail, Pheasant, Chukar, Ducks; **Dogs**
Avail/HDW; **Packages** 1/2 Day, 1-20 guns
O NAGA/See Pg. 107

Oakview II Hunting Club
12726 Hwy. F 70 W, Runnells, IA 50237
(515) 966-2095 Glenn D. Neideigh
Shoots Field; **Birds** Quail, Pheasant, Chukar, Turkey
O NAGA/See Pg. 107

Outdoorsman Hunting Club
RR1, Box 32, Webb, IA 51366
(712) 838-4890 Larry Buettner
90 mi. NE of Sioux City
Est 1968; **Acres** 1,000; **Type** Public, Member/Avail;
On Site Clubhouse, Lodging; **Shoots** Field; **Birds**
Quail, Pheasant, Chukar, Turkey, Ducks, Geese; **Dogs**
Avail/HDW

Pheasant Haven
1485 110th St., Kanawha, IA 50447
(515) 762-3432 Marvin Stupka
Shoots Field; **Birds** Pheasant, Chukar, Turkey
O NAGA/See Pg. 107

Pheasants Galore
Box 83, Corning, IA 50841
(515) 322-3749 Darwin Linn 8-5
125 mi. SW of Des Moines
Est 1986; **Acres** 300,000; **Hunters/yr** 1,000;
Type Public; **Shoots** Field; **Birds** Quail, Pheasant,
Huns, Ducks, Geese; **Dogs** Avail/HDW; **Packages** 2
Days, 1-12 guns

Safari Iowa Hunting Farms
3018 "O" Ave., Parnell, IA 52325
(319) 664-3472 Larry or Jan Statler 7am-6pm
40 mi. SW of Cedar Rapids
Est 1988; **Acres** 2,700; **Type** Public, Member/Avail,
Corp.; **On Site** Clubhouse, Lodging, Meals, Clays;
Shoots Field; **Birds** Quail, Pheasant, Chukar, Turkey,
Ducks, Geese; **Dogs** Avail/HDW; **Packages** 1/2 Day
O NAGA/See Pg. 107

Timber Ridge Hunting Preserve
RR1, Box 203A, Castana, IA 51010
(712) 353-6517 Richard Bumann
90 mi. N of Omaha, NE
Est 1990; **Acres** 1,200; **Type** Public, Member/Avail;
On Site Clubhouse, Lodging, Meals, Clays; **Shoots**
Field; **Birds** Quail, Pheasant; **Dogs** Avail/HDW;
Packages 1/2 Day, 1-20 guns

Triple H Ranch
Hunting Preserve
16365 70th Avenue, Burlington, IA 52601
(319) 985-2253 Keith A. Hoelzen 7am-8pm
140 mi. SE of Des Moines
Est 1986; **Acres** 950; **Hunters/yr** 300; **Type**
Public; **On Site** Clubhouse, Meals, Clays; **Shoots**
Field, Tower, Driven, Blinds, Boat; **Birds** Quail,
Woodcock, Pheasant, Chukar, Turkey, Ducks, Geese;
Dogs Avail/HDW; **Packages** 1/2 Day, 1-25 guns O
NAGA/See Pg. 107
O Nearby Burlington Airport handles corporate jets
and is served by two major airlines
See Our Ad Pg. 329

Wingshoot Iowa
RR1, Box 35C, Vinton, IA 52349
(319) 472-4484 Dave Wessling 8pm-10pm
25 mi. from Cedar Rapids
Est 1991; **Acres** 1,000; **Hunters/yr** 40; **Type**
Public; **On Site** Clubhouse, Lodging, Meals; **Shoots**
Field; **Birds** Quail, Pheasant, Huns, Ducks, Geese;
Dogs Avail/HDW; **Packages** 2 Days, 4-12 guns

Winterset Hunt Club and Lodge
RR1, Box 100, Lorimor, IA 50419
(515) 763-2505 Curt Sandahl 7-7
47 mi. SW of Des Moines
Est 1981; **Acres** 1,670; **Hunters/yr** 600; **Type**
Public, Member/Avail; **On Site** Clubhouse, Lodging,
Meals, Clays; **Shoots** Field; **Birds** Quail, Pheasant,
Chukar, Turkey; **Dogs** Avail/HDW; **Packages** 1 Day,
1-20 guns O NAGA/See Pg. 107

David Robertson 9-5

Wing & Clay

Est 1... **On Site** Clubhouse,
Lodging, ...ts Field; **Birds** Dove, Quail,
Pheasant, ... ns, Turkey; **Dogs** Avail/HDW;
Packages 1 Day, ...12 guns

Blue Line Club
Rt. 1, Box 139A, Solomon, KS 67480
(913) 488-3785 Bernie Janssen After 8pm
25 mi. NE of Salina
Est 1969; **Acres** 640; **Hunters/yr** 200; **Type**
Public; **Shoots** Field, Driven; **Birds** Dove, Quail,
Pheasant, Chukar, Turkey, Prairie Chicken; **Dogs**
Avail/HDW; **Packages** 1/2 Day, 1-30 guns
○ NAGA/See Pg. 107

Broken Bar 7 Hunting Safari
HC1, Box 19, St. Francis, KS 67756
(913) 332-2416 Dean/Kaye O'Brien
160 mi. E of Denver, CO
Est 1989; **Acres** 1,280; **Type** Public; **On Site**
Clubhouse, Lodging, Meals, Clays; **Shoots** Field;
Birds Quail, Pheasant, Huns; **Dogs** Avail/HDW;
Packages 1 Day, 1-10 guns

Clark's Creek Outfitters, Inc.

RR1, Box 23, White City, KS 66872
(800) 856-6636 Ron Britt or (913) 349-2280 Anytime
20 mi. S of Junction City
Est 1995; **Acres** 6,000; **Hunters/yr** 40; **On Site**
Clubhouse, Lodging, Meals, Clays; **Shoots** Field;
Birds Dove, Quail, Pheasant, Turkey, Prairie Chicken,
Ducks, Geese; **Dogs** Avail/HDW; **Packages** 2 Days,
2-10 guns
See Our Ad Pg. 334

Classic Upland Pheasant Hunting
RR1, Box 209, Liberal, KS 67901
(316) 624-2245 Stan Boles
6 mi. W of Liberal
Acres 2,200; **Hunters/yr** 200; **Type** Public; **On
Site** Clubhouse, Meals; **Shoots** Field; **Birds** Quail,
Pheasant; **Dogs** Avail

Claythorne Lodge
Rt. 1, Box 13, Hallowell, KS 66725
(316) 597-2568 Sam or Frieda Lancaster
150 mi. S of Kansas City
Acres 300; **Type** Public, Member/Avail; **On Site**
Clubhouse, Lodging, Meals, Clays; **Shoots** Field,
Driven; **Birds** Quail, Pheasant, Chukar; **Dogs**
Avail/HDW; **Packages** 1/2 Day, 1-10 guns
○ NAGA/See Pg. 107

Cokeley Farms

RR1, Box 149, Delia, KS 66418

(913) 771-3817 Will Cokeley

22 mi. NW of Topeka

Est 1988; **Acres** 2,000; **Type** Public, Member/Avail, Corp.; **On Site** Clubhouse, Lodging, Meals, Clays; **Shoots** Field, Driven, Blinds; **Birds** Quail, Pheasant, Chukar, Huns, Turkey, Prairie Chicken, Ducks, Geese; **Dogs** Avail/HDW; **Packages** 1/2 Day, 1-20 guns

See Our Ad Below

The Farm

HC1, Box 61, Clayton, KS 67629

(913) 567-4646 Raymond Scheetz

100 mi. NW of Hays

Est 1989; **Acres** 3,000; **Type** Public, Member/Avail, Corp.; **On Site** Lodging, Meals, Clays; **Shoots** Field; **Birds** Dove, Quail, Pheasant, Chukar; **Dogs** Avail/HDW; **Packages** 2 Days, 2-6 guns O NAGA/See Pg. 107

Five Double Bar Farms

RR1, Box 55, Selden, KS 67757

(913) 687-3785 Tom Beckman 7-10pm

270 mi. E of Denver

Est 1989; **Acres** 15,000; **Hunters/yr** 70; **Type** Public; **On Site** Meals; **Shoots** Field; **Birds** Quail, Pheasant, Turkey; **Dogs** Avail/HDW; **Packages** 1 Day, 2-8 guns

Flint Hills

PO Box 33, Atlanta, KS 67008

(316) 394-2345 Brent Flemming

45 mi. SE of Witchita

Est 1991; **Type** Public; **On Site** Clubhouse, Lodging, Meals, Clays; **Shoots** Field; **Birds** Dove, Quail, Prairie Chicken; **Dogs** Avail/HDW; **Packages** 1/2 Day, 2-10 guns

Flint Oak

Rt. 1, Box 262, Fall River, KS 67047

(316) 658-4401 Pete Laughlin 8:30am-5pm

75 mi. E of Wichita

Est 1979; **Acres** 2,800; **Type** Public, Member/Avail, Corp.; **On Site** Clubhouse, Lodging, Meals, Clays; **Shoots** Field, Driven; **Birds** Dove, Quail, Pheasant, Chukar, Turkey; **Dogs** Avail/HDW; **Packages** 1/2 Day, 1-78 guns O NAGA/See Pg. 107

Flying W Pheasant Ranch
6199 4 Rd., Plains, KS 67869
(316) 563-7679 Leon Winfrey
50 mi. SW of Dodge City
Est 1990; **Acres** 2,500; **Hunters/yr** 200; **Type**
Public; **On Site** Clubhouse, Lodging, Meals; **Shoots**
Field; **Birds** Pheasant, Chukar; **Dogs** Avail/HDW;
Packages 1/2 Day, 2-15 guns

Golden Prairie Hunting Svc.
PO Box 119, Sublette, KS 67877
(316) 675-8490 Jeff & Debbie White

Gunsmoke Hunting
PO Box 128, Hanston, KS 67849
(800) 476-6827 Walt/Gwen Salmans
35 mi. NE of Dodge City   **Est** 1982; **Acres** 4,000;
Hunters/yr 200; **Type** Public, Member/Avail; **On
Site** Lodging, Meals; **Shoots** Field; **Birds** Dove,
Quail, Pheasant, Chukar; **Dogs** Avail/HDW;
Packages 1 Day, 2-14 guns

Gunthunder
RR3, Great Bend, KS 67530
(316) 793-3738 John R. Miorandi Anytime
80 mi. NW of Wichita   **Est** 1974; **Acres** 60,000;
Hunters/yr 65; **Type** Public; **On Site** Clubhouse,
Lodging, Meals, Clays; **Shoots** Field, Blinds; **Birds**
Dove, Quail, Pheasant, Prairie Chicken, Snipe, Sharp
Tail Grouse, Ducks, Geese; **Dogs** Avail/HDW;
Packages 2 Days, 1-5 guns

Hidden Hollow Farm
26835 Ellis Rd., Havensville, KS 66432
(913) 948-3477 Thomas Routh 50 mi. from Topkea
Acres 240; **Hunters/yr** 100; **Type** Public; **Shoots**
Field; **Birds** Quail, Pheasant, Dogs Avail/HDW;
Packages 1/2 Day, 1-10 guns

The Hunnewell
Hunting Club, Inc.
105 N. 6th, Hunnewell, KS 67140
(316) 892-5821 Allan Helsel 9-3 Wkdays
50 mi. S of Wichita **Est** 1991; **Acres** 3,000; **Hunt-
ers/yr** 50; **Type** Public; **On Site** Clubhouse,
Lodging, Meals, Clays; **Shoots** Field; **Birds** Quail,
Pheasant, Huns; **Dogs** Avail/HDW; **Packages** 1/2
Day, 1-12 guns
If you're looking for the kind of wingshooting experience that Kansas is justly famous for, look no further
than The Hunnewell Hunting Club. Our packages include meals and the use of a roomy, comfortable
lodge. We provide you with the best Kansas wild and
released pheasant and released Hungarian partridge
hunting experience imaginable. Wild quail hunting,
too! Small groups are our specialty and personal attention is a Hunnewell Hallmark. Call today for more
information and reservations.

See Our Ad Below

Lil' Toledo Lodge

In Beautiful Southeast Kansas

1,000 Acres on the Neosho River

PHEASANT • CHUKAR • QUAIL DUCK & GOOSE HUNTING
From Heated Blinds

- Excellent Guides & Dogs
- Overnight Lodging Available
- Corporate & Private Meetings
- Sporting Clays & Five Stand
- Airport & Airport Limo Available

Call for information and reservations:

316-244-5668 or 316-763-2494

Fax: 316-763-2000

Rt. #4, Box 117, Chanute KS 66720

Hunting Sports Plus
710 Main St., Ste. E, Blue Springs, MO, Hunting in 4 states including, KS
(800) 729-1924 Dan Gasser
Est 1989; **Acres** 200,000; **Type** Public, Member/Avail; **On Site** Clubhouse, Lodging, Meals, Clays; **Shoots** Field, Blinds, Boat; **Birds** Quail, Pheasant, Turkey, Prairie Chicken, Ducks, Geese; **Dogs** Avail/HDW; **Packages** 1 Day, 1-24 guns
See Our Ad Pg. 331

EAST CENTRAL KANSAS –6,000 Private Acres–

Visit our ranch and enjoy an abundance of Pheasant, Quail, Prairie Chicken, Ducks, Geese, and Wild Turkey. Trophy Whitetail deer, too!

Individuals and groups as large as 10 people can hunt with our first rate dogs or use their own (our kennels are top notch). Excellent accommodations and meals.

Call or write today for more information:
Ron Britt • Clark's Creek Outfitters, Inc.
812 S. 2700 Rd. • White City, KS 66872

–800-856-6636–

Jayhawk Outfitting
PO Box 117, Hill City, KS 67642
(913) 674-2284 Steve Lewis
180 mi. NW of Wichita
Est 1989; **Acres** 18,000; **Hunters/yr** 150; **Type** Public; **On Site** Clubhouse, Lodging, Meals; **Shoots** Field; **Birds** Quail, Pheasant; **Dogs** Avail/HDW; **Packages** 1 Day, 1-15 guns
See Our Ad Across

Lasada Hunting Service
PO Box 1, Russell, KS 67665
(913) 483-3758 Ron or Scott Young
On Site Lodging; **Shoots** Field; **Birds** Quail, Pheasant, Turkey O NAGA/See Pg. 107

Lazy J Hunting Service
PO Box 832, Sublette, KS 67877
(316) 675-2338 Dave Holloway
50 mi. W of Dodge City
Est 1980; **Acres** 10,000; **Hunters/yr** 400; **Type** Public; **On Site** Clubhouse, Meals; **Shoots** Field; **Birds** Pheasant, Chukar; **Dogs** Avail; **Packages** 1/2 Day, 1-40 guns

Lil' Toledo Lodge
Rt. 4, Box 117, Chanute, KS 66720
(316) 244-5668 Ron King 8-5
100 mi. SW of Kansas City
Est 1991; **Acres** 2,000; **Type** Public, Member/Avail; **On Site** Clubhouse, Lodging, Meals, Clays; **Shoots** Field; **Birds** Quail, Pheasant, Chukar, Huns, Turkey, Sage Grouse; **Dogs** Avail/HDW; **Packages** 1/2 Day, 1-5 guns
See Our Ad Above, Left

Lone Pine Shooting Preserve
RR#1, Box 79, Toronto, KS 66777
(316) 637-2967 Mike Hammon
75 mi. E of Wichita
Acres 550; **Type** Public; **Shoots** Field; **Birds** Quail, Pheasant, Chukar; **Dogs** Avail/HDW
O NAGA/See Pg. 107

Mid America Adventure
11565 E. Plymell Rd., Pierceville, KS 67860
(316) 335-5522 Earl & Crystal Reist
Type Public; **Shoots** Field; **Birds** Pheasant, Chukar
O NAGA/See Pg. 107

Mill Creek Hunting Preserve
RR2, Box 78, Washington, KS 66968
(913) 325-3103 Charles Penning
100 mi. NW of Topeka
Est 1994; **Acres** 680; **Type** Public; **On Site** Clays;
Shoots Field; **Birds** Quail, Pheasant
○ NAGA/See Pg. 107

Ole Olson's Wild Bird Hunts
225 S. Main, Lindsborg, KS 67456
(913) 227-2528 Jeffrey D. Olson After 6pm
Est 1982; **Acres** 15,000; **Type** Member/Avail;
Shoots Field; **Birds** Dove, Quail, Pheasant, Prairie
Chicken; **Dogs** Avail/HDW; **Packages** 1 Day

Pheasant Creek
Box 209, Lakin, KS 67860
(316) 355-7118 J.R. Dienst 8am-12noon
210 mi. W of Wichita
Est 1988; **Acres** 15,000; **Hunters/yr** 200; **Type**
Public; **On Site** Clubhouse, Lodging, Meals; **Shoots**
Field; **Birds** Quail, Pheasant, Chukar, Turkey, Prairie
Chicken; **Dogs** Avail; **Packages** 1 Day, 1-30 guns
○ NAGA/See Pg. 107

Pheasants Galore
HCR1, Box 5, Sublette, KS 67877
(316) 675-8418 Jill or Vern Hibbard

Prairie Land Wildlife, Inc.
2009 South Sylvia Rd., Sylvia, KS 67581
(316) 486-2496 Rodney or Marilyn Hurst
80 mi. NW of Witchita
Est 1995; **Acres** 3,500; **Type** Public; **Shoots** Field,
Blinds; **Birds** Dove, Quail, Pheasant, Turkey, Ducks,
Geese; **Dogs** Avail/HDW; **Packages** 1 Day, 1-5 guns

Prairie Winds Guide Service
1611 K-157 Hwy., Junction City, KS 66441
(913) 257-3234 Thomas D. Slick After 9pm
120 mi. W of Kansas City
Est 1988; **Acres** 4,000; **Type** Public; **On Site**
Lodging, Meals; **Shoots** Field; **Birds** Dove, Quail,
Pheasant, Turkey, Prairie Chicken, Ducks, Geese;
Dogs Avail/HDW; **Packages** 1 Day, 1-10 guns

Quail Valley
Sporting Clays & Hunt Club
16501 NW 72nd; RR1, Box 134, Moundridge, KS 67107
(316) 345-8367 Mike & Barbara Stucky 8-10 evenings
35 mi. NW of Wichita
Est 1992; **Acres** 320; **Type** Public; **On Site**
Clubhouse, Lodging, Meals, Clays; **Shoots** Field;
Birds Quail, Pheasant, Chukar; **Dogs** Avail/HDW;
Packages 1/2 Day, 1-10 guns ○ NAGA/See Pg. 107

RMF Guide Service
PO Box 1924, Manhattan, KS 66502
(913) 537-4682 Ronald M. Ford 5-6am; 7-10pm

Ravenwood Hunting
Preserve & Sporting Clays
10147 SW 61 St., Topeka, KS 66610
(800) 656-2454 Ken Corbet (913) 256-6444
50 mi. W of Kansas City
Est 1985; **Acres** 1,500; **Type** Public, Member/Avail,
Corp.; **On Site** Clubhouse, Meals, Clays; **Shoots**
Field; **Birds** Dove, Quail, Pheasant, Chukar, Turkey,
Prairie Chicken, Ducks, Geese; **Dogs** Avail/HDW;
Packages 1/2 Day, 1-20 guns ○ NAGA/See Pg. 107
See Our Ad Across, Left

Red Rock Game Farm
10855 Broderick, Wamago, KS 66547
(913) 456-7664 Lynn Pugh
10 mi. N of Wamego   **Acres** 320; **Type** Public;
On Site Clays; **Shoots** Field; **Birds** Quail, Pheasant,
Chukar; **Dogs** Avail/HDW

Republican Valley Hunting
PO Box 208, Scandia, KS 66966
(913) 335-2658 Elise Gile
75 mi. N of Salina
Est 1996; **Acres** 4,000; **Hunters/yr** 200; **Type**
Public; **On Site** Clubhouse, Lodging, Meals; **Shoots**
Field; **Birds** Dove, Quail, Pheasant, Turkey; **Dogs**
Avail/HDW; **Packages** 1 Day, up to 12 guns

Ringneck Ranch Inc.
HC61, Box 7, Tipton, KS 67485
(913) 373-4835 Keith or Debra Houghton Day or eve
75 mi. NW of Salina
Est 1983; **Acres** 10,000; **Hunters/yr** 900; **Type**
Public; **On Site** Clubhouse, Lodging, Meals, Clays;
Shoots Field, Blinds; **Birds** Dove, Quail, Pheasant,
Turkey, Prairie Chicken, Ducks, Geese; **Dogs**
Avail/HDW; **Packages** 1 Day, 1-30 guns
○ NAGA/See Pg. 107
See Our Ad, Right

Shawnee Creek Preserve
Rt. 2, Box 50-B, Columbus, KS 66725
(316) 429-2315 Jon Holt After 7pm
140 mi. S of Kansas City, MO
Est 1987; **Acres** 729; **Hunters/yr** 150; **Type**
Public; **On Site** Lodging, Meals, Clays; **Shoots** Field;
Birds Quail, Pheasant; **Dogs** Avail; **Packages** 1/2
Day, 2-5 guns

Show-Me Bird Hunting Resort
Rt. 1, Box 134, Baxter Springs, KS 66713
(316) 674-8863 Kim Shira
Type Public; **On Site** Lodging; **Shoots** Field; **Birds**
Pheasant, Chukar ○ NAGA/See Pg. 107

Solomon Valley Farm
1894 W. 70th Dr., Alton, KS 67623
(913) 346-2570 Bob Saylor
6 mi. N of Osborne
Acres 1,100; **Hunters/yr** 200; **Type** Public; **On
Site** Lodging, Meals, Clays; **Shoots** Field; **Birds**
Quail, Pheasant, Turkey, Prairie Chicken; **Dogs** Avail

Spillman Creek Lodge
RD1, Box 40, Sylvan Grove, KS 67481
(913) 277-3424 Merrill Nielsen
55 mi. NW of Salina
Est 1987; **Acres** 1,200; **Type** Public; **On Site**
Clubhouse, Lodging, Meals; **Shoots** Field; **Birds**
Quail, Pheasant; **Dogs** Avail/HDW; **Packages** 1/2
Day, 1-16 guns ○ NAGA/See Pg. 107
See Our Ad Pg. 331

3019 North Road G, Ulysses, KS 67880
(316) 356-3924 Shane/Mary Sullivan
200 mi. W of Wichita
Est 1988; **Acres** 1,500; **Hunters/yr** 50; **Type**
Public, Corp.; **On Site** Lodging, Meals, Clays;
Shoots Field; **Birds** Quail, Pheasant, Chukar, Huns;
Dogs Avail/HDW; **Packages** 1 Day, 2-15 guns
○ NAGA/See Pg. 107

Eldon R. Trost
RR#2, Box 70, Belleville, KS 66935
(913) 243-3934 Eldon R. Trost Before 7:30am/After 6pm
60 mi. N of Salina
Est 1986; **Acres** 6,000; **Hunters/yr** 200; **Type**
Public; **On Site** Lodging; **Shoots** Field; **Birds** Dove,
Quail, Pheasant, Turkey, Prairie Chicken, Snipe, Ducks,
Geese; **Dogs** Avail/HDW; **Packages** 1 Day, 1-15 guns

Twin Mounds Lodge
1850 22 Rd., Plainville, KS 67663
(913) 434-2488 Phil Hinger 6-8pm
30 mi. N of Hays
Est 1988; **Acres** 3,000; **Hunters/yr** 100; **Type**
Public; **On Site** Clubhouse, Lodging, Meals; **Shoots**
Field; **Birds** Dove, Quail, Pheasant, Prairie Chicken;
Dogs Avail/HDW; **Packages** 1 Day, 1-10 guns

Uhlik Hunting Grounds
RR1, Box 51, Washington, KS 66968
(913) 325-2747 Mark Uhlik After 7 pm
150 mi. NW of Kansas City
Est 1987; **Acres** 12,000; **Type** Public; **Shoots**
Field; **Birds** Quail, Pheasant, Turkey, Prairie Chicken;
Dogs Avail/HDW; **Packages** 1 Day, 2-18 guns

Walnut Ridge Hunting Preserve
RR1, Box 35A, Walnut, KS 66780
(316) 354-6713 Mike or Barb Duling
120 mi. S of Kansas City
Est 1988; **Acres** 760; **Type** Public; **On Site**
Clubhouse, Clays; **Shoots** Field; **Birds** Quail,
Pheasant, Chukar; **Dogs** Avail/HDW; **Packages** 1/2
Day ○ NAGA/See Pg. 107

Walnut Valley Guide Service
Rt. 2, Box 250, Arkansas City, KS 67005
(316) 442-6442 Steve Shirley Anytime
40 mi. SE of Wichita
Est 1989; **Type** Public; **On Site** Clubhouse, Lodging,
Clays; **Shoots** Field; **Birds** Dove, Quail, Pheasant,
Chukar, Turkey, Prairie Chicken, Ducks, Geese; **Dogs**
Avail/HDW; **Packages** 2 Days, up to 1 guns

*Whenever you contact one of the
companies listed or advertising in Wing &
Clay, please remember to tell them that you
benefitted from the information you found
here. And don't forget to say : "I saw it in
Wing & Clay."*

KENTUCKY

Cane Spring Hunting Preserve
4156 Deatsville Rd., Shepherdsville, KY 40165
(502) 543-6327 Gussy Allen
Type Public; **On Site** Lodging; **Birds** Quail,
Pheasant, Chukar ○ NAGA/See Pg.107

Circle Saw Hunting Preserve
Rt. 3, Box 54, Clinton, KY 42031
(502) 653-4224 James Neil Mathis
Type Public; **Shoots** Field; **Birds** Quail, Pheasant,
Chukar ○ NAGA/See Pg. 107

The Cooper Field Hunting Club
641 Colvin Lk. Rd., Kevil, KY 42053
(502) 224-2668 Ed Allcock
120 mi. N of Nashville, TN
Est 1983; **Acres** 3,000; **Hunters/yr** 700; **Type**
Public; **On Site** Clubhouse, Lodging, Meals, Clays;
Shoots Field, Blinds; **Birds** Quail, Pheasant, Chukar,
Ducks, Geese; **Dogs** Avail/HDW; **Packages** 2 Days

Deer Creek Outfitters
P.O. Box 39, Sebree, KY 42455
(502) 835-2424 Tim Stull
140 mi. SW of Louisville   **Est** 1984; **Acres** 5,000;
Type Public, Member/Avail; **On Site** Clubhouse,
Lodging, Meals, Clays; **Shoots** Field, Blinds; **Birds**
Dove, Quail, Pheasant, Chukar, Turkey, Ducks, Geese;
Dogs Avail/HDW; **Packages** 1/2 Day, 1-12 guns
See Our Ad Pg. 340

Flatrock Hunting Preserve
5188 W SR 244, Milroy, IN 46156
(317) 629-2354 Merrill Carrigan 6am to 10pm

Gary & Jerry Shooting Preserve
3415 Ashbyburg Rd., Slaughters, KY 42456
(502) 884-7760 Jerry Morehead After 4 pm
50 mi. S of Evansville, IN
Est 1994; **Acres** 183; **Type** Public; **Shoots** Field;
Birds Quail, Woodcock, Pheasant, Chukar, Huns;
Dogs Avail/HDW; **Packages** 1/2 Day, 1-8 guns

▼ ORVIS ENDORSED ▼

Grassy Lake Lodge
PO Box 319, Wickliffe, KY 42087
(800) 526-0095 Greg Joles
32 mi. SW of Paducah
Est 1985; **Acres** 4,000; **Type** Public, Member/Avail;
On Site Clubhouse, Lodging, Meals, Clays; **Shoots**
Field, Blinds; **Birds** Dove, Ducks, Geese; **Dogs**
Avail/HDW; **Packages** 3 Days, 4-12 guns
See Our Ad Across

▲ ORVIS ENDORSED ▲

Kentucky's Grassy Lake Lodge, Orvis Endorsed. . . Wingshooting Satisfaction Guaranteed

by Ronald H. Jones

The waterfowl season was a disaster in our end of Michigan. In an attempt to salvage it, I searched for late season alternatives. While hunt opportunities abounded in the deep south, Grassy Lake Lodge in Wickliffe, Kentucky, offered the best opportunity for a gentleman hunter to share the experience with his wife and dog.

The extraordinary Grassy Lake Lodge.

Located at the confluence of the Mississippi and Ohio rivers, Grassy Lake consists of some of the finest waterfowl habitat in the country. The owners have spared no expense in providing a premium hunting experience. Their efforts have been recognized by no other than the Orvis organization, which recently bestowed its much sought after wingshooting endorsement on the Lodge.

The best of both worlds

Anyone familiar with Orvis knows that superlative hunting alone is not enough to win an endorsement. Great accommodations, dining and service are just as important. And here too, Grassy Lake excels. Frankly, no words can adequately describe the lodge. Elevated on pillars in the center of the marsh, 25 feet above the flood plain, Grassy Lake Lodge provides a panoramic view of cypress-studded Minor Lake and marshland below. Its great room and bedrooms are exquisitely appointed in varying waterfowl motifs. If you have any personal needs, no matter how slight, the lodge staff will attend to them all. The chef's always ply their culinary talents to a meal that leaves you (sheepishly) asking for thirds.

Experienced Guides

But as formidable as they are, the lodging, food and service act only as supporting cast to the Lodge's true star: World Class Waterfowling. Grassy Lake is encircled by eight major waterfowl refuges and is directly bounded by the Swan Lake Refuge on the Ohio River, which together provide daily flights of geese and ducks. Each hunting group is always accompanied by two resident guides. On our first hunt, Donny Haynes and David Courtney, handled the guiding and catered to our every need.

These two quickly demonstrated the value of 40 years of waterfowling experience. As if by magic, they summoned mallards and divers alike from distant levees and floated them over and into the decoys for an easy harvest.

After a complete country breakfast, Operations Manager Greg Joles started our Friday hunt at 6:15 AM at the edge of a line of willows. Small bunches of mallards traversed in the flooded fields to the west for the first hour. But then...the birds began to respond to our pleas, and by 9 AM we had our limit of three mallards, a widgeon and a bluebill. Three other small groups occupied blinds that morning, but over 30 blinds were purposely left idle, as is Grassy Lake's custom throughout the season. Hunting, by club edict, stops at 1 PM daily, allowing the birds to settle down for the evening.

Other diversions

But don't think the fun has ended when you leave the field. Hidden away on an adjacent tract of land is a complete John Woolley-designed sporting clays course and a shooting preserve that allows each guest to pass-shoot six resident mallards from spacious, comfortable blinds. When you visit, make time to shoot both. The lodge also offers shooting instruction, clinics and schools.

Grassy Lake Lodge invites you to inquire. Write to Greg Joles, Grassy Lake Lodge, 2957 Barlow Road, P.O. Box 319, Wickliffe, KY 42087; or call 1-800-526-0095.

Ronald H. Jones of Saginaw, Michigan, is an NSCA Certified Instructor with 40 years of hunting experience.

Happy Ridge Quail Farm & Preserve
111 Shucks Rd., Pleasureville, KY 40057
(502) 878-4903 Eddie Shuck 6-10pm
45 mi. NE of Louisville
Est 1988; **Acres** 122; **Hunters/yr** 40; **Type** Public; **On Site** Clubhouse; **Shoots** Field; **Birds** Quail, Chukar; **Dogs** Avail/HDW; **Packages** 1/2 Day, 2-3 guns ○ NAGA/See Pg. 107

Kentucky Wonderland Hunting Preserve
14301 Castle Hwy., Pleasureville, KY 40057
(502) 878-4412 Murray Armstrong
80 mi. W of Lexington
Acres 350; **Shoots** Field; **Birds** Quail, Pheasant, Chukar, Turkey; **Dogs** Avail
Want some exciting hunting this fall? Get in on the action at the Kentucky Wonderland Hunting Preserve. For the first time, controlled Turkey Hunts. Early morning hunts only. Turkey can be taken with muzzle loaders, bow, rifles or shotguns. Also available: Pheasant, Quail and Chukar. Give us a call!

Kentucky-Tennessee Quail Plantation
4785 Huffman Mill Rd., Hopkinsville, KY 42240
(502) 885-8877 Donnie or Goebel Adams After 4 pm
75 mi. NW of Nashville
Est 1988; **Acres** 550; **Type** Public; **On Site** Clubhouse, Lodging, Meals, Clays; **Shoots** Field; **Birds** Dove, Quail, Pheasant, Chukar; **Dogs** Avail/HDW; **Packages** 1/2 Day, 2-6 guns

Knotty Pine Hunting Preserve
2511 Coldwater Rd., Murray, KY 42071
(502) 753-5261 Paul Butterworth, Jr. Evenings
50 mi. S of Paducah, KY
Est 1989; **Acres** 200; **Hunters/yr** 100; **Type** Public; **On Site** Clubhouse; **Shoots** Field; **Birds** Quail, Pheasant, Chukar; **Dogs** Avail/HDW; **Packages** 1/2 Day, 1-4 guns ○ NAGA/See Pg. 107

Little Southfork Quail Preserve
1205 Hickory Ridge Rd., Waddy, KY 40076
(502) 223-2935 James S. Miller
7 mi. SW of Frankfort
Acres 130; **Type** Public, Member/Avail; **On Site** Lodging, Meals; **Shoots** Field; **Birds** Quail, Pheasant, Chukar; **Dogs** Avail/HDW; **Packages** 1/2 Day ○ NAGA/See Pg. 107

Quail Run
Hunting Preserve
Box 164, Walton, KY 41094
(502) 463-0912 Kelly Hance
45 mi. SW of Cincinnati, OH
Acres 250; **Hunters/yr** 350; **Type** Public; **On Site** Clubhouse; **Shoots** Field; **Birds** Dove, Quail, Pheasant, Turkey; **Dogs** Avail
See Our Ad Above

Shoot Fire Sportsman's Farm
290 Koostra Rd., Bowling Green, KY 42101
(502) 781-9545 Kent Koostra
60 mi. N of Nashville
Est 1991; **Acres** 1,000; **Type** Public; **On Site** Clubhouse, Meals, Clays; **Shoots** Field; **Birds** Quail, Pheasant, Chukar, Turkey; **Dogs** Avail/HDW; **Packages** 1/2 Day, 3-15 guns ○ NAGA/See Pg. 107

Sugar Creek Hunting
& Sporting Clays
RR2, Box 413, Mitchell, KY 47446
(812) 849-2296 Dale Waldbieser or (812) 849-5020
54 mi. NE of Lousiville
Est 1992; **Acres** 500; **Type** Public; **On Site** Clubhouse, Meals, Clays; **Shoots** Field; **Birds** Quail, Pheasant, Chukar; **Dogs** Avail/HDW; **Packages** 1/2 Day, 1-6 guns ○ NAGA/See Pg. 107

Turkey Creek Hunting Preserve
2145 Turkey Town Rd., Crab Orchard, KY 40419
(606) 355-7301 John Blanton 6-8 pm
40 mi. W of Lexington

Est 1992; **Acres** 255; **Type** Public; **Shoots** Field, Tower, Driven; **Birds** Quail, Pheasant, Chukar; **Dogs** Avail/HDW

Waldon Lodge
779 Colvin Lake Rd., Kevil, KY 42053
(502) 224-2020 Ricky Waldon
30 mi. W of Paducah
Acres 1,400; **Type** Public; **On Site** Clubhouse, Lodging, Meals, Clays; **Shoots** Field; **Birds** Dove, Turkey, Ducks, Geese; **Packages** 1 Day, 4-24 guns

LOUISIANA

Ace Hunting Club
Rt. 1, Box 1465, Abbeville, LA 70510
(318) 643-2910 Gerald Patin
40 mi. from Lafayette
Acres 12,000; **Hunters/yr** 400; **Type** Public, Member/Avail; **On Site** Clubhouse, Meals; **Shoots** Tower, Blinds; **Birds** Ducks, Geese; **Dogs** Avail

Bon Amis'
167 North Platte, Vile Platte, LA 70586
(318) 837-5944 J.P. Theriot
Shoots Field; **Birds** Quail, Pheasant, Chukar, Ducks ○ NAGA/See Pg. 107

C&C Game Birds Hunting Preserve
612 W. Main St., Broussard, LA 70518
(318) 837-6782 Charles E. Langlinais Anytime
150 mi. W of New Orleans
Est 1980; **Acres** 1,000; **Type** Public; **Shoots** Field; **Birds** Chukar; **Dogs** Avail/HDW; **Packages** 1/2 Day, 1-4 guns ○ NAGA/See Pg. 107

Doug's Hunting Lodge
Rt. 1, Box 143, Gueydan, LA 70542
(800) 888-0960 Doug Sonnier Anytime
40 mi. SW of Lafayette
Est 1991; **Acres** 200; **Type** Public, Corp.; **On Site**

Clubhouse, Lodging, Meals, Clays; **Shoots** Field, Tower, Blinds, Boat; **Birds** Dove, Quail, Pheasant, Chukar, Snipe, Ducks, Geese; **Dogs** Avail/HDW; **Packages** 1/2 Day, 1-54 guns

Dry Creek Ranch
Rt. 2, Box 510A, Ragley, LA 70657
(318) 666-2657 Josh & Rane Sills 6:30-5
30 mi. NE of Lake Charles
Acres 2,000; **Hunters/yr** 1,000; **Type** Public; **On Site** Clubhouse, Lodging, Meals, Clays; **Shoots** Field, Tower, Blinds; **Birds** Dove, Quail, Pheasant, Chukar, Ducks; **Dogs** Avail/HDW; **Packages** 1/2 Day, 2-20 guns O NAGA/See Pg. 107

The Florence Club
PO Box 8470, Metairie, LA 70011
(504) 837-5766 Jean Messmer
Est 1926; **Acres** 5,000; **Type** Public; **On Site** Clubhouse, Lodging, Meals; **Shoots** Field; **Birds** Pheasant, Ducks, Geese; **Dogs** Avail; **Packages** 1/2 Day

Hilltop Quail Farm & Preserve
287 Hwy. 135, Winnsboro, LA 71295
(318) 435-6318 Sherman Phillips 9am-12pm; 1-9pm
Est 1985; **Acres** 150; **Type** Public; **Shoots** Field; **Birds** Quail; **Dogs** Avail/HDW; **Packages** 1/2 Day, 1-4 guns O NAGA/See Pg. 107

Land of Lakes
Rt. 3, Box 93, Ville Platte, LA 70586
(318) 363-6310 Woodson Harvey
150 mi. W of New Orleans
Type Public; **On Site** Clubhouse, Lodging, Meals; **Shoots** Field; **Birds** Dove, Pheasant, Chukar; **Dogs** Avail; **Packages** 1/2 Day

Ace Cullum's
PIN OAK MALLARDS

Pin Oak Mallards
711 Hwy. 15, Rayville, LA 71269
(800) 259-3827 Ace Cullum (318) 248-3549
15 mi. E of Monroe
Acres 1,000; **Type** Public, Member/Avail; **On Site** Clubhouse, Lodging, Meals, Clays; **Shoots** Field; **Birds** Ducks; **Dogs** Avail/HDW
PIN OAK MALLARDS "Best Damn Duck Club in Louisiana(R) with modern rustic lodge overlooking duck reservoir. 3 Meals; Experienced guides, excellent callers; Loaner Guns; Bird Processing; Crappie fishing; Brochure available; Flooded timber hunting; Boat to heated blinds or wade hunts; $225 per gun per day; airport pickup; clay shoots. Call Ace Cullum (318) 248-3549.

Plum Ridge Shooting Preserve
PO Box 364, Arcadia, LA 71001
(318) 263-2850 John M. Futch
50 mi. E of Shreveport

Type Public, Member/Avail; **Shoots** Field; **Birds** Quail; **Dogs** Avail/HDW; **Packages** 1/2 Day, up to 3 guns

SHOOTING GROUNDS

Tallow Creek Shooting Grounds
4990 Hwy. 22, Mandeville, LA 70471
(504) 893-1951 Rick Adams/P.J. Demarie Anytime
35 mi. N of New Orleans
Est 1994; **Acres** 450; **Hunters/yr** 200; **Type** Public, Member/Avail, Corp.; **On Site** Clubhouse, Meals, Clays; **Shoots** Field, Tower; **Birds** Quail, Chukar; **Dogs** Avail/HDW; **Packages** 1/2 Day, 2-4 guns O Home of the "Louisiana Governors Cup Sporting Clays Open"

Wild Wings Hunting Preserve
Rt. 2, Box 26, Downsville, LA 71234
(318) 982-7777 Steve Bryan
75 mi. NE of Shreveport
Est 1979; **Acres** 2,000; **Type** Public, Member/Avail, Corp.; **On Site** Clubhouse, Lodging, Meals, Clays; **Shoots** Field; **Birds** Dove, Quail, Pheasant, Chukar, Turkey, Ducks; **Dogs** Avail/HDW

MAINE

Bosebuck Mtn. Camps
Rt. 16, Box 330, Wilsons Mills, ME 03579
(207) 243-2945 Tom Rideout 8 am to 10 pm
90 mi. N of Portland
Est 1907; **Acres** 200,000; **Hunters/yr** 150; **Type** Public; **On Site** Clubhouse, Lodging, Meals; **Shoots** Field; **Birds** Ruffed Grouse, Woodcock; **Dogs** Avail/HDW; **Packages** 1 Day, 1-20 guns

The Bradford Camps

PO Box 729, Ashland, ME 04732
(207) 746-7777 Karen & Igor Sikorsky
90 mi. N of Greenville
Est 1890; **Acres** 1,000,000; **Type** Public; **On Site** Clubhouse, Lodging, Meals, Clays; **Shoots** Field; **Birds** Ruffed Grouse, Woodcock; **Dogs** HDW; **Packages** 3 Days, up to 10 guns
Enjoy the magic of the Maine woods in this remote sportsman's paradise. Century old waterfront log cabins on pristine Munsungan Lake. Ruffed grouse and woodcock abound on the trails and woods roads around camp. Ten station sporting clays, guided hunts, three home cooked meals, comfortable cabins– Four Star service. Free brochure.

Freehold Lodge Club, Inc.
RFD1, Box 141, Perry, ME 04667
(207) 726-5093 George W. Fennell
100 mi. E of Bangor
Est 1992; **Acres** 500; **Type** Public; **On Site** Clubhouse, Lodging, Meals; **Shoots** Field; **Birds** Ruffed Grouse, Woodcock, Ducks, Geese; **Dogs** HDW; **Packages** 1 Day, up to 1 guns

Georges River Outfitters
1364 Atlantic Hwy., Warren, ME 04864
(207) 273-3818 Jeff Bellmore
Est 1986; **Type** Public; **On Site** Clubhouse, Lodging, Meals; **Shoots** Field, Blinds, Boat; **Birds** Ruffed Grouse, Woodcock, Ducks; **Dogs** Avail/HDW; **Packages** 1 Day, 2-6 guns

King & Bartlett Fish & Game Club
PO Box 4, Eustis, ME 04936
(207) 243-2956 Buzz Cox
120 mi. NW of Portland
Est 1894; **Acres** 24,000; **Type** Public; **On Site** Clubhouse, Lodging, Meals, Clays; **Shoots** Field, Blinds; **Birds** Ruffed Grouse, Woodcock, Ducks, Geese; **Dogs** Avail/HDW; **Packages** 1 Day, 1-12 guns

Maine Game Bird Guides
RR#2, Box 468, Belfast, ME 04915
(207) 722-3664 Jo-Ann Moody Evenings
40 mi. S of Bangor
Est 1987; **Hunters/yr** 50; **Type** Public; **On Site** Lodging, Meals; **Shoots** Driven; **Birds** Ruffed Grouse, Woodcock, Pheasant; **Dogs** Avail/HDW; **Packages** 1 Day, 1-8 guns

Maine Sea Ducks
18 Pine St., Thomaston, ME 04861
(207) 354-6520 Bill Wasson Evening
60 mi. NE of Portland
Est 1989; **Hunters/yr** 150; **Type** Public; **Shoots** Blinds; **Birds** Ducks; **Dogs** Avail/HDW; **Packages** 1 Day, 1-4 guns

Medawisla on Second Roach Pond
RR 76, Box 592, Greenville, ME 04441
(207) 695-2690 Larry LeRoy Daytime
70 mi. NW of Bangor
Acres 10,000; **Type** Public; **On Site** Lodging, Clays; **Shoots** Field; **Birds** Ruffed Grouse, Woodcock; **Dogs** HDW

Northern Outdoors
Rt. 201, PO Box 100, The Forks, ME 04985
(800) 765-7238 Wayne Hockmeyer
100 mi. NW of Bangor
Type Public; **On Site** Clubhouse, Lodging, Meals; **Shoots** Field; **Birds** Ruffed Grouse, Woodcock; **Dogs** Avail

Nugent's Chamberlain Lake Camps
HCR 76, Box 632, Greenville, ME 04441
(207) 944-5991 John Richardson
75 mi. N of Bangor **Type** Public; **On Site** Clubhouse, Lodging, Meals; **Shoots** Field; **Birds** Ruffed Grouse, Chukar; **Dogs** Avail

Pathfinder Guide Service
RR1, Box 4173, Camden, ME 04843
(207) 236-0832 Bob Foshay 8am-8pm
50 mi. S of Bangor
Est 1989; **Type** Public; **On Site** Meals; **Shoots** Field, Driven; **Birds** Ruffed Grouse, Woodcock; **Dogs** Avail/HDW; **Packages** 1 Day, 1-3 guns

Red River Camps
PO Box 320, Portage, ME 04765
(207) 435-6000 Mike Brophy
135 mi. N of Bangor
Est 1900; **Acres** 1,000; **Hunters/yr** 50; **Type** Public; **On Site** Clubhouse, Lodging, Meals; **Shoots** Field; **Birds** Ruffed Grouse; **Dogs** HDW; **Packages** 2 Days, 4-12 guns

Ridge Runner Guide Service
RFD1, Box 645, Monroe, ME 04951
(207) 525-3588 Les Thompson
24 mi. SW of Bangor
Est 1988; **Type** Public; **On Site** Clubhouse, Lodging; **Shoots** Field; **Birds** Ruffed Grouse, Woodcock; **Dogs** Avail/HDW; **Packages** 1 Day, 1-3 guns

River View Hunting Preserve
PO Box 278, Anson, ME 04911
(207) 696-3076 Chet Flanagin 9-4, M-S
10 mi. N of Madison
Est 1990; **Acres** 200; **Hunters/yr** 150; **Type** Public; **Shoots** Field; **Birds** Quail, Pheasant; **Dogs** Avail/HDW; **Packages** 1/2 Day, 1-4 guns

The Village Camps
Box 101-W, Forest City, ME 04413
(207) 448-7726 Lance Wheaton
110 mi. NE of Bangor
Est 1989; **Type** Public; **On Site** Lodging; **Shoots** Field; **Birds** Ruffed Grouse, Woodcock, Ducks, Geese; **Dogs** Avail/HDW

MARYLAND

Alexander Sporting Farms
13503 Alexander Rd., Golt, MD 21637
(410) 928-3549 James/Samuel Alexander
5 mi. N of Millington
Type Public; **On Site** Clays; **Shoots** Field;

B&J Goose Hunting
31106 Chesterville Bridge Rd., Millington, MD 21651
(410) 928-5260 Joe Kuhn
Est 1973; **Type** Public; **Shoots** Field, Blinds, Boat;
Birds Ducks, Geese; **Dogs** Avail; **Packages** 1 Day,
1-5 guns

Bourbon Brook Hunting Preserve
141 Seney Rd., Church Hill, MD 21623
(410) 556-6177 Wayne or Donnie McFarland Evenings
40 mi. E of Annapolis
Est 1989; **Acres** 400; **Hunters/yr** 250; **Type**
Public; **Shoots** Field, Blinds; **Birds** Quail, Pheasant,
Chukar, Huns, Turkey, Geese; **Dogs** Avail/HDW;
Packages 1/2 Day, 1-10 guns

Campbell's Covey
Box 127, Galesville, MD 20765
(410) 867-7144 Steve Campbell
Type Public, Member/Avail; **Shoots** Field; **Birds**
Quail, Pheasant, Chukar   O NAGA/See Pg. 107

Caroline County Shooting Preserve
8785 New Bridge Rd., Denton, MD 21629
(410) 479-2364 Tom/Don/Steve Swann 6 to 10 pm
60 mi. E of Washington, DC
Est 1963; **Acres** 400; **Hunters/yr** 1,200; **Type**
Public; **On Site** Clubhouse; **Shoots** Field, Blinds;
Birds Dove, Quail, Pheasant, Chukar, Huns, Ducks;
Dogs Avail/HDW; **Packages** 1/2 Day, 1-10 guns

Chesapeake Sporting Clays
16090 Oakland Rd. (Rt. 312, Bridgetown),
Henderson, MD 21640
(410) 758-1824 Bill Connors 7 Days, 9am-6pm
65 mi. NE of Washington, DC
Est 1990; **Acres** 419; **Hunters/yr** 150; **Type**
Public; **On Site** Clubhouse, Lodging, Meals, Clays;
Shoots Field, Tower, Driven, Blinds; **Birds** Dove,
Quail, Pheasant, Chukar, Turkey, Ducks, Geese; **Dogs**
Avail/HDW

O Sporting Clays   O Gourmet Meals
O Deer Hunting   O Quality Clubhouse
O Shooting Instruction   O Private Bedrooms

Bill Clark's Goose Hunting
23141 Schooner Rd., Chestertown, MD 21620
(410) 778-5854 Bill Clark
50 mi. E of Baltimore
Acres 2,000; **Type** Public, Member/Avail, Corp.;
On Site Lodging; **Shoots** Blinds, Boat; **Birds** Ducks,
Geese; **Dogs** Avail/HDW

Jeffrey Barnett Clark, Sr.
405 Spider Web Rd., Centreville, MD 21617
(410) 758-2763 Jeff Clark
W of Centreville
Acres 1,000; **Hunters/yr** 400; **Type** Public;
Shoots Field, Blinds; **Birds** Dove, Quail, Pheasant,
Chukar, Ducks, Geese; **Dogs** Avail

Fair Winds Gun Club
5886 Quaker Neck Rd., Chestertown, MD 21620
(410) 778-5363 Clint Evans 9-5
from Chestertown   .
Est 1980; **Acres** 2,500; **Hunters/yr** 750; **Type**
Public, Corp.; **On Site** Lodging, Meals; **Shoots**
Field, Blinds, Boat; **Birds** Dove, Ducks, Geese; **Dogs**
HDW; **Packages** 1 Day
O Hunting License
O Airport Pickup
O Bird Processing
O Gourmet Meals
O Brochure Available
O Seasonal Packages Available
Fair Winds Gun Club manages over 2,200 acres in
and around Chestertown on Maryland's Eastern
Shore. We have day hunts with fully trained, experi-
enced professionals. Through its habitat
management program, the September Dove shoot-
ing is superb. Diverse hunting grounds provide for
widest variety of waterfowl shooting – including Can-
ada & Snow Geese, puddle, diving & Sea Ducks.
Early reservations are urged. We will arrange for accommodations & meals per your request.

Fairs Regulated Shooting Area
1605 Old Virginia Rd., Pocomoke City, MD 21851
(410) 957-1749 Ray Fair
30 mi. S of Salisbury
Acres 270; **Type** Public; **On Site** Clubhouse, Clays;
Shoots Field; **Birds** Quail, Pheasant, Chukar, Huns;
Dogs Avail/HDW   O NAGA/See Pg.107

Fly-By-Island, Inc.
3052 Crosiadore Lane, Trappe, MD 21673
(410) 476-3843 Bo Kennedy Evenings
17 mi. from Easton
Est 1975; **Acres** 1,500; **Type** Public; **On Site**
Meals, Clays; **Shoots** Field, Blinds; **Birds** Ducks,
Geese; **Packages** 1 Day

Goose Valley Farming & Outfitting
12504 Augustine Herman Hwy., Kennedyville, MD 21645
(410) 778-5300 Floyd-Tom-Kay 10 to 5
35 mi. E of Baltimore
Est 1956; **Acres** 5,000; **Hunters/yr** 561; **Type**
Public, Member/Avail, Corp.; **On Site** Lodging,
Meals; **Shoots** Field, Tower, Blinds; **Birds** Dove,
Pheasant, Chukar, Ducks, Geese; **Dogs** Avail/HDW;
Packages 1 Day, up to 150 guns

Green Rest Hunting Preserve
Star Rt. 2, Box 2, Valley Lee, MD 20692
(301) 994-2104 Ronnie Carter Evenings
60 mi. SE of Washington, DC

Est 1990; **Acres** 450; **Type** Public; **On Site** Clubhouse; **Shoots** Field, Tower; **Birds** Dove, Quail, Pheasant, Chukar, Huns; **Dogs** Avail/HDW; **Packages** 1/2 Day, 2-8 guns

Greensboro Regulated Hunting Preserve
PO Box 159, Greensboro, MD 21639
(410) 482-6873 A.W. Spiering, Jr.
60 mi. E of Washington, DC
Est 1980; **Acres** 500; **Type** Public, Member/Avail, Corp.; **On Site** Clubhouse, Lodging, Clays; **Shoots** Field, Blinds; **Birds** Dove, Quail, Pheasant, Chukar, Huns, Ducks, Geese; **Dogs** Avail/HDW; **Packages** 1/2 Day, 2-10 guns

Gunpowder Game Farm
17904 Gunpowder Rd., Hampstead, MD 21074
(410) 374-1434 David or Wendy Tracey
30 mi. N of Baltimore
Est 1991; **Acres** 300; **Type** Public; **Shoots** Field; **Birds** Quail, Pheasant, Chukar; **Dogs** Avail/HDW; **Packages** 1/2 Day, 1-4 guns O NAGA/See Pg. 107

O Brochure Available
O Entertain Clients
O Wide Variety of Hunts
O Overnight Accommodations
O Family Run Business
O Hard Flying Birds

J&P Hunting Lodge, Inc.
1105 Benton Corner Rd., Sudlersville, MD 21668
(410) 438-3832 John E. George, Jr. 9-4, T-Su
20 mi. W of Dover, DE
Est 1982; **Acres** 1,100; **Hunters/yr** 400; **Type** Public; **On Site** Clubhouse, Meals, Clays; **Shoots** Field, Tower, Blinds; **Birds** Dove, Quail, Pheasant, Chukar, Huns, Ducks, Geese; **Dogs** Avail/HDW; **Packages** 1/2 Day, 2-16 guns

Masons Branch Hunting Preserve
22 Mason Branch, Queen Anne, MD 21657
(410) 758-0162 Donald Lee Dean, Jr. After 6 pm
Est 1989; **Acres** 300; **Hunters/yr** 150; **Type** Public, Member/Avail; **On Site** Meals; **Shoots** Field, Blinds; **Birds** Dove, Quail, Pheasant, Chukar, Huns, Turkey, Ducks, Geese; **Dogs** Avail/HDW; **Packages** 1/2 Day, 1-10 guns

Native Shore Hunting Preserve
800 Grange Hall Rd., Centreville, MD 21617
(410) 758-2428 Keith R. Leaverton
Est 1981; **Acres** 1,500; **Type** Public; **Shoots** Field, Tower; **Birds** Quail, Pheasant, Chukar, Huns, Ducks; **Dogs** Avail/HDW; **Packages** 1/2 Day, up to 4 guns O NAGA/See Pg. 107

Pintail Point

511 Pintail Point Farm Lane, Queenstown, MD 21658
(410) 827-7029
from Eastern Shore, 20 mi. E of Bay Bridge
Est 1993; **Acres** 1,100; **Type** Public, Member/Avail,
Corp.; **On Site** Clubhouse, Lodging, Meals, Clays;
Shoots Field, Blinds, Boat; **Birds** Dove, Quail,
Pheasant, Chukar, Huns, Ducks; **Dogs** Avail/HDW;
Packages 1/2 Day, 1-16 guns   ○ NAGA/See Pg.107
○ Shooting Shop   ○ Rental Guns
○ Hunting & Fishing Licenses
○ Airport Pickup   ○ Sporting Clays/5-Stand
See Our Ad Pg. 345

Quaker Neck Gun Club, Inc.

PO Box 2600, Chestertown, MD 21620
(410) 778-6965 F. Tyler Johnson 8-4
3 mi. SE of Chestertown
Est 1981; **Acres** 3,500; **Type** Public, Member/Avail,
Corp.; **On Site** Clubhouse, Lodging, Clays; **Shoots**
Blinds, Boat; **Birds** Dove, Turkey, Ducks, Geese;
Dogs Avail/HDW; **Packages** 1 Day, 1-20 guns

Schrader's Hunting

900 Red Lion Branch Rd., Millington, MD 21651
(410) 778-1895 Ken, Owner/Operator
50 mi. E of Washington, DC
Est 1982; **Acres** 10,000; **Type** Public,
Member/Avail; **On Site** Clubhouse, Lodging, Meals;
Shoots Field, Blinds, Boat; **Birds** Dove, Quail,
Pheasant, Chukar, Huns, Ducks, Geese; **Dogs**
Avail/HDW; **Packages** 1/2 Day, 1-16 guns
○ NAGA/See Pg. 107
○ Hunting License
○ Deer Hunting
○ Train Bird Dogs
○ Brochure Available
○ Fishing

Sheaffer's Hunting Preserve

PO Box 28, Pioneer Point, Centreville, MD 21617
(410) 778-0185 John Whaley 7-10 pm
50 mi. E of Washington, DC
Est 1985; **Acres** 350; **Type** Public; **Shoots** Field,
Tower; **Birds** Quail, Pheasant, Chukar; **Dogs**
Avail/HDW; **Packages** 1/2 Day, up to 4 guns

Southern Maryland Gun Club

Southern Maryland Gun Club
PO Box 332, West River, MD 20778
(410) 823-4399 Kevin Colbeck
20 mi. S of Annapolis
Est 1993; **Acres** 1,400; **Type** Public, Corp.; **On
Site** Meals; **Shoots** Field; **Birds** Dove, Quail; **Dogs**
Avail/HDW; **Packages** 1/2 Day, 1-25 guns
The Southern Maryland Gun Club offers classic
wing shooting at its finest. Join us for a September
afternoon dove shoot over well-managed Sunflower fields or a timeless waterfowl hunt over
hand-carved and painted decoys on a crisp autumn
morning. The Southern Maryland Gun Club prides
itself on professional yet personal service to make
your outdoor experience truly memorable.

MASSACHUSETTS

Fullflight Game Farm & Preserve
4 Brattleboro Rd., Bernardston, MA 01337
(413) 648-9580 Edwin Gray
Type Public, Member/Avail; **Shoots** Field; **Birds**
Quail, Pheasant, Chukar, Huns ○ NAGA/See Pg. 107

Hedgerow Kennel & Hunt Club
Rt. 32, RFD2, Athol, MA 01331
(508) 249-7115 Patrick Perry
70 mi. W of Boston
Est 1986; **Acres** 108; **Hunters/yr** 300; **Type**
Public, Member/Avail, Corp.; **On Site** Clubhouse;
Shoots Field, Tower; **Birds** Quail, Pheasant, Chukar;
Dogs Avail/HDW; **Packages** 1/2 Day, 1-3 guns

Lissivigeen
Spooner Rd., Barre, MA 01005
(413) 477-8783 Kevin J. Coakley or (508) 355-0280
55 mi. W of Boston
Est 1988; **Acres** 240; **Hunters/yr** 250; **Type**
Public, Member/Avail, Corp.; **On Site** Clubhouse,
Meals, Clays; **Shoots** Field, Tower; **Birds** Quail,
Ruffed Grouse, Woodcock, Pheasant, Chukar, Ducks,
Geese; **Dogs** Avail/HDW; **Packages** 1/2 Day, 1-8
guns ○ NAGA/See Pg. 107

Royal Hunt Club, Inc.
Plain St., Middleboro, MA 02346
(508) 947-8141 Joseph L Di Santis/Joe
Turcotte/William Cunningham
1 hr. from Boston/Providence/Worcester
Est 1967; **Acres** 2,000; **Type** Member/Avail; **On
Site** Clubhouse, Lodging, Meals, Clays; **Shoots** Field,
Driven; **Birds** Quail, Pheasant, Chukar, Huns; **Dogs**
Avail/HDW; **Packages** 1 Day, 1-32 guns
o The Royal Hunt Club features many hundreds of
acres of land consisting of excellent wildlife habitat
and a warm and beautiful clubhouse.
o The club prides itself with our success of natural-like
pheasant and chukar partridge hunts.
o There is also vast acreage of low bush blueberry and
open hard woods that lend themselves to
memorable bobwhite quail hunts.
o This is a true sporting club with a keen eye toward
conservation and the principles of sound wildlife
management upheld.
o We have an international membership. Privacy and
confidentiality is in place at all times.
o If there is a heaven for sportsmen, it's here at this club.

MICHIGAN

Andy's Acres
Shooting Preserve
14902 A Dr. N., Marshall, MI 49068
(616) 781-8676 Jack H. Anderson 8am-10pm
80 mi. S of Lansing or 50 mi. N of Ft. Wayne, IN
Est 1977; **Acres** 118; **Type** Public, Member/Avail,
Corp.; **On Site** Clubhouse; **Shoots** Field; **Birds**
Quail, Pheasant, Chukar, Ducks, Geese; **Dogs**
Avail/HDW; **Packages** 1/2 Day, 1-8 guns
o Airport Pickup   o Loaner Guns
o Family Recreation o Quality Clubhouse
o Shooting Instruction o Family Run Business
o Train Bird Dogs

Big Creek Shooting Preserve
PO Box 369, 269 Zimowske Rd., Mio, MI 48647
(517) 826-3606 Steven A. Basl 8am-5pm
130 mi. NE of Grand Rapids
Est 1991; **Acres** 365; **Hunters/yr** 500; **Type**
Public, Member/Avail, Corp.; **On Site** Clubhouse,
Clays; **Shoots** Field, Tower, Blinds; **Birds** Ruffed
Grouse, Woodcock, Pheasant, Chukar, Turkey, Ducks,
Geese; **Dogs** Avail/HDW; **Packages** 1/2 Day, 1-32
guns o NAGA/See Pg. 107

Blendon Pines
8455 88th Ave., Zeeland, MI 49464
(616) 875-7000 Phil Van Til
20 mi. W of Grand Rapids
Est 1990; **Acres** 200; **Type** Public, Member/Avail;
On Site Clubhouse, Meals, Clays; **Shoots** Field;
Birds Pheasant, Chukar; **Dogs** Avail/HDW

Ciavola Ranch Shooting Preserve
77377 McKay, Romeo, MI 48065
(810) 752-2133 Howard Ciavola
Type Public; **On Site** Clubhouse; **Shoots** Field;
Birds Pheasant; **Dogs** HDW o NAGA/See Pg. 107

Country Glen Pheasants
12800 Pfaus, Manchester, MI 48158
(313) 428-9100 John Hochstetler
On Site Lodging; **Shoots** Field; **Birds** Quail,
Pheasant, Chukar o NAGA/See Pg. 107

Deer Creek Hunt Club
18000 Basswood Rd., Three Oaks, MI 49128
(616) 756-6600 George W. Daniels
from At IN/MI border with Lake Michigan
Est 1993; **Acres** 500; **Type** Member/Avail; **On
Site** Clubhouse, Meals, Clays; **Shoots** Field; **Birds**
Quail, Pheasant, Chukar, Huns; **Dogs** Avail/HDW;
Packages 1/2 Day o NAGA/See Pg. 107
o European Shoots
o Wild Waterfowl

Farmland Pheasant
Hunters, Inc.
7104 Gosline Rd., Brown City, MI 48416
(810) 346-3672 Preston H. Mann 7am-9pm
45 mi. NE of Flint
Est 1987; **Acres** 5,000; **Type** Member/Avail;
Shoots Field; **Birds** Quail, Woodcock, Pheasant,
Chukar; **Dogs** HDW; **Packages** 1 Day, 1-120 guns
o NAGA/See Pg. 107
o Wild Grouse

Fowler Farms Shooting Preserve
RR2, Box 298, S. Haven, MI 49090
(616) 637-4381 Carter Fowler
50 mi. SW of Grand Rapids
Est 1980; **Acres** 640; **Type** Public; **On Site**
Clubhouse, Lodging; **Shoots** Field; **Birds** Quail,
Pheasant, Geese; **Dogs** Avail/HDW; **Packages** 1/2
Day, 1-30 guns o NAGA/See Pg. 107

Grandview Shooting Preserve
3151 Kelso Rd., North Adams, MI 49262
(517) 287-4752 Tim Kelley Anytime
26 mi. S of Jackson
Est 1994; **Acres** 219; **Hunters/yr** 100; **Type**
Public; **On Site** Lodging, Clays; **Shoots** Field; **Birds**
Pheasant, Chukar; **Dogs** Avail/HDW; **Packages** 1/2
Day, 1-8 guns o NAGA/See Pg. 107

Hunter's Creek Club
675 Sutton Rd., Metamora, MI 48455
(810) 664-4307 Charlie Mann
30 mi. N of Detroit
Est 1957; **Acres** 860; **Type** Member/Avail, Corp.;
On Site Clubhouse, Meals, Clays; **Shoots** Field,
Driven; **Birds** Quail, Pheasant, Chukar, Huns, Ducks;
Dogs Avail/HDW; **Packages** 1/2 Day, 1-100 guns
○ NAGA/See Pg. 107
See Our Ad Across

Hunter's Ridge Hunt Club
3921 Barber, Oxford, MI 48371
(810) 628-4868 Dave Fischer 9-5, T-Su
25 mi. N of Detroit
Est 1981; **Acres** 650; **Hunters/yr** 5,000; **Type**
Member/Avail, Corp.; **On Site** Clubhouse, Lodging,
Meals, Clays; **Shoots** Field, Tower; **Birds** Pheasant,
Chukar, Huns; **Dogs** Avail/HDW; **Packages** 1/2
Day, 4-25 guns ○ NAGA/See Pg. 107

Hunters Quest Game Ranch
Box 158, Onondaga, MI 49264
(810) 254-4746 Ted Fitzgerald Anytime
20 mi. S of Lansing
Est 1990; **Acres** 315; **Type** Public; **On Site**
Clubhouse, Lodging, Meals; **Shoots** Field, Tower;
Birds Pheasant, Turkey; **Dogs** Avail/HDW;
Packages 1 Day, 4-16 guns

▼ ORVIS ENDORSED ▼
The Huntsman
Hunt Club Inc.
3166 Havens Rd., Dryden, MI 48428
(810) 796-3000 Craig Novotney
40 mi. N of Detroit
Est 1979; **Acres** 850; **Type** Member/Avail, Corp.;
On Site Clubhouse, Meals, Clays; **Shoots** Field, Tower,
Driven, Blinds; **Birds** Quail, Pheasant, Chukar, Ducks;
Dogs Avail/HDW; **Packages** 1/2 Day, 2-30 guns
See Our Ad Pg. 351

▲ ORVIS ENDORSED ▲

Lost Arrow Resort & Hunting Lodge
1749 Bomanville Rd., Gladwin, MI 48624
(517) 345-7774 Avery Sterling 9-5
45 mi. N of Saginaw
Est 1994; **Acres** 160; **Type** Public; **On Site**
Clubhouse, Lodging, Meals, Clays; **Shoots** Field,
Tower; **Birds** Pheasant, Chukar, Huns; **Dogs**
Avail/HDW; **Packages** 1/2 Day, 1-24 guns
○ NAGA/See Pg. 107

Lucky Feather Game Farm
2040 N. Pittsford Rd., Hillsdale, MI 49242
(517) 523-2050 Hal/Karen Bennett
80 mi. SW of Detroit
Est 1988; **Acres** 856; **Hunters/yr** 600; **Type**
Public, Member/Avail, Corp.; **On Site** Clubhouse,
Meals, Clays; **Shoots** Field, Blinds; **Birds** Quail,
Pheasant, Chukar, Huns, Ducks, Geese; **Dogs**
Avail/HDW; **Packages** 1/2 Day, 1-40 guns
○ NAGA/See Pg. 107
○ Hunting License
○ Airport Pickup
○ Bird Processing
○ Kennel Bird Dogs
○ Sporting Clays (50 & 100 target ranges)
Lucky Feather is a family-run business specializing
in flighty birds and fine dogwork in a wilderness
setting. In addition to upland bird hunting, we've
got 2 Sporting clay ranges, clubhouse and local ac-
commodations. Ask about our Family
Memberships. Call today!

M L Shooting Preserve
7169 W4 Rd., Mesick, MI 49668
(616) 269-3137 Mike Luther
Type Public, Member/Avail; **On Site** Clays; **Shoots**
Field; **Birds** Quail, Pheasant, Chukar
○ NAGA/See Pg. 107

Michigan Sportsmen's Hunt Club
4242 Oak Rd., Vassar, MI 48768
(517) 823-2157 Lawrence S. Joseph
40 mi. NE of Flint
Est 1969; **Acres** 600; **Type** Member/Avail, Corp.;
On Site Clubhouse, Meals, Clays; **Shoots** Field,
Tower; **Birds** Quail, Ruffed Grouse, Woodcock,
Pheasant, Chukar, Huns; **Dogs** Avail/HDW

Midland Michigan -Mel Su Jac
140 Camelot, Apt. I-11, Saginaw, MI 48603
(517) 793-0712 John W. Manning
30 mi. NW of Flint
Est 1967; **Acres** 275; **Hunters/yr** 40; **Type**
Public, Member/Avail; **Shoots** Field; **Birds** Ruffed
Grouse, Pheasant, Turkey; **Dogs** HDW; **Packages**
1/2 Day, 1-20 guns

Mitchell Farms Hunt Club
10542 McWain Rd., Grand Blanc, MI 48439
(810) 694-2281 Bill Teer 9-5
10 mi. S of Flint
Est 1985; **Acres** 500; **Type** Member/Avail, Corp.;
On Site Clubhouse; **Shoots** Field; **Birds** Pheasant,
Chukar; **Dogs** Avail/HDW ○ NAGA/See Pg. 107

Mitchell Hill Pheasant Hunting Preserve
Rt. 1, Box 130B, Ellsworth, MI 49729
(616) 588-6063 James Ruster After 5pm

World Class Dog Training, Shooting Instruction, Hunting and More at Michigan's Hunters Creek Club

Metamora, MI — If you've been running a bird hunting preserve for nearly 41 years ... and if, in the process, you've become one of the best known and most popular establishments in the state ... you must be doing something right! And doing it right they are at Hunters Creek Club in southeastern Michigan, about an hour's drive from Detroit.

Hunters Creek encompasses 1,000 acres of woods, meadows, and fields of sorghum, timothy and brome grass, and boasts an impressive array of attractions and activities designed to appeal to a broad segment of sportsmen. Bird hunters, clay shooters, fishermen, and even gourmets, express constant enthusiasm for Hunters Creek.

Founder Preston Mann and members of the Class of '98.

Founded by Preston Mann in 1958, when hunting preserves in the United States were few and far between, Hunters Creek is a private club that is renowned for its attention to member needs. Certain Club services, however, are available to non-members, notably dog training and professional shooting instruction.

Dogs to Savvy Hunting Companions

With on-site kennels that can accommodate 60 dogs, Hunters Creek's widely acclaimed dog-training program converts untutored animals into obedient—and savvy—hunting companions. Charlie Mann, club owner, puts retrievers through their paces, while club manager Dale Jarvis handles pointers. Hunters Creek also sells pedigreed pups, including Brittany Spaniels and Labs.

Shooting School...The More You Know

Headed by Sporting Clays All American Pat Lieske, the shooting school offers intensive individual instruction by appointment on all aspects of gun safety, shooting etiquette and proper technique. The school is open to all levels, beginner to advanced. Quarterly stock fitting seminars, monthly group and kids' shooting clinics are also part of the program.

"Hunting and clay shooting are like any other human activity," Charlie Mann says. "The more you know about something, the

better you'll become at it. And the better you become, the more you'll enjoy yourself."

To ensure that dog and hunter are never disappointed, the club, under the guidance of Charlie Mann—a former president of the North American Gamebird Association—stocks thousands upon thousands of gamebirds. Hunters Creek Club provides a cornucopia of benefits for its members. A spacious clubhouse, for example, includes private lockers so time-pressured business people can leave the office, drive to the site, and change quickly into field gear. And a Pro Shop is generously stocked with accessories and equipment.

Catering To Clay Shooters

Clay shooters are catered to at Hunters Creek, with trap and skeet fields and a sporting clays course that entice novices and challenge old-timers. "We're never entirely satisfied with the ranges," Charlie Mann says. "Like everything else at Hunters Creek, there's not a year goes by that we don't try to improve them."

Hunters Creek also satisfied the appetite. It is a favorite location for group picnics. And folks are more than willing to drive from the city to feast on home cooked pheasant, duck in orange sauce, pan fried trout or New York strip steak.

For more information on membership, dog training and shooting instruction at Hunters Creek, where "doing things right" is a way of life, write Charlie Mann at the club, **675 Sutton Road, Metamora, MI 48455, or phone (810) 664-4307.**

160 mi. N of Grand Rapids
Est 1988;   **Acres** 340;   **Hunters/yr** 200;   **Type** Public;
On Site Meals;   **Shoots** Field;   **Birds** Pheasant;   **Dogs**
Avail/HDW;   **Packages** 1/2 Day, 1-5 guns

Orchard Hill Sporting Clays Inc.
PO Box 463, Escanaba, MI 49829
(906) 466-2887 Mike Gierke
4 mi. S of Bark River
Est 1993;   **Type** Public;   **On Site** Clubhouse,
Lodging, Clays;   **Shoots** Field;   **Birds** Ruffed Grouse,
Woodcock, Pheasant, Turkey, Geese;   **Dogs** HDW

PGW Haymarsh Hunt Club
9215 Jefferson, Lakeview, MI 48850
(517) 352-6727 Bud Gummer 7:30am-9pm
50 mi. N of Grand Rapids
Est 1990;   **Acres** 640;   **Type** Public, Member/Avail,
Corp.;   **On Site** Clays;   **Shoots** Field;   **Birds** Quail,
Ruffed Grouse, Woodcock, Pheasant, Chukar, Huns;
Dogs Avail/HDW;   **Packages** 1/2 Day, 2-30 guns
○ NAGA/See Pg. 107

Paradise Shooting Preserve
1300 State St., Carsonville, MI 48419
(810) 622-9800 Don Mackley
80 mi. N of Detroit
Acres 180;   **Type** Public, Member/Avail, Corp.;   **On
Site** Clubhouse, Meals;   **Shoots** Field, Tower;   **Birds**
Quail, Pheasant, Chukar;   **Dogs** Avail/HDW
○ NAGA/See Pg. 107

Pine Hill Kennels & Sportsmen's Club
8347 10 Mile Rd. NE, Rockford, MI 49341
(616) 874-8459 Jim Rypkema
15 mi. NE of Grand Rapids
Est 1980;   **Acres** 190;   **Type** Public;   **On Site**
Clubhouse, Clays;   **Shoots** Field;   **Birds** Quail,
Pheasant, Chukar, Huns;   **Dogs** Avail/HDW;
Packages 1/2 Day, 1-5 guns

Pleasant Lake Farm
PO Box 465, Delton, MI 49046
(616) 623-5853 James Alden 5-11pm
20 mi. NE of Kalamazoo
Est 1988;   **Acres** 410;   **Type** Member/Avail;   **On
Site** Clubhouse, Lodging, Meals, Clays;   **Shoots** Field,
Blinds;   **Birds** Pheasant;   **Dogs** Avail/HDW;
Packages 1/2 Day, 1-32 guns
○ Airport Pickup
○ Bird Processing
○ Kennel Bird Dogs
○ Deer Hunting
○ Family Run Business

Republic Ridge Shooting Preserve
PO box 516, Ishpeming, MI 49849
(906) 376-2106 Brian Racine am or after dark
45 mi. SW of Marquette   **Acres** 130;   **Hunters/yr**
250;   **Type** Public, Member/Avail;   **On Site**
Clubhouse, Lodging, Meals;   **Shoots** Field, Blinds;
Birds Quail, Ruffed Grouse, Woodcock, Pheasant,
Chukar, Ducks, Geese;   **Dogs** Avail/HDW;   **Packages**
1/2 Day, 2-12 guns   ○ NAGA/See Pg. 107

Rolling Hills Shooting Preserve
17025 McKenzie St., Marcellus, MI 49067
(616) 646-9164 Curt Johnson Evenings
60 mi. SW of Grand Rapids
Est 1982;   **Acres** 275;   **Hunters/yr** 500;   **Type**
Public;   **On Site** Clubhouse, Clays;   **Shoots** Field;
Birds Quail, Pheasant, Chukar;   **Dogs** Avail/HDW;
Packages 1/2 Day, 1-15 guns   ○ NAGA/See Pg. 107

Rooster Ranch Hunt Club
7480 Germania, Ubly, MI 48475
(517) 658-2332 R. Kim Anthony Days
90 mi. N of Detroit
Est 1987;   **Acres** 600;   **Hunters/yr** 800;   **Type**
Public, Member/Avail, Corp.;   **On Site** Clubhouse,
Lodging, Meals;   **Shoots** Field;   **Birds** Quail,
Pheasant, Chukar;   **Dogs** Avail/HDW;   **Packages** 1/2
Day, 1-40 guns   ○ NAGA/See Pg. 107

Rustic Ridge Hunt Club, Inc.
1332 12th St., Martin, MI 49070
(800) 392-7721 Mike Shoup
On Site Clays;   **Shoots** Field;   **Birds** Quail, Pheasant,
Chukar, Huns   ○ NAGA/See Pg. 107

Smith Creek Hunt Club
8669 Lashbrook, Goodlles, MI 48027
(810) 325-1135 Joe Musu Anytime
40 mi. E of Detroit
Est 1985;   **Acres** 200;   **Type** Public, Member/Avail;
On Site Clubhouse, Meals, Clays;   **Shoots** Field,
Tower;   **Birds** Quail, Pheasant, Chukar, Ducks;   **Dogs**
Avail/HDW;   **Packages** 1/2 Day, 1-20 guns

Thundering Aspens
4421 N. 5 1/2 Rd., Mesick, MI 49668
(616) 885-2420 Greg Wright
110 mi. N of Grand Rapids
Est 1989;   **Acres** 400;   **Hunters/yr** 500;   **Type**
Public, Member/Avail, Corp.;   **On Site** Clays;   **Shoots**
Field;   **Birds** Quail, Ruffed Grouse, Woodcock,
Pheasant, Chukar, Huns, Turkey, Geese;   **Dogs**
Avail/HDW;   **Packages** 1/2 Day, 1-25 guns
○ NAGA/See Pg. 107

Michigan's Premiere Shooting Preserve
— 40 Miles North of Detroit —

Welcome to **The Huntsman Hunt Club**, where our philosophy is to rekindle the sporting traditions of the past. Located in rural Michigan about an hour north of Detroit, our formerly private preserve is now proud to welcome wingshooters from across the country.

At **The Huntsman** you'll take pleasure in the finest upland bird hunting available. Our professional guides with their superbly-trained dogs will point the Hungarian partridge or flush the ringneck from his cover in the sorghum thicket.

A day at **The Huntsman** begins with a home-cooked country breakfast and a classic morning hunt. Weather permitting, a first-rate lunch, served in the field, is followed by more hunting or a round of sporting clays on our world class course.

The evening will afford a savory full course gourmet dinner served at the main lodge. You may select a premium wine for our cellar to compliment your repast. A lovely country farmhouse will beckon you to its charming stone fireplace at the end of an exhilarating day.

Come rekindle the sporting traditions of the past at **The Huntsman**. Call or write today for complete details and reservations:

810-796-3000 • FAX 810-796-9205
3166 Havens Road • Dryden, MI 48428

Wycamp Lake Club

Shooting Preserve

Upland Bird & Waterfowl Hunting in Northern Michigan's Most Scenic Cover

ANNUAL DRIVEN PHEASANT

Each Fall, Driven Pheasant are offered in the finest European tradition. Huntsmen are placed in a line of blinds & move to a new peg for each drive. At the sound of a hunting horn, Pheasant are driven toward the blinds for challenging overhead shooting. Exciting pass shooting from side-to-side often occurs. Some birds fly as high as 50 yards. Shoots are based on 20 guns and include a luncheon. An afternoon walk-up hunt follows with guide and dog except during "The Shooting Party"* on Oct. 25th & 26th, which has 2 great drives each day & walk-up hunt on Oct. 27th for a grand total of 1,600 Pheasant released.

— Fall '96 Schedule —

Day & Date		Release	Cost *
Sat.,	Oct. 5th	300 pheasant	$295/gun
Sat.,	Oct. 12th	300 pheasant	$295/gun
Sat.,	Oct. 19th	300 pheasant	$295/gun
*Fri. a.m.	Oct. 25th	400 pheasant	$375/gun
*Fri. p.m.	Oct. 25th	400 pheasant	$375/gun
*Sat. a.m.	Oct. 26th	400 pheasant	$375/gun
*Sat. p.m.	Oct. 26th	400 pheasant	$375/gun
*Sun.	Oct. 27th	Walk-up Hunt	$125/gun
Sat.	Nov. 2nd	300 pheasant	$295/gun
Sat.,	Nov. 30th	300 pheasant	$295/gun
Sat.	Dec. 7th	300 pheasant	$295/gun
Thur.	Dec. 28th	300 pheasant	$295/gun
Fri.	Dec. 29th	400 pheasant	$375/gun
Sat.,	Dec. 30th	400 pheasant	$375/gun

* Shoot 4 "Shooting Party" Drives & Walk-Up, Spec. Rate

Also : Custom Drives and Field Hunts
Guided Grouse and Woodcock Hunts
Complete Sporting Clays Course

Call: Dirk Shorter, Wycamp Lake Club, Inc.

(616) 537-4830 or Office: 526-6651

c/o 5484 Pleasantview Rd., Harbor Springs, MI 49740

Trapper Jim's Hunt Club
4300 E. Sanilac Rd., Kingston, MI 48741
(517) 683-2620 Jim Pruett 8am-5pm
40 mi. NE of Flint
Est 1967; **Acres** 500; **Hunters/yr** 1,200; **Type** Member/Avail, Corp.; **On Site** Clubhouse, Meals, Clays; **Shoots** Field, Tower; **Birds** Quail, Pheasant, Chukar, Huns; **Dogs** Avail/HDW; **Packages** 1/2 Day, 1-80 guns

Wild Wings Game Farm
PO Box 1232, Gaylord, MI 49735
(616) 584-3350 James W. Avery 8am-5:30pm
160 mi. N of Lansing
Type Public; **On Site** Clays; **Shoots** Field; **Birds** Pheasant, Chukar, Huns; **Dogs** Avail/HDW
O NAGA/See Pg. 107

Willow Lake Sportsmen's Club
51704 U.S. 131, Three Rivers, MI 49093
(616) 279-7124 Woodrow R. Thompson
65 mi. S of Grand Rapids
Est 1976; **Acres** 250; **Hunters/yr** 1,000; **Type** Member/Avail, Corp.; **On Site** Clubhouse, Lodging, Meals, Clays; **Shoots** Field, Tower; **Birds** Quail, Pheasant, Chukar, Huns, Turkey; **Dogs** Avail/HDW; **Packages** 1/2 Day, 1-35 guns O NAGA/See Pg. 107

▼ ORVIS ENDORSED ▼

Woodmoor
26 Maxton Rd., Drummond Isl., MI 49726
(906) 493-1039 Steve Gilbert 9-5,M-F
40 mi. SE of Sault Ste. Marie
Est 1986; **Acres** 2,000; **Type** Public; **On Site** Clubhouse, Lodging, Meals, Clays; **Shoots** Field, Blinds, Boat; **Birds** Ruffed Grouse, Woodcock, Pheasant, Huns, Ducks, Geese; **Dogs** Avail/HDW
O NAGA/See Pg. 107
See Our Ad Across, Right

▲ ORVIS ENDORSED ▲

Wycamp Lake Club, Inc.
c/o 5484 Pleasantview Rd., Harbor Springs, MI 49740
(616) 526-6651 Dirk Shorter 8am-8pm
16 mi. SW of Macinaw City
Est 1983; **Type** Public, Member/Avail, Corp.; **On Site** Clubhouse, Lodging, Meals, Clays; **Shoots** Field, Driven, Blinds, Boat; **Birds** Quail, Ruffed Grouse, Woodcock, Pheasant, Chukar, Ducks, Geese; **Dogs** Avail/HDW; **Packages** 1/2 Day, 2-24 guns O NAGA/See Pg. 107
See Our Ad, Left

Orvis Endorsed Woodmoor:
The Challenge of Ruffed Grouse & Woodcock

Here's a recipe for sportsmen that never fails to please. Mix wingshooting, sporting clays, fishing, hiking, boating, horseback riding and a championship golf course. Add luxurious accommodations and gourmet dining. The result is Woodmoor on Drummond Island, a resort masterpiece in northern Michigan that more than satisfies the appetite for outdoor adventure.

Among the Elite

The Woodmoor experience—and no other term describes a visit as well—is unique.And the quality of its wingshooting program is such that the resort has been designated an Orvis endorsed wingshooting lodge.

Private cabins in a wooded setting.

Encompassing 2,000 acres, and situated on Drummond Island in the state's Upper Peninsula, Woodmoor is a sporting enthusiast's dream come true. Among its attractions are professionally guided hunts over well-trained pointers and retrievers. Fifty thousand nearby acres of state and federally-managed land offer the challenges of ruffed grouse, woodcock, ducks and geese.

Woodmoor also offers world-class sporting clays with targets released in a blur of angles and speeds from covers of every description and shooting instruction provided by Orvis-trained personnel.

Fishing Hemingway Admired

The salmon fishing at Woodmoor will test the mettle of the most avid sportsman. Established near the island's shores, these pugnacious beauties feed only on flies, and roam the waters at depths of ten feet or less. Additional thrills are available at the rapids at Sault Ste. Marie, where fly fishing reaches a zenith that Ernest Hemingway admired.

Is it golf you crave? Woodmoor brings you The Rock, named one of Michigan's top ten courses by *Michigan Golfer Magazine*. A visual treat, this championship-caliber course demands skill, patience and perseverance of duffer and pro alike.

Scenic Splendor

And, when you're not shooting, casting or golfing, you're sure to enjoy the scenic wonders of Woodmoor's many hiking trails, the invigorating pleasure of horseback riding, or the pure fun of boating on Lake Huron.

Not the least of Woodmoor's attractions, however, are those that invite relaxation. Supervised by General Manager Dan Serrine, Woodmoor includes a 40-room log lodge with conference facilities for ten to 150, and the Bayside dining room that overlooks nearby islands. Quiet times are also the promise of eight large private cabins in wooded settings, five of traditional log construction and three in the architectural style of Frank Lloyd Wright.

Woodmoor, on Drummond Island is accessible by car ferry or plane (a 4,000 foot runway, ADF/NDB rated, with hangar facilities, is available). Out of the way, to be sure. But the Woodmoor experience is one you'll never forget. And one, we are certain, that you'll want to repeat again and again!

For further information, or to make reservations, please contact **Dan Serrine, Director of Orvis Services, at (906) 493-1039 or Fax at (906) 493-5576; write: 26 Maxton Road, Drummond Island, MI 49726.**

MINNESOTA

American Heritage Hunting Club
Rt. 2, Box 131, Eagle Bend, MN 56446
(218) 738-5143 Don/Sue Ellwanger 8am-10pm

Bader's Pheasant Run
Box 270, Federal Dam, MN 56641
(218) 654-5097 Wade or Deb Huotari
110 mi. W of Duluth, WI **Type** Public; **On Site**
Clubhouse, Lodging, Meals; **Shoots** Field; **Birds**
Quail, Pheasant; **Dogs** Avail/HDW o NAGA

Bullseye Hunting Preserve & Game Farm
R2, Box 140A, Aitkin, MN 56431
(218) 678-2910 Dan Schmidt
100 mi. NW of Minneapolis
Est 1988; **Acres** 300; **Type** Public, Member/Avail,
Corp.; **On Site** Clubhouse, Clays; **Shoots** Field,
Blinds, Boat; **Birds** Pheasant, Chukar, Turkey, Ducks;
Dogs Avail/HDW; **Packages** 1/2 Day, 1-10 guns

Caribou Gun Club
Shooting Preserve
Rt. 1, Box 26, Le Sueur, MN 56058
(800) 672-3936 Randy Voss
60 mi. SW of Minneapolis-St. Paul
Est 1953; **Acres** 600; **Hunters/yr** 2,500; **Type**
Public, Member/Avail, Corp.; **On Site** Clubhouse,
Lodging, Meals, Clays; **Shoots** Field, Tower; **Birds**
Quail, Pheasant, Chukar; **Dogs** Avail/HDW;
Packages 1/2 Day, 1-50 guns o NAGA/See Pg. 107

Charlie's Hunting Club
RR1, Box 173, Danvers, MN 56231
(612) 567-2276 Jim Langan
115 mi. W of Minneapolis
Acres 2,000; **Type** Public; **On Site** Clubhouse,
Lodging, Meals, Clays; **Shoots** Field; **Birds**
Pheasant, Geese; **Dogs** Avail/HDW
o NAGA/See Pg. 107

Charlie's is committed to quality hunting. Two thousand acres of prime habitat supports a large native
pheasant population. Goose hunting is available at
near-by Lac Qui Parle goose refuge. Finish the day
at Charlie's. The farm, homesteaded in the early
1900s, has a renovated dairy barn that serves as
the clubhouse. Call today!

Clear Creek Outdoors
2550 Hwy. 23, Wrenshall, MN 55797
(218) 384-3670 Patrick LaBoone 8-8
6 mi. SW of Duluth
Est 1983; **Acres** 300; **Type** Member/Avail, Corp.;
On Site Clubhouse, Meals, Clays; **Shoots** Field,
Driven; **Birds** Quail, Ruffed Grouse, Woodcock,
Pheasant, Chukar, Huns, Turkey; **Dogs** Avail/HDW;
Packages 1/2 Day, up to 25 guns
o NAGA/See Pg. 107

Dead Horse Creek Shooting Preserve
RR 2, Box 103, Frazee, MN 56544
(218) 334-4868 Chris or Ben Wacker All Day
180 mi. NW of Minneapolis
Est 1993; **Acres** 1,000; **Type** Public, Member/Avail;
On Site Clubhouse, Lodging, Clays; **Shoots** Field;
Birds Pheasant, Chukar; **Dogs** Avail/HDW;
Packages 1/2 Day, 1-70 guns o NAGA/See Pg.107

Deer Ridge Hunting
5050 470th St., Harris, MN 55032
(612) 288-0020 Henry J. Gregoire, Jr.
Type Public, Member/Avail; **On Site** Clays; **Shoots**
Field; **Birds** Quail, Pheasant, Chukar, Ducks
o NAGA/See Pg. 107

Elk Lake Heritage Preserve
PO Box 422, Hoffman, MN 56339
(320) 986-2200 Ed Loeffler
On Site Lodging, Clays; **Shoots** Field; **Birds**
Pheasant, Chukar o NAGA/See Pg. 107

Elsing Prairies & Wildlife
107 Johnson Dr., Box 58, Rushmore, MN 56168
(507) 478-4482 Willie Elsing Evening
50 mi. E of Sioux Falls, SD
Est 1986; **Acres** 320; **Type** Public, Member/Avail,
Corp.; **On Site** Clubhouse, Lodging; **Shoots** Field,
Driven, Blinds; **Birds** Quail, Pheasant, Chukar, Huns,
Ducks, Geese; **Dogs** Avail/HDW; **Packages** 1/2
Day, 1-8 guns o NAGA/See Pg. 107

Fischer's Kennels & Hunt Club
29512 223rd Ave., Albany, MN 56307
(320) 597-2729 Pete Fischer
Acres 320; **Hunters/yr** 1,000; **Type**
Member/Avail, Corp.; **On Site** Clubhouse, Clays;
Shoots Field; **Birds** Pheasant; **Dogs** Avail/HDW;
Packages 1/2 Day, 1-40 guns o NAGA/See Pg. 107

Gold Meadows Hunting Preserve
18506 260th St., Richmond, MN 56368
(612) 597-2747 Joe Doubek
Est 1968; **Acres** 800; **Type** Public; **On Site**
Clubhouse; **Shoots** Field; **Birds** Quail, Pheasant,
Chukar, Turkey; **Dogs** Avail/HDW
o NAGA/See Pg. 107

Golden Valley Pheasant Run
HCR4, Box 116A, Roseau, MN 56751
(218) 425-7401 Rod Wulff/Steve Johnson 8am-10pm
120 mi. NE of Grand Forks, ND

Est 1988; **Acres** 550; **Hunters/yr** 200; **Type** Public; **On Site** Clubhouse, Lodging, Meals, Clays; **Shoots** Field; **Birds** Quail, Pheasant, Chukar, Turkey; **Dogs** Avail/HDW

H&R Shooting Preserve
34934 140th Ave., Avon, MN 56310
(612) 356-7427 David J. Raab
Hidden Valley Game Birds, Inc.
RR1, Box 323, Pine Island, MN 55963
(507) 356-8887 Butch Owens 8am-Sundown
55 mi. SE of Minneapolis
Est 1989; **Acres** 850; **Hunters/yr** 200; **Type** Public, Member/Avail, Corp.; **On Site** Clubhouse, Clays; **Shoots** Field, Driven; **Birds** Quail, Pheasant, Chukar, Huns; **Dogs** Avail/HDW; **Packages** 1/2 Day, up to 12 guns O NAGA/See Pg. 107

Horse Barn & Hunt Club
RR1, Box 103, Lakefield, MN 56150
(507) 662-5490 Brent or Lori Rossow Before 8am
20 mi. N of Iowa Great Lakes **Est** 1994; **Acres** 390; **Type** Public, Member/Avail; **On Site** Clubhouse, Lodging, Meals, Clays; **Shoots** Field; **Birds** Pheasant; **Dogs** Avail/HDW; **Packages** 1/2 Day

Lac Qui Parle Hunting Camp
RR5, Box 67A, Montevideo, MN 56265
(612) 269-9769 Steve or Stan Baldwin 8am-10pm

Langhei Hills
Rt. 1, Box 29, Hancock, MN 56244
(612) 392-5808 Ken Reese
Acres 1,000; **Type** Public, Member/Avail, Corp.; **On Site** Clubhouse, Lodging, Meals, Clays; **Shoots** Field; **Birds** Pheasant; **Dogs** Avail/HDW
O NAGA/See Pg. 107

Don Le Blanc Hunting Preserve
Rt. 5, Box 228, Little Falls, MN 56345
(612) 745-2522 Don or Marge Le Blanc

LeBlanc Rice Creek Hunting
Rt. 5, Box 213, Little Falls, MN 56345
(612) 745-2451 Gregg LeBlanc 8am-12 Noon
85 mi. N of Minneapolis
Est 1982; **Acres** 1,500; **Type** Public, Member/Avail, Corp.; **On Site** Clubhouse, Lodging, Meals, Clays; **Shoots** Field, Blinds; **Birds** Quail, Pheasant, Chukar, Turkey, Ducks; **Dogs** Avail/HDW; **Packages** 1/2 Day, 1-50 guns O NAGA/See Pg. 107

Leech Lake Hunting Area
Box 310, Federal Dam, MN 56641
(218) 654-3998 Robert A. Wake Anytime
110 mi. W of Duluth
Est 1962; **Acres** 1,000; **Type** Public; **Shoots** Field; **Birds** Pheasant; **Dogs** Avail/HDW

Little Moran Hunting Club
Rt. 1, Pheasant Valley Rd., Staples, MN 56479
(218) 894-3852 Steve & Gayle Grossman
130 mi. NW of Minneapolis

Est 1984; **Acres** 320; **Type** Public, Member/Avail, Corp.; **On Site** Clubhouse, Lodging, Meals, Clays; **Shoots** Field; **Birds** Ruffed Grouse, Woodcock, Pheasant, Chukar, Turkey, Ducks, Geese; **Dogs** Avail/HDW O NAGA/See Pg. 107

Major Ave. Hunt Club
11721 Major Ave., Glencoe, MN 55336
(320) 864-6025 Gerald G. Martin Daylight Hours
45 mi. W of Minneapolis
Est 1988; **Acres** 360; **Type** Public, Member/Avail, Corp.; **On Site** Clubhouse, Lodging, Meals, Clays; **Shoots** Field, Tower; **Birds** Quail, Pheasant, Chukar; **Dogs** Avail/HDW; **Packages** 1/2 Day, 2-50 guns O NAGA/See Pg. 107

Maple Landing Preserve
RR3, Box 113, Erksine, MN 56535
(218) 687-2175 Mike Kolden
110 mi. NE of Fargo, ND
Acres 340; **Type** Public; **On Site** Clubhouse, Meals; **Shoots** Field; **Birds** Pheasant, Chukar, Turkey; **Dogs** Avail/HDW

McCollum's Hunting Preserve
Rt. 1, Box 9, Bejou, MN 56516
(218) 935-2468 Terry/Theresa McCollum 7am-10pm
75 mi. NE of Fargo, ND
Est 1989; **Acres** 520; **Type** Public; **On Site** Clubhouse, Lodging, Meals, Clays; **Shoots** Field, Driven; **Birds** Quail, Pheasant, Chukar; **Dogs** Avail/HDW; **Packages** 1/2 Day, 1-30 guns

Mille Lacs Hunting Lodge
8673 340 St., Onamia, MN 56359
(800) 743-2768 John or Dave Barsody
90 mi. N of Minneapolis
Est 1993; **Acres** 2,500; **Type** Public, Member/Avail; **On Site** Clubhouse, Lodging, Meals, Clays; **Shoots** Field, Blinds; **Birds** Pheasant, Chukar, Huns; **Dogs** Avail/HDW; **Packages** 1/2 Day, 2-25 guns O NAGA/See Pg. 107
The Mille Lacs Hunting Lodge is Minnesota's only Orvis Endorsed Wingshooting Lodge. Located on an early 1900's farmstead in beautiful central Minnesota, the area is known for an abundance of Ruffed Grouse, Woodcock, Pheasant, and Duck. Located 2 hours north of the Minneapolis/St. Paul Airport. Single and multiple day packages with meals.

Minnesota Horse & Hunt Club
2920 220th St., Prior Lake, MN 55372
(612) 447-2272 Terry Correll 8am-5pm, M-Su

Mission Creek Hunting Preserve
Rt. 2, Box 119A, Hinckley, MN 55037
(612) 450-1036 George Markgraf
70 mi. N of Minneapolis
Acres 300; **Type** Public, Member/Avail, Corp.;
On Site Clubhouse, Meals; **Shoots** Field; **Birds**
Pheasant, Chukar, Turkey; **Dogs** Avail/HDW

Misty Meadows Shooting Preserve
HC9, Box 439, Detroit Lakes, MN 56501
(218) 847-4680 Steve Laine After 6pm
16 mi. E of Detroit Lakes
Est 1988; **Acres** 300; **Hunters/yr** 500; **Type**
Public, Member/Avail, Corp.; **On Site** Clubhouse,
Meals, Clays; **Shoots** Field, Tower, Driven; **Birds**
Quail, Pheasant, Chukar, Turkey, Ducks; **Dogs**
Avail/HDW; **Packages** 1/2 Day ○ NAGA/See Pg. 107

North Star Hunting Preserve
Rt. 1, Box 190, Ft. Ripley, MN 56449
(218) 829-1042 Randy Tomberlin Evenings
125 mi. N of Minneapolis-St. Paul
Est 1985; **Acres** 520; **Hunters/yr** 200; **Type**
Public; **On Site** Clubhouse; **Shoots** Field; **Birds**
Pheasant, Chukar, Turkey; **Dogs** Avail/HDW;
Packages 1/2 Day, 1-6 guns

Oak Point Shooting Preserve
RR3, Box 44-A, Wadena, MN 56482
(218) 631-4467 Don Dykhoff
Type Public; **On Site** Lodging, Clays; **Shoots** Field;
Birds Quail, Pheasant, Chukar ○ NAGA/See Pg. 107

Oakdale Ridge Hunting Preserve
8900 Union Hill Blvd., Belle Plaine, MN 56011
(612) 873-6423 Dale Stender

Pheasant Dreams
15033 70th St., Elk River, MN 55330
(612) 441-7204 Greg Lefebvre 9-10am, After 7pm

Pheasants Plus, Inc.
HCR01, Box 16, Warba, MN 55793
(218) 492-4450 Keith Austin Anytime
16 mi. SE of Grand Rapids
Est 1993; **Acres** 805; **Hunters/yr** 700; **Type**
Public; **On Site** Clubhouse, Meals, Clays; **Shoots**
Field; **Birds** Pheasant, Chukar, Turkey; **Dogs**
Avail/HDW; **Packages** 1 Day, 1-20 guns

Pleasant Acres
RR 1, Box 129, Courtland, MN 56021
(507) 359-5770 Lester Zwach 8-5

Need another copy of Black's Wing & Clay?
To order, call 800-224-9464, 9am -5pm

Ringneck Ranch
RR1, Box 8C, Wheaton, MN 56296
(320) 563-4705 Peter & Miki Bertram
55 mi. W of Alexandria
Est 1985; **Acres** 850; **Type** Public, Member/Avail;
On Site Clubhouse, Lodging, Meals; **Shoots** Field;
Birds Quail, Pheasant, Chukar; **Dogs** Avail/HDW;
Packages 1/2 Day, 1-30 guns

Ringneck Ranch Hunting Preserve
Rt. 2, Box 373, Aitkin, MN 56431
(218) 678-2169 Clark Holcomb 6-8am

Ringneck Ridge Shooting Preserve
Rt. 1, Box 319, Motley, MN 56466
(218) 575-2913 John & Carol Jacklitch Anytime

Rooster Ridge Hunting Club
PO Box 7, Browerville, MN 56438
(612) 594-6031 Russ Noland/Ev Sykora
120 mi. NW of Minneapolis
Est 1989; **Acres** 465; **Hunters/yr** 480; **Type**
Member/Avail, Corp.; **On Site** Clubhouse, Meals;
Shoots Field, Tower; **Birds** Pheasant, Chukar, Turkey;
Dogs Avail/HDW; **Packages** 1/2 Day, 1-30 guns

Rudquist's Shooting Preserve
HC76, Box 105, Backus, MN 56435
(218) 947-3044 George Rudquist
150 mi. N of Minneapolis
Est 1991; **Acres** 900; **Hunters/yr** 400; **Type**
Public; **Shoots** Field; **Birds** Quail, Pheasant, Chukar;
Dogs Avail/HDW; **Packages** 1/2 Day, 1-36 guns

Rum River Pheasant Club
30925 CR 5 NW, Princeton, MN 55371
(612) 389-2316 Rick Johnson

Shamrock Shooting Preserve
59563 300th St., RR3, Litchfield, MN 55355
(612) 693-8725 Mark/Jon/Pat Finnegan 7am-10pm

Spunk River Hunting Club
15718 390th St., Avon, MN 56310
(320) 746-2442 Tom Dickhausen
75 mi. NW of Minneapolis
Acres 500; **Type** Public; **On Site** Clubhouse,
Lodging, Meals, Clays; **Shoots** Field, Blinds; **Birds**
Quail, Pheasant, Chukar, Ducks; **Dogs** Avail/HDW
○ NAGA/See Pg. 107

Stoney Flats Hunting Preserve
Rt. 3, Box 102A, Milaca, MN 56353
(612) 753-1057 Jack Wenz

Ten Mile Creek Hunting Preserve
Rt. 1, Box 85, Dunnell, MN 56127
(507) 695-2544 Michael Honnette Evenings
140 mi. SW of Minneapolis
Acres 200; **Type** Public; **On Site** Meals; **Shoots**
Field; **Birds** Pheasant; **Dogs** Avail/HDW

Thompson Hunting Preserve
PO Box 613, Barnesville, MN 56514

(218) 493-4222 Eldon Thompson 7am-10pm
30 mi. SE of Fargo, ND
Est 1987; **Acres** 240; **Hunters/yr** 400; **Type**
Public; **On Site** Clubhouse, Lodging, Meals, Clays;
Shoots Field; **Birds** Pheasant, Chukar; **Dogs**
Avail/HDW; **Packages** 1/2 Day, 1-30 guns

Traxler's Hunting Preserve
R2, LeCenter, MN 56057
(612) 357-6940 Jeff Traxler 7am-6pm

Valhalla Hunt Club
RR1, Albert Lea, MN 56007
(507) 377-7225 Gary Pestorious

Viking Valley Hunt Club
Rt. 1, Box 198, Ashby, MN 56309
(218) 747-2121 Les Bensch 8-6

Voyager Sportsmans Paradise
PO Box 1236, International Falls, MN 55649
(800) 814-4868 Kenneth & Brian Bahr
Type Public; **On Site** Clubhouse, Clays; **Shoots**
Field; **Birds** Quail, Pheasant, Turkey; **Dogs**
Avail/HDW ○ NAGA/See Pg. 107

Western Wild Wings
13766 55th St., NW, Annandale, MN 55302
(612) 274-3513 Doug Streu
Type Public, Member/Avail; **Shoots** Field; **Birds**
Pheasant ○ NAGA/See Pg. 107

Wild Acres Hunting Club
HC83, Box 108, Pequot Lakes, MN 56472
(218) 568-5024 Mary Ebnet 7am-7pm
150 mi. N of Minneapolis
Est 1970; **Acres** 400; **Hunters/yr** 600; **Type**
Public, Member/Avail, Corp.; **On Site** Clubhouse,
Lodging, Meals, Clays; **Shoots** Field, Tower, Blinds;
Birds Quail, Pheasant, Chukar, Turkey, Ducks; **Dogs**
Avail/HDW; **Packages** 1/2 Day, 2-20 guns
○ NAGA/See Pg. 107

Wild Wings of Oneka
9491 152nd St., N., Hugo, MN 55038
(612) 439-4287 Jeff Hughes/Gary Schulte Anytime
15 mi. NE of Minneapolis
Est 1956; **Acres** 500; **Hunters/yr** 9,000; **Type**
Member/Avail; **On Site** Clubhouse, Meals, Clays;
Shoots Field, Driven, Blinds; **Birds** Quail, Pheasant,
Chukar, Huns, Turkey, Ducks; **Dogs** Avail/HDW;
Packages 1/2 Day, 4-50 guns ○ NAGA/See Pg. 107

MISSISSIPPI

Clear Creek Quail Farm
& Shooting Preserve
156 Oilfield Rd., Lumberton, MS 39455
(601) 796-5063 Herman B. Morgan
90 mi. N of New Orleans & 70 mi. N of Gulf Coast
Est 1991; **Acres** 200; **Hunters/yr** 45; **Type**
Public; **On Site** Lodging, Meals; **Shoots** Field;
Birds Quail; **Dogs** Avail/HDW; **Packages** 1/2 Day,
1-9 guns ○ NAGA/See Pg. 107
○ Bird Processing
○ Kennel Bird Dogs
○ Hunting Jeeps
○ Family Run Business
○ RV Parking Available

Dunn's Shooting Grounds
Rt. 3, Box 39D4, Holly Springs, MS 38635
(601) 564-1111 Jim Cassidy 8-5, M-S
35 mi. SE of Memphis
Est 1993; **Acres** 1,000; **Hunters/yr** 100; **Type**
Public; **On Site** Clubhouse, Lodging, Meals, Clays;
Shoots Field; **Birds** Quail, Pheasant, Chukar; **Dogs**
Avail/HDW; **Packages** 1/2 Day, 1-16 guns
○ NAGA/See Pg. 107
○ Airport Pickup   ○ Hunting Jeeps
○ Bird Processing   ○ Brochure Available
○ Kennel Bird Dogs   ○ On-Site Pro Shop
○ Sporting Clays   ○ Factory Ammunition
○ Quality Clubhouse   ○ Private Bedrooms
○ Mule Drawn Hunting Carriage

Get Away Place
PO Box 472, Waynesboro, MS 39367
(601) 735-5764 Dan Young
125 mi. SE of Jackson
Acres 900; **Type** Public, Member/Avail; **On Site**
Clubhouse, Lodging, Meals, Clays; **Shoots** Field;
Birds Quail, Pheasant, Turkey; **Dogs** Avail/HDW;
Packages 1/2 Day, 2-4 guns

Kearney Park Shooting Preserve
151 Ergon Rd., Flora, MS 39071
(601) 879-3249 Chuck Boyer/T.W. Tolleson
10 mi. N of Jackson
Est 1980; **Acres** 600; **Hunters/yr** 342; **Type**
Public; **On Site** Clubhouse, Lodging, Meals, Clays;
Shoots Field; **Birds** Quail; **Dogs** Avail/HDW;
Packages 1/2 Day, 1-16 guns

Levee Break Outfitters

253 Avondale Rd., Greenville, MS 38703
(601) 335-8489 Tom Eubank
7 mi. N of Greenville
Est 1992; **Acres** 800; **Type** Public, Corp.; **On Site**
Meals, Clays; **Shoots** Field; **Birds** Quail, Pheasant,
Chukar; **Dogs** Avail/HDW; **Packages** 1/2 Day, 2-8 guns

Longleaf Plantation

PO Box 511, Lumberton, MS 39455
(601) 794-6001 George Alexander M-F, 8 to 4:30
90 mi. N of New Orleans **Est** 1970; **Acres** 3,200;
Type Public; **On Site** Clubhouse, Lodging, Meals,
Clays; **Shoots** Field; **Birds** Quail; **Dogs** Avail/HDW;
Packages 1/2 Day, 6-24 guns

Prairie Shooting Preserve

20645 Old Magnolia Hwy., Prairie, MS 39756
(601) 369-9291 Harold Loftin 5:30 to 7:30 pm
35 mi. S of Tupelo
Est 1987; **Acres** 1,200; **Hunters/yr** 45; **Type**
Public; **On Site** Clubhouse, Lodging, Meals; **Shoots**
Field; **Birds** Quail; **Dogs** Avail/HDW; **Packages**
1/2 Day, 2-12 guns

Prospect Farms Shooting Preserve

30353 Hwy. 41, Nettleton, MS 38858
(601) 256-8227 Bud & Patsy Stevens
20 mi. S of Tupelo
Est 1987; **Acres** 800; **Type** Public, Member/Avail;
On Site Clubhouse, Lodging, Meals, Clays; **Shoots**
Field; **Birds** Quail, Pheasant; **Dogs** Avail/HDW;
Packages 1/2 Day, 2-20 guns O NAGA/See Pg. 107

Savage Quail Hunting Preserve

Rt. 1, Box 840, Coldwater, MS 38618
(601) 562-4083 Bobby or Eddie Savage
43 mi. S of Memphis, TN   **Acres** 400; **Hunters/yr**
100; **Type** Public; **Shoots** Field; **Birds** Quail;
Dogs Avail

Tara Wildlife Management

6791 Eagle Lake Shore Rd., Vicksburg, MS 39180
(601) 279-4261 Sidney Montgomery 7:30am-6pm (cst)
25 mi. NW of Vicksburg
Est 1806; **Acres** 20,000; **Hunters/yr** 800; **Type**
Public, Member/Avail; **On Site** Clubhouse, Lodging,
Meals, Clays; **Shoots** Field, Blinds; **Birds** Dove,
Quail, Turkey, Ducks, Geese; **Dogs** Avail/HDW;
Packages 1/2 Day, 1-35 guns

Wildwood Hunt Club

Box 7, Wildwood Rd., Benton, MS 39039
(601) 673-9717 Thomas E. Johnson Anytime
45 mi. N of Jackson
Est 1989; **Acres** 2,500; **Hunters/yr** 500; **Type**
Public, Member/Avail, Corp.; **On Site** Clubhouse,
Lodging, Meals, Clays; **Shoots** Field; **Birds** Quail,
Ducks; **Dogs** Avail/HDW; **Packages** 1/2 Day, 2-10
guns O NAGA/See Pg. 107

MISSOURI

Ace Fence

9816 E. 41st St., Kansas City, MO 64133
(816) 353-3445 Ed Davis
Acres 617; **Type** Public; **On Site** Clubhouse;
Shoots Field; **Birds** Quail, Pheasant
O NAGA/See Pg. 107

B&C Game Farm

RFD1, St. Catherine, MO 64677
(816) 258-2973 Jeff Sayre
Type Public, Member/Avail, Corp.; **On Site**
Clubhouse, Clays; **Shoots** Field, Tower; **Birds** Dove,
Quail, Pheasant, Chukar, Turkey; **Dogs** Avail/HDW

B&L Hunting

RR1, Box 28, Monticello, MO 63457
(314) 767-5367 Bruce Hinton Evenings
125 mi. NW of St. Louis
Acres 500; **Type** Public; **On Site** Lodging, Meals;
Shoots Field; **Birds** Quail, Pheasant, Turkey; **Dogs**
HDW

Baier Den Kennels
& Hunting Preserve

Peculiar, MO 64078
(816) 758-5234 Bud Baier 9-6
25 mi. S of Kansas City
Est 1951; **Acres** 4,000; **Type** Public, Member/Avail;
On Site Clubhouse, Lodging, Meals; **Shoots** Field;
Birds Quail, Pheasant, Chukar, Turkey; **Dogs**
Avail/HDW; **Packages** 1/2 Day, 2-4 guns
O NAGA/See Pg. 107

O Hunting License   O Shooting Instruction
O Bird Processing   O Brochure Available
O Kennel Bird Dogs   O On-Site Pro Shop
O Deer Hunting   O Factory Ammunition
O Quality Clubhouse   O Family Run Business
O Train Bird Dogs-No Electric Collars

Bird Dogs & Retrievers Trained The Old Fashioned
Proven Way. Patience and hard work on quail, partridge or pheasants (ducks for retrievers) with
plenty of birds...actual field conditions. Special attention paid to developing staunchness on point,
retrieving and hunting dead. All dogs broke to whistle. Monthly report with pictures on dog's
progress. Clean, modern cement kennels in the
heart of Missouri quail country. Write or phone for
free folder. Come visit our kennels and hunt our
preserve!

Rich Baumgartner

610 Camborne, St. Louis, MO 63125
(314) 892-7967
33 mi. SW of St. Louis

Big River Hunting Club & Kennels
PO Box 30, Fletcher, MO 63030
(314) 452-3511 Evenings
33 mi. SW of St. Louis
Est 1993; **Acres** 300; **Type** Member/Avail, Corp.;
On Site Clubhouse, Lodging, Meals, Clays; **Shoots**
Field; **Birds** Dove, Quail, Pheasant, Chukar, Huns;
Dogs Avail/HDW; **Packages** 1/2 Day, 1-12 guns

Blackhawk Valley
Hunting Preserve
Rt. 1, Box 118, Old Monroe, MO 63369
(314) 665-5459 Mickey Palmer After 6pm
40 mi. NW of St. Louis
Est 1968; **Acres** 600; **Hunters/yr** 75; **Type**
Member/Avail, Corp.; **On Site** Clubhouse, Meals,
Clays; **Shoots** Field; **Birds** Dove, Quail, Pheasant,
Chukar; **Dogs** Avail/HDW; **Packages** 1/2 Day, 1-16
guns ○ NAGA/See Pg. 107

Brush Creek
RR#1, Box 41, Mayview, MO 64071
(816) 237-4212 Todd Hulver
40 mi. E of Kansas City
Acres 240; **Type** Member/Avail; **On Site**
Clubhouse, Meals; **Shoots** Field; **Birds** Quail,
Pheasant, Chukar; **Dogs** Avail

Clear Fork Hunting Preserve
321 SE 671, Warrensburg, MO 64093
(816) 747-2588 Ruth or Ron Dillingham
50 mi. SE of Kansas City
Est 1993; **Acres** 600; **Type** Public; **On Site**
Clubhouse, Clays; **Shoots** Field; **Birds** Quail,
Pheasant, Chukar; **Dogs** Avail/HDW; **Packages** 1/2
Day, 1-20 guns ○ NAGA/See Pg. 107

Double Tree Farms
Rt. 1, Box 467, Licking, MO 65542
(573) 674-4142 Jim Ludan

The Fraley Ranch
16300 County Road 7250, Newburg, MO 65550
(573) 364-3017 Tom or Barb Fraley Anytime
110 mi. SW of St. Louis
Est 1986; **Acres** 1,000; **Type** Public; **On Site**
Clubhouse, Lodging, Meals; **Shoots** Field; **Birds**
Turkey; **Packages** 3 Days

Hi Point Hunting Club
R1, Box 28, Breckenridge, MO 64625
(816) 644-5708 Brian Guffey
65 mi. NE of Kansas City
Est 1968; **Acres** 1,200; **Hunters/yr** 900; **Type**
Public, Member/Avail, Corp.; **On Site** Clubhouse,
Meals, Clays; **Shoots** Field; **Birds** Quail, Pheasant,
Chukar, Huns, Turkey; **Dogs** Avail/HDW; **Packages**
1/2 Day, 2-30 guns ○ NAGA/See Pg. 107
"Not a country club, just a club in the country."
That's Hi Point, located in beautiful Northwest Missouri with good motels & restaurants nearby. Our
business is built by return customers. We can handle any type of hunting, from one man working a
young dog to a corporate outing. Visit us for a challenging and sporty hunt you'll long remember. Call
today!

High Adventure Ranch
20 Worthington Access Dr., Maryland Hts., MO 63043
(314) 434-0506 Charles J. Puff 12-5pm

High Meadow Hunt Club
828 Wild Horse Valley, Chesterfield, MO 63005
(314) 458-3550 John O'Shaugnessy
10 mi. NW of Chesterfield
Acres 256; **Type** Member/Avail; **On Site** Clays;
Shoots Field; **Birds** Quail, Pheasant, Turkey; **Dogs** Avail

Hopewell Views Hunting Club
Rt. 2, Box 232, Rockport, IL 62370
(217) 734-9234 Rick Wombles
85 mi. NE of St. Louis, MO
Acres 1,900; **Type** Public, Member/Avail, Corp.;
On Site Clubhouse, Lodging, Meals, Clays; **Shoots**
Field; **Birds** Dove, Quail, Pheasant, Chukar, Turkey,
Ducks, Geese; **Dogs** Avail/HDW; **Packages** 1/2 Day

Hunting Farms

Management
RR1, Box 244, Browning, MO 69630
(816) 946-4153 Beth & Jim Dwiggins 8-9pm
100 mi. NE of Kansas City
Est 1990; **Acres** 360; **Type** Public; **On Site**
Clubhouse, Lodging, Meals; **Shoots** Field; **Birds**
Dove, Quail, Pheasant, Turkey, Ducks, Geese; **Dogs**
Avail/HDW; **Packages** 2 Days, 3-9 guns

Hunting Sports Plus

710 Main St., Suite E, Blue Springs, MO 64015
(800) 729-1924 Dan Gasser
from Locations in 5 Midwest States
Est 1989; **Acres** 200,000; **Type** Public,
Member/Avail; **On Site** Clubhouse, Lodging, Meals,
Clays; **Shoots** Field, Blinds, Boat; **Birds** Quail,
Pheasant, Turkey, Prairie Chicken, Ducks, Geese;
Dogs Avail/HDW; **Packages** 1 Day, 1-24 guns

Quality hunting on over 200,000 acres of private
farm land in 7 Midwest States–AR, IA, IL, KS, MO,
NE, OK. Hunt quail, pheasant, turkey, deer, prairie
chicken, ducks and geese. Affordable Midwestern
hospitality. Large seclection of low cost memberships, daily plans or hunting vacation package
hunts. Call today for more information.
See Our Ad Pg. 359 or 361

Kena Shooting Preserve
RR1, Emden, MO 63439
(314) 439-5075 Ken Rowden
110 mi. NW of St. Louis **Est** 1990; **Acres** 480;
Type Public; **Shoots** Field; **Birds** Quail, Pheasant,
Chukar; **Dogs** Avail; **Packages** 1/2 Day

Lake of the Ozarks

Hunting Preserve
Rt. 70, Box 964, Camdenton, MO 65020
(314) 873-3566 Gloria Beattie 9-5, Th-Su
9 mi. N of Camdenton
Est 1994; **Acres** 480; **Type** Public, Member/Avail,
Corp.; **On Site** Clubhouse, Clays; **Shoots** Field;
Birds Quail, Pheasant, Chukar; **Dogs** Avail/HDW;
Packages 1/2 Day, up to 3 guns

O Hunting License
O Airport Pickup   O Loaner Guns
O Kennel Bird Dogs   O Brochure Available
O Sporting Clays   O Factory Ammunition
O Train Bird Dogs   O Family Run Business
O 3-Day Permits Only

Malinmor Hunt Club
RR4, Box 108, Eolia, MO 63344
(573) 324-3366 Rick Merritt 8-4
65 mi. NW of St. Louis
Est 1987; **Acres** 2,100; **Type** Member/Avail; **On
Site** Clubhouse, Lodging, Meals, Clays; **Shoots** Field;
Birds Dove, Quail, Woodcock, Pheasant, Chukar,
Huns, Turkey; **Dogs** Avail/HDW; **Packages** 1/2 Day,
2-12 guns O NAGA/See Pg. 107

McCutchan Ent. Inc. Shooting Division
R2, Box 35, Monticello, MO 63457
(573) 767-5359 Dennis McCutchan
35 mi. from Quincy, IL
Acres 311; **Type** Public; **On Site** Clays; **Shoots**
Field; **Birds** Quail, Pheasant, Turkey; **Dogs** Avail

Midway Farms, Inc.
700 County Rd. 404, Fayette, MO 65248
(816) 248-3838 Lee Myers 8-5:30
125 mi. E of Kansas City
Est 1991; **Acres** 1,250; **Hunters/yr** 500; **Type**
Public, Member/Avail; **On Site** Clubhouse, Meals,
Clays; **Shoots** Field; **Birds** Quail, Pheasant, Chukar;
Dogs Avail/HDW; **Packages** 1/2 Day, 4-24 guns
O NAGA/See Pg. 107

Moser's Pheasant Creek
502 County Rd. 327, Franklin, MO 65250
(816) 848-2621 Bonnie & Mike Moser
100 mi. E of Kansas City
Est 1985; **Acres** 480; **Type** Public; **On Site** Meals;
Shoots Field; **Birds** Pheasant; **Dogs** Avail/HDW
O NAGA/See Pg. 107

New London Hunting Club
Rt. 1, Box 269a, New London, MO 63459
(314) 985-7477 Steve & Pam Swon anytime
88 mi. N of St. Louis
Est 1988; **Acres** 1,500; **Hunters/yr** 1,200; **Type**
Public, Member/Avail, Corp.; **On Site** Clubhouse,
Lodging, Meals, Clays; **Shoots** Field; **Birds** Dove,
Quail, Woodcock, Pheasant, Chukar, Turkey; **Dogs**
Avail/HDW; **Packages** 1/2 Day, 1-40 guns

Newcastle Hunt Club
3100 Broadway, #711, Kansas City, MO 64111
(816) 931-9551 Larry Carter 8-6
75 mi. NE of Kansas City
Est 1989; **Acres** 582; **Type** Public, Member/Avail,
Corp.; **On Site** Meals, Clays; **Shoots** Field; **Birds**
Quail, Pheasant, Chukar; **Dogs** Avail/HDW;
Packages 1/2 Day, 4-20 guns

Pond Fort Hunt Club & Kennels
8860 Hwy. N., O'Fallon, MO 63366
(314) 332-9084 Kerry Mische

Range Line Hunt Club
Rt. 1, Box 31, Osborn, MO 64474
(816) 449-2670 Leslie Kerns
50 mi. N of Kansas City
Type Public; **On Site** Clubhouse, Meals, Clays;
Shoots Field, Blinds; **Birds** Dove, Quail, Pheasant,
Chukar, Turkey, Ducks, Geese; **Dogs** Avail/HDW;
Packages 1/2 Day, up to 10 guns

Salt Creek Game Farm & Hunting Preserve
Rt. 1, Box 62, Farber, MO 63345
(314) 249-5048 Dave or Lori Sutton After 5pm
100 mi. W of St. Louis
Est 1992; **Acres** 172; **Type** Public; **On Site**
Clubhouse, Lodging; **Shoots** Field; **Birds** Quail,
Pheasant; **Dogs** Avail/HDW O NAGA/See Pg. 107

Show-Me Safaris
PO Box 108, Summersville, MO 65571
(417) 932-4423 Mark Hampton Evenings

Snow White Hunting Preserve
Rt. 1, Box 40, Carrollton, MO 64633
(816) 542-3037 Carol L. Atherton
50 mi. E of Kansas City **Type** Public; **Shoots** Field;
Birds Quail, Pheasant, Chukar; **Dogs** Avail/HDW;
Packages 1/2 Day O NAGA/See Pg. 107

Sorenson's S.C. & Preserve Hunting
1703 Hwy. DD, Defiance, MO 63341
(314) 828-5149 Tom & Kay Sorenson 8am-6pm
19 mi. W of St. Louis
Est 1963; **Acres** 250; **Type** Public; **On Site**
Clubhouse, Meals, Clays; **Shoots** Field, Tower;
Birds Quail, Pheasant, Chukar; **Dogs** Avail/HDW;
Packages 1/2 Day, 2-4 guns

Stillwater Kennel & Game Farm
Rt. 2, Box 239, Silex, MO 63377
(314) 384-6290 Ron & Monica Garringer
60 mi. NW of St. Louis **Est** 1989; **Acres** 180; **Type**
Public; **On Site** Clubhouse; **Shoots** Field; **Birds**
Quail, Pheasant, Chukar; **Dogs** Avail/HDW

Street's Wild Game Farm & Hunt Club
Rt. 1, Box 106, Eolia, MO 63344
(573) 384-5489 Dave Street Anytime

Sumgoose Club, Inc.
30 Sumgoose Rd., Box 30A, Sumner, MO 64681
(816) 856-3348 Roy McCallum
Type Public, Member/Avail; **On Site** Lodging, Clays;
Shoots Field; **Birds** Quail, Pheasant, Chukar, Turkey,
Ducks O NAGA/See Pg. 107

Tall Oaks Club
295 Tall Oaks Rd., Warrenton, MO 63383
(314) 456-8427 Jeff Brand
Type Public, Member/Avail; **On Site** Lodging;
Shoots Field; **Birds** Quail, Pheasant, Chukar, Huns,
Ducks O NAGA/See Pg. 107

Turkey Creek Hunting Preserve
RR1, Box 117A, LaClede, MO 64651
(816) 963-2538 Jim Tollerton

Twin Lakes Sporting Club
Rt. 1, Box 203, Mexico, MO 65265
(314) 581-1877 Wally Feutz 7am-9pm
110 mi. NW of St. Louis **Est** 1991; **Acres** 1,280;
Hunters/yr 200; **Type** Public, Member/Avail; **On Site**
Clubhouse, Meals, Clays; **Shoots** Field, Blinds; **Birds**
Dove, Quail, Pheasant, Chukar, Turkey, Ducks, Geese;
Dogs Avail/HDW; **Packages** 1/2 Day, 1-15 guns
O NAGA/See Pg. 107

Wildwood Hunting & Sporting Clays
RR1, Box 143, Houstonia, MO 65333
(816) 879-4451 Bill Wall After 5pm
100 mi. SE of Kansas City
Est 1986; **Acres** 1,100; **Type** Public, Member/Avail;
On Site Clubhouse, Lodging, Meals, Clays; **Shoots**
Field; **Birds** Dove, Quail, Woodcock, Pheasant,
Chukar, Turkey; **Dogs** Avail/HDW; **Packages** 1/2
Day, 1-35 guns

Wilson Creek Hunts
Rt. 1, Box 74, Eldorado Springs, MO 64744
(417) 465-2240 Kent Ablee
Type Public, Member/Avail; **On Site** Lodging;
Shoots Field; **Birds** Quail, Pheasant, Chukar
O NAGA/See Pg. 107

Wings - St. Albans Properties, L.L.C.
PO Box 49, St. Albans, MO 63073
(314) 458-6523 Gale Braswell 8-5
35 mi. W of St. Louis
Est 1963; **Acres** 320; **Type** Member/Avail, Corp.;
On Site Clubhouse, Lodging, Meals, Clays; **Shoots**
Field, Blinds; **Birds** Quail, Pheasant, Chukar, Ducks;
Dogs Avail/HDW; **Packages** 1/2 Day, 2-9 guns
O NAGA/See Pg. 107

Wingtip Game Ranch & Kennel
RR1, Cainsville, MO 64632
(816) 893-5880 John & Mary Jo Rouse 9-5
100 mi. NE of Kansas City
Est 1985; **Acres** 780; **Hunters/yr** 600; **Type**
Public, Member/Avail, Corp.; **On Site** Clubhouse,
Lodging, Meals, Clays; **Shoots** Field; **Birds** Quail,
Pheasant, Chukar; **Dogs** Avail/HDW; **Packages** 1
Day, 4-20 guns

MONTANA

Big Island Shooting Preserve
HC53, Box 31C, Columbus, MT 59019
(406) 322-5339 John Sherwood
32 mi. W of Billings
Acres 122; **Hunters/yr** 50; **Type** Public; **On Site**
Clubhouse, Clays; **Shoots** Field; **Birds** Quail,
Pheasant; **Dogs** Avail/HDW; **Packages** 1/2 Day

Big Sky Hunting
at Van Voast's Farm
3100 Irvine Flats, Polson, MT 59860
(406) 883-2000 Rick Van Voast
4 mi. NW of Polson In The Beautiful Flathead Valley
Est 1985; **Acres** 7,500; **Type** Public, Member/Avail;
On Site Clubhouse, Meals, Clays; **Shoots** Field, Blinds,
Boat; **Birds** Pheasant, Chukar, Huns, Ducks, Geese;
Dogs Avail/HDW; **Packages** 1/2 Day, 1-48 guns
See Our Ad Pg. 364

Birds of Plenty
PO Box 427, Broadus, MT 59317
(406) 436-2433 Dennis Schaffer
Type Public, Member/Avail; **Shoots** Field; **Birds**
Quail, Pheasant, Chukar, Huns, Turkey
○ NAGA/See Pg. 107

Eagle Nest Lodge
PO Box 509, Hardin, MT 59034
(406) 665-3711 Keith or Alan Kelly
45 mi. S of Billings
Est 1981; **Acres** 50,000; **Hunters/yr** 20; **Type**
Public; **On Site** Clubhouse, Lodging, Meals, Clays;
Shoots Field; **Birds** Pheasant, Chukar, Huns, Turkey,
Sharp Tail Grouse, Ducks, Geese; **Dogs** Avail/HDW;
Packages 2 Days, 2-6 guns
See Our Ad Pg. 365

Fetch Inn Hunting Preserve
PO Drawer 1429, Hamilton, MT 59840
(406) 363-5111 Tom Fox 8-6
40 mi. S of Missoula   **Est** 1973; **Acres** 1,000;
Hunters/yr 100; **Type** Public, Member/Avail, Corp.;
On Site Clubhouse, Lodging, Meals, Clays; **Shoots**
Field, Blinds; **Birds** Quail, Pheasant, Chukar, Huns,
Turkey, Ducks, Geese; **Dogs** Avail/HDW; **Packages**
1/2 Day, 1-8 guns   ○ NAGA/See Pg. 107

High Mountain Ranch
HC55, Box 331, Fishtail, MT 59028
(406) 328-6198 Barbara Kohler
25 mi. NW of Red Lodge
Acres 750; **Type** Member/Avail; **On Site** Lodging;
Shoots Field; **Birds** Quail, Chukar, Huns, Turkey,
Sage Grouse, Snipe; **Dogs** HDW; **Packages** 1/2 Day
○ NAGA/See Pg. 107

Mike/Elaine Krueger
4155 W. Kootenai Rd., Rexford, MT 59930
(406) 889-3297 Mike Krueger
100 mi. NW of Kalispell   **Acres** 250; **Hunters/yr**
30; **Type** Public; **On Site** Lodging, Meals; **Shoots**
Field; **Birds** Pheasant, Chukar

Montana Bird Hunts
Box 5031, Bozeman, MT 59717
(406) 587-5923 Dennis Kavanagh 7am-9pm
60 mi. E of Bozeman   **Est** 1982; **Acres** 50,000;
Type Public; **On Site** Lodging, Meals; **Shoots** Field;
Birds Ruffed Grouse, Pheasant, Huns, Sage Grouse,
Snipe, Sharp Tail Grouse, Ducks; **Dogs** Avail/HDW;
Packages 3 Days, 2-9 guns

Montana Outdoor Expeditions
76370 Gallatin Rd., Gallatin Gateway, MT 59730
(406) 763-4749 Bob Griffith
10 mi. SW of Bozeman
Type Public; **On Site** Clubhouse, Lodging, Meals;
Shoots Field; **Birds** Quail, Pheasant, Chukar, Huns,
Turkey, Sharp Tail Grouse; **Dogs** Avail/HDW;
Packages 1 Day

The Diamond J: A Little Montana Magic

In 1959, Peter and Jinny Combs were on their way to Alaska, looking to move from the ever-increasing development of southern California. They stopped at the Diamond J Ranch, and the rest is history—and a little Montana Magic.

Located in the Madison River Valley just outside Ennis, the Diamond J, nestled in a separate canyon at 5,800 feet with Jack Creek running along side, is a sportsman's delight: an Orvis Endorsed fishing and wingshooting lodge and a whole lot more.

Today Pete, Jinny and their son, Tim, manage the ranch. Together they see to it that all thirty-six guests are well looked after.

Your hosts, Jinny and Pete Combs

Orvis Endorsed Hunting

The Diamond J offers exceptional private upland bird-hunting on a 30,000 acre ranch located on the east side of the famous Madison River. So exceptional is the hunting, that the Diamond J is one of a handful of Lodges across the U.S. endorsed by the Orvis Wingshooting Program.

An abundance of Hungarian & Chukar Partridge, Ring-necked Pheasant, Blue & Ruffed Grouse (and ducks and geese in season) can be hunted September through December on terrain consisting of river bottom, hay meadows, willows and natural grass cover. Expert guides and dogs are provided by the Diamond J at no additional cost says Tim Combs, but guests are welcome to hunt with their own dogs and "we have excellent facilities to shelter and care for the dogs while they are here." A typical hunt starts with a morning round of sporting clays, a mid-day break for a delicious home-cooked lunch from the ranch kitchen, and an afternoon afield. (No need to panic if you've forgotten your bird-hunting equipment or need additional clothing, ammunition or a gun. The Diamond J's gift shop is fully stocked with Orvis hunting and fishing equipment.)

Orvis Endorsed Fishing, Too!

Whether you're a seasoned veteran of fly fishing or an eager beginner, fishing at the Diamond J is an experience you will long remember. From June through October the fishing includes anything from wet to dry flies. From the outlet of Quake Lake and running 52 miles downstream to Ennis Lake, the famous and swift upper Madison River offers some of the most consistent fishing for Rainbow and Brown Trout you will ever find—anywhere. There's private stream and lake fishing, too. (The adventuresome fisherman can opt for an all-day to three-day pack trip by horseback to fish mountain lakes.)

Welcome Pardner

The Diamond J's appeal doesn't end with fine fishing and hunting. A fully operational dude ranch, the Diamond J offers a range of activities tailored to individual, family or corporate needs: horseback riding, hiking, square dancing, camp fire sing-a-longs, a pool, and, even, an excellent library. Ten log cabins, each with its own rock fireplace and full bath, but no telephones or television, accommodate up to 36 guests. Meals—hearty and delicious— are served family style three times a day in the Main Lodge.

Getting to the Diamond J in Ennis is very easy. A commercial airport, Gallatin Field in Belgrade, is a little more than an hour's drive from the ranch, and is served by Delta, Northwest and Frontier Airlines. Ennis has a 4,800 foot paved runway that can accommodate private planes and corporate jets.

Finally, a word of caution: One trip to the Diamond J—alone, with friends, or family—may start an annual tradition. And the Combs wouldn't have it any other way!

Call (406) 682-4867 or write Diamond J Ranch, Box 577W, Ennis, Montana 59729 for more information, a beautiful color brochure or reservations.

Pigeye Basin Outfitters

HCR81, Box 25-(4), Utica, MT 59452
(406) 423-5223 Pete Rogers 8am-9pm
85 mi. SE of Great Falls Est 1986; **Acres** 200,000; **Hunters/yr** 50; **Type** Public; **On Site** Lodging, Meals; **Shoots** Field, Blinds; **Birds** Ruffed Grouse, Pheasant, Huns, Sage Grouse, Sharp Tail Grouse, Ducks; **Dogs** Avail/HDW; **Packages** 3 Days, 3-6 guns

Rainwater's Whispering Pines Ranch & Hunt Club

10500 Lost Prairie Rd., Marion, MT 59925
(406) 858-2292 Michael Canavan
or (406) 293-8666 Dave Giradot
35 mi. W of Kalispel Est 1996; **Acres** 600; **Type** Public, Member/Avail, Corp.; **On Site** Clubhouse, Lodging, Meals, Clays; **Shoots** Field; **Birds** Quail, Pheasant, Chukar, Huns; **Dogs** Avail/HDW; **Packages** 1/2 Day, 1-10 guns
O Game Preserve & Sporting Clays Instruction
O Professional Licensed Outfitter Available For: Ruffed Franklin Blue Grouse Partridge & Pheasants
O Fly Fishing & Large Game Hunts
O Hunting Permit Access to 300,000 Acres

Rock Creek Outfitters

PO Box 152, Hinsdale, MT 59241
(406) 648-5524 Dean Armbrister
17 mi. N of Hinsdale
Acres 47,000; **Hunters/yr** 50; **Type** Public; **On Site** Clubhouse, Lodging, Meals; **Shoots** Field, Blinds; **Birds** Pheasant, Turkey, Sage Grouse, Sharp Tail Grouse, Ducks, Geese; **Packages** 3 Days, 1-8 guns

Stillwater Shooting Preserve

1141 Church Dr., Kalispell, MT 59901
(406) 755-1959 Brian Tutvedt
10 mi. NW of Kalispell
Acres 500; **Type** Public; **On Site** Clays; **Shoots** Field, Blinds; **Birds** Quail, Pheasant, Chukar, Ducks, Geese; **Dogs** Avail

Tamarack Lodge

32855 South Fork Rd., Troy, MT 59935
(406) 295-4880 Bill & Judy McAfee
Type Public; **On Site** Clubhouse, Lodging, Meals, Clays; **Shoots** Field; **Birds** Ruffed Grouse; **Dogs** Avail/HDW

Troilus Kennels & Guide Service

RR 1, Box 1213, Bridger, MT 59014
(406) 662-3576
Est 1994; **Acres** 2,000,000; **Type** Public; **Shoots** Field; **Birds** Pheasant, Huns, Sage Grouse, Sharp Tail Grouse; **Packages** 5 Days, 4-100 guns

Two Leggins Outfitters

Box 2120, Star Rt., Hardin, MT 59034
(406) 665-2825 David Schaff
49 mi. SE of Billings
Acres 80,000; **Hunters/yr** 40; **Type** Public; **On**

Eagle Nest Lodge: Great Fishing & Wingshooting

Birds and trout in abundance. Scenic splendor. Restful accommodations. Sumptuous meals. They all contribute to the allure of one of the nation's great sporting destinations, Eagle Nest Lodge.

Exceptional wingshooting

Eagle Nest Lodge, owned since its inception by the Kelly family, was the first lodge in the country to earn a coveted Orvis double-endorsement for fishing and hunting. The hills, coulees and stubble fields surrounding the lodge provide premier habitat for some of the world's finest upland bird hunting. Pheasants, Hungarian partridge and sharptail grouse abound on the 35,000 acre private ranch where Eagle Nest guides conduct traditional western hunts, from September through early December, over German shorthairs, Brittanies, and English pointers. (For those who have not encountered Huns on the Montana prairie, the experience is exceptionally challenging.)

To sharpen your shooting skills, an instructional clay course is available, and the lodge manager is an Orvis certified wingshooting instructor.

Extraordinary fishing

Fifty five miles from Billings, Montana, Eagle Nest lodge sits on the Bighorn River, one of the nation's best trout fisheries.

Providing mile upon mile of blue ribbon water, the Bighorn is renowned for the quality and quantity of its rainbow and brown trout. So it's not unusual for the average angler, assisted by one of the lodge's professional guides, to land 20 fish between 16 and 22 inches in a single day.

What's more, the same guides who know just where the trout are rising are also qualified instructors, eager to teach beginners the fundamentals of fly fishing, to help intermediate anglers improve their skills, and to show experts new and exciting ways to take trophy trout.

World class amenities

Not the least of Eagle Nest's attractions is the lodge itself, a well planned combination of rustic beauty and modern comfort. Six spacious guest rooms, each with two single beds and a full bath, are designed for rest and relaxation. The great trophy room includes a huge screened in porch with rockers and a swing. And the lodge's dining room features

Eagle Nest Lodge combines rustic beauty with the comforts of the modern age.

fresh Montana meats and wild game delicacies, complemented by salads and side dishes that are meals in themselves. The lodge also operates its own tackle shop with a full line of fishing and hunting gear.

A choice of packages

Eagle Nest offers a trout fishing package from May through October; a bird-hunting package from September through early December; and combination packages—a lodge specialty— from September through October. Custom packages and exclusive stays are available. The lodge recommends making reservations well in advance of a desired stay. Write or phone A. Keith Kelly, Eagle Nest Lodge, PO Box 509, Hardin, MT 59034; (406) 665-3711.

Orvis Endorsed:
A Lodge of Double Distinction

Eagle Nest Lodge enjoys the distinction of being the first in the world to achieve an Orvis endorsement for both fly fishing and wingshooting.

The credit for that achievement goes to lodge's founders: the Kelly family. Alan Kelly, the former U.S. Fish & Wildlife biologist on the Bighorn, and his wife, Wanda, maintain quality control. While their two sons, Keith an Orvis flyfishing and shooting instructor, and Matthew, an experienced Western guide, are in charge of daily operations. Together they invite you to join them for "the experience of a lifetime, in what has been aptly called 'The Last Best Place: Montana'."

Site Lodging, Meals;   Shoots Field, Blinds;   Birds
Pheasant, Chukar, Turkey, Sharp Tail Grouse, Ducks,
Geese;   Dogs Avail

Whispering Wind Ranch
69 Cottonwood Rd., Cardwell, MT 59721
(406) 285-6715 Sharon Buckallew
Shoots Field;   Birds Pheasant, Turkey
O NAGA/See Pg. 107

Whitcomb Lodge
Box 1173, Malta, MT 59538
(406) 654-2089 Roy Ereaux Anytime
200 mi. N of Billings
Est 1985;   Acres 30,000;   Hunters/yr 50;   Type
Public;   On Site Clubhouse, Lodging, Meals, Clays;
Shoots Field, Driven, Blinds;   Birds Pheasant, Chukar,
Huns, Sage Grouse, Sharp Tail Grouse, Ducks, Geese;
Dogs Avail/HDW;   Packages 3 Days, 1-14 guns

Wolf Creek Shooting Preserve
HC76, Box 45, Denton, MT 59435
(406) 567-2436 Floyd Blair
40 mi. N of Lewistown
Acres 1,280;   Type Public;   Birds Pheasant, Chukar,
Huns, Ducks, Geese

Yaak River Lodge
27744 Yaak River Rd., Troy, MT 59935
(406) 295-5463 Gloria Racine/Donald Belcher
On Site Clubhouse, Lodging, Meals;   Birds Ruffed
Grouse;   Dogs Avail

NEBRASKA

Blackbird Valley Ringnecks
RR1, Box 60, O'Neill, NE 68763
(402) 336-3858 Denny Drayton
On Site Lodging, Clays;   Shoots Field;   Birds Quail,
Pheasant   O NAGA/See Pg. 107

Boardman Springs
HC32, Box 31, Valentine, NE 69201
(402) 376-1498 Bill Weller
110 mi. N of North Platte
Acres 20,000;   Type Public;   On Site Lodging,
Meals;   Shoots Field;   Birds Dove, Pheasant, Sharp
Tail Grouse, Ducks, Geese;   Dogs Avail/HDW;
Packages 2 Days, 3-12 guns

Calamus Safari
HC79, Box 2-1, Burwell, NE 68823
(308) 346-5330 Mick Phillipps
Type Public;   Shoots Field;   Birds Quail, Pheasant
O NAGA/See Pg. 107

Can-Hunt
RR1, Box 10A, Garland, NE 68360
(402) 588-2448 Todd Halle After 8pm
60 mi. SW of Omaha
Est 1988;   Acres 440;   Hunters/yr 150;   Type
Public, Member/Avail, Corp.;   On Site Clubhouse,
Clays;   Shoots Field;   Birds Dove, Quail, Pheasant,
Chukar;   Dogs Avail/HDW;   Packages 1/2 Day, 1-15
guns O NAGA/See Pg. 107

Frenchman River Hunting
HC65, Box 113, Wauneta, NE 69045
(308) 394-5511 Pat Kitt
65 mi. S of North Platte
Est 1989; **Acres** 3,000; **Hunters/yr** 100; **Type** Public; **On Site** Lodging, Meals, Clays; **Shoots** Field, Blinds; **Birds** Dove, Quail, Pheasant, Chukar, Ducks, Geese; **Dogs** Avail/HDW; **Packages** 1/2 Day, 1-7 guns

H&H
PO Box 334, Cozad, NE 69130
(308) 784-2410 Dean Herrington
Acres 160; **Hunters/yr** 160; **Type** Public; **Shoots** Field; **Birds** Quail, Pheasant ○ NAGA/See Pg. 107

Honore Hilltop Shooting Preserve
1605 North E Rd., Phillips, NE 68865
(402) 886-2215 Nina & John Honore 6am-10pm
130 mi. W of Omaha **Est** 1985; **Acres** 1,000; **Type** Public; **On Site** Clubhouse, Meals, Clays; **Shoots** Field, Tower; **Birds** Quail, Pheasant, Chukar, Huns, Turkey; **Dogs** Avail/HDW; **Packages** 1/2 Day, 1-30 guns ○ NAGA/See Pg. 107

Hunt Nebraska, Inc.
PO Box 328, Arapahoe, NE 68922
(800) 486-8632 Johnny Hemelstrand
180 mi. W of Lincoln
Est 1986; **Acres** 10,000; **Hunters/yr** 300; **Type** Public; **On Site** Clubhouse, Lodging, Meals, Clays; **Shoots** Field, Blinds; **Birds** Dove, Quail, Pheasant, Chukar, Turkey, Sharp Tail Grouse, Ducks, Geese; **Dogs** Avail/HDW; **Packages** 1 Day, 1-20 guns ○ NAGA/See Pg. 107

Hunting Sports Plus
710 Main St., Ste. E, Blue Springs, MO, Hunting in 4 States including, NE
(800) 729-1924 Dan Gasser
Est 1989; **Acres** 200,000; **Type** Public, Member/Avail; **On Site** Clubhouse, Lodging, Meals, Clays; **Shoots** Field, Blinds, Boat; **Birds** Quail, Pheasant, Turkey, Prairie Chicken, Ducks, Geese; **Dogs** Avail/HDW; **Packages** 1 Day, 1-24 guns
See Our Ad Pg. 368

K-D Hunting Acres
RR1, Box 182A, Tekamah, NE 68061
(402) 374-1428 Kim or Dee Snow Anytime
40 mi. N of Omaha **Est** 1992; **Acres** 1,000; **Hunters/yr** 700; **Type** Public, Member/Avail, Corp.; **On Site** Clubhouse, Lodging, Meals, Clays; **Shoots** Field; **Birds** Quail, Pheasant, Chukar; **Dogs** Avail/HDW; **Packages** 1/2 Day, 1-15 guns ○ NAGA/See Pg. 107

L and P Ranch
RR2, Box 80A, Orchard, NE 68764
(402) 655-2244 Linda or Paul Hayes 9am-5pm
75 mi. NW of Norfolk; **Type** Public; **On Site** Clubhouse, Lodging, Meals; **Shoots** Field; **Birds** Pheasant; **Dogs** Avail/HDW; **Packages** 1/2 Day, 1-6 guns ○ NAGA/See Pg. 107

Pheasant Haven Hunting Acres
PO Box 650, Elkhorn, NE 68022
(402) 779-2608 Scott Bruhn 7am
15 mi. NW of Omaha
Est 1987; **Acres** 1,000; **Hunters/yr** 500; **Type** Public, Member/Avail, Corp.; **On Site** Clubhouse, Lodging, Meals; **Shoots** Field; **Birds** Quail, Pheasant, Chukar; **Dogs** Avail/HDW; **Packages** 1/2 Day, 1-24 guns ○ NAGA/See Pg. 107

Prairie Hills Hunting Club
1267 2nd Ave., Dannebrog, NE 68831
(308) 226-2540 John & Kathleen McElroy 8-5
13 mi. NW of Grand Island
Est 1985; **Acres** 1,200; **Hunters/yr** 600; **Type** Public, Member/Avail, Corp.; **On Site** Clubhouse, Lodging, Meals, Clays; **Shoots** Field; **Birds** Dove, Quail, Pheasant, Chukar, Prairie Chicken; **Dogs** Avail/HDW; **Packages** 1/2 Day, 4-20 guns ○ NAGA/See Pg. 107

Rooster Ranch
RR1, Box 51, Ruskin, NE 68974
(402) 279-2035 Rocky Renz 8-5
130 mi. SW of Omaha
Est 1989; **Acres** 120; **Hunters/yr** 20; **Type**
Public; **On Site** Clubhouse, Lodging, Meals; **Birds**
Dove, Quail, Pheasant, Chukar; **Dogs** Avail/HDW;
Packages 1 Day, 3-6 guns

Sand Prairie Preserve
Box 94, Alliance, NE 69301
(308) 762-2735 William or Bev Lore Evenings
6 mi. SE of Alliance
Est 1992; **Acres** 360; **Type** Public; **On Site**
Clubhouse, Lodging, Meals, Clays; **Shoots** Field;
Birds Quail, Pheasant, Chukar, Turkey; **Dogs**
Avail/HDW; **Packages** 1/2 Day, 4-20 guns
o NAGA/See Pg. 107

Sandhills Adventures
HC63, Box 29, Brewster, NE 68821
(308) 547-2450 Delten or Tracy Rhoads
125 mi. NW of Grand Island
Est 1989; **Acres** 16,000; **Type** Public, Corp.; **On
Site** Clubhouse, Lodging, Meals, Clays; **Shoots** Field,
Driven, Blinds; **Birds** Dove, Pheasant, Chukar, Huns,
Turkey, Prairie Chicken, Ducks, Geese; **Dogs**
Avail/HDW; **Packages** 1 Day, 1-24 guns
See Our Ad Pg. 366

Sappa Creek Hunt Preserve
PO Box 357, Orleans, NE 68966
(308) 473-3308 Tim Rief
165 mi. SW of Lincoln
Est 1993; **Acres** 76,000; **Type** Public; **On Site**
Clubhouse, Lodging, Meals, Clays; **Shoots** Field,
Driven; **Birds** Quail, Pheasant, Chukar; **Dogs**
Avail/HDW; **Packages** 1 Day, 2-12 guns

Seifer Farms
Hunting Preserve
RR1, Box 90, Sutherland, NE 69165
(308) 386-2394 Ray Seifer
23 mi. W of North Platte
Est 1993; **Acres** 5,000; **Type** Public; **On Site**
Lodging, Meals, Clays; **Shoots** Field, Blinds; **Birds**
Dove, Quail, Pheasant, Prairie Chicken, Ducks, Geese;
Dogs Avail/HDW; **Packages** 1/2 Day, 1-5 guns
See Our Ad Pg. 367

Swanson Hunting Acres, Inc.
PO Box 99, Niobrara, NE 68760
(402) 857-3514 Janet Swanson
85 mi. W of Sioux City, IA
Est 1983; **Acres** 2,200; **Type** Public; **On Site**
Clubhouse, Lodging, Meals, Clays; **Shoots** Field;
Birds Quail, Pheasant, Chukar; **Dogs** Avail/HDW
o NAGA/See Pg. 107

Table Top Hunting Preserve
1011 Table Rd., Chadron, NE 69337
(308) 432-5828 Melvin Bruns
23.5 mi. SW of Chadron
Acres 1,000; **Type** Public; **On Site** Meals; **Shoots**
Field; **Birds** Pheasant; **Dogs** Avail
o NAGA/See Pg. 107

Trapper's Creek Outdoors
RR1, Box 64, Burwell, NE 68823
(308) 346-5024 Gary & Mary Hughes
90 mi. NE of Grand Island
Acres 251; **Type** Public; **On Site** Lodging, Meals;
Shoots Field; **Birds** Quail, Pheasant, Chukar; **Dogs**
Avail o NAGA/See Pg. 107

Turtle Creek Hunting Preserve
Rt. 1, Box 89, Hoskins, NE 68740
(402) 565-4581 Randy Wagner After 6pm
50 mi. SW of Sioux City, IA
Est 1991; **Acres** 1,500; **Hunters/yr** 50; **Type**
Public; **On Site** Clubhouse, Lodging, Meals, Clays;
Shoots Field; **Birds** Dove, Quail, Pheasant; **Dogs**
Avail/HDW; **Packages** 1 Day, 2-16 guns

Upland Hunts
PO Box 58, Broken Bow, NE 68822
(308) 872-2998 Keith "Cas" McCaslin
70 mi. NE of North Platte
Est 1985; **Acres** 15,000; **Hunters/yr** 150; **Type**
Public, Corp.; **On Site** Clubhouse, Lodging, Meals;
Shoots Field; **Birds** Quail, Pheasant, Huns, Turkey,
Prairie Chicken, Sharp Tail Grouse; **Dogs** Avail/HDW;
Packages 1 Day, 2-12 guns o NAGA/See Pg. 107

NEVADA

Canyon Pheasant Club
HC62, Box 300, Wells, NV 89835
(702) 752-3065 Sterling Nixon
60 mi. NE of Elko
Acres 13,000; **Hunters/yr** 100; **Type** Public,
Member/Avail; **On Site** Lodging, Meals, Clays;
Shoots Field; **Birds** Dove, Pheasant, Chukar, Turkey,
Prairie Chicken, Ducks, Geese; **Dogs** Avail

Casino West/LM Ranches
11 N. Main St., Yerington, NV 89447
(702) 463-2481 L. Bryan Masini Wkdys, 8-5
90 mi. SE of Reno
Est 1979; **Acres** 3,000; **Hunters/yr** 500; **Type**
Public; **On Site** Clubhouse, Meals; **Shoots** Field,
Blinds; **Birds** Dove, Quail, Pheasant, Chukar, Geese;
Dogs Avail/HDW; **Packages** 1 Day, 10-100 guns

Circle HH
Hunting Preserve
HCR#1, Box 512, Nipton, CA 92364
(702) 642-9405 Fred Hymes/Jessie Hymes 5pm-10pm
**78 mi. S of Las Vegas, NV - 100 mi. E of
Barstow/20 mi N. I-40**
Est 1988; **Acres** 200; **Hunters/yr** 72; **Type**
Public, Member/Avail, Corp.; **On Site** Clubhouse,
Meals, Clays; **Shoots** Field; **Birds** Dove, Quail,
Pheasant, Chukar, Turkey; **Dogs** Avail/HDW;
Packages 1/2 Day, 1-6 guns

The Humboldt Hunting Club
PO Box 70341, Reno, NV 89570
(702) 356-6080
72 mi. N of Winnemucca
Acres 17,000; **Type** Member/Avail; **On Site**
Clubhouse; **Shoots** Field; **Birds** Dove, Quail,
Pheasant, Chukar; **Dogs** HDW

Red Hills Hunting Preserve
PO Box 493, Gardnerville, NV 89410
(702) 266-3856 George Asay
60 mi. S of Reno
Acres 10,000; **Type** Public, Member/Avail; **On Site**
Clubhouse, Meals, Clays; **Shoots** Field; **Birds** Quail,
Pheasant, Chukar, Ducks, Geese; **Dogs** Avail/HDW
O NAGA/See Pg. 107

Sage Hill Clay Sports & Game Hunting
11500 Mira Loma Rd., Reno, NV 89511
(702) 851-1123 Rich & Darlene Bullard
12 mi. SE of Reno
Est 1991; **Acres** 1,900; **Type** Public, Member/Avail,
Corp.; **On Site** Clubhouse, Meals, Clays; **Shoots**
Field; **Birds** Quail, Pheasant, Chukar; **Dogs**
Avail/HDW; **Packages** 1 Day, 1-10 guns

NEW HAMPSHIRE

Green Boughs
& Tail Feathers
Center Hill Rd., Epsom, NH 03234
(617) 665-5011 John Baldi/Mike Hickey after 5
72 mi. N of Boston
Est 1990; **Acres** 400; **Type** Public, Member/Avail;
On Site Clubhouse; **Shoots** Field, Driven; **Birds**
Quail, Pheasant, Chukar; **Dogs** Avail/HDW;
Packages 1/2 Day, up to 4 guns

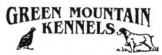

Green Mountain
Kennels Hunting Preserve
RR1, Box 438F, Center Ossipee, NH 03814
(603) 539-2106 David Bardzik 8-5
50 mi. NE of Concord
Est 1995; **Acres** 400; **Type** Public, Member/Avail,
Corp.; **On Site** Clubhouse, Lodging, Meals, Clays;
Shoots Field, Driven; **Birds** Quail, Pheasant, Chukar,
Huns; **Dogs** Avail/HDW; **Packages** 1/2 Day, 1-12 guns
O Airport Pickup   O Train Bird Dogs
O Bird Processing   O Brochure Available
O Kennel Bird Dogs   O On-Site Pro Shop
O Sporting Clays   O Factory Ammunition
O Shooting Instruction   O Quality Clubhouse
O Gourmet Meals   O Family Run Business
O Hunting Jeeps   O Authorized Browning Dealer

Hidden Meadow Farm
PO Box 64, Webster Rd., Temple, NH 03084
(603) 924-6030 Martin T. Connolly
50 mi. NW of Boston   **Est** 1986; **Acres** 1,200;
Type Member/Avail, Corp.; **On Site** Clubhouse;
Shoots Field; **Birds** Quail, Pheasant, Chukar, Huns,
Ducks; **Dogs** Avail/HDW O NAGA/See Pg. 107

High Point
Upland Game Preserve
Rte. 28 S., Alton, NH 03809
(603) 875-3552 Jonathan & Bob Caley
75 mi. N of Boston   Est 1993; **Acres** 140; **Type**
Public, Member/Avail, Corp.; **On Site** Clubhouse, Clays;
Shoots Field, Tower; **Birds** Quail, Pheasant, Chukar;
Dogs Avail/HDW; **Packages** 1/2 Day, 1-5 guns
O NAGA/See Pg.
O Gun Dog Training - Specialty Pointing Breeds
O Quality Clubhouse
O World Class Five Stand (SCA Sanctioned)
O Bird Processing
O Just 15 minutes East of State Hwy. 93

New England Estate Hunting
PO Box 64, Temple, NH 03084
(603) 924-6030 Martin T. Connolly
Est 1992; **Acres** 4,000; **Type** Public; **On Site**
Clubhouse, Lodging, Meals; **Shoots** Field; **Birds**
Quail, Pheasant, Chukar, Huns, Ducks; **Dogs**
Avail/HDW; **Packages** 1 Day

SKAT
PO Box 137, New Ipswich, NH 03071
(603) 878-1257 Tony Haigh
50 mi. NW of Boston
Est 1952; **Acres** 350; **Hunters/yr** 1,000; **Type**
Public, Member/Avail, Corp.; **On Site** Clubhouse,
Lodging, Meals, Clays; **Birds** Pheasant, Chukar, Huns,
Ducks; **Dogs** Avail/HDW; **Packages** 1/2 Day, 2-30 guns

Sportsmen's Hill Hunting Preserve
Old Leonard Farm Rd., West Swanzey, NH 03469
(603) 357-0386 Gary or Joan Polishan
6 mi. S of Keene
Est 1986; **Acres** 125; **Type** Public; **On Site**
Clubhouse, Clays; **Shoots** Field; **Birds** Pheasant,
Chukar; **Dogs** Avail/HDW; **Packages** 1/2 Day, 1-4 guns

Tall Timber Lodge
231 Beach Rd., Pittsburg, NH 03592
(800) 835-6343 Cindy Sullivan
180 mi. N of Manchester
Est 1946; **Type** Public; **On Site** Clubhouse,
Lodging, Meals; **Shoots** Field; **Birds** Ruffed Grouse,
Woodcock, Pheasant; **Dogs** HDW; **Packages** 1 Day

The Timberdoodle Club

One Webster Hwy., Temple, NH 03084
(603) 654-9510 Randall Martin
55 mi. NW of Boston
Est 1967; **Acres** 1,000; **Type** Member/Ltd, Corp.;
On Site Clubhouse, Lodging, Meals, Clays; **Shoots**
Field, Tower, Driven; **Birds** Quail, Pheasant, Chukar,
Huns; **Dogs** Avail/HDW
O Airport Pickup   O On-Site Pro Shop
O Bird Processing   O Quality Clubhouse
O Sporting Clays   O Quality Fly Fishing Program
O Family Recreation
O Gunsmith and Fitting Service

NEW JERSEY

B&B Pheasantry
78 Whitehall Rd., Pittstown, NJ 08867
(908) 735-6501 Ben Beckage Nights
50 mi. SW of New York City
Est 1979; **Acres** 1,000; **Hunters/yr** 5,000; **Type**
Public, Member/Avail; **Shoots** Field, Tower, Blinds;
Birds Quail, Pheasant, Chukar, Huns, Geese; **Dogs**
Avail/HDW; **Packages** 1/2 Day, up to 20 guns
O NAGA/See Pg. 107
O Hunting License   O Factory Ammunition
O Bird Processing   O German Shorthairs
O Loaner Guns

Belleplain Farms
Shooting Preserve
346 Handsmill Rd., Belleplain, NJ 08270
(609) 861-2345 Nick Germanio 8 to 6
50 mi. SE of Philadelphia
Est 1983; **Acres** 1,200; **Hunters/yr** 1,500; **Type**
Public, Member/Avail, Corp.; **On Site** Clubhouse,
Lodging, Clays; **Shoots** Field, Tower; **Birds** Quail,
Ruffed Grouse, Woodcock, Pheasant, Chukar; **Dogs**
Avail/HDW; **Packages** 1 Day, 1-40 guns
O NAGA/See Pg. 107
O On Site Gun Center   O Great Deer Hunting
O Family Run Business   O Bird Processing
O Rifle/Pistol Range

Big Spring Game Farm
RD#3, Box 591, Sussex, NJ 07461
(201) 875-3373 Bob Hogg 8am-4pm
50 mi. NW of New York City
Est 1967; **Acres** 180; **Hunters/yr** 150; **Type**
Public, Member/Avail, Corp.; **On Site** Clubhouse,
Clays; **Shoots** Field; **Birds** Quail, Pheasant, Chukar;
Dogs Avail/HDW; **Packages** 1/2 Day, 1-8 guns

Bradway's Hunting
149 Jericho Rd., RD2, Salem, NJ 08079
(609) 935-5698 Joan/John/Mike Bradway 9am-9pm
30 mi. SW of Philadelphia
Est 1970; **Acres** 315; **Hunters/yr** 300; **Type**
Public; **On Site** Clubhouse, Lodging, Meals; **Shoots**
Field, Blinds; **Birds** Quail, Pheasant, Chukar, Turkey,
Ducks; **Dogs** Avail/HDW; **Packages** 1/2 Day, up to
16 guns
O Deer Hunting

Buttonwood
Game Preserve
810 Harmony Station Rd., Phillipsburg, NJ 08865
(908) 454-8377 Gail & Frank Vargo
60 mi. W of New York
Est 1994; **Acres** 150; **Type** Public, Member/Avail;
On Site Clays; **Shoots** Field, Tower; **Birds** Quail,
Pheasant, Chukar, Huns; **Dogs** Avail/HDW;
Packages 1/2 Day, 1-8 guns   O NAGA/See Pg. 107
See Our Ad Above

Game Creek Hunting Farms
RR#2, Box 195, Woodstown, NJ 08098
(609) 769-0035 John or Cheryl DiGregorio 7am-8pm
20 mi. SE of Philadelphia
Est 1983; **Acres** 450; **Type** Public, Member/Avail, Corp.; **On Site** Clubhouse, Lodging, Meals; **Shoots** Field, Tower, Driven; **Birds** Quail, Pheasant, Chukar, Geese; **Dogs** Avail/HDW; **Packages** 1/2 Day, 1-4 guns ○ NAGA/See Pg. 107
○ Family Run Business
○ Excellent Trainings Site for Dogs-Special in Oct.
○ Secluded Acres-Just You, Your Party, Your Dog
○ Comfortable Clubhouse
○ Excellent Cover-Natural & Managed
○ 20 Minutes from Philadelphia & Wilmington & 2 hrs. New York City

Gibersons Game Farm & Hunting Preserve
317 Sooys Landing Rd., Port Republic, NJ 08241
(609) 652-1939 Clem or Lois Giberson Evenings

M&M Hunting Preserve
Hook & Winslow Rds., Pennsville, NJ 08070
(609) 935-1230 Anthony Matarese 9-3
20 mi. SW of Philadelphia
Est 1980; **Acres** 1,500; **Hunters/yr** 8,000; **Type** Public, Member/Avail; **On Site** Clubhouse, Meals, Clays; **Shoots** Field, Tower, Blinds, Boat; **Birds** Pheasant, Chukar, Ducks, Geese; **Dogs** Avail/HDW; **Packages** 1/2 Day, 1-48 guns ○ NAGA/See Pg. 107
See Our Ad, Left

Meadows Grove Sportsmen
58 West Chrystal St., Dover, NJ 07801
(201) 366-3687 Frank G. Hulsman, Pres. After 6 pm
50 mi. W of New York City
Est 1981; **Acres** 800; **Type** Member/Avail; **On Site** Clubhouse; **Shoots** Field; **Birds** Quail, Woodcock, Pheasant, Chukar, Geese; **Dogs** Avail/HDW
○ Kennel Bird Dogs
○ Deer Hunting
○ Family Recreation
○ Train Bird Dogs

Meadowview Sporting
Dog Club & Preserve
P.O. Box 486, Hancock's Bridge, NJ 08038
(609) 935-8077 Steven Veltman
15 mi. SE of Wilmington
Est 1993; **Acres** 1,400; **Type** Public, Member/Avail, Corp.; **On Site** Clubhouse, Lodging, Meals, Clays; **Shoots** Field, Tower, Blinds, Boat; **Birds** Quail, Pheasant, Chukar, Huns, Ducks; **Dogs** Avail/HDW; **Packages** 1/2 Day, 1-24 guns
See Our Ad, Right

Oak Lane Farms
Dutch Mill Rd., Piney Hollow, NJ 08344
(609) 697-2196 John Scavelli day or evening
Est 1974; Acres 200; Type Public; On Site
Clubhouse, Lodging, Meals, Clays; Shoots Field,
Tower, Blinds; Birds Quail, Pheasant, Ducks; Dogs
Avail/HDW; Packages 1/2 Day, 1-4 guns
○ NAGA/See Pg. 107

Oak Ridge Sportsman Club

261 Garrison Rd., Phillipsburg, NJ 08865
(908) 859-1615 William MacQueen
50 mi. W of New York
Est 1975; Acres 425; Type Public, Member/Avail;
On Site Clubhouse, Clays; Shoots Field; Birds
Quail, Pheasant, Chukar, Huns; Dogs Avail/HDW;
Packages 1/2 Day, 1-10 guns ○ NAGA/See Pg. 107
○ Family Run Business
○ Less than 1 Hr. from NYC
○ Day Hunts Available
○ Season Memberships: $600-$800
○ Target Shooting: Pistol, Rifle, Bow

One Flew Over the Hedgerow
748 Coles Mill Rd., Franklinvolle, NJ 08322
(609) 728-6454 Mike Moffa 25 mi. SE of
Philadelphia Acres 200; Type Public; Shoots Field;
Birds Quail, Pheasant, Ducks; Dogs Avail/HDW;
Packages 1/2 Day, 1-6 guns ○ NAGA/See Pg. 107

Shallow Brook Sportsmen
982 Fairview Lake Rd., Newton, NJ 07821
(201) 579-9443 Lindsey Dwyer
60 mi. W of New York City Type Public,
Member/Avail; Shoots Field; Birds Pheasant;
Dogs Avail; Packages 1/2 Day ○ NAGA/See Pg. 107

Shorewinds Farm & Kennel
5392 Rt. 49, Millville, NJ 08332
Jerry Lynch Shoots Field; Birds Quail, Pheasant
○ NAGA/See Pg. 107

Wing & Shot
64 Fern St., Browns Mills, NJ 08015
(609) 893-6266 Keith 4 to 9 pm
25 mi. E of Philadelphia Est 1985; Acres 1,100;
Type Public, Member/Avail; Shoots Field; Birds
Quail, Pheasant, Chukar, Turkey, Ducks; Dogs
Avail/HDW; Packages 1/2 Day, 2-4 guns

NEW MEXICO

Stanley Hunting

PO Box 614, Stanley, NM 87056

(505) 832-6356 Bob Stitt Evenings

35 mi. NE of Albuquerque

Est 1988; **Acres** 6,800; **Hunters/yr** 300; **Type** Public, Member/Avail, Corp.; **Shoots** Field; **Birds** Dove, Quail, Pheasant; **Dogs** Avail/HDW; **Packages** 1/2 Day, 1-4 guns ○ NAGA/See Pg. 107

Less than an hour's drive from Santa Fe and Albuquerque! We're a "low key", "no fancy stuff" operation, but if you want to stretch your legs, huntin' quail, pheasant or chukars on our 6800 acres can't be beat. Hunt with your dog or one of our LOS CASADORES PUDLEPOINTERS. Puppies, started dogs and trained dogs sometimes available. Call today. Thanks.

Tinnin Hunt Club

20 First Plaza NW, Suite 518, Albuquerque, NM 87103

(505) 242-2871 Tom Tinnin

45 mi. S of Albuquerque

Est 1992; **Acres** 500; **Type** Public; **On Site** Clubhouse, Meals, Clays; **Shoots** Field, Blinds; **Birds** Dove, Quail, Pheasant, Chukar, Ducks, Geese; **Dogs** Avail/HDW; **Packages** 1/2 Day, 3-50 guns ○ NAGA/See Pg. 107

○ Kennel Bird Dogs   ○ Sporting Clays
○ Brochure Available   ○ Factory Ammunition
○ Family Run Business   ○ Cranes

NEW YORK

Austerlitz Club

634 Dugway Rd., Chatham, NY 12037

(518) 392-9879 Terry Cozzolino 7am-9pm

40 mi. S of Albany

Est 1928; **Acres** 500; **Type** Public, Member/Avail; **On Site** Clubhouse, Meals; **Shoots** Field, Tower; **Birds** Pheasant, Chukar; **Dogs** Avail/HDW; **Packages** 1/2 Day, 1-30 guns ○ NAGA/See Pg. 107

Bill's Hunting

RD2, Box 288A, Mohawk, NY 13407

(315) 823-1708 John or Linda Bills

Type Member/Avail; **Shoots** Field; **Birds** Pheasant ○ NAGA/See Pg. 107

Bobwhite Ridge Kennel

PO Box 55, West Eaton, NY 13484

(315) 245-4510 Frederick G. Bastable, III

Shoots Field; **Birds** Quail, Pheasant, Chukar, Huns ○ NAGA/See Pg. 107

Catskill Pheasantry & Sporting Clays

PO Box 42, Long Eddy, NY 12760

(914) 887-4487 Alex Papp 8am-8pm

100 mi. NW of New York City

Est 1981; **Acres** 400; **Type** Public, Member/Avail, Corp.; **On Site** Clubhouse, Lodging, Meals, Clays; **Shoots** Field; **Birds** Quail, Pheasant, Chukar; **Dogs** Avail/HDW; **Packages** 1/2 Day, 1-4 guns ○ NAGA/See Pg. 107

Chemung Shooting Preserve

115 Lilac Dr., Horseheads, NY 14845

(607) 739-9238 Pat Colligan Anytime

70 mi. S of Syracuse

Est 1995; **Acres** 300; **Type** Public, Member/Avail; **On Site** Clubhouse, Meals, Clays; **Shoots** Field; **Birds** Quail, Pheasant, Chukar; **Dogs** Avail/HDW; **Packages** 1/2 Day, 1-15 guns ○ NAGA/See Pg. 107

Chenango Valley Kennels

PO Box 502, Greene, NY 13778

(607) 656-7257 Vincent & Irene Guglielmo Nights

15 mi. N of Binghampton

Est 1987; **Acres** 110; **On Site** Clays; **Shoots** Field; **Birds** Quail, Pheasant, Chukar; **Dogs** Avail/HDW; **Packages** 1/2 Day, 1-4 guns

East Mountain Shooting Preserve

150 McCarthy Rd., Dover Plains, NY 12522

(914) 877-6274 Victor D'Avanzo 6am-9pm

80 mi. N of New York City

Acres 500; **Type** Public; **On Site** Clubhouse, Clays; **Shoots** Field, Tower; **Birds** Quail, Pheasant, Chukar, Ducks; **Dogs** Avail/HDW; **Packages** 1/2 Day, 1-12 guns

○ Kennel Bird Dogs
○ Sporting Clays
○ Factory Ammunition
○ Quality Clubhouse
○ Family Run Business

Eldred Preserve

1040 Rt. 55, Eldred, NY 12732

(914) 557-8316 Bonnie Robertson 8-4pm

16 mi. from Monticello

Est 1967; **Acres** 600; **Type** Public, Member/Avail; **On Site** Clubhouse, Lodging, Meals, Clays; **Shoots** Field; **Birds** Turkey; **Packages** 1 Day, up to 25 guns

Empire Game Farm

3720 Rt. 41, Solon, NY 13040

(607) 836-6620 W. Douglas Whittaker

30 mi. S of Syracuse

Est 1987; **Acres** 275; **Hunters/yr** 60; **Type** Public; **Shoots** Field; **Birds** Quail, Pheasant; **Dogs** Avail/HDW; **Packages** 1/2 Day, 1-4 guns

Forrestal Farm Hunting Preserve
4660 Water Works Rd., Medina, NY 14103
(716) 798-0222 Bill Keppler
30 mi. NE of Buffalo
Est 1975; **Acres** 680; **Hunters/yr** 500; **Type**
Public, Member/Avail; **On Site** Clubhouse, Lodging,
Meals; **Shoots** Field, Tower, Blinds; **Birds** Pheasant,
Ducks, Geese; **Dogs** Avail/HDW; **Packages** 1/2
Day, up to 16 guns ○ NAGA/See Pg. 107

Four Winds Hunting Club
542 Maple Dr., PO Box 133, East Chatham, NY 12060
(718) 996-4115 Peter Giakoumis Weekdays (518)
392-2559 Weekends
100 mi. N of New York City
Est 1982; **Acres** 205; **Hunters/yr** 180; **Type**
Public, Member/Avail; **On Site** Clubhouse, Meals,
Clays; **Shoots** Field, Tower; **Birds** Quail, Pheasant,
Chukar, Turkey; **Dogs** Avail/HDW; **Packages** 1 Day,
1-8 guns

Friar Tuck Clay & Shooting Preserve
4858 Rt. 32, Catskill, NY 12414
(800) 832-7600 Mick Howells Ext. 447, 9-5
18 mi. S of Kingston
Est 1994; **Acres** 125; **Hunters/yr** 250; **Type**
Public, Member/Avail; **On Site** Clubhouse, Lodging,
Meals, Clays; **Shoots** Field; **Birds** Ruffed Grouse,
Woodcock, Pheasant, Chukar, Turkey, Snipe, Ducks,
Geese; **Dogs** Avail/HDW; **Packages** 1/2 Day, 2-6 guns

Golden Blew Acres Shooting Preserve
1835 Lewiston Rd., Basom, NY 14013
(716) 948-5690 Terry Blew Anytime
25 mi. W of Buffalo **Est** 1970; **Acres** 300;
Hunters/yr 125; **Type** Public, Member/Avail;
Shoots Field; **Birds** Pheasant; **Dogs** Avail/HDW;
Packages 1/2 Day, 1-12 guns

Gray's Farms
2839 Lockport Rd., Oakfield, NY 14125
(716) 948-9269 David Gray 9-5
30 mi. E of Buffalo
Est 1947; **Acres** 600; **Hunters/yr** 800; **Type**
Public; **On Site** Clubhouse; **Shoots** Field; **Birds**
Pheasant; **Dogs** Avail/HDW; **Packages** 1/2 Day,
1-20 guns ○ NAGA/See Pg. 107

Green Mountain Shooting Preserve
PO Box 12, Denver, NY 12421
(914) 586-4831 Craig Massell
5 mi. N of Margaretville
Acres 158; **Type** Public; **On Site** Lodging, Meals,
Clays; **Shoots** Field; **Birds** Ruffed Grouse, Pheasant,
Turkey; **Dogs** Avail/HDW; **Packages** 1/2 Day

Highland Farm
Pheasant Preserve
Box 193, Highland Rd., Old Chatham, NY 12136
(518) 784-2614 Joe Nastke 9-9
25 mi. SE of Albany Est 1985; **Acres** 500; **Type**
Public; **On Site** Clubhouse, Lodging, Meals; **Shoots**
Field, Tower; **Birds** Quail, Ruffed Grouse, Pheasant,
Chukar, Turkey; **Dogs** Avail/HDW; **Packages** 1/2
Day, 1-16 guns — Located only 25 miles southeast of
Albany and just 2 1/2 hours from Downtown Manhattan, Highland Farm Pheasant Club is a sportsman's
paradise. At Highland you'll hunt on over 500 acres of
some of the best pheasant cover in the northeast. Joe
Nastke, Highland's Coordinator of Events will personally see that your visit will be eventful and rewarding.
Overnight accommodations are available in large
peaceful rooms with private baths. In addition to walk-
up pheasant hunts, English-style pheasant tower
releases, guided grouse and springtime turkey hunts
are offered. Call today for information and don't forget to ask about our special Youth and Ladies
programs.

Hull-O-Farms Game Preserve
Box 48, Cochrane Rd., Durham, NY 12422
(518) 239-6950 Frank Hull
Type Public; **On Site** Lodging; **Shoots** Field; **Birds** Pheasant, Chukar, Turkey, Ducks o NAGA/See Pg.107

Indian Mountain Lodge
RR1, Box 17, Millerton, NY 12546
(518) 789-6801 Joseph L. Blank 8am-5pm
100 mi. N of Manhattan
Est 1994; **Acres** 532; **Type** Public, Member/Avail, Corp.; **On Site** Clubhouse, Meals, Clays; **Shoots** Field, Tower, Driven, Blinds, Boat; **Birds** Quail, Pheasant, Chukar, Huns, Turkey, Ducks, Geese; **Dogs** Avail/HDW; **Packages** 1/2 Day, 1-24 guns o NAGA/See Pg. 107

Kidney Creek Farms & Preserve
PO Box 27, Schaghticoke, NY 12154
(518) 753-0309 Gary Breski
Type Public, Member/Avail; **Shoots** Field; **Birds** Quail, Pheasant, Chukar, Turkey o NAGA/See Pg. 107

Lazy River Game Bird Farm
341 Lazy River Rd., Hermon, NY 13652
(315) 347-4960 Michael Watkins
Shoots Field; **Birds** Quail o NAGA/See Pg. 107

Lido's Game Farm
68 Berkshire Rd., Box 277, Hillsdale, NY 12529
(518) 329-1551 Lido or Francine 12-3pm
45 mi. S of Albany **Acres** 6,000; **Hunters/yr** 2,000; **Type** Public, Member/Avail; **On Site** Clubhouse, Meals; **Shoots** Field, Tower; **Birds** Quail, Pheasant, Chukar; **Dogs** Avail; **Packages** 1/2 Day, 1-10 guns o NAGA/See Pg. 107

LoPinto Farms Lodge
355 Sheldon Rd., Freeville, NY 13068
(800) 551-5806 Joe LoPinto
10 mi. N of Ithaca
Est 1993; **Acres** 320; **Type** Public, Member/Avail, Corp.; **On Site** Clubhouse, Lodging, Meals; **Shoots** Field; **Birds** Quail, Pheasant, Turkey; **Dogs** Avail/HDW; **Packages** 1/2 Day, up to 9 guns o NAGA/See Pg. 107

Mountain View
Shooting Preserve
1123 Albany Post Rd., Gardiner, NY 12525
(914) 255-5398 John/Pat Leavitt Evening
85 mi. N of New York City
Est 1981; **Acres** 450; **Hunters/yr** 700; **Type** Public, Member/Avail, Corp.; **On Site** Clubhouse; **Shoots** Field, Tower, Blinds; **Birds** Quail, Woodcock, Pheasant, Chukar, Ducks; **Dogs** Avail/HDW; **Packages** 1/2 Day, 2-5 guns

Nine Partners Pheasant Farm
RR#3, Box 47, Millbrook, NY 12545
(914) 677-3114 Jonathan L. Wicker
80 mi. N of New York City
Est 1982; **Type** Public, Member/Avail; **On Site**

Clubhouse, Clays; **Shoots** Field, Tower; **Birds** Quail, Pheasant, Chukar, Huns, Ducks; **Dogs** Avail/HDW; **Packages** 1/2 Day, 1-24 guns o NAGA/See Pg. 107

North Fork Preserve, Inc.
5330 Sound Ave. (Mail to:349 Penny's Rd),
Riverhead, NY 11901
(516) 369-1728 Brett Jayne or Robert H. Krudop 8-4
70 mi. E of New York
Est 1984; **Acres** 400; **Type** Member/Avail; **On Site** Clubhouse, Meals, Clays; **Shoots** Field, Tower; **Birds** Quail, Woodcock, Pheasant, Chukar, Ducks, Geese; **Dogs** Avail/HDW; **Packages** 1/2 Day, 1-3 guns
o Shooting Instruction - Under the direction of Mark Elliot, formerly of the West London Shooting School, with over 20 yrs. experience teaching and fitting for Britain's major gunmakers
Exclusive Sportsman's Club on Eastern Long Island - has limited owner/memberships available. Facilities include sporting clays, FITASC, skeet, excellent upland game and cover, deer, bass ponds, clubhouse and tennis courts. Non-member, private and corporate shoots and functions may be arranged. Call: North Fork Preserve: (516) 369-1728 (days); (516) 722-3152 (evenings).
See Our Ad Across

Orvis Sandanona
PO Box 450, Millbrook, NY 12545
(914) 677-9701 Brian Long
60 mi. N of New York City
Est 1995; **Type** Member/Avail; **On Site** Clubhouse, Meals, Clays; **Shoots** Field, Tower, Blinds; **Birds** Quail, Pheasant, Chukar, Huns, Ducks; **Dogs** Avail/HDW

Pawling Mountain Club
PO Box 573, Pawling, NY 12564
(914) 855-3825 Gary Hall
80 mi. N of New York City
Est 1987; **Acres** 900; **Type** Member/Ltd, Corp.; **On Site** Clubhouse, Lodging, Meals, Clays; **Shoots** Field, Tower; **Birds** Quail, Pheasant, Chukar, Turkey, Ducks; **Dogs** Avail/HDW o NAGA/See Pg. 107
o Shooting Instruction Available

Petan Farms Shooting Preserve
South Quaker Hill Rd., Pawling, NY 12564
(914) 878-3183 John O'Hara 5:30-8:30 pm
50 mi. N of New York City
Est 1980; **Acres** 150; **Hunters/yr** 75; **Type** Public; **On Site** Clubhouse; **Shoots** Field; **Birds** Quail, Pheasant, Chukar; **Dogs** Avail/HDW; **Packages** 1/2 Day, 2-6 guns

Pheasant Hollow Gun Dogs
5629 Canadice Hollow Rd., Springwater, NY 14560
(716) 367-3535 Lorraine Carpenter
Type Public, Member/Avail; **Shoots** Field; **Birds** Quail, Pheasant, Chukar o NAGA/See Pg. 107

Pheasant Ridge at Saratoga
Rt. 40 North, Greenwich, NY 12834
(518) 692-9464 V.A. Mallon
13 mi. E of Saratoga
Est 1989; **Acres** 102; **Type** Public, Corp.; **On Site** Clubhouse, Meals; **Shoots** Field, Tower; **Birds** Pheasant; **Dogs** Avail; **Packages** 1/2 Day, 1-24 guns ○ NAGA/See Pg. 107
Set in the foothills of the Adirondacks, just 13 miles from Saratoga Springs, Pheasant Ridge offers hunters 100 acres of prime pheasant habitat. On Saturdays during the hunting season, novice and veteran shooters alike can experience the unmatched thrill of a traditional English Style Continental Pheasant Shoot. Nearby inns and the Little Colfax Executive Retreat provide charming and comfortable accommodations. Shooting lessons are available. The splendid foliage makes a visit to Pheasant Ridge a special treat in Autumn. Call today for information.

Pond Hollow Hunting Preserve
676 North Sanford Rd., Deposit, NY 13754
(607) 467-4165 Kevin J. McGibney
150 mi. NW of New York City
Est 1986; **Type** Public, Member/Avail; **On Site** Clubhouse, Lodging; **Shoots** Field; **Birds** Quail, Pheasant, Chukar; **Dogs** Avail/HDW; **Packages** 1/2 Day, 1-8 guns ○ NAGA/See Pg. 107

Port of Missing Men
, Township of Southampton, NY
(516) 354-3442 Robert Penn 9-5
120 mi. E of New York City
Acres 2,000; **Type** Public; **Shoots** Field, Tower, Driven, Blinds; **Birds** Pheasant, Ducks; **Packages** 1 Day, 2-12 guns

Quail Run Sportsman's Club
, Speonk, NY 11972
(516) 325-1180 Brian or (516) 325-5535
W of West Hampton
Est 1995; **Acres** 150; **Type** Member/Avail; **On Site** Clubhouse; **Shoots** Field; **Birds** Quail, Pheasant, Chukar; **Dogs** Avail/HDW; **Packages** 1/2 Day, 1-3 guns

Quigg Hollow Hunting Preserve
3130 Quigg Hollow Rd., Andover, NY 14806
(607) 478-8576 Rod & Phyllis Walker
90 mi. S of Rochester
Est 1965; **Acres** 225; **Hunters/yr** 320; **Type** Public, Member/Avail, Corp.; **On Site** Clubhouse, Meals, Clays; **Shoots** Field, Blinds; **Birds** Quail, Pheasant, Chukar, Ducks; **Dogs** Avail/HDW; **Packages** 1/2 Day, 1-20 guns ○ NAGA/See Pg. 107

Rainbow Ridge Pheasants
47 Farnsworth Ave., Oakfield, NY 14125
(716) 948-9123 Jason Haacke
Type Public, Member/Avail; **On Site** Clubhouse; **Shoots** Field; **Birds** Quail, Pheasant, Chukar; **Dogs** Avail/HDW; **Packages** 1/2 Day, 1-20 guns

Ringneck Hunting Preserve
2407 Broadway, Darien Center, NY 14040
(716) 547-3749 Eugene Bontrager after 5pm
28 mi. E of Buffalo Est 1988; **Acres** 120;
Hunters/yr 130; **Type** Public; **On Site** Clubhouse, Lodging; **Shoots** Field; **Birds** Quail, Pheasant, Chukar; **Dogs** Avail/HDW; **Packages** 1/2 Day, 1-4 guns

Rock Tavern

Hunting Preserve
156 Beattie Rd., Rock Tavern, NY 12575
(914) 497-7071 Charlie Popek
50 mi. N of New York City
Est 1996; **Acres** 300; **Type** Public, Member/Avail,
Corp.; **On Site** Clubhouse, Meals; **Shoots** Field,
Tower, Driven, Blinds; **Birds** Quail, Pheasant, Chukar,
Turkey, Sage Grouse, Ducks, Geese; **Dogs**
Avail/HDW; **Packages** 1/2 Day, 1-4 guns
See Our Ad Pg. 375

H. Rottmoss & Sons
508 Col. Cty. Rt. 3, Anciandale, NY 12503
(518) 329-1369 Henry Rottmoss
Acres 700; **Type** Public; **On Site** Clays; **Shoots**
Field; **Birds** Pheasant, Turkey, Ducks, Geese

Seneca River Hunting Preserve
11915 Rt. 176, Cato, NY 13033
(315) 626-2834 Virgil Perry
Type Public, Member/Avail; **Shoots** Field; **Birds**
Quail, Pheasant, Chukar, Huns   O NAGA/See Pg. 107

Serendipity Farms

12201 Rt. 62, Lawtons, NY 14091
(716) 337-9828 Vincent E. Lorenz
25 mi. S of Buffalo
Est 1991; **Acres** 200; **Type** Public, Member/Avail;
On Site Clubhouse, Clays; **Shoots** Field; **Birds**
Quail, Pheasant, Chukar; **Dogs** Avail/HDW;
Packages 1/2 Day, 1-16 guns   O NAGA/See Pg. 107
O Bird Processing
O Sporting Clays
O Family Run Business
O Train Your Dog Here

R.L. Sheltra's Upland Outfitters
40 North St., Pulaski, NY 13142
(315) 298-3803 Robin L. Sheltra Anytime

Sherburne Shooting Preserve
RR#1, Box 148-J, Skinner Hill Rd., Sherburne, NY 13460
(607) 674-4707 Joe Regan Morning or Evening
45 mi. SE of Syracuse
Est 1985; **Acres** 300; **Type** Public; **Shoots** Field;
Birds Quail, Pheasant, Chukar; **Dogs** Avail/HDW;
Packages 1/2 Day, 1-4 guns

Sno-Fun Hunting Preserve

26809 Beckwith Rd., Evans Mills, NY 13637
(315) 629-4801 Richard Farr 6-9
6 mi. N of Watertown
Est 1985; **Acres** 500; **Hunters/yr** 300; **Type**
Public; **On Site** Clubhouse, Lodging, Meals, Clays;
Shoots Field; **Birds** Quail, Pheasant, Chukar; **Dogs**
Avail/HDW; **Packages** 1/2 Day, 1-12 guns
O NAGA/See Pg. 107

The Sportsman's Shooting Preserve
19 Auburn St., Wolcott, NY 14590
(315) 594-2527 Danny Valentine
45 mi. E of Rochester
Acres 220; **Hunters/yr** 100; **Type** Public,
Member/Avail; **On Site** Clubhouse; **Shoots** Field;
Birds Quail, Pheasant, Chukar; **Dogs** Avail;
Packages 1/2 Day

Spring Farm
PO Box 301, Sag Harbor, NY 11963
(516) 725-0038 Dave Schellinger
100 mi. E of New York City
Est 1940; **Acres** 150; **Type** Public; **On Site**
Clubhouse; **Shoots** Field, Tower, Blinds; **Birds**
Pheasant, Chukar, Huns, Ducks; **Dogs** Avail/HDW;
Packages 1/2 Day, 1-8 guns   O NAGA/See Pg. 107
O Bird Processing
O Loaner Guns
O Family Run Business

Stoney Lane Pheasant Farm
2967 Quaker Rd., Gasport, NY 14067
(716) 772-2744 Martin L. Richardson
50 mi. W of Rochester
Est 1990; **Acres** 200; **Type** Public; **On Site** Clays;
Shoots Field; **Birds** Pheasant, Ducks; **Dogs**
Avail/HDW; **Packages** 1/2 Day, 1-4 guns

T-M-T Hunting Preserve, Inc.

RR1, Box 297, School House Rd., Staatsburg, NY 12580
(914) 266-5108 Thomas F. Mackin Anytime
55 mi. N of New York City
Est 1966; **Acres** 209; **Hunters/yr** 1,500; **Type**
Public; **On Site** Clubhouse, Clays; **Shoots** Field,
Blinds; **Birds** Pheasant, Chukar, Ducks; **Dogs**
Avail/HDW; **Packages** 1/2 Day, 1-16 guns
O NAGA/See Pg. 107
O Bird Processing
O Sporting Clays
O Hunting Jeeps
O Quality Clubhouse
O Family Run Business

Tailfeathers Game Farm
Rt. Box 23C, Geer Rd., Chaffee, NY 14030
(716) 496-5162 Bill Howell 9-5
30 mi. S of Buffalo **Est** 1991; **Acres** 700;
Hunters/yr 500; **Type** Public, Member/Avail, Corp.;
Shoots Field; **Birds** Quail, Pheasant, Chukar, Ducks;
Dogs Avail/HDW; **Packages** 1/2 Day, 1-20 guns

Tamarack Preserve Ltd.
RR#1, Box 111B, Millbrook, NY 12545
(914) 373-7084 Tim Bontecou
65 mi. N of New York

Est 1991; **Acres** 2,400; **Hunters/yr** 150; **Type** Member/Avail, Corp.; **On Site** Clubhouse, Lodging, Meals, Clays; **Shoots** Field, Driven, Blinds; **Birds** Quail, Pheasant, Chukar, Huns, Turkey, Ducks, Geese; **Dogs** Avail/HDW; **Packages** 1/2 Day, 1-40 guns O NAGA/See Pg. 107

Chuck Tiranno Kennels & Game Farm
5409 Salt Works Rd., Middleport, NY 14105
(716) 798-1522 Chuck or Carolyn Tiranno 7 pm
38 mi. NE of Buffalo
Est 1975; **Acres** 2,400; **Type** Public, Member/Avail, Corp.; **On Site** Clays; **Shoots** Field, Blinds; **Birds** Pheasant, Turkey, Ducks, Geese; **Dogs** Avail/HDW; **Packages** 1/2 Day

Tompkins Hunting Club
Box 682, Hancock, NY 13783
(607) 637-4574 Art Tompkins
Type Public, Member/Avail; **Birds** Turkey, Ducks
O NAGA/See Pg.

Turkey Trot Acres
Tubbs Hill Rd., Candor, NY 13743
(607) 659-7849 Peter M. Clare Days & Evenings
20 mi. S of Ithaca
Est 1987; **Acres** 25,000; **Hunters/yr** 175; **Type** Public; **On Site** Clubhouse, Meals; **Shoots** Field; **Birds** Turkey; **Dogs** Avail/HDW; **Packages** 3 Days, 1-8 guns

Ed Viola-Waterfowl Guide
87 Job's Lane, Southampton, NY 11968
(516) 287-1181 Ed Viola
90 mi. E of New York City
Est 1979; **Acres** 200; **Type** Public; **Shoots** Blinds; **Birds** Ducks, Geese; **Dogs** HDW; **Packages** 1/2 Day, 2-4 guns

Whispering Pines
Hideaway
548 Townline Rd., Lyons, NY 14489
(315) 946-6170 Charlie & Jane Buisch
30 mi. E of Rochester
Est 1985; **Acres** 2,700; **Type** Public, Member/Avail, Corp.; **On Site** Clubhouse, Lodging, Meals, Clays; **Shoots** Field; **Birds** Quail, Pheasant, Chukar, Huns; **Dogs** Avail/HDW; **Packages** 1/2 Day, 1-28 guns O NAGA/See Pg. 107
We offer 2,600 acres of scenic Finger Lakes countryside for your hunting pleasure. Natural and farmed cover. Hunt with our dogs or your own. Morning, afternoon or all day hunts. No hunting license required. Bird processing available. Season-long hunting passes, too! Special prices for Husband/ Wife, Father/Daughter and Father/Son hunts. Call for information.

Wild Wings Hunting Retreat
12404 Trevett Rd., Springville, NY 14141
(716) 592-7875 Robert Robinson
Type Public; **Shoots** Field; **Birds** Quail, Pheasant, Chukar, Turkey O NAGA/See Pg. 107

NORTH CAROLINA

Adams Creek Gunning Lodge
6240 Adams Creek Rd., Havelock, NC 28532
(919) 447-6808 Rusty or June Bryan (919) 447-7688
125 mi. SE of Raleigh near Morehead City
Est 1933; **Acres** 800; **Type** Public, Member/Avail, Corp.; **On Site** Clubhouse, Lodging, Meals, Clays; **Shoots** Field, Tower, Blinds; **Birds** Dove, Quail, Pheasant, Ducks; **Dogs** Avail/HDW; **Packages** 1/2 Day, 1-12 guns O NAGA/See Pg. 107

Black River Hunting Preserve
Rt. 3, Box 477, Dunn, NC 28334
(910) 897-5490 Ron Hicks
5 mi. NE of Coats **Type** Public; **Shoots** Field; **Birds** Dove, Quail, Pheasant, Chukar; **Dogs** Avail/HDW

BUSICK QUAIL FARMS
HUNTING PRESERVE
Busick Quail Farms & Hunting Preserve
11933 NC Hwy. 119 South, Burlington, NC 27217
(910) 421-5758 Roger D. Busick Anytime
40 mi. NW of Durham or 35 mi. E of Greensboro
Est 1987; **Acres** 1,600; **Hunters/yr** 400; **Type** Public, Member/Ltd; **On Site** Clubhouse, Lodging, Meals, Clays; **Shoots** Field; **Birds** Quail, Pheasant, Chukar; **Dogs** Avail/HDW; **Packages** 1/2 Day, 1-20 guns O NAGA/See Pg. 107
O Bird Processing
O Kennel Bird Dogs
O Less than 15 minutes from off I-85
O Come shoot our brand new 10 station sporting clays course
O Hospitality is our trademark!

Can't Miss Shooting Preserve
Rt. 1, Box 530, Aurora, NC 27806
(919) 322-5227 Earl Bonner/O.C. Bennett 6 am to 10 pm
40 mi. E of Greenville
Est 1987; **Acres** 600; **Hunters/yr** 250; **Type** Public; **Shoots** Field; **Birds** Quail, Pheasant; **Dogs** Avail/HDW; **Packages** 1/2 Day, 1-10 guns

Catawba Hunting Preserve
345 Hackett St., Salisbury, NC 28144
(704) 642-1710 Drew Arey
30 mi. N of Charlotte **Est** 1996; **Acres** 400; **Type** Public, Member/Avail; **On Site** Clubhouse, Meals, Clays; **Shoots** Field, Blinds; **Birds** Quail, Pheasant, Chukar, Ducks; **Dogs** Avail/HDW; **Packages** 1/2 Day, 1-20 guns

Chestnut Hunting Lodge
Rt. 2, Box 236, Taylorsville, NC 28681
(704) 632-3916 Jerry Rushing
50 mi. NW of Charlotte
Acres 700; **Type** Public; **On Site** Lodging; **Shoots**
Field; **Birds** Turkey; **Dogs** Avail/HDW

Contentnea Creek
Hunting Preserve - Kennel- Clays
Rt. 5, Box 60, Snow Hill, NC 28530
(919) 747-2020 S.M. Gray/Bob Steed
60 mi. SE of Raleigh
Est 1986; **Acres** 2,000; **Hunters/yr** 1,000; **Type**
Public, Member/Avail, Corp.; **On Site** Clubhouse,
Lodging, Meals, Clays; **Shoots** Field, Tower, Blinds,
Boat; **Birds** Dove, Quail, Pheasant, Chukar, Ducks;
Dogs Avail/HDW; **Packages** 1/2 Day, 2-30 guns

Crow Hill Farm, Inc.
758 Crow Hill Rd., Beaufort, NC 28516
(919) 728-7233 Charles Roffey
Type Member/Ltd; **Shoots** Field; **Birds** Quail,
Ducks ○ NAGA/See Pg. 107

Davis Farms Preserve
314 Joan Court, Beaufort, NC 28516
(919) 728-2199 Warren J. Davis 8-8
Est 1991; **Acres** 250; **Type** Public, Member/Avail;
On Site Clays; **Shoots** Field; **Birds** Quail, Pheasant,
Chukar; **Dogs** Avail/HDW; **Packages** 1 Day, up to
2 guns ○ NAGA/See Pg. 107

Flint Ridge Shooting Preserve, Inc.
Rt. 2, Box 118, Polkton, NC 28135
(704) 826-8107 Keith Edwards
45 mi. SE of Charlotte
Est 1987; **Type** Public; **On Site** Clubhouse, Lodging,
Meals, Clays; **Shoots** Field; **Birds** Quail, Pheasant,
Chukar; **Dogs** Avail/HDW; **Packages** 1/2 Day

George Hi Plantation
PO Box 1068, Roseboro, NC 28382
(910) 525-4524 Charles DuBose 9-5
Est 1987; **Acres** 2,000; **Type** Public; **On Site**
Clubhouse, Lodging, Meals; **Shoots** Field; **Birds**
Quail; **Dogs** Avail/HDW; **Packages** 1 Day, 1-16 guns

Gold Mine Hunting Preserve
6464 Smith Rd., Stanfield, NC 28163
(704) 786-0619 G.M. Almond Evenings
Est 1979; **Type** Public; **On Site** Clubhouse,
Lodging, Meals; **Shoots** Field; **Birds** Turkey; **Dogs**
Avail/HDW; **Packages** 1 Day, up to 1 guns

Griffin Hill
Hunting Preserve
Rt. 3, Box 222, Wadesboro, NC 28170
(704) 694-5086 Al or Phyllis Griffin After 6 pm
50 mi. E of Charlotte
Est 1977; **Acres** 550; **Type** Public, Corp.; **On Site**
Clubhouse, Lodging, Meals, Clays; **Shoots** Field;
Birds Quail; **Dogs** Avail/HDW; **Packages** 1/2 Day,
1-12 guns ○ NAGA/See Pg. 107
See Our Ad Below

Gunners Point Plantation
PO Box 221, Harrells, NC 28444
(910) 532-4520 John Melvin
85 mi. S of Raleigh
Est 1991; **Acres** 600; **Type** Public, Member/Avail;
Shoots Field; **Birds** Dove, Quail; **Dogs** Avail/HDW;
Packages 1/2 Day, 1-3 guns

Haddock's
Shooting Preserve
Rt. 1, Box 467-10, Winterville, NC 28590
(919) 355-6539 David Haddock 7 am to 7 pm
65 mi. SE of Raleigh
Est 1985; **Acres** 5,000; **Hunters/yr** 500; **Type**
Public; **On Site** Clubhouse, Lodging; **Shoots** Field,
Driven, Blinds, Boat; **Birds** Dove, Quail, Pheasant,
Ducks, Geese; **Dogs** Avail/HDW; **Packages** 1/2
Day, 1-8 guns
See Our Ad, Right

Hunting Creek Quail & Pheasant Hunting
Rt. 2, Box 394, Hamptonville, NC 27020
(910) 468-4591 Bill Hudson After 5 pm
25 mi. W of Winston-Salem
Acres 500; **Type** Public; **On Site** Clubhouse, Clays;
Shoots Field; **Birds** Quail, Pheasant; **Dogs**
Avail/HDW; **Packages** 1/2 Day, 1-8 guns
○ NAGA/See Pg. 107

Jones Island Hunt Club
PO Box 8365, Hobucken, NC 28537
(919) 745-7877 Fred Hampton
Type Member/Avail; **On Site** Lodging; **Shoots**
Field; **Birds** Quail, Pheasant, Ducks
○ NAGA/See Pg. 107

Kennis Creek Hunting Preserve
Rt. 2, Box 55A, Fuquay-Varina, NC 27526
(919) 552-9156 Frank Howard 8-11 pm
20 mi. S of Raleigh
Est 1991; **Acres** 600; **Hunters/yr** 200; **Type**
Public; **On Site** Lodging, Meals, Clays; **Shoots** Field;
Birds Quail; **Dogs** Avail/HDW; **Packages** 1/2 Day,
1-10 guns

Lee Farms Hunting Preserve
Rt. 1, Box 357, Rocky Point, NC 28457
(910) 259-5550 R. Eric Lee
105 mi. SE of Raleigh
Acres 400; **Type** Public; **Shoots** Field; **Birds** Quail;
Packages 1/2 Day, 1-4 guns ○ NAGA/See Pg. 107

Louisburg Shooting Preserve
947 N. Main St., Louisburg, NC 27549
(919) 496-5076 Johnny King After 8 pm
25 mi. NE of Raleigh
Est 1992; **Acres** 175; **Hunters/yr** 250; **Type**
Public; **On Site** Clubhouse; **Shoots** Field; **Birds**
Quail, Pheasant, Chukar; **Dogs** Avail; **Packages** 1/2
Day, 2-6 guns

Lowes Shooting Preserve
108 Lowe St., Lawndale, NC 28090
(704) 538-7254 J.D. Lowe 8 to 11 pm
40 mi. W of Charlotte
Est 1983; **Acres** 175; **Hunters/yr** 250; **Type**
Public; **On Site** Clubhouse, Clays; **Shoots** Field;
Birds Quail, Pheasant; **Dogs** Avail/HDW; **Packages**
1/2 Day, 3-10 guns

Mauney Hunting Preserve
548 Mauney Lane, Gastonia, NC 28052
(704) 861-8735 Roger Mauney
Type Public, Member/Avail; **Shoots** Field; **Birds**
Quail ○ NAGA/See Pg. 107

Maxwell Creek Plantation
707 Blind Bridge Rd., Magnolia, NC 28453
(910) 289-2171 Wendell Evans, Jr.
70 mi. E of Raleigh
Est 1979; **Acres** 1,000; **Type** Public; **On Site** Clubhouse, Lodging, Meals, Clays; **Shoots** Field, Blinds; **Birds** Dove, Quail, Ducks; **Dogs** Avail/HDW; **Packages** 1/2 Day, 1-8 guns

Occoneechee Shooting Preserve
Rt. 1, Box 435, Jackson, NC 27845
(919) 583-1799 Gill Cutchin
90 mi. NE of Raleigh
Acres 5,000; **Type** Public; **On Site** Clubhouse, Lodging, Meals, Clays; **Shoots** Field; **Birds** Turkey; **Dogs** Avail/HDW

OLD HOMEPLACE
SHOOTING PRESERVE

Old Homeplace Shooting Preserve
5000 Holly Ridge Farm Rd., Raleigh, NC 27604
(919) 878-9183 Don Jones 8am-9pm
45 mi. S of Raleigh
Est 1992; **Acres** 500; **Hunters/yr** 150; **Type** Public; **On Site** Clubhouse, Meals; **Shoots** Field; **Birds** Quail, Pheasant, Chukar, Huns; **Dogs** Avail/HDW; **Packages** 1/2 Day, 1-12 guns
At the "Old Homeplace" you'll hunt the best flying quail available in natural fields of oak and pine ridges. Pheasant and chukar are available, too. (Ask about our combination hunt packages.) All hunts include a guide and a dog. Overnight accommodations for up to 6 people–including an old fashioned country breakfast–are available in our recently renovated lodge that has a big porch, tongue and groove floors and ceilings, and a fireplace in each room. The quality and low-price of our no-limit hunts cannot be beat. Call today!

Paul's Place Hunting Preserve
11725 Hwy. 117 S., Rocky Point, NC 28457
(910) 675-2345 Dave Paul Anytime
12 mi. N of Wilmington
Est 1991; **Acres** 250; **Hunters/yr** 100; **Type** Member/Avail, Corp.; **On Site** Lodging, Meals, Clays; **Shoots** Field, Blinds; **Birds** Quail, Pheasant, Chukar, Ducks; **Dogs** Avail/HDW

C. Pierce Farms Shooting Preserve
Rt. 2, Box 38, Ahoskie, NC 27910
(919) 332-5360 Cedric Pierce
6 mi. NE of Ahoskie
Acres 1,000; **Hunters/yr** 500; **Type** Public; **On Site** Clubhouse, Lodging, Meals, Clays; **Shoots** Field, Tower, Blinds; **Birds** Quail, Pheasant, Chukar, Ducks; **Dogs** Avail

Pine Lake Plantation
Beulah Hill Church Rd., West End, NC 27376
(910) 947-1696 J. Clayton Myrick
70 mi. S of Raleigh
Acres 4,000; **Type** Public; **Shoots** Field; **Birds** Quail; **Dogs** Avail

Pungo Acres Hunting Retreat
PO Box 55, Pantego, NC 24860
(919) 935-5415 Edwin "Booger" Harris
115 mi. E of Raleigh
Est 1985; **Acres** 12,000; **Hunters/yr** 600; **Type** Public, Member/Avail, Corp.; **On Site** Clubhouse, Lodging, Meals, Clays; **Shoots** Field, Blinds; **Birds** Dove, Quail, Pheasant, Ducks, Geese; **Dogs** Avail/HDW; **Packages** 1/2 Day, 2-15 guns

Quail Creek Hunting Preserve
3461 Macon Farm Rd., Ramseur, NC 27316
(919) 879-4187 Stephen A. Grubb
8 mi. E of Asheboro
Acres 500; **Hunters/yr** 100; **Type** Member/Avail; **On Site** Clubhouse, Lodging, Meals, Clays; **Shoots** Field; **Birds** Dove, Quail; **Dogs** Avail

Quail Hatchery Shooting Preserve
1618 Friendship, Statesville, NC 28677
(704) 592-2935 Paul Harmon or Alma before 10 pm
40 mi. N of Charlotte
Est 1970; **Acres** 300; **Type** Public; **On Site** Lodging; **Shoots** Field; **Birds** Quail; **Dogs** HDW; **Packages** 1/2 Day, up to 1 guns

Quail Ridge Shooting Preserve
Rt. 1, Box 165, Hookerton, NC 28538
(919) 747-5210 R.E. Carraway
75 mi. SE of Raleigh
Est 1991; **Acres** 1,000; **Hunters/yr** 500; **Type** Public, Member/Avail, Corp.; **On Site** Clubhouse, Lodging, Meals, Clays; **Shoots** Field; **Birds** Quail, Pheasant; **Dogs** Avail/HDW; **Packages** 1/2 Day, 1-15 guns

Ray Ingold's Shooting Preserve
PO Box 381, Mt. Gilead, NC 27306
(910) 439-6318 Ray Ingold
50 mi. E of Charlotte
Type Public; **Shoots** Field; **Birds** Quail; **Dogs** Avail/HDW

Salem Kennels & Shooting Preserve
Rt. 2, Box 107, Whitakers, NC 27891
(919) 443-5660 Craig Reid
45 mi. NE of Raleigh
Est 1983; **Acres** 300; **Type** Public; **Shoots** Field; **Birds** Quail, Pheasant; **Dogs** Avail/HDW; **Packages** 1/2 Day, 1-6 guns

Shady Knoll Preserve
3642 Shady Knoll Dr., Asheboro, NC 27203
(919) 879-3663 John W. Maness After 6 pm
8 mi. E of Asheboro
Est 1987; **Acres** 150; **Type** Public, Member/Avail, Corp.; **On Site** Meals; **Shoots** Field, Blinds; **Birds**

Six Runs Plantation

The Only ORVIS® Endorsed Wingshooting Lodge In the Carolinas

Quail hunting is our business at Six Runs Plantation. Over 50 different feeding plots, plenty of underbrush and cover provide for excellent bird concentrations.

At Six Runs, setters are our specialty. Some of the finest English and Irish Setters campaigned today in National competition were bred and trained here. We are very proud of our dogs and know you will be too, after the hunt.

While quail is the primary game sought here, there are also abundant populations of ducks and deer on over 2,000 acres. Quail hunters may hunt duck and deer at no additional charge.

After a challenging day's hunt—walking, aboard our 6-wheel hunting vehicles, or riding our Tennessee Walking horses you'll appreciate our deluxe lodge. An historic structure of heart pine and juniper logs, the main house boasts an extrarordinarily large great room, lounge with bar, and a conference/formal dining room.

Six Runs Lodge accommodates up to 20 guests in eight spacious bedrooms. Overnight guests enjoy gourmet meals of pheasant, quail, chicken, duck, venison and cabrito.

Truly a hunter's paradise, Six Runs has earned a coveted endorsement from ORVIS. Come and enjoy covey shooting at its best.

For more information and reservations, call or write:

910-532-4810 *or* 800-685-7221 (PIN # 2019)

Six Runs Plantation • 2794 Register-Sutton Rd. • Rose Hill, NC 28458

Quail, Pheasant, Chukar, Ducks;   **Dogs** Avail/HDW;
Packages 1/2 Day, up to 6 guns
o NAGA/See Pg. 107

Shelter Creek Plantation & Hunting
1523 N. Kerr Ave., Wilmington, NC 28405
(910) 791-7778 Jerry Simmons
22 mi. from Wilmington
Acres 1,500;   **Hunters/yr** 124;   **Type** Public,
Member/Avail;   **On Site** Clubhouse, Lodging, Meals,
Clays;   **Shoots** Field;   **Birds** Quail, Pheasant, Ducks;
Dogs Avail/HDW;   **Packages** 1/2 Day, 2-4 guns

▼ ORVIS ENDORSED ▼

Six Runs Plantation
Rt. 1, Box 179, Rose Hill, NC 28458
(910) 532-4810 Rebecca Todd-Edwards 6-9 pm
75 mi. SE of Raleigh
Est 1979;   **Acres** 2,000;   **Hunters/yr** 200;   **Type**
Public;   **On Site** Clubhouse, Lodging, Meals, Clays;
Shoots Field, Blinds, Boat;   **Birds** Dove, Quail,
Chukar, Turkey, Ducks;   **Dogs** Avail/HDW;   **Packages**
1 Day, 2-12 guns
See Our Ad Pg. 383

▲ ORVIS ENDORSED ▲

Stadler's Quail Farm
3412 NC 87, Reidsville, NC 27320
(910) 349-5531 Miles Stadler
25 mi. N of Greensboro
Acres 300;   **Type** Public, Member/Avail, Corp.;
Shoots Field;   **Birds** Quail, Pheasant;   **Dogs**
Avail/HDW;   **Packages** 1/2 Day
o NAGA/See Pg. 107

Sun Valley Shooting Preserve
104 Griffin Circle, Monroe, NC 28110
(704) 289-3501 Jack Haney After 6 pm
15 mi. E of Charlotte
Acres 100;   **Type** Public;   **Shoots** Field;   **Birds** Quail;
Dogs Avail/HDW

Tall Cotton Plantation
Rt. 1, Box 260-B, Murfreesboro, NC 27855
(919) 398-8284 E.R. Evans
6 mi. E of Murfreesboro
Type Public, Member/Avail;   **On Site** Clubhouse;
Shoots Field, Blinds;   **Birds** Quail, Pheasant, Chukar,
Ducks;   **Dogs** Avail o NAGA/See Pg. 107

Tobacco Stick Shooting Preserve
PO Box 310, Candor, NC 27229
(910) 974-7197 C.J. Reynolds
50 mi. S of Greensboro
Acres 500;   **Hunters/yr** 100;   **Type** Public;   **On Site**
Clubhouse, Lodging, Clays;   **Shoots** Field, Blinds;
Birds Quail, Pheasant, Chukar, Ducks;   **Dogs** Avail;
Packages 1/2 Day, up to 10 guns

Voncannon's Shooting Preserve
2382 Old Humble Rd., Asheboro, NC 27203

(910) 629-9253 Nolan K. Voncannon
25 mi. S of Greensboro **Acres** 340;   **Type** Public,
Member/Avail;   **On Site** Clubhouse;   **Shoots** Field;
Birds Quail, Pheasant, Chukar;   **Dogs** Avail/HDW;
Packages 1/2 Day, 1-9 guns

Wintergreen
Hunting Preserve
PO Box 981, Bladenboro, NC 28320
(910) 648-6171 Boyce White 7 am to 6 pm
85 mi. S of Raleigh
Est 1988;   **Acres** 500;   **Hunters/yr** 800;   **Type**
Public;   **On Site** Clubhouse, Clays;   **Shoots** Field;
Birds Quail, Pheasant, Chukar;   **Dogs** Avail/HDW;
Packages 1/2 Day, 2-12 guns o NAGA/See Pg. 107

Yadkin Point Hunt & Sporting Clays
PO Box 313, Advance, NC 27006
(910) 998-9518 Howell W. Woltz
10 mi. W of Winston-Salem
Est 1991;   **Acres** 300;   **Type** Public, Member/Avail,
Corp.;   **On Site** Clubhouse, Lodging, Meals, Clays;
Shoots Field;   **Birds** Dove, Quail;   **Dogs** Avail/HDW;
Packages 1/2 Day, 1-15 guns

NORTH DAKOTA

Bois de Sioux Game Farm
18270 95 R St. SE, Fairmount, ND 58030
(701) 474-5879 Arlen Spear
65 mi. S of Fargo
Type Public;   **Shoots** Field;   **Birds** Quail, Pheasant,
Chukar, Ducks;   **Dogs** Avail/HDW
o NAGA/See Pg. 107

Dakota Hunting Club
& Kennels
PO Box 13623, Grand Forks, ND 58208
(701) 775-2074 George Newton 8-5
12 mi. SW of Grand Forks
Est 1969;   **Acres** 900;   **Hunters/yr** 500;   **Type**
Public, Member/Avail, Corp.;   **On Site** Clubhouse,
Clays;   **Shoots** Field;   **Birds** Quail, Pheasant, Chukar,
Huns, Turkey;   **Dogs** Avail/HDW;   **Packages** 1/2 Day,
3-12 guns o NAGA/See Pg. 107

Hillview Hunting Acres, Inc.
RR4, Box 171A, Minot, ND 58701
(800) 838-1057 Bob Saunders
4.5 mi. SE of Minot
Acres 250;   **Hunters/yr** 60;   **Type** Public;   **Shoots**
Field;   **Birds** Pheasant, Chukar;   **Dogs** Avail/HDW;
Packages 1/2 Day, 1-6 guns o NAGA/See Pg. 107

Pride of the Prairie Hunts
HCR01, Box 75, Regent, ND 58650
(701) 563-4526 Brad & Cheryl Nasset

110 mi. SW of Bismarck   **Acres** 20,000; **Type** Public;
On Site Lodging, Meals; **Shoots** Field; **Birds**
Pheasant, Huns, Sharp Tail Grouse; **Dogs** Avail/HDW;
Packages 1 Day, 2-8 guns

Ringnecks Unlimited, Inc.
Rt. 1, Box 12, Flasher, ND 58535
(701) 597-3032 Steve Craine
45 mi. SW of Bismarck **Acres** 640; **Type** Public; **On
Site** Clubhouse, Lodging, Meals, Clays; **Shoots** Field;
Birds Quail, Pheasant, Chukar, Turkey; **Dogs**
Avail/HDW; **Packages** 1/2 Day ○ NAGA/See Pg. 107

Sheyenne Valley Lodge
RR1, Box 27, Goodrich, ND 58444
(701) 884-2432 Ted or Orlan Mertz
80 mi. NE of Bismarck
Acres 50,000; **Type** Public; **On Site** Clubhouse,
Lodging, Meals, Clays; **Shoots** Field; **Birds** Dove,
Pheasant, Huns, Sharp Tail Grouse, Ducks, Geese;
Dogs Avail/HDW; **Packages** 1 Day, 1-8 guns

Windmill Pheasant Farm
7504 130th Ave., SE, Lisbon, ND 58054
(701) 678-2652 Gene or Kandyce Sandstrom
75 mi. SW of Fargo **Est** 1987; **Acres** 320; **Type**
Public; **On Site** Meals; **Shoots** Field; **Birds**
Pheasant; **Dogs** Avail/HDW; **Packages** 1 Day

OHIO

Brier Oak Hunt Club
5316 Sandhill Rd., Bellevue, OH 44811
(419) 483-4953 Kevin or Denise Schaeffer 9-5
65 mi. W of Cleveland
Est 1989; **Acres** 400; **Hunters/yr** 100; **Type**
Public, Member/Avail, Corp.; **On Site** Clubhouse,
Clays; **Shoots** Field; **Birds** Quail, Pheasant, Chukar;
Dogs Avail/HDW; **Packages** 1/2 Day, 1-32 guns
○ NAGA/See Pg. 107

Buckeye Pheasants Hunting Preserve
1608 S. Clayton Rd., New Lebanon, OH 45345
(513) 687-2523 Terry/Robert Parks Anytime
10 mi. W of Dayton
Est 1989; **Acres** 90; **Type** Public; **On Site**
Clubhouse, Meals; **Shoots** Field; **Birds** Quail,
Pheasant, Chukar, Huns; **Dogs** Avail/HDW;
Packages 1/2 Day, 1-6 guns ○ NAGA/See Pg. 107

Cherrybend Pheasant Farm

2326 Cherrybend Rd., Wilmington, OH 45177
(513) 584-4269 Mary Hollister 8am-6pm
40 mi. NE of Cincinnati
Est 1956; **Acres** 368; **Type** Public, Member/Avail;
On Site Clubhouse, Meals, Clays; **Shoots** Field;
Birds Quail, Pheasant, Chukar; **Dogs** Avail/HDW;
Packages 1/2 Day, 1-20 guns ○ NAGA/See Pg. 107

Conneaut Creek Club
2265 Harcourt Dr., Cleveland, OH 44106
(216) 368-1565 H.F. Biggar, III 6-9pm
70 mi. NE of Cleveland; **Type** Member/Avail, Corp.;
On Site Clubhouse, Lodging, Clays; **Shoots** Field;
Birds Quail, Pheasant, Chukar; **Dogs** Avail/HDW;
Packages 1/2 Day, 1-5 guns

Brad Dysinger's Preserve
520 W. Wayne, Paulding, OH 45879
(419) 399-3415 Brad Dysinger
On Site Clays; **Shoots** Field; **Birds** Pheasant,
Chukar ○ NAGA/See Pg. 107

Elkhorn Hunt Club

4146 Klopfenstein Rd., Bucyrus, OH 44820
(419) 562-6131 Samuel A. Ballou Evenings
55 mi. N of Columbus
Est 1962; **Acres** 300; **Hunters/yr** 1,500; **Type**
Public, Member/Avail, Corp.; **On Site** Clubhouse,
Clays; **Shoots** Field; **Birds** Quail, Pheasant, Chukar,
Huns; **Dogs** Avail/HDW; **Packages** 1/2 Day, 1-24
guns ○ NAGA/See Pg. 107

Federal Valley Pheasant Farm
16171 E. Kasler Creek Rd., Amesville, OH 45711
(614) 448-6747 Gene/Roseanna Hines

Flatrock Hunting Preserve
5188 W SR 244, Milroy, IN 46156
(317) 629-2354 Merrill Carrigan 6am to 10pm
85 mi. NW of Cincinnati **Est** 1991; **Acres** 104;
Type Public; **On Site** Clubhouse; **Shoots** Field;
Birds Quail, Pheasant, Chukar; **Packages** 1/2 Day

Grand Valley
Hunting Ranch

10198 Penniman Rd., Orwell, OH 44076
(216) 437-6440 Scott Adams W-Su, 9-4
40 mi. E of Cleveland
Est 1991; **Acres** 1,230; **Type** Public, Member/Avail,
Corp.; **On Site** Clubhouse, Clays; **Shoots** Field;
Birds Dove, Quail, Pheasant, Chukar, Ducks, Geese;
Dogs Avail/HDW; **Packages** 1/2 Day, 1-12 guns

Hidden Haven
Shooting Preserve

9257 Buckeye Rd., Sugar Grove, OH 43155
(614) 746-8568 Ronald Blosser Anytime
50 mi. SE of Columbus
Est 1969; **Acres** 93; **Hunters/yr** 184; **Type**
Public, Member/Avail; **On Site** Clubhouse, Lodging,
Meals, Clays; **Shoots** Field; **Birds** Quail, Pheasant,
Chukar; **Dogs** Avail/HDW; **Packages** 1/2 Day, 2-20
guns ○ NAGA/See Pg. 107

○ Hunting License   ○ Quality Clubhouse
○ Airport Pickup   ○ 5-Stand Sporting & FITASC
○ Shooting Instruction   ○ Sporting Clays-10 Courses
○ Loaner Guns   ○ Factory Ammunition

Hill 'N Dale Club

3605 Poe Rd., Medina, OH 44256
(330) 725-2097 Terry L. Eicher 8-5
50 mi. S of Cleveland
Est 1952; **Acres** 300; **Hunters/yr** 400; **Type**
Member/Avail; **On Site** Clubhouse, Lodging, Meals,
Clays; **Shoots** Field, Tower, Driven; **Birds** Quail,
Pheasant, Chukar, Huns; **Dogs** Avail/HDW;
Packages 1/2 Day, 1-4 guns

Lone Oak Farm

3318 Panhandle Rd., Delaware, OH 43015
(614) 363-7219 Bill Oman
Type Public; **Shoots** Field; **Birds** Quail, Pheasant,
Chukar ○ NAGA/See Pg.107

Mad River
Sportsman's Club

1055 County Rd. 25, Bellefontaine, OH 43311
(513) 593-8245 Tony Stratton, Mgr. 8am-5pm
45 mi. NW of Columbus
Est 1991; **Acres** 300; **Hunters/yr** 1,200; **Type**
Member/Avail, Corp.; **On Site** Clubhouse, Lodging,
Meals, Clays; **Shoots** Field; **Birds** Quail, Pheasant,
Chukar, Huns; **Dogs** Avail/HDW; **Packages** 1/2
Day, 1-4 guns ○ NAGA/See Pg. 107

○ Hunting License   ○ Gourmet Meals
○ Bird Processing   ○ Hunting Jeeps
○ Kennel Bird Dogs   ○ Brochure Available
○ Sporting Clays   ○ On-Site Pro Shop
○ Shooting Instruction   ○ Factory Ammunition
○ Quality Clubhouse

Pheasant Recreation Inc.

18376 London Rd., Circleville, OH 43113
(614) 477-1587 Jack E. Carpenter
25 mi. S of Columbus
Acres 550; **Type** Public, Member/Avail, Corp.; **On**
Site Clubhouse, Lodging, Meals, Clays; **Shoots** Field;
Birds Dove, Quail, Pheasant, Chukar, Ducks; **Dogs**
Avail/HDW; **Packages** 1/2 Day

Quail Run
Hunting Preserve

Box 164, Walton, KY 41094
(502) 463-0912 Kelly Hance
45 mi. SW of Cincinnati, OH
Acres 250; **Hunters/yr** 350; **Type** Public;
On Site Clubhouse; **Shoots** Field; **Birds** Dove,
Quail, Pheasant, Turkey; **Dogs** Avail

See Our Ad Across

Ridgeway Preserves

60 West St., LaRue, OH 43332
(800) 323-3825 Dean or John Ridgeway
50 mi. N of Columbus
Est 1993; **Acres** 190; **Type** Public; **Shoots** Field;
Birds Quail, Pheasant, Ducks; **Dogs** Avail/HDW;
Packages 1/2 Day, 1-10 guns

Ringneck Ridge Sporting Club

1818 County Rd. 74, Gibsonburg, OH 43431
(419) 637-2332 Pete Ochs 8-5
85 mi. W of Cleveland
Est 1986; **Acres** 360; **Type** Member/Avail; **On**
Site Clubhouse, Lodging, Meals, Clays; **Shoots** Field;
Birds Quail, Pheasant, Chukar; **Dogs** Avail/HDW;
Packages 1/2 Day, 1-16 guns ○ NAGA/See Pg. 107

Scioto River Hunting Club

17226 St. Rt. 235, Waynesfield, OH 45896
(513) 464-6560 Mary Zirkle 8am-5pm
○ NAGA/See Pg. 107

Southern Ohio Exotics

31625 Goose Creek Rd., McArthur, OH 45651
(614) 596-5917 Butch Alexander 9-5
70 mi. SE of Columbus **Est** 1991; **Acres** 123;
Type Public; **On Site** Clubhouse, Lodging, Meals;
Shoots Field; **Birds** Pheasant; **Dogs** Avail/HDW;
Packages 1/2 Day, 1-8 guns

Sportsman's Haven Gun Club

14695 E. Pike Rd., Cambridge, OH 43725
Brent Umberger
80 mi. E of Columbus **Est** 1982; **Type**
Member/Avail; **On Site** Clubhouse, Lodging, Clays;

Stinson Farms Hunting Preserve

5920 Good Hope Rd., Frankfort, OH 45628
(614) 998-4977 Manly Stinson 9pm
5 mi. SW of Frankfort
Est 1990; **Acres** 400; **Hunters/yr** 125; **Type**
Public; **On Site** Clubhouse; **Shoots** Field; **Birds**
Quail, Pheasant; **Dogs** Avail/HDW; **Packages** 1/2
Day, 2-10 guns ○ NAGA/See Pg. 107

Stull Hunting Preserve

10738 Ellen Dr., New Carlisle, OH 45344
(513) 845-3901 Dale Stull Eve.
17 mi. N of Dayton **Est** 1991; **Acres** 165; **Type**
Public; **Shoots** Field; **Birds** Pheasant, Chukar;
Dogs Avail/HDW ○ NAGA/See Pg.

Tallmadge Pheasant Farm
& Hunting Preserve

16 County Rd. 1950, Jeromesville, OH 44840
(419) 368-3457 N.L. Tallmadge
50 mi. SW of Cleveland
Est 1922; **Acres** 300; **Type** Public; **On Site**
Clubhouse, Clays; **Shoots** Field; **Birds** Pheasant;
Dogs Avail/HDW; **Packages** 1/2 Day, 2-12 guns
○ NAGA/See Pg. 107

Treddolphin Hunting Preserve
3145 US 62, Hillsboro, OH 45133
(513) 927-5203 Claire S. Smith
Shoots Field; **Birds** Quail, Pheasant
O NAGA/See Pg. 107

Triple Creek Farms, Ltd.
6737 Dueber Ave., SW, East Sparta, OH 44626
(216) 484-3734 Ralph Soehnlen
Shoots Field; **Birds** Pheasant O NAGA/See Pg. 107

WR Hunt Club
5690 CR237, Clyde, OH 43410
(419) 547-8550 Betty or Robert Wright 7am-12noon
50 mi. W of Cleveland
Est 1986; **Acres** 300; **Hunters/yr** 400; **Type** Public, Member/Avail, Corp.; **On Site** Clubhouse, Lodging, Meals, Clays; **Shoots** Field; **Birds** Quail, Pheasant, Chukar; **Dogs** Avail/HDW; **Packages** 1/2 Day, 1-5 guns O NAGA/See Pg. 107

Wild Wings Expeditions
52441 CR 16, West Lafayette, OH 43845
(614) 622-8942 James Schumaker
Shoots Field; **Birds** Pheasant O NAGA/See Pg. 107

Wooster Duck & Pheasant Hunting
470 Carter Dr., Wooster, OH 44691
(330) 262-1671 Louie Carter
Acres 585; **Hunters/yr** 1,200; **Type** Public, Member/Avail, Corp.; **On Site** Clubhouse; **Shoots** Field; **Birds** Pheasant; **Dogs** Avail/HDW; **Packages** 1/2 Day, 1-32 guns O NAGA/See Pg. 107

Wrestle Creek Game Club
23605 Fairmont - CR180, Waynesfield, OH 45896
(419) 568-2867 Jim Hardin 9am-6pm
12 mi. SE of Lima **Est** 1990; **Acres** 160;
Hunters/yr 400; **Type** Public; **On Site** Clubhouse, Clays; **Shoots** Field; **Birds** Quail, Pheasant, Chukar; **Dogs** Avail/HDW; **Packages** 1/2 Day, 1-15 guns

OKLAHOMA

3H Hunting Ranch
608 Cedar Lane, Frederick, OK 73542
(405) 335-5385 Joe Horton
13 mi. NW of Frederick Est 1995; **Acres** 6,000;
Type Public; **On Site** Clubhouse, Lodging, Meals, Clays; **Shoots** Field; **Birds** Dove, Quail, Turkey, Ducks, Geese; **Dogs** Avail

Anderson Commercial
Rt. 1, Box 1, Sweetwater, OK 73666
(405) 534-2305 James Anderson
30 mi. W of Sweetwater **Type** Public; **Shoots** Field;
Birds Quail, Pheasant; **Dogs** Avail

Antelope Hills Hunting
Box 65, Durham, OK 73642
(405) 983-2462 Max Montgomery After 6pm

Bar B Commercial Hunting Area
Rt. 2, Box 130, Pawhuska, OK 74056
(918) 349-2231 Robert A. Boulanger
45 mi. NW of Tulsa Est 1986; **Acres** 2,200;
Hunters/yr 300; **Type** Public; **On Site** Clubhouse, Meals; **Shoots** Field, Tower; **Birds** Quail, Pheasant, Chukar, Turkey; **Dogs** Avail/HDW; **Packages** 1/2 Day, 1-40 guns

Boxcar Hunting Club
3201 N.W. 13th, Oklahoma City, OK 73107
(405) 947-7525 Glen Decker 8am-10am
160 mi. SW of Oklahoma City
Est 1991; **Acres** 700; **Hunters/yr** 65; **Type**
Public; **On Site** Clubhouse, Lodging, Meals, Clays;
Shoots Field; **Birds** Dove, Quail, Turkey, Ducks;
Dogs Avail/HDW; **Packages** 1 Day, 4-6 guns

Canadian River Recreational Club
HC62, Box 146, Eufaula, OK 74432
(918) 689-5085 David/Patty Fisher 8-10am, 5-10pm

Cimarron Hunting Preserve
Rt. 1, Box 163, Hennessey, OK 73742
(405) 853-2737 Donald Miller Evenings
60 mi. NW of Oklahoma City
Est 1988; **Acres** 10,000; **Type** Public, Corp.; **On
Site** Lodging, Meals; **Shoots** Field; **Birds** Quail,
Pheasant, Chukar, Huns, Turkey; **Dogs** Avail/HDW;
Packages 1/2 Day, up to 1 guns O NAGA/See Pg. 107

The Covey Connection
Rt. 2, Box 251, Macomb, OK 74852
(405) 333-2324 Marty S. Swinney

Deer Creek Outfitters
Rt. 2, Box 315A, Guthrie, OK 73044
(405) 348-8723 Steve Humphrey Evenings
60 mi. NW of Oklahoma City

Est 1987; **Acres** 9,000; **Hunters/yr** 200; **Type**
Public; **On Site** Clubhouse, Lodging, Meals; **Shoots**
Field; **Birds** Quail, Turkey; **Dogs** Avail/HDW;
Packages 1 Day, 3-5 guns

Moorland Sportsman's Country Club
Box 454, Moorland, OK 73852
(405) 994-2755 C.M. Crawford Between 9-12
10 mi. E of Woodward
Est 1994; **Type** Member/Avail; **On Site** Clubhouse;
Shoots Field, Blinds; **Birds** Quail, Turkey, Ducks,
Geese; **Dogs** Avail/HDW O NAGA/See Pg. 107

Oklahoma City Hunting Preserve
PO Box 91, Arcadia, OK 73007
(405) 396-2661 Jim & Bobbie Jolly
10 mi. NE of Oklahoma City
Est 1994; **Acres** 75; **Type** Public, Member/Avail,
Corp.; **On Site** Clubhouse, Meals, Clays; **Shoots**
Field; **Birds** Quail, Pheasant, Chukar; **Dogs**
Avail/HDW; **Packages** 1/2 Day, 3-5 guns

Red Rock Ranch
Rt. 1, Box 64-M, Marland, OK 74644
(405) 268-9663 Bill Spires 8am-6pm
25 mi. SE of Ponca City
Est 1985; **Acres** 5,400; **Type** Public, Member/Avail;
On Site Clubhouse, Lodging, Meals, Clays; **Shoots**
Field; **Birds** Quail, Pheasant, Chukar, Turkey; **Dogs**
Avail/HDW; **Packages** 1 Day, 6-10 guns
O NAGA/See Pg. 107

Oklahoma's Woods & Water:
The Shooting's Simply Great!

Want to put your shooting skills to the test? Lots of opportunities await you at Woods & Water, a popular gun club just 7 miles east of Tulsa in northeastern Oklahoma. Doves, waterfowl and upland birds abound in Woods & Water's 4,000-acre hunting arena, as do deer.

Early season dove hunting brings plentiful numbers of the elusive birds, and many hunters take their 15-bird limit in two hours or less. Excellent duck hunting is found at four lakes and 300 acres of flooded timber on the hunt club, which is situated in a large loop of the Verdigris River, a major waterfowl flyway.

Manicured paths lead to challenging stands.

Upland bird hunters find Woods & Water a welcome venue, too, with well trained dogs available and multitudes of quail, pheasants and chukars in natural cover. The resort also conducts European style pheasant shoots. And for those who prefer the challenge of tracking deer, the resort's hunting arena offers perfect habitat.

Outstanding Bass Fishing

But there's more to Woods & Water than hunting. The resort is a favorite destination of fishermen, with largemouth bass—some in the 12-pound range—swimming in the shallow waters of a 110-acre lake. Smaller bass are so abundant elsewhere in the lake that, on a typical spring or early summer day, a pair of anglers can boat 50 to 100, most in the 2 1/2- to 6-pound range.

Bass fishing is catch-and-release only, notes club manager Doug Fuller, and all barbs must be bent flat or filed off hooks. Anglers can fish by themselves, or accompanied by guides who are thoroughly knowledgeable about the lake.

Top 100 Clays Course

Another of Woods & Water's attractions is a sporting clays course designated one of the top 100 courses in the country by *Rifle & Shotgun* magazine. Designed to tax the skills of accomplished shooters, the course presents stand-and-trap combinations that frequently surprise a shotgunner, and often leave him shaking his head.

At the first stand, for example, a pair of hard crossers zip over a pond from right to left to sharpen your shooting eye. At the next, broadside falling battues give you just enough time to break both before they splash into the water. Another stand combines a fast, low-flying crosser with a high-bounding rabbit target, both coming from left to right. Tough by themselves. But the Woods & Water course designers made sure that a sizable tree stands in your way.

The club also boosts a 5-Stand® range whose covered deck overlooks a rugged downward slope. Traps are set at a variety of locations and angles. The sharp slope contributes to the range's challenge by making angles difficult to determine. Another test is the club's wobble-trap range, a variety of shooting favored by a number of club members and visitors.

With a 3,200 sq. ft. clubhouse, and a well stocked pro shop, Woods & Water is not unmindful of the amenities and creature comforts that sportsman enjoy. Professional shoooting instruction, under the tutelage of top shooter Doug Fuller is available. And out-of-town visitors can extend a visit with an overnight stay at a delightful bed & breakfast on the nearby Diamond Bar-D Ranch.

But for those who relish shooting of every sort, the club remains most notable for the year-round variety it offers. Simply put, Woods & Water has it all!

For additional information on Woods & Water, you're invited to contact Doug Fuller or Shane Dillon at Rt. 1, Box 319, 269 N. 305th E. Ave., Catoosa, OK 74015; (918) 266-5551; fax: 918-266-6960.

Rock Creek
Commercial Hunting Area
Rt. 2, Box 130, Pawhuska, OK 74056
(918) 349-2231 Robert Boulanger
13 mi. W of Bartlesville
Acres 4,000; **Type** Public; **On Site** Lodging, Meals;
Shoots Field, Tower; **Birds** Quail, Pheasant, Chukar,
Turkey; **Dogs** Avail

Southern Ranch Hunting Club
Rt. 2, Box 75, Chandler, OK 74834
Dean/Terri Caton (405) 258-0000, 9-5
45 mi. NE of Oklahoma City
Est 1987; **Acres** 1,500; **Hunters/yr** 350; **Type**
Public, Member/Avail, Corp.; **On Site** Clubhouse,
Lodging, Meals, Clays; **Shoots** Field, Tower; **Birds**
Quail, Pheasant, Chukar, Turkey; **Dogs** Avail/HDW;
Packages 1/2 Day, 2-24 guns O NAGA/See Pg. 107

Woods and Water, inc.
Rt. 1, Box 319, Catoosa, OK 74015
(918) 266-5551 Doug Fuller M-F, 9-5
6.5 mi. E of Tulsa
Est 1994; **Acres** 4,000; **Type** Public, Member/Avail;
On Site Clubhouse, Lodging, Meals, Clays; **Shoots**
Field, Tower, Driven, Blinds, Boat; **Birds** Dove, Quail,
Pheasant, Chukar, Turkey, Ducks, Geese; **Dogs**
Avail/HDW; **Packages** 1/2 Day, 2-12 guns
See Our Ad Pg. 388 & 389

OREGON

Bear Creek Pheasant Farm
PO Box 514, Noti, OR 97461
(541) 935-2014 Julie Haney
On Site Lodging; **Shoots** Field; **Birds** Pheasant,
Ducks O NAGA/See Pg. 107

Bear Creek Shooting Preserve
827519 Crooked River Hwy., Prineville, OR 97754
(541) 576-2096 Dan Greenfield
26 mi. SE of Primeville
Acres 640; **Hunters/yr** 200; **Type** Public; **On Site**
Clays; **Shoots** Field; **Birds** Quail, Pheasant; **Dogs**
Avail O NAGA/See Pg. 107

Fish & Wildlife Resources
5014 Rosewood St., Lake Oswego, OR 97035
(503) 636-6744 Barry Morinaka
Type Public; **Shoots** Field; **Birds** Quail, Pheasant,
Chukar O NAGA/See Pg. 107

Great Basin Game Birds
PO Box 613, Burns, OR 97720
(800) 646-0058 Lance Okeson
from 3 Hrs. W of Boise, ID
Est 1990; **Type** Public; **On Site** Clays; **Shoots**
Field; **Birds** Pheasant, Chukar; **Dogs** Avail/HDW;
Packages 1/2 Day, 1-10 guns

Great Expectations Hunting Preserve
HC82, Box 234, Kimberly, OR 97848
(541) 934-2117 Jerry Russell
70 mi. NW of John Day
Est 1994; **Acres** 556; **Hunters/yr** 250; **Type**
Public, Member/Avail; **On Site** Clubhouse, Lodging,
Meals, Clays; **Shoots** Field; **Birds** Quail, Pheasant,
Chukar, Huns; **Dogs** Avail/HDW; **Packages** 1/2
Day, 2-8 guns O NAGA/See Pg. 107
See Our Ad Across

Helms Canyon Hunt Club
200 West 9th St., The Dalles, OR 97058
(503) 296-9535 Doug Reid Evenings
115 mi. E of Portland
Est 1993; **Acres** 2,500; **Hunters/yr** 350; **Type**
Public, Member/Avail, Corp.; **On Site** Clubhouse,
Lodging, Meals, Clays; **Shoots** Field; **Birds** Dove,
Quail, Pheasant, Chukar, Huns, Geese; **Dogs**
Avail/HDW; **Packages** 1 Day, 2-5 guns
O NAGA/See Pg. 107

Hulse Pheasant & Sporting Clay Ranch
60277 Tygh Ridge Rd., Dufur, OR 97021
(503) 467-2513 Mike & Debbie Hulse
100 mi. E of Portland
Est 1988; **Acres** 3,000; **Type** Public, Corp.; **On
Site** Clubhouse, Meals, Clays; **Shoots** Field; **Birds**
Dove, Quail, Pheasant, Chukar, Huns; **Dogs**
Avail/HDW

Lonsford Pheasants
851 NE Yamhill, Sheridan, OR 97378
(503) 843-2684 Charles Lonsford 7pm-10pm
25 mi. NW of Salem
Est 1990; **Acres** 120; **Type** Public, Member/Avail; **On
Site** Meals, Clays; **Shoots** Field; **Birds** Quail, Pheasant;
Dogs Avail/HDW; **Packages** 1/2 Day, 1-4 guns

Muddy Creek Sporting Club
29499 Buchanan Rd., Corvallis, OR 97333
(503) 753-9679 Don Hamblin

Great Expectations Hunting Preserve. . . Oregon's Finest Upland Gamebird Hideaway

Spend the day hunting at Oregon's Great Expectations and you'll find yourself suggesting that the name of the place be changed to "Great Expectations...Met and Exceeded!"

The reason? A formula for sure-fire success developed by owner/managers Jerry and Kitty Russell: First, offer world-class upland game hunting in some of the best native and planted habitat in the West; second, add the challenge of one of the best and most remote sporting clays' circuits in the world; and third, complete the package with comfortable lodging and great service.

A magnificent setting for hunting and clays.

You'll find Great Expectations in Eastern Oregon—the sunny side of the state—about 120 miles south of Pendleton and 70 miles northwest of John Day. Jerry, who holds a degree in natural resources, moved to the area with his wife, Kitty, nearly two decades ago. Two years ago, they purchased the 556 acre Cupper Ranch with the specific intent of developing one of the finest upland game hunting preserves in the country. After an extensive remodeling of the lodge and planting specifically for bird feed and habitat, Jerry and Kitty are well on their way to meeting their goal.

Quality and Privacy

"Great Expectations is a remote destination location," says Jerry. "We manage it with the idea of providing a quality experience where sportsmen can virtually have the entire preserve to themselves."

The posh lodge comfortably accommodates 10 people and offers every convenience, including a complete kitchen, satellite television and laundry. For those who prefer to be catered to, a professional cook is available to prepare hearty lunches and dinners.

A typical day in the field at Great Expectations is a mixed *no-bag-limit* affair. Hunters may work their own dogs or one or more of the preserve's well-trained canine crew. The quarry? Hard-flying pheasant, chukar, bobwhite and valley quail found in secluded canyons of swales and thickets and in fields awash with color.

Sporting Clays At Its Best

Great Expectations sporting clays course has been called "America's premier remote sporting clays course." Designed by U.S. National Champion, Dan Carlisle, the course consists of Honker Hill, a five-station Hunter's Clays range, and the Merkel Challenge, a 10-station sporting clays course.

The beauty of Carlisle's set-up, Jerry explains, is that the wireless, remote controlled traps on the courses can be adjusted to fit the skill level of the shooter—from novice to world-class competitor. Open year-round to the public, (reservations are needed) Great Expectations clays courses are a serious and immensely enjoyable diversion for hunting guests.

A recent visitor summed it up best when he said: "Great Expectations is a great retreat. The bird hunting, the accommodations, the scenery, the sporting clays, and the hosts are all first rate." In short, Great Expectations...Met and Exceeded!

For more information about Great Expectations, call or write Jerry and Kitty at Star Rt. 2, Kimberly, OR 97848; call toll free, 888-581-0550; phone or fax, 541-934-2117.

22 mi. N of Eugene
Est 1989; **Acres** 115; **Type** Public; **On Site**
Clubhouse, Clays; **Shoots** Blinds; **Birds** Ducks;
Dogs Avail/HDW

Oregon Blacktails Guide Service
PO Box 1737, Jacksonville, OR 97530
(541) 772-1010 Perry Allen 6-9

Pheasant Ridge, Inc.
80420 Ross Rd., Tygh Valley, OR 97063
(541) 544-2183 Steve Pierce, Mgr.
115 mi. E of Portland
Est 1987; **Acres** 2,500; **Type** Public, Member/Avail;
On Site Clubhouse, Lodging, Meals, Clays; **Shoots**
Field; **Birds** Dove, Quail, Pheasant, Chukar, Ducks,
Geese; **Dogs** Avail/HDW ○ NAGA/See Pg. 107

R&M Game Birds & Sporting Clays
Hood River, OR
(509) 365-3245 Rodger L. Ford Web site:
http://www.americaoutdoors.com/r&m
80 mi. E of Vancouver, WA or Portland, OR
Est 1986; **Acres** 1,100; **Type** Public, Member/Avail,
Corp.; **On Site** Clubhouse, Meals, Clays; **Shoots**
Field; **Birds** Quail, Pheasant, Chukar, Huns, Turkey;
Dogs Avail/HDW; **Packages** 1/2 Day, 1-20 guns

Ringneck Ranch
PO Box 316, Christmas Village, OR 97641
(541) 576-2532 Wayne Stutzman **Type** Public; **On
Site** Lodging; **Shoots** Field; **Birds** Quail, Pheasant,
Chukar; **Dogs** Avail ○ NAGA/See Pg. 107

Round Barn Pheasant Farm
93614 Swamp Creek Rd., Blachly, OR 97412
(541) 927-3767 Chris Mooney
115 mi. SW of Portland
Type Public; **Shoots** Field; **Birds** Pheasant

Summer Ridge Shooting Preserve
3759 Reed Rd., Vale, OR 97918
(541) 473-3355 Tim McGuffin
65 mi. NW of Boise, ID **Acres** 390; **Type** Public;
On Site Lodging, Meals; **Shoots** Field; **Birds** Quail,
Pheasant, Ducks, Geese; **Dogs** Avail

TKO - Thompson Krein Outdoors
Rt. 1, Box 3346, Heppner, OR 97836
(541) 676-5005 Bob Krein
190 mi. SE of Portland
Est 1995; **Acres** 35,000; **Hunters/yr** 350; **Type**
Public; **On Site** Clubhouse, Lodging, Meals, Clays;
Shoots Field; **Birds** Pheasant, Chukar; **Dogs**
Avail/HDW; **Packages** 1 Day, 2-10 guns
○ NAGA/See Pg. 107

TREO Ranches
Rt. 1, Box 3171, Heppner, OR 97836
(503) 676-5840 Phil Carlson Anytime
180 mi. E of Portland
Est 1987; **Acres** 4,200; **Type** Public; **On Site**
Clubhouse, Lodging, Meals, Clays; **Shoots** Field;
Birds Pheasant, Chukar, Huns; **Dogs** Avail/HDW;
Packages 1 Day, 2-10 guns
See Our Ad Across

Upland Meadows Hunting
1903 SW Jackson, Portland, OR 97201
(503) 640-5757 Charles Lilley
25 mi. W of Portland
Acres 300; **Type** Public; **On Site** Clays; **Shoots**
Field, Driven; **Birds** Quail, Pheasant, Chukar; **Dogs**
Avail/HDW; **Packages** 1/2 Day, 2-6 guns
○ NAGA/See Pg.
○ Hunting License
○ Airport Pickup
○ Sporting Clays
○ Brochure Available
○ Family Run Business

White River Ranch
Box 274, Tygh Valley, OR 97063
(541) 483-2211 Bruce Meredith
Type Public, Member/Avail; **On Site** Clubhouse,
Clays; **Shoots** Field; **Birds** Quail, Pheasant, Chukar,
Ducks, Geese ○ NAGA/See Pg. 107

PENNSYLVANIA

Allegheny Bird Dog Club
RD 5, Box 213, Somerset, PA 15501
(814) 443-3326 Mark Holliday 9-9
Est 1990; **Acres** 250; **Type** Public, Member/Avail;
On Site Clubhouse, Lodging, Meals; **Shoots** Field;
Birds Quail, Pheasant, Chukar; **Dogs** Avail/HDW;
Packages 1/2 Day, 1-8 guns

Angus Conservation & Hunting Farms
RD#1, Box 260, Latrobe, PA 15650
(412) 423-4022 Jay Angus 9-5
Est 1980; **Acres** 600; **Type** Public, Member/Avail;
On Site Lodging, Meals, Clays; **Shoots** Field, Tower,
Driven; **Birds** Quail, Pheasant, Chukar, Ducks; **Dogs**
Avail/HDW; **Packages** 1/2 Day, 1-25 guns
○ NAGA/See Pg. 107

Ayers Hill Farm
Box 197, R.D.#3, Coudersport, PA 16915
(814) 274-7922 Lowell W. Ayers 5pm-8pm
80 mi. NW of Williamsport
Est 1995; **Acres** 475; **Hunters/yr** 50; **Type**
Public, Member/Avail, Corp.; **On Site** Lodging;

TREO'S Magic Recipe Is Really No Secret

Many of TREO's customers are repeaters—they enjoy the experience so much they must do it again.

What magic ingredient brings them back? The TREO recipe is no secret, but it is unique. It includes:

- Excellent Hunting for pheasants, chukars and Hungarian partridges.
- Unexcelled working bird dogs.
- A variety of terrain and cover.
- The efforts of all the staff, from guide to cook, to make your stay enjoyable.
- No limit on fresh air and fun.
- Gourmet meals and comfortable beds.
- Peace and quiet, no matter which TREO facility you stay at.

Molly, Haley and Ebony helped!

Each of TREO's lodges is equipped with a full-service kitchen, comfortable new beds, trap-shooting opportunities, hot tubs, comfortable big chairs for evening relaxation.

Quality & Variety

Quality comes first. Everything's constant. The faces may change but the experience does not: Game birds holding tight on a crisp morning...the pleasure of seeing the best dogs in the West work the surge of appetite as the aroma of roasting pheasant floats from the tidy kitchen.

Whether you hunt with Phil or Clint, or on your own in a non-guided hunt, the emphasis at TREO is always to provide you with a quality experience. The folks at TREO strive to make everything about your stay memorable.

Variety is another TREO trademark—pheasants, chukars, Hungarian partridge, trap and sporting clays are included in the shooting options.

But bring good boots. This is a real hunting experience. The hunt will work up a comfortable sweat, but it's not overly strenuous. And you'll always see birds and have plenty of shooting.

The flushes can be unnerving even when you've watched Molly or one of the other German Wirehaired pointers move in on a bird, and the guide tells Haley or Ebony, "Flush 'em up!"

You will encounter a variety of flushes—some rocketing upward, others up and turning back over your head, or low and rapid over the plentiful cover. If you miss the first shot, usually there's time for a second chance.

After the first exciting hunt, you'll break for cold drinks on a warm day, coffee if you want, maybe a light snack. Then it's back to more birds, more shooting, more excitement.

By noon you'll be ready for a great lunch of, say, pheasant soup and a bratwurst, or a stack-it-yourself sandwich. A cheerful campfire may make you want to linger, but, sorry, it's back to the hunt.

What A Life!

After the final hunt, it's time for one of TREO's first-rate dinners. The menu will be built around cognac pheasant, beef tenderloin, prime rib, or leg of lamb, accompanied by fresh hot biscuits, crisp salads, and a dessert—homemade apple pie and ice cream, for one. The table groans with goodies.

Later, after an evening with your friends talking, playing cards or reading, you will drift off to sleep thinking about the great moments of the day, and the hunt that awaits you in the morning. What a life!

TREO magic: Memorable and dependable. No matter which hunt you choose. [For more information and reservations call or write: Phil Carlson, TREO, Rt.1, Box 3171, Heppner, OR 97836; (503) 676-5840].

Shoots Field; **Birds** Pheasant, Huns; **Dogs** Avail/HDW; **Packages** 1/2 Day, 1-4 guns

Big Pine Hunting Club
PO Box 45, Prompton, PA 18456
(908) 362-9008 George Rabtzow
20 mi. NE of Scranton
Est 1960; **Acres** 175; **Hunters/yr** 15; **Type** Public, Member/Avail, Corp.; **On Site** Clubhouse, Lodging, Clays; **Shoots** Field; **Birds** Dove, Quail, Woodcock, Pheasant, Chukar, Turkey, Ducks; **Dogs** HDW; **Packages** 1 Day, 3-15 guns

Blacklick Shooting Preserve
PO Box 191, Blairsville, PA 15717
(412) 459-8869 Daryl Thomas

Mr. Britt's Game Farm
PO Box 925, RD2, Homer City, PA 15748
(412) 479-9813 John A. Boris After 5
45 mi. E of Pittsburgh
Est 1980; **Acres** 2,300; **Hunters/yr** 700; **Type** Public, Member/Avail, Corp.; **On Site** Clubhouse, Meals, Clays; **Shoots** Field, Tower; **Birds** Dove, Quail, Ruffed Grouse, Pheasant, Chukar, Turkey; **Dogs** Avail/HDW; **Packages** 1 Day, 1-60 guns

Clover Hollow Hunting Preserve
6951 Lime Kiln Rd., Slatington, PA 18080
(610) 767-3319 Wilmer H. Dise
15 mi. N of Allentown
Acres 400; **Type** Public, Member/Avail, Corp.; **On Site** Clubhouse; **Shoots** Field; **Birds** Quail, Pheasant, Chukar; **Dogs** Avail/HDW; **Packages** 1/2 Day, 1-6 guns

Codorus Duck & Goose Guided Hunts
RD#3, Box 50, Glen Rock, PA 17327
(717) 227-0212 Lee Irwin 9-9
46 mi. S of Harrisburg
Est 1991; **Acres** 1,000; **Hunters/yr** 125; **Type** Public, Member/Avail, Corp.; **Shoots** Field, Blinds; **Birds** Ducks, Geese; **Dogs** Avail/HDW; **Packages** 1/2 Day, 1-16 guns

Cross Keys Pheasantry
PO Box 594, Hollidaysburg, PA 16648
(814) 695-3063 David A. Creuzberger
Type Member/Avail; **Shoots** Field; **Birds** Pheasant
○ NAGA/See Pg. 107

Dancing Fields Farm
27386 Guys Mills Rd., Meadville, PA 16335
(814) 789-3276 Joseph W. Tinko
Est 1994; **Acres** 200; **Type** Public, Member/Avail; **On Site** Meals; **Shoots** Field, Blinds; **Birds** Dove, Quail, Pheasant, Chukar, Huns, Turkey, Ducks, Geese; **Dogs** Avail/HDW; **Packages** 1/2 Day, 1-8 guns
○ NAGA/See Pg. 107

Gaybird Farms
6063 Sawmill Rd., Box 1, Carversville, PA 18913
(215) 297-5553 Barney Berlinger 8 am or noon
10 mi. N of Philadelphia
Type Member/Avail; **Shoots** Field; **Birds** Pheasant; **Dogs** Avail/HDW; **Packages** 1/2 Day

Greater Pittsburgh Gun Club
RD1, Bulger, PA 15019
(412) 796-9111 Tex Freund Anytime
Est 1968; **Acres** 700; **Type** Public, Member/Avail; **On Site** Clubhouse, Meals, Clays; **Shoots** Field; **Birds** Pheasant, Turkey, Ducks, Geese; **Dogs** HDW; **Packages** 1/2 Day, up to 1 guns

Hay's Pheasant Hunt, Inc.
625 Meadowbrook Ln., Gettysburg, PA 17325
(717) 334-1588 Robert Hay
55 mi. N of Baltimore
Est 1988; **Acres** 200; **Hunters/yr** 300; **Type** Public; **On Site** Clubhouse; **Shoots** Field; **Birds** Pheasant; **Dogs** Avail/HDW; **Packages** 1/2 Day, 1-12 guns

Hemlock Acres Hunting Club
RR3, Box 87-1-A, Benton, PA 17814
(717) 458-5930 Jim LeVan
6 mi. from Benton
Acres 250; **Type** Public, Member/Avail; **On Site** Lodging, Meals; **Shoots** Field; **Birds** Quail, Pheasant, Chukar; **Dogs** Avail/HDW

Hemlock Hill Preserve
39 Odell Rd., Mandfield, PA 16933
(717) 662-3927 David Russell
5 mi. E of Mansfield
Acres 197; **Hunters/yr** 50; **Type** Public; **Shoots** Field; **Birds** Quail, Pheasant; **Dogs** Avail

Hill's Twin Spruce Lodge
Box 212, Equinunk, PA 18417
(717) 224-4845 Adam Hill
45 mi. NE of Scranton
Est 1990; **Acres** 4,000; **Type** Public, Member/Avail; **On Site** Clubhouse, Clays; **Shoots** Field, Driven, Blinds; **Birds** Dove, Quail, Ruffed Grouse, Pheasant, Chukar, Turkey, Ducks, Geese; **Dogs** Avail/HDW; **Packages** 1/2 Day, 1-4 guns
○ Spacious 20 room lodge on the Delaware
○ Private access to 1 1/2 mi. of river frontage
○ Guaranteed Private Group Hunts!
○ Great Location for Corporate Entertaining–Cast & Blast Packages Available
○ Challenging Sporting Clays–Just off PA Rt. 191 and NY Rt. 97

Hillendale Hunt Club
RD#1, Box 390, Tyrone, PA 16686
(814) 684-5015 Tom Crawford 7-8pm

Sporting Clays available year around.

THE WARRINGTON CLUB

- Comfortable facilities with a gracious atmosphere.
- Complete pro shop.
- Located two hour drive from Philadelphia and Washington D.C.

Discover

The

GAME BIRD HUNTING

- Quail, Pheasant, Chukars and Huns.
- 365 acres of varied terrain, including 140 specialty planted acres.
- Dogs and guides available.

For information please complete the coupon below or call (717) 432-0643 or (717) 741-7214.

Please send me information on:
- ☐ Warrington Hunt Club
- ☐ Warrington Sporting Clays Course
- ☐ Both of the above

Name: _____

Address:_____

City/Town:_____State_____Zip_____

Tel:_____ Best time to call _____

Please return to: the Warrington Club, 400 Yeager Road, Wellsville, PA 17365

Hillside Hunting Preserve
PO Box 56, Berlin, PA 15530
(814) 267-5301 James Scurfield 9-5
60 mi. SE of Pittsburgh
Est 1983; Acres 300; Hunters/yr 600; Type
Public, Member/Avail, Corp.; On Site Clubhouse,
Lodging, Meals, Clays; Shoots Field, Tower, Driven;
Birds Quail, Pheasant, Chukar; Dogs Avail/HDW;
Packages 1 Day, up to 10 guns
○ NAGA/See Pg. 107

Hopewell Pheasantry, Inc.
RD3, Box 680, Felton, PA 17322
(800) 847-8881 Bill or Gail Rinas
20 mi. S of York
Est 1987; Acres 300; Type Public, Member/Avail,
Corp.; Shoots Field, Blinds; Birds Quail, Pheasant,
Chukar, Geese; Dogs Avail/HDW; Packages 1/2
Day, 1-20 guns

Indian Run Country
Rt. 2, Centerville, PA 16404
(814) 967-2635 Dave & Nancy Stutzman
85 mi. N of Pittsburgh
Est 1986; Acres 380; Type Public, Member/Avail;
On Site Clubhouse, Meals, Clays; Shoots Field,
Tower; Birds Quail, Pheasant, Chukar; Dogs
Avail/HDW; Packages 1/2 Day, 1-24 guns
○ NAGA/See Pg. 107

JDZ Game Farm
RD#2, Box 75, Watsontown, PA 17777
(717) 649-5881 John Zaktansky Evenings
70 mi. SW of Scranton
Est 1988; Acres 80; Type Public, Member/Avail; On
Site Clays; Shoots Field; Birds Quail, Pheasant, Chukar;
Dogs Avail/HDW; Packages 1/2 Day, 1-4 guns

Juniata River Game Farm
52 Goose Lane, McClure, PA 17841
(717) 543-6281 Doug Boreman
On Site Clays; Shoots Field; Birds Quail, Pheasant,
Chukar, Ducks ○ NAGA/See Pg. 107

Kettle Creek Lodge
HCR62, Box 14B, Cross Fork, PA 17729
(814) 435-1019 Steve Benna
Acres 282,000; Type Public; Shoots Field; Birds
Turkey; Dogs Avail/HDW

Kimble's Regulated Hunting Grounds
321 Newport Rd., Duncannon, PA 17020
(717) 834-5122 Dan Kimble
15 mi. NW of Harrisburg
Acres 226; Type Public, Member/Avail; On Site
Clubhouse, Meals; Shoots Field; Birds Quail,
Pheasant, Chukar; Dogs Avail; Packages 1/2 Day
○ NAGA/See Pg. 107

La-Da-Jo Pines
RD2, Box 67, New Ringgold, PA 17960
(717) 943-2213 Larry Delp 7am-9pm
65 mi. NW of Philadelphia
Est 1960; Acres 600; Type Public, Member/Avail,

Corp.; On Site Clubhouse, Meals, Clays; Shoots
Field, Tower, Driven; Birds Dove, Quail, Ruffed
Grouse, Woodcock, Pheasant, Chukar, Huns, Turkey;
Dogs Avail/HDW; Packages 1/2 Day, 3-15 guns
○ NAGA/See Pg. 107

Laurel Springs Hunt-Fishing Club
RD#2, Box 162, Rockwood, PA 15557
(814) 352-8803 Bob Weston
60 mi. SE of Pittsburgh
Est 1995; Acres 350; Type Public, Member/Avail,
Corp.; On Site Clubhouse, Lodging, Meals, Clays;
Shoots Field, Tower, Driven; Birds Quail, Pheasant,
Chukar; Dogs Avail/HDW; Packages 1/2 Day, 1-10
guns

Lazy E Hunting Grounds
RD#4, Box 304, Tyrone, PA 16686
(814) 632-5291 Gary Eyer
90 mi. E of Pittsburg
Est 1990; Acres 200; Type Public, Member/Avail;
On Site Lodging, Meals; Shoots Field; Birds Quail,
Pheasant, Chukar; Dogs Avail/HDW; Packages 1/2
Day, 1-4 guns

Lucky Buck
RR2, Box 225, Saltsburg, PA 15681
(412) 468-6579 Gregory McQuaide
30 mi. E of Pittsburg
Est 1990; Acres 700; Type Public; On Site
Clubhouse, Meals; Shoots Field; Birds Pheasant;
Dogs Avail/HDW; Packages 1/2 Day, 1-50 guns

Martz's Gap View Hunting Preserve
RR#1, Box 85, Dalmatia, PA 17017
(800) 326-8442 Don Martz 8am-5pm
38 mi. N of Harrisburg
Est 1955; Acres 1,300; Hunters/yr 5,000; Type
Public, Member/Avail; On Site Clubhouse, Lodging,
Meals, Clays; Shoots Field, Tower; Birds Pheasant,
Chukar, Huns; Dogs Avail/HDW; Packages 1/2
Day, 1-15 guns ○ NAGA/See Pg. 107
See Our Ad Across

Mascari Shooting Grounds
RD#1, Levis Rd., Knox, PA 16232
(412) 366-7163 Don Mascari
65 mi. N of Pittsburgh
Acres 257; Hunters/yr 30; Type Public,
Member/Avail; On Site Clubhouse, Meals, Clays;
Shoots Field, Tower; Birds Pheasant

Mason Dixon Hunting Farm
RD3, Box 233, Glen Rock, PA 17327
(717) 235-2308 Jerry & Michele Walker
20 mi. S of York
Est 1990; Acres 190; Hunters/yr 100; Type
Public; Shoots Field; Birds Quail, Pheasant, Chukar;
Dogs Avail/HDW; Packages 1/2 Day, 1-6 guns

Medhia Shooting Preserve
Box 64, E. Waterford, PA 17021

(717) 734-3965 Donald Singer 6-10 pm
Est 1988; **Acres** 611; **Hunters/yr** 800; **Type**
Public, Member/Avail, Corp.; **Shoots** Field; **Birds**
Pheasant, Chukar; **Dogs** Avail/HDW; **Packages** 1
Day, up to 16 guns O NAGA/See Pg. 107

Moore's Run Fish & Game Preserve
RR1, Box 280, Austin, PA 16720
(814) 647-5563 Roy Magarigal, Jr.
Type Public, Member/Avail; **Shoots** Field; **Birds**
Chukar; **Dogs** HDW; **Packages** 1/2 Day

Nightingale Shooting Preserve
RD#7, Box 485, Muncy, PA 17756
(717) 584-2274 Raymond P. Sones
Type Public; **On Site** Lodging; **Shoots** Field; **Birds**
Pheasant, Chukar; **Dogs** Avail/HDW; **Packages** 1/2
Day, 1-36 guns

Pheasant Hill Farms
RD#6, Box 331, Wellsboro, PA 16901
(717) 724-3274 George S. Myers 8 am - 10 pm
50 mi. N of Williamsport
Acres 375; **Hunters/yr** 150; **Type** Public,
Member/Avail; **On Site** Lodging, Meals, Clays;
Shoots Field; **Birds** Quail, Pheasant; **Dogs**
Avail/HDW; **Packages** 1/2 Day, up to 5 guns
O NAGA/See Pg. 107

Quail Hill Hunting Preserve
PO Box 79A, Templeton, PA 16259
(412) 868-2245 Barbara Wolfe
Est 1991; **Acres** 350; **Hunters/yr** 300; **Type**
Public, Member/Avail, Corp.; **On Site** Clubhouse,
Lodging, Meals; **Shoots** Field; **Birds** Quail,
Pheasant, Chukar; **Dogs** Avail/HDW; **Packages** 1/2
Day, 1-25 guns

Quemahoning Trap & Field Club
RR7, Box 178-A, Somerset, PA 15501
(814) 443-4460 Kent Landefeld
15 mi. S of Johnstown
Acres 1,001; **Type** Member/Avail; **On Site**
Clubhouse; **Shoots** Field; **Birds** Quail, Ruffed
Grouse, Pheasant

Reading Regulated
Hunting Area, Inc.
RD1, Box 220A, Birdsboro, PA 19508
(610) 856-7671 Margaret Wisner After 4pm
42 mi. NW of Philadelphia
Est 1941; **Acres** 220; **Hunters/yr** 600; **Type**
Public, Member/Avail, Corp.; **On Site** Clubhouse,
Meals, Clays; **Shoots** Field; **Birds** Dove, Pheasant;
Dogs Avail/HDW; **Packages** 1/2 Day, 1-20 guns
O Bird Processing
O Kennel Bird Dogs
O Sporting Clays
O Brochure Available
O Factory Ammunition
O Family owned & operated 46 years

Rock Ridge Hunting Preserve
RD#3, Box 77M, Pine Grove, PA 17963
(717) 345-8900 Gregory Fedechko
Acres 1,300; **Type** Public; **On Site** Clubhouse,
Meals, Clays; **Shoots** Field, Tower, Driven, Blinds;
Birds Quail, Pheasant, Chukar, Turkey, Ducks; **Dogs**
Avail/HDW; **Packages** 1/2 Day, 1-8 guns
O NAGA/See Pg. 107

Sagulla Hunting Ground
826 Millbrook Rd., Jackson Center, PA 16133
(814) 786-7368 Joe or Pauline Sagulla Evening
60 mi. N of Pittsburgh
Est 1953; **Acres** 650; **Hunters/yr** 600; **Type**
Public; **On Site** Clubhouse; **Shoots** Field, Blinds;
Birds Pheasant, Chukar, Ducks; **Dogs** Avail/HDW;
Packages 1/2 Day

Shaner Sportsman's Club
RD#1, Malicki Lane, Irwin, PA
(412) 446-1313 Bob Morgan Fri, 6-9
20 mi. E of Pittsburgh
Est 1940; **Acres** 100; **Type** Public, Member/Avail;
On Site Clubhouse, Clays; **Shoots** Field; **Birds**
Dove, Ruffed Grouse, Pheasant, Turkey; **Dogs**
Avail/HDW

Smith Game Farm
206 Kepple Rd., Sarver, PA 16055
(412) 353-1107 Larry Smith
20 mi. NE of Pittsburgh
Est 1991; **Acres** 150; **Hunters/yr** 300; **Type**
Public; **On Site** Clubhouse, Meals; **Shoots** Field;
Birds Quail, Pheasant, Chukar; **Dogs** Avail/HDW;
Packages 1/2 Day, 1-6 guns

Spruce Hollow Hunting Farms, Ltd.
RD#2, Box 353, Kunkletown, PA 18058
(610) 381-3406 Junie & Cindy Kuehner Anytime
20 mi. N of Allentown
Est 1985; **Acres** 1,200; **Type** Public, Member/Avail,

Corp.; **On Site** Clubhouse, Lodging, Meals, Clays;
Shoots Field, Tower; **Birds** Quail, Pheasant, Chukar;
Dogs Avail/HDW; **Packages** 1/2 Day
o NAGA/See Pg. 107

Susquehanna Valley
Game Farm
Box 8, RD2, McClure, PA 17841
(800) 338-7389 Ken Snyder 9-4
20 mi. S of Lewistown off US Rt. 522
Est 1990; **Acres** 800; **Hunters/yr** 400; **Type**
Public, Member/Avail, Corp.; **On Site** Clubhouse,
Meals, Clays; **Shoots** Field; **Birds** Quail, Pheasant,
Chukar, Huns; **Dogs** Avail/HDW; **Packages** 1/2
Day, 2-4 guns o NAGA/See Pg.
o 3-D Archery/Video Archery System
o Archery Pro-Shop

Sutersville Sportsman's Club
PO Box 41, Sutersville, PA 15083
(412) 872-0910 John Vezzani Mon. 6-9
20 mi. SE of Pittsburgh
Est 1940; **Acres** 10; **Type** Public, Member/Avail;
On Site Clubhouse, Clays; **Shoots** Field; **Birds**
Dove, Ruffed Grouse, Pheasant, Turkey; **Dogs**
Avail/HDW

TNT Shooting Grounds
PO Box 236, Waltersburg, PA 15488
(412) 677-2609 Thomas Stewart 8-5
48 mi. S of Pittsburgh
Est 1980; **Acres** 400; **Hunters/yr** 1,800; **Type**
Public, Member/Avail, Corp.; **On Site** Clubhouse,
Meals, Clays; **Shoots** Field, Tower; **Birds** Quail,
Pheasant, Chukar, Ducks; **Dogs** Avail/HDW;
Packages 1/2 Day, 1-15 guns o NAGA/See Pg. 107

Timberdoodle Farms
832 Cardinal Rd., St. Marys, PA 15857
(814) 781-7256 Robert Friedl
24 mi. E of Bradford
Acres 125; **Hunters/yr** 50; **Type** Public; **On Site**
Clubhouse, Lodging; **Shoots** Field; **Birds** Quail,
Ruffed Grouse, Woodcock, Pheasant, Chukar, Turkey;
Dogs Avail

Triple "L" Farms Upland Gamebird Hunts
RD#3, Box 50, Glen Rock, PA 17327
(717) 227-0212 Lee Irwin 9-9
46 mi. S of Harrisburg
Est 1993; **Acres** 160; **Hunters/yr** 125; **Type**
Public, Member/Avail, Corp.; **On Site** Clubhouse,
Meals, Clays; **Shoots** Field, Blinds; **Birds** Quail,
Pheasant, Chukar, Huns, Ducks; **Dogs** Avail/HDW;
Packages 1/2 Day, 1-12 guns o NAGA/See Pg. 107

W.C.J. Ranch
305 Jefferson St., Meadville, PA 16335
(814) 724-1930 Charles E. Schmitz
10 mi. NE of Meadville
Acres 258; **Type** Public; **On Site** Clubhouse, Clays;
Shoots Field; **Birds** Pheasant; **Dogs** Avail/HDW;
Packages 1/2 Day

The Warrington Club
400 Yeager Rd., Wellsville, PA 17365
(717) 741-7214 Reservations
15 mi. S of Harrisburg
Est 1991; **Acres** 365; **Type** Member/Avail, Corp.;
On Site Clubhouse, Lodging, Clays; **Shoots** Field;
Birds Quail, Pheasant, Chukar, Huns; **Dogs**
Avail/HDW; **Packages** 1/2 Day, 1-2 guns
o Complete On-Site Pro Shop
See Our Ad Pg. 395

Whitetail Enterprises
PO Box 1233, Conyngham, PA 18219
(717) 384-2314 Fran Curran
10 mi. NW of Hazleton
Acres 700; **Type** Public, Member/Avail; **On Site**
Clubhouse, Meals; **Shoots** Field, Tower; **Birds**
Quail, Pheasant, Chukar; **Dogs** Avail/HDW
o NAGA/See Pg. 107

Windy Ridge
Game Farm & Kennels
RD#1, Box 59C, Tioga, PA 16946
(717) 835-5427 Robert Stewart/Tom Bower 7am-9pm
25 mi. S of Corning, NY
Est 1987; **Acres** 1,400; **Hunters/yr** 300; **Type**
Public, Member/Avail, Corp.; **On Site** Clubhouse,
Lodging, Meals, Clays; **Shoots** Field; **Birds** Quail,
Ruffed Grouse, Pheasant, Chukar, Turkey; **Dogs**
Avail/HDW; **Packages** 1/2 Day, 1-20 guns o
NAGA/See Pg. 107
Return to the "Good Old Days!" We have the finest
near natural upland bird hunting in Northern Penn-
sylvania. Releasing pheasants, chukars and quail
9/15 through 4/15. Use your dog or ours. Moder-
ate rates. Modern lodge available year round.
Deer, turkey and grouse hunting in PA season.
Skeet by reservation. Contact (717) 835-5427.

Wing & Shot Hunting Preserve
465 Camp Hebron Rd., Halifax, PA 17032
(717) 896-9077 Kirk Hartlaub 9-9
15 mi. NE of Harrisburg
Est 1990; **Acres** 240; **Hunters/yr** 400; **Type**
Member/Avail, Corp.; **Shoots** Field; **Birds** Quail,
Pheasant, Chukar; **Dogs** HDW o NAGA/See Pg. 107

RHODE ISLAND

Addieville East Farm
200 Pheasant Dr., Mapleville, RI 02839
(401) 568-3185 Geoff Gaebe 7am-8pm
20 mi. N of Providence
Est 1979; **Acres** 600; **Hunters/yr** 2,000; **Type** Public, Member/Avail, Corp.; **On Site** Clubhouse, Lodging, Meals, Clays; **Shoots** Field, Driven; **Birds** Quail, Pheasant, Chukar, Huns; **Dogs** HDW
O NAGA/See Pg. 107

Peace Dale Shooting Preserve
441 Rose Hill Rd., Peace Dale, RI 02879
(401) 789-3730 Richie Frisella
20 mi. S of Providence
Est 1950; **Acres** 200; **Type** Public; **On Site** Clubhouse, Clays; **Shoots** Field, Tower; **Birds** Quail, Pheasant, Chukar; **Dogs** Avail/HDW

SOUTH CAROLINA

Back 40 Wing & Clay
4671 Timrod Rd., Bethune, SC 29009
(803) 475-4408 Grady Roscoe 7am-10pm
53 mi. NE of Columbia
Est 1995; **Acres** 1,100; **Type** Public, Member/Avail, Corp.; **On Site** Clubhouse, Meals, Clays; **Shoots** Field, Tower, Blinds; **Birds** Dove, Quail, Pheasant, Chukar, Turkey, Ducks; **Dogs** Avail/HDW; **Packages** 1/2 Day, 1-12 guns

BACK WOODS QUAIL CLUB

Back Woods Quail Club
Rt. 3, Box 253F, Georgetown, SC 29440
(803) 546-1466 Rick Hemingway 7am-5pm
65 mi. N of Charleston
Est 1987; **Acres** 14,000; **Hunters/yr** 600; **Type** Public, Member/Ltd, Corp.; **On Site** Clubhouse, Lodging, Meals, Clays; **Shoots** Field; **Birds** Dove, Quail, Turkey; **Dogs** Avail/HDW; **Packages** 1/2 Day, 2-18 guns O NAGA/See Pg. 107

Set on nearly 15,000 acres of open fields, timber lands, and wooded areas, Back Woods offers sport-

ing variety few hunting operations can match. At Back Woods you can hunt with us for days and never work the same field twice—our five separate hunting areas make that possible. You can also hunt Trophy Deer from tree stands over corn and sunflower fields. Our three comfortable guest lodges can accommodate up to 18 hunters. Sporting clays, too! Enjoy great hunting and Good Ol' Southern Hospitality at Back Woods. Call today!

Bostick Plantation Hunting Club
PO Box 728, Estill, SC 29918
(803) 625-4512 Joe Bostick 9-5
50 mi. NW of Savannah, GA
Est 1977; **Acres** 9,000; **Hunters/yr** 450; **Type** Public; **On Site** Clubhouse, Lodging, Meals, Clays; **Shoots** Field; **Birds** Quail, Turkey; **Dogs** Avail/HDW; **Packages** 1/2 Day, 2-12 guns
See Our Ad Pg. 400

Brays Island Plantation
PO Box 30, Sheldon, SC 29941
(803) 846-3100 Owner Services M-F, 9-5
50 mi. SW of Charleston
Est 1988; **Acres** 5,000; **Hunters/yr** 700; **Type** Member/Avail; **On Site** Clubhouse, Lodging, Meals, Clays; **Shoots** Field, Blinds; **Birds** Dove, Quail, Chukar, Ducks; **Dogs** Avail/HDW; **Packages** 1/2 Day, 1-6 guns O NAGA/See Pg. 107

Broxton Bridge Plantation
PO Box 97, Hwy. 601, Ehrhardt, SC 29081
(800) 437-4868 Jerry Varn, Jr. 7 am to 9 pm
60 mi. W of Charleston
Est 1965; **Acres** 7,000; **Hunters/yr** 600; **Type** Public, Member/Avail; **On Site** Clubhouse, Lodging, Meals, Clays; **Shoots** Field, Tower, Blinds; **Birds** Dove, Quail, Pheasant, Turkey, Ducks; **Dogs** Avail/HDW; **Packages** 1/2 Day, 2-12 guns
O NAGA/See Pg. 107
See Our Ad Pg. 401

Buck Ridge Plantation
PO Box 2785, Orangeburg, SC 29116
(803) 531-8408 Michael C. Tourvilte
Type Member/Avail; **On Site** Lodging, Clays; **Shoots** Field; **Birds** Pheasant, Chukar, Turkey
O NAGA/See Pg. 107

Canvasback Kennel & Hunt Club
872 Gary Rd., Camden, SC 29020
(803) 432-4451 Felix Mock 8-6
35 mi. NE of Columbia
Est 1993; **Acres** 300; **Type** Public; **On Site** Meals; **Shoots** Field, Tower, Blinds; **Birds** Quail, Pheasant, Ducks; **Dogs** Avail/HDW; **Packages** 1/2 Day, up to 8 guns O NAGA/See Pg. 107

Carter Shooting Preserve
2480 Hwy. 521 South, Sumter, SC 29153

(803) 481-2732 David C. Carter 8am-11pm
50 mi. E of Columbia **Est** 1984; **Acres** 150; **Type** Public; **Shoots** Field; **Birds** Quail; **Dogs** Avail/HDW; **Packages** 1/2 Day, 1-3 guns

Chelsea Plantation
Rt. 1, Box 310, Ridgeland, SC 29936
(803) 726-6887 Bill Apps 8am-5pm
35 mi. NE of Savannah, GA **Est** 1872; **Acres** 5,300; **Hunters/yr** 200; **Type** Public, Member/Avail; **On Site** Clubhouse, Lodging, Meals, Clays; **Shoots** Field, Blinds; **Birds** Dove, Quail, Ducks; **Dogs** Avail/HDW; **Packages** 1 Day, 4-8 guns O NAGA/See Pg. 107

Eleven Oaks Farm
3067 Highpoint Rd., Hartsville, SC 29550
(803) 332-9191 Stephen Beasley after 5pm
Est 1995; **Acres** 600; **Type** Public; **On Site** Clubhouse, Lodging; **Shoots** Field; **Birds** Quail, Pheasant, Chukar; **Dogs** Avail/HDW; **Packages** 1/2 Day, 1-8 guns O NAGA/See Pg. 107

Graham & Carroll Shooting Preserve
PO Box 37, Smoaks, SC 29481
(803) 562-2574 John Graham
50 mi. NW of Charleston
Acres 400; **Hunters/yr** 150; **Type** Member/Avail; **On Site** Clubhouse, Lodging, Meals, Clays; **Shoots** Field; **Birds** Dove, Quail, Turkey; **Dogs** Avail/HDW; **Packages** 1/2 Day, 1-3 guns O NAGA/See Pg. 107

Groton Plantation
Rt. 1, Box 98, Luray, SC 29932
(803) 625-4160 Robert Winthrop, II 8am-6pm
55 mi. NW of Savannah
Est 1975; **Acres** 23,000; **Hunters/yr** 200; **Type** Member/Avail; **On Site** Clubhouse, Lodging, Meals; **Shoots** Field; **Birds** Dove, Quail, Turkey, Ducks; **Dogs** Avail; **Packages** 1 Day, 2-8 guns

Jack Island Gun Club
2602 Mullet Hall Rd., John's Island, SC 29455
(803) 729-3541 Sidi Limehouse

Little River Plantation
PO Box 1129, Abbeville, SC 29620
(864) 391-2300 Jim & John Edens 8am-9pm
54 mi. N of Augusta **Est** 1980; **Acres** 4,200; **Hunters/yr** 400; **Type** Public, Member/Avail, Corp.; **On Site** Clubhouse, Lodging, Meals, Clays; **Shoots** Field; **Birds** Dove, Quail, Pheasant, Chukar, Turkey, Ducks; **Dogs** Avail/HDW; **Packages** 1/2 Day, 1-20 guns — DESIGN YOUR OWN HUNT! At Little River Plantation flexibility is the key: You tell us what gamebirds you want to hunt and how many–our top-notch guides and well-trained dogs will do the rest. Wild and liberated bird shooting available on several thousand acres of prime wildlife habitat. Spacious lodge and home-cooked meals. Sporting clays course. Deer and turkey hunting, too. Call today!
See Our Ad Pg. 402

Broxton Bridge Plantation

By: Peggy Boehmer

We recently had the pleasure of meeting G.D. "Jerry" Varn, who, along with his family, operates Broxton Bridge Plantation in Ehrhardt, South Carolina.

Towering almost seven feet tall, Jerry is easy to spot in a crowd. A charismatic guy with a heart as overwhelming as his stature, Jerry can quote chapter and verse from the bible or the constitution with equal eloquence. He is a true southern gentleman, and a shrewd businessman.

Broxton Bridge offers 7,000 acres of hunting land, and, according to its brochure, "Lasting memories for the serious sportsman." It even have a grass air strip. (Jerry, by the way, is a licensed pilot.)

Hunts

Broxton Bridge Plantation offers a wide variety of hunting opportunities—deer hunting, duck hunting over decoys, in addition to pheasants, chukar and, of course, quail.

Deer season opens August 15th, ends January 1st; bird hunting is available October 1st through March 31st. The deer hunting "package" includes meals and lodging and costs $225 per day. For groups of three or more the rate drops to $175 per day. There is a three day minimum.

The duck hunt—minimum four to a group, maximum, 20 (an individual can "join in" if he doesn't have enough guests)—is conducted from a blind using hand calls. The cost for a half-day (morning or after lunch) is $245, lunch included. Hunters have the opportunity to bag 8 mallards (the group divides the total bag evenly).

For safety's sake, only two hunters are allowed "on the ground" at one time during quail hunts. A half-day quail hunt (includes guide, dogs, 12 quail and bird cleaning) is priced at $160. An all day quail hunt includes all of that plus lunch and features 18 quail. The cost is $275. Broxton also offers an "ALL DAY SPECIAL" for $495. Guests hunt five different types of birds. The day begins with a duck hunt, then a trip through the sporting clays course. After lunch hunters have the opportunity to bag 2 pheasant, 3 chukar, and 6 quail. All game is cleaned and packaged.

Rooms to suit

Jerry offers his customers a wide variety of services and experiences. Guests can even choose accomodations to suit their style. There is a hunting lodge that I believe can accomodate 15-20 guests. The "hundred year old" lodge is comfortable (right down to the air conditioning) and rustic . Accomodations start at $30.

Hunting guests who prefer luxury can stay at "Ehrhardt Hall" (a restored mansion next to Jerry's house in town, about 5 miles from the plantation.), offering "Bed & Breakfast" style accomodations in spacious rooms with private bath, fireplaces, remote television and VCR's. The rate is $55 per night or $80 for two people in one room. (Continental breakfast is included.) Broxton also offers a "Victorian Cottage" across the street for $35 single, $65 double.

Sporting clays

At Broxton you can shoot one of four sporting clays ranges (25 shots each, for $10) or all four courses (100 shots for $35). (One course is named the "Dan Carlisle". after the champion shooter who designed it.) Broxton also has a 65 foot tower that offers a variety of shots, including one that simulates mallards "settling in" around decoys and another shot very similar to dove shooting.

Jerry requires a 50% deposit (non-refundable, but it may be transferred or rescheduled with 3 weeks prior notice). Broxton accepts Visa, Mastercard, and American Express. Jerry and his fine family offer quite a unique and extremely attractive hunting/outdoor experience. Call (1-800-437-HUNT) for information and reservations.

Moree's Sportsman's Preserve
PO Box 118, Society Hill, SC 29593
(803) 378-4831 Gus Tucker 8:30 am to 5 pm
40 mi. SW of Columbia
Acres 1,000; **Type** Public; **On Site** Clubhouse;
Shoots Field, Blinds; **Birds** Quail, Pheasant, Chukar,
Ducks; **Dogs** Avail/HDW; **Packages** 1/2 Day, up to
4 guns ○ NAGA/See Pg. 107

Norfolk Southern Railroad
PO Box 27, Dorchester, SC 29437
(803) 563-5720 J.I. Chapman
Type Member/Avail; **On Site** Lodging; **Shoots**
Field; **Birds** Quail, Chukar, Turkey, Ducks
○ NAGA/See Pg. 107

Oak Ridge Hunting Preserve
1002 Hatchaway Bridge Rd., Aiken, SC 29803
(803) 648-3489 Clarence Chapman
25 mi. E of Augusta
Est 1966; **Acres** 5,000; **Type** Public; **On Site**
Clubhouse, Meals, Clays; **Shoots** Field; **Birds** Dove,
Quail, Turkey; **Dogs** Avail/HDW; **Packages** 1/2
Day, up to 12 guns ○ NAGA/See Pg. 107

Oaks Gun Club, Ltd.
1276 Oaks Plantation Rd., Georgetown, SC 29440
(803) 527-1861 Heyward Talley Anytime
48 mi. N of Charleston
Est 1987; **Acres** 2,000; **Type** Member/Avail, Corp.;
On Site Clubhouse, Clays; **Shoots** Field, Blinds;
Birds Quail, Pheasant, Ducks; **Dogs** Avail
○ NAGA/See Pg. 107

Quail Trough Hunting Preserve
2032 Edgefield Hwy., Aiken, SC 29801
(803) 648-5483 Dennis Willing
50 mi. W of Colombia
Est 1994; **Acres** 450; **Type** Public, Member/Avail;

On Site Lodging; **Shoots** Field; **Birds** Dove, Quail,
Chukar, Turkey; **Dogs** Avail/HDW; **Packages** 1/2
Day, 1-12 guns

River Bend Sportsman's Resort
PO Box 279, Fingerville, SC 29338
(864) 592-1348 Ralph N. Brendle 8am-5pm
15 mi. NW of Spartanburg
Est 1985; **Acres** 535; **Hunters/yr** 3,000; **Type**
Public, Member/Avail, Corp.; **On Site** Clubhouse,
Lodging, Meals, Clays; **Shoots** Field; **Birds**
Quail, Pheasant, Chukar; **Dogs** Avail/HDW;
Packages 1/2 Day, 1-36 guns ○ NAGA/See Pg. 107
○ Hunting License   ○ Sporting Clays
○ Airport Pickup   ○ Shooting Instruction
○ Bird Processing   ○ Loaner Guns
○ Kennel Bird Dogs   ○ Brochure Available

Round O Kennel & Quail
Rt. 1, Box 296, Round O, SC 29474
(803) 835-5532 John Agee
Type Public, Member/Avail; **Shoots** Field; **Birds**
Quail ○ NAGA/See Pg. 107

Sandhill Sportsman's Club
421 Tap Harley Rd., Swansea, SC 29160
(803) 568-3126 Gene Jeffcoat
21 mi. S of Columbia
Acres 4,200; **Hunters/yr** 82; **Type** Public,
Member/Avail; **On Site** Clubhouse, Lodging, Meals,
Clays; **Shoots** Field; **Birds** Dove, Quail, Turkey;
Dogs Avail; **Packages** 1/2 Day, 2-3 guns

Sardis Shooting Preserve
4142 Sardis Hwy., Timmonsville, SC 29161
(803) 346-2497 J.D. Matthews
Type Member/Avail; **Shoots** Field; **Birds** Quail
○ NAGA/See Pg. 107

Singletree Hunting Plantation
Rt. 1, Box 564, Clinton, SC 29325
(803) 833-5477 C.C. May
55 mi. NW of Columbia
Est 1982; **Acres** 1,700; **Type** Public, Member/Avail;
On Site Clubhouse, Lodging, Meals, Clays; **Shoots**
Field, Tower; **Birds** Dove, Quail, Pheasant, Chukar,
Turkey, Ducks, Geese; **Dogs** Avail/HDW; **Packages**
1/2 Day, 2-15 guns O NAGA/See Pg. 107

South Carolina Outdoor Shooting
371 Cedar Branch Road, Windsor, SC 29856
(803) 648-5132 Richard Sherman 9 to 5
17 mi. E of Augusta, GA
Acres 400; **Type** Public, Member/Avail; **On Site**
Clubhouse, Meals, Clays; **Shoots** Field, Tower;
Birds Dove, Pheasant, Chukar; **Dogs** Avail/HDW;
Packages 1/2 Day, 2-12 guns

Springrove
Shooting Preserve
PO Box 397, St. Stephen, SC 29479
(803) 567-3830 David Shealy
40 mi. N of Charleston
Est 1971; **Acres** 1,500; **Hunters/yr** 1,200; **Type**
Public; **On Site** Clubhouse, Lodging, Meals, Clays;
Shoots Field; **Birds** Quail, Pheasant, Chukar; **Dogs**
Avail/HDW; **Packages** 1/2 Day, 1-16 guns

Tinker Creek Shooting Preserve
Rt. 2, Box 76, Williston, SC 29853
(803) 266-4840 Gregg or Roger Bates 7pm-10pm

Tri-State Hunting Club
PO Box 101, Estill, SC 29918
(803) 625-4009 Tommy Rhodes
60 mi. N of Savannah
Type Public, Member/Avail; **Birds** Turkey

Wassamassaw Shooting Preserve
1405 Sandy Run Circle, Summerville, SC 29483
(803) 688-5941 Robert J. Welch
12 mi. NE of Summerville
Acres 162; **Type** Public; **Shoots** Field; **Birds** Quail;
Dogs Avail/HDW

SOUTH DAKOTA

Audiss Hunting Service
RR2, Box 61, Dallas, SD 57529
(605) 835-9439 Cecil Audiss
3 mi. W of Gregory Acres 1,500; Type Public; On
Site Clubhouse, Lodging, Meals; Shoots Field; Birds
Dove, Pheasant, Sharp Tail Grouse; Dogs Avail;
Packages 1 Day

Bass Pheasant Hunting
R-2, Box 15, Kimball, SD 57355
(605) 778-6842 Jim & Patsy Bass
120 mi. W of Sioux Falls
Est 1989; **Acres** 640; **Hunters/yr** 750; **Type**
Public; **On Site** Clubhouse, Lodging; **Shoots** Field;
Birds Pheasant; **Dogs** HDW; **Packages** 1/2 Day,
1-20 guns

▼ ORVIS ENDORSED ▼
Big Bend Ranch
1301 N. 4th St., Aberdeen, SD 57401
(605) 229-3035 Alex Falk
28 mi. SE of Pierre
Est 1955; **Acres** 10,000; **Type** Public,
Member/Avail, Corp.; **On Site** Clubhouse, Lodging,
Meals, Clays; **Shoots** Field, Blinds; **Birds** Pheasant,
Huns, Prairie Chicken, Sharp Tail Grouse, Ducks,
Geese; **Dogs** Avail/HDW; **Packages** 2 Days, 1-16
guns O NAGA/See Pg. 107
O Orvis Endorsed Lodge
See Our Ads Pgs. 404 & 407

▲ ORVIS ENDORSED ▲

Biggins Hunting Service
Box 1, RR3, Gregory, SD 57533
(605) 835-8518 Gregg Biggins Anytime
145 mi. SW of Sioux Falls
Est 1980; **Acres** 12,000; **Hunters/yr** 100; **Type**
Public, Member/Avail, Corp.; **On Site** Clubhouse,
Lodging, Meals; **Shoots** Field; **Birds** Dove, Ruffed
Grouse, Pheasant, Chukar, Turkey, Prairie Chicken,
Sharp Tail Grouse, Geese; **Dogs** Avail/HDW;
Packages 2 Days, 1-40 guns
The land we hunt around Gregory has, without a
doubt, the best wild pheasant population in South
Dakota. At Biggins we don't have to guarantee
your limit because you will get your limit. Delicious
meals, spacious lodging, family hospitality and
genuine concern for the quality of your hunt are
what make Biggins special. Call today for information. And tell Gregg you "Saw it in Wing & Clay."

Circle CE Ranch
RR5, Box 98, Dixon, SD 57533
(605) 835-8281 Dick & Sally Shaffer Anytime
145 mi. W of Sioux Falls
Est 1988; **Acres** 3,000; **Type** Public; **On Site**
Clubhouse, Lodging, Meals; **Shoots** Field; **Birds**
Pheasant; **Dogs** Avail/HDW; **Packages** 3 Days, 8-12
guns ○ NAGA/See Pg. 107

Circle H Ranch
1300 W. 57th St., Sioux Falls, SD 57108
(605) 336-2111 Peter Hegg 8-6
8 mi. S of Gregory
Est 1990; **Acres** 3,000; **Type** Public; **On Site**
Clubhouse, Lodging, Meals, Clays; **Shoots** Field;
Birds Dove, Pheasant; **Dogs** Avail/HDW; **Packages**
2 Days, 3-20 guns

Cocks Unlimited
RR2, Box 29, Gregory, SD 57533
(605) 835-8479 Bruce/Alice Shaffer
180 mi. SW of Sioux Falls
Est 1981; **Acres** 6,000; **Hunters/yr** 125; **Type**
Public; **On Site** Clubhouse, Lodging, Meals; **Shoots**
Field; **Birds** Dove, Pheasant, Prairie Chicken, Sharp
Tail Grouse, Ducks, Geese; **Dogs** Avail/HDW;
Packages 1 Day, 5-20 guns

Connie Farms Inc.
HCR57, Box 38, Ideal, SD 57541
(605) 842-2904 Wayne L. Lapsley
55 mi. SE of Pierre
Est 1980; **Acres** 3,000; **Hunters/yr** 200; **Type**
Public; **On Site** Clubhouse, Lodging, Meals; **Shoots**
Field; **Birds** Pheasant; **Dogs** Avail/HDW; **Packages**
1 Day, 1-20 guns ○ NAGA/See Pg. 107

Dakota Dream Hunts, Inc.
20223 452nd Ave., Arlington, SD 57212
(605) 983-5033 Doug/Richard Converse Anytime
65 mi. NW of Sioux Falls
Est 1979; **Acres** 1,140; **Type** Public, Member/Avail;
On Site Clubhouse, Lodging, Meals, Clays; **Shoots**
Field, Blinds; **Birds** Dove, Pheasant, Huns, Snipe,
Ducks, Geese; **Dogs** Avail/HDW; **Packages** 1 Day,
1-30 guns ○ NAGA/See Pg. 107

Dakota Expeditions
HC64, Box 109, Miller, SD 57362
(605) 853-2545 Clint Smith After 6pm
63 mi. E of Pierre
Est 1980; **Acres** 10,000; **Hunters/yr** 300; **Type**
Public, Member/Avail, Corp.; **On Site** Clubhouse,
Lodging, Meals, Clays; **Shoots** Field; **Birds** Dove,
Pheasant, Chukar, Huns, Turkey, Prairie Chicken, Sharp
Tail Grouse, Ducks, Geese; **Dogs** Avail/HDW;
Packages 2 Days, 1-30 guns ○ NAGA/See Pg. 107

Dakota Hills Private Shooting Preserve
HC56, Box 90, Oral, SD 57766
(800) 622-3603 Tom Lauing
60 mi. S of Rapid City Airport
Est 1988; **Acres** 6,000; **Hunters/yr** 150; **Type**
Public; **On Site** Clubhouse, Lodging, Meals, Clays;
Shoots Field, Driven, Blinds; **Birds** Dove, Pheasant,
Chukar, Huns, Turkey, Sharp Tail Grouse, Ducks;
Dogs Avail/HDW; **Packages** 1 Day, 1-14 guns
○ NAGA/See Pg. 107
See Our Ad, Right

Dakota Hunting Farms
RR1, Box 100, Hecla, SD 57446
(800) 356-5281 Tim or Julie Mertz
40 mi. NE of Aberdeen
Est 1985; **Acres** 20,000; **Hunters/yr** 200; **Type**
Public; **On Site** Clubhouse, Lodging, Meals, Clays;
Shoots Field, Driven, Blinds; **Birds** Dove, Pheasant,
Turkey, Ducks, Geese; **Dogs** Avail/HDW; **Packages**
1 Day, 1-40 guns

Dakota Prairie Holidays
1108 South 3rd Ave., Sioux Falls, SD 57105
(605) 373-8931 Don Drake
30 mi. W of Mitchell
Est 1996; **Acres** 4,500; **Type** Public; **On Site**
Clubhouse, Lodging, Meals, Clays; **Shoots** Field;
Birds Pheasant; **Dogs** Avail/HDW; **Packages** 2
Days, 2-20 guns
See Our Ad Pg. 406

Dakota Ridge
RR2, Box 67, Altamont, SD 57226
(605) 874-2813 Charles Shomaker noon & 8pm
95 mi. N of Sioux Falls
Est 1988; **Acres** 2,500; **Hunters/yr** 200; **Type**
Public; **On Site** Clubhouse, Lodging, Meals, Clays;
Shoots Field, Blinds; **Birds** Pheasant, Chukar, Huns,
Ducks, Geese; **Dogs** Avail/HDW; **Packages** 1/2
Day, 1-20 guns ○ NAGA/See Pg. 107

Etzkorn's Goose Camp
HCR531, Box 39, Pierre, SD 57501
(605) 875-3338 Terry Etzkorn
Type Public; **On Site** Meals; **Birds** Pheasant, Ducks,
Geese

Folan Ranch
RR1, Box 128, Plankinton, SD 57368
(605) 942-7228 Bill Folan
90 mi. W of Sioux Falls
Acres 2,000; **Type** Public; **On Site** Clubhouse,
Lodging; **Shoots** Field; **Birds** Pheasant, Ducks;
Dogs Avail/HDW; **Packages** 1 Day, 1-8 guns

Forester Ranches
PO Box 102, Oacoma, SD 57365
(800) 982-6841 John Forester
125 mi. W of Sioux Falls
Est 1967; **Acres** 70,000; **Type** Public; **On Site**
Lodging, Meals; **Shoots** Field; **Birds** Dove, Quail,
Pheasant, Huns, Turkey, Prairie Chicken, Sharp Tail
Grouse, Ducks, Geese; **Dogs** Avail/HDW; **Packages**
3 Days, up to 6 guns ○ NAGA/See Pg. 107

Fort Randall
PO Box 459, Lake Andes, SD 57356
(605) 337-2301 J.A. Tonelli
115 mi. SW of Sioux Falls
Est 1965; **Acres** 1,300; **Hunters/yr** 60; **Type**
Public; **On Site** Clubhouse, Lodging, Meals; **Shoots**
Field, Blinds; **Birds** Dove, Pheasant, Prairie Chicken,
Sharp Tail Grouse, Ducks, Geese; **Dogs** Avail/HDW;
Packages 2 Days, 3-7 guns ○ NAGA/See Pg. 107

Funkrest Hunting Preserve
RR3, Box 167, Madison, SD 57042
(800) 351-1477 Don or Bonnie Funk 9-dusk
50 mi. NW of Sioux Falls
Est 1985; **Acres** 800; **Hunters/yr** 300; **Type**
Public, Member/Avail, Corp.; **On Site** Clubhouse,
Lodging, Meals, Clays; **Shoots** Field; **Birds**
Pheasant, Chukar, Turkey; **Dogs** Avail/HDW
○ NAGA/See Pg. 107

Great Plains Hunting
RR#2, Box 33, Wessington, SD 57381
(605) 883-4526 Clyde L. Zepp Evenings
22 mi. W of Huron
Est 1990; **Acres** 5,000; **Type** Public, Member/Avail;
On Site Clubhouse, Lodging, Meals; **Shoots** Field;
Birds Dove, Pheasant, Huns, Prairie Chicken, Sharp Tail
Grouse, Ducks; **Dogs** Avail/HDW; **Packages** 1 Day,
1-10 guns

Haines Hunting Service
RR1, Box 18, Gregory, SD 57533
(605) 835-9280 Edward Haines
90 mi. SE of Pierre
Acres 7,500; **Type** Public; **On Site** Clubhouse,
Lodging, Meals; **Shoots** Field; **Birds** Pheasant,
Prairie Chicken, Sharp Tail Grouse, Ducks, Geese;
Dogs HDW; **Packages** 2 Days, 1-10 guns

Heartland Pheasant Acres
Rt. 1, Box 14, Ree Heights, SD 57371
(605) 943-5586 Kenneth Werdel Evenings
Type Public; **On Site** Clubhouse; **Shoots** Field;
Birds Ruffed Grouse, Pheasant, Huns; **Dogs**
Avail/HDW

Hidden Valley Hunting Club
HC56, Box 51, Oral, SD 57766
(605) 424-2895 Bob Anderson Daytime
50 mi. S of Rapid City
Est 1985; **Acres** 640; **Type** Public, Corp.; **On Site**
Meals, Clays; **Shoots** Field; **Birds** Dove, Pheasant,
Ducks; **Dogs** Avail/HDW; **Packages** 1 Day, 1-6 guns

High Brass, Inc.
RR1, Box 4X, Chamberlain, SD 57325
(605) 734-6047 Tom Koehn Early morning/evening
120 mi. W of Sioux Falls
Est 1980; **Acres** 50,000; **Hunters/yr** 300; **Type**
Public; **On Site** Meals; **Shoots** Field; **Birds**
Pheasant, Prairie Chicken, Sharp Tail Grouse, Geese;
Dogs Avail/HDW; **Packages** 3 Days, 1-20 guns
○ NAGA/See Pg. 107

High Plains Game Ranch
HCR76, Box 192, Nisland, SD 57762
(605) 257-2365 Randy Vallery 7am-8pm
55 mi. N of Rapid City
Est 1986; **Acres** 1,280; **Hunters/yr** 200; **Type**
Public; **On Site** Clubhouse, Lodging, Meals, Clays;
Shoots Field; **Birds** Pheasant, Chukar, Turkey;
Dogs Avail/HDW; **Packages** 1/2 Day, 1-15 guns
○ NAGA/See Pg. 107

Orvis Discovers A Star: *South Dakota's Big Bend Ranch*

Pierre, SD - The world's best hotels rate 5 Stars from Mobil...the best restaurants, 3 Stars from Michelin...and the very best hunting lodges an endorsement from The Orvis Company. So it came as no surprise when an operation as rich in hunting tradition as Big Bend Ranch won a role in Orvis's star-studded cast of Endorsed Wingshooting Lodges.

Orvis Endorsed

Orvis, America's oldest mail order company, created its Wingshooting Lodge Program to help clients find the best bird-shooting experiences in the country. "To qualify for the program, you have to meet stringent criteria established by Orvis," says Big Bend Ranch owner-operator Alex Falk. "First and foremost, you have to offer a complete and totally uncompromising bird hunting experience. But just as important," he adds, "is the quality of the lodging, dining and service."

Big Bend, a sprawling hunting paradise along the scenic Missouri River near Pierre, South Dakota, has clearly mastered both sides of the Orvis equation. Here, world class wingshooting—upland game and waterfowl—is the rule rather than the exception. In fact, the Ranch has been cited by knowledgeable hunters as the #1 Canada Goose hunting location in the world and has hosted the Annual South Dakota Governor's Pheasant Hunt for the past several years.

Spectacular hunting & shooting

Falk traces much of his success to aggressive habitat management. The Ranch's varied terrain includes farm fields, CRP, shelterbelts and river breaks where Ringneck Pheasant and Hungarian Partridge predominate, but coveys of Prairie Chicken and Sharptail Grouse are also encountered.

Big Bend Ranch is renowned for spectacular waterfowl pass and field shooting. Canada Geese are the primary waterfowl species but large flights of Northern mallards, White Front, Snow and Blue Geese are also seen frequently.

Throughout the hunting season guests begin the day with a big country style breakfast and then, in September and Octo-

Hunting the wily South Dakota Ringneck.

ber, set off in pursuit of upland game—Hungarian Partridge, Sharptail Grouse or Prairie Chicken. Or, if they prefer, they can enjoy decoying Northern Mallards into one of Big Bend Ranch's many ponds. In November and December, early morning hunters can experience the finest Canada Goose hunting imaginable.

Morning hunts are followed by a break for a hearty home cooked lunch and then a trip afield to hunt the wily South Dakota Ringneck Pheasant. After a challenging but invariably successful pheasant hunt, many sportsman opt to return to the duck or goose blinds, while some head for the Ranch's private trout pond.

World class service

Big Bend's comfortable lodge is the perfect spot to reflect on a great day in the field and to anticipate a fine evening meal. Personal attention, service and hospitality are a hallmark at Big Bend. The Ranch staff is experienced, professional and attentive to their guests' every need.

Expert guides and professionally trained dogs earn their share of accolades from hunters at Big Bend. "We specialize in small groups," says Falk, "and we're always happy to customize a hunt to our guests' needs."

Big Bend is located 28 miles southeast of Pierre, South Dakota's capital. The Pierre airport has a 6800 foot airstrip with full service FBO. If you're interested in adding Big Bend's spectacular outdoor experience and hospitality to your memories, contact **Alex or Annie Falk, Big Bend Ranch 1301 N. 4th St., Aberdeen, SD 57401; Hunting Season:(605) 875-3445 or (605) 229-3035.**

Horseshoe K Ranch
RR1, Box 94, Kimball, SD 57355
(605) 778-6714 8pm
110 mi. W of Sioux Falls
Est 1982; **Acres** 2,400; **Hunters/yr** 30; **Type**
Public, Member/Avail; **On Site** Clubhouse, Lodging,
Meals; **Shoots** Field; **Birds** Dove, Ruffed Grouse,
Pheasant, Huns, Sharp Tail Grouse; **Dogs** Avail/HDW

Ingall's Prairie Wildfowl Hunts
RR1, Box 111, Bryant, SD 57221
(605) 628-2327 Jim/Joyce Ingalls
100 mi. NW of Sioux Falls
Est 1980; **Acres** 2,500; **On Site** Clubhouse,
Lodging, Meals; **Shoots** Field, Blinds; **Birds**
Pheasant, Ducks, Geese; **Dogs** Avail/HDW;
Packages 1 Day, 1-15 guns ○ NAGA/See Pg. 107

James Valley Hunting Resort, Inc.
43765 298 St., Utica, SD 57067
(605) 364-7468 Harold or Jan Klimisch Evenings
55 mi. SW of Sioux Falls
Est 1985; **Acres** 1,200; **Type** Public, Member/Avail,
Corp.; **On Site** Clubhouse, Lodging, Meals, Clays;
Shoots Field; **Birds** Quail, Pheasant, Chukar, Turkey;
Dogs Avail/HDW; **Packages** 1 Day, 1-20 guns
○ NAGA/See Pg. 107

K&M Hunting
Rt. 3, Box 15, Plankinton, SD 57368
(605) 942-7516 Michael & Kathye Miller
85 mi. W of Sioux Falls
Est 1982; **Acres** 1,200; **Type** Public; **On Site**
Clubhouse, Lodging, Meals; **Shoots** Field; **Birds**
Pheasant; **Dogs** Avail/HDW; **Packages** 1 Day, 1-12 guns

Lake's Byron Lodge
109 Bluebell Dr., Pierre, SD 57501
(605) 352-3241 Doug Lake
17 mi. NE of Huron
Acres 2,000; **Hunters/yr** 70; **Type** Public; **On
Site** Lodging, Meals; **Shoots** Field, Blinds; **Birds**
Pheasant, Huns, Sharp Tail Grouse, Ducks, Geese;
Dogs Avail

Lubber's Farms Hunting Service
Rt. 1, Box 119, Gregory, SD 57533
(605) 835-9134 Jim Lubbers
120 mi. SE of Pierre
Est 1987; **Type** Public; **On Site** Clubhouse,
Lodging, Meals; **Shoots** Field; **Birds** Quail,
Pheasant, Chukar, Turkey, Prairie Chicken, Sharp Tail
Grouse; **Dogs** Avail

Medicine Creek
Pheasant Ranch, Inc.
PO Box 63, Vivian, SD 57576
(605) 683-6411 Mike Authier
30 mi. S of Pierre
Est 1986; **Acres** 4,000; **Type** Public; **On Site**
Clubhouse, Lodging, Meals, Clays; **Shoots** Field,
Blinds; **Birds** Pheasant, Prairie Chicken, Sharp Tail
Grouse, Ducks, Geese; **Dogs** Avail/HDW; **Packages**
2 Days, 1-8 guns
Satisfied clients and hunting on nearly 10,000
owned and leased acres, you can be confident of a
successful hunt. A 3-day package includes on-site
luxurious lodging, meals, guide, dogs, etc. starting
at $825. Call Mike Authier, 605-683-6411 or write
Box 63, Vivian, SD 57576.

Morris Game Farm
Box 126, Artesian, SD 57314
(605) 527-2424 Thomas Morris **Type** Public,
Member/Avail; **On Site** Lodging; **Shoots** Field;
Birds Pheasant, Chukar ○ NAGA/See Pg. 107

Paul Nelson Farm
119 Hilltop Dr., PO Box 183, Gettysburg, SD 57442
(605) 765-2469 Paul Nelson
65 mi. NE of Pierre
Acres 8,000; **Type** Public; **On Site** Clubhouse,
Lodging, Meals, Clays; **Shoots** Field; **Birds**
Pheasant; **Dogs** Avail/HDW; **Packages** 3 Days, 1-20
guns ○ NAGA/See Pg. 107
See Our Ad Across

P&R Hunting Lodge
Rt. 5, Box 117, Dallas, SD 57529
(605) 835-8050 Paul Taggart 8am-10pm
110 mi. SE of Pierre   **Type** Public; **On Site**
Clubhouse, Lodging, Meals, Clays; **Shoots** Field;
Birds Pheasant, Turkey, Sharp Tail Grouse, Geese;

Pearson's Hunting
Adventures, Inc.
HC74, 256, Forestburg, SD 57314
(612) 935-2514 Marvin R. Pearson
16 mi. SE of Huron
Est 1946; **Acres** 2,000; **Type** Public, Corp.; **On
Site** Clubhouse, Lodging, Meals, Clays; **Shoots** Field,
Driven, Blinds; **Birds** Dove, Quail, Pheasant, Huns,
Turkey, Sharp Tail Grouse, Ducks, Geese; **Dogs**
Avail/HDW; **Packages** 2 Days, 1-20 guns
○ NAGA/See Pg. 107
See Our Ad Pg. 410

Reprinted from: THE WALL STREET JOURNAL THURSDAY, FEBRUARY 8, 1996

LEISURE & ARTS

Where Pheasants Swarm as Thick as Locusts

By Michael Pearce

The lodge at Paul Nelson Farm.

Not unlike much of America's wildlife, South Dakota's pheasant population has risen and fallen at the whims of Mother Nature. Worse yet, it suffered at the hands of modern agriculture, which steadily replaced needed nestling and winter cover with sprawling inland seas of corn and wheat. But the tide has turned. South Dakota's pheasant hunting has been nothing short of phenomenal lately.

"Thanks to several things—mild winters, the cover of the Conservation Reserve Program, and private habitat programs—our pheasant population has been incredible the last few years," said Paul Nelson, president of Paul Nelson Farm, of Gettysburg, South Dakota. "Most of our guests have simply never seen anything like it, or compare it to the glory days of the 1950s. It's not uncommon for our guests to flush 200 pheasants from just one field."

Mind-Boggling Bird Numbers

Not surprisingly, the mind-boggling bird numbers have again brought sportsmen from around the world to the place where pheasants outnumber people many, many times over. "Pheasant hunting is really, really big in South Dakota. People come from all over the world," said Mark Kayser, outdoor promotions manager, South Dakota Department of Tourism.

And in recent years a number of businesses have blossomed that cater to sportsmen who want the creme de la creme of wingshooting action and worldly accommodations, such as Mr. Nelson's legendary establishment.

One of the Best in the Nation

Picked up in nearby Pierre, guests are taken along a back road maze that soon places them at the huge lodge that features a country opulence and is rated among the best in the nation. Served by a hand-picked staff from across the state, Mr. Nelson's guests feast on five-star cuisine as they talk business or simply relax.

But there is no time for total relaxation when taken afield by Mr. Nelson's guides and dogs. Proof that agriculture and wildlife can coexist, Paul Nelson Farm's thousands of acres spew birds like bees from a shaken hive. The wingshooting is indeed so good that Mr. Nelson had to seek special regulation that allows gunners to take more than the state-regulated three-bird-per-day limit.

Hunters Return Again and Again

Still, the action is hot enough that most guests are back at the lodge by late afternoon, where they can bang a round of sporting clays or simply sit quietly on a balcony, favored drink in hand as they watch scores of gaudy cockbirds sail into a small sanctuary just yards from the lodge. Mr. Nelson reports that few who depart fail to leave a deposit for another all-inclusive hunt, which will cost around $2,000 for three days. For more information about Paul Nelson Farm call or write: P.O. Box 183, Gettysburg, SD 57442; (605) 765-2469.

Pheasant Haven Farms
Box 373, Wagner, SD 57380
(605) 384-3296 Dennis Kuhlman
120 mi. SW of Sioux Falls
Est 1986; **Acres** 2,500; **Hunters/yr** 50; **Type**
Public; **On Site** Lodging, Meals, Clays; **Shoots** Field;
Birds Pheasant, Chukar, Geese; **Dogs** Avail/HDW;
Packages 1 Day, 3-20 guns

Prairie Bird Paradise
1212 Rice St., Gregory, SD 57533
(605) 835-9522 Tom Falencik
Acres 17,000; **Hunters/yr** 100; **Shoots** Field;
Birds Dove, Pheasant, Turkey, Prairie Chicken, Sharp
Tail Grouse, Ducks, Geese; **Dogs** Avail

Prairie Paradise Hunts
325 Crow, Pierre, SD 57501
(605) 224-5573 Verne Olson
30 mi. W of Pierre
Hunters/yr 200; **Type** Public; **On Site** Lodging,
Meals; **Shoots** Field; **Birds** Dove, Pheasant, Prairie
Chicken, Sharp Tail Grouse, Geese; **Dogs** Avail

Bob Priebe Pheasant Hunting Country
HC69, Box 36, Chamberlain, SD 57325
(605) 734-6153 Bob Priebe
140 mi. W of Sioux Falls
Est 1986; **Acres** 1,000; **Hunters/yr** 130; **Type**
Public; **On Site** Lodging, Meals; **Shoots** Field;
Birds Dove, Pheasant; **Dogs** Avail/HDW; **Packages**
1/2 Day, 1-20 guns

Ralph Erickson Hunting Preserve
RR1, Box 50, Humboldt, SD 57035
(605) 297-3561 Ralph Erickson Late evenings
15 mi. W of Sioux Falls
Est 1990; **Acres** 1,000; **Hunters/yr** 100; **Type**
Public; **On Site** Meals; **Shoots** Field; **Birds**
Pheasant; **Dogs** Avail/HDW; **Packages** 1/2 Day, up
to 12 guns

Don Reeves
Pheasant Ranch
Rt. 2, Box 30, White Lake, SD 57383
(605) 249-2693 Genevieve Reeves 7am-10pm
100 mi. W of Sioux Falls
Est 1984; **Acres** 1,270; **Hunters/yr** 400; **Type**
Public; **On Site** Lodging, Meals; **Shoots** Field;
Birds Pheasant; **Dogs** Avail/HDW

Rooster Roost Ranch
25699 407th Ave., Mitchell, SD 57301
(605) 996-4676 Dean Strand 7-10pm
4 mi. SW of Mitchell
Est 1988; **Acres** 5,000; **Hunters/yr** 80; **Type**
Public; **On Site** Clubhouse, Lodging, Meals; **Shoots**
Field; **Birds** Dove, Pheasant, Huns; **Dogs**
Avail/HDW; **Packages** 3 Days, 1-10 guns
O NAGA/See Pg. 107
Light hunting pressure at Rooster Ranch–we will
not book over 80 guests in any season–results in
some of the most fantastic hunting you've ever experienced. By keeping things "small" we can offer
uncomparable personalized service, including excellent home cooked farm meals and extremely
comfortable lodging. Our spacious and clean kennels are at your disposal, if you'd like to hunt with
your own dogs. Other South Dakota operations are
larger, but none offers better hunting or more reasonable prices. Call today.

S&S Hunting
RR1, Box 64, Burke, SD 57523
(605) 775-2262 Mary Ann Shaffer Late evenings
160 mi. W of Sioux Falls
Est 1984; **Acres** 1,000; **Hunters/yr** 100; **Type**
Public, Member/Avail; **On Site** Clubhouse, Lodging,
Meals, Clays; **Shoots** Field; **Birds** Quail, Pheasant,
Chukar, Huns, Turkey, Prairie Chicken, Sharp Tail
Grouse; **Dogs** Avail/HDW; **Packages** 1 Day, 3-10
guns

HUNT WILD
SOUTH DAKOTA
PHEASANTS • DUCKS • GEESE

3 FULL DAYS OF HUNTING
$2150.00

Includes guides, accommodations, dogs, licenses, ammunition, gourmet meals, open bar, game cleaning and applicable taxes.
A first quality hunt with no itemized bill at days end.

Each day mallards over decoys on stock dams or out of our custom duck boats on big water, or Honker hunting from corn field pits. Pheasants and grouse at noon in cornfields, weed patches and tree strips. After hunting open bar, wines and outstanding dinners.

Private hunts for as few as 4 guns, for as large as 8.
A perfect corporate program.

P.O. Box 27, Pierre, SD 57501
(619) 296–8533
Brochures • Videos • References Available on Request

South Dakota Hunting Service
PO Box 324, Herrick, SD 57538
(605) 775-2460 Mike Moody

South Dakota Pheasant Acres
Rt. 1, Box 56, Armour, SD 57313
(605) 337-3523 Jay Jensen Evenings
90 mi. SW of Sioux Falls **Est** 1980; **Acres** 2,000;
Type Public; **On Site** Clubhouse, Lodging, Meals;
Shoots Field; **Birds** Pheasant; **Dogs** Avail/HDW;
Packages 1 Day, 1-36 guns O NAGA/See Pg. 107

South Dakota Pheasant Hunts
RR1, Box 260, Gary, SD 57237
(605) 272-5608 William E. Stone
90 mi. N of Sioux Falls **Est** 1985; **Acres** 800; **Type**
Public; **Shoots** Field; **Birds** Dove, Pheasant, Ducks,
Geese; **Dogs** Avail/HDW; **Packages** 1 Day, 1-10 guns

South Dakota
Pheasant Safaris
PO Box 27, Pierre, SD 57501
(619) 296-8533 Darwin Dapper Early am
20 mi. E of Pierre
Est 1980; **Acres** 10,000; **Hunters/yr** 125; **Type**
Public, Member/Avail, Corp.; **On Site** Clubhouse,
Lodging, Meals, Clays; **Shoots** Field, Blinds; **Birds**
Pheasant, Huns, Prairie Chicken, Sharp Tail Grouse,
Ducks, Geese; **Dogs** Avail/HDW; **Packages** 31/2
Days, 4-16 guns
See Our Ad Pg. 411

South Dakota Wildfowl
RR2, Box 134, Dell Rapids, SD 57022
(605) 428-5743 David Lenth
30 mi. NW of Sioux Falls
Acres 4,200; **Hunters/yr** 150; **Type** Public; **On
Site** Lodging, Meals; **Shoots** Field, Driven; **Birds**
Dove, Pheasant, Chukar, Huns, Ducks, Geese; **Dogs**
Avail/HDW

Stukel's Birds & Bucks
Rt. 1, Box 112W, Gregory, SD 57533
(605) 835-8941 Frank Stukel
90 mi. SE of Pierre
Est 1981; **Acres** 10,000; **Hunters/yr** 250; **Type**
Public; **On Site** Clubhouse, Lodging, Meals, Clays;
Shoots Field, Blinds; **Birds** Pheasant, Turkey, Sharp
Tail Grouse; **Dogs** Avail/HDW; **Packages** 2 Days,
1-20 guns O NAGA/See Pg. 107
O Family Run Business
O Quality Clubhouse
O Onsite Pro Shop
O Sporting Clays
O Award Winning Habitat
See Our Ad, Right

Swisher Hunting
RR2, Box 163, Groton, SD 57445
(605) 294-5860 Robert Swisher 11:30 am - 1:30 pm
25 mi. NE of Aberdeen Airport
Est 1986; **Acres** 2,000; **Hunters/yr** 150; **Type** Public; **On Site** Clubhouse, Meals; **Shoots** Field; **Birds** Dove, Pheasant, Huns, Ducks, Geese; **Dogs** Avail/HDW; **Packages** 1/2 Day, 10-15 guns

Thunderstik Lodge
RR1, Box 10T, Chamberlain, SD 55459
(800) 888-1601 Chuck Ross M-F, 8-5
125 mi. W of Sioux Falls
Est 1988; **Acres** 8,000; **Hunters/yr** 300; **Type** Public; **On Site** Clubhouse, Lodging, Meals; **Shoots** Field, Blinds; **Birds** Pheasant, Ducks, Geese; **Dogs** Avail/HDW; **Packages** 3 Days, 2-30 guns ○ NAGA/See Pg. 107

Tinker Kennels
3031 Sussex Pl., Pierre, SD 57501
(605) 224-5414 Bob Tinker
Est 1989; **Acres** 50,000; **Type** Public; **On Site** Clubhouse, Lodging, Meals; **Shoots** Field, Blinds; **Birds** Quail, Pheasant, Chukar, Huns, Turkey, Prairie Chicken, Sharp Tail Grouse, Ducks, Geese; **Dogs** Avail/HDW; **Packages** 1 Day, 1-5 guns

Unlimited Ringnecks
Rt. 1, Box 67A, Cresbard, SD 57435
(800) 645-3850 Jon Batteen Anytime
30 mi. NW of Redfield
Est 1976; **Acres** 3,000; **Type** Public; **On Site** Lodging, Meals; **Shoots** Field; **Birds** Pheasant; **Dogs** Avail/HDW; **Packages** 2 Days, 1-20 guns

Valley West
Hunting Preserve
809 W. 10th St., Sioux Falls, SD 57104
(800) 424-2047 Daniel Stock or Francis Phillips 8am-5pm
5 mi. W of Empire Mall at Sioux Falls
Est 1990; **Acres** 700; **Hunters/yr** 5,000; **Type** Public, Member/Avail, Corp.; **On Site** Clubhouse, Lodging, Meals, Clays; **Shoots** Field, Tower, Blinds; **Birds** Pheasant; **Dogs** Avail/HDW; **Packages** 1/2 Day, 2-20 guns ○ NAGA/See Pg. 107
See Our Ad Across, Left

Wells Shooting Preserve
R1, Box 44, Oldham, SD 57051
(605) 854-3284 Dale E. Wells
65 mi. NW of Sioux Falls
Est 1945; **Acres** 1,100; **Hunters/yr** 600; **Type** Public; **On Site** Clubhouse, Lodging, Meals; **Shoots** Field; **Birds** Pheasant, Ducks, Geese; **Dogs** Avail/HDW

Wild Flush, Inc.
RR2, Box 75, Waubay, SD 57273
(800) 599-2393 Mike Frederick 7am-7pm
20 mi. NW of Watertown
Est 1992; **Acres** 1,000; **Hunters/yr** 65; **Type** Public, Member/Avail, Corp.; **On Site** Lodging, Meals, Clays; **Shoots** Field, Blinds; **Birds** Dove, Pheasant, Huns, Ducks, Geese; **Dogs** Avail/HDW; **Packages** 1/2 Day, 1-20 guns ○ NAGA/See Pg. 107

Wild Wings
Box 149, Gregory, SD 57533
(605) 835-8391 Rick Johnson 9-5
160 mi. SE of Sioux Falls
Est 1987; **Acres** 3,000; **Hunters/yr** 200; **Type** Public, Member/Avail; **On Site** Clubhouse, Lodging, Meals, Clays; **Shoots** Field; **Birds** Pheasant, Turkey; **Dogs** Avail/HDW; **Packages** 2 Days, 8-20 guns

TENNESSEE

Arrowhead Hunt Club
PO Box 598, Whiteville, TN 38075
(901) 231-8684 Elmer Kahl
45 mi. E of Memphis **Type** Public, Member/Avail;
On Site Clubhouse, Lodging, Meals, Clays; **Shoots**
Field, Tower, Driven; **Birds** Dove, Quail, Woodcock,
Pheasant; **Dogs** Avail/HDW; **Packages** 1/2 Day,
2-12 guns ○ NAGA/See Pg. 107

Babe's Bird Farm
303 Cedar Mt. Rd., Decherd, TN 37324
(615) 967-9601 Kenneth Perry
Shoots Field; **Birds** Quail, Chukar
○ NAGA/See Pg. 107

CBD Hunting Preserve
13800 Cookeville Dock Rd., Baxter, TN 38544
(615) 858-2185 Reece Nash 9 to 5
64 mi. E of Nashville **Est** 1991; **Acres** 280; **Type**
Public; **On Site** Clubhouse, Meals; **Shoots** Field;
Birds Quail, Pheasant; **Dogs** Avail/HDW; **Packages**
1/2 Day, up to 2 guns

Caryonah Hunting Lodge

Rt. 10, Box 264, Crossville, TN 38555
(615) 277-3113 Bobbie Jean Garrison 7am-10pm
14 mi. NW of Crossville
Est 1950; **Acres** 2,000; **Type** Public; **On Site**
Clubhouse, Lodging, Meals; **Shoots** Field; **Birds** Quail,
Turkey; **Dogs** Avail; **Packages** 1 Day, 1-32 guns

Cedar Hill Shooting Preserve
714 S. Cumberland St., Morristown, TN 37814
(423) 587-6486 B.G. McFall/T. Newcomb
Acres 240; **Hunters/yr** 80; **Type** Public; **On Site**
Meals, Clays; **Shoots** Field; **Birds** Quail, Pheasant;
Dogs Avail

Crockett Pheasant Farm & Hunting
1213 Woodgate, Humboldt, TN 38343
(901) 784-5368 Van Holyfield After 5pm
75 mi. NE of Memphis
Est 1991; **Type** Public; **On Site** Clubhouse,
Lodging, Clays; **Shoots** Field; **Birds** Quail, Pheasant;
Dogs Avail/HDW; **Packages** 1/2 Day
○ NAGA/See Pg. 107

Deer Creek Outfitters

PO Box 39, Sebree, KY 42455
(502) 835-2424 Tim Stull
from 2 hours North of Nashville
Est 1984; **Acres** 5,000; **Type** Public, Member/Avail;
On Site Clubhouse, Lodging, Meals, Clays; **Shoots**
Field, Blinds; **Birds** Dove, Quail, Pheasant, Chukar,
Turkey, Ducks, Geese; **Dogs** Avail/HDW; **Packages**
1/2 Day, 1-12 guns

Estanaula Hunt Club
PO Box 26, Brownsville, TN 38012
(901) 772-9780 Harbert Mulherin
50 mi. NE of Memphis
Est 1977; **Acres** 6,000; **Type** Public; **On Site**
Clubhouse, Lodging, Meals, Clays; **Shoots** Field;
Birds Quail; **Dogs** Avail; **Packages** 1/2 Day

Falls Creek Hunt Club
HC69, Box 234, Spencer, TN 38585
(615) 946-2095 Frank Hanwright
85 mi. SE of Nashville
Est 1989; **Acres** 280; **Type** Public, Member/Avail;
On Site Clubhouse, Lodging, Meals, Clays; **Shoots**
Field; **Birds** Quail, Pheasant, Chukar; **Dogs**
Avail/HDW

Goose Busters Guide Service
PO Box 176, Rt. 4, Martin, TN 38237
(901) 587-9397 Johnny Gibson
15 mi. SE of Stuttgart
Acres 50,000; **Type** Public; **On Site** Clubhouse,
Lodging, Meals; **Shoots** Blinds; **Birds** Ducks, Geese;
Dogs Avail/HDW; **Packages** 1/2 Day, 4-8 guns

Goose Creek Hunting Preserve
659 Nicholson Rd., Jefferson City, TN 37760
(423) 397-7406 Tom Jenkins 6-9pm
35 mi. E of Knoxville
Est 1990; **Acres** 220; **Hunters/yr** 100; **Type**
Member/Avail; **Shoots** Field; **Birds** Quail, Pheasant;
Dogs HDW; **Packages** 1/2 Day, 1-3 guns
○ NAGA/See Pg. 107

Hamilton's Resort
Rt. 1, Hornbeak, TN 38232
(901) 538-2325 Bonnie
80 mi. NE of Memphis
Est 1945; **Acres** 1,300; **Type** Public; **On Site**
Lodging; **Shoots** Field, Blinds; **Birds** Dove, Turkey,
Snipe, Ducks, Geese; **Dogs** Avail; **Packages** 1 Day,
2-30 guns

Honey Creek Hunting Preserve
Star Rt., Box 171, Allardt, TN 38504
(615) 879-9796 Royal D. Tompkins
87 mi. NW of Knoxville
Type Public; **Shoots** Field; **Birds** Quail, Pheasant,
Chukar ○ NAGA/See Pg. 107

The Hunting Lodge
PO Box 381, Manchester, TN 37355
(615) 728-7260 Harry L. Taylor
75 mi. SE of Nashville
Est 1991; **Acres** 565; **Type** Public; **On Site**
Clubhouse, Lodging, Meals, Clays; **Shoots** Field;
Birds Quail, Pheasant, Chukar; **Dogs** Avail/HDW;
Packages 1/2 Day

Meadowbrook Game Farm
1600 Meadowbrook Dr., Westmoreland, TN 37186
(615) 888-2411 G.D. Denning
40 mi. N of Nashville
Est 1950; **Acres** 1,600; **Hunters/yr** 700; **Type**

Public, Member/Avail; **Shoots** Field; **Birds** Dove,
Quail, Pheasant, Chukar; **Dogs** Avail/HDW
O NAGA/See Pg. 107

Nestegg Ranch
1326 Warner Bridge Rd., Shelbyville, TN 37160
(615) 684-9814 Steve Smith
On Site Lodging; **Shoots** Field; **Birds** Quail,
Pheasant, Chukar O NAGA/See Pg. 107

Pheasant Creek Hunting Preserve
692 Huddleston Rd., Lascassas, TN 37085
(615) 286-2499 Jesse Dunaway Anytime
25 mi. E of Nashville
Acres 410; **Type** Public, Member/Avail; **On Site**
Clubhouse, Clays; **Shoots** Field, Tower; **Birds** Dove,
Quail, Pheasant, Chukar, Turkey, Ducks; **Dogs**
Avail/HDW; **Packages** 1/2 Day, 1-12 guns
O NAGA/See Pg. 107

Quail Valley Hunt Club
506 Bryant St., Shelbyville, TN 37160
(615) 685-4628 Jim Walker
50 mi. SE of Nashville
Est 1986; **Type** Public, Member/Avail, Corp.; **On
Site** Lodging, Clays; **Shoots** Field; **Birds** Quail,
Pheasant, Chukar; **Dogs** Avail/HDW; **Packages** 1/2
Day O NAGA/See Pg. 107

Quail Walk
1212 Evans Lane, Brownsville, TN 38012
(901) 772-3213 D. Clinton Evans
50 mi. NE of Memphis
Est 1990; **Acres** 200; **Hunters/yr** 200; **Type**
Public; **On Site** Clubhouse, Meals, Clays; **Shoots**
Field; **Birds** Quail, Pheasant, Chukar; **Dogs**
Avail/HDW; **Packages** 1/2 Day, 1-6 guns

Shaw Creek Shooting Preserve
2055 Burnett Rd., Williston, TN 38076
(901) 854-0121 Randy Reeves 9 to 5
29 mi. E of Memphis
Est 1988; **Acres** 900; **Type** Public; **On Site**
Clubhouse, Lodging, Clays; **Shoots** Field; **Birds**
Dove, Quail, Pheasant, Chukar; **Dogs** Avail/HDW;
Packages 1/2 Day, 2-9 guns

Teal Hollow Hunting Club
PO Box 10, Fayetteville, TN 37334
(615) 937-8441 Donny Ray Hudson
50 mi. NE of Memphis
Type Public; **Shoots** Field; **Birds** Quail; **Dogs**
Avail/HDW

TEXAS

3G's Lodge & Kennel
PO Box 56, Mineral, TX 78125
(512) 375-2814 Tom Godlewski
70 mi. N of Corpus Christi
Est 1990; **Acres** 8,000; **Type** Public; **On Site**
Clubhouse, Lodging, Meals, Clays; **Shoots** Field, Tower,
Driven; **Birds** Dove, Quail, Pheasant, Chukar, Turkey;
Dogs Avail/HDW; **Packages** 1/2 Day, 4-12 guns

Adobe Lodge Hunting Camp
9660 S. US Hwy. 67, San Angelo, TX 76904
(915) 942-8040 Skipper Duncan
10 mi. SW of San Angelo
Est 1985; **Acres** 50,000; **Hunters/yr** 117; **Type**
Public; **On Site** Clubhouse, Lodging, Meals; **Shoots**
Field; **Birds** Turkey; **Dogs** Avail/HDW; **Packages**
31/2 Days, 1-8 guns

Allen Ranches
574 Dana Lane, Houston, TX 77056
(713) 465-2298 Ranch Phone
100 mi. SW of Houston
Acres 1,000; **Type** Public, Member/Avail, Corp.;
On Site Clubhouse, Lodging, Clays; **Shoots** Field;
Birds Quail, Pheasant, Chukar; **Dogs** Avail/HDW;
Packages 1/2 Day, 2-20 guns O NAGA/See Pg. 107
O Bird Processing
O Loaner Guns
O Plantation Wagon Hunts
O Field Trial Headquarters

L.D. Anderson
1802 Ave. Q, Lubbock, TX 79401
50 mi. SE of Lubbock
Acres 1,100; **Hunters/yr** 20; **Type** Member/Avail;
Shoots Field; **Birds** Pheasant, Chukar; **Dogs** Avail

B-Bar-B Ranch
Rt. 1, Box 457, Kingsville, TX 78363
(512) 296-3331 Luther or Patti Young
45 mi. SW of Corpus Christi
Est 1992; **Acres** 20,000; **Type** Public; **On Site**
Clubhouse, Lodging, Meals, Clays; **Shoots** Field;
Birds Dove, Quail, Turkey; **Dogs** Avail/HDW;
Packages 1 Day, 4-16 guns

Bajio Ranch
PO Box 502, Fowlerton, TX 78021
(800) 528-8725 Warren Vecker
65 mi. S of San Antonio
Acres 600; **Type** Public; **On Site** Lodging; **Shoots**
Field; **Birds** Quail; **Packages** 1 Day

Bar H Dude Ranch
Box 1191, Clarendon, TX 79226
(806) 874-2634 Frank Hommel
45 mi. SE of Amarillo

Acres 1,500; **Hunters/yr** 30; **Type** Public; **On Site** Lodging, Meals; **Shoots** Field, Blinds; **Birds** Dove, Quail, Chukar, Turkey; **Dogs** Avail

Bar K Hunting Lodge
10000 County Road 430, San Angelo, TX 76901
(915) 949-2229 Dale Bates
30 mi. W of San Angelo
Acres 5,000; **Type** Public; **On Site** Clubhouse, Lodging, Meals; **Shoots** Field; **Birds** Turkey; **Packages** 3 Days, 1-22 guns

Bay Prairie Outfitters
PO Box 35378, Houston, TX 77235
(800) 242-1374 Mike Ladnier Web Site:
http://www.texas-goose-hunting.com
80 mi. SW of Houston
Type Public; **Shoots** Field, Blinds; **Birds** Ducks, Geese; **Dogs** Avail; **Packages** 1/2 Day, 1-4 guns
o Morning hunts for Geese, Duck and Sandhill Crane
o Affordable package hunts include lodging, breakfast, morning hunt, bird processing & freezing
o Afternoon hunts on Bay Flats for Pintails, Redheads, Widgeon and Teal
o License, stamps and shotgun shells available at the Lodge

Big County Game Bird Farm
PO Box 1880, Abilene, TX 79604
(915) 677-0866 Norman Dozier
Type Public, Member/Avail; **Birds** Quail, Pheasant, Chukar

HUNTING PRESERVE

Black Creek Ranch
26081 Bulverde Rd., San Antonio, TX 78261
(210) 438-4188 Lee McClintick 9-5
58 mi. S of San Antonio
Est 1988; **Acres** 1,200; **Hunters/yr** 200; **Type** Public; **On Site** Clubhouse, Lodging, Meals, Clays; **Shoots** Field, Tower; **Birds** Dove, Quail, Pheasant, Chukar, Huns, Turkey, Ducks; **Dogs** Avail/HDW; **Packages** 1/2 Day, 2-16 guns o NAGA/See Pg. 107
o Half and Full Day Hunts for Quail, Dove & Duck
o 4,500 Sq. Ft. Lodge With Private Bedrooms
o Excellent Business Retreat
o Sporting Clays Course/60' Dove Tower
o Featured in Sporting Clays Magazine and On ESPN
See Our Ad Across

Blue Goose Hunting Club
PO Box M, Altair, TX 77412
(409) 234-3597 John R. Fields Anytime
50 mi. W of Houston
Est 1953; **Acres** 150,000; **Hunters/yr** 4,000; **Type** Public; **On Site** Clubhouse, Lodging, Meals, Clays; **Shoots** Field; **Birds** Dove, Quail, Pheasant, Chukar, Ducks, Geese; **Dogs** Avail/HDW; **Packages** 1/2 Day, 4-100 guns

Brush Country Outfitters
PO Box 1310, Three Rivers, TX 78071
(210) 935-4674 Marty Brown
Type Public; **On Site** Lodging, Meals; **Shoots** Field; **Birds** Dove, Quail, Turkey; **Dogs** Avail/HDW; **Packages** 2 Days, up to 4 guns

Butch's Guide Service
2806 Patna, Katy, TX 77493
(713) 391-4381 Butch Waggoner
25 mi. W of Houston
Est 1970; **Acres** 9,000; **Hunters/yr** 1,500; **Type** Public, Member/Avail; **On Site** Meals; **Shoots** Field; **Birds** Dove, Quail, Pheasant, Chukar, Ducks, Geese; **Dogs** Avail/HDW; **Packages** 1/2 Day

CF Ranch
Box 689, Alpine, TX 79831
(915) 364-2251 Lashawn McIvor 8am-5pm
13 mi. N of Alpine
Acres 1,000; **Hunters/yr** 100; **Type** Public; **On Site** Clubhouse, Lodging, Meals; **Shoots** Tower; **Birds** Pheasant, Chukar; **Dogs** Avail/HDW; **Packages** 2 Days, 6-12 guns

William Carl, Jr.
1640 Fountain View Dr., Houston, TX 77057
(713) 785-5788 W. Noble Carl Ext. 123
60 mi. SW of Houston
Acres 1,600; **Hunters/yr** 12; **Type** Member/Avail; **On Site** Clubhouse, Lodging, Meals; **Shoots** Field, Blinds; **Birds** Dove, Quail, Ducks, Geese

Caverhill Ranch
HCR81, Box 312, Junction, TX 76849
(915) 446-2448 John T. Fargason
100 mi. NW of San Antonio
Est 1987; **Acres** 640; **Hunters/yr** 30; **Type** Public; **On Site** Clubhouse, Lodging; **Shoots** Field; **Birds** Turkey; **Packages** 1/2 Day, 1-6 guns

Cedar Creek Ranch
Rt. 1, Box 84A, Rochelle, TX 76872
(915) 463-5547 Rawley Curry Anytime
30 mi. S of Brownwood
Est 1984; **Acres** 20,000; **Type** Public; **On Site** Clubhouse, Lodging, Meals, Clays; **Shoots** Field; **Birds** Dove, Quail, Turkey; **Dogs** Avail/HDW; **Packages** 2 Days

Central Texas Hunts
Rt. 1, Box 52, Medina, TX 78055
(210) 589-7703 Tommy Thompson

HUNTING PRESERVE

"A Unique South Texas Hunting Experience "

Located just 60 miles south of San Antonio, Black Creek Ranch is a true hunter's paradise, covering more than 2,400 acres of brush, grasslands, creeks and lakes.

Set in the gently rolling hills of South Texas, the Ranch provides a place for the sportsman to get away—for a day, overnight or longer, with friends, family, or business associates.

A full-time staff of seven provides professional guide services, superbly trained English pointers, and half and full day hunts for quail, dove and duck.

The 4,500 sq. ft. main lodge is rich, homey and relaxed, with private bedrooms for up to 16 guests. The country kitchen pleases any and all appetites. The spacious porches, "great room", game parlor, and library offer ample space to visit and relax—if you can tear yourself away from the spa and heated soaking pool, the largest in South Texas.

Excellent fishing and sporting clay target shooting with 66 ft. dove tower. Hog, coyote, and bobcat hunting, also available.

Whether your looking for a personal or corporate sporting retreat, a truly unique South Texas hunting experience awaits at Black Creek Ranch. Call today!

Contact Lee McClintick for Information, Reservations or a Brochure.

— Black Creek Ranch —

26081 Bulverde Road • San Antonio, TX 78261

Office: (210) 438-4188 • FAX: (210) 438-3534

55 mi. NW of San Antonio
Est 1982; **Acres** 100,000; **Type** Public; **On Site**
Lodging, Meals; **Shoots** Field; **Birds** Turkey

Central Texas Shooting Reserve
Rt. 4, Box 288, Elgin, TX 78621
(512) 856-2200 Oscar Albert
40 mi. NE of Austin
Est 1988; **Acres** 500; **Hunters/yr** 350; **Type**
Public; **On Site** Clubhouse, Meals, Clays; **Shoots**
Field, Tower; **Birds** Quail, Pheasant, Chukar; **Dogs**
Avail/HDW; **Packages** 1/2 Day, 1-12 guns

Choctaw Preserve
PO Box 556, McKinney, TX 75070
(214) 221-4646 J.V. Lattimore
65 mi. N of Dallas **Est** 1992; **Acres** 4,000; **Type**
Public; **On Site** Clubhouse, Lodging, Meals, Clays;
Shoots Field; **Birds** Pheasant, Chukar, Huns; **Dogs**
Avail; **Packages** 1/2 Day, 1-12 guns

Cinco Ranch
PO Box 55, El Indio, TX 78860
(210) 773-1131 Steve Robishaw
Type Public; **On Site** Lodging, Meals, Clays; **Birds**
Dove, Quail, Turkey; **Dogs** Avail

Circle (H) Outfitters

Circle H Outfitters
2019 Cutter Dr., League City, TX 77573
(713) 480-8824 Scott & Gary Hickman 7am-10pm
45 mi. E of & W of Houston
Est 1983; **Acres** 33,000; **Hunters/yr** 1,200; **Type**
Public, Member/Avail, Corp.; **On Site** Clubhouse,
Lodging, Meals; **Shoots** Field, Blinds, Boat; **Birds**
Dove, Quail, Ducks, Geese; **Dogs** Avail/HDW;
Packages 1/2 Day, 1-40 guns

Circle Rocking N Ranch
PO Box 449, Texarkana, TX 75504
(903) 793-4647 Fred Norton
Est 1993; **Acres** 1,000; **Type** Public; **On Site**
Clubhouse, Lodging, Meals, Clays; **Shoots** Field;
Birds Quail; **Dogs** Avail/HDW; **Packages** 1/2 Day,
2-8 guns

Clear Creek Gun Range
306 Crystal, League City, TX 77573
(713) 337-1722 Ernest Randall 1-8, T-Th, S/Su
Est 1976; **Acres** 82; **Type** Public; **On Site**
Clubhouse, Meals, Clays;

Clear Creek Shooting Club
PO Box 744, Bellville, TX 77418
(409) 865-2689 David Charpiot 9-5

Cold River Land & Cattle Co.
Rt. 2, Box 77C, San Juan, TX 78589
(210) 783-0870 Bobbie Brown Anytime
45 mi. NW of McAllen
Est 1971; **Acres** 13,000; **Hunters/yr** 200; **Type**
Public; **On Site** Clubhouse, Lodging, Meals, Clays;
Shoots Field; **Birds** Dove, Quail, Turkey; **Dogs**
Avail/HDW; **Packages** 2 Days, 2-24 guns

Cypress Valley Preserve
PO Box 162525, Austin, TX 78716
(512) 328-5279 Phillip C. Walker
25 mi. N of Austin
Est 1986; **Acres** 515; **Type** Member/Avail; **On
Site** Clubhouse, Lodging, Meals, Clays; **Shoots** Field,
Tower, Blinds; **Birds** Quail, Pheasant, Chukar, Ducks;
Dogs Avail/HDW; **Packages** 1/2 Day, 2-12 guns

Dancing Dogs Ranch & Lodge
PO Box 226, Wingate, TX 79566
(915) 743-2084 Patty or Bob Curnutte 8am-5pm
40 mi. SW of Abilene
Est 1988; **Acres** 7,000; **Hunters/yr** 100; **Type**
Public; **On Site** Clubhouse, Lodging, Meals, Clays;
Shoots Field; **Birds** Dove, Quail, Turkey, Ducks;
Dogs Avail/HDW; **Packages** 2 Days, 2-8 guns

Divin Hunting Services, Inc.
11303 El Sendero, San Antonio, TX 78233
(210) 646-6817 Mike Divin
55 mi. E of Laredo
Est 1976; **Acres** 21,000; **Hunters/yr** 200; **Type**
Public, Corp.; **On Site** Lodging, Meals, Clays;
Shoots Field; **Birds** Dove, Quail; **Dogs** Avail/HDW;
Packages 2 Days, 4-10 guns

Dolan Creek Ranches
PO Box 420069, Del Rio, TX 78842
(210) 775-3129 John Finegan after 6pm
Est 1970; **Acres** 35,000; **Type** Public; **On Site**
Meals; **Shoots** Field; **Birds** Dove, Quail, Turkey;
Dogs Avail

El Canelo Ranch:
A South Texas Wingshooting Paradise

From a distance, the sprawling, hacienda-style Inn at the El Canelo Ranch rises like a mirage from the surrounding mesquite and cactus. But as visiting sportsmen from around the world will tell you, the quality of the hunting at El Canelo is anything but an illusion. This is a wingshooting paradise just north of the Texas/Mexico border.

El Canelo's lodge—a hunting oasis.

Managing Quality

Much of the credit for El Canelo's growing reputation goes to the Ranch's operators, Monica and Ray Burdette. El Canelo has been continuously owned and operated as a working cattle ranch by Monica's family for 150 years. Monica, a classically trained chef, manages guest services and Ray, a retired Army officer, looks after the hunting. "We're proud of our Inn and guest facilities," says Ray, "but it's the hunting that keeps our customers coming back year after year."

A 10-year long committment to wildlife management has left local populations of bobwhite quail, dove, deer, turkey, nilgai, boar and javalina in excellent condition. Sportsmen will enjoy hundreds of acres of unspoiled natural beauty and hours of unforgettable hunting.

From the time each each guest arrives at the ranch or is picked up at the Harlingen, Texas, airport, it is Ray and Monica's goal to provide the ultimate hunting experience. El Canelo Ranch offers world-class wingshooting for the South Texas bobwhite quail. (These quail, Ray points out, "are not the 'gentlemen bobs' of the east." Hunters can expect 12 to 15 coveys a day during average years and up to 40 coveys a day during the best seasons. Dove hunters will enjoy afternoon shoots over crotten (dove weed) and sunset hunts at water holes.

A Typical Day

A typical day of hunting at El Canelo begins with a Mexican accented breakfast in the spacious Trophy Room. Then, led by seasoned guides and superbly trained dogs, hunters head out for a morning hunt for native bobwhite quail, mourning dove, or pheasant and chukar. Following the morning hunt, hunters return to the Inn for a hearty lunch prepared by Monica, before testing their shooting mettle on the Ranch's world class sporting sporting clays course. By mid-afternoon hunters are out in the unique South Texas brush country for more wingshooting. The day's take of birds will be carefully processed by the staff for the hunter's trip home.

A Chance to Kick Back

When the hunting is done, guests return to El Canelo's oasis-like compound for champagne margaritas on the patio. After a little time to freshen up and relax, guests enjoy a gourmet dinner served in an elegant dining room or a delicious barbecue on the Ranch's spacious covered patio. Tempting desserts that showcase Monica's considerable skill in the kitchen complete the meal.

After dinner many guests are drawn outdoors to gaze at the stars and listen to the coyotes song. Guests then retire to elegantly decorated bedrooms in the main house, each with private baths and balconies, or to the nearby guest house with large living room and bedrooms.

El Canelo Ranch is located just five miles from I-77, 10 miles from Raymondville, 90 miles south of Corpus Christi. Guests may fly into Harlingen airport, approximately 40 miles from the Ranch, on American, Continental and Southwest Airlines.

For more information and reservations, call Monica and Ray Burdette at 210-689-5042; or write El Canelo Ranch, P.O. Box 487, Raymondville, TX 78580.

Dos Vaqueros
PO Box 1035, Refugio, TX 78377
(512) 543-4905 Joan Rooke 9-5
45 mi. N of Corpus Christi
Est 1990; **Acres** 12,000; **Hunters/yr** 100; **Type** Public; **On Site** Clubhouse, Lodging, Meals, Clays; **Shoots** Field; **Birds** Dove, Quail, Turkey; **Dogs** Avail; **Packages** 1/2 Day, 2-9 guns
See Our Ad Below

Double E Kennels
2863 Speegleville Rd., Waco, TX 76712
(817) 848-4658 Earl Elkins
20 mi. SW of Waco
Acres 600; **Hunters/yr** 50; **Type** Public; **Shoots** Field; **Birds** Quail, Pheasant

Double R Ranch Hunting Preserve
2035 Victoria Garden Drive, Richmond, TX 77469
(713) 342-9361 Roland Reichardt
45 mi. W of Houston

Est 1995; **Acres** 640; **Type** Public, Member/Avail; **On Site** Clubhouse, Lodging, Meals, Clays; **Shoots** Field; **Birds** Quail, Pheasant, Chukar; **Dogs** Avail/HDW; **Packages** 1/2 Day, 2-4 guns

Eagle Lake & Katy Prairie Outfitters
PO Box 129, Katy, TX 77492
(888) 894-6673 Larry Gore 8:30am-5:30pm
35 mi. W of Houston
Est 1977; **Acres** 40,000; **Type** Member/Avail, Corp.; **On Site** Lodging, Meals; **Shoots** Field, Blinds; **Birds** Ducks, Geese; **Dogs** Avail/HDW; **Packages** 1 Day, 1-100 guns

El Canelo Ranch

El Canelo Ranch
PO Box 487, Raymondville, TX 78580
(210) 689-5042 Ray Burdette
75 mi. S of Corpus Christi
Est 1990; **Acres** 11,000; **Type** Public; **On Site** Clubhouse, Lodging, Meals, Clays; **Shoots** Field; **Birds** Dove, Quail, Pheasant, Chukar, Turkey; **Dogs** Avail/HDW; **Packages** 1/2 Day, 4-25 guns
NAGA/See Pg. 107

- O Airport Pickup
- O Bird Processing
- O Sporting Clays
- O Deer Hunting
- O Gourmet Meals
- O Brochure Available
- O Factory Ammunition
- O Quality Clubhouse
- O Family Run Business
- O Private Bedrooms

See Our Ad Pg. 419

Eshleman-Vogt Ranch
PO Box 2442, Corpus Christi, TX 78403
(512) 888-4888 William T. Vogt, Jr. 8:30-5
100 mi. SW of Corpus Christi
Est 1984; **Acres** 25,000; **Hunters/yr** 200; **Type** Public, Member/Avail, Corp.; **On Site** Clays; **Shoots** Field; **Birds** Dove, Quail; **Dogs** Avail/HDW; **Packages** 2 Days, 3-12 guns

Executive Outfitters
6956 Meadowbriar Lane, Dallas, TX 75230
(214) 638-9200 Richard R. Lee
Est 1964; **Type** Public; **On Site** Clubhouse, Lodging, Meals, Clays; **Shoots** Field; **Birds** Dove; **Packages** 2 Days

Flying Feathers
Rt. 1, Box 468C, Winnie, TX 77665
(409) 296-2348 Billy Ray Hickman
45 mi. E of Houston
Est 1993; **Acres** 1,000; **Type** Public, Member/Avail; **On Site** Clubhouse, Meals, Clays; **Shoots** Field; **Birds** Quail, Pheasant, Chukar; **Dogs** Avail/HDW; **Packages** 1/2 Day, 1-8 guns O NAGA/See Pg. 107

Flying O Ranch
Rt. 1, Box 151A, Ore City, TX 75683

(903) 762-2148 Ed B. Orms
40 mi. N of Tyler
Est 1993; **Type** Public; **Shoots** Field; **Birds** Dove,
Quail, Pheasant; **Dogs** Avail/HDW; **Packages** 1/2
Day, up to 1 guns

Flying P Outdoors
PO Box C, Hico, TX 76457
(817) 968-5434 Bobby Pettijohn
On Site Lodging; **Shoots** Field; **Birds** Quail,
Pheasant, Chukar, Turkey, Ducks ○ NAGA/See Pg. 107

Ford Ranch
Rt. 1, Box 81, Melvin, TX 76858
(915) 286-4572 Forrest/Ellen Armke 8-10pm
150 mi. NW of San Antonio
Est 1894; **Acres** 33,000; **Hunters/yr** 300; **Type**
Public; **On Site** Clubhouse, Lodging, Meals; **Shoots**
Field; **Birds** Dove, Quail, Turkey; **Dogs** HDW;
Packages 2 Days, 1-20 guns

GB Flyers
3221 Jack Beaver Rd., Santa Fe, TX 77517
(409) 925-2433 Greg Blackburn
20 mi. S of Houston
Est 1992; **Acres** 2,000; **Type** Public, Member/Avail;
On Site Clubhouse; **Shoots** Field; **Birds** Quail,
Pheasant, Chukar; **Dogs** Avail/HDW; **Packages** 1/2
Day, 1-30 guns ○ NAGA/See Pg. 107

Graves Hunting
Rt. 2, Box 136, Shelbyville, TX 75973
(409) 598-2751 Aubrey Graves
180 mi. E of Houston
Est 1989; **Acres** 800; **Type** Public; **Shoots** Field;
Birds Quail, Pheasant, Chukar; **Dogs** Avail/HDW;
Packages 1/2 Day, 1-30 guns ○ NAGA/See Pg. 107

 ### Greystone Castle Sporting Club

Greystone Castle Sporting Club
PO Box 158, Mingus, TX 76463
(817) 672-5927 Dan VanSchaik
70 mi. W of Ft. Worth
Est 1993; **Acres** 4,000; **Type** Member/Avail, Corp.;
On Site Clubhouse, Lodging, Meals, Clays; **Shoots**
Field, Driven, Blinds; **Birds** Dove, Quail, Pheasant,
Chukar, Turkey, Ducks, Geese; **Dogs** Avail/HDW;
Packages 1/2 Day, 2-20 guns ○ NAGA/See Pg. 107

Harper's Hunting Preserve
Rt. 2, Box 484 WC, Booker, TX 79005
(806) 435-3495 Gilbert & Clydeene Harper before
8am or evenings
130 mi. NE of Amarillo
Est 1989; **Acres** 1,200; **Hunters/yr** 100; **Type**
Public; **Shoots** Field; **Birds** Dove, Quail, Pheasant,
Chukar; **Dogs** Avail/HDW; **Packages** 1/2 Day, 2-40
guns ○ NAGA/See Pg. 107

Hawkeye Hunting Club
PO Box 27, Center, TX 75935
(409) 598-2424 9-6pm
55 mi. SW of Shreveport, LA
Est 1955; **Acres** 4,000; **Type** Member/Ltd, Corp.;
On Site Clubhouse, Lodging, Meals, Clays; **Shoots**
Field, Driven; **Birds** Quail, Pheasant, Chukar; **Dogs**
Avail; **Packages** 1/2 Day, 1-35 guns
○ NAGA/See Pg. 107

Herradura Ranch Inc.
PO Drawer 698, Cotulla, TX 78014
(210) 373-4492 David Schuster 9:30-4:30
95 mi. W of Corpus Christi
Est 1988; **Acres** 15,000; **Hunters/yr** 300; **Type**
Public; **On Site** Clubhouse, Lodging, Meals, Clays;
Shoots Field, Driven, Blinds; **Birds** Dove, Quail,
Pheasant, Chukar, Turkey, Ducks, Geese; **Dogs**
Avail/HDW; **Packages** 1/2 Day, up to 16 guns

Hickman's
Gamebird Hunting
PO Box 1871, Beeville, TX 78104
(512) 362-2473 Priscilla Hickman
60 mi. N of Corpus Christi
Est 1991; **Acres** 400; **Hunters/yr** 100; **Type**
Public, Member/Avail; **On Site** Clubhouse, Lodging,
Meals, Clays; **Shoots** Field; **Birds** Dove, Quail,
Pheasant, Chukar; **Dogs** Avail/HDW; **Packages** 1/2
Day, 1-4 guns ○ NAGA/See Pg. 107
○ Bird Processing   ○ Fishing
○ Family Recreation   ○ Family Run Business
○ Loaner Guns   ○ 90 Mi. So. of San Antonio
○ Brochure Available

Hill Country Hunting Resort
PO Box 5634, Valley Spring, TX 76885
(915) 247-3137 Tim Bauman
Shoots Field; **Birds** Quail, Pheasant
○ NAGA/See Pg. 107

HILLTOP FISH&GAME RANCH

Hilltop Fish & Game Ranch
HCR67, Box 58C, Pleasanton, TX 78064
(210) 569-HILL Steve Hill (4455) Call: Daily, 8-5
35 mi. S of San Antonio
Est 1994; **Acres** 1,200; **Type** Public; **On Site**
Clubhouse, Lodging, Meals, Clays; **Shoots** Field,
Blinds; **Birds** Dove, Quail, Pheasant, Chukar, Ducks;
Dogs Avail/HDW; **Packages** 1/2 Day, 2-12 guns
○ Call about the ultimate trout and bass fly fishing
  experience with our partners Guadalupe Trout
  Outfitters

Idania Hunter
Rt. 9, Box 1428, Sour Lake, TX 77659
(504) 279-0452

Acres 2,000; **Hunters/yr** 40; **Type** Public,
Member/Avail; **On Site** Lodging, Meals, Clays;
Shoots Field, Blinds; **Birds** Dove, Quail, Pheasant,
Chukar, Ducks, Geese; **Dogs** Avail

J&L Game Bird Farm
1176 US Hwy. 180 W., Rotan, TX 79546
(915) 776-2852 Jackie W. Etheredge 8-10pm
75 mi. NW of Abilene
Est 1990; **Acres** 34,000; **Hunters/yr** 400; **Type**
Public; **Shoots** Field; **Birds** Dove, Quail, Pheasant,
Chukar; **Dogs** Avail/HDW; **Packages** 1 Day, 1-12
guns ○ NAGA/See Pg. 107

Jenkins Ranch Dove Hunt
1803 West Crescent, Odessa, TX 79761
(915) 367-9592 Jon & Dolly Thomas
60 mi. W of Odessa
Est 1992; **Acres** 100,000; **Type** Public; **Shoots**
Field; **Birds** Dove; **Packages** 3 Days, 1-8 guns

Pat Johnson's Wild Goose Hunting Club
2718 West Creek, El Campo, TX 77437
(409) 543-7553 Pat Johnson
70 mi. SW of Houston
Est 1982; **Acres** 30,000; **Hunters/yr** 1,200; **Type**
Public, Member/Avail; **On Site** Clubhouse, Lodging,
Meals, Clays; **Shoots** Field, Blinds; **Birds** Dove,
Quail, Pheasant, Snipe, Ducks, Geese; **Dogs**
Avail/HDW; **Packages** 1/2 Day, 3-35 guns

Joshua Creek Ranch
PO Box 1946, Boerne, TX 78006
(210) 537-5090 Ann Kercheville 9-6
25 mi. NW of San Antonio
Est 1990; **Acres** 1,000; **Hunters/yr** 500; **Type**
Public, Member/Avail; **On Site** Clubhouse, Lodging,
Meals, Clays; **Shoots** Field, Driven, Blinds; **Birds**
Dove, Quail, Pheasant, Chukar, Huns, Turkey, Ducks;
Dogs Avail/HDW; **Packages** 1/2 Day, 1-34 guns
○ NAGA/See Pg. 107
○ Hunting License   ○ Train Bird Dogs
○ Airport Pickup   ○ Loaner Guns
○ Bird Processing   ○ Brochure Available
○ Deer Hunting   ○ On-Site Pro Shop
○ Shooting Instruction   ○ Fishing
○ Gourmet Meals   ○ Factory Ammunition
See Our Ads Pgs. 421, 423-425

Kat Creek Hunting Club & Sporting Clays
PO Box 987, Henderson, TX 75653
(903) 854-2232 Chester Martin
135 mi. SE of Dallas/Ft. Worth
Acres 1,200; **Type** Public, Member/Avail; **On Site**
Clubhouse, Meals, Clays; **Shoots** Field; **Birds** Quail,
Pheasant; **Dogs** Avail; **Packages** 1/2 Day
○ NAGA/See Pg. 107

Joshua Creek Ranch: Hill Country's Best Kept Secret

By Bob Rivard
Deputy Managing Editor, San Antonio Light

Joe & Ann Kercheville at one of Joshua Creek Ranch's Driven Pheasant shoots.

WELFARE, Texas - Call me Buddy. Buddy Gough, Light Outdoors Editor, that is. For a day and night, I recently filled ol' Buddy's shoes while he was out of town inspecting ancient cave paintings, chasing giant, mutant bass or doing something that wouldn't sound much like work to you or me. I stepped into the breach.

My assignment: Explore Joshua Creek Ranch, a one-year-old scenic hunting and fishing preserve located on the Guadalupe River, in the company of Bill Morrill, noted wildlife biologist and owner of Wildlife Management, Inc. in Boerne.

I also took along John Maeckle, my father-in-law, as friend and witness in the event I caught any fish on the flies I recently learned to tie under master fly-tyer Pete Jones at the Tackle Box. John introduced me to the Texas outdoors and it only seemed fair to deal him into my new career as outdoor writer.

Buddy, ol' boy, you should have stayed in town. Joshua Creek is one of the Hill country's best kept secrets. It is hard to believe a 1,000 acre ranch this beautiful, this alive with fish and game, this secluded, sits only 45 minutes from my downtown office.

On another matter, Buddy, I owe you an apology. I have always thought you guys stretched the truth a little bit, if you know what I mean, but after the great hunting and fishing John and I enjoyed at Joshua Creek Ranch, I'm beginning to believe what I read. Why, we came away with a few stories of our own. But first the facts.

Deluxe Ranch

Joshua Creek Ranch is a deluxe, guest oriented fish and game ranch—"an outdoor recreation enterprise," in the words of Morrill—designed to serve a limited membership, and for a few more months, the occasional day fishers and hunters. Right now it's a great place to fish for rainbow trout at $25 a day, but the ranch's reputa-

tion is growing fast and the enterprise will shift to members only in October.

"We call it hunting like Granddad used to know", Morrill said.

Granddad was never so lucky.

Joe and Ann Kercheville, successful San Antonio business people and avid outdoorsmen themselves (the lodge's African trophies came from their honeymoon), own and operate Joshua Creek Ranch. They have set an ambitious goal for themselves in offering members a well managed highly serviced ranch resort at very competitive prices.

Success seems possible, even in this economy, with a strong business plan based on location, a guest oriented ambience, superb service and excellent game and habitat management.

Guaranteed Good Time

Joshua Creek Ranch is geared toward the family and corporations and offers a variety of activities for those who choose not to hunt or fish, including a world class sporting clays course, nature hikes, volleyball, croquet,canoeing, fishing or simply relaxing.

"A lot of people out there work very hard and simply do not have very much time for shooting and fishing or recreating", Ann Kercheville, our gracious host said over a superb lunch of homemade soup and pasta salad prepared by chef and director of member services Sue Wetmore. "We guarantee that every person has a very good time. We take care of every detail. We offer quality experience. I think the future of hunting in Texas, is this."

The ranch is an ideal balance of water, fields, pasture and hills, open spaces and thick cover. Half the ranch has been cleared of cedar, the other half remains thick with cedar and live oak.

Morrill was brought in to match the habitat with game and to make sure ideal conditions were achieved and maintained. The result is a balance that seems natural when experienced, but actually is the product of much work and understanding complex relationships up and down the food chain.

While the ranch offers traditional white tail deer and wild turkey hunting for an additional harvest fee, the emphasis here is on wing shooting: pheasant, chukar, and quail. Mallard duck and Hungarian partridge are also available.

Families and corporations can buy either

Professional guides and well trained dogs conduct walk-up shooting for upland birds.

fishing or hunting and fishing memberships and select the number and types of birds they will hunt during the season. Fishing and sporting clays are year round activities.

Hunting

I've visited two game shooting resorts in the past, and each one featured birds that

Traditional European Estate Shoots Just 25 Miles From San Antonio? Yes! At Joshua Creek Ranch
by Chuck Wechsler

When Joe and Ann Kercheville purchased Joshua Creek Ranch eight years ago, they set in motion plans for developing a world-class hunting preserve that would replicate the traditional estate shoots of Europe.

Ann explained: "Joe and I have shot in countries around the world. We've seen what it takes to provide a top-flight shooting experience, and we're determined to offer that to sportsmen over here--but at a greatly reduced cost."

If what wildlife artist Ron Van Gilder and I saw during our brief stay at Joshua Creek is any indication, they've succeeded in becoming a leader in stateside driven shoots. After a memorable morning of walk-up shooting, Ron and I watched three husbands and their wives shoot flighted mallards. The birds were released above a plunging wooded ravine, where the guns were stationed several hundred feet apart. Most of the mallards made a beeline toward a pond at the bottom of the canyon. Shooters on the slopes were challenged by birds that careened just above the treetops, while those along the valley floor had

to pick out their targets through small openings in the woodland canopy.

The next day's shoot was even more impressive. This time the guns were positioned over a picked cornfield at the base of a tree-covered bluff, where a string of beaters pushed pheasants into the air. A few of the birds sliced through the trees, but most climbed high above them, offering difficult, straight-up shots of forty yards or more.

The limestone cliff was like a natural amphitheater, intensifying the sights and sounds of the hunt. All in all it was a wonderful spectacle and a challenging shoot, even for the best gunners.

Most driven shoots at Joshua Creek total about 400 birds, though as many as 650 have been presented in a single day. After completing the drives, the guides take the hunters down to the fields where they can gun the escaped birds over dogs.

Ann told us that she is able to set up a shoot with very little notice and carry it off in just one day. "For an American to plan a driven shoot in Europe , he'd have to set aside a week to ten days," she added. For more information about estate shoots and Joshua Creek's many other sporting amenities call Ann Kercheville at 210-537-5090. [A longer version of this article appeared in the March/April, 1994 issue of *Sporting Classics* Magazine.]

actically came when you called, embar-
ssing guides when they refused to flush.
t Joshua Creek, the quail appear fully ac-
imated to their wooded cover. They
ushed high and hard and flew strongly
en on a second flush.

John, my father-in-law, is a robust 70
ar old, but he has had all the hunting he
ants and now limits himself to fly fish-
g. I, on the other hand, had never hunted
uail with well trained pointers.

Morrill and I met up with guide James
arnes, a friendly 21 year old graduate of
omfort High School who also was a mem-
r of his school's nationally ranked range
d pasture team. All day, in between
ooting, I had the pleasure of Jim's tutor-
g on plants and flowers whose names
ve always eluded me. Silver leaf night
ade was my favorite.

The morning started, predictably, with
orrill's Browning, 20-gauge functioning
uch better than my Beretta, 20-gauge.
hatever was wrong with my gun, it disap-
ared as the morning wore on, and I
ished the quail hunt quite nicely. By the
me we switched to chukar, and had
alked the rows of trampled corn stalks
ce or twice, I was close to acting cocky.

Later in the day, while hunting pheasant
an old pea field on the edge of sloping
oods, we paused to watch a pair of point-
s work the field in tandem. It was a
easure to watch the two, well trained dogs
veep through the high grass. Even if
orrill and I hadn't each knocked down a
n, watching the dogs would have made
e trip worthwhile.

That night we dined on pheasant, again
epared by Chef Wetmore, and then reed to the flagstone patio for a view of a
ll moon and a long evening of stories..

I stayed up late in the lodge's great room,
owsing the well stocked periodical table
miring spear points, measuring the enor-
ous fireplace and wondering who built
e lodge. We slept in one of the two bed-
oms, each containing eight deluxe bunk
ds, fireplaces and whirlpool baths.

The lodge, available to members or guests
$35 a night per person, inclusive of con-
ental breakfast, seems ideal for family
therings, company picnics or small cor-
rate retreats.

*Fly Fishermen catch rainbow trout in the brisk
spring waters of Joshua Creek.*

Fishing, too

The next morning we rose early to fish.
Pete, it was an epiphany. The flies, that is,
my flies, actually worked. They fooled the
fish. At one point, fishing a deep, secluded
blue hole located on the backside of Joshua
Creek, John and I landed and released more
than a dozen rainbow trout, all measuring
14 inches or more, in the space of 30 minutes. The trout fought and leapt and
shimmered like wild rainbows. The
Kerchevilles hope that the cool, spring fed
blue hole and larger lake that cascades into
the creek just below the old stone lodge will
stay cool enough for the trout to survive
and breed.

Another secret to divulge here, Buddy,
we caught those fat rainbows below the surface on olive bodied woolly buggers,
leadwing coachmen nymphs and a small
green pupa. We failed, in the afternoon
heat, to get the rainbows to rise to my dryfl-
ies, though the flies seemed to sit up and
sail nicely. Joshua Creek Ranch, inciden-
tally has to be about the southern most
location in Texas offering rainbow trout.

Buddy, I wrote out a check for my birds
and a couple of Joshua Creek caps and was
handed back neatly packaged vacuum packed
birds. I'm saving them for a backyard cook-
out, maybe with a few of my fellow editors,
including the real outdoor editor.

[This article originally appeared in the
San Antonio Light, Outdoors, April 28,
1991. For more information about Joshua
Creek Ranch, call or write Ann & Joe
Kercheville at P.O. Box 1946, Boerne, TX
78006, (210) 537-5090.]

King Pheasant Farm & Hunting Preserve
1608 71st St., Lubbock, TX 79412
(806) 745-4003 Ray King
10 mi. W of Lubbock
Acres 640; **Hunters/yr** 100; **Type** Public; **Shoots** Field; **Birds** Pheasant, Chukar; **Dogs** Avail; **Packages** 1/2 Day O NAGA/See Pg. 107

Krooked River
Ranch Outfitters
PO Box 85, Haskell, TX 79521
(915) 773-2457 Roy & Becky Wilson 9-5
200 mi. W of Dallas/Ft. Worth
Est 1985; **Acres** 80,000; **Hunters/yr** 350; **Type** Public; **On Site** Clubhouse, Lodging, Meals, Clays; **Shoots** Field, Blinds; **Birds** Dove, Quail, Turkey, Ducks, Geese; **Dogs** Avail/HDW; **Packages** 2 Days, 1-25 guns
See Our Ad Across

La Media Sportsman's Lodge
PO Box 319, Linn, TX 78563
(800) 437-3903 Jerry & Karen Pippen
110 mi. S of Corpus Christi
Type Public; **On Site** Clubhouse, Lodging, Meals, Clays; **Shoots** Field; **Birds** Dove, Quail, Turkey; **Dogs** Avail; **Packages** 1 Day O NAGA/See Pg. 107

LaPaloma Sporting Club
PO Box 160516, San Antonio, TX 78280
(210) 980-4424 Henry Burns 9am-Dark
Est 1987; **Acres** 70; **Type** Public, Member/Avail; **On Site** Clubhouse, Meals, Clays; **Shoots** Field, Driven; **Birds** Quail, Pheasant, Chukar; **Dogs** Avail/HDW; **Packages** 1/2 Day, 2-4 guns

Lazy WJ Ranch
Rt. 5, Box 51952, Winnsboro, TX 75494
(903) 365-2610 Wayne or Jane Daniels After 6pm
120 mi. NE of Dallas
Est 1987; **Acres** 500; **Type** Public; **Shoots** Field; **Birds** Quail; **Dogs** Avail/HDW; **Packages** 1/2 Day, 1-8 guns O NAGA/See Pg. 107

Jonathan Letz
Rt. 1, Box 71, Comfort, TX 78013
(210) 995-2120
11 mi. NW of San Antonio
Acres 7,000; **Hunters/yr** 30; **Type** Member/Avail; **On Site** Clubhouse, Lodging; **Shoots** Field; **Birds** Quail, Turkey; **Dogs** Avail

Los Cuernos Ranch
PO Box 200105, San Antonio, TX 78220
(210) 676-3317 Pat Moore/Sonny Hild 7am-8pm
132 mi. SW of San Antonio
Est 1993; **Acres** 5,500; **Hunters/yr** 100; **Type** Public, Member/Avail, Corp.; **On Site** Clubhouse, Lodging, Meals, Clays; **Shoots** Field, Driven, Blinds; **Birds** Dove, Quail, Pheasant, Chukar, Huns, Turkey, Ducks; **Dogs** Avail/HDW; **Packages** 1/2 Day, 2-15 guns

O Hunting License   O Gourmet Meals
O Airport Pickup   O Hunting Jeeps
O Bird Processing   O Train Bird Dogs
O Sporting Clays   O Fishing
O Shooting Instruction   O Factory Ammunition
O Quality Clubhouse   O 5,000 Ft. Landing Strip

Los Patos Lodge
18907 Tranquility Dr., Houston, TX 77346
(409) 286-5767 Forrest West Anytime
Est 1964; **Acres** 45,000; **Type** Public, Member/Avail; **On Site** Clubhouse, Lodging, Meals, Clays; **Shoots** Field, Blinds; **Birds** Dove, Quail, Snipe, Ducks, Geese; **Dogs** Avail/HDW; **Packages** 1/2 Day, up to 40 guns

Lynn Manor Hunting Preserve & Kennels
3808 Curry Rd., Manvel, TX 77578
(713) 489-0315 C.B. Watts/Glenda Watts

Mariposa Ranch-SK Corporation
Rt. 1, Box 33, Falfurrias, TX 78355
(512) 325-5752 Dan Sullivan/Robert King 8am-5pm
75 mi. SW of Corpus Christi
Est 1985; **Acres** 45,000; **Hunters/yr** 240; **Type** Public; **On Site** Clubhouse, Lodging, Meals, Clays; **Shoots** Field; **Birds** Dove, Quail; **Dogs** Avail; **Packages** 1 Day, 2-12 guns

Mesquite Canyon Game
Rt. 1, Box 104-D, Shamrock, TX 79079
(806) 256-3724 William Howe
On Site Lodging; **Shoots** Field; **Birds** Dove, Quail, Chukar, Turkey, Geese O NAGA/See Pg. 107

More or Less Game Ranch
2626 N 2nd, Abilene, TX 79603
(915) 673-7208 Toad Leon
25 mi. S of Abilene
Acres 2,000; **Type** Public; **On Site** Clubhouse, Lodging, Meals, Clays; **Shoots** Field; **Birds** Dove, Quail, Pheasant, Turkey

Nail Ranch
Rt. 1, Box 106, Albany, TX 76430
(915) 762-2974 Craig Winters 8am-6pm
35 mi. NE of Abilene

Est 1900; **Acres** 57,000; **Hunters/yr** 400; **Type** Public; **On Site** Clubhouse, Lodging, Meals; **Shoots** Field; **Birds** Quail, Turkey; **Dogs** HDW; **Packages** 3 Days, up to 8 guns

Earl Nobles
Rt. 5, Box 430, Beaumont, TX 77713
(409) 866-1310 Earl H. Nobles
90 mi. NE of Houston
Type Public; **Shoots** Field; **Birds** Turkey

Jeff Pegg & Son Hunting
Rt. 1, Box 593-A, Springtown, TX 76082
(817) 748-2729 Jeff Pegg After 7pm
30 mi. W of Ft. Worth
Est 1990; **Acres** 500; **Type** Public, Corp.; **On Site** Clubhouse, Meals; **Shoots** Field, Tower, Blinds; **Birds** Dove, Quail, Pheasant, Chukar, Turkey, Ducks; **Dogs** Avail/HDW; **Packages** 1/2 Day, 2-15 guns

Possum Walk Ranch
Rt. 2, Box 174, Huntsville, TX 77340
(409) 291-1891 Buddy Smith 6am-9pm
70 mi. N of Houston
Est 1990; **Acres** 1,350; **Hunters/yr** 250; **Type** Public, Member/Avail, Corp.; **On Site** Clubhouse; **Shoots** Field, Tower; **Birds** Dove, Quail, Pheasant, Chukar; **Dogs** Avail/HDW ○ NAGA/See Pg. 107

Pringle Pheasant Farm & Hunting Area
PO Box 274, Girvin, TX 79740
(915) 652-8245 Burl or Frankie Pringle After 7pm
75 mi. SW of Midland/Odessa
Est 1986; **Acres** 160; **Hunters/yr** 100; **Type**

Public; **On Site** Clubhouse, Meals; **Shoots** Field, Tower; **Birds** Dove, Quail, Pheasant, Chukar, Turkey; **Dogs** HDW; **Packages** 1/2 Day, 2-20 guns ○ NAGA/See Pg. 107

Quail America
PO Box 1364, Mineral Wells, TX 76531
(800) 588-3633 Gene Ender
Type Public, Member/Avail; **Shoots** Field; **Birds** Quail, Pheasant, Chukar

Rafter W Ranches
Box 944, Sonora, TX 76950
(915) 387-3377 Jack Wardlew
Type Public; **Shoots** Field; **Birds** Quail, Turkey

Raisin L Ranch
PO Box 1710, Pearland, TX 77588
(713) 485-2300 Darryl Lilie
79 mi. SW of Houston
Acres 640; **Hunters/yr** 600; **Type** Public; **On Site** Clubhouse, Lodging, Meals; **Shoots** Field; **Birds** Quail, Pheasant; **Dogs** Avail

Rio Paisano Ranch
PO Box 130, Riviera, TX 78379
(512) 294-5281 Casey Taub/Frank Horlock 7-5:30
55 mi. SW of Corpus Christi
Est 1978; **Acres** 10,000; **Hunters/yr** 100; **Type** Public; **On Site** Clubhouse, Lodging, Meals, Clays; **Shoots** Field, Driven, Blinds; **Birds** Dove, Quail, Turkey, Ducks, Geese; **Dogs** Avail/HDW; **Packages** 3 Days, 1-18 guns

Riverside Farms
Rt. 3, Box 217-R, Hamilton, TX 76531
(214) 953-2850

Robby Robinson Ranches
PO Box 274, Junction, TX 76849
(915) 446-3165 Robby Robinson
100 mi. NW of San Antonio
Est 1956; **Acres** 20,000; **Type** Public,
Member/Avail; **On Site** Lodging, Meals; **Shoots**
Field; **Birds** Turkey

Royal Flush Outfitters
Box 236, Garden City, TX 79739
(915) 354-2560 or (314) 256-8269 (off season)
35 mi. SE of Midland
Acres 15,000; **Type** Public; **On Site** Lodging,
Meals; **Shoots** Field; **Birds** Quail, Turkey; **Dogs**
Avail/HDW; **Packages** 3 Days

Rustic Range
Rt. 2, Box 182, Slaton, TX 79364
(806) 828-4820 Dub Dillard 1-Sunset
11 mi. E of Lubbock
Est 1990; **Acres** 10; **Hunters/yr** 100; **Type**
Public; **On Site** Clubhouse, Clays; **Shoots** Tower;
Birds Quail, Pheasant, Chukar; **Dogs** HDW;
Packages 1/2 Day

SF Ranch
Rt. 4, Box 153, Comanche, TX 76442
(817) 842-5456 Clayton Parker Before 8 & after 5
100 mi. SW of Dallas
Est 1989; **Acres** 650; **Type** Public; **On Site** Clays;
Shoots Field; **Birds** Quail, Pheasant, Chukar; **Dogs**
Avail/HDW; **Packages** 1/2 Day, 1-4 guns
○ NAGA/See Pg. 107

Santa Anna Hunting Area
Rt. 1, Box 102A, Santa Anna, TX 76878
(915) 348-9267 John/Gerry Stearns 7am-10pm
60 mi. SE of Abilene
Est 1986; **Acres** 600; **Hunters/yr** 600; **Type**
Public; **On Site** Clays; **Shoots** Field; **Birds** Quail,
Pheasant, Chukar; **Dogs** Avail/HDW; **Packages** 1/2
Day, 1-30 guns ○ NAGA/See Pg. 107

74 Ranch Hunting Resort
5005 Riverway, Houston, TX 77056
(800) 874-7411 John Burdett 9am-5pm, cst
50 mi. S of San Antonio
Est 1987; **Acres** 27,000; **Hunters/yr** 100; **Type**
Public, Member/Avail; **On Site** Clubhouse, Lodging,
Meals, Clays; **Shoots** Field; **Birds** Dove, Quail,
Turkey; **Dogs** Avail; **Packages** 1 Day
○ NAGA/See Pg. 107

W.S. Sherrill Waterfowl Hunting
1702 Garrett Court, Wharton, TX 77488
(409) 532-1789 W.S. Sherrill
45 mi. SW of Houston
Acres 40,000; **Type** Public; **On Site** Clubhouse,
Lodging, Meals, Clays; **Birds** Ducks, Geese; **Dogs**
Avail; **Packages** 1/2 Day, 4-30 guns

Southwest Safaris
PO Box 38, Campbellton, TX 78008
(210) 579-4808 R.P. Hodges Anytime
60 mi. S of San Antonio
Est 1987; **Acres** 30,000; **Hunters/yr** 400; **Type**
Public; **On Site** Clubhouse, Lodging, Meals, Clays;
Shoots Field, Blinds; **Birds** Dove, Quail, Turkey, Ducks;
Dogs Avail/HDW; **Packages** 2 Days, 2-12 guns

Spanish Dagger Hunting Resort
PO Box 1325, Uvalde, TX 78802
(210) 278-2998 George Cooper
70 mi. W of San Antonio
Est 1987; **Acres** 2,000; **Type** Public; **On Site**
Lodging, Meals, Clays; **Shoots** Field, Driven; **Birds**
Dove, Quail, Pheasant, Chukar, Ducks; **Dogs**
Avail/HDW; **Packages** 1/2 Day
○ NAGA/See Pg. 107

Sporting Pheasants
Rt. 1, Box 56, Ivanhoe, TX 75447
(903) 664-4205 John Haynes
Type Member/Avail; **Birds** Pheasant
○ NAGA/See Pg. 107

Stasney's Cook Ranch
PO Drawer 1826, Albany, TX 76430
(915) 762-3695 Johnnie Hudman
30 mi. N of Abilene
Acres 25,000; **Hunters/yr** 400; **Type** Public; **On
Site** Clubhouse, Lodging, Meals, Clays; **Shoots** Field;
Birds Dove, Quail, Pheasant, Chukar, Turkey, Ducks;
Dogs Avail/HDW; **Packages** 2 Days, 2-8 guns

Sun Land Game Farm
910 W. 1st, Amarillo, TX 79116
(806) 374-8121 Dewayne Weatherly
Type Public; **On Site** Lodging; **Shoots** Field; **Birds**
Quail, Pheasant, Chukar ○ NAGA/See Pg. 107

T.G.R. Gamebird Preserve
6501 CR 118, Bullard, TX 75757
(903) 894-6320 Rob Martin
Type Public, Member/Avail; **On Site** Clays; **Shoots**
Field; **Birds** Quail, Pheasant, Chukar
○ NAGA/See Pg. 107

Texas Rice Belt Hunt Club
PO Box 274, Garwood, TX 77447
David Ordonez
70 mi. SW of Houston
Est 1982; **Acres** 40,000; **Hunters/yr** 1,500; **Type**
Public, Member/Avail; **On Site** Clubhouse, Lodging,
Clays; **Shoots** Field, Blinds; **Birds** Dove, Pheasant,
Chukar, Snipe, Ducks, Geese; **Dogs** Avail/HDW;
Packages 1/2 Day, 4-100 guns

Texas Waterfowl Outfitters
22413 Katy Frwy., Katy, TX 77450
(800) 899-2650 Tony Hurst 9-5
20 mi. W of Houston
Est 1984; **Acres** 35,000; **Hunters/yr** 3,000; **Type**
Public, Member/Avail, Corp.; **On Site** Lodging,
Meals, Clays; **Shoots** Field, Tower, Driven, Blinds,

Boat; **Birds** Dove, Quail, Pheasant, Chukar, Huns, Snipe, Ducks, Geese; **Dogs** Avail/HDW; **Packages** 1/2 Day, 1-100 guns

Texas Wings - Sporting Charters
PO Box 160818, Austin, TX 78716
(800) 448-8994
Anywhere in Texas
Type Public; **On Site** Clubhouse, Lodging, Meals; **Shoots** Field; **Birds** Dove, Quail, Turkey, Ducks; **Dogs** Avail/HDW

Texas-Oklahoma Quail Hunts
PO Box 464, Nocona, TX 76255
(817) 995-2210 John Cox
30 mi. N of Abilene/Oklahoma City, OK
Est 1984; **Acres** 150,000; **Hunters/yr** 300; **Type** Public; **On Site** Clubhouse, Lodging, Meals; **Shoots** Field; **Birds** Dove, Quail, Turkey; **Dogs** Avail/HDW; **Packages** 3 Days, 3-12 guns

Third Coast Outfitters
PO Box 1351, Bay City, TX 77404
(409) 245-3071 Bobby Hale Anytime
78 mi. SW of Houston
Est 1986; **Acres** 40,000; **Type** Public, Member/Avail, Corp.; **Shoots** Field, Blinds; **Birds** Dove, Quail, Snipe, Ducks, Geese; **Dogs** Avail/HDW; **Packages** 3 Days, 1-50 guns

Thunderbird Ranch
768 South Main, Lumberton, TX 77657
(409) 755-7204 Lee Riston
5 mi. N of Beaumont
Type Public; **Shoots** Field; **Birds** Pheasant, Chukar; **Dogs** Avail

O Hunting License	O Hunting Jeeps
O Airport Pickup	O Train Bird Dogs
O Bird Processing	O Family Run Business

Tierra Colinas
5200 FM 1885, Weatherford, TX 76088
(817) 596-4827 Joe Bishop
30 mi. W of Dallas/Ft. Worth
Acres 1,200; **Type** Member/Avail, Corp.; **On Site** Clubhouse, Meals, Clays; **Shoots** Field; **Birds** Quail, Pheasant, Chukar, Huns; **Dogs** Avail/HDW; **Packages** 1/2 Day, 1-30 guns

O Bird Processing
O Kennel Bird Dogs
O Sporting Clays
O Shooting Instruction
O Quality Clubhouse

Top Flight Hunting Preserve
Rt. 1, Box 233, Beasley, TX 77417
(409) 387-2284 Leon Randermann anytime
30 mi. W of Houston
Est 1990; **Acres** 1,100; **Hunters/yr** 250; **Type** Public, Member/Avail, Corp.; **On Site** Clubhouse, Meals, Clays; **Shoots** Field; **Birds** Dove, Quail,

Pheasant, Chukar; **Dogs** Avail/HDW; **Packages** 1/2 Day, 2-24 guns

Torel Wildlife
PO Box 65 (Duval County), Freer, TX 78357
(512) 394-6684 B.R. Thompson After 7pm
65 mi. W of Corpus Christi
Est 1976; **Acres** 6,000; **Type** Public; **On Site** Clubhouse, Lodging; **Shoots** Field; **Birds** Dove, Quail, Turkey; **Dogs** HDW

Upland Bird Country
PO Box 730, Corsicana, TX 75151
(903) 872-5663 Steve Stroube 8:30-4:30
55 mi. SE of Dallas
Est 1985; **Acres** 640; **Hunters/yr** 700; **Type** Public; **On Site** Clubhouse, Meals, Clays; **Shoots** Field, Tower; **Birds** Quail, Pheasant, Chukar; **Dogs** Avail/HDW; **Packages** 1/2 Day, 2-18 guns
O NAGA/See Pg. 107

Waterfowl Specialties, Inc.
PO Box 411, El Campo, TX 77437
(409) 543-1109 Terry Karstedt Anytime
74 mi. SW of Houston
Est 1984; **Acres** 60,000; **Hunters/yr** 2,000; **Type** Public; **On Site** Lodging, Meals; **Shoots** Field, Blinds; **Birds** Dove, Ducks, Geese; **Dogs** Avail/HDW; **Packages** 1/2 Day, 4-40 guns

Wild Wings Hunting Club
Rt. 4, Box 11, El Campo, TX 77437
(409) 543-6075 Lonnie Neel 6-10pm
60 mi. SW of Houston
Est 1976; **Acres** 40,000; **Hunters/yr** 1,000; **Type** Public; **On Site** Clubhouse, Lodging, Meals; **Shoots** Field; **Birds** Dove, Quail, Ducks, Geese; **Dogs** Avail/HDW; **Packages** 1/2 Day, up to 4 guns

Wing & Shot Shooting Resort
2209 Stroker Rd., Crosby, TX 77532
(713) 328-3439 Gus Holmelin
35 mi. NE of Houston
Acres 940; **Type** Public, Member/Avail; **On Site** Clubhouse, Lodging, Clays; **Shoots** Field, Blinds; **Birds** Dove, Quail, Pheasant, Chukar, Huns, Ducks, Geese; **Dogs** Avail; **Packages** 1/2 Day

Y.O. Ranch Onion Creek Lodge
, Mountain Home, TX 78025
(210) 640-3222 Bo Wafford
30 mi. S of Austin
Acres 5,000; **Type** Public; **On Site** Clubhouse, Lodging, Meals; **Shoots** Field; **Birds** Dove, Quail, Turkey; **Dogs** Avail

UTAH

4 Mile Hunting Club
PO Box 261, Mona, UT 84645
(801) 623-0704 Earl Sutherland
Est 1992; Acres 1,900; Hunters/yr 1,100; Type Public, Member/Avail; On Site Clubhouse, Lodging, Meals, Clays; Shoots Field; Birds Quail, Pheasant, Chukar; Dogs Avail/HDW; Packages 1/2 Day, 1-20 guns O NAGA/See Pg. 107

Beer Creek Farms
1085 E. 1050 S., Spanish Fork, UT 84660
(801) 798-6355 Bob Llewellyn
10 mi. S of Provo
Acres 387; Type Public; On Site Meals, Clays; Shoots Field; Birds Quail, Pheasant, Chukar; Dogs Avail/HDW O NAGA/See Pg. 107

Chicken Creek Hunting Club
PO Box 12, Levan, UT 84639
(801) 623-0656 Tom or Ryan Aagard
45 mi. S of Provo
Acres 3,800; Hunters/yr 200; Type Public, Member/Avail; Shoots Field, Blinds; Birds Pheasant, Chukar, Ducks, Geese; Dogs Avail

Diamond Bar Ranch
4832 W. 8800 S., Payson, UT 84651
(801) 465-9173 Jay or Ben Isaac 7am-10pm
20 mi. S of Provo
Est 1989; Acres 350; Hunters/yr 600; Type Public, Member/Avail, Corp.; On Site Clays; Shoots Field; Birds Pheasant, Chukar; Dogs Avail/HDW; Packages 1/2 Day, 1-20 guns O NAGA/See Pg. 107

Falcon's Ledge
PO Box 67, Altamont, UT 84001
(801) 454-3737 Howard Brinkerhoff
85 mi. SE of Salt Lake City
Acres 5,000; Type Public; On Site Clubhouse, Lodging, Meals; Shoots Field, Blinds; Birds Dove, Ruffed Grouse, Pheasant, Chukar, Sage Grouse, Ducks, Geese; Dogs Avail/HDW; Packages 1 Day, 1-20 guns

Hatt's Ranch
Box 275, Green River, UT 84525
(801) 564-3224 Rey Lloyd Hatt
16 mi. SW of Green River
Est 1976; Acres 1,000; Hunters/yr 1,800; Type Member/Avail; On Site Clubhouse, Meals, Clays; Shoots Field; Birds Pheasant, Chukar, Huns; Dogs Avail/HDW; Packages 1/2 Day O NAGA/See Pg. 107

L&R Bird Ranch
816 S. 600 E. Circle, St. George, UT 84770
(801) 628-7132 Lee Scott 5-10pm
34 mi. W of St. George
Est 1988; Acres 1,020; Hunters/yr 600; Type Public; On Site Clubhouse, Clays; Shoots Field; Birds Dove, Quail, Pheasant, Chukar; Dogs Avail/HDW; Packages 1/2 Day, 1-25 guns O NAGA/See Pg. 107

Lakeview Pheasantry
1494 S. Carterville Rd., Orem, UT 84058
(801) 224-5223 Jerry Cross
Type Public, Member/Avail; Shoots Field; Birds Quail, Pheasant, Huns, Turkey O NAGA/See Pg. 107

Mosida
PO Box 120, Elberta, UT 84626
(801) 667-3282 Lance
40 mi. S of Salt Lake City
Est 1986; Acres 2,700; Hunters/yr 60; Type Member/Ltd; On Site Lodging, Meals; Shoots Field, Blinds; Birds Pheasant, Chukar, Ducks, Geese; Dogs HDW

Pheasant Grove Hunting Preserve
4230 North Hwy. 13, Corinne, UT 84307
(801) 744-2284 Ken Dillree
Est 1994; Acres 400; Type Public, Member/Avail; Shoots Field; Birds Quail, Pheasant, Chukar; Dogs Avail/HDW; Packages 1/2 Day, 1-16 guns O NAGA/See Pg. 107

Pheasant Valley Hunting Club
16840 W. 12800 N., Howell, UT 84316
(801) 471-2245 Carlos Christensen Evenings
Est 1981; Acres 3,500; Hunters/yr 1,250; Type Public, Member/Avail, Corp.; On Site Clubhouse, Lodging, Clays; Shoots Field; Birds Dove, Quail, Pheasant, Chukar, Huns, Turkey; Dogs Avail/HDW O NAGA/See Pg. 107

River Hollow Hunting Club & Kennel
68 N. 3rd E., Hyrum, UT 84319
(801) 245-6150 Randy A. Burbank 4-10pm
70 mi. N of Salt Lake City
Est 1988; Acres 500; Type Public, Member/Avail, Corp.; On Site Clubhouse; Shoots Field, Tower; Birds Quail, Pheasant, Chukar; Dogs Avail/HDW; Packages 1/2 Day O NAGA/See Pg. 107

Road Creek Rod & Gun Club
90 S. Main, Loa, UT 84747
(801) 836-2485 Mark Leavitt
1 mi. W of Loa
Acres 2,100; Type Public, Member/Avail; On Site Lodging, Meals, Clays; Shoots Field, Blinds; Birds Quail, Pheasant, Chukar, Huns; Dogs Avail

Rooster Valley Pheasants
855 North 300 West, Richfield, UT 84701
(801) 896-4868 Russ Peterson
2 mi. S of Richfield
Acres 2,000; Hunters/yr 500; Type Public, Member/Avail; On Site Clubhouse, Lodging, Meals, Clays; Shoots Field, Blinds; Birds Dove, Pheasant, Chukar, Huns, Ducks, Geese; Dogs Avail

Split Mountain
Hunting Club
PO Box 540, Jensen, UT 84035
(801) 789-9247 Dave Snow or (801) 789-5271
200 mi. E of Salt Lake City
Est 1994; **Acres** 800; **Type** Public, Member/Avail,
Corp.; **On Site** Meals; **Shoots** Field; **Birds**
Pheasant; **Dogs** Avail/HDW; **Packages** 1/2 Day, up
to 8 guns

W.C. Flyers
1580 N. 5600 W., Corinne, UT 84307
(801) 744-2975 Scott Forsgren
50 mi. N of Salt Lake
Acres 466; **Type** Public, Member/Avail; **On Site**
Clubhouse; **Shoots** Field; **Birds** Quail, Pheasant;
Dogs Avail; **Packages** 1/2 Day, 1-20 guns
○ NAGA/See Pg. 107

Wings Unlimited
PO Box 334, Wellington, UT 84542
(801) 637-2057 Dale Norton
100 mi. SE of Provo
Est 1990; **Acres** 1,200; **Hunters/yr** 600; **Type**
Public, Member/Avail, Corp.; **On Site** Clubhouse,
Meals; **Shoots** Field; **Birds** Quail, Pheasant, Chukar;
Dogs Avail/HDW; **Packages** 1/2 Day, 2-20 guns
○ NAGA/See Pg. 107

VERMONT

Hermitage Inn
Coldbrook Rd., Wilmington, VT 05363
(802) 464-3511 Jim McGovern 9-5
25 mi. E of Bennington
Est 1980; **Acres** 200; **Hunters/yr** 50; **Type**
Public, Member/Avail; **On Site** Clubhouse, Lodging,
Meals, Clays; **Shoots** Field; **Birds** Pheasant; **Dogs**
Avail/HDW; **Packages** 1/2 Day, 1-4 guns
○ NAGA/See Pg. 107

Tinmouth Hunting Preserve
Box 556, Wallingford, VT 05773
(802) 446-2337 Rick Fallar 8am-5pm
70 mi. NE of Albany
Est 1977; **Acres** 800; **Hunters/yr** 500; **Type**
Public, Member/Avail; **On Site** Clubhouse, Meals,
Clays; **Shoots** Field, Tower, Driven; **Birds** Quail,
Ruffed Grouse, Woodcock, Pheasant, Chukar, Ducks;
Dogs Avail/HDW; **Packages** 1/2 Day, 1-25 guns
○ NAGA/See Pg. 107

Upland Sports of South Hero, Inc.
PO Box 260, South Hero, VT 05486
(802) 372-6648 Daniel Farnham
Type Public; **Shoots** Field; **Birds** Quail, Pheasant,
Chukar ○ NAGA/See Pg. 107

The Vermont Sportsman
HCR70, Box 42, Morgan, VT 05853
(802) 895-4209 Bob/Maryann/Andy Beaupre
12 mi. E of Newport
Type Public; **On Site** Clubhouse, Lodging, Meals;
Shoots Field; **Birds** Ruffed Grouse, Woodcock;
Dogs HDW

VIRGINIA

• *See Pgs. 16-17 for Virginia State Ad*

Christmas Hill Game Preserve
7060 Esmont Farm, Esmont, VA 22937
(804) 286-2870 John Ambrose **Shoots** Field; **Birds**
Quail, Pheasant, Chukar ○ NAGA/See Pg. 107

EASTERN SHORE SAFARIS
AND
SPORTING CLAYS

Eastern Shore Safaris
6276 Sturgis House Rd., Jamesville, VA 23398
(757) 442-6035 Tom Webb
40 mi. E of VA Beach
Est 1982; **Acres** 2,000; **Hunters/yr** 500; **Type**
Public; **On Site** Clubhouse, Lodging, Meals, Clays;
Shoots Field, Blinds, Boat; **Birds** Dove, Quail,
Woodcock, Ducks, Geese; **Dogs** Avail/HDW;
Packages 1/2 Day, 2-50 guns ○ NAGA/See Pg. 107

Falkland Farms
PO Box 1297, Halifax, VA 24558
(804) 575-1400 Tom Rowland 8-5
90 mi. SW of Richmond
Est 1991; **Acres** 7,700; **Hunters/yr** 150; **Type**
Public; **On Site** Clubhouse, Lodging, Meals, Clays;
Shoots Field, Driven, Blinds, Boat; **Birds** Dove, Quail,
Turkey, Ducks; **Dogs** Avail/HDW; **Packages** 1 Day

Feathers-Fur & Fin Kennels
Rt. 1, Box 255, Keysville, VA 23947
(804) 568-3944 Bill Hall
50 mi. SE of Lynchburg **Acres** 600; **Type** Public;
On Site Clubhouse, Lodging, Clays; **Shoots** Field,
Blinds; **Birds** Dove, Quail, Ducks; **Dogs** Avail

Forest Green Shooting Preserve
Forest Green Ln., PO Box 361, Spotsylvania, VA 22553
(540) 582-2566 Thad Sutter 8-8
Est 1989; **Acres** 380; **Type** Public, Member/Avail,
Corp.; **On Site** Clubhouse, Clays; **Shoots** Field;
Birds Dove, Quail, Pheasant; **Dogs** Avail/HDW;
Packages 1/2 Day, 1-4 guns ○ NAGA/See Pg. 107

Jonakin Creek Hunt Club
Rt. 1, Box 417, Gladehill, VA 24092
(540) 576-1223 Eddie Shelton

26 mi. S of Roanoke
Est 1990; **Acres** 1,200; **Type** Public, Member/Avail;
On Site Clubhouse; **Shoots** Field; **Birds** Quail;
Dogs Avail/HDW; **Packages** 1/2 Day, 2-12 guns

King Kennels & Shooting Preserve
PO Box 563, Rixeyville, VA 22737
(540) 937-4310 Naomi Ray
Est 1936; **Acres** 123; **Type** Public; **Shoots** Field;
Birds Quail, Pheasant; **Dogs** Avail/HDW; **Packages**
1/2 Day, 1-6 guns

Magnolia Shooting Preserve
101 Philhower Dr., Suffolk, VA 23434
(804) 539-6296 M. Dewey Howell
65 mi. SW of Norfolk
Est 1979; **Acres** 420; **Hunters/yr** 300; **Type**
Public, Member/Avail; **Shoots** Field; **Birds** Quail,
Pheasant, Chukar, Huns; **Dogs** Avail/HDW;
Packages 1/2 Day, 1-6 guns

Merrimac Farm Hunting Preserve
14710 Deepwood Lane, Nokesville, VA 20181
(703) 594-2276 Dean N. McDowell
30 mi. SW of Washington, DC
Est 1971; **Acres** 296; **Type** Public, Member/Avail;
Shoots Field; **Birds** Quail, Pheasant, Chukar, Huns;
Dogs Avail/HDW; **Packages** 1/2 Day, 1-12 guns
○ NAGA/See Pg. 107

Mountain Empire Quail Ranch
Rt. 2, Box 550, Marion, VA 24354
(540) 646-5452 Fred Rupard
85 mi. SW of Roanoke **Acres** 125; **Type** Public;
Shoots Field; **Birds** Quail; **Dogs** Avail

Old Coppermine Hunting Preserve
PO Box 450, Keysville, VA 23947
(804) 736-9495 J.W. Bolton
70 mi. SW of Richmond
Acres 5,400; **Hunters/yr** 400; **Type** Public;
Shoots Field; **Birds** Quail

Orapax Plantation
3831 River Rd. W., Goochland, VA 23063
(804) 556-4856 Nancy Dykers 8 to 8
35 mi. NW of Richmond
Est 1987; **Acres** 675; **Hunters/yr** 500; **Type**
Public; **Shoots** Field, Tower; **Birds** Quail, Turkey;
Dogs HDW; **Packages** 1/2 Day, 1-4 guns
○ NAGA/See Pg. 107

Plain Dealing Hunting Preserve
Rt. 2, Box 72, Center Cross, VA 22437
(804) 443-4592 Ron Edwards Evening
Est 1983; **Acres** 280; **Type** Public, Member/Avail,
Corp.; **Shoots** Field, Tower, Driven; **Birds** Quail,
Woodcock, Pheasant, Turkey, Ducks; **Dogs**
Avail/HDW; **Packages** 1/2 Day, 2-12 guns

Primland
Rt. 1, Box 265-C, Claudville, VA 24076
(540) 251-8012 Johnny Lambert 8:30-5, M-F
60 mi. N of Greensboro
Est 1987; **Acres** 14,000; **Type** Public, Corp.; **On
Site** Clubhouse, Lodging, Meals, Clays; **Shoots** Field,
Tower, Driven; **Birds** Quail, Pheasant, Turkey, Ducks;
Dogs Avail/HDW; **Packages** 1/2 Day, 1-12 guns
○ NAGA/See Pg. 107
See Our Ads Left & Across

Primland Hunting Reserve...The Secret's Out

Long the "best kept secret" of a small group of discriminating sportsmen, Primland Hunting Reserve is emerging to take its place as one of the finest facilities of its type in the United States.

Located in the beautiful Blue Ridge Mountains of Patrick County, VA, the Reserve is easily reached from Greensboro, Winston-Salem, and Charlotte, NC, Richmond and Roanoke, VA and worth a trip from practically anywhere. And no wonder: Primland's combination of hunting--ranging from European Style Pheasant Shoots to Deer Hunts--sporting clays, and private dining lodging is difficult to match.

The pulse-quickening action of a traditional English pheasant shoot.

Upland Style Hunts

If Primland specializes in anything, it's fully guided upland style pheasant and quail hunts catered to the individual demands of the hunter, whether new to the sport or a "campaign" veteran. Primland's varied cover--grain and corn fields, thickets and forested ravines--are intensely managed to provide abundant game and ample shooting opportunities. Hunters may bring their own dogs or shoot over one of Primland's healthy and highly trained pointers, setters, brittanys, short hairs or labradors.

European Style Pheasant Shoots

Not long ago, you'd have to make the costly and time-consuming trip to Europe to experience the exhilaration of a traditional British pheasant shoot. No longer. The rolling hills and mountains of Primland's Estate creates a terrain almost custom designed for this type of challenging shoot. Each shooter is paired with a loader and moves from marked station to station aboard horse drawn wagons. Birds are pushed over the guns and retrievers pick up downed birds. Hardy and sporty flying ringnecks are released the day of the shoot and throughout the year and these birds, flying from 20 to 50 yards aloft, create challenging and competitive shooting. Loaders and dog handlers on the shoot are dressed in European style shooting attire--an added touch that lends air of authenticity.

Deer hunting and a unique released duck hunt round out Primland's hunting menu and trout fishing in one of the Estate's 3 ponds provides a thoroughly relaxing counterpoint to the pulse-quickening hunting available.

Sporting Clays--Rated Tops

Majestically laid out in the foothills of the Blue Ridge Mountains, Primland's 12 station sporting clays course was chosen one of the top 25 in the country by Esquire Magazine. Shooters traverse the 1 mile course on foot or golf cart and are challenged by simulated hunting shots. Primland also offers a fast and furious five stand clay game. At Primland, guests find either game a great way to spend quality time with friends, family, colleagues or clients.

Lodging and Dining

Virtually the only thing to challenge the sporting opportunities at Primland is the quality of its lodging and dining services. Captivating chalets and cabins, each different in character and most with majestic mountain or valley views, provide a welcome retreat for weary hunters.

Hunters and guests find their day in the field or on the sporting clays course punctuated by superb meals prepared by Primland's chef de cuisine and staff at a private restaurant located on the property. The restaurant's dining room will seat up to 100 people and is perfect for corporate meetings.

Primland Hunting Reserve offers something for everyone—individuals, families and corporations. Reservations are required, so make plans to visit soon. **Write Primland Hunting Reserve, Rt. 1, Box 265-C, Claudville, VA 24076; Fax 540-251-8244; or call 540-251-8012.**

Red Oak Ranch-Virginia Upland Outfitters
Red Oak Ranch, Hightown, VA 24444
(540) 468-2949 Ken Martin 8:30am-Dark
90 mi. NW of Roanoke
Est 1985; **Acres** 4,500; **Hunters/yr** 200; **Type** Public; **On Site** Clubhouse, Lodging, Meals, Clays; **Shoots** Field; **Birds** Turkey; **Dogs** Avail/HDW; **Packages** 3 Days, 1-16 guns

Sandy Point
Recreational Park
3551 Hunsucker Lane, Charles City, VA 23030
(804) 966-2421 Rick Hunsucker
30 mi. NE of Richmond
Est 1995; **Acres** 3,000; **Type** Public, Member/Avail, Corp.; **On Site** Clubhouse, Meals, Clays; **Shoots** Field, Tower, Driven, Blinds; **Birds** Quail, Pheasant, Chukar, Huns, Ducks; **Dogs** Avail/HDW; **Packages** 1/2 Day, 1-32 guns
O 3-D Archery Course/20 Target Practice Range

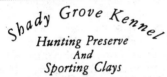

Shady Grove Kennel & Hunting Preserve
11986 Lucky Hill Rd., Remington, VA 22734
(540) 439-2683 Neil Selby 8am-5pm
45 mi. SW of Washington, DC
Est 1989; **Acres** 504; **Type** Public, Member/Avail; **On Site** Clubhouse, Clays; **Shoots** Field, Driven, Blinds, Boat; **Birds** Quail, Woodcock, Pheasant, Chukar, Huns, Turkey, Ducks, Geese; **Dogs** Avail/HDW; **Packages** 1/2 Day, 1-24 guns
O Bird Processing
O Sporting Clays
O Shooting Instruction
O Hunting Jeeps
O Train Bird Dogs
O New Virginia Hunting Season: Sept. 1 - April 30

Sundance Hunting Preserve, Inc.
PO Box 91, Orlean, VA 22128
(540) 364-9525 Dave Bierlein
35 mi. W of Washington, DC
Est 1989; **Acres** 400; **Hunters/yr** 100; **Type** Public; **On Site** Clubhouse; **Shoots** Field; **Birds** Quail, Pheasant, Geese; **Dogs** Avail/HDW; **Packages** 1/2 Day, up to 3 guns

Sussex Shooting Sports
Box 624 (Rt. 460), Waverly, VA 23890
(804) 834-3200 Bob Hall
35 mi. SE of Richmond

Est 1991; **Acres** 300; **Type** Public; **On Site** Clubhouse, Clays; **Shoots** Field; **Birds** Quail, Ducks; **Dogs** Avail/HDW; **Packages** 1/2 Day, 1-4 guns

Walnut Run Shooting Preserve
26233 Raccoon Ford Rd., Culpeper, VA 22701
(540) 423-1569 Don Taylor 7 to 9 pm
55 mi. SW of Washington, DC
Est 1989; **Acres** 170; **Hunters/yr** 80; **Type** Member/Ltd; **Shoots** Field; **Birds** Quail, Pheasant; **Dogs** Avail/HDW; **Packages** 1/2 Day, 2-6 guns

Windwood Farm
2014 Martinsburg Pike, Winchester, VA 22603
(540) 667-1045 Linwood R. Williamson 7 to 10 pm
65 mi. NW of Washington, DC
Est 1986; **Acres** 166; **Hunters/yr** 200; **Type** Public; **On Site** Clubhouse; **Shoots** Field; **Birds** Pheasant; **Dogs** Avail/HDW; **Packages** 1/2 Day, 4-6 guns

WASHINGTON

Acme Hunting Club
3110 Standard Rd., Acme, WA 98220
(360) 595-2725 Jim Lallas
Acres 200; **Type** Public, Member/Avail; **On Site** Lodging, Clays; **Shoots** Field; **Birds** Quail, Pheasant, Chukar, Ducks O NAGA/See Pg. 107

Cooke Canyon Hunt Club
861 Cooke Canyon Rd., Ellensburg, WA 98926
(509) 968-4844 Ed Nestler, Pres.
115 mi. E of Seattle
Est 1991; **Acres** 1,400; **Hunters/yr** 300; **Type** Member/Avail, Corp.; **On Site** Clubhouse, Clays; **Shoots** Field, Blinds; **Birds** Quail, Pheasant, Chukar, Turkey, Ducks; **Dogs** Avail/HDW; **Packages** 1/2 Day, 1-4 guns O NAGA/See Pg. 107

Landt Farms Shooting Preserve
W. 16308 Four Mound Rd., Nine Mile Falls, WA 99026
(509) 466-4036 Ellwood/Dolly Landt 6-9am, 4-9pm
10 mi. NW of Spokane
Est 1984; **Acres** 500; **Hunters/yr** 1,200; **Type** Public, Member/Avail, Corp.; **On Site** Clubhouse, Clays; **Shoots** Field; **Birds** Pheasant, Chukar; **Packages** 1/2 Day O NAGA/See Pg. 107

Lincoln Creek Hunting Club
1401 Lincoln Creek Rd., Rochester, WA 98579
(360) 736-6609 Lorraine Smith Evenings

Est 1962; **Type** Public; **On Site** Clubhouse, Clays; **Shoots** Field, Blinds; **Birds** Pheasant, Ducks; **Dogs** Avail/HDW; **Packages** 1/2 Day, up to 3 guns

Nate Johnson Hunting Club
1929 A Dry Slough Rd., Mount Vernon, WA 98273
(360) 445-6015 Nate Johnson
Est 1985; **Acres** 1,200; **Type** Public, Member/Avail; **Shoots** Field, Blinds; **Birds** Ducks; **Dogs** HDW

Pheasant Valley Shooting Preserve
PO Box 201, LaCrosse, WA 99143
(509) 549-3912 Jerry Townsend Anytime
75 mi. SW of Spokane
Acres 1,500; **Type** Public, Member/Avail, Corp.; **On Site** Clubhouse, Lodging, Meals, Clays; **Shoots** Field; **Birds** Dove, Pheasant, Huns, Ducks, Geese; **Dogs** Avail/HDW; **Packages** 1/2 Day, 1-6 guns

Pitts Game Farm
HCR Box 357-A, Coulee City, WA 99115
(509) 632-5502 Jimmy Pitts 6-8am; 7-9pm
100 mi. W of Spokane
Acres 17,000; **Type** Public, Member/Avail, Corp.; **On Site** Clubhouse; **Shoots** Field; **Birds** Dove, Quail, Pheasant, Chukar, Huns, Ducks, Geese; **Dogs** Avail/HDW; **Packages** 1/2 Day, 1-10 guns O NAGA/See Pg. 107

R&M Game Birds
& Sporting Clays
495 Fisher Hill Rd., Lyle, WA 98635
(509) 365-3245 Rodger L. Ford Web Site: http://www.americaoutdoors.com/r&m
80 mi. E of Vancouver, WA or Portland, OR
Est 1986; **Acres** 1,100; **Hunters/yr** 500; **Type** Public, Member/Avail, Corp.; **On Site** Clubhouse, Meals, Clays; **Shoots** Field; **Birds** Quail, Pheasant, Chukar, Huns, Turkey; **Dogs** Avail/HDW; **Packages** 1/2 Day, 1-20 guns O NAGA/See Pg. 107

Reecer Creek Gamebird Ranch
6623 196th SW, Lynnwood, WA 98036
(206) 776-0189 Claude Frable Anytime
12 mi. NW of Ellensburg
Est 1991; **Acres** 800; **Hunters/yr** 400; **Type** Public; **On Site** Clubhouse, Lodging, Meals, Clays; **Shoots** Field; **Birds** Quail, Pheasant, Chukar, Huns; **Dogs** Avail/HDW; **Packages** 1/2 Day, 1-4 guns O NAGA/See Pg. 107

Snoqualmie Valley Hunting
4638 9th Ave., NE, Belleuve, WA 98004
(360) 805-8592 Al Erickson
Shoots Field; **Birds** Quail, Pheasant, Chukar
O NAGA/See Pg. 107

Triple B Ranch
1131 Maloy Rd., Selah, WA 98942
(509) 697-7675 Tom Bass, Jr.
Est 1985; **Acres** 2,100; **Type** Public, Member/Avail; **On Site** Clubhouse, Lodging, Meals, Clays; **Shoots** Field; **Birds** Pheasant, Chukar; **Dogs** Avail/HDW

WEST VIRGINIA

The Greenbrier Hunting Preserve
300 West Main St., White Sulpher Springs, WV 24986
(800) 624-6070 Neal Roth Ext. 7183; 10am-5pm
80 mi. W of Roanoke, VA
Est 1994; **Acres** 1,000; **Hunters/yr** 125; **Type** Public; **On Site** Clubhouse, Lodging, Meals, Clays; **Shoots** Field; **Birds** Quail, Pheasant, Chukar; **Dogs** Avail/HDW; **Packages** 1/2 Day, 1-8 guns

Kincheloe Pheasant Hunting Preserve
Rt. 2, Box 88A, Jane Lew, WV 26378
(304) 884-7431 Paul Hughes 8-10pm
123 mi. N of Charleston
Est 1983; **Acres** 1,000; **Hunters/yr** 2,000; **Type** Public, Corp.; **On Site** Clubhouse, Lodging, Meals, Clays; **Shoots** Field; **Birds** Dove, Quail, Ruffed Grouse, Woodcock, Pheasant, Chukar, Turkey; **Dogs** Avail/HDW; **Packages** 1/2 Day, 1-8 guns
O NAGA/See Pg. 107

Prospect Hall
Rt. 1, Box 370, Kearneysville, WV 25430
(304) 728-8213 Christine Martin 8am-6pm
60 mi. NW of Washington, DC
Est 1985; **Acres** 400; **Hunters/yr** 500; **Type** Member/Avail, Corp.; **On Site** Clubhouse, Lodging, Meals, Clays; **Shoots** Field, Tower, Driven, Blinds; **Birds** Dove, Quail, Pheasant, Chukar, Huns, Turkey, Ducks; **Dogs** Avail/HDW; **Packages** 1/2 Day, 2-24 guns O NAGA/See Pg. 107

White Oak Mountain Preserve
PO Box 859, Beaver, WV 25813
(304) 763-5266 Mike Estes
10 mi. SE of Beckley
Type Public; **On Site** Clubhouse, Meals, Clays; **Shoots** Field; **Birds** Quail, Pheasant; **Dogs** Avail/HDW

WISCONSIN

Acorn Acres Hunting Club
E. 7920 Hoppe Rd., Spring Green, WI 53588
(608) 544-5451 Lester Schulenburg
50 mi. W of Madison
Type Member/Avail, Corp.; **On Site** Clubhouse; **Shoots** Field; **Dogs** Avail/HDW

Back Forty Hunting Preserve
N11055 Bandy Rd., Phillips, WI 54555
(715) 339-2823 Peter G. Jesunas After 6pm
150 mi. SE of Duluth, MN
Est 1992; **Acres** 470; **Type** Public, Member/Avail; **On Site** Lodging, Meals; **Shoots** Field; **Birds** Quail, Ruffed Grouse, Woodcock, Pheasant, Chukar; **Dogs** Avail/HDW; **Packages** 1/2 Day, 1-6 guns

Bearskin Wildlife Reserve
8915 Church Rd., Harshaw, WI 54529
(715) 282-5362 John Hendrickson 7-9am, 6-10pm
Est 1984; **Acres** 400; **Type** Public; **Shoots** Field,
Driven; **Birds** Quail, Ruffed Grouse, Pheasant,
Chukar, Turkey, Ducks, Geese; **Dogs** Avail/HDW;
Packages 1/2 Day, up to 2 guns
○ NAGA/See Pg. 107

Big Country Shooting Preserve
14626 Berg Rd., Orfordville, WI 53576
(608) 879-2354 Rick Schneider
Shoots Field; **Birds** Quail, Pheasant, Chukar, Huns
○ NAGA/See Pg. 107

Big Rock Hunting Preserve
W15664 Chuck Rd., Gilman, WI 54433
(715) 668-5557 Chuck Birkenholz 7am or 7pm
60 mi. NE of Eau Claire
Est 1989; **Acres** 600; **Hunters/yr** 1,500; **Type**
Public, Member/Avail, Corp.; **On Site** Clubhouse,
Lodging, Clays; **Shoots** Field; **Birds** Quail, Ruffed
Grouse, Woodcock, Pheasant, Chukar; **Dogs**
Avail/HDW; **Packages** 1/2 Day, 1-20 guns
○ NAGA/See Pg. 107

Black Slough Conservation Club
59 Racine St., Menasha, WI 54952
(414) 722-4293 Dr. Vern Larsen
Est 1971; **Acres** 1,300; **Hunters/yr** 20; **Type**
Member/Ltd; **On Site** Clubhouse, Lodging, Clays;
Shoots Field, Blinds, Boat; **Birds** Pheasant, Ducks,
Geese; **Dogs** Avail/HDW ○ NAGA/See Pg. 107

Blonhaven Hunting Preserve
8006 N. John Paul Rd., Milton, WI 53563
(608) 868-3176 Jim Clark 7am-8pm
60 mi. SW of Milwaukee
Est 1953; **Acres** 250; **Hunters/yr** 3,000; **Type**
Public, Member/Avail; **On Site** Clubhouse, Clays;
Shoots Field, Tower; **Birds** Pheasant, Chukar, Huns;
Dogs Avail/HDW; **Packages** 1/2 Day, 1-40 guns
○ NAGA/See Pg. 107

BURNETT
GAME FARM
& HUNT CLUB

Burnett Game Farm & Hunt Club
4430 Imperial Dr., Brookfield, WI 53045
(414) 781-9156 Bob Voit 8-8
**60 mi. NW of Milwaukee on the
famed Horicon Marsh**
Est 1964; **Acres** 6,800; **Hunters/yr** 130; **Type**
Member/Avail, Corp.; **On Site** Clubhouse, Lodging,
Meals, Clays; **Shoots** Field, Driven, Blinds, Boat;
Birds Quail, Woodcock, Pheasant, Chukar, Huns,
Ducks, Geese; **Dogs** Avail/HDW; **Packages** 1/2
Day, 2-8 guns

Cadens Kennels & Hunt Club
W2738 Scenic Dr., Campbellsport, WI 53010
(414) 533-8579 Dennis Brath 8-5pm
40 mi. NW of Milwaukee
Est 1989; **Acres** 600; **Hunters/yr** 120; **Type**
Public, Member/Avail, Corp.; **On Site** Clubhouse,
Lodging, Meals, Clays; **Shoots** Field, Tower, Blinds;
Birds Quail, Pheasant, Chukar, Huns, Geese; **Dogs**
Avail/HDW; **Packages** 1/2 Day, 1-25 guns

County Line Hunt Club
W7163 Grouse Dr., Portage, WI 53901
(608) 981-2691 Don Gneiser
40 mi. N of Madison
Est 1992; **Acres** 145; **Type** Public, Member/Avail,
Corp.; **On Site** Clubhouse; **Shoots** Field; **Birds**
Pheasant, Chukar; **Dogs** Avail/HDW; **Packages** 1/2
Day, 1-6 guns

Crawfish River
Sportsmen's Club
N5659 Popp Rd., Jefferson, WI 53549
(414) 674-3709 Peter Thomsen
30 mi. E of Madison
Est 1991; **Acres** 500; **Type** Public, Member/Avail,
Corp.; **On Site** Clubhouse; **Shoots** Field; **Birds**
Pheasant, Chukar; **Dogs** Avail/HDW; **Packages** 1/2
Day ○ NAGA/See Pg. 107
○ 40 Mi. West of Milwaukee

Crooked Creek Hunt Club
W1896 Prairie Rd., Burlington, WI 53105
(414) 763-6597 John Parat 8am-8pm
5 mi. W of Lake Geneva
Est 1993; **Acres** 120; **Hunters/yr** 500; **Type**
Public, Member/Avail, Corp.; **On Site** Clubhouse;
Shoots Field; **Birds** Quail, Pheasant, Chukar, Huns;
Dogs Avail/HDW; **Packages** 1/2 Day, 1-12 guns
○ NAGA/See Pg. 107

E&E Game Farm
102 County Line Lane, Kewaskum, WI 53040
(414) 626-3365 Perry Etta/Greg Engelhardt
25 mi. from Milwaukee
Est 1994; **Acres** 360; **Hunters/yr** 1,200; **Type**
Public; **On Site** Clubhouse; **Shoots** Field; **Birds**
Quail, Pheasant, Chukar, Huns; **Dogs** Avail/HDW;
Packages 1/2 Day, 1-30 guns ○ NAGA/See Pg. 107

Eastman Hunting Club, Inc.
527 Hillside Rd., Edgerton, WI 53534
(608) 884-6588 Tom Eastman
30 mi. S of Madison
Acres 700; **Type** Member/Ltd, Corp.; **On Site**
Clubhouse, Clays; **Shoots** Field; **Birds** Quail,
Pheasant, Chukar, Huns ○ NAGA/See Pg. 107
Eastman Hunting Club is an exclusive recreational
game farm. Membership is limited to minimize
crowding. A maximum of two new members are
accepted per year. At Eastman's, fields and hunting conditions are maintained to recreate the
rugged natural hunting of a bygone era. Only serious inquiries welcome.

David A. Eilertson
2611 Baumgartner Dr., LaCrosse, WI 54603
(608) 781-7519 David A. Eilertson 6:30-9:30pm
120 mi. SE of Minneapolis
Est 1984; **Acres** 165; **Hunters/yr** 30; **Type**
Member/Avail; **On Site** Clubhouse, Meals, Clays;
Shoots Field; **Birds** Pheasant; **Dogs** Avail/HDW;
Packages 1/2 Day, up to 6 guns

Fence Line Hunt Club
10759 W. 8 Mile Rd., Franksville, WI 53126
(414) 425-8112 Richard Prihoda
15 mi. SW of Milwaukee
Acres 105; **Type** Public, Member/Avail; **On Site**
Clubhouse; **Shoots** Field; **Birds** Quail, Pheasant;
Dogs HDW; **Packages** 1/2 Day, 1-4 guns
○ NAGA/See Pg. 107

Forest Ridge Hunt Club
PO Box 128, Glenwood City, WI 54013
(715) 265-4286 Tom Whitten
55 mi. NE of Minneapolis
Est 1990; **Acres** 1,600; **Type** Public, Member/Avail,
Corp.; **On Site** Clubhouse, Lodging, Meals; **Shoots**
Field; **Birds** Quail, Pheasant, Chukar; **Dogs**
Avail/HDW; **Packages** 1/2 Day, 1-30 guns

Fox Ridge Game Farm
8585 Valley Line Rd., Oconto Falls, WI 54154
(414) 846-2508 Bill or Kathy 7am-1pm
135 mi. N of Milwaukee
Est 1988; **Acres** 1,000; **Hunters/yr** 700; **Type**
Public, Member/Avail; **On Site** Clubhouse, Lodging,
Clays; **Shoots** Field, Tower; **Birds** Quail, Pheasant,
Chukar; **Dogs** Avail/HDW; **Packages** 1/2 Day, 1-6
guns ○ NAGA/See Pg. 107

Game Unlimited Hunting Club
871 Ct. Rd. E., Hudson, WI 54016
(715) 246-2350 Patrick Melloy 6am-10pm
20 mi. E of Minneapolis

Est 1963; **Acres** 1,000; **Type** Member/Avail, Corp.;
On Site Clubhouse, Lodging, Meals, Clays; **Shoots**
Field, Tower, Blinds; **Birds** Quail, Pheasant, Chukar,
Ducks; **Dogs** Avail/HDW

Geneva National Hunt Club
555 Hunt Club Court, Lake Geneva, WI 53147
(414) 245-7205 Mark Hanna 9-5, T-Su
45 mi. from Milwaukee
Est 1990; **Acres** 400; **Hunters/yr** 2,000; **Type**
Public, Member/Avail, Corp.; **On Site** Clubhouse,
Lodging, Meals, Clays; **Shoots** Field, Blinds, Boat;
Birds Quail, Woodcock, Pheasant, Chukar, Huns,
Snipe, Ducks, Geese; **Dogs** Avail/HDW; **Packages**
1/2 Day, 2-5 guns ○ NAGA/See Pg. 107

Ghost Lake Lodge
Rt. 7, Box 7450, Hayward, WI 54843
(715) 462-3939 Bill Gryzik
140 mi. NE of Minneapolis-St.Paul
Acres 900,000; **Type** Public; **On Site** Clubhouse,
Lodging, Meals; **Shoots** Field; **Birds** Ruffed Grouse,
Woodcock, Ducks; **Dogs** Avail/HDW; **Packages** 3
Days, 2-40 guns

Golden Heritage Farms
5221 County Rd. N., Pickett, WI 54964
(414) 589-4852 Dic Schultz After 7pm
60 mi. NW of Milwaukee
Est 1985; **Acres** 82; **Hunters/yr** 50; **Type** Public,
Corp.; **On Site** Clubhouse, Meals, Clays; **Shoots**
Field, Blinds; **Birds** Pheasant, Ducks, Geese; **Dogs**
Avail/HDW; **Packages** 1/2 Day, 2-4 guns

Halter Wildlife
9626 113th St., Kenosha, WI 53140
(414) 697-0070 John Burke
Shoots Field; **Birds** Quail, Pheasant, Chukar, Huns,
Turkey ○ NAGA/See Pg. 107

Hawe Hunting Preserve
N2594 Blueberry Lane, Waldo, WI 53093
(414) 528-8388 Tom Hawe
35 mi. N of Milwaukee
Est 1950; **Acres** 700; **Type** Public, Member/Avail,
Corp.; **On Site** Clubhouse, Clays; **Shoots** Field;
Birds Quail, Woodcock, Pheasant, Chukar, Ducks;
Dogs Avail/HDW; **Packages** 1/2 Day, 2-20 guns
○ NAGA/See Pg. 107

Highland Hunt Club
N3041W Cty A, Cascade, WI 53011
(414) 528-8848 Mike or Joann Sommers 8-7, T-Su
50 mi. N of Milwaukee
Est 1989; **Acres** 291; **Type** Public, Member/Avail;
On Site Clubhouse, Meals; **Shoots** Field, Driven;
Birds Quail, Pheasant, Chukar, Huns, Ducks; **Dogs**
Avail/HDW; **Packages** 1/2 Day, 1-4 guns
○ NAGA/See Pg. 107

Isaacson's Pheasant Pharm
N2780 Cty. Hwy. M, Sarona, WI 54870
(715) 635-9586 Sylvia & Scott Isaacson Anytime

85 mi. S of Duluth
Est 1988; **Acres** 200; **Type** Public; **Shoots** Field;
Birds Pheasant; **Dogs** Avail/HDW; **Packages** 1/2
Day, 2-4 guns ○ NAGA/See Pg. 107

J&H Game Farm
W5810 J&H Rd., Shiocton, WI 54170
(715) 758-8134 James or Joanne Johnson 8-6
27 mi. W of Green Bay
Est 1968; **Acres** 400; **Hunters/yr** 1,000; **Type**
Member/Avail, Corp.; **On Site** Clubhouse, Meals,
Clays; **Shoots** Field, Tower; **Birds** Pheasant, Chukar;
Dogs Avail/HDW; **Packages** 1/2 Day, 1-4 guns
○ NAGA/See Pg. 107

K 'N K Hi Lo, Inc.
N265 County "T", Endeavor, WI 53930
(608) 587-2696 Darwin or Peggy Kottka
Est 1963; **Acres** 760; **Type** Public, Member/Avail,
Corp.; **On Site** Clubhouse; **Shoots** Field; **Birds**
Pheasant; **Dogs** Avail/HDW; **Packages** 1/2 Day,
1-25 guns

Kidder Game Farm
3219 E. County Rd. N, Milton, WI 53563
(608) 868-2376 Warren/Nancy/Clark 8am-10pm
30 mi. from Madison
Est 1960; **Acres** 300; **Type** Public; **Shoots** Field;
Birds Quail, Pheasant, Chukar, Turkey; **Dogs**
Avail/HDW; **Packages** 1/2 Day, up to 1 guns
○ NAGA/See Pg. 107

Little Creek Lodge Hunt Club
4408 Sampson Rd., Little Suamico, WI 54141
(414) 826-7382 Jerry or Linda Boomsma Anytime
18 mi. N of Green Bay
Est 1995; **Acres** 700; **Hunters/yr** 400; **Type**
Public, Member/Avail, Corp.; **On Site** Clubhouse,
Clays; **Shoots** Field; **Birds** Quail, Pheasant, Chukar;
Dogs Avail/HDW; **Packages** 1/2 Day, 1-40 guns
○ NAGA/See Pg. 107

Lone Oak Shooting Preserve
N4028 Cty. C, Montello, WI 53949
(608) 297-7104 Jon & Gertrude Polcyn
8 mi. from Montello
Acres 567; **Type** Public; **Birds** Pheasant

Longshot Sportsman's Club
N8995 Townline Rd., Van Dyne, WI 54979
(414) 688-2314 John Eiden
75 mi. NW of Milwaukee
Est 1987; **Acres** 410; **Hunters/yr** 250; **Type**
Public, Member/Avail, Corp.; **On Site** Clubhouse,
Meals, Clays; **Shoots** Field, Driven, Blinds; **Birds**
Quail, Pheasant, Chukar, Ducks, Geese; **Dogs**
Avail/HDW; **Packages** 1/2 Day, 1-24 guns

Martin Fish & Game Farm
W10681 Hwy. 127, Portage, WI 53901
(608) 742-7205 Jim Martin
Type Public, Member/Avail; **Shoots** Field; **Birds**
Quail, Pheasant, Chukar, Huns, Ducks
○ NAGA/See Pg. 107

Mecan River Outfitters
Rt. 2, Box 103, Princeton, WI 54968
(414) 295-3439 Paul Harvey
45 mi. W of Oshkosh
Acres 400; **Hunters/yr** 600; **Type** Public, Member/
Avail; **On Site** Clubhouse, Lodging, Meals, Clays;
Shoots Field; **Birds** Pheasant, Chukar; **Dogs** Avail

○ Airport Pickup ○ Brochure Available
○ Bird Processing ○ Quality Clubhouse
○ Family Recreation ○ Family Run Business
○ Gourmet Meals ○ Private Bedrooms

Oak Hill Hunting Preserve
W8718 Forest Ave., Eldorado, WI 54932
(414) 921-2776 Paul Snider
50 mi. N of Milwaukee
Acres 500; **Type** Public, Member/Avail, Corp.; **On
Site** Clubhouse; **Shoots** Field; **Birds** Quail,
Pheasant, Chukar, Ducks, Geese; **Dogs** Avail/HDW
○ NAGA/See Pg. 107

Oakwood Kennel & Game Farm
7149 Badger Lane, Allenton, WI 53002
(414) 488-5852 Ron or Dianne Norman 7am-7pm
30 mi. NW of Milwaukee
Est 1989; **Acres** 150; **Hunters/yr** 100; **Type**
Public, Member/Avail, Corp.; **On Site** Clubhouse,
Clays; **Shoots** Field, Blinds; **Birds** Quail, Pheasant,
Chukar, Huns, Ducks, Geese; **Dogs** Avail/HDW;
Packages 1/2 Day ○ NAGA/See Pg. 107

Our Farm
PO Box 108, Eastman, WI 54626
(608) 874-4556 Rudy Wendt
Est 1992; **Acres** 278; **Type** Public, Member/Avail,
Corp.; **On Site** Clays; **Shoots** Field; **Birds** Quail,
Pheasant, Chukar, Huns, Turkey; **Dogs** Avail/HDW;
Packages 1/2 Day, 1-4 guns ○ NAGA/See Pg. 107

Palmquist's "The Farm"
N5136 River Rd., Brantwood, WI 54513
(800) 519-2558 Helen & Jim Palmquist
60 mi. N of Wausau **Est** 1949; **Acres** 800; **Type**
Public; **On Site** Clubhouse, Lodging, Meals; **Shoots**
Field; **Birds** Ruffed Grouse, Woodcock, Ducks,
Geese; **Dogs** Avail/HDW

Pheasant City Hunt Club
R#1, Box 272, Markesan, WI 53946
(414) 324-5813 Bill/Debbie Scallon
65 mi. NW of Milwaukee
Est 1957; **Acres** 640; **Type** Public, Member/Avail,
Corp.; **On Site** Clubhouse, Lodging, Meals, Clays;
Shoots Field, Tower, Blinds; **Birds** Quail, Pheasant,
Chukar, Ducks, Geese; **Dogs** Avail/HDW; **Packages**
1/2 Day

Pheasant Retreat Game Farm
7617 Prellwitz Rd., Ripon, WI 54971
(414) 748-9427 Dick & Deb 6am-10pm
Est 1983; **Acres** 527; **Type** Public, Member/Avail;
On Site Clubhouse; **Shoots** Field; **Birds** Quail,
Pheasant, Chukar; **Dogs** Avail/HDW
O NAGA/See Pg. 107

Quail Haven Hunt Club
Rt. 4, Box 821, Clintonville, WI 54929
(715) 823-6123 Michael K. Duffey 6:30-9am
35 mi. W of Green Bay
Est 1985; **Acres** 200; **Hunters/yr** 20; **Type** Public;
On Site Clubhouse, Clays; **Shoots** Field; **Birds** Quail,
Ruffed Grouse, Woodcock, Pheasant, Chukar; **Dogs**
Avail/HDW; **Packages** 1/2 Day, 2-4 guns

R&R Ranch
8923 Richfield Dr., Marshfield, WI 54449
(715) 676-3365 Steve Strong
6 mi. S of Marshfield
Est 1985; **Acres** 700; **Hunters/yr** 300; **Type**
Public, Member/Avail; **On Site** Clubhouse, Lodging,
Meals, Clays; **Shoots** Field; **Birds** Quail, Ruffed
Grouse, Pheasant, Chukar; **Dogs** Avail/HDW;
Packages 1/2 Day, 1-100 guns

Richford Game Club
Rt. 1, Box 107, Coloma, WI 54930
(715) 228-3052 Vern Slife/Debb Semrow
50 mi. N of Madison
Est 1987; **Acres** 80; **Hunters/yr** 75; **Type**
Member/Avail; **Shoots** Field; **Birds** Pheasant;
Dogs HDW; **Packages** 1/2 Day, up to 20 guns

River Wildlife
Kohler, WI 53044
(414) 457-0134 Max Grube 7am-6pm
55 mi. N of Milwaukee
Est 1977; **Acres** 250; **Hunters/yr** 1,000; **Type**
Member/Avail, Corp.; **On Site** Clubhouse, Lodging,
Meals, Clays; **Shoots** Field; **Birds** Pheasant, Chukar,
Turkey; **Dogs** Avail/HDW; **Packages** 1/2 Day, 1-15
guns O NAGA/See Pg. 107

Rush Creek Hunt Club
400 Springs Dr., Spring Green, WI 53588
(608) 588-2219 Lee Bilke
40 mi. W of Madison
Est 1995; **Acres** 3,000; **Type** Public, Member/Avail,
Corp.; **On Site** Clubhouse, Lodging, Meals, Clays;
Shoots Field, Tower; **Birds** Quail, Pheasant, Chukar,
Ducks; **Dogs** Avail/HDW; **Packages** 1/2 Day, 2-50
guns O NAGA/See Pg. 107
See Our Ad Above, Right

Smoky Lake Reserve
1 Lake St., PO Box 100, Phelps, WI 54554
(715) 545-2333 Miriam Saucke 9-5, M-F
45 mi. NE of Rhinelander
Est 1966; **Acres** 6,000; **Hunters/yr** 100; **Type**
Member/Avail, Corp.; **On Site** Clubhouse, Lodging,
Meals, Clays; **Shoots** Field, Blinds; **Birds** Quail,

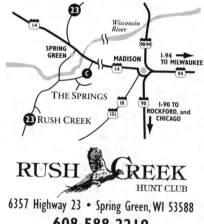
Ruffed Grouse, Woodcock, Pheasant, Chukar, Turkey,
Ducks; **Dogs** Avail/HDW; **Packages** 1/2 Day, 1-16
guns O NAGA/See Pg. 107

Spring Creek Farm
W8797 Hwy. P, Oxford, WI 53952
(608) 586-5858 Eugene Schmidt
Shoots Field; **Birds** Pheasant O NAGA/See Pg. 107

Spring Valley Hunting Preserve
15201 Lang Rd., Orfordville, WI 53576
(608) 879-2628 Lyle Yaun 7am-9pm
15 mi. W of Janesville
Est 1985; **Acres** 130; **Hunters/yr** 400; **Type**
Public; **On Site** Clubhouse; **Shoots** Field; **Birds**
Quail, Pheasant; **Dogs** Avail/HDW; **Packages** 1/2
Day, 2-12 guns O NAGA/See Pg. 107

Strebig's Game Farm & Shooting Preserve
N 3215 CTHE, Medford, WI 54451
(715) 748-2883 Tim Strebig
50 mi. NW of Wausau

Est 1990;   Acres 600;   Type Public, Member/Avail,
Corp.;   On Site Clubhouse;   Shoots Field;   Birds
Pheasant;   Dogs Avail/HDW;   Packages 1/2 Day
O NAGA/See Pg. 107

Summit Lake Game Farm

PO Box 810, Hayward, WI 54843
(715) 354-7241 John Treslley
75 mi. SE of Superior
Est 1990;   Acres 5,000;   Hunters/yr 1,500;   Type
Public, Member/Avail, Corp.;   On Site Clubhouse,
Lodging, Meals, Clays;   Shoots Field, Blinds, Boat;
Birds Quail, Ruffed Grouse, Woodcock, Pheasant,
Chukar, Huns, Turkey, Ducks, Geese;   Dogs
Avail/HDW;   Packages 1/2 Day, 1-5 guns
ENJOY THE BEST HUNTING WISCONSIN HAS TO
OFFER! Summit Lake Game Farm is a sportsman's
paradise, a 6,250 acre game preserve. A 60 acre
private lake, numerous creeks, ponds and marshes
are found amidst the 6 square miles of woodlands.
Here sportsmen will find abundant deer, bear,
grouse, woodcock and upland birds. Upon arrival
at Summit Lake, we will provide you with everything you need to make your stay as enjoyable as
possible. We offer two lake-side lodges and one
right in the middle of the preserve. After the hunt,
relax in our Club House, nestled among towering
pines, and watch majestic bald eagles soar overhead. Quality upland bird hunts ensured. Fishing,
too. A pro shop, shooting instruction, dog training,
trap range and bird processing also available. Call
today for more information.

Tall Feathers Corporation

PO Box 37, Nashotah, WI 53058
(414) 781-2270 Barth Chudik
Type Member/Avail;   On Site Lodging;   Shoots
Field;   Birds Pheasant, Chukar O NAGA/See Pg. 107

Tamarack Game Farm

N8745 Cty. Rd. G, Colfax, WI 54730
(715) 632-2346 Stan Lorenz Eve.
65 mi. E of Minneapolis, MN
Est 1987;   Acres 240;   Hunters/yr 25;   Type
Public;   Shoots Field;   ;   Dogs Avail/HDW;
Packages 1/2 Day, 1-8 guns O NAGA/See Pg. 107

Three Lakes Preserve

PO Box 440, Three Lakes, WI 54562
(715) 546-8289 Roger Devenport
Type Public;   On Site Lodging;   Shoots Field;   Birds
Pheasant, Turkey O NAGA/See Pg. 107

Thunderbird Game Farm

W23119 Thunderbird Rd., Chilton, WI 53014
(414) 853-3030 Todd Doughty
30 mi. S of Green Bay
Est 1967;   Acres 600;   Type Public, Member/Avail,
Corp.;   On Site Clubhouse, Meals, Clays;   Shoots
Field, Tower, Blinds;   Birds Pheasant, Ducks, Geese;
Dogs Avail/HDW;   Packages 1/2 Day, 1-20 guns
O NAGA/See Pg. 107

Tumm's Pine View Game Farm

PO Box 240, Fall Creek, WI 54742
(715) 877-2434 James W. Tumm 7am-8pm
100 mi. SE of Minneapolis
Est 1988;   Type Public;   On Site Clubhouse;
Shoots Field;   Birds Quail, Pheasant;   Dogs
Avail/HDW;   Packages 1/2 Day, 1-4 guns
O NAGA/See Pg. 107

Wern Valley Sportsmen's Club

S36 W19657 Wern Way, Waukesha, WI 53188
(414) 968-2400 Steve Williams
20 mi. W of Milwaukee
Acres 700;   Type Public, Member/Avail, Corp.;   On
Site Clubhouse, Meals, Clays;   Shoots Field, Tower;
Birds Quail, Pheasant, Chukar, Huns;   Dogs
Avail/HDW;   Packages 1/2 Day, 1-40 guns
O NAGA/See Pg. 107

Whispering Emerald Ridge Game Farm

N3952 640th St., Menomonie, WI 54751
(715) 235-1720 Mike Kettner/Bruce Olson anytime
60 mi. E of Minneapolis-St. Paul
Est 1989;   Type Public;   On Site Clubhouse, Clays;
Shoots Field;   Birds Quail, Pheasant;   Dogs
Avail/HDW;   Packages 1/2 Day, 1-6 guns

Wild Wings Hunting & Fishing

N. 865 Hwy. W., Campbellsport, WI 53010
(414) 533-8738 Jim Coblentz 8-5
40 mi. N of Milwaukee
Est 1974;   Acres 120;   Type Public, Member/Avail,
Corp.;   On Site Clubhouse, Meals, Clays;   Shoots
Field;   Birds Quail, Pheasant, Chukar;   Dogs
Avail/HDW;   Packages 1/2 Day, 1-50 guns

Willow Creek Ranch

N710 Bloomer Mill Rd., LaCrosse, WI 54601
(608) 788-8662 Kevin Churchill
Type Public;   On Site Lodging, Clays;   Shoots Field;
Birds Quail, Pheasant O NAGA/See Pg. 107

Wolf River Game Farm

W6796 St. Rd. 156, Shiocton, WI 54170
(715) 758-8106 Dean Daebler
30 mi. W of Green Bay Est 1986;   Type Public,
Member/Avail;   On Site Clubhouse;   Shoots Field;
Birds Quail, Pheasant, Chukar;   Packages 1/2 Day,
1-8 guns O NAGA/See Pg. 107

Woods & Meadows Game Farm

Rt. 1, Warrens, WI 54666
(608) 378-4223 Scott Goetzka Evenings
Type Public;   On Site Clubhouse, Lodging, Clays;
Shoots Field;   Birds Quail, Pheasant, Chukar;   Dogs
Avail/HDW;   Packages 1/2 Day, 1-12 guns
O NAGA/See Pg. 107

WYOMING

Bear Mountain Back Trails
PO Box 37, LaGrange, WY 82221
(307) 834-2281 Ellis or Linda Kessler
56 mi. NE of Cheyenne
Est 1987; **Acres** 2,000; **Type** Public, Member/Avail;
On Site Lodging, Meals, Clays; **Shoots** Field; **Birds**
Quail, Pheasant, Chukar; **Dogs** Avail/HDW;
Packages 1/2 Day, 2-10 guns ○ NAGA/See Pg. 107

Big Willow Pheasant Pharm
HC76, Box 47, Hawk Springs, WY 82217
(307) 532-3442 Dennis Simmons
Type Public, Member/Avail; **Shoots** Field; **Birds**
Quail, Pheasant, Chukar ○ NAGA/See Pg. 107

Canyon Ranch Gun Club
PO Box 629, Big Horn, WY 82833
(307) 674-9097 Jim Roach Evenings
15 mi. S of Sheridan
Est 1985; **Acres** 4,000; **Hunters/yr** 150; **Type**
Member/Ltd; **On Site** Clubhouse, Lodging, Meals,
Clays; **Shoots** Field, Driven; **Birds** Pheasant, Huns,
Turkey, Sharp Tail Grouse; **Dogs** Avail/HDW;
Packages 1/2 Day, 4-8 guns ○ NAGA/See Pg. 107

Clear Creek
Hunting Preserve
3004 Hwy. 14-16 East, Clearmont, WY 82835
(307) 737-2217 Doug Kauffman 7am-9pm
125 mi. N of Casper
Est 1980; **Acres** 700; **Hunters/yr** 800; **Type**
Public, Member/Avail, Corp.; **On Site** Clubhouse,
Lodging, Meals, Clays; **Shoots** Field, Tower, Blinds;
Birds Dove, Pheasant, Chukar, Huns, Sage Grouse,
Ducks, Geese; **Dogs** Avail/HDW; **Packages** 1/2
Day, 1-30 guns ○ NAGA/See Pg. 107
Clear Creek offers some of the finest Upland Game
Bird hunting in the Rocky Mountain region at the
foot of the Big Horn Mountains in secluded northeastern Wyoming. Our full-time conservationists
have worked for years cultivating habitats for our
Upland Game Bird hunting areas. Released
ringnecked pheasants, Chukar and Hungarian partridges supplement native stock. Whether you opt
for a morning, afternoon or all-day hunt, our experienced guides and well-trained bird dogs–Labradors,
pointers and Brittany Spaniels–work hard to make
it successful and pleasurable. Your birds can be
dressed and quick frozen after each hunt. Clear
Creek's excellent sporting clays course, including
Duck Tower, Grouse Butte, and Crazy Quail (skeet,
too), allows you to tune up before your hunt or simply enjoy an afternoon of recreation.

Milliron 2 Outfitting
1513 Culbertson, Worland, WY 82401
(307) 347-2574 Billy & Barbara Sinclair Anytime
160 mi. N of Casper, WY
Est 1992; **Acres** 1,300; **Hunters/yr** 150; **Type**
Public; **On Site** Meals; **Shoots** Field, Blinds, Boat;
Birds Quail, Pheasant, Chukar, Turkey, Sage Grouse,
Ducks, Geese; **Dogs** Avail/HDW; **Packages** 1/2 Day
○ NAGA/See Pg. 107

Nowood River Game Bird Farm
915 Obie Sue, Worland, WY 82401
(307) 347-8726 Ron Overcast
On Site Lodging; **Shoots** Field; **Birds** Pheasant
○ NAGA/See Pg. 107

ARGENTINA

Argentina Estancias
(800) 778-4778 (Orvis)   011-54-972-27391
FAX: 011-54-972-27111   **Birds** Dove & Waterfowl
Argentina Estancias, an Orvis Endorsed Wingshooting
Lodge, offers "never-to-be-forgotten" hunting and
shooting in Argentina. English speaking guides and
superb accommodations. Call today!
See Our Ad Pg. 269

Argentina Wings
20780 Temelec Dr., Sonoma, CA 95476
(800) 946-4486 FAX: (707) 938-0937
Contact: Carlos A. Brouard
Birds: Duck, Partridge, Dove
Wingshooting and fishing with first class lodging at
exclusively private country estates (Estancias). Excellent
options for non-shooting guests.
See Our Ad Page 270

Gage Outdoor Expeditions
608 2nd Ave., So., Suite 166, Minneapolis, MN 55402 ·
(800) 888-1601 FAX: (612) 339-0964
Contact: Baird Pittman   Destinations: Argentina,
Mexico, South Dakota
Birds: Dove, Duck, Goose, Quail, Pheasants
We offer destinations that are plentiful in game and
partner with outfitters who have years of experience
hosting guests from around the world.
See Our Ad Page 271

High Adventure Company
2941 Little River Rd., Madison, GA 30650
(800) 847-0834 Contact: Chuck Humphrey
Birds: Dove, Duck, Geese, Quail, Perdiz, Francolin;
Also Big Game & Sportfishing Packages.
The world's best high volume dove and duck hunting
as well as perdiz over pointing dogs. A minimum
group size of four shooters is required and we will
assist you in putting your group together. Private
ranch accommodations, great food and wine, and a
superb staff make for an outstanding trip!
See Our Ad Page 273

Luis Sier Safaris
8168 Sierra Ventana, Buenos Aires, Argentina
FAX: 011-54-91-91-5268
Birds: Geese, Duck, Pigeon, Partridge
Looking for the world's finest wingshooting? Contact
Luis Sier Safaris for incredible hunts in Argentina.
Operating from a five-star ranch, Luis Sier Safaris has
served the world's wingshooters for more than 20 years.
Fax today to arrange your most unforgettable hunt.
See Our Ad Page 275

Wings, Inc.
403 Greene St., PO Box 743, Camden, SC 29020-0743
(803) 425-7260 (Day)   (803) 432-5877 (Eve)
FAX: (803) 425-7270
Contact: Don Terrell   Birds: Dove, Duck
See our ad for special 3-day packages to Argentina
and Eastern Mexico.
See Our Ad Page 277

MEXICO

Gage Outdoor Expeditions
608 2nd Ave., So., Suite 166
Minneapolis, MN 55402
(800) 888-1601 FAX: (612) 339-0964
Contact: Baird Pittman
Destinations: Argentina, Mexico, South Dakota
Birds: Dove, Duck, Goose, Quail, Pheasants
We offer destinations that are plentiful in game and
partner with outfitters who have years of experience
hosting guests from around the world.
See Our Ad Page 271

Las Palomas
de Loma Colorada
PO Box 202, Linn, TX 78563
(800) 375-4868 FAX: (210) 380-3723
Contact: Don Turner or Phillip Veale
Birds: Dove, Duck, Quail, Geese
Location: San Fernando, Mex.–85 mi. S. of McAllen, TX
See Our Ad Page 272

Los Patos
PO Box 202, Linn, TX 78563
(800) 375-4868   FAX: (210) 380-3723
Contact: Don Turner or Phillip Veale
Location: 30 miles E. of San Fernando
Birds: Duck, Geese
See Our Ad Page 272

Rancho El Palomar
Alamos, Sonora, Mexico
Mail: Box 820, Ennis, MT 59729
(406) 682-4764   Contact: Felipe & Cherisse Acosta
Birds: Dove, Blue Pigeon, Quail
Located in the White Wing capital of western Mexico,
Rancho El Palomar offers a hunting experience with a
"south of the border flair." Family owned and
operated, El Palomar has over thirty years of
experience and over 100,000 acres. From November
through March, Wingshooters enjoy shooting white
wing, mounring dove, blue pigeon and quail in
semi-tropical vegatation. Superb accommodations and
gourmet meals. Call or write today for information.

Wings, Inc.
403 Greene St., PO Box 743
Camden, SC 29020-0743
(803) 425-7260 (Day)   (803) 432-5877 (Eve)
FAX: (803) 425-7270
Contact: Don Terrell Birds: Dove, Duck
See our ad for special 3-day packages to Argentina
and Eastern Mexico.
See Our Ad Page 277

COLOMBIA

Safari de Colombia
Hunting & Fishing
(800) 684-5110 (U.S.A.)
Contact: Kjell Erland von Sneidern
FAX: 011-572-555-1581 (Colombia)
FAX: 011-572-555-2740
Birds Hunted: Dove & Pigeon Year Round
See Our Ad Page 274

UNITED KINGDOM

Supreme Sporting Tours
Supreme Sporting U.K. Ltd.
Bordesley House, Birmingham
Rd., Redditch, Worcestershire, B97 6RH England
Phone/Fax: 011-44-1527-61000
Contact: Ashton D. Hall
Experience the finest in traditional British
games/shooting. Supreme Sporting Tours guides you
to the most challenging of English sporting birds on
long established estates (many with Royal Patronage).
Enjoy classic double gun days with experienced loaders
or instructors. Complete packages include airport
pickup and accommodations to make your sporting
holiday trouble free and carefree.
See Our Ad Page 276

How to Use Wing & Clay's Sporting Clays, Trap & Skeet Directory

Near home or far away

Finding a place to shoot clays—especially when you're away from home—can be difficult. This is especially true of sporting clays. Dozens of new courses are coming on line monthly and even more are in the planning stages. Fortunately, you now have a copy of Wing & Clay to make the job easier and less time consuming.

Extensive listings

The heart of the Clays Directory is its extensive listings of sporting clay courses—some affiliated with the National Sporting Clays Association or Sporting Clays of America and yet other unaffiliated courses—across the country. A complete listing includes the operation's name, address and telephone number, a contact name, membership type, days and hours of operation, reservation policy (this information given in advertiser and enhanced listings only) , sporting clay course description, and the availability of trap, skeet, five stand, wobble traps, high towers and other clay games. [Look for detailed explanations in the numbered Typical Listing on the following page.]

The listings in each state begin with the sub-head **SPORTING & 5 STAND**, followed by an alphabetical listing of locations that offer sporting clays, five stand (or both) and in many instances trap, skeet or other clay games.

This year for the first time, the Clays directory section includes individual listings of locations that offer trap or skeet, but no sporting of five stand. Here listings follow the **TRAP & SKEET** sub-head in alphbetical order. The listings include the operation's name, address, telephone number, contact name and the number of trap and skeet fields at the location.

Your primary source

In short, the Clays Directory is your primary source of information on clay shooting opportunities anywhere in the country. Please use it at home and whenever you travel. And when you do, remember to say you "saw it in Wing & Clay." (Note: The information contained in the Clays section is provided by the operator or a reliable source, but is not verified by Wing & Clay. Call ahead to confirm listing data, before visiting a location.)

CLAY TARGETS

STANDARD
4 ¼ inches in diameter, 1 ⅛ inches thick; dome shaped; standard in trap and skeet.

BATTUE
4 ¼ inches in diameter; ⅜ inch thick; "flying razor blade," difficult to pick up edge-on; does rolls and wingovers.

ROCKET
4 ¼ inches in diameter; ⅝ inch thick; deceptive in flight; appears to float, but retains more velocity than the standard.

MIDI
3 ½ inches in diameter, ⅞ inch thick; smaller size make it appear farther away than it actually is; retains initial velocity longer than other targets.

RABBIT
4 ¼ inches in diameter; ½ inch thick; rolls and bounces on the ground; thick rim, density prevent shattering on impact with ground.

MINI
2 ⅜ inches in diameter, ⅝ inch thick; deceptive because small size makes it appear to be moving faster than it actually is; slows quickly because it's light.

TYPICAL LISTING

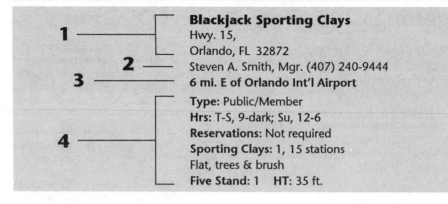

1 ─── **Blackjack Sporting Clays**
Hwy. 15,
Orlando, FL 32872
2 ── Steven A. Smith, Mgr. (407) 240-9444
3 ─── **6 mi. E of Orlando Int'l Airport**

Type: Public/Member
Hrs: T-S, 9-dark; Su, 12-6
Reservations: Not required
4 ─── Sporting Clays: 1, 15 stations
Flat, trees & brush
Five Stand: 1   HT: 35 ft.

HOW THE DIRECTORY IS ORGANIZED

Listings in Wing & Clay's Sporting Clay Directory are organized alphabetically first by state (followed by foreign listings). Within state, listings appear in alphabetical order by operation name, beginning with operations that offer sporting clays or five stand. These listings are followed by an alphabetical listing of locations within the state that offer trap or skeet.

1 CLAY SHOOTING LOCATION NAME & ADDRESS

2 CONTACT NAME(S) & TELEPHONE NUMBER:
The name of the person and the telephone number to call when you're looking for information or making a reservation. When you call, please remember to tell the contact you saw the location's advertisement or listing in Wing & Clay

3 NEAREST MAJOR TOWN/CITY:
Distance in miles and direction from a large city or town or ,in some cases, an airport ; intended to give you a better general idea of where the sporting clays course is located, especially if you are unfamiliar with an area.

4 PARTICULARS

Type Specifically, type of membership. That is whether the sporting clays course is open to the public (**Public**) or to members only—individual or corporate. "**Member**" usually means an annual fee is required. **Public/Member** means the club is a membership club that is also open to the public, though public access may be limited. (Contact the club directly for information on membership cost and availability and policies governing public access.)

Hours: The operating schedule of the sporting clays location—days and hours open. For example: **T-Su, 9-dk** means that the operation is open Tuesday through Sunday from 9 a.m. to dusk or dark. Seasonal information is provided in some instances, space allowing. Always call ahead to confirm.

Reservations: (Information provided in enhanced listings only.) Course reservation policy, specifically whether they are: **Not Required, Recommended** or **Strongly Recommended**.

Sporting clays & terrain description: (Terrain and coverage information is found only in enhanced listings.) Number of sporting clays courses on the property, total number of shooting stations; topography (**Flat, Rolling, Hilly**) and coverage or foliage (**Light, Brush, Trees & Brush, Heavily Wooded**). A listing that reads "**Sporting Clays: 3, 36 stations, Mostly flat and heavily wooded**" means that the location has 3 courses with a total of 36 shooting stations that are laid out on flat, densely wooded land. (A station is defined as a position along the course at which a shooter receives a score.)

Clay shooting games & high tower: The availability of other clay shooting games or disciplines—**Trap, Skeet, Wobble Trap, Five Stand, Olympic Trap, Double Trap ,Universal Trench**—and whether the operation has a High Tower from which targets are thrown. A "**Y**" appearing after "**Skeet**" or "**Trap**" indicates that these games are available at the location; a number following these words (or **Five Stand**) indicates the number of shooting fields available for that particular game or discipline. "**HT**" indicates the presence of at least one High Tower at the location (whenever possible the height of the tallest tower is printed in the listing).

CLAY LOCATIONS
STATE/PAGE INDEX

ALABAMA

SPORTING & 5-STAND

Dixieland Plantation
Box 168, Hatchechubbee, AL 36858
Donald Dixon (334) 667-7876
25 mi. SW of Columbus, GA
Type: Public **Hrs:** 8am-5pm
Sporting: 1, 11 stations
Skeet: 1 **Five Stand:** 1 **HT**

Doublehead Resort & Lodge
145 Cty. Rd 314,
Town Creek, AL 35672
Donny Patrick (800) 685-9267
20 mi. W of Florence
Type: Public
Hrs: M-S, 10-Dark; Su, 1-Dark
Sporting: None
Five Stand: 1

Greenfield Hunting
Hwy. 4 West, PO Box 174,
Pittsview, AL 36871
Rick Cunningham (334) 855-9118
25 mi. S of Columbus, GA
Type: Public
Hrs: S, 10-Dk; W/F, 2-Dk; Su, 1-Dk
Sporting: 11, 20 stations **HT:** 25'

Mars Skeet Club
107 Parcus Rd., SE,
Huntsville, AL 35803
Richard Sheppard (205) 544-7198
80 mi. N of Birmingham
Type: Member/Avail
Sporting: 1, 8 stations
Trap: 1 **Skeet:** 2

Mobile Shooting Center
710 Dykes Rd., Mobile, AL 36608
Sandra Green (334) 633-8629
3 mi. W of Mobile Airport
Type: Public **Hrs:** T-Su, 10-5
Sporting: 1, 8 stations
Trap: 1 **Skeet:** 5 **HT:** 40 ft.

Parches Cove
4415 Parches Cove Rd.,
Union Grove, AL 35175
Houston Lindsay (205) 498-2447
20 mi. from Huntsville
Type: Public
Hrs: Call for information
Sporting: 1, 10 stations

Rockfence Station
4388 Chmbrs. Cty Rd. 160,
Lafayette, AL 36862
Kane Hudmon (334) 864-0217
95 mi. SW of Atlanta
Type: Public/Member
Hrs: Su-S, 8am-6pm
Reservs: Recommended
Sporting: 1, 16 stations
Trap: 1 **Skeet:** 1
Five Stand: 1 **HT:** 25 ft.
O Lodging/16 Guest
O Meals/100 Seated
O Metal Rifle & Pistol Targets
O Open Year Around/
  Conference Facility
O Hunting

Rocky Top Sporting Clays
135 Rogers Circle,
Notasulga, AL 36866
Darsic Rogers (334) 887-9240
5 mi. N of Tallasse
Type: Public/Member
Hrs: Su, 1-5; Other days by appt;
closed June & July
Sporting: 1, 8 stations **HT:** 32 ft.

Selwood Sporting Clays
706 Selwood Rd.,
Alpine, AL 35014
Alan Hill (800) 522-0403
40 mi. SE of Birmingham
Type: Public/Member
Hrs: M-S, 8-dark
Reservs: Strongly recommended
Sporting: 2, 28 stations
Five Stand: 1 **HT:** 30 ft.
O Loaner Guns
O Factory Ammunition
O On-Site Pro Shop
O Shooting Lodge
O Formal Instructions
O Golf Carts

Seven Bridges Sporting
Rt. 2, Box 633, Ramer, AL 36069
Quincy Stacey (334) 288-5150
10 mi. S of Montgomery
Type: Public/Member
Hrs: W-Su, 9-5 **Sporting:** 2, 20 sta.
Five Stand: 1 **HT:** 40 ft.

Tannehill Sporting Clays
PO Box 187, Woodstock, AL 35188
Hunter Faulconer (205) 938-3379
35 mi. S of Birmingham
Type: Public/Member
Hrs: W-S, 12-Dusk; Su, 1-Dusk
Sporting: 1, 12 stations
Five Stand: 5   HT: 60 ft.

Westervelt Sporting Clays
Box 2362, Tuscaloosa, AL 35403
Charles Bedwell (205) 373-8212
50 mi. SW of Tuscaloosa
Type: Public
Hrs: Booking required with 10 or
more; and hunt package
Reservs: Recommended
Sporting: 1, 7 stations
Trap: 1   Skeet: 1
See Our Ad Pg. 291

Wheeler Station
1316 Stratford Rd., SE,
Decatur, AL 35601
Scottie Letson (205) 637-6400
35 mi. W of Huntsville
Type: Public/Member
Hrs: M-F, by appt; S, 9-Dk; Su, 1-5
Sporting: 1, 13 stations HT: 60 ft.

White Oak Plantation
5215 B County Road 10,
Tuskegee, AL 36083
Matthew or Robert Pitman
(334) 727-9258
20 mi. SW of Auburn
Type: Member/Avail
Hrs: M-Su, By Appt.
Reservs: Strongly recommended
Sporting: 1, 17 stations
Five Stand: 1   HT: 40 ft.
Wobble Trap
http://www.americaoutdoors.com
/woak
Recognized as one of the top
courses in the nation, White Oak
is designed with a variety of
rolling terrains, wooded to
lakeside, and several stations
over water. A completely
automated course and
innovative target presentations
produce a course that is
constantly changing and
challenging.

TRAP & SKEET

Big Sky Skeet & Trap Club
Box 14396, Huntsville, AL 35802
Norman Lindsey (205) 586-1970
Hrs: W/F/S, 12-5; Su, 8-5
Trap: 2   Skeet: 4

Dixie Trap
315 West Fleming Rd.,
Montgomery, AL 36105
Bill Parson (334) 288-5427
Trap: 3

Ft. Rucker Skeet Club
Box 620992, Ft. Rucker, AL 36362
Ralph Aaron (334) 347-8363
Hrs: S/Su/Holidays, 10-5
Trap: 1   Skeet: 6

Headland Skeet & Gun Club
2874 Denton Rd.,
Dothan, AL 36303
Ronald Bass (334) 793-3111
Hrs: S/Su, 12-6   Skeet: 2

Honey Do Retreat
Rt. 3, Box 346A,
Enterprise, AL 36330
Harrell Howell (334) 293-2843
Hrs: By invitation   Skeet: 1

Maxwell Skeet & Trap Club
Rt. 3, Box 7, Newton, AL 36352
Stuart Cope, Jr. (334) 598-4485
Hrs: Oct/Nov, S/Su, 12-5
Trap: 1   Skeet: 3

Muscle Shoals Skeet & Trap
PO Box 334, Florence, AL 35631
Eric Massey (205) 757-1481
Hrs: Su, pm; Th/S
Trap: 5   Skeet: 3

Red Eagle Skeet & Trap
Box 280, Childersburg, AL 35044
Neil Pillar (205) 426-0545
Hrs: S, all day; W/Su, 12-Dark
Trap: 1   Skeet: 6

Southern Skeet & Trap
Box 101012, Irondale, AL 35210
Larry Sexton (205) 956-6800
Type: Public   Hrs: W, 11-10; Th,
5-10; F, 2-10; S, 9-10; Su, 9-Dark
Trap: 9   Skeet: 7

Styx River Shooting Center
Box 1457, Robertsdale, AL 36567
Robert Garner (334) 964-7066
Type: Public/Member
Hrs: W-Su, 8-6:30
Trap: 3   Skeet: 2

War Eagle Gun Club
300 Mockingbird Lane,
Auburn, AL 36830
John David Vedder (334) 826-6381
Hrs: By appt.   Skeet: 1

ALASKA

SPORTING & 5-STAND

Chugach Skeet Association
7230 Dorchester, Anchor., AK 99502
Chris Hafer (907) 428-0001
Hrs: W/Th, 4-6; S/Su, 10-4
Trap: 3   Skeet: 4 Five Stand: 1

Eagles' Ridge Ranch
HC62, Box 5780,
Delta Junction, AK 99737
Mike Crouch (907) 895-4329
100 mi. S of Fairbanks
Type: Public Hrs: Su-S, 8-10
Reservs: Strongly recommended
Sporting: 2, 27 stations
HT: 50 ft. Wobble Trap
○ Loaner Guns
○ On-Site Pro Shop
○ NSCA Certified Instructor
○ Visa & Mastercard Accepted
○ Meals, Lodging & RV Parking
   Available
○ Wingshooting Available (Apr. 1 -
   October 31)

Ft. Wainwright S&T
Box 35046,
Ft. Wainwright, AK 99703
David Fischer (907) 353-7869
Hrs: W-Th, 4-8; S/Su, Noon-6
Trap: 2   Skeet: 3 Five Stand: 1

Izaak Walton Recreation Pk.
Box 670650, Chugiak, AK 99567
Mac McCord (907) 688-2809
21 mi. N of Anchorage
Type: Public Hrs: W/Th, 3-10; F,
5-10; S/Su, 10-6 Sporting: 1, 15
stations Trap: 12 Skeet: 4

Sporting Clays of Alaska
Box 774547, Eagle River, AK 99577
Rick Allen (907) 688-2529
21 mi. N of Anchorage
Type: Public/Member Hrs:
Summer: 9am-9pm; Closed Winter
Reservs: Strongly recommended
Sporting: 1, 20 stations HT: 35 ft.

TRAP & SKEET

Eielson Skeet & Trap
Box 4644, Eielson AFB, AK 99702
Robert Setren (907) 377-5338
Hrs: S, 12-5; T/Th, 5-9
Trap: 1 **Skeet:** 2

Fairbanks Trap Club
Box 71447, Fairbanks, AK 99707
Kathy Parker (907) 457-6116
6.5 mi. N of Fairbanks
Type: Public
Hrs: W/Th, 6-9; Su, 12-5
Trap: 5

Nanook Skeet & Trap
Box 1041,
Delta Junction, AK 99737
Michael W. Koke (907) 873-1240
Hrs: T-F, 11-7; S/Su, 10-6
Trap: 1 **Skeet:** 4

Valdez Sportsmens
Box 1921, Valdez, AK 99686
Club Manager (907) 835-9503
Type: Public
Hrs: W, 6-9; Su, 12-9 (May-Oct)
Trap: Y

ARIZONA

SPORTING & 5-STAND

Arizona Hunt Club
Box 1021, Mayer, AZ 86333
Kent Henry (520) 632-7709
65 mi. N of Phoenix
Type: Public/Member
Hrs: T-Su, 8-5
Reservs: Strongly recommended
Sporting: 1, 10 stations **HT:** 55 ft.
○ Factory Ammunition
○ On-Site Snack Bar
○ Rental Guns Available
○ Shooting Instruction Available
○ Pheasant/Chukar Hunting
   Oct.-March

Ben Avery Shooting Facility
4044 W. Black Canyon Blvd.,
Phoenix, AZ 85027
Don Turner (602) 582-8313
Sporting: 1 **Trap:** 19 **Skeet:** 15

Bird Busters of Payson, Inc.
606 N. Hideway Cir.,
Payson, AZ 85541
Ernest Rogers (520) 474-9781
Hrs: W & Sat., 8-3 or by appt.
Sporting: 1 **Skeet:** 1

Black Canyon Gun Club
37016 N. Archery Dr.,
Phoenix, AZ 85027
Mark & Gerri August (602)
258-1901
20 mi. N of Phoenix
Type: Public/Member
Hrs: Th/F, 1-9:30; S/Su, 8-5
Reservs: Not required
Sporting: 1, 10 stations
Trap: 16 **Skeet:** 16 **Five Stand:** 1
○ Loaner Guns
○ Factory Ammunition
○ On-Site Meals
○ Formal Instructions
○ Golf Carts
○ On Site Kitchen
○ ZZ Bird

Bullhead City Gun Club
Box 1026, Bullhead City, AZ 86430
Linda Bell (520) 754-2606
Hrs: W/S/Su, 9-12
Sporting: None
Trap: 4 **Skeet:** 1 **Five Stand:** 1

Double Adobe
5057 West Double Adobe Rd.,
McNeal, AZ 85617
Mike McNeeley (520) 364-4000
90 mi. SE of Tucson
Type: Public **Hrs:** Daily, 9-6
Sporting: 1, 15 stations
Trap: 3 **HT:** 40 ft. **Wobble Trap**

Long Meadow Preserve
HC30, Box 1030,
Prescott, AZ 86301
Jim Puntenney (520) 778-9563
20 mi. NW of Prescott
Type: Public/Member
Hrs: F-Su, 8-4 **Sporting:** 1, 5 sta.

Phoenix Trap & Skeet Club
12450 W. Indian School Rd.,
Litchfield Park, AZ 85340
Hal Getzan (602) 935-2691
10 mi. W of Phoenix
Type: Public/Member
Hrs: W/Th, 1-10; F, 12-8; S/Su, 7-4
Sporting: None
Trap: 48 **Skeet:** 10 **Five Stand:** 1
Wobble Trap

Prescott Gun Club
PO Box 1881, Prescott, AZ 86302
Alix Lafontant (520) 778-4153
Hrs: T/Th/S/Su, 12-5
Sporting: None
Trap: 5 **Skeet:** 2 **Five Stand:** 1

Red Mountain T & S Club
15001 N. Beeline Hwy.,
Scottsdale, AZ 85256
Jim Bob Vaughn (602) 990-9994
Type: Public/Member
Hrs: T-F, 10-10; S/Su, 10-5
Sporting: None
Trap: 9 **Skeet:** 5 **Five Stand:** 1

River's Edge Sporting Retreat
HC1, Box 742, Benson, AZ 85602
Norm Crawford (520) 212-4868
70 mi. E of Tucson
Type: Public/Member
Hrs: Yr. Round, Th-M, 7:30-5:30
Reservs: Strongly recommended
Sporting: 1, 12 stations

Tucson Trap & Skeet Club
131 E. 6th St., Tucson, AZ 85705
Ron Wilson (520) 883-6426
8 mi. W of Tucson
Sporting: None
Trap: 18 **Skeet:** 14 **Five Stand:** 2

TRAP & SKEET

Casa Grande Trap Club
1320 N. Arbor,
Casa Grande, AZ 85222
Sam Stedman (602) 836-8300
Trap: 10

DMAFB Rod & Gun
355 SVS/SVRO, 5465 E. Nuggat
St., Davis-Monthan AFB, AZ 85707
James E. Bunch (520) 228-3736
Hrs: S/Su, 8-12; T-Th, 4-7
Trap: 2 **Skeet:** 2

Flagstaff Clay Target Shoot.
PO Box 2456, Flagstaff, AZ 86004
Toby Johnson (520) 526-9409
Trap: 5 **Skeet:** 2

Ft. Huachuca Sportsman's
4575 Calle Encina, Siera, AZ 85635
Barbara Dallavo (602) 533-7085
Hrs: W-Su, 10-6 **Trap:** 5 **Skeet:** 4

Garden Canyon Trap Club
27 W. Kayeton Dr.,
Sierra Vista, AZ 85635
Rod Ritter (602) 533-7085
Hrs: W/F, 11-7; Th, 11-9; S/Su, 10-6
Trap: 4

Phantom Skeet & Trap
8427 N. 17th Pl.,
Phoenix, AZ 85020
Barney C. Fagan (602) 856-3928
Hrs: Apr-Oct, 9-2; Nov-Mar, 10-3
Skeet: 2

Sedona Sportsmens Club
PO Box 2552, Sedona, AZ 86339
Jim Sullivan (602) 282-7787
Hrs: Su, 1-5; others by appt.
Skeet: 2

Yuma Trap & Skeet Club
PO Box 6397, Yuma, AZ 85366
Hrs: S, 9-2; Su, 12-4
Trap: 5 **Skeet:** 21

ARKANSAS

SPORTING & 5-STAND

Blue Rock Sportsman Club
Box 6612, Sherwood, AR 72116
Blanchard Causey (501) 374-5275
Type: Public/Member
Hrs: S/Su, 1-5 **Sporting:** None
Skeet: 4 **Five Stand:** 1

Crowley Ridge Shooting Resort
112 SFC 434,
Forrest City, AR 72335
Dale Horton (501) 633-3352
42 mi. W of Memphis, TN
Type: Public/Member **Hrs:** Su-S
Reservs: Strongly recommended
Sporting: 1, 13 stations
HT: 30 ft. **Wobble Trap**

Drake's Landing
Rt. 1, Box 177, Tichnor, AR 72166
Tommy Turner (800) 548-4389
45 mi. SE of Stuttgart
Type: Public **Hrs:** 7 days/week; by appt. **Sporting:** 1

Grandview Plantation
PO Box 201, Columbus, AR 71831
Charles Butler (501) 983-2526
Type: Public/Member
Sporting: 1, 15 stations **HT**

Great Guns
20492 Raceway Rd.,
Harrisburg, AR 72432
Steve Skillern (501) 578-9700
60 mi. NW of Memphis, TN
Type: Public/Member
Hrs: M-S, by app't, Su, 10-Dark
Reservs: Recommended
Sporting: 1, 13 stations
Five Stand: 1   **HT:** 40 ft.
O On-Site Meals
O Golf Carts
O Rental Guns
O Pro Shop/Instruction
O Archery, Pistol & Rifle Ranges
O 1/2 hr. West of I-55

Gunsmoke Sporting Clays
16414 North Hwy. 94,
Pea Ridge, AR 72751
Lee Anderson (501) 451-8306
30 mi. N of Fayette
Type: Public
Hrs: F/S/Su, 9-5 by appt.
Sporting: 1, 12 stations
Wobble Trap

Hawk's Range Sporting Clays
PO Box 589, Foreman, AR 71836
Paul Hawkins, Jr. (501) 542-7350
30 mi. W of Texarkana
Type: Public/Member
Hrs: S/Su, 10-6; W, 4-Dk; & by appt.
Sporting: 1, 20 stations **HT:** 25 ft.

Miriah Sporting Clays
CR 492, Wesley, AR 72773
Mike & Theresa Carfagno (501) 456-2533
20 mi. E of Fayetteville
Type: Public/Member
Hrs: S/Su, 9-5
Reservs: Recommended
Sporting: 1, 25 stations **HT:** 50 ft.
O Full Service Conference Lodge
O Rifle & Pistol Ranges
O 8 Station Practice Course
O Rental Guns Available
O Shooting Instruction
O On Site Fishing & Camping

Nevada Gamebirds
Rt. 1, Box 171, Buckner, AR 71827
Karl Salb (501) 899-2902
100 mi. S of Little Rock
Type: Public **Hrs:** M-F, 1-7; S/Su, 10-7
Sporting: 1, 10 stations
Skeet: 1   **HT:** 40 ft.

Pajaro Gun Club
Old Hwy. 271, Ft. Smith, AR 72903
Don Barksdale (501) 785-2891
Sporting: 1
Trap: 1 **Skeet:** 3

Point Remove WMA, Inc.
PO Box 133, Hattieville, AR 72063
Scott Kaufman (501) 354-0136
60 mi. NW of Little Rock
Type: Public/Member
Sporting: 2, 10 stations
Trap: 1 **Skeet:** 1 **Five Stand:** 1
HT: 60 ft.

Quail Ridge Sporting Clays
8821 North Lake Ln.,
Hackett, AR 72937
Randy Jacobs (501) 638-8156
135 mi. W of Little Rock
Type: Public/Member
Hrs: S/Su, 9-4
Sporting: 1, 26 stations

Sand Creek Sporting Clays
Rt. 2, Box 218-A,
Lockesburg, AR 71846
Randy Goldman (501) 289-3373
40 mi. N of Texarkana
Type: Public/Member
Hrs: By appt.
Sporting: 1, 16 stations
Wobble Trap

Sanders LaGrue Hunt Club
PO Box 171, Humphrey, AR 72073
C.S. anders, Sr. (501) 673-2796
50 mi. SE of Little Rock
Type: Public **Hrs:** Call for appt.
Sporting: 2, 16 stations
Skeet: 1   **HT:** 60 ft.

Thunder Valley Sptg. Clays
PO Box 2401, Batesville, AR 72501
John Clouse (501) 793-6350
80 mi. NE of Little Rock
Type: Public
Hrs: Th, 4-Dark; S/Su, 9-Dark
Sporting: 1, 12 stations
Skeet: 1   **HT:** 24 ft. **Wobble Trap**

TRAP & SKEET

Aux Arc Gun Club, Inc.
PO Box 511, Ozark, AR 72949
Virgil Pratt
Trap: 1 **Skeet:** 1

Barkman Gun Club
PO Box 118, Friendship, AR 71942
John Fowler (501) 384-5357
Hrs: M-F, 8-5 **Skeet:** 1

Malloy Sportsman Club
PO Box 7020, El Dorado, AR 71731
Joe Whatley (501) 862-5141
Trap: 1 **Skeet:** 1

North Delta Gun Club
116 Avalon Pl., Helena, AR 72342
Jimmy Hobson (501) 338-7415
Hrs: By Appt.
Trap: 1 **Skeet:** 2

Remington Gun Club
Rt. I-40 & Remington Rd.,
Lonoke, AR 72086
Billy Crutchfield (501) 676-2677
Hrs: W/Th, 2-6:30; S/Su, 1-5:30
Trap: 7 **Skeet:** 5

Twin Lakes Gun Club, Inc.
Box 199, Mountain Home, AR 72653
John McKinney (501) 425-7640
Hrs: 8-Sundown
Trap: 2 **Skeet:** 2

West Poinsett Gun Club
PO Box 336, Weiner, AR 72479
Lloyd Wofford (501) 684-2271
Hrs: Su, 1-6 (Apr-Oct)
Trap: 2 **Skeet:** 2

CALIFORNIA

SPORTING & 5-STAND

5 Dogs Range, Inc.
20238 Woody Rd.,
Bakersfield, CA 93308
David Olds (805) 399-7296
18 mi. NE of Bakersfield
Type: Public/Member
Hrs: W-S, by appt; Su, 8-Dark
Sporting: 1, 10 stations **HT:** 50 ft.

6B Sportsman's Club
3100 West Gaffery Rd.,
Tracy, CA 95376
Paul Bogetti (209) 832-5672
10 mi. SE of Tracy
Type: Public **Hrs:** W-Su, 8am-5pm
Sporting: 1, 12 stations
Five Stand: 1

Angeles Shooting Club
12651 Little Tujunga Canyon Rd.,
San Fernando, CA 91342
(818) 899-2255
Type: Member/Avail
Sporting: 1, 15 stations

Antelope Valley/ Whiteside's Sporting Clays
45408 160th St., W.,
Lancaster, CA 93536
David Whiteside (805) 724-1291
60 mi. N of Los Angeles
Type: Public/Member
Hrs: S/Su, 9-Dusk; Others by appt.
Reservs: Recommended
Sporting: 1, 15 stations
Trap: 1 **Five Stand:** 1
See Our Ad Pg. 450

Beale AFB Rod & Gun Club
9 MWRSS/MWBR 6000 C St., Rm.
111, Beale AFB, CA 95903
Jay Hammond (916) 788-2473
10 mi. N of Marysville
Type: Public/Member
Hrs: T-F, 2-8; S, 9-2
Sporting: 1, 13 stations
Trap: 1 **Skeet:** 2 **Five Stand:** 1

Birds Landing Sptg. Clays
PO Box 5, Birds Landing, CA 94512
Dan Cirillo (707) 374-5092
60 mi. NE of San Francisco
Type: Public/Member
Hrs: W/S/Su, 9-5 by appt.
Reservs: Recommended
Sporting: 1, 15 stations
Five Stand: 1
○ Napa Valley's Closest
  Sporting Clays
○ 60 Mi. NE of San Francisco
○ 45 Mi. SW of Sacramento
○ 5-Stand, Pro Shop &
  Corporate Events
○ Call for Info & Reservations
  (707) 374-5092

Black Point Game Bird Club
7711 Lakeville Hwy.,
Petaluma, CA 94954
Mike Sutsos (707) 763-0076
25 mi. N of San Francisco
Hrs: W/S/Su, 10-4
Sporting: 1, 5 stations **HT:** 30 ft.

Blythe Skeet & Trap Club
PO Box 558, Blythe, CA 92226
Joanne Prochaka (619) 922-8890
120 mi. E of Palm Springs
Hrs: Summer: Sat, 6pm; Winter:
Sun, 1pm **Sporting:** None
Trap: 2 **Skeet:** 1 **Five Stand:** 2

Cahoon Pheasant Club
31249 E. Combs Rd.,
Escalon, CA 95320
Dave & Patti Cahoon (209) 838-6233
3 mi. N of Escalon
Hrs: Year round
Sporting: 1, 13 stations

Camanche Hills Hunting Preserve
2951 Curran Rd., Ione, CA 95640
Larry L. Skinner (209) 763-5270
40 mi. S of Sacramento
Type: Public
Hrs: Year round; Closed Tuesdays
Reservs: Recommended
Sporting: 1, 10 stations **Trap:** 1
○ Factory Ammunition
○ Easy Drive From San Francisco
○ On-Site & Close By Meals
○ One of the Most Challenging
  Courses in CA
○ See Our Listing CA Wings Section

Carr Creek Sporting Clays
PO Box 1502, Hayfork, CA 96041
Steve Beck (916) 628-5888
Type: Public **Hrs:** S/Su
Sporting: 1, 16 stations

Circle HH Sporting Clays
HCR#1, Box 512,
Nipton, CA 92364
Fred Hymes (702) 642-9405
78 mi. S of Las Vegas, NV - 100 mi.
E of Barstow/20 mi. N I-40
Type: Public/Member
Hrs: F-Su, 8-6; others by appt.
Sporting: 1, 6 stations
Trap: 1

Clear Creek Sports Club
3971 Keefer Rd., Chico, CA 95926
Bob Henman (916) 343-9263
45 mi. N of Sacramento
Type: Public/Member
Sporting: 1

Coon Creek Trap & Skeet
5393 Waltz Rd., PO Box 460,
Lincoln, CA 95648
George Ahart (916) 539-8544
Hrs: T/Th/S/Su, 10-Dark
Sporting: None
Trap: 8 **Skeet:** 3 **Five Stand:** 1

Cordova Shooting Center
100 Sanborn Ct., Folsom, CA 95630
Pat Glaze (916) 351-0538
10 mi. E of Sacramento
Type: Public/Member
Hrs: S/Su, 9-5; M/F, 10-6; T-Th, 10-8
Sporting: None
Trap: 4 **Skeet:** 5

Coyote Valley Sporting Clays
1000 San Bruno Avenue,
Morgan Hill, CA 95037
Tom Ebert (408) 778-3600
15 mi. S of San Jose
Type: Public/Member
Hrs: W-Th - 12-8; F - 9-5; S/Su - 8-5
Reservs: Recommended
Sporting: 2, 22 stations
Trap: 1 **Skeet:** 1 **Five Stand:** 1
○ Loaner Guns
○ On-Site Pro Shop
○ Formal Instructions

Creekside Pheasant Club
Box 3640, Pkfield Rt., San Miguel,
CA 93451
Larry Hamilton (805) 463-2349
115 mi. NW of Los Angeles
Type: Member/Avail
Sporting: 1, 5 stations
Trap: Y

EAFB Rod & Gun Activity
95 SPTG/SVRO, 115 Methusa,
Edwards AFB, CA 93524
Hugh Jamison (805) 277-3182
11 mi. N of Lancaster
Type: Public/Member
Hrs: T/Th, 10-8; S/Su, 9-6
Sporting: None
Trap: 6 **Skeet:** 2 **Five Stand:** 1
HT: 40 ft.

Fresno Trap & Skeet Club
5195 N. Humboldt,
Kerman, CA 93630
Joe Young (209) 846-8750
15 mi. S of Fresno
Type: Public
Hrs: 7 days a week, 9-5
Sporting: 1, 10 stations
Trap: 13 **Skeet:** 10 **Five Stand:** 1
Wobble Trap

G&G Pheasant Shoot
PO Box 116, Gazelle, CA 96034
John or Dot Giorgi (916) 435-2309
60 mi. S of Oregon Border
Type: Public/Member
Hrs: Open Fall of '96; Daily by app't
Sporting: 1, 10 stations

Green Head Hunting Club
PO Box 552, Pine Valley, CA 91962
(619) 473-8668
26 mi. E of San Diego
Type: Public/Member
Hrs: W/Th/F, noon; S/Su, all day
Sporting: 1, 10 stations
Trap: Y **Skeet:** Y

Hunter's Retreat/Palm Springs Sporting Clays
67-555 Hwy. 111, C115,
Cathedral City, CA 92234
(619) 324-0099 or (619) 321-1817
5 mi. E of Downtown Palm Springs
Type: Public, Public/Member
Hrs: W-Su/& by app't
Reservs: Recommended
Sporting: 1, 10 stations
○ Factory Ammunition
○ On-Site Pro Shop
○ Formal Instructions
○ Rental Guns
○ Full Service Gun Shop - Gunsmith
  & Gunfitting Service
○ Indoor Handgun Range
○ The Only Sporting Clays Course
  in Palm Springs!

Knowles Ranch Sporting Clays
PO Box 982, Willows, CA 95988
Tom Knowles (916) 934-5595
75 mi. N of Sacramento
Type: Public/Member
Hrs: W/F/S/Su, By Appt. All Day
Reservs: Strongly recommended
Sporting: 2, 20 stations
Five Stand: Y **HT:** 40 ft.
See Our Ad Below

Livermore - Pleasanton Rod & Gun
PO Box 786, Livermore, CA 94551
James Boatman (510) 449-8780
Hrs: S/Su, 10-4
Reservs: Not required
Sporting: None
Trap: 18 **Five Stand:** 1

Miramar Trap & Skeet Club
Box 82181, San Diego, CA 92138
Harvey Fischer (619) 278-3173
Type: Public/Member
Hrs: W/S/Su, 8-5; F, 11-4
Sporting: 1, 5 stations
Trap: 10 **Skeet:** 8 **Wobble Trap**

Moore-N-Moore Sporting Clays
12651 N. Little Tujunga Cyn Rd.,
San Fernando, CA 91342
Pat & Cory Moore (818) 890-4788
15 mi. NE of Los Angeles
Type: Public/Member
Hrs: W/Th, 12-9; F, 12-5; S/Su, 9-5
Reservs: Recommended
Sporting: 1, 12 stations
Five Stand: 1 **HT:** 100 ft.
○ Factory Ammunition
○ On-Site Pro Shop
○ Formal Instructions
○ Organized Leagues
○ Gun Fitting

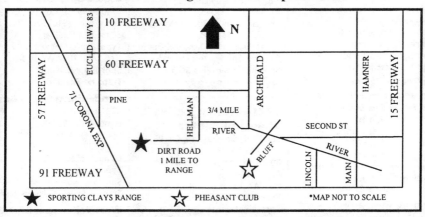

Pachmayr International Shooting Sports Park
831 N. Rosemead Blvd., S. El Monte, CA 91733
(818) 579-5201
20 mi. SE of Los Angeles
Type: Public
Hrs: T/W/Th, 12-9; F, 3-9; S/Su, 8-5
Reservs: Not required
Sporting: 1, 10 stations
Trap: 14 **Skeet:** 8 **HT:** 45 ft.
Wobble Trap
○ Loaner Guns
○ On-Site Pro Shop
○ Formal Instructions
○ Gunsmith Service
○ Gun Fitting

Pacific Rod & Gun Club
PO Box 3276, Daly City, CA 94015
(415) 586-8349
in SW San Francisco on Lake Merced
Type: Public/Member
Hrs: W/S/Su, 11-5
Sporting: 1, 5 stations **Trap:** 7
Skeet: 6 **HT Wobble Trap**

Potter Valley Sportsmen's
6950 Hwy. 20, Ukiah, CA 95482
Jim Guntly (707) 485-5188
50 mi. N of Santa Rosa
Type: Public/Member
Hrs: 1st & 3rd Sun./mo. (10-dark);
Club shoots by resrv
Sporting: 1, 12 stations

Mike Raahauge Shooting Enterprises
5800 Bluff St., Norco, CA 91760
Mike Raahauge (909) 735-7981
35 mi. E of Los Angeles
Type: Public/Member
Hrs: W/F, 11-6; S/Su, 9-6
Reservs: Not required
Sporting: 2, 10 stations
Trap: 1 **Skeet:** 1 **HT:** 75 ft.
See Our Ad Pg. 451

Red Bank Ale & Quail Gamebird Club
PO Box 8295, Red Bluff, CA 96080
Brian Rielly (916) 529-9435
170 mi. N of San Francisco
Reservs: Strongly recommended
Sporting: 1, 20 stations

Redding Gun Club
Box 493847, Redding, CA 96049
Merle Huffman (916) 549-4652
Type: Public
Hrs: Su, 10-4; W, 2-Dark
Sporting: Y **Trap:** 5 **Skeet:** 1

Redlands Trap & Skeet
PO Box 2231, Redlands, CA 92373
Margaret Yochem (909) 792-5780
55 mi. E of Los Angeles
Type: Public **Hrs:** W, 9-10pm; Th, 5-10; F, 12-5; S/Su, 9-5
Sporting: 1, 5 stations
Trap: 12 **Skeet:** 6 **Five Stand:** 1

River Road Sporting Clays
PO Box 3016, Gonzales, CA 93926
Bruce Barsotti (408) 675-2473
30 mi. NE of Carmel-Monterey Peninsula
Type: Public/Member
Hrs: T-Su, 9-5 **Reservs:** Recommended
Sporting: 3, 45 stations
Trap: 1 **Skeet:** 1 **Five Stand:** Y
HT: 60 ft.
○ Loaner Guns
○ Factory Ammunition
○ On-Site Pro Shop
○ On-Site Meals
○ Shooting Lodge
○ Formal Instructions
○ Golf Carts
○ Gunsmith Service
○ Gun Fitting
○ Overnight Accommodations

Rock Springs Ranch
11000 Old Hernandez Rd., Paicines, CA 95043
Ken Range (800) 209-5175
75 mi. S of San Jose
Type: Public **Hrs:** Daily, 8am-5pm
Reservs: Strongly recommended
Sporting: None **Five Stand:** 1
See Our Ad Pg. 297

Sacramento Valley Shooting Center
Box 1407, Sloughhouse, CA 95683
Walt Mansell (916) 952-3780
30 mi. SE of Sacramento
Type: Public/Member
Hrs: Weekends only, 8-5
Reservs: Not required
Sporting: None
Trap: 5 **Skeet:** 2 **Five Stand:** 1

Stockton Trap & Skeet Club
4343 N. Ashley Lane, Stockton, CA 95215
Norm Volponi, Mgr. (209) 931-6803
Type: Public/Member
Hrs: S/Su, 10-5; W, 10-9
Sporting: None
Trap: 20 **Skeet:** 7 **Five Stand:** 1
○ Factory Ammunition
○ On-Site Meals
○ Golf Carts

Sun Mountain Sportsman
PO Box 58, Coarse Gold, CA 93644
Vivian Phelan (209) 683-3669
30 mi. N of Fresno
Type: Public **Hrs:** Th-Su, 10-5
Sporting: 1, 12 stations
Trap: 3 **Wobble Trap**

Target Tossers
5350 Otay Valley Rd., San Ysidro, CA 92073
Chip Enniss (619) 661-1400
10 mi. S of San Diego
Type: Public
Hrs: W/Th, 12-10; S/Su, 9-5
Reservs: Not required
Sporting: 1, 10 stations **Trap:** 5
Skeet: 1 **Five Stand:** 1 **HT:** 40 ft.

Timbuctoo Sporting Estate
PO Box 357, Smartville, CA 95977
Randy Rigdon (916) 639-2200
50 mi. NW of Sacramento
Type: Public **Hrs:** Daily by appt.
Sporting: 1, 12 stations

United Sportsmen Inc.
4700 Evora Rd., Concord, CA 94522
Ben Wright (510) 676-1963
30 mi. E of San Francisco
Type: Public/Member
Hrs: S/Su, 10-6; W/Th, 3-10
Sporting: None
Trap: 12 **Skeet:** 6 **Five Stand:** 1

Vandenburg Rod & Gun
537 Venus Ave., Lompoc, CA 93436
Levi Lee H. Miller, Jr. (805) 734-8232
60 mi. N of Santa Barbara
Type: Public **Hrs:** M-S, 11-1
Sporting: None
Trap: 1 **Skeet:** 1 **Five Stand:** 1

West Valley Sportsmen's
PO Box 257, Gustine, CA 95322
Robert Kloepfer (209) 634-1547
80 mi. SE of San Francisco
Type: Public/Member

Hrs: W-Su
Sporting: 1, 10 stations
Trap: Y **Skeet:** Y **Five Stand:** 1
HT: 40 ft.

Winchester Canyon
Box 3306, Santa
Barbara, CA 93130
Tony Urwick (805) 965-9890
90 mi. NW of Los Angeles
Type: Public/Member
Hrs: Trap/Skeet, S/Su/W, 10-4;
Clays 1st Sun. of month
Sporting: 1, 30 stations
Trap: 3 **Skeet:** 1 **HT:** 60 ft.
Wobble Trap

Yolo Sportsmen's Assn.
PO Box 82, Woodland, CA 95776
Phil DeCarlo (916) 662-2349
Hrs: 9-Dark
Sporting: 1 **Trap:** 4 **Skeet:** 2

TRAP & SKEET

Barstow Gun Club
16152 Pamela St.,
Victorville, CA 92392
Allen Seymour (619) 247-2299
Type: Public/Member
Hrs: T, 6-10; Su, 10-5
Trap: 4 **Skeet:** 1 **Wobble Trap**

Chabot Gun Club
Box 2246, Castro Valley, CA 94563
John Maunder (510) 569-0213
5.5 mi. N of Castro Valley
Type: Public/Member
Hrs: W-F, 10-5; S/Su, 9-5
Trap: 6 **Skeet:** 1

Concord Sportsmans Club
PO Box 1121, Concord, CA 94521
Dan Fowler, Sr. (510) 686-5654
Hrs: T/F, 4:30-9; S/Su, 9-5

Diablo Rod & Gun Club
PO Box 393, Concord, CA 94522
Charles Hunter (510) 676-1987
Hrs: W/Th, 3-10; S/Su, 10-6
Sporting: 1 **Trap:** 5 **Skeet:** 8

Edwards AFB R&GC
6500 ABW/SSRO,
Edwards AFB, CA 93523
Bruce Jones
Type: Member/Avail
Hrs: T/Th, 10-8; S/Su, 9-6
Trap: 6 **Skeet:** 2

Fraternal Order of Eagles
16287-24 1/2,
Chowchilla, CA 93610
H.K. Crow (209) 665-1723
Hrs: S, 1-5 **Trap:** 2

Kern County Gun Club
2818 China Grade Loop,
Bakersfield, CA 93308

Paul Mooney (805) 871-9977
Hrs: W/F, 3-9; Su, 9-3
Trap: 6 **Skeet:** 4

Los Cazadores Gun Club
PO Box 6700, Oxnard, CA 93030
Bob Reitz (805) 984-9651
Hrs: Su, 10-5 **Trap:** 1

Newman Swamp Rats T&S
806 Orestimba Rd.,
Newman, CA 95360
George Siler (209) 523-8423
Type: Public/Member
Hrs: M-F, 8-5 **Trap:** 5

Novato Trap Club
PO Box 482, Novato, CA 94948
Rick Gustin (415) 897-9712
Hrs: Th, 6-10; Su, 9-3
Trap: 9

Petersen Productions, Inc.
17501 Pomona Rincon Rd.,
Chino, CA 91710
Wayne Moulton (714) 597-4794
Hrs: W/F, 11-5; Th, 11-9; S/Su, 8-5
Trap: 9 **Skeet:** 5

Point Mugu Gun Club
Box 42246,
Nas Pt. Mugu, CA 93044
Lou Gleason (805) 989-8225
Trap: 1 **Skeet:** 2

Prado Tiro Club
6420 Wilshire Blvd.,
Los Angeles, CA 90048
Robert O'Deane (909) 597-4794
Trap: 8 **Skeet:** 5

Richmond Rod & Gun Club
3155 Goodrick Ave.,
Richmond, CA 94801
Billy DeFries (510) 741-1700
Hrs: W/F/S/Su, 10-4
Trap: 4 **Skeet:** 5

Sacramento Trap Club
3701 Fulton Ave.,
Sacramento, CA 95821
Charlette Shaw (916) 484-9889
Type: Public/Member
Hrs: W, 11-7; S, 11-4; Su, 12-4
Trap: 10

San Benito Co Skeet & Trap
4351 Pacheco Pass Hwy., Hollister,
CA 95023
Dan Lanini (408) 637-2310
Trap: 1 **Skeet:** 1

San Gabriel Valley Gun Club
4001 Fish Canyon Rd.,
Duarte, CA 91010
Richard Phillips (818) 358-9906
Hrs: T/W/F, 10-4; S/Su, 8:30-4:30
Trap: 2 **Skeet:** 4

San Joaquin Valley R&G
1169 Beverly Dr., #40,
Lemoore, CA 93245
John Cortner (209) 998-4072
Hrs: Su, 9-4; W, 6-8
Trap: 1 **Skeet:** 2

Santa Maria Trap Club
3150 Telephone Rd., PO Box 867,
Santa Maria, CA 93456
Club Manager (805) 295-6673
Hrs: Su, 9am; W, 5:30-Dark
Trap: 8 **Skeet:** 1

Santa Ynez Valley Sportsmen
Box 453, Santa Ynez, CA 93460
Vickie Craine (805) 688-8176
Hrs: Scheduled events only
Trap: 3 **Skeet:** 1

Tulare County Trap Club
8601 W. Roosevelt,
Visalia, CA 93291
Club Manager (209) 651-2525
Hrs: Su, 9am; W, 5:30-Dark
Trap: 6 **Skeet:** 1

Vado Del Rio Skeet/Trap
11110 Red Cedar Dr., San Diego,
CA 92131
Anthony Erbacher (619) 725-4832
Hrs: W-Su, Daylight Hrs.
Trap: 2 **Skeet:** 2

COLORADO

SPORTING & 5-STAND

American Sporting Clay
Road 53, Kiowa, CO 80117
Clay Blyth (303) 621-2841
30 mi. SE of Denver
Type: Public/Member
Hrs: F-Su, 9-4
Sporting: 1, 10 stations **HT:** 25 ft.

Aurora Gun Club
301 S. Gun Club Rd.,
Aurora, CO 80041
Dave Allen (303) 366-9030
20 mi. E of Denver
Type: Public/Member
Hrs: M-F (Members); S/Su, 9-3
Sporting: 1, 13 stations **Trap:** 5

Bang-A-Away Gun Club
17629 Weld County Rd. 5,
Berthoud, CO 80513
Bill Voigt (970) 535-4538
45 mi. N of Denver
Type: Public/Member
Hrs: T-Su, 8:30-4:30
Sporting: 2, 10 stations **Trap:** 1

Broadmoor
4570 Cheyenne Mt. Zoo Rd.,
Colorado Springs, CO 80906
Jack Bath, Jr. (719) 635-3438
3 mi. SW of Colorado Springs
Type: Public **Hrs:** M-F, 12-4; S/Su,
10-4; closed 12/1-4/1
Sporting: 1, 5 stations
Trap: 2 **Skeet:** 2

Cherry Creek Sporting Clays
10325 C.R. 250,
Durango, CO 81301
Rob Conaty (970) 247-2250
28 mi. from Durango
Type: Public/Member
Hrs: April-Nov., by appt.
Sporting: 1, 11 stations **HT**

Chipeta Guest Ranch
1938 Hwy. 133, Paonia, CO 81428
Larry Mautz (303) 929-6260
70 mi. W of Aspen
Type: Public
Hrs: Su-S, call for resrv.
Sporting: 1, 10 stations **HT:** 12 ft.

Glenarm Sporting Clays
68202 Trout Rd.,
Montrose, CO 81404
C. C. Antrim (970) 249-6490
60 mi. S of Grand Junction
Type: Public **Hrs:** Daily by appt.
Sporting: 1, 12 stations

Glenwood Springs Gun Club
Box 2362,
Glenwood Springs, CO 81602
Linden Burnsworth (970) 945-5346
5 mi. SW of Glenwood Springs
Type: Public/Member
Hrs: Th, 4:30-Dark; S, 9-5
(Spring/Summer/Fall)
Sporting: 2, 10 stations
Trap: 3 **Skeet:** 1 **HT:** 100 ft.
Wobble Trap

High Country Game Birds
33300 County Rd. 25,
Elizabeth, CO 80107
Todd Pederson (303) 646-3315
35 mi. SE of Denver
Type: Public/Member
Hrs: Year Round
Sporting: 1, 10 stations

Izaak Walton League of America
450 Francsville Rd., Colorado
Springs, CO 80929
Bill Jacobs/William Bell
(719) 683-4420
Type: Public/Member
Sporting: 1, 10 stations
Trap: 5 **Five Stand:** 1

La Junta Rifle Club
215 Garden, La Junta, CO 81050
Terry Davis (719) 384-6643
65 mi. E of Pueblo
Type: Public/Member
Hrs: Th, 4-Dark; 1st & 4th Sun., 9-1
Sporting: None
Trap: 2 **Skeet:** 1 **Five Stand:** 1

Mt. Blanca Game Bird & Trout
PO Box 236, Blanca, CO 81123
Bill Binnian (719) 379-3825
150 mi. SW of Colorado Springs
Type: Public/Member
Hrs: M-Su, 7-10 (June-Dec); W-Su,
7-10 (Feb-May)
Reservs: Recommended
Sporting: 1, 10 stations **Skeet:** 1
HT: 35 ft. **Wobble Trap**
See Our Ad Pg. 303

Pagosa Clay & Trout Ranch
End of Harvard, Pagosa Springs,
CO 81147
Bobby or Susan (970) 731-9830
50 mi. E of Durango
Type: Public
Hrs: 7 Days, 10am-Dusk by reserv.
Sporting: 1, 13 stations

R&T Gun Club
9912 Downing, Thornton, CO 80229
Dave Redell (303) 452-4777
100 mi. NE of Denver
Type: Public/Member
Hrs: Weekends, 8-dark
Sporting: 1, 10 stations
Trap: 1 **HT:** 40 ft. **Wobble Trap**

Renegade Gun Club, Inc.
3570 Weld County Road #23, Fort
Lupton, CO 80621
Dick Chikuma (303) 857-6000
20 mi. N of Denver
Type: Public/Member
Hrs: S/Su, 9-5; W, 1pm
Reservs: Strongly recommended
Sporting: 3, 20 stations
Mostly Flat, trees & brush
Five Stand: 1 **HT:** 30 ft.
Wobble Trap
○ All Automated Seasonal FITASC

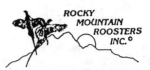

Rocky Mountain Roosters
PO Box 10164,
Colorado Springs, CO 80932
Brett M. Axton (719) 635-3257
35 mi. E of Colorado Springs
Type: Public/Member
Hrs: Su-S, by rsv. only
Reservs: Strongly recommended
Sporting: 1, 10 stations
Rolling, light coverage
Wobble Trap

Rocky Ridge Hunting Club
633 Gait Circle,
Ft. Collins, CO 80524
Michael Moreng (970) 221-4868
55 mi. N of Denver
Type: Public/Member
Hrs: Proposed 4/96
Sporting: 1 **Trap:** Y

Seven Lakes Lodge
738 CR 59, Meeker, CO 81641
(970) 878-4772
100 mi. NE of Grand Junction
Type: Public **Hrs:** **Sporting:** Y

SPORTHAVEN, LTD.
50500 E. 72nd Ave.,
Bennett, CO 80102
D. A. Lincoln, Jr. (303) 644-3030
20 mi. NE of Denver
Type: Public/Member
Hrs: W-Su, all day
Reservs: Recommended
Sporting: 1, 30 stations
Rolling, heavily wooded**HT:** 35 ft.
○ On-Site Pro Shop
○ Visa/Mastercard Accepted
○ Tower Ht. 35 ft.
○ Denver's Most Complete
    Sporting Facility
○ Closed Monday/Tuesday

Vail Rod & Gun Club
PO Box 1848, Vail, CO 81658
M. Murphy (970) 926-3472
120 mi. W of Denver
Type: Public/Member
Hrs: Th-Su, 9-5 (Oct-Mar); Daily,
10-5 (June-Sep)
Sporting: 1, 18 stations **HT:** 100'

Valhalla-Bijou Inc.
450 County Rd. 133,
Bennett, CO 80102
Rich Cummings (303) 644-4300
20 mi. E of Denver
Type: Member/Avail
Hrs: By appt. only
Sporting: 1, 10 stations HT: 30 ft.

Western Col. Sporting Clays
375 A W. Valley,
Grand Junction, CO 81503
Jim Lander, VP (970) 242-9196
30 mi. E of Grand Junction
Type: Public/Member
Hrs: Call for appt.
Sporting: 1, 10 stations HT: 125 ft.

TRAP & SKEET

Buckeye Trap & Skeet Range
6255 WCR#74, Windsor, CO 80524
Tim or Lisa Brough (970) 686-5210
Type: Public
Hrs: S/Su, 10-4; T/Th, 4-8
Trap: 6 Skeet: 2 Wobble Trap

Colorado West Gun Club
2913 Hwy. 92, Hotchkiss, CO 81419
Gerhart L. Stengel (970) 872-3748
Hrs: Call for appt.
Trap: 1 Skeet: 1

Cortez Trap Club
PO Box 48, Cortez, CO 81321
Pat Woosley (303) 565-7396
Hrs: Th, 6-10; Su, 1-5 Trap: 8

Delta Trap Club
PO Box 1061, Delta, CO 81416
John Lowe (308) 874-4980
Type: Public
Hrs: W, Eve. League; Su, 11-2:30
Trap: 9

ENT Gun Club
Box 14002, Peterson AFB, CO 80914
Judy Kelly (719) 596-7688
Hrs: Th/S/Su, 10-5
Trap: 8 Skeet: 7

Golden Gun Club, Inc.
PO Box 471, Golden, CO 80402
Rod Ott (303) 366-6970
Trap: 10 Skeet: 6

Grand Junction Trap Club
PO Box 334,
Grand Junction, CO 81502
Al Strecker (303) 245-0780
Hrs: T, 7-10; Su, 1-4
Trap: 4 Skeet: 1

Haxton Gun Club
12350 RD 11, Haxton, CO 80731
Rod Ham (303) 774-7504
Type: Public/Member
Trap: 2

Mile Hi Shooting Park
1745 Co Hwy. 7, Erie, CO 80516
Ida L. Wiens (303) 665-9991
Hrs: T-Th, 3-6; S/Su, 10-4
Trap: 16 Skeet: 2

Montrose Rod & Gun Club
2226 Devon Ct.,
Montrose, CO 81401
Ben Harris (970) 249-4346
Hrs: Su, pm (Winter); M, Eve.
(Summer) Trap: 1 Skeet: 1

OTC Olympic Shooting Club
1 Olympic Plaza,
Colorado Springs, CO 80909
Randy Moeller (719) 578-4882

Skyline Hunting Club
2418 Bitterfoot Ln.,
Golden, CO 80401
Joe Profera (303) 526-9858
Trap: 1 Skeet: 1

Tri Service Sportsmans
7664 W. Ontario Place,
Littleton, CO 80123
Mike Gutirrez (303) 340-9889
Hrs: W/S/Su, 9-3
Trap: 2 Skeet: 5

USA Shooting
One Olympic Plaza,
Colorado Springs, CO
Randy Moeller (719) 578-4883
Trap: 4 Skeet: 4

Watkins Skeet Club
PO Box 21, Watkins, CO 80137
Felix Lopez (303) 366-6970
Trap: 10 Skeet: 6

CONNECTICUT

SPORTING & 5-STAND

Blue Trail Range & Gun Store
316 N. Branford Rd.,
Wallingford, CT 06492
David Lyman (203) 269-3280
30 mi. N of New Haven
Type: Public
Hrs: Throw your own clays: M-F,
9-8; S/Su, 9-5 Sporting:

Bristol Game & Fish Assoc.
PO Box 175, Bristol, CT 06010
James Strecker (203) 879-9938
75 mi. NE of New York
Type: Public/Member
Hrs: S, 9-1 Sporting: 1, 20 stations
Trap: 4 Skeet: 1

Fin Fur & Feather Club
Box 81, North Windam, CT 06256
Dick White (203) 455-9516
30 mi. E of Hartford

Type: Member/Avail
Hrs: Daily, during daylight hours
Sporting: Y Trap: 1 Skeet: 8

Guilford Sportsmans Assoc.
PO Box 286, Guilford, CT 06437
D. Summerton (203) 457-9931
Type: Member/Avail
Hrs: 9-Dark
Sporting: 1, 7 stations
Trap: 2 Skeet: 2 Five Stand: 1

Ledyard Sportsmen's Club
PO Box 112, Ledyard, CT 06339
Jerry May (401) 596-3909
15 mi. S of Norwich
Type: Public/Member
Hrs: Su-S, 9-1 (open to public)
Sporting: None
Trap: 1 Skeet: 2 Five Stand: 1

Markover Hunting Preserve
719 Cook Hill Rd.,
Danielson, CT 06239
Kevin Olsen (860) 774-4116
75 mi. SW of Boston, MA
Type: Public
Hrs: Su-S, by appt.
Sporting: 1, 6 stations

TRAP & SKEET

Eastern CT Skeet Club Inc.
43 Evergreen Lane,
Oakdale, CT 06370
C.. McPherson (203) 433-0296

Fairfield Co. Fish & Game
53 Wood Ave., Trumbull, CT 06611
William Morey (203) 426-9400
Trap: 5 Skeet: 5

Golden Gunners Skeet Club
53 Wood Ave.,
Trumbull, CT 06611
William Morey (203) 426-9400

Hamden Fish & Game
PO Box 5619, Hamden, CT 06518
S. Amendola (203) 281-9440
Hrs: Su, 9:30-2:30
Trap: 4 Skeet: 4

Hartford Gun Club
157 S. Main St.,
East Granby, CT 06026
Dick Masterpole (203) 658-1614
Hrs: S/Su, 12-5; T/Th, 4-8
(May-Sept.1)
Trap: 12 Skeet: 6

Mukluk Skeet Club
RD7, #502, Norwich, CT 06360
Hervey LaLiberte (203) 822-6938
Hrs: S, 1-4; W, 5-Dark
Skeet: 2

Mystic Rod & Gun Club
272 Haley Rd., Mystic, CT 06355
Rod Dougherty (203) 536-6324
5 mi. E of New London
Type: Member/Avail
Hrs: Su, 9-2; Th, 6-10
Trap: 1 **Skeet:** 1

Niantic Sportsmen's Club
4 York Ave., Niantic, CT 06357
Belinda Gribosky (203) 739-5322
Skeet: 2

Northfield Rod & Gun Club
PO Box 639, Watertown, CT 06795
Edward Kalita (203) 383-8955
Trap: 2

Nutmeg Skeet Club
26 A Golden Hill St., South
Norwalk, CT 06854
Howard Altman (203) 866-3569

Pahquioque Rod & Gun
615 S. Salem Rd.,
Ridgefield, CT 06877
Fran Redman (203) 792-5222
Type: Public **Hrs:** T, 3-Dark
Trap: 4

Quaker Hill Rod & Gun
PO Box 80, Oak Dale, CT 06370
Mario Montalbini (203) 848-7884
Hrs: Su-S, 9-Dusk
Trap: 1 **Skeet:** 2

Rockville Fish & Game Club
999 Ellington Rd.,
S. Windsor, CT 06074
Howard Jorgensen (203) 872-3528
Hrs: S/Su, 9-4
Trap: 3 **Skeet:** 3

**Seymour
Fish & Game**
57 Greenbriar Rd., Oxford, CT 06478
Raymond P. Manzella
(203) 888-2805
Hrs: T/Th, 3:30-9; Su, 9:30-3
Trap: 2 **Skeet:** 2
○ Factory Ammunition
○ Shooting Lodge
○ Organized Leagues

Torrington Fish & Game
1229 Winsted Rd., Unit 89,
Torrington, CT 06790
Jack Consolini (203) 521-8505
5 mi. N of Torrington
Type: Public/Member
Hrs: W-F, 5-9 (Year Round)
Skeet: 1

DELAWARE

SPORTING & 5-STAND

Eagle Wing Sporting Clays
436 SVS/SVRO, 262 Chaust,
Dover AFB, DE 19902
Carl Barnes (302) 677-6308
Type: Public **Hrs:** W, 4-11; Su,
10-4:30 **Sporting:** None
Skeet: 3 **Five Stand:** Y

Ommelanden Range
1205 River Rd.,
New Castle, DE 19720
Michael Friel (302) 323-5333
35 mi. SE of Philadelphia
Type: Public **Hrs:** T-Su 9-4; W, 4-9
Reservs: Recommended
Sporting: 1, 28 stations
Trap: 6 **Skeet:** 2 **Five Stand:** 1
HT: 45 ft.
○ Loaner Guns
○ Factory Ammunition
○ Formal Instructions
○ Organized Leagues
○ Hunter Education &
　Gun Safety Classes

Owens Station
RD1, Box 203,
Greenwood, DE 19950
Bill Wolter (302) 349-4434
75 mi. E of Washington, DC
Type: Public **Hrs:** T-S, 9-dusk; Su, 10-4
Sporting: 3, 43 stations
Five Stand: 1 **HT:** 60 ft.
Wobble Trap

**Sporting Clays
Unlimited, Inc.**
3719 Lafayette St.,
Wilmington, DE 19808
Mark H. Davis (302) 998-2004
Hrs: Mobile unit for sporting clays
Sporting: 1
○ Available to travel to your club
　within 2-3 hr. drive from
　Wilmington

TRAP & SKEET

Dupont Fish & Game Assn.
701 Faun Rd., Newark, DE 19711
E.J. Hackman (302) 366-2484
Trap: 5 **Skeet:** 5

Wilmington Trapshooting
PO Box 9203, Newark, DE 19714
Thelma E. Clagett (302) 738-6600
Trap: 14 **Skeet:** 2

FLORIDA

SPORTING & 5-STAND

**Adams Farms, Inc.
Pheasant Shooting
Preserve**
2575 County Hwy. 185,
Glendale, FL 32433
Dr. Tom Guyton or Leonard Adams
(904) 837-2957
**12 mi. N of DeFuniak Springs,
12 mi. N of I-10**
Type: Public
Hrs: We/Sa/Su - 9-dk; & by app't
Reservs: Recommended
Sporting: 1, 13 stations

BIG D
•PLANTATION•

Big D Sporting Clays
Rt. 15, Box 1760,
Lake City, FL 32024
Charlie Parnell (800) 437-4441
70 mi. W of Jacksonville
Type: Public **Hrs:** Tu-S, 10-Dusk
Reservs: Recommended
Sporting: 1, 20 stations
HT: 40 ft. **Wobble Trap**
○ Loaner Guns
○ Factory Ammunition
○ On-Site Meals
○ Organized Leagues
○ Golf Carts

Blackjack Sporting Clays
Hwy. 15, Box 721412,
Orlando, FL 32872
Steven A. Smith, Mgr.
(407) 240-9444
6 mi. E of Orlando Int'l. Airport
Type: Public/Member
Hrs: T-S, 9-Dark; Su, 12-6
Reservs: Recommended
Sporting: 1, 24 stations
Five Stand: 1 **HT:** 35 ft.
See Our Ad Across

Bonnette HuntingClub
5309 Hood Rd., Palm Beach
Gardens, FL 33418
Tom Sheppard (561) 626-4309
70 mi. N of Miami

Type: Member/Avail
Hrs: M/T/Th/F, 10-6; S/Su, 10-5
Sporting: 1, 12 stations **Trap:** 5

Bradford Sportsmen's
S.W. 106th St., Graham, FL 32042
Patrick B. Welch (904) 485-2302
15 mi. N of Gainesville
Type: Member/Avail
Hrs: W, 12-Sundown; S/Su,
9-Sundown
Sporting: 3, 24 stations **HT**

Coon Bottom Gun Club
2995 Lake Bradford Rd.,
Tallahassee, FL 32310
Willis L. Heath (904) 539-0293
Hrs: W/S/Su, 1-Dark
Sporting: None
Skeet: 3 **Five Stand:** 1

Double WW Sporting Clays
1200 Cassat Ave.,
Jacksonville, FL 32205
Ken Branham (904) 266-1121
12 mi. SW of Jacksonville
Type: Public
Hrs: W/F, noon-dusk; S/Su, all day
Reservs: Not required
Sporting: 2, 36 stations
Five Stand: 1 **HT:** 40 ft.
○ Factory Ammunition
○ NSCA Certified Instructor
○ Dove Tower Game
○ Plantation Quail Hunts
○ Just 8 mi. off I-10 West

Everglades
Sporting Clays
4750 CR951 Florida Sports Park,
Naples, FL 33962
Susan Branco (941) 793-0086
3 mi. S of I-75 Exit 15
Type: Public/Member
Hrs: W&F, 10-4; S&Su, 9-3
Reservs: Strongly recommended
Sporting: 1, 16 stations **HT:** 30 ft.
○ Loaner Guns
○ Factory Ammunition
○ On-Site Pro Shop
○ Shooting Lessons Available
○ 30 mi. South of Ft. Myers

Gator Skeet & Trap Club
5202 NE 46th Ave.,
Gainesville, FL 32609
Wayne Pearce (904) 372-1044
60 mi. SW of Jacksonville
Type: Public/Member

Hrs: W/S/Su, 1:30-7
Sporting: None
Trap: 9 **Skeet:** 4 **Five Stand:** 1

Harvins' Hammock Sporting
1790 Poa Boy Farms Rd., St.
Augustine, FL 32092
Dennis Harvin (904) 829-6000
30 mi. S of Jacksonville
Type: Public
Hrs: W-F, by appt; S/Su, 1-6
Sporting: 1, 10 stations

Indian River T&S Club
699 17th St., Suite B,
Vero Beach, FL 32960
Annette Miller (407) 567-0011
100 mi. SE of Orlando
Type: Member/Avail
Hrs: W/Su, 1-5
Sporting: 1, 10 stations
Trap: 1 **Skeet:** 2 **Five Stand:** 1

J&R Hunting Preserve
8400 SW Fox Brown Rd.,
Indiantown, FL 34956
Joe or Liz O'Bannon (407) 597-4757
30 mi. NW of West Palm Beach
Type: Public/Member
Hrs: Anytime, by reservation
Sporting: 1, 13 stations **HT:** 12 ft.

Jacksonville Gun Club
12125 New Berlin Rd.,
Jacksonville, FL 32226
Richard Lacey (904) 272-5609
5 mi. NE of Jacksonville
Type: Public **Hrs:** W-Su, 1-Dark
Trap: 10 **Skeet:** 10 **Five Stand:** 1

Jennings Bluff
Rt. 2, Box 4250, Jennings, FL 32053
Troy Tolbert (904) 938-5555
65 mi. NE of Tallahassee
Type: Public **Hrs:** By Appt.
Sporting: 1, 8 stations

Markham Park/ South Florida Sporting Clays

16001 W. State Rd. 84,
Sunrise, FL 33326
Ron Cadurette (954) 370-9597
12 mi. W of Ft. Lauderdale
Type: Public/Member
Hrs: T-Su, 12-5; S/Su, 9-5; F/S/Su,
by appt (Clays)
Reservs: Not required
Sporting: 1, 12 stations **Trap:** 5
Skeet: 5 **Five Stand:** 1 **HT:** 40 ft

Okefenokee Sporting Clays

Rt. 2, Box 3778, Folkston, GA 31537
H.J. "Ronnie" Murray
(912) 496-2417
40 mi. N of Jacksonville, FL
Type: Public
Hrs: S/Su, 12-5 by appt.
Reservs: Not required
Sporting: 4, 14 stations
Skeet: 1   **HT:** 100 ft.
○ Instruction Available
○ NSCA Level II
○ NSSA Level I
○ 25 miles West of I-95 (Exit 2)
100 Ft. Tower! Come See Us!

Palm Beach Sporting Clays at Bonnette's Hunting & Fishing Club

5312 Hood Rd., Palm Beach
Gardens, FL 33418
Ryner Raeppold (561) 622-7300
**15 mi. N of West Palm
Beach Airport**
Type: Public/Member
Hrs: Tu-Su, 9-dusk
Reservs: Strongly recommended
Sporting: 1, 12 stations **HT:** 40 ft.
See Our Ad Below

Palm Beach Trap & Skeet Club

2950 Pierson Rd.,
West Palm Beach, FL 33414
Joe Fordham (407) 793-8787
**7 mi. W of Palm Beach Int'l Air-
port Type:** Public/Member
Hrs: S/Su, 10 to 5
Reservs: Recommended
Sporting: 1, 10 stations   **Trap:** 20
Skeet: 5 **Five Stand:** 1 **HT:** 30 ft.
○ Loaner Guns
○ Int'l. Olympic Bunker Trap
○ Quality New & Used Shotguns
○ Outstanding Snack Bar
○ Shooting Lessons Available
○ Complete Pro Shop

Polk County Skeet & Trap

151 Racepit Rd.,
Winter Haven, FL 33880
Harry Smiley (941) 291-0459
40 mi. SW of Orlando
Type: Public
Hrs: We & Su, 1-6; Th, 6-10; Sa, 9-6
Sporting: 1, 10 stations
Trap: 9 **Skeet:** 5 **Five Stand:** 1
Wobble Trap

Port Malabar Rifle & Pistol

Box 060307, Palm Bay, FL 32906
Rick Pepin (407) 777-6405
Hrs: Call for info
Sporting: 1
Trap: 3 **Skeet:** 2 **Five Stand:** 1

Shoal River Gun Club

PO Box 1293, Crestview, FL 32536
Jim Griffin (904) 689-1997
6 mi. E of Crestview
Type: Public/Member

Hrs: T-S, 9-6; Su, 1-6
Sporting: 1, 10 stations
Trap: 1 **Skeet:** 1

Silver Dollar Trap Club

17000 Patterson Rd.,
Odessa, FL 33556
Edna Mollohan (813) 920-3231
15 mi. NE of Tampa
Type: Public/Member
Hrs: W/S/Su, 10-6 (Summer); T-Su,
10-6 (Winter)
Sporting: None
Trap: 26 **Five Stand:** 1

Spaceport Gun Club

PO Box 540995,
Merritt Island, FL 32954
Al Luther (407) 459-2605
8 mi. S of Kennedy Space Center
Type: Public/Member
Hrs: W/Su afternoons (5-Stand)
Sporting: 1, 28 stations
Trap: 4 **Skeet:** 10 **Five Stand:** 1.

Sporting Clays of Tampa Bay

15720 Apache Dr., PO Box 16998,
Tampa, FL 33687
Steve Stewart (813) 986-7888
70 mi. SW of Orlando
Type: Public/Member
Hrs: W/S/Su, 8-6
Reservs: Recommended
Sporting: 2, 20 stations
Mostly Flat, trees & brush
Skeet: 1 **Five Stand:** 1 **HT:** 50 ft.
○ Open All Holidays Except Easter,
Thanksgiving & Christmas

Telegraph Cypress Field Club

45501 Bermont Rd. (CR74), Punta
Gorda, FL 33982
Gene McMillan (941) 575-0550
30 mi. N of Ft. Myers
Type: Public/Member
Hrs: W, 2-10; Th/S/Su, 8-Dusk;
Closed M/T/F
Reservs: Recommended
Sporting: 2, 30 stations
Trap: 1 **Skeet:** 1 **Five Stand:** 1
○ On-Site Pro Shop
○ NSCA Instructors Available
○ Fax: (941) 575-0544
See Our Ad Pg. 460

Trail Glades Range

10901 SW 24th St.,
Miami, FL 33165
Janie Clark (305) 226-1823
18 mi. W of Miami
Type: Public **Hrs:**
Sporting: 1, 10 stations
Trap: 6 **Skeet:** 5 **HT:** 25 ft.

Allen Smith Shooting Sports, Inc.
Orlando World Shooting Center at Lake Nona

BEELINE EXPRESSWAY #528 — To Cape Canaveral
2 mi.
(15)
Orlando International Airport
3 mi.
BLACKJACK'S
N
Greenway Toll Road #417

Welcome to Blackjack Sporting Clays, located just 6.5 miles east of Orlando International Airport. Visit Blackjack and shoot its challenging 15-station fully automated course, designed by Bob Edwards and general manager, Steven A. Smith. International Five-Stand and FITASC are also available.

Blackjack offers many amenities to the public and its members including a *Lodge Style Club-house, Remington & Beretta Loaner Guns, Gunsmith Service and Golf Carts.* Factory ammunition is available at the *On-site Pro Shop.*

Blackjack is the southern home of the Remington Shooting School.

Shooting instruction, available daily from certified, resident instructors, is supplemented by clinics held throughout the year by touring instructors.

Visit Blackjack Sporting Clays whenever you are in Orlando. Ask about our Special Packages for area attractions. Call today for reservations and membership information:

407-240-9444 • Fax 407-240-5103
Blackjack Sporting Clays • Orlando World Shooting Center
P.O. Box 721412 Orlando, FL 32872

Trail Trap and Skeet Club
6913 SW 139th Pl., Miami, FL 33193
Fred Azan (305) 223-8969
Hrs: M-F, 12-Sundown; S/Su,
9-Sundown Sporting: None
Trap: 2 Skeet: 5 Five Stand: 1

Turkey Run Gun Clubs
Rt. 3, Box 221, Alachua, FL 32615
Jack Baier, Mgr. (904) 462-5303
13 mi. N of Gainesville
Type: Public Hrs: W-Su, 9-6
Reservs: Recommended
Sporting: 2, 19 stations HT: 25 ft.
O Fully Stocked On-Site Pro Shop
See Our Ad Pg. 457

TRAP & SKEET

Cecil Field Skeet Club
MWR Dept., PO Box 109,
Jacksonville, FL 32215
Thomas Beets (904) 778-5181
Skeet: 2

Chairscholars Foundation
17000 Patterson Rd.,
Odessa, FL 33556
Hugo A. Keim (813) 920-2737
Hrs: 9-4 Trap: 4 Skeet: 2

Imperial Polk County S & T
Box 1915, Winter Haven, FL 33880
(941) 299-4853
Hrs: W/S/Su, 1-5; Th, 6:30-10:30
Trap: 6

Indian Hammock Skeet
32801 Hwy. 441,
Okeechobee, FL 34972
Charles Whipple (813) 763-9401
Hrs: By Appt.
Trap: 2 Skeet: 2

Key West Skeet Club
2108 Harris Ave.,
Key West, FL 33040
Johnnie Yongue (305) 294-1394
Hrs: Su, 9-3; W, 4:30-Sundown
Skeet: 2

Keystone Heights Skeet
1403 Ree St., Starke, FL 32091
Janet Kimutis (904) 964-8804
Hrs: W, 7-11 Skeet: 1

Li Bi Ho Gun Club
Rt. 3, Box 475, Perry, FL 32347
Henry Lee (904) 584-6550

Hrs: W, 3-9; S/Su, 1-9
Trap: 1 **Skeet:** 1

MacDill AFB Skeet & Trap
10303 Marina Bay Dr., MacDill
AFB, FL 33621
Nancy Wheeler (800) 821-4982
Trap: 2 **Skeet:** 2

Mayport Skeet Club
11049 Jean Ribault Ct.,
Jacksonville, FL 32225
Ken Krueger (904) 270-5627
Hrs: Su, 12-5 **Skeet:** 1

Nas Jax Skeet Club
Box 14, Bldg. 621, Nas Jax, FL 32212
Larry A. Rich (904) 272-1472
Hrs: W, 3-6; S, 8-1
Trap: 1 **Skeet:** 1

Orange Bend Skeet Club
Box 492810, Leesburg, FL 34749
B. M. Tucker, Jr. (352) 787-3157
Hrs: Varies **Skeet:** 1

Orange County Trap & Skeet
10955 Smith-Bennett Rd.,
Orlando, FL 32811
Tom Jones (407) 351-1230
Type: Public/Member
Trap: 9 **Skeet:** 4

Palatka Skeet & Trap Club
PO Box 1546, Palatka, FL 32177
Roy Dear (904) 325-5425
Hrs: W-Su, 1-Dark **Skeet:** 7

Palm Beach Gun Club
3001 S.W. 10th St., Pompano
Beach, FL 33069
David Humble (305) 425-7800

Patrick Skeet & Trap Range
320 Maple Dr.,
Satellite Beach, FL 32937
Adrian Troy (407) 783-6166
Hrs: W, 3-7; S/Su, 12-5
Trap: 1 **Skeet:** 4

Port of the Islands
12425 Union Rd., Naples, FL
33961
Russ Howard (813) 394-8666
90 mi. NW of Miami
Type: Public **Hrs:** W/Su, 9-4
Trap: 3 **Skeet:** 5

Sarasota Trap & Skeet
1743 D Lake Pl., Venice, FL 34293
Harold Babcock (941) 488-3223
105 mi. SW of Orlando
Type: Public/Member
Hrs: S/Su/W, 12-8
Trap: 9 **Skeet:** 3

Skyway Trap & Skeet Club
3200 74th Ave., N.,
St. Petersburg, FL 33702
J.W. Smith (813) 526-8993
70 mi. SW of Orlando
Type: Public **Hrs:** W/Th/S/Su
Trap: 10 **Skeet:** 2

St. Augustine Rod & Gun
1019 San Rafael St.,
St. Augustine, FL 32084
Barbara Bozard (904) 829-6011
Trap: 1 **Skeet:** 5

Tyndall AFB Trap & Skeet
6616 Lance St.,
Callaway, FL 32404
Luke Heitkamp (904) 283-3855
Hrs: W/F, 3-7; S, 9-5; Su, 11-5
Trap: 3 **Skeet:** 3

GEORGIA

SPORTING & 5-STAND

Ashburn Hill
PO Box 128, Moultrie, GA 31776
F.R. Pidcock, III (912) 985-1507
60 mi. NE of Tallahassee
Type: Public
Hrs: Su-S, Oct. thru March
Sporting: 1, 9 stations
Trap: 1 **Skeet:** 1 **HT:** 60 ft.

Barksdale Sporting Clays
Rt. 4, Longstreet Rd., P.O. Box 851, Cochran, GA 31014
Ronnie Wright (912) 934-6916
35 mi. S of Macon
Type: Public/Member
Hrs: W/S, 9-Dusk; Su, 1-Dusk; Other days by appt.
Sporting: 1, 11 stations
Skeet: 1 **Five Stand:** 1 **HT:** 50 ft.

Bevy Burst
Rt. 2, Box 245, Edison, GA 31746
Kathy Gray (912) 835-2156
40 mi. SW of Albany
Type: Public **Hrs:** By appt.
Sporting: 1, 9 stations

Boggy Pond Plantation
1084 Lanier Road,
Moultrie, GA 31768
Mack W. Dekle, Jr. (912) 985-5395
55 mi. NE of Tallahassee, FL
Type: Public

Hrs: October 1 thru March 31st
Sporting: 1, 14 stations **HT:** 50 ft.

Boll Weevil Plantation
4264 Thompson Bridge Rd.,
Waynesboro, GA 30830
Al McClain (706) 554-6227
35 mi. S of Augusta
Type: Public
Hrs: M-S, 9-Dark; Su, 1-Dark
Sporting: 1, 24 stations

Cat Creek Sporting Clays
N. Main St., PO Box 52,
Pavo, GA 31778
Buddy Lewis (912) 859-2075
30 mi. W of Valdosta
Type: Public **Hrs:** W-Su
Sporting: 1, 14 stations
Five Stand: 1 **Wobble Trap**

Cherokee Gun Club
PO Box 941, Gainesville, GA 30503
Earle Darby, Jr. (770) 531-9493
45 mi. NE of Atlanta
Type: Member/Avail
Hrs: By appointment
Sporting: 1, 15 stations
Trap: 3 **Skeet:** 3 **Five Stand:** 1
HT: 12 ft.

Climax Clays
PO Box 248, Climax, GA 31734
Eugene Oviatt (912) 246-3214
35 mi. N of Tallahassee
Type: Public/Member
Hrs: M-S, by appt.
Sporting: 1, 15 stations
Five Stand: 1

Floyd County Wildlife
PO Box 646, Rome, GA 30162
George Holder (706) 234-7879
10 mi. W of Rome
Type: Public/Member
Hrs: T-Su, Daylight-Dark; Closed
Mondays **Sporting:** None
Trap: 1 **Skeet:** 2 **Five Stand:** 1

Forest City Gun Club
9203 Ferguson Ave.,
Savannah, GA 31406
Carl Cole (912) 354-0210
1 mi. SE of Savannah
Type: Member/Avail
Hrs: W/S/Su, 2-8
Sporting: 1, 14 stations
Trap: 22 **Skeet:** 42 **Five Stand:** 1
HT: 45 ft.

Gum Swamp Country Club
PO Box 4116, Eastman, GA 31023
Lister Harrell (912) 374-5097
5 mi. E of Eastman
Type: Public **Hrs:** By Appt. Only
Sporting: 1, 22 stations **HT:** 60 ft.

Llewellin's PointHunting Preserve & Kennel
4897 Salem Rd., Pine Mountain, GA 31822
Floyd Clements (800) 636-9819
70 mi. SW of Atlanta
Type: Public/Member
Hrs: W-F, 1-9; S, 10-8; Su, 2-8
Reservs: Recommended
Sporting: 2, 20 stations
Rolling, trees & brush
Trap: 4 **Skeet:** 4 **Five Stand:** 1
HT: 50 ft.
O On-site Pro Shop
O Professional Shooting Instruction Available
See Our Ad Across

Manbone Run
270 Trinty Rd.,
Whigham, GA 31797
Julian Knight (912) 762-4315
10 mi. NW of Cairo
Type: Public **Hrs:** S/Su, 9-6
Sporting: 2, 20 stations
Five Stand: 2   **HT:** 30 ft.

The Meadows Nat'l. Gun
PO Box 377, Smarr, GA 31086
Cliff M. Evans (912) 994-9910
Type: Member/Avail
Sporting: 1, 17 stations
HT: 50 ft. **Wobble Trap**

Millcreek Hunting Preserve
PO Box 131, Rincon, GA 31326
William Exley/Jesse (912) 826-4968
15 mi. N of Savannah
Type: Public/Member
Hrs: Su-S, Dawn-Dusk
Sporting: 1, 25 stations

Myrtlewood Sporting Clays
Box 199, Thomasville, GA 31799
Bob or John (912) 228-0987
55 mi. S of Albany
Type: Public
Hrs: M-Sa, daylight to dusk
Sporting: 1, 24 stations
HT: 35 ft. **Wobble Trap**

Ocmulgee River Gun Club
169 Marcar Rd., Macon, GA 31206
Kenny Lassiter (912) 788-7989
Type: Public/Member
Hrs: W/Th/S/Su, 2-Dark
Sporting: None
Trap: 1 **Skeet:** 6 **Five Stand:** 1

Okefenokee Sporting Clays
Rt. 2, Box 3778,
Folkston, GA 31537
H.J. "Ronnie" Murray
(912) 496-2417
40 mi. N of Jacksonville, FL
Type: Public
Hrs: S/Su, 12-5 by appt.
Reservs: Not required
Sporting: 4, 14 stations
Skeet: 1   **HT:** 100 ft.
O Instruction Available
O NSCA Level II
O NSSA Level I
O 25 miles West of I-95 (Exit 2)
O 100 Ft. Tower! Come See Us!

Outback Gun & Bow Club
Rt. 1, Box 1815,
Hazelhurst, GA 31539
Rhonwyn Dawson (912) 375-0765
100 mi. S of Macon
Type: Public/Member
Hrs: T-S, 9:30-Dark; Su, 1:30-6
Sporting: 1, 30 stations **HT:** 40 ft.

Pinetucky Skeet & Trap Club, Inc.
2676 Gordon Hwy.,
Augusta, GA 30909
Stephen Melbrum (706) 592-4230
135 mi. E of Atlanta
Type: Public
Hrs: W/Th/F, 2-10; S/Su, 12-10
Reservs: Recommended
Sporting: 1, 12 stations
Trap: 4 **Skeet:** 5 **Five Stand:** 1
HT: 60 ft.
See Our Ad Below

Quailridge Plantation
Box 155, Norman Park, GA 31771
Edwin Norman (912) 985-5011
70 mi. N of Tallahasse, FL
Type: Public
Hrs: Oct. 1 thru March 31
Sporting: 1, 4 stations **Trap:** 1

Shirahland Plantation
Rt. 1, Box 340, Camilla, GA 31730
Ray Shirah (912) 294-4805
25 mi. S of Albany
Type: Public/Member
Hrs: Th 3-8; S 1:30-8; & by appt.
Reservs: Strongly recommended
Sporting: 1, 10 stations
Five Stand: 1   **HT:** 66 ft.
Wobble Trap
See Our Ad Pg. 319

South River Gun Club
5205 Hwy. 212,
Covington, GA 30209
Pete Gunn (770) 786-3752
30 mi. E of Atlanta
Type: Public/Member
Hrs: W, 11-9; T-F, 11-7; S/Su, 9-6
Sporting: None
Trap: 9 **Skeet:** 5 **Five Stand:** 1

Southpoint Plantation
PO Box 4309, Albany, GA 31706
Jimmy Harris (912) 888-6598
20 mi. NW of Albany
Type: Public **Hrs:**
Sporting: 1, 6 stations

At Callaway Gardens

Llewellin's Point Gun Club & Sporting Clays at Callaway Gardens offers the premier clay shooting experience in Georgia. Two world-class sporting clays courses, trap & skeet fields and 5-stand sporting clays offer a wide array of shooting challenges.

In addition, certified instructors are available to assist novices and experienced gunners alike improve their skills. Rental guns, factory ammunition and a fully stocked, on-site pro shop complete the "picture perfect" clay shooting experience.

Llewellin's Point is also a world-renowned hunting preserve. Its staff of hunting professionals grew up hunting quail, and have put themselves and an excellent kennel of experienced Llewellin setters at your disposal. There's nothing they'd rather do than put you over an exploding covey of quail. No matter what your level of expertise, Llewellin's Point guides can outfit and guide you to a great day's hunting.

And there's more. Guests of the Club enjoy accommodations ranging from the 345-room inn at Callaway Gardens to 2-bedroom cottages or 4-bedroom villas, the ultimate in privacy and elegance. There are seven restaurants to choose from, all offering their unique brand of Southern fare. Fly fishing, golf and tennis, too! Easily accessible by car, only 70 miles south of Atlanta and just 2 miles off I-185. Or fly in by private plane to our 5,000 ft. paved, lighted airport.

Call Today For Information, Reservations Or A Color Brochure:

800-636-9819

4897 Salem Road • Pine Mountain, GA 31822

Starrsville Plantation
283 Bo Jones Rd.,
Covington, GA 30209
N. Hendriks, III (770) 787-1366
30 mi. E of Atlanta
Type: Public
Hrs: Daily, 8:30-5; Year Round
Sporting: 3, 6 stations
Trap: 1 HT: 45 ft.

Tannenwood-A Shooting
Box 130, Davidsboro, GA 31018
Chad Tanner (912) 348-4931
60 mi. SW of Augusta
Type: Public/Member
Hrs: W, 9-til; Su, 1-til
Sporting: 1, 10 stations
Five Stand: 1

Tri-County Gun Club, Inc.
PO Box 1815, Odum, GA 31555
Ray Russell (912) 586-2723
72 mi. SW of Savannah
Type: Public
Hrs: W/S/Su, 2-Dark
Sporting: 1, 20 stations
Trap: 1 Skeet: 4

Wolf Creek Sport Shooting
3070 Merk Rd., SW,
Atlanta, GA 30349
Rusty Morris, Mgr. (404) 346-8382
2 mi. SW of Atlanta
Type: Public
Hrs: T-F, 1 to 9; S/Su, 10 to 5
Sporting: 3, 10 stations
Trap: 19 Skeet: 19 Five Stand: 1
HT: 40 ft.
O Shooting Instruction Available —
See Ad Pg. 215

TRAP & SKEET

Athens Rifle Club
1131 Hollow Creek Lane,
Watkinsville, GA 30677
Henry A. Burkes (706) 549-0936
Hrs: Su, 2-5 Trap: 1 Skeet: 2

Bleckley County Sportsman
PO Box 670, Cochran, GA 31014
Randy Bryan (912) 934-6306
Skeet: 1

Burke Co. Rifle/Pistol Club
394 D. Knight Rd.,
Waynesboro, GA 30830
Gordon Hull Hrs: Upon Request
Skeet: 1

Chickasaw Rod & Gun Club
PO Box 191, Pelham, GA 31779
R.G. Rogers, Sr. (912) 294-8240
Hrs: Appt. only Skeet: 6

Elbert Co. Gun Club
Rt. 2, Box 644, Carlton, GA 30627
Mike Metternick (706) 213-0098

Hrs: W, 5; Su, 1-6
Trap: 1 Skeet: 2

Flint Skeet & Trap Club
PO Box 1853, Albany, GA 31702
Randy Tyson (912) 432-6603
Hrs: W, 3-9; S/Su/Holidays, 1-9
Trap: 2 Skeet: 5

Fort Benning, US Army Base
US Army Marksmanship Unit, Fort
Benning, GA 31905
Burl Branham (706) 545-7916

Griffin Gun Club
120 Allie Dr.,
McDonough, GA 30252
Larry Lyskowinski (770) 228-4872
Type: Member/Avail
Hrs: S/Su, 9-5
Trap: 1 Skeet: 4

Little River Gun Club
174 Folds Rd.,
Carrolton, GA 30116
Jim Bake (770) 834-3076
Type: Public Hrs: Su, 1-6
Trap: 1 Skeet: 2

Moultrie Gun Club
Rt. 1, Box 516,
Moultrie, GA 31768
Hrs: Su, 2-5; Sat. on request
Skeet: 2

Ora Gun Club
PO Box 211, Statesville, GA 31648
Leo L. Miller (912) 559-7025
Trap: 1 Skeet: 1

Pounderosa Plantation
Rt. 1, Box 267 K, Hwy. 15 S, White
Plains, GA 30678
Dee Lindsey (800) 215-4196
75 mi. SE of Atlanta
Type: Public Hrs: Skeet: 1

RPM Gun Club
PO Box 40, Coleman, GA 31736
Billy Moore (912) 732-3416
Hrs: S/Su, 2-7 Skeet: 1

Robins Skeet & Trap Range
2669 Hwy. 127,
Kathleen, GA 31047
Alan Ray (912) 926-4733
Hrs: T/W, 3-9; S/Su, 12-6
Trap: 1 Skeet: 3

Sea Island Gun Club
Box 30296, Sea Island, GA 31561
Fred D. Missildine (912) 638-3611
45 mi. N of Jacksonville, FL
Type: Public Hrs: Daily, 2:30-4
Trap: 1 Skeet: 3

Sportsman's Gun Club
PO Box 146, Royston, GA 30662
Wray Brown (800) 451-7626
Hrs: W/S/Su Trap: 1 Skeet: 5

HAWAII

SPORTING & 5-STAND

Lanai Pine Sporting Clays
PO Box 310, Lanai City, HI 96763
Bob Donovan (808) 565-3803
7 mi. W of Maui
Type: Public Hrs: 7 Days/Week
Sporting: 1, 14 stations
Trap: 1 Skeet: 1 Five Stand: 1
HT: 30 ft.

Maui Trap & Gun Club
PO Box 963, Ulupalakua, HI 96790
Sam King (808) 572-0689

Papaka Sporting Clays, Maui
1325 S. Kihei Rd. Suite 212, Kihei,
Maui, HI 96753
Dave Barnes (808) 879-5649
5 mi. S of Makena
Type: Public/Member
Hrs: By app't. only; 7 days: 9 - dusk
Sporting: 1, 30 stations
Trap: Y Five Stand: 1 HT: 90 ft.

Westside Sporting Clays Kapalua
2600 Liaholo Pl., Kihei, HI 96753
Mickey Hewitt (808) 669-SHOT
Type: Public Hrs: Su-S, 9-Dark
Sporting: 1, 6 stations Skeet: 1

TRAP & SKEET

Big Island Trap Club
PO Box 10645, Hilo, HI 96721
Garrett Zane (808) 935-6111
Hrs: W/S/Su Trap: 4

Kilauea Sporting Skeet Club
6 Hokupaa St., Nilo, HI 96720
Noel Aoki (808) 982-5700
Hrs: W, 12:30-3:45; S/Su, 9-3:45
Trap: 4 Skeet: 5

Koko Head Skeet Club
96-1225 Waihona St.,
Pearl City, HI 96782
Patrick Nolan (808) 455-4444
Hrs: S/Su, 8-4 Skeet: 2

IDAHO

SPORTING & 5-STAND

Blaine County Gun Club
Box 2940, Ketchum, ID 83340
David Rosser (208) 788-2681
7 mi. S of Sun Valley
Type: Public **Hrs:** Th-Su, 11-6
Sporting: 1, 10 stations
Trap: 4 **Skeet:** 1 **Five Stand:** 1

Clays West, Inc.
2915 El Rio, Meridian, ID 83628
Wayne P. Bayne (208) 362-6688
2 mi. S of Boise
Type: Public
Hrs: W/Th, 1-10; S/Su, 10-6
Sporting: 1, 11 stations
Trap: 3 **Skeet:** 2 **Five Stand:** 1

Idaho Gamebirds
Rt. 1, Box 1212,
Homedale, ID 83628
Jim Davenport (208) 337-4826
40 mi. W of Boise
Type: Public/Member
Hrs: Open daily; dawn to dark
Sporting: 1, 12 stations **HT:** 30 ft.

Idaho Sporting Clays
Rt. 1, Box 1212,
Homedale, ID 83628
Jim Davenport (208) 337-4826
Type: Public
Hrs: M-F, 2-7; S/Su, 9-Dark
Sporting: 1, 9 stations

Skyline Gun Club, Inc.
5888 W. Arco Hwy-PO Box 50774,
Idaho Falls, ID 83405
W.R. Lloyd (208) 525-8575
185 mi. E of Boise
Type: Public **Hrs:** S/Su, 12-5
Sporting: 1, 11 stations
Trap: 9 **Skeet:** 1 **Five Stand:** 1

Skyline
Hunting Club & Clays
Rt. 2, Box 14A,
Homedale, ID 83628
George Hyer (208) 337-4443
40 mi. W of Boise
Type: Public/Member
Hrs: Daily
Reservs: Strongly recommended
Sporting: 1, 26 stations **HT:** 38 ft.

TRAVELING WITH YOUR SHOTGUN

Flying within the United States on a commercial airliner with your unloaded shotgun is easy and legal. All airlines require a hard-shell, crush proof, lockable gun case (priced from $150 to $700). And just to be safe, you should allow an additional 15 minutes at check-in.

Each airline has its own rules governing firearms, but they are basically similar. If you follow the steps outlined in the article on traveling with your shotgun that appears on page 152, you'll breeze through the process and wonder why you ever left your shotgun at home. Oh! If you need a case for your gun, don't forget to turn to the Gun Case section beginning on page 151.

Teton Ridge Guest Ranch
200 Valley View Rd.,
Tetonia, ID 83452
Albert Tilt (208) 456-2650
40 mi. NW of Jackson Hole, WY
Type: Member/Avail
Hrs: (Summer) Daily, 2-6
Sporting: 2, 15 stations **HT:** 60 ft.

Tews Ranches
745 N. 550 W.,
Shoshone, ID 83352
Rusty (208) 886-2100
50 mi. S of Sun Valley, ID
Type: Public/Member
Hrs: S/Su, 10-Dark
Sporting: 1, 10 stations **HT:** 47 ft.

TRAP & SKEET

Boise Gun Club
PO Box 2293, Boise, ID 83701
Abe Wilson (208) 342-0892
Hrs: Su, 12-5; W, 5-10
Trap: 14 **Skeet:** 3

CDA Skeet & Trap Club
Box 1281, Coeur D'Alene, ID 83816
John Bainter (208) 772-2275
Hrs: Th, 12-9; S/Su, 9-4
Trap: 4 **Skeet:** 4

Caldwell Gun Club
Box 1363, Caldwell, ID 83605
R.W. Murphey (208) 459-2616
Hrs: T, 6-10; S, 12-5 **Trap:** 6

Lewiston Gun Club
1165 Miller Rd.,
Lewiston, ID 83501
Gary Schwank (208) 746-4938
Hrs: S, 12-Dusk; Su, 9-5
Trap: 18 **Skeet:** 4

MHAFB Trap & Skeet Range
366 SV/SVRT, 710 Trap Dr., Bldg.
2222, Mtn. Home, ID 83648
Harley Lekvold (208) 828-6093
Hrs: W-S, 11-8; Su, for reg. shoots
Trap: 7 **Skeet:** 3

Pleasant Valley Skeet Club
2703 Smith Ave., Boise, ID 83702
Don Mues (208) 336-3018
Hrs: By appt. **Skeet:** 1

Skeet Farm
1165 Miller Rd.,
Lewistown, ID 83501
Gary Schwank (208) 743-5622
Hrs: By appt. only **Skeet:** 1

St. Maries Gun Club
323 10th St., St. Maries, ID 83861
Robert Grieser (208) 245-4101
Type: Public **Hrs:** Dec-April,
Sundays 10-3 **Trap:** 3

Sun Valley Gun Club
Sun Valley Resort,
Sun Valley, ID 83353
Tom Neely (208) 622-2111
1 mi. E of Sun Valley
Type: Public/Member
Hrs: 7 Days (May-Oct); 10-6pm
Trap: 4 **Skeet:** 1 **HT:** 35 ft.

ILLINOIS

SPORTING & 5-STAND

Bi-State Sportsmen's Assoc.
Colon, IL
Duane Sassen (319) 355-6605
160 mi. E of Des Moines
Type: Public/Member
Hrs: Su, 10-5
Sporting: 1, 20 stations
Trap: 3 **Skeet:** 5 **Five Stand:** 1
HT: 40 ft.

Best Shot Sporting Clays
2610 Willow Grove Rd.,
Harrisburg, IL 62946
Alan Pulliam (618) 268-4629
Type: Public/Member
Hrs: S, 9-Dusk; Wkdys by appt.
Sporting: 2, 20 stations **HT:** 40 ft.

Bloomington Gun Club
RR2, Box 96, Colfax, IL 61728
Tim Schierl (309) 724-8516
Hrs: W/Th, 12-10; F/S/Su, 8-10
Sporting: 2 **Trap:** 3 **Skeet:** 3

Callahan Ranch Hunting
RR2, Box 26N, Dieterich, IL 62424
Tom & Dana Thull (217) 924-4412
100 mi. NE of St. Louis, MO
Type: Public **Hrs:** Su-S, 8-Dusk
Sporting: 2, 20 stations **Trap:** 1

Decatur Gun Club
PO Box 3062, Decatur, IL 62525
Mike Turner (217) 877-0400
2 mi. S of Decatur
Type: Public
Hrs: S, 11-4; Su, 9-4; Th, 5-9
Sporting: None
Trap: 9 **Skeet:** 8 **Five Stand:** 1

Diamond S Sporting Clays
27211 Townline Rd.,
Tremont, IL 61568
Karen or Cory Stowell
(309) 449-5500
25 mi. SE of Peoria
Type: Public **Hrs:** Th/Su, 8-5:30
Reservs: Recommended
Sporting: 1, 16 stations **HT:** 65 ft.

Garden Plain Hunt Club
7737 Long Rd., Fulton, IL 61252
Curt Ebersohl (309) 887-4439
120 mi. W of Chicago
Type: Public/Member
Hrs: Su-S, 8-Dusk
Sporting: 4, 56 stations

Highland Shooting Grounds
N3041W Cty A,
Cascade, WI 53011
Mike or Joann Sommers
50 mi. N of Milwaukee
Type: Public/Member
Hrs: May 1-Sep 30: We-Fr, 1-7;
Sa-Su, 10-5
Reservs: Strongly recommended
Sporting: 1, 18 stations **HT:** 60 ft.

Hopewell Views Hunting
Rt. 2, Box 232, Rockport, IL 62370
Rick Wombles (217) 734-9234
85 mi. NW of St. Louis, MO
Type: Member/Avail **Sporting:** 1

Hot Shot Sporting Clays, Ltd.
4945 State Rt. 156,
Waterloo, IL 62298
Steve King (618) 939-3015
Hrs: By Appt. **Sporting:** 1, 13 sta.

Hunting Unlimited
RR4, Box 98, Mt. Sterling, IL 62353
Larry Hanold (217) 289-3366
Type: Public/Member
Hrs: 8-5, by app't
Sporting: 2, 15 stations **Trap:** 1

Lefthanders Gun Club
121 South Main, Box 82,
Loami, IL 62661
George Moon (217) 624-4001
12 mi. SW of Springfield
Type: Public/Member
Hrs: 1st Sunday/mo. (5-stand), 9-1;
Other times by appt
Reservs: Not required
Sporting: 1, 10 stations
Trap: 1 **Five Stand:** 1   **HT:** 30 ft.

Millbrook Hunting Club
7519 Finnie Rd., Newark, IL 60541
Dick Carlson (708) 553-5407
60 mi. SW of Chicago
Type: Member/Avail
Hrs: Su-S, by appt.
Reservs: Strongly recommended
Sporting: 1, 14 stations

Nishkawee Preserve
21887 Pigeon Rd.,
Morrison, IL 61270
Norman F. Spencer (815) 772-3394
140 mi. W of Chicago
Type: Public/Member
Hrs: 4/16-9/20; 8-5 daily by app't
Sporting: 1, 10 stations **HT:** 16 ft.

North Pike Hunting Club
RR2, Griggsville, IL 62340
Donovan Baldwin (217) 236-3131
Type: Public/Member
Hrs: S/Su, 8-5; Wkdys by Appt.
Sporting: 1, 13 stations **Trap:** Y

Northbrook Sports Club
PO Box 766, Grayslake, IL 60030
Frank Kasper (847) 223-5700
Type: Member/Avail
Hrs: W, 12-5; Th, 12-10; S/Su, 10-5
Sporting: 1, 10 stations
Trap: 10 **Skeet:** 12 **Five Stand:** 1

Oakmount Game Club
30808 N. Darrell Rd.,
McHenry, IL 60050
Peter Reiland, Jr. (815) 385-2144
45 mi. NW of Chicago
Type: Public **Hrs:** W-S, 9-5; Su, 10-5
Reservs: Strongly recommended
Sporting: 1, 18 stations **HT:** 55 ft.

Olde Barn Sporting Clays
RR2, Box 143A, Rt. 130,
Oakland, IL 61943
B.C. McQueen (217) 346-3211
85 mi. E of Springfield
Type: Public **Hrs:** Th/F/S/Su,
8:30-5; M/T/W by appt.
Reservs: Recommended
Sporting: 2, 20 stations
Five Stand: 1   **HT:** 40 ft.

Otter Creek Hunting Club
Rt. 3, Box 125G,
Jerseyville, IL 62052
Mike Runge (618) 376-7601
40 mi. NE of St. Louis, MO
Type: Public/Member
Hrs: M-F, by appt; S/Su, 8-?
Sporting: 2, 27 stations
Trap: Y **Skeet:** Y **Five Stand:** 1
Wobble Trap

Pheasant Valley Hunt Club
R#1, Box 360,
Bunker Hill, IL 62014
Sharon Wilkinson (618) 585-3956
30 mi. NE of St. Louis, MO
Type: Public/Member
Hrs: W-Su, 9am-dusk
Sporting: 1, 10 stations
Five Stand: 1   **HT:** 40 ft.

PINEWOOD HUNTING CLUB

Pinewood Hunt Club
RR#1, Box 36, Beaverville, IL 60912
Wayne DeYoung (815) 435-2314
55 mi. S of Chicago
Type: Member/Avail
Hrs: 8am-7pm
Reservs: Strongly recommended
Sporting: 1, 25 stations

Prairie Chicken Sport.Clays
4121 Illinois Rt. 127,
Hillsboro, IL 62049
Pat Boehler (217) 537-3085
40 mi. N of St. Louis, MO
Type: Public
Hrs: S/Su, 9-5; Wkdays by appt.
Sporting: 1, 25 stations

Rend Lake Trap Field
Rt. 3, Box 242, Benton, IL 62812
Tom Winn (618) 629-9920
Type: Public **Hrs:**
Sporting: 1, 10 stations
Trap: 10 **Skeet:** 1   **Wobble Trap**

Richmond Hunting Club
Hwy. 173, Rt. 12,
Richmond, IL 60071
Mike Daniels (815) 678-3271
50 mi. NW of Chicago
Type: Public/Member
Hrs: Su-S, 8-5
Sporting: 1, 10 stations
Trap: 3   **HT:** 25 ft.

Sand Prairie Farms, Inc.
185 Rogers Rd., Ohio, IL 61349
Tom Yucus (815) 376-6641
90 mi. W of Chicago
Type: Public/Member
Hrs: M-S, Dawn-Dusk, year-round
Sporting: 1, 10 stations **Trap:** 1

Seneca Hunt Club
PO Box 824, Seneca, IL 60098
Larry Higdon (815) 357-8080
60 mi. SW of Chicago
Type: Public/Member
Hrs: T-Su, 8-4:30
Sporting: 4, 15 stations
Five Stand: 1   **HT:** 45 ft.

Smokin' Gun Hunt Club
995 E. County Rd. 1550,
Hamilton, IL 62341
Terry Phillips (217) 847-2227
100 mi. NW of Springfield
Type: Public/Member
Hrs: Daily by appt.
Sporting: None
Trap: 2 **Skeet:** 1 **Five Stand:** 1

St. Charles Sportsmens Club
8N365 Shady Lane, Elgin, IL 60123
Robert Scherf (708) 365-9881
25 mi. W of Chicago
Type: Public/Member
Hrs: Th, 6pm-10pm; S, 1pm-4pm;
Su, 9:30-1pm
Sporting: 1, 10 stations
Trap: 7 **Skeet:** 1

Streamline Sporting Clays
Rt. 1, Box 204, Percy, IL 62272
Ron Doering (618) 497-2539
50 mi. SE of St. Louis, MO
Type: Member/Avail
Hrs: S/Su, 10-4; Weekdays by Appt.
Sporting: 1, 10 stations

Tamarack Farm Hunt Club
7210 Keystone Rd.,
Richmond, IL 60071
Dick Hendricksen (815) 678-4506
40 mi. NW of Chicago
Type: Member/Avail
Hrs: Group Resrv. Only
Sporting: 1, 10 stations
Trap: Y **Five Stand:** 1
Wobble Trap

Timberview Lakes Sporting Clays
23200 North 2000 Rd.,
Bushnell, IL 61422
Ken Stone (309) 772-3609
30 mi. S of Galesburg
Type: Public
Hrs: Daily by Appt.
Sporting: 2, 25 stations

Trail of Tears Lodge
1575 Fair City Rd.,
Jonesboro, IL 62952
Ron & Deb Charles (618) 833-8697
15 mi. NE of Cape Girardeau
Type: Public/Member
Sporting: 2, 10 stations

Upland Bay Hunt Club
Rt. 173 & Lakeview 4218,
Richmond, IL 60071
Mike Mathews (815) 678-4411
50 mi. NW of Chicago
Type: Public/Member
Sporting: 1, 10 stations **HT:** 40 ft.

Upland Hunt Club & Sporting Clays
14755 Edson Rd.,
Davis Junction, IL 61020
Mike McInerney, Mgr.
(815) 874-7444
55 mi. NW of Chicago
Type: Public/Member
Hrs: Daily by reservation
Reservs: Strongly recommended
Sporting: 8, 40 stations
HT: 60 ft. **Wobble Trap**
See Our Ad Across

X Sporting Clays
Rt. 3, Box 165, Pana, IL 62557
James Eck (217) 562-5272
45 mi. SE of Springfield
Type: Public
Hrs: S/Su, 8:30-5; M-F, By Appt.
Sporting: 1, 10 stations
Trap: 2   **HT:** 30 ft. **Wobble Trap**

TRAP & SKEET

Brittany Shooting Park
RR2, Box 224,
Bunker Hill, IL 62014
Larry Mohr (618) 362-6265
Hrs: T/S, 6-11; Su, 12-6
Trap: 9 **Skeet:** 2

Edgewood Shooting Park
1008 W. Madison St.,
Auburn, IL 62615
James Ketchum (217) 438-6327
Type: Public **Hrs:** Th, 6-10; Su, 1-4
Trap: Y

Edwardsville Gun Club
PO Box 557, Edwardsville, IL 62025
Chuck Malmgren (618) 656-2875
Hrs: Th, 7-10; S/Su, 1-5 **Trap:** Y

Effingham Co. Sportsman's
306 S. 8th St., Altamont, IL 62411
David Miller (618) 483-6241
Trap: 2 **Skeet:** 2

Frankfort Sportsmans Club
8200 W. 191st St.,
Mokena, IL 60448
(815) 469-9887   **Hrs:** W/F,
6-10:30; Su, 10-4   **Trap:** 4

Gordon Gun Club
Gun Club Rd., Robinson, IL 62454
Brett Richeson (618) 584-3827
50 mi. SW of Terre Haute, IN
Type: Public/Member
Hrs: Trap, Sat. 11-4; Skeet, Sun. 1-5
Trap: 4 **Skeet:** 1

Grayville Gun Club
PO Box 125, Albion, IL 62806
Dick Gumbrell (618) 446-3129
Trap: Y

Hi-Lo Club, Inc.
47 Fox Court, Mahomet, IL 61853
Wayne R. Cluver (217) 495-3576
Hrs: S/Su, 10-4; W, 4-6 (Summer)
Trap: 2 **Skeet:** 2

Highland Pistol/Rifle Club
1910 Olive St., Highland, IL 62249
Wes Stueber (618) 654-5971
Hrs: M-F, 6-10; S/Su, 12-5
Trap: 5 **Skeet:** 1

Hilldale
18 N. 681 Rt. 31, Dundee, IL 60118
Fred Lawrence (708) 428-2816
Hrs: F, 1-Dark; S/Su, 10-6
Trap: 4 **Skeet:** 4

Illinois State Trap Assn.
624 Lakeview, E. Peoria, IL 61611
Roger Rocke (309) 699-6202
Type: Public **Hrs:** S/Su
Trap: Y **Skeet:** Y

Knollwood Gun Club
3 Hampton Rd.,
Montgomery, IL 60538
William Barnett (708) 553-7585
Hrs: Su, 10-4 **Skeet:** 3

Marble Gun Club
RR5, Box 285A, Danville, IL 61832
Todd Marble (217) 431-3014
Trap: 4 **Skeet:** 1

McHenry Sportsmen's Club
N. Weingart Rd.
@ Rolling Ln., McHenry, IL
Harvey Scharlau (708) 894-9135
Hrs: S, 1-5; 2nd & 4th Sun, 10-4
Trap: 4

New Boston Gun Club
403 SE 3rd Ave., Box 208,
Aledo, IL 61231
(309) 582-5327
Type: Public **Hrs:** 1st Sunday/mo.
Trap: 5

Oak Park Country Club
PO Box 109, Oak Park, IL 60303
Tom Geraghty (708) 456-7600
Hrs: S, 10-2; Su, 9-3 (Nov-Mar)
Trap: 1 **Skeet:** 2

Olin Gun Club
427 Shamrock St.,
East Alton, IL 62024
Cindy R. Wattles
Trap: 2 **Skeet:** 4

Palos Sportsman's Club
24038 S. Harlem,
Frankfort, IL 60423
Robert Osterberg (815) 469-4446
Hrs: W, 12-Dusk; S/Su, 9-5
Trap: 4 **Skeet:** 5

Peoria Skeet & Trap Club
515 W. Kellar Pkwy.,
Peoria, IL 61614
Becky McCumber (309) 822-8146
Type: Public/Member
Hrs: Th/S/Su, 11-5
Trap: 10 **Skeet:** 10

Quincy Gun Club
930 Maine, Quincy, IL 62301
Henry Geise, III (217) 222-8462
Type: Public/Member
Hrs: Th, 5-8; S/Su, 12-4
Trap: 5 **Skeet:** 5

Rockford Skeet Club
8101 Lindenwood Rd.,
Rockford, IL 61107
James E. Gaddis (815) 398-7708
Type: Member/Avail
Hrs: S/Su, 9-5
Trap: 1 **Skeet:** 3

Scott AFB Rod & Gun Club
D#9 Meadowbruck La.,
Belleville, IL 62221
Kevin Pellone (618) 256-2052
Hrs: Th, 5-10; S, 10-3; Su, 12-5
Trap: 2 **Skeet:** 3

Voorhees Street Gun Club
15886 First St., Westville, IL 61883
John Kocurek (217) 267-2510
Hrs: S/Su, 9-3
Trap: 1 **Skeet:** 1

X-Line Gun Club
1157 Pheasant, Bradley, IL 60915
Jack or Jan Miller (815) 932-0877
Type: Public
Hrs: T/F, 6pm; S, 11-3; Reg. Shoots
Trap: 9

INDIANA

SPORTING & 5-STAND

Back 40 Sporting Clays
9442 Beech Rd., Bourbon, IN 46504
Larry Meister (219) 342-4665
45 mi. W of Fort Wayne
Type: Public
Hrs: S, 9-6; Sun, 12-6; M-F, by appt.
Sporting: 2, 20 stations **HT:** 20 ft.

Bearcreek
Bearcreek Sporting Clays
R4, Box 268-A (500 North),
Portland, IN 47371
John Lawrence (219) 726-8646
40 mi. S of Fort Wayne
Type: Public/Member
Hrs: M-F, call for hrs; S/Su, 8-dark
Reservs: Not required
Sporting: 3, 45 stations
Skeet: 1 **Five Stand:** 1 **HT:** 25 ft.
Wobble Trap
○ Factory Ammunition
○ On Site Gun Shop & Pro Shop
○ Come Shoot Our Brand New
   Covey Chucker
○ NSCA Fun Shoot Every Month!
○ Less than 1/2 mi off U.S. 27

Circle City Sporting Clays
14926 E. 113th St.,
Fortville, IN 46040
Marc Waltzer (317) 485-7044
6 mi. NE of Indianapolis
Type: Public/Member
Reservs: Recommended
Sporting: 2, 20 stations
Trap: 20 **Skeet:** 6 **Five Stand:** 1
HT Wobble Trap
○ Tell Marc You Saw His Listing in
   Wing & Clay

Clear Creek Sporting Clays
7944 W. Country Rd. 100 North,
Danville, IN 46122
J. D. Mendenhall (317) 539-2869
25 mi. W of Indianapolis
Type: Public
Hrs: W-S, 10-Dusk; Su, 1-Dusk
Sporting: 3, 15 stations **HT:** 40 ft.

Crooked Creek Conservation
13203 E. 246th St.,
Noblesville, IN 46060
Dennis Trice (317) 552-8925
Type: Member/Avail **Hrs:** S/Su,
12-5 **Sporting:** 1, 10 sta. **Skeet:** 2

Evansville Gun Club

RD#2, Box 89D,
Haubstadt, IN 47639
Ron Eberhard (812) 768-6370
15 mi. N of Evansville
Type: Public/Member
Hrs: T/W/Th, 12-9; S/Su, 8-4
Sporting: 1, 14 stations
Trap: 9 **Skeet:** 2 **Five Stand:** 1

Graham Creek Sporting Clays

3700 E. Private Rd., #390S,
N. Vernon, IN 47265
George Cummins (812) 873-2529
70 mi. S of Indianapolis
Type: Public
Hrs: S/Su, 9-5; M-F, by appt.
Reservs: Recommended
Sporting: 3, 11 stations
Five Stand: 1   **Wobble Trap**

Graham Creek offers sporting clays shooters 3 courses, pro-shop, picnic area and course instruction. Beginner or pro can enjoy shooting the two 100 target eleven stations. Woodlands I and II designed by Jon Kruger winds through heavily wooded rolling terrain with crushed stone paths. One FITASC style course, Meadows offer a variety of long crossing targets and wide spread pairs.

Hard Scrabble

PO Box 1313, Warsaw, IN 46580
Roy Gregory (219) 566-2511
40 mi. SW of Fort Wayne
Type: Public
Hrs: S, 9-3; Wkdays. by appt.
Sporting: 3, 33 stations **HT:** 40 ft.

Indian Creek Shooting Ctr

5950 Gun Club Rd., NE,
Georgetown, IN 47122
Wanda Seitz (812) 951-3031
15 mi. W of Louisville, KY
Type: Public/Member
Hrs: M/W/F, by appt., 1st, 3rd & 5th Weekends
Sporting: 1, 11 stations **Trap:** 4

Indiana Gun Club

14926 E. 113th St.,
Fortville, IN 46040
Steve Smith (317) 485-6540
8 mi. NE of Indianapolis
Type: Public
Hrs: W, 12-10:30; Th/F, 12-6; S/Su, 10-6
Sporting: 1, 12 stations
Trap: 23 **Skeet:** 5 **Five Stand:** 1

Kosko Conservation Inc.

PO Box 801, Warsaw, IN 46580
Jim Gast (219) 267-7599
35 mi. W of Ft. Wayne
Type: Public
Hrs: W, 4-10; S, 9-3; Su, 8:30-3
Sporting: None
Trap: 2 **Skeet:** 2 **Five Stand:** 1

Quail Ridge Sportsman's

PO Box 148, Sunman, IN 47041
Shawn D. Hance, Mgr.
(812) 926-4999
60 mi. E of Indianapolis
Type: Public/Member
Hrs: Th-Su, 9-dusk
Reservs: Strongly recommended
Sporting: 1, 25 stations **HT:** 60 ft.

Scott County Sporting

3331 E. Harrod Rd.,
Scottsburg, IN 47170
Patricia Lytle (812) 794-2382
10 mi. NE of Scottsburg
Type: Public
Hrs: S/Su, 9-Dusk; M-F, by appt.
Sporting: 1, 10 stations

Springer Run Hunting

Box 816, New Albany, IN 47151
Tony Thomas (812) 739-4848
3 mi. N of Levenworth
Type: Public
Hrs: S/Su, 9-5; Wkdays by appt.
Sporting: 1, 11 stations
Five Stand: 1   **HT:** 15 ft.

Sugar Creek Sporting Clays

RR2, Box 413, Mitchell, IN 47446
Dale Waldbieser (812) 849-2296
40 mi. S of Bloomington
Type: Public
Hrs: S/Su, 10-Dark; W/Th/F, 8-Dark by appt.
Reservs: Recommended
Sporting: 2, 20 stations
Trap: 2 **Skeet:** 2
○ Loaner Guns
○ Less than 1 hour from Louisville, KY
○ Just 35 minutes off I-65
○ Family Owned & Operated
○ Quail, Chukar & Pheasant
  Hunting 9/1/96-4/30/97

West Creek Shooting

15547 W. 169th Ave.,
Cedar Lake, IN 46303
Randy Lukasik (219) 696-6101
50 mi. SE of Chicago
Type: Public/Member
Hrs: Su-S, 9am & 1pm
Sporting: 2, 15 stations **HT:** 40 ft.

Wild Wing Sporting Center

RR1, Box 1, Center Pointe, IN 47840
James Andrews (812) 986-2828
20 mi. E of Terre Haute
Type: Public
Hrs: W-Su, 8:30-5; M/T, By appt.
Sporting: 1, 15 stations
Trap: 1   **HT:** 45 ft.

TRAP & SKEET

Albion Conservation Club

1591 W. 300 N., PO Box 81,
Albion, IN 46701
Terry Askren (219) 636-7150
32 mi. NW of Ft. Wayne
Type: Public/Member
Hrs: Th, 6-10; 3rd Sun/month, 12-5
Trap: 2

Chain O Lakes Gun Club

1601 Kings Court,
Mishawaka, IN 46544
Art Horvath (219) 259-7333
Type: Public/Member
Hrs: S/Su, 1-5
Trap: 5 **Skeet:** 3

Columbus Gun Club

CR 525 E., Columbus, IN 47203
Curt McIntosh (812) 377-6441
Trap: 3 **Skeet:** 1

Daleville Skeet & Trap Club

6701 S. Co. Rd. 900 W.,
Daleville, IN 47334
John Swift (317) 378-5122
40 mi. NE of Indianapolis
Type: Public
Hrs: W, 9-7; S/Su, 9-5
Trap: 1 **Skeet:** 5

Deer Creek Conservation

6203 S. 375 East,
Jonesboro, IN 46938
Toni or Jim Ehle (317) 677-8281
Type: Public/Member
Hrs: S, 6; 1st Su/month-Reg. 11am
Trap: 5   **Wobble Trap**

Evansville Izaak Walton

PO Box 2468, Evansville, IN 47728
Howard Shrode (812) 897-2746
Hrs: S-Th, 8-10
Trap: 2 **Skeet:** 2

Fall Creek Valley CC

2306 Nichol Ave.,
Anderson, IN 46016
Thomas Daily (317) 644-0421
Type: Public/Member
Hrs: Reg. Trap, 2nd Sun; Practice, T, 6pm (Apr-Nov) **Trap:** 4

Frontier Gun Club

RR2, Box 235,
Roachdale, IN 46172
Steve Smith (317) 522-2084

Type: Public/Member **Hrs:** 2nd & 3rd S/Su, 10-6 **Trap:** 13

Fulton County Gun Club
3916 N. Meridian Rd.,
Rochester, IN 46975
Don E. Cain (219) 223-2072
Type: Public/Member
Hrs: F, 6:30-11pm; 2nd, 4th & 5th Sundays, 9:30am **Trap:** 4

Henry County Conservation
PO Box 35, New Castle, IN 47362
Gil Lee (317) 533-6602
Type: Public/Member
Hrs: Th, 6pm-11pm; Su, 10-2; ATA Shoot 1st Sun/month
Trap: 4 **Wobble Trap**

I U Skeet Range
HPER Bldg., Room 290,
Bloomington, IN 47405
Jack Mills (812) 855-0244
Hrs: Su, 12-5 **Trap:** 2 **Skeet:** 2

Indiana State Trap Assn.
PO Box 121, Orleans, IN 47452
Velton Smith (317) 485-6540
Type: Public/Member
Hrs: W, 12-10; Th/F/S/Su, 10-6
Trap: 23 **Skeet:** 6

Kingen Gun Club
5190 N. 500 W.,
McCordsville, IN 46055
Dennis Kingen (317) 335-3781
Hrs: W/S, 11-5 **Trap:** 19

Oakwood Gun Club
RR2, Box 736, Wheatfield, IN 46392
Dave Glissman (219) 956-4615
Hrs: W, 5:30-10:30; S, 10-3
Trap: 4

St. Joe Valley Conservation
7222 State Rd. #8, Butler, IN 46721
Tom Bassett (219) 337-5234
Type: Public/Member
Hrs: 1st Su/mo. W, 12-8 (June-Aug)
Trap: 5 **Skeet:** 2

Vincennes Gun Club
PO Box 538, Vincennes, IN 47591
Robert V. Bierhaus (812) 882-0990
Type: Public/Member
Hrs: Skeet, Sat. 1-5; ATA Shoots, 2nd Sundays **Trap:** 4 **Skeet:** 1

Wallace Traps
R#1, Box 95, Hillsboro, IN 47949
Charles Bryant (317) 397-3568
Type: Public **Hrs:** 4th Sunday, April-Sept. **Trap:** 5

White River Gun Club
3221 29th St., Bedford, IN 47421
Robert Snyder (812) 275-3697
Type: Public/Member
Hrs: 1st & 3rd Sun/month
Trap: 5

IOWA

SPORTING & 5-STAND

Arrowhead Hunting Club
3529 170th St.,
Goose Lake, IA 52750
Gloria Mullin (319) 577-2267
165 mi. E of Des Moines
Type: Public/Member
Hrs: By Appt.
Reservs: Strongly recommended
Sporting: 1, 5 stations **Trap:** 5
○ Loaner Guns
○ Factory Ammunition
○ On-Site Meals
○ Shooting Lodge
○ Formal Instructions

Bi-State Sportsman's Assn.
1603 Central Ave.,
Bettendorf, IA 52722
Duane Sassen (319) 355-6605
E of Davenport
Type: Public/Member
Hrs: T, 4-10; Su, 9:30-4
Sporting: 1, 20 stations **Trap:** 2

Black Hawk Sporting Clays
2407 Valley High Dr.,
Cedar Falls, IA 50613
Mike Grieger (319) 266-7262
90 mi. NE of Des Moines
Type: Public
Hrs: Su, 9-5; W, 4-Dark
Sporting: 1, 8 stations
Trap: 1 **Skeet:** 1 **HT:** 45 ft.

Coyote Run Sporting Clays
21957 U U Ave., Eldora, IA 50627
Terry Steding (515) 858-5773
65 mi. NE of Des Moines
Type: Public
Hrs: S/Su, 9-5; M-F, by appt.
Sporting: 1, 10 stations

Flood Creek
708 Taylor St., Rudd, IA 50471
Mike Kelsey (515) 395-2694
120 mi. N of Des Moines
Type: Public/Member
Hrs: W, 5-dark; Su, 11-5
Sporting: 1, 12 stations **HT:** 80 ft.

Hawkeye Area Sport. Clays
PO Box 75, Tiffin, IA 52340
Jim Rogers (319) 645-2093
95 mi. E of Des Moines
Type: Public/Member
Hrs: T/Th, 5-10; S/Su, 12-5
Sporting: 1, 10 stations
Trap: 4 **Skeet:** 2 **HT:** 50 ft.

Hunter's Knob Gun Club
623 Pershing St., St.
Charles, IA 50240
Daryl Brown (515) 297-2250
25 mi. S of Des Moines
Type: Public
Hrs: Th, 6-Dark, 1st & 3rd Wkends
Sporting: 1, 11 stations

Kruger Clay World
RR1, Box 213, St. Ansgar, IA 50472
Jon Kruger (515) 736-4893
20 mi. NE of Mason City
Type: Public
Hrs: M/Th/F, 5; S/Su, 1-5; T, 5-Dark
Reservs: Not required
Sporting: 1, 16 stations
Mostly Flat, trees & brush
Trap: 1 **Skeet:** 1 **Five Stand:** 1
Wobble Trap
○ Shooting Instruction Available—
See Pgs. 211-12

Bill Kuntz's Oakwood Sporting Resort
RR#2, Box 69, Sigourney, IA 52591
Bill Kuntz (800) 432-3290
40 mi. SW of Iowa City
Type: Public **Hrs:** By Appt.
Reservs: Recommended
Sporting: 1, 10 stations **HT:** 40 ft.

Lazy H Hunting Club
RR#2, Woodbine, IA 51579
Murray Hubbard (712) 647-2877
45 mi. NE of Omaha/Co. Bluffs
Type: Public/Member
Hrs: S/Su, 9-dk; Wkdays, by appt.
Sporting: 1, 27 stations **HT:** 90 ft.

New Pioneer Gun Club
PO Box 219, Waukee, IA 50263
Jeff Brammer (515) 987-4415
7 mi. W of Des Moines
Type: Public/Member
Hrs: W/Th, 1-6; S/Su, 10-5
Sporting: 1, 10 stations
Trap: 4 **Skeet:** 6 **HT:** 65 ft.

Outpost Clays Range
Rt. 1, Box 211, Logan, IA 51546
Bob Spencer (712) 644-2222
30 mi. N of Omaha, NE
Type: Public **Hrs:** Su-S, by appt.
Sporting: 1, 10 stations
Trap: 1 **HT:** 100 ft.

Shell Rock Area Sportsmens

PO Box 12, Shell Rock, IA 50670
Ernest W. Ramige (319) 885-6521
20 mi. NW of Waterloo
Type: Public/Member
Hrs: Twice a month by appt.
Sporting: 1, 5 stations

Southern Iowa Sporting

RR2, Box 91, Moulton, IA 52572
Bruce Burgher (515) 642-3256
70 mi. SE of Des Moines
Type: Public
Hrs: Weekends & Evenings by appt.
Sporting: 1, 10 stations **HT:** 30 ft.

Spring Run

1886 B 280th Ave.,
Spirit Lake, IA 51360
Marty Loos (712) 336-0882
85 mi. E of Sioux Falls
Type: Public **Hrs:** Daily, 7-Dark
Reservs: Recommended
Sporting: 1, 10 stations
Trap: Y **Skeet:** Y
O Factory Ammunition
O On-Site Pro Shop
O On-Site Meals
O Shooting Lodge
O Organized Leagues

Steelclay Shooting Sports

3353 Plymouth Ave.,
Eddyville, IA 52553
Larry Dunn (515) 969-4387
60 mi. SE of Des Moines
Type: Public/Member
Hrs: Su-S, 9-7
Sporting: 1, 10 stations
HT: 40 ft. **Wobble Trap**

Timber Ridge

RR1, Box 203A, Castana, IA 51010
Richard Bumann (712) 353-6517
90 mi. N of Omaha, NE
Type: Public **Hrs:** By appt. only
Sporting: 1, 10 stations

Triple H Ranch Hunting Preserve

16365 70th Avenue, Burlington, IA
52601
Keith A. Hoelzen (319) 985-2253
140 mi. SE of Des Moines
Type: Public
Hrs: S/Su, 9-5; M-F, by Appt.
Reservs: Strongly recommended
Sporting: 2, 15 stations
Five Stand: 1 **HT:** 60 ft.

TRAP & SKEET

Ames Izaak Walton League

3121 Aspen, Ames, IA 50014
Martin Simpson (512) 233-1105
Hrs: W, 6:30-11:30; Su, 3-5
Trap: 2 **Skeet:** 1

DLS Gun Club

PO Box 72, McCausland, IA 52758
Linda Sawvell (319) 225-2311
1 mi. W of McCausland
Type: Public
Hrs: W/Th, 3-9; S/Su, 9-5
Trap: 8 **Skeet:** 4

Jefferson Cty. Ikes Gun Club

2153 175th St., Fairfield, IA 52556
Don Schiedel (515) 472-1641
Hrs: T, 6-12 **Trap:** 4 **Skeet:** 2

Marion Co. Sportsmens

926 128th Ave., Knoxville, IA 50138
Stephen C. Coon (515) 828-7392
Hrs: W/Th, Evenings
Trap: 4 **Skeet:** 2

Marshall Gun Club

812 Washington,
Marshalltown, IA 50158
Allen Huseboe (515) 752-1760
Type: Public/Member
Hrs: Su, 1pm; T/W/Th, 5pm
Trap: Y **Skeet:** Y

Otter Creek Sportsmens

PO Box 31, Hiawatha, IA 52233
Joanne DeLong
Type: Public/Member
Hrs: T/Th, 5-9:30; S, 12-4; Su, 12-5
Trap: 6 **Skeet:** 1

Pella Trap Range

906 W. South, Knoxville, IA 50138
Karl Crook (515) 842-6078
Hrs: Th, 5pm **Trap:** 4

Stockdale Gun Club

RR2, Box 42, Ackley, IA 50601
Dale Stockdale (516) 648-4779
Type: Public/Member
Hrs: By request, resrv.; ATA Shoots
May-Sept. **Trap:** Y

Tri-State Gun Club

Box 336, Montrose, IA 52639
Glen Van Pelt
Type: Public/Member
Hrs: T/W, 5-9pm; S/Su, 12:00
Trap: Y

Going on a sporting adventure?

That't great! But to get the most out of your trip, you'll want to go fully outfitted. A new travel gun case might be called for. New clothes? Boots? Perhaps, a brand new shotgun. If it's a trip that will include sporting clays, you may want to get a new set of chokes, or perhaps have that gunfitting you've put off for a while. Fortunately, you're in the right place. Turn to the following sections to begin. And enjoy your trip!

KANSAS

SPORTING & 5-STAND

BLUEROCK TARGET PARK

Blue Rock Target Park
4500 E. 117th North,
Sedgwick, KS 67135
Todd Beers (316) 744-8366
10 mi. N of Wichita
Type: Public/Member
Hrs: W/Th/F, 2-7; Sa, 10-7; Su, 11-7
Reservs: Recommended
Sporting: 1, 10 stations **Trap:** 5
Skeet: 5 **Five Stand:** 1 **HT:** 35 ft.
○ Just 2 1/2 miles East of I-235
and I-35

Capital City Gun Club
100 E. Ninth St., Topeka, KS 66612
Whitney Damrom (913) 354-1354
8 mi. W of Topeka
Type: Public/Member
Sporting: None **Trap:** 2 **Skeet:** 4

Cedar Hill Gun Club & Sporting Clays
918 E. 1650 Road,
Baldwin, KS 66006
Mary Watson (913) 843-8213
30 mi. SW of Kansas City
Type: Public/Member
Hrs: S/Su, 10-5; M-F, By Appt.
Reservs: Strongly recommended
Sporting: 1, 13 stations **Trap:** 5
Five Stand: 1 **Wobble Trap**
○ Loaner Guns
○ Factory Ammunition
○ On-Site Meals
○ Organized Leagues
○ Golf Carts

Cimarron Sporting Clays
Box 575, Cimarron, KS 67835
Gavin Unruh (316) 855-7050
180 mi. E of Wichita
Type: Public/Member
Hrs: Su, 1-6; Other days by appt.
Sporting: 1, 8 stations **HT:** 30 ft.

Claythorne Lodge
R1, Box 13, Hallowell, KS 66725
Sam or Frieda Lancaster
(316) 597-2568
150 mi. S of Kansas City
Type: Public/Member
Hrs: W/S/Su, 9-dusk; & by reserv.
Reservs: Recommended
Sporting: 2, 60 stations **Trap:** 1
Skeet: 1 **Five Stand:** 1 **HT:** 85 ft.
○ Just 1 1/2 miles off of Hwy. 96
○ Chief Instructor, '90 World
    Professional Clay Target
    Champion, Steve Middleditch

Doug's Trap & Skeet
8601 Monticello Rd.,
Lenexa, KS 66227
Doug Montis (913) 422-5063
10 mi. S of Kansas City, MO
Type: Public/Member
Hrs: T/F, 2-11; S/Su, 10-5
Sporting: 1, 10 stations
Trap: 5 **Skeet:** 3 **HT:** 40 ft.
Wobble Trap

Elkhorn Ranch
Rt. 1, Box 113, Fredonia, KS 66736
Lee White (316) 378-2306

80 mi. E of Wichita
Type: Public **Hrs:** Su, 9-5; Other days by appt. **Sporting:** 1, 18 sta. **HT:** 35 ft. **Wobble Trap**

Flint Oak
Rt. 1, Box 262, Fall River, KS 67047
Pete Laughlin (316) 658-4401
75 mi. E of Wichita
Type: Public/Member
Hrs: T-S, 10-dusk; Su, 10-5
Reservs: Recommended
Sporting: 2, 5 stations
Trap: Y **Skeet:** Y   **HT:** 157 ft.
See Our Ad Left, Below

Fossil Creek Sporting Clays
PO Box 811, Russell, KS 67665
Jack Yost (913) 483-6456
70 mi. W of Salina
Type: Public/Member
Hrs: Varies, call to check days & hours of operation
Sporting: 1, 10 stations

Geary County F&G Club
1519 Hale Dr.,
Junction City, KS 66441
Easy Ed Augustine (913) 238-8727
60 mi. W of Topeka
Type: Public
Hrs: Su, 1-5; T, 6-10; W/S, 1-5 (S)
Sporting: 1, 13 stations **Trap:** 3

Gypsum Valley Sport. Clays
5668 South Kipp Rd.,
Gypsum, KS 67448
Craig Stephenson (913) 536-4535
15 mi. SE of Gypsum
Type: Public **Hrs:** W, 5-Dk; S/Su, 9-6
Sporting: 1, 12 stations **HT:** 20 ft.

Kansas Field & Gun Dog
8601 Monticello Rd., Lenexa, KS
Doug Montis (913) 422-5063
Hrs: T/F, 5-11; S/Su, 10-5
Sporting: 1, 10 stations
Trap: 6 **Skeet:** 3

Lil' Toledo Lodge
Rt. 4, Box 117, Chanute, KS 66720
Ron King (316) 244-5668
100 mi. SW of Kansas City
Type: Public/Member **Hrs:** S/Su, 9-4
Reservs: Recommended
Sporting: 1, 18 stations
Skeet: 1 **Five Stand:** 1 **HT:** 27 ft.
Wobble Trap
See Our Ad Left, Above

Locust Point Gun Club
19939 S. Berryton Rd.,
Lyndon, KS 66451
Doug Koehler (913) 828-3406
25 mi. S of Topeka
Type: Public/Member
Hrs: S-Su, 8-dark; Evenings & Weekdays by app't
Reservs: Recommended
Sporting: 2, 10 stations
Skeet: Y **Five Stand:** 1 **HT:** 50 ft.

Lynbrooke Sporting Clays
1900 State St., Augusta, KS 67010
Ross Lietzke (316) 775-1715
Type: Public **Hrs:** Summer: Th, 4-dk; S/Su, 9-6 **Sporting:** Y

Marais des Cygnes
2103 E. 15th St., PO Box 811,
Ottawa, KS 66067
Georgia Blacketer (913) 242-7468
Type: Public/Member
Hrs: M/Th/S/Su, 10am-5pm
Sporting: 1, 10 stations
Trap: 1   **Wobble Trap**

Michael Murphy & Sons
6400 S.W. Hunter Rd.,
Augusta, KS 67010
Daryl Banmister (316) 775-2137
15 mi. E of Wichita
Type: Public
Hrs: W/F/Su, pm; S, am/pm
Reservs: Recommended
Sporting: 1, 10 stations
Skeet: 1 **Five Stand:** 1
HT: 35 ft. **Wobble Trap**
See Our Ad Pgs. 217-19

Pine Ridge Sporting Clays
Rt. 1, Box 161C, Alma, KS 66401
Keith Tolbert, Mgr. (913) 765-3709
32 mi. W of Topeka
Type: Public
Hrs: M-F, by appt; S/Su, 9-dusk
Sporting: 1, 10 stations

Pleasant Valley
4078 NW US Hwy. 281,
Sawyer, KS 67134
Carolyn/David Keller (316) 594-2238
70 mi. SW of Wichita
Type: Public
Hrs: S/Su, 10-5; Weekdays by appt.
Sporting: 1, 12 stations

Quail Valley Sporting Clays & Hunt Club

16501 NW 72nd, RR1, Box 134
Moundridge, KS 67107
Mike & Barbara Stucky
(316) 345-8367
35 mi. NW of Wichita
Type: Public **Hrs:** S, 9-Dusk; Su,
1:30-Dusk; W, 4:30-Dusk
Reservs: Not required
Sporting: 1, 13 stations
HT: 35 ft. **Wobble Trap**

Ravenwood Hunting Preserve & Sporting Clays

10147 SW 61 St.,
Topeka, KS 66610
Ken Corbet (800) 656-2454
50 mi. W of Kansas City
Type: Public/Member
Hrs: M-F; by appt; S/Su; 9-Dark
Reservs: Recommended
Sporting: 1, 20 stations
Rolling, light coverage
HT: 50 ft. **Wobble Trap**
See Our Ad Pg. 473

Rohrer's Sporting Clays

RR1, Box 45, Troy, KS 66087
Sandy Rohrer (913) 985-2635
15 mi. W of St. Joseph
Type: Public
Hrs: By Reservation, 7 days/week
Sporting: 2, 18 stations

Shawnee Creek Preserve

Rt. 2, Box 50-B,
Columbus, KS 66725
Jon Holt (316) 674-8563
140 mi. S of Kansas City, MO
Type: Public/Member
Sporting: 1 **Trap:** 1 **Skeet:** 1
Wobble Trap

Starbird Sporting Clays

RR1, Box 149, Delia, KS 66418
Gary Starbird (913) 771-3141
22 mi. NW of Topeka
Type: Public/Member
Hrs: M/T, by Appt; W-Su, 9-Dk
Sporting: 2, 20 stations
HT: 35 ft. **Wobble Trap**

Sullivan Sand and Sage

3019 North Road G,
Ulysses, KS 67880
Shane Sullivan (316) 356-3924
200 mi. W of Wichita
Type: Public
Hrs: By Reservations
Sporting: 1, 12 stations

Walnut Ridge Hunting

RR1, Box 35A, Walnut, KS 66780
Mike (316) 354-6713
120 mi. S of Kansas City
Type: Public **Hrs:**
Sporting: 1, 13 stations

Windridge Sporting Clays

8601 Monticello Rd.,
Lenexa, KS 66227
Doug Montis (913) 422-5063
4 mi. W of Lenexa
Type: Public/Member
Hrs: S/Su, 10-5; T/F, 3-Dark
Sporting: 1, 10 stations
Trap: 4 **Skeet:** 3 **HT**

TRAP & SKEET

Ark Valley Gun Club

PO Box 781553, Wichita, KS 67278
Patrick H. Streiff (316) 776-0809
Hrs: Varies **Skeet:** 3

Beech Gun Club

9709 East Central,
Wichita, KS 67201
Dean Hilton (316) 676-8133
Trap: 3 **Skeet:** 3

Cadmus Skeet Range

12604 High Dr., Leawood, KS 66209
Harry Wilber (913) 491-5496

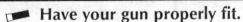
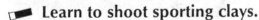

Type: Member/Avail
Hrs: By invitation **Skeet:** 1

Coffeyville Sportsmans
701 Lincoln, Coffeyville, KS 67337
Wes Stewart (316) 251-0637
Hrs: S, 8-12
Trap: 1 **Skeet:** 1

Dodge City Gun Club
PO Box 181, Dodge City, KS 67801
Club Manager **Type:** Public/Member
Trap: Y

Ft. Leavenworth Skeet/Trap
Box 3107, Leavenworth, KS 66027
Dan Lombard (913) 651-8132
Hrs: S/Su, 12-5; W, 11-4; Th,
11-8:30 **Trap:** 2 **Skeet:** 4

Kansas Trapshooters
PO Box 133, Kanopolis, KS 67454
Luke Seitz (913) 472-5266
Hrs: T, 6:30-10 **Trap:** 20

Kinsley Gun Club
115 Sunnyside Dr., Lewis, KS 67552
Frank O'Brien (316) 324-5693
Type: Public **Hrs:** W, Evening
Trap: 5

Liberal Gun Club
1210 N. Cain, Liberal, KS 67901
Bud Perry (316) 624-5810
Hrs: T/Th, 6-7; Sun, 1
Trap: 5 **Skeet:** 1

Prairie Dog Trap Range
510 N. Grant Ave.,
Norton, KS 67654
Bruce Reeves (913) 877-5545
150 mi. NW of Salina
Type: Public **Hrs:** Tues. eve.
Trap: 5 **Skeet:** 1

Rawlins Cty. Sportsmans
PO Box 162, Atwood, KS 67730
Scott W. Carlson (913) 626-3700
Type: Public/Member
Hrs: S/Su, by appt.
Trap: 2 **Skeet:** 1

Salt City Trap Park
203 N. 5th, Box 256,
Sterling, KS 67579
Glenn Gable (316) 278-3301
Type: Public
Hrs: Th, 5-9; Su, 1-5 **Trap:** 5

Tuttle Creek Trap Park
1712 Ranser Rd.,
Manhattan, KS 66502
C. A. Lamaster (913) 539-4392
Hrs: Th, 7pm; Su, 1;30 **Trap:** 4

Wheatbelt Gun Club
RR2, Russell, KS 67665
Loren Keil (913) 483-3459
Hrs: W, 5pm   **Trap:** 2

KENTUCKY

SPORTING & 5-STAND

**Blue Grass Skeet &
Sporting Clays Club**
392 Cromwell Hwy.,
Lexington, KY 40503
Mike Howard (606) 223-9160
Type: Public/Member
Hrs: T, 5-9; Su, 11-5
Sporting: 1, 10 stations
Trap: 6 **Skeet:** 2

Bush Road Sporting Clays
888 Bush Rd., Cadiz, KY 42211
Robert Bush (502) 522-6193
Type: Public **Hrs:** SA, 9-Dk; Su,
12-Dk; & by appt. **Sporting:** 2, 20

Deer Creek Outfitters
P.O. Box 39, Sebree, KY 42455
Tim Stull (502) 835-2424
140 mi. SW of Louisville
Type: Public/Member
Hrs: Open daily by app't
Sporting: 1, 10 stations

Flush-A-Covey
1403 Ealy Branch Rd.,
Owingsville, KY 40360
E. Wells/M. Miller (606) 674-6554
Type: Public
Hrs: S/Su, 8-dusk; Wkdays by appt.
Sporting: 2, 27 stations **Trap:** 2

Grassy Lake Lodge
PO Box 319, Wickliffe, KY 42087
Greg Joles (502) 462-3595
32 mi. SW of Paducah
Type: Public/Member
Sporting: 1
O Shooting Instruction Available—
See Ad Pg. 225
See Our Ad Pg. 339

Hammond
Sycamore Hill
Sporting Club
70 Three Lick Rd.,
Harrodsburg, KY 40330
W.C. Hammond (606) 366-9198
35 mi. W of Lexington
Type: Public **Hrs:** S, 8-5; Su/W,
12-5; & by appt.
Reservs: Recommended
Sporting: 1, 14 stations
Five Stand: Y

Hummin' Birds Sporting
9110 Wall Rd., Utica, KY 42376
Tom O'Daniel (502) 785-9429
Type: Public **Hrs:** S, 10-Dk; Su, 1-Dk
Sporting: 1, 20 stations

Jackson Purchase Gun Club
Rt. 1, Box 724, Ridgeland Dr.,
Mayfield, KY 42066
William R. Miller (502) 247-2903
Type: Public/Member
Hrs: Th, 5:30-10; Su, 12-Dark
Sporting: 1, 5 stations **Trap:** 4

Mudlick Gun Club
223 Highland Ave.,
Cynthiana, KY 41031
Larry Ritchie (606) 234-2511
35 mi. NE of Lexington
Type: Public
Hrs: M/T/W/F, by Rsrv; S, 9-6; 2nd
& 4th Su, 12-6
Reservs: Recommended
Sporting: 2, 27 stations
Trap: 2 **HT:** 14 ft.

Shoot Fire Sportsman's
290 Koostra Rd.,
Bowling Green, KY 42101
Kent Koostra (502) 781-9545
60 mi. N of Nashville
Type: Public
Hrs: M-F, by appt; S, 9-dusk; Su,
1-dusk **Sporting:** 2, 15 stations
Trap: Y **Skeet:** Y **Five Stand:** 1

Shooter's
Sporting Clays
11958 Big Bone Rd.,
Union, KY 41091
Jim McHale (606) 643-3411
35 mi. S of Cincinnati on I-71 in KY
Type: Public/Member
Hrs: S, 9-Dusk; Su, 10-Dusk; Wkdys
by resrv. only
Reservs: Strongly recommended
Sporting: 2, 20 stations **HT:** 60 ft.
O On I-71, less than 1/2 hr.
from I-75
O 5 Station/5 Trap Practice Field
O Factory Ammo/Rental Guns &
Golf Course

Sugar Creek
Sporting Clays
RR2, Box 413, Mitchell, KY 47446
Dale Waldbieser (812) 849-2296
40 mi. S of Bloomington
Type: Public **Hrs:** S/Su, 10-Dk;
W/Th/F, 8-Dk by app't
Reservs: Recommended
Sporting: 2, 20 stations
Trap: 2 **Skeet:** 2

TRAP & SKEET

Ashland Gun Club
PO Box 422, Ashland, KY 41105
Louis Clark (606) 836-3284
Hrs: Th, 4-Dark; Su, 9-Dark
Skeet: 4

Calvert City Gun Club
1218 US Hwy. 95,
Calvert City, KY 42029
Milton Stevenson (502) 395-5676
Hrs: Th, night; Sun, afternoon
Skeet: 2

Casey County Sportsman
Rt. 1, Box 94B, Liberty, KY 42539
Phillip Randolph (606) 787-9815
Hrs: Su-S Trap: 1 Skeet: 1

Chief Paduke Gun Club
1501 Clay St., Paducah, KY 42001
Tommy Lynn (502) 488-3248
Hrs: W, 4-9; S/Su, 12-9
Trap: 2 Skeet: 4

Ft. Knox Skeet Club
Bldg. 9333 French Range,
Ft. Knox, KY 40121
Edward Peterson (502) 624-7754
Type: Public
Hrs: W, 12-5; F-Su, 10-6
Trap: 2 Skeet: 4

Knob Creek Range
690 Richey Lane,
West Point, KY 40177
Kenny Sumner (502) 922-4457
18 mi. S of Louisville
Type: Public Hrs: M/T/Th, 7pm;
Su, 1pm Trap: 1

Lloyd Area Skeet Club
Box 272, Crittenden, KY 41030
Harry R. Rieder (606) 428-2323
Hrs: W, 7-11; Su, 1-5 (Yr round)
Skeet: 3

Madison Co. Game Club
Box 13083, Lexington, KY 40583
F. D. Marcum (606) 263-4625
Hrs: Th, 6-10 Skeet: 2

Powder Ridge
PO Box 436, Warsaw, KY 41095
Bill Eckler (606) 567-4113
Hrs: S/Su, 12-6 Skeet: 1

Pulaski Outdoorsmen
PO Box 704, Somerset, KY 42501
Harold Hamon (606) 382-5398
Type: Public/Member
Hrs: T, 7-10:30; Other times
scheduled Trap: 2 Skeet: 2

LOUISIANA

SPORTING & 5-STAND

Fort Polk Recreational
PO Box 3909, Fort Polk, LA 71459
Jim Callaway (318) 531-6591
120 mi. S of Shreveport
Type: Public Hrs: F, 4-8 (summer);
2-5 (winter) Sporting: 1, 10 sta.
Trap: 1 Skeet: 2

**High Point
Shooting Grounds**
1637 Marengo St.,
New Orleans, LA 70115
Donald Vallee (504) 656-7575
15 mi. SE of New Orleans
Type: Public/Member
Hrs: W-F, 1-Dark; S, 10-Dark; Su,
12-Dark Reservs: Not required
Sporting: 3, 33 stations
Five Stand: 2   HT: 90 ft.
Wobble Trap

Jean LaFitte Shooting Ctr.
2304 Constance Lane,
Lake Charles, LA 70605
Clem Myers (318) 478-2672
Hrs: W-Su, 2-Dark
Sporting: 1, 10 stations
Trap: 1 Skeet: 7 Five Stand: 1

Louisiana Sporting Clays
790 Lake Martin Rd.,
Breaux Bridge, LA 70517
Clayton Phillip (318) 235-9655
5 mi. NE of Lafayette
Type: Public/Member
Hrs: W-F, 2-Dark; S/Su, 9-Dark
Sporting: 1, 12 stations Skeet: 2

Natchitoches
Shooting Range
1421 Washington Ave.,
Natchitoches, LA 71457
Louis F. "Pop" Hyams, Jr. (318)
352-2785
6 mi. NE of Natchitoches
Type: Public/Member
Hrs: S/Su/Bank Holidays,
9am-9pm; W/Th/F, 2pm-9pm
Reservs: Recommended
Sporting: 1, 30 stations
Trap: 1 Skeet: 1 Five Stand: 1
HT: 40 ft.

Pin Oak Mallards
711 Hwy. 15, Rayville, LA 71269
Ace Cullum (318) 248-3549
15 mi. E of Monroe
Type: Public/Member
Sporting: 1, 10 stations

Red Chute Shotgun Club
Barksdale AFB, LA 71110
Capt. Nolen Grogan
(318) 456-2849
10 mi. E of Shreveport
Type: Public/Member
Hrs: Th, 3-dk; Sa, 9-dk; Su, 12-dk
Sporting: 1, 13 stations
Trap: 1 Skeet: 1 Wobble Trap

Shreveport Gun Club
4435 Meriwether Rd.,
Shreveport, LA 71118
Robert LaBorde (318) 686-9810
1 mi. W of Shreveport
Type: Public/Member
Hrs: W, 3-Dark; S/Su, 1-Dark
Trap: 9 Skeet: 1 Five Stand: 1
Wobble Trap

Tallow Creek
Shooting Grounds
4990 Hwy. 22,
Mandeville, LA 70471
Rick Adams/P.J. Demarie
(504) 893-1951
35 mi. N of New Orleans
Type: Public/Member
Hrs: W/F, 3:45-Dark; S/Su,
10:45-Dark; Others by appt.
Reservs: Not required
Sporting: 1, 14 stations
Trap: 1 Skeet: 1 Five Stand: 1
HT: 40 ft.
○ Home of the Open "Louisiana
Governors Cup Sporting
Clays Open"

Wild Wings
Rt. 2, Box 26, Downsville, LA 71234
Steve Bryan (318) 982-7777
75 mi. NE of Shreveport
Type: Public/Member
Hrs: W/Th/F/Su, 1-6; S, 9-6
Sporting: 1, 10 stations
Five Stand: 1   HT: 40 ft.

TRAP & SKEET

Arcadia Gun Club Inc.
Rt. 1, Box 594, Arcadia, LA 71001
R.T. Sherrill (318) 263-8319
Type: Public Hrs: Th, 3-Dark; Su,
1-Dark Trap: 2 Skeet: 2

Bayou Boeuf Skeet Range
PO Box 488, LeCompte, LA 71346
Wade Jones (318) 776-9301
Skeet: 2

Bogalusa Skeet Club
106 Suzanne St.,
Bogalusa, LA 70427
Paul Capo (504) 735-9173
Hrs: Su, 1-Dark   **Skeet:** 5

Florida Parishes Skeet
107 E. Mulberry St.,
Amite, LA 70422
Sally Smith (504) 748-8025
60 mi. NW of New Orleans
Hrs: W/S/Su, 2-Dark
Skeet: 6

Hunters Run Gun Club, Inc.
3636 S. Sherwood Forest Blvd.,
#590, Baton Rouge, LA 70816
(504) 387-3507
Hrs: W-Su, 10-7
Trap: 1   **Skeet:** 5

Lafayette Gun Club
Box 93043, Lafayette, LA 70509
Edward Francez (318) 234-2203
Hrs: Call for appt.   **Skeet:** 2

Pine Hills Gun Club
Box 1293, West Monroe, LA 71294
Jim Steele, III (318) 396-1495
Hrs: Su, 1-Sundown; Th,
4:30-Sundown   **Trap:** 2   **Skeet:** 2

South Louisiana Gun Club
149 Blanche Dr.,
Avondale, LA 70094
Russell Walker (504) 436-9901
Hrs: W/Th, 1-Dark; S/Su, 1-6
Trap: 3   **Skeet:** 5

MAINE

SPORTING & 5-STAND

The Bradford Camps
PO Box 729, Ashland, ME 04732
Karen & Igor Sikorsky
(207) 746-7777
75 mi. W of Presque Isle
Type: Public   **Hrs:** Daily
Sporting: 1, 10 stations

Foggy Ridge
PO Box 211, Warren, ME 04864
Jim Olmsted (207) 273-2357
80 mi. NE of Portland
Type: Public/Member
Hrs: M-S, day hrs; Su, after 9am
Sporting: 1, 20 stations

Hermon Skeet & Trap Club
RR#1, Box 292, Clifton, ME 04428
Marty Millett (207) 843-5323
10 mi. W of Bangor
Type: Public/Member
Hrs: Su, 9-1; W, 1-Dark
Sporting: None
Trap: 1   **Skeet:** 1   **Five Stand:** 1

Presque Isle Fish & Game
Box 375, Presque Isle, ME 04769
Bill Norsworthy (207) 764-0162
160 mi. N of Bangor
Type: Public/Member
Hrs: Su, 9-3; W, 5-Dk
Sporting: None
Trap: 1   **Skeet:** 1   **Five Stand:** 1

Scarborough Fish & Game
Box 952, Scarborough, ME 04070
Brad Varney (207) 865-4825
10 mi. S of Portland
Type: Public/Member
Hrs: Clays-1st Sun. of month, 9-5;
call for tr/sk times
Sporting: 1, 15 stations
Trap: 9   **Skeet:** 3

Sheepscot Ridge Sporting Cl.
Box 185, Wiscasset, ME 04578
David Laemmle (207) 882-5033
38 mi. E of Portland
Type: Public/Member
Hrs: S/Su, by appt.
Sporting: 1, 22 stations   **HT:** 20 ft.

TRAP & SKEET

Arnold Trail Sportsmans
6 Allen St., Augusta, ME 04330
Russell Hubbard (207) 622-7339
Hrs: Su, 10-4   **Trap:** 1   **Skeet:** 3

Durham Rod & Gun Club
288 US Rt. 1, N., Freeport, ME 04032
Peter MacDonald (207) 665-9409
Hrs: Su, 10-4; Wed., Night
Trap: 1   **Skeet:** 1

Richmond Gun Club
Reed Rd., Richmond, ME 04357
Leland Smith (207) 737-2620
Type: Public   **Hrs:** Tues. Nights
Trap: 9   **Skeet:** 1

Windham Gorham Gun Club
Great Falls Rd., Gorham, ME 04107
David LaRose/Joe Hall
Type: Public   **Hrs:** T, 4-Dusk; Su, 9-1
Trap: 4

MARYLAND

SPORTING & 5-STAND

Alexander Sporting Farms
13503 Alexander Rd.,
Golt, MD 21635
Jim/Sam Alexander
(410) 928-3549
2 mi. N of Massey
Type: Public
Hrs: M, 9-4; T-Su, 9-6
Reservs: Not required
Sporting: 1, 70 stations
Five Stand: 1   **HT:** 30 ft.
O Factory Ammunition
O Organized Leagues
O Golf Carts

BCC/Izaak Walton League
Izaak Walton Way,
Poolesville, MD 20837
Bill Thelemann (301) 620-1535
Type: Public/Member
Hrs: S/Su, call for hours
Sporting: 1   **Trap:** 1   **Skeet:** 1

Chesapeake Clays
16090 Oakland Rd.
Henderson, MD 21640
Bill Connors (410) 758-1824
Type: Public   **Hrs:** Su-S, 9am-6pm
Sporting: 1, 25 stations   **HT:** 100'

DELMARVA SPORTING CLAYS

Del-Mar-Va Sporting Clays
23501 Marsh Rd.,
Mardela Springs, MD 21837
Bryon Richardson (410) 742-2023
75 mi. SE of Washington, DC
Type: Public
Hrs: 7 days a week, 9-5
Reservs: Not required
Sporting: 2, 40 stations
Five Stand: 1   **HT:** 60 ft.

Fairs Regulated Sport. Clays
1605 Old Virginia Rd.,
Pocomoke City, MD 21851
Ray Fair (410) 957-1749
30 mi. S of Salisbury
Type: Public

Hrs: W-F, 1; S/Su, 9-5; Closed M/T
Sporting: 1, 25 stations HT: 40 ft.

Gunsmoke
Sporting Clays
Bethel Rd.(Mail: 6860 Bent Pine
Rd), Willards, MD 21874
Richard Laws (410) 835-2324
18 mi. W of Ocean City
Type: Public
Hrs: Su-S, starting @ 8am
Reservs: Not required
Sporting: 1, 15 stations HT
○ Loaner Guns
○ Factory Ammunition
○ On-Site Pro Shop
○ Formal Instructions
○ Organized Leagues
○ Gary Phillips, Shooting Instructor

Hopkins Game Farm
Box 218, Kennedyville, MD 21645
George or Patti (410) 348-5287
35 mi. E of Baltimore
Type: Public Hrs: Year Round
Sporting: 3 Five Stand: 1 HT

J&P Hunting Lodge, Inc.
1105 Benton Corner Rd.,
Sudlersville, MD 21668
John George, Jr. (410) 438-3832
20 mi. W of Delaware
Type: Public Hrs: T-Su, 10-4
Reservs: Recommended
Sporting: 1, 20 stations
Mostly Flat, trees & brush
Five Stand: 1 HT: 30 ft.

Skeet & Trap Club
**National Capital
Skeet & Trap**
16700 Riffleford Rd.,
Darnestown, MD 20878
Kurt & Al (301) 948-2266
Type: Public/Member
Hrs: T/Th, 4-9; S/Su/Holiday, 10-4
Sporting: None
Trap: 9 Skeet: 9 Five Stand: 1

Pintail Point
511 Pintail Point Farm Lane,
Queenstown, MD 21658
(410) 827-7029
Eastern Shore, 20 minutes E of
Bay Bridge
Type: Public/Member
Hrs: Range closed Mondays; Year
Round Shooting from 9am
Reservs: Not required
Sporting: 1, 16 stations
Mostly Flat, trees & brush
Five Stand: 1 HT: 35 ft.
○ Rental Guns
○ Shooting Shop
○ Instruction
See Our Ad Right, Above

Prince George's
County Trap & Skeet
Center
10400 Goodluck Rd.,
Glen Dale, MD 20769
Mark Biggins (301) 577-7178
5 mi. E of Washington, DC
Type: Public
Hrs: M&F, 10-5; T/W/Th, 1-8:30;
S/Su, 10-5 Reservs: Not required
Sporting: 1, 23 stations
Trap: 9 Skeet: 13 Five Stand: 1
HT: 45 ft.
See Our Ad Below

Sanner's Lake Sportsmans
Box 1300,
Lexington Park, MD 20653
Vernon Gray (301) 863-5589
65 mi. SE of Washington, DC
Type: Public/Member
Hrs: Wed. & Sun., Noon-Sunset
Sporting: 1, 6 stations Skeet: 1

Tuscarora Gun Club
5694 Glen Rock Dr.,
Frederick, MD 21790
John R. Ortaldo (301) 695-8322
10 mi. SW of Frederick
Type: Public
Hrs: Th, Eve. (Apr-Sept); Reg.
Shoots Sun. Sporting: 2, 10 sta.
Trap: 9 Skeet: 1 Wobble Trap

The Woodlands
Sporting Clays, Inc.
4633 Ocean Gateway (Rt. 50),
Vienna, MD 21869
Carol Baker (410) 376-0200
63 mi. N of Bay Bridge
Type: Public
Hrs: W, 10-6; Th-Su, 10-5
Reservs: Not required
Sporting: 1, 42 stations
Mostly Flat, light coverage
Five Stand: 1 HT: 60 ft.
○ 1 1/2 hrs. from Washington, DC,
on Rt. 50, Mile Marker 93

TRAP & SKEET

Andrews Rod & Gun Club
PO Box 857, Clinton, MD 20735
Kenneth Crump (301) 981-5985
Hrs: W, 1-5; S/Su, 9-5
Trap: 1 Skeet: 3

Cambridge Skeet/Gun Club
Box 1281, Cambridge, MD 21613
Dennis Roe (410) 228-8199
Hrs: Th, 5-8; Su, 11-6
Trap: 1 Skeet: 3

The Best on Maryland's Eastern Shore...

1,000 acres of forests, fields and Wye River waterfront, just 20 minutes from the Bay Bridge. An ideal location for hunting, shooting, fishing and recreating. Less than 1 hour from Baltimore and Washington D.C., two hours from Philadelphia. Individuals, families and corporate groups welcome.

- Guided hunts with top notch dogs
- Pheasant, quail, chukar and Hungarian partridge
- Realistic & challenging released mallard duck hunts
- Wild duck hunts
- Dove and deer
- Boarding kennels; started dogs and puppies for sale
- Sporting clays & 5 Stand
- Shooting instruction

—PINTAIL POINT FARM—
511 Pintail Point Farm Lane • Queenstown, MD 21658 • (410) 827-7029

Carroll County Gun Club
8009 Windsor Mill Rd.,
Baltimore, MD 21244
Don Kirk (410) 655-5223
Type: Public **Hrs:** W/F, 6pm;
S-Noon; **Trap:** 9

Loch Raven Skeet/Trap Club
PO Box 6846, Towson, MD 21204
Greg Hay (410) 252-3851
Hrs: W, 12-7; Th, 12-9; F, 12-6;
S/Su, 10-6 **Trap:** 7 **Skeet:** 7

Maryland State Sportsmens
3332 Woodside Ave.,
Baltimore, MD 21234
Gene Mullinix (410) 665-9185
Trap: 28

Millington Sportsmens
335 N. Ferry Point Rd.,
Pasadena, MD 21122
Ohmer Webb, Jr. (410) 360-1013
Type: Member/Avail **Trap:** 22

Potomac River Gun Club
Box 264, Indian Head, MD 20640
Larry A. Buckley (301) 743-6986
Hrs: T/Th, 4-9; Su, 9-4
Trap: 2 **Skeet:** 2

Salisbury Gun Club
PO Box 4061, Salisbury, MD 21801
John Lee Taylor (301) 749-0337
Hrs: W/F, 12-Dark; S/Su, 9-Dark
Trap: 2 **Skeet:** 7

Sudlersville Skeet Club
935 Coon Box Rd.,
Centerville, MD 21617
Marvin Coppage (410) 438-3880
Hrs: Su, 1-5 **Trap:** 1 **Skeet:** 4

Synepuxent Gun Club
PO Box 724, Berlin, MD 21811
Roger Taylor (410) 641-0326
Type: Public **Hrs:** W, 6-10pm; Su,
1-4pm **Trap:** 5

Talbot Rod & Gun Club
F28132 Pleasant Valley Dr.,
Easton, MD 21601
John K. Waters (301) 822-6928
Hrs: W, 4-7; Su/Su, 11-5
Trap: 1 **Skeet:** 6

Thurmont Sportsmans Club
13404 Rabbit Run Terrace, Union
Bridge, MD 21791
John R. Dodd, Sr. (301) 898-9093
Trap: 16

MASSACHUSETTS

SPORTING & 5-STAND

Angle Tree Stone R&G
PO Box 1243 (Kelly Blvd.), N.
Attleboro, MA 02761
James Bolton (508) 695-0902
40 mi. SW of Boston
Type: Public/Member
Hrs: S/Su, 12-4
Sporting: 1, 10 stations
Trap: 1 **Skeet:** 2

Cape Cod's Sporting Clays
PO Box 3157, Waquoit, MA 02586
Lenny Rentel (508) 540-2851
60 mi. SE of Boston
Type: Public **Hrs:** Sunday, 9-3
Sporting: 1, 12 stations
Trap: 1 **Skeet:** 2

Fall River Rod & Gun Club
PO Box 571, Fall River, MA 02723
Gus Yankopoulos (508) 673-4535
40 mi. S of Boston
Type: Public/Member
Hrs: T/Th/S/Su, 10-5
Sporting: 1, 6 stations
Trap: 2 **Skeet:** 2

Falmouth Skeet Club
PO Box 157, Waquoit, MA 02536
Stuart Gifford (508) 540-3177
Hrs: W/S, 1-4; Su, 9-1
Sporting: 1, 10 stations
Trap: 1 **Skeet:** 2

Fin Fur & Feather Club
25 Mallard Rd.,
Needham, MA 02192
Richard Lyons (508) 376-2977
20 mi. W of Boston
Type: Public/Member
Hrs: S/Su, 11-4 (Nov-Apr); 12-4
(May-Oct)
Sporting: None
Trap: 2 **Skeet:** 2 **Five Stand:** 1

Hamilton Rod & Gun Club
Hamilton Rd., PO Box 954,
Sturbridge, MA 01566
(508) 347-3389
50 mi. W of Boston
Type: Public
Hrs: S, 10-4; Su, 11-4; & by appt.
Sporting: 1, 13 stations
Trap: 4

Hopkinton Sportsmens
95 Lumber ST.,
Hopkinton, MA 01748
Wayne Nigro (508) 435-3838
16 mi. SE of Worcester
Type: Public
Hrs: T, 6:30-9; Su, 9:30-1
Sporting: 1, 14 stations
Trap: 1 **Skeet:** 2

Independent Sportsmen's
36 Mirimichi Rd.,
Foxboro, MA 02035
Charles Langille (508) 543-9887
35 mi. SW of Boston
Type: Public/Member
Hrs: S/Su, 1-4; W, 6-9
Sporting: 1, 10 stations
Trap: 2 **Skeet:** 3 **Five Stand:** 1

Lee Gun Club
PO Box 178, Fairview St.,
Lee, MA 01238
Fred Wood (413) 243-9721
14 mi. S of Pittsfield
Type: Public
Hrs: S, 11; Su, 9; W/Th, 12
Sporting: None
Trap: 1 **Skeet:** 3 **Five Stand:** 1
Wobble Trap

Lee Sportsman Club
66 Mill St., RR2, Lee, MA 01238
Phil Hiser, Jr. (413) 243-9721
15 mi. S of Pittsfield
Type: Public/Member
Hrs: W, 12-Dusk; S, 12-Dusk; Su, 9-1
Sporting: None
Trap: 1 **Skeet:** 3 **Five Stand:** 1

Lissivigeen
Private Hunting Club

Lissivigeen
Spooner Rd., Barre, MA 01005
Kevin J. Coakley (413) 477-8783
55 mi. W of Boston
Type: Public/Member
Hrs: 9/15-3/31, Su-S, 8-4:30pm
Reservs: Strongly recommended
Sporting: 1, 5 stations
Five Stand: 5

Old Colony Sportsmens
PO Box 523, Pembroke, MA 02359
Nancy Allen/Phil Turner (617)
293-9980
Hrs: S/Su, 10-3; W, Afternoons
Sporting: None
Trap: 2 Skeet: 2 Five Stand: 1

Plymouth Rod & Gun Club
PO Box 3121, S. Meadow Rd.,
Plymouth, MA 02360
Steve Ruas (508) 746-9805
35 mi. SE of Boston
Type: Public Hrs: Su, 9-2
Sporting: 1, 10 stations
Trap: 2 Skeet: 4 Five Stand: 1

Springfield Sportsmen's
179 Birch Rd.,
Longmeadow, MA 01106
Dick Haskins (413) 267-9652
75 mi. from Boston
Type: Public Hrs: T/S/Su, 9-5
Sporting: 1, 8 stations
Trap: 1 Skeet: 3 Five Stand: 1

Walpole Sportsmen's Assn.
PO Box 91, Walpole, MA 02081
Barry Parker (508) 668-6919
30 mi. W of Boston
Type: Public/Member
Hrs: Th, 5-Dark; Su, 11-3
Sporting: 1, 15 stations
Trap: 4 Skeet: 1 HT: 30 ft.

Wilderness Adventures
219 John Wise Ave.,
Essex, MA 01929
Allan F. Guminski (508) 768-3338
33 mi. NE of Boston
Type: Public
Hrs: S, 9-6; Su, 12-6 By Appt.
Sporting: Y Trap: 1 Skeet: 1

TRAP & SKEET

Danvers Fish & Game Club
3 Judith Rd., Peabody, MA 01960
Charlie Parziale (508) 774-9541
Trap: 2 Skeet: 2

The Eight Point Sportsmen's
PO Box 235, Sterling, MA 01564
Richard Hewett (508) 278-3095
Hrs: Su/T, 1-4; Th, 6-9; S, 1-5
Trap: 2 Skeet: 1

Fitchburg Sportsmen's
Box 624, Ashburnham, MA 01430
Richard Moorcroft (508) 827-6641
Hrs: T, 5-10
Sporting: Y Trap: 1 Skeet: 2

Franklin Co. League
19 James St., Greenfield, MA
01301
Dr. Norman Pike (413) 773-8750
Hrs: S/Su, Noon-5; W, 5-Dusk
Trap: 4 Skeet: 2

Holbrook Sportsmen's Club
PO Box 275, Holbrook, MA 02343
Arthur Lavallee (617) 767-4971
Hrs: W, 6-9; S, 12:30-4; Su, 9-3
Trap: 4

Ludlow Fish & Game Club
28 Crown St., Westfield, MA 01085
Porter Burns (413) 583-4055
Trap: 1 Skeet: 7

Martha's Vineyard R&G Club
PO Box 2157,
Vineyard Haven, MA 02568
Harold Green (508) 627-3537
2.5 mi. NE of Edgartown
Type: Member/Avail
Hrs: Su, 12-5
Trap: 1 Skeet: 1

Massapoag Sportsmens
21 Clark St., Braintree, MA 02184
Ralph Newman (617) 784-5856
Hrs: Su, 10-3; S, 12-3
Trap: 1 Skeet: 3

Minute Man Sportsmans
15 S. Bedford St.,
Burlington, MA 01803
Andy Greene (617) 272-7169
Hrs: W/Su, 12-Sunset; S, 10-Sunset
Trap: 14 Skeet: 10

Nauset Rod & Gun Club
83 Fortune Farrow Way,
Brewster, MA 02651

Ronald P. Goguen (508) 240-0198
Hrs: Su, 9:30-1; W, 1-3:30; S,
9:30-11 Skeet: 2

North Leominster R&G
PO Box 25, Leominster, MA 01453
G. W. Makrianis (508) 840-6322
18 mi. N of Worcester
Type: Public/Member
Hrs: Th, 6-10; Su, 9-1
Sporting: 1, 11 stations
Trap: 6 Skeet: 3

Riverside Gun Club
48 Crestwood Lane,
Marlboro, MA 01752
Lenny O'Reilly (508) 562-2404
Hrs: Daily, 9-9
Trap: 2 Skeet: 2

Royalston Fish & Game
New Boston Rd.,
S. Royalston, MA 01331
Roy Smith, Jr. (508) 249-9687
Hrs: S, 1-5; W, 6-9
Trap: 8

Scituate Rod & Gun Club
Box 321, N. Scituate, MA 02060
Bill Gray (617) 545-1510
Hrs: W, 6-9; Su, 12-6
Skeet: 1

Sheffield Sporting Club
PO Box 1033, Sheffield, MA 01257
Wayne Palmer (413) 229-8766
Hrs: W, 5-8; Su, 9-1
Trap: 1 Skeet: 2

Shirley Rod & Gun Club
28 Rodman Ave., Shirley, MA 01464
Richard Pontbriand (617) 425-4039
Hrs: W, 6-9; Su, 1-6
Trap: 2

Singletary Rod & Gun Club
11 Wesley Dr., Leicester, MA 01524
Frank Laureyns (617) 987-8783
Hrs: W, 6:30-10; S, 1-5
Trap: 6

Stockbridge Sportsmen's
Rt. 102, Stockbridge, MA 01262
Gary Johnston (413) 298-3623
30 mi. E of Albany, NY
Type: Public/Member
Hrs: T/Th, 5-Dark; Su, 9-Noon;
Others by appt. Skeet: 2

4-Square Sportsmans
6777 Cline Rd., Jeddo, MI 48032
Roger Pilos (810) 327-6859
60 mi. N of Detroit
Type: Public/Member
Hrs: S/Su, 10-5; Wed. night shoots
Sporting: 1, 22 stations
Trap: 3

MICHIGAN

SPORTING & 5-STAND

Alpena
Sportsman Club
4260 M-32 West, Alpena, MI 49707
Frank Malenski (517) 354-2582
3.5 mi. W of Alpena
Type: Public/Member
Hrs: S, 9-3; Su, 9-4; W (Summer), 3-6
Reservs: Recommended
Sporting: 1, 11 stations

Bald Mountain Gun Range
2500 Kern Rd.,
Lake Orion, MI 48360
Larry Woo (810) 814-9193
30 mi. N of Detroit
Type: Public
Hrs: S/Su, 10-6; W, 1-Dark; M/T,
12-Dark **Sporting:** 1, 12 stations
Trap: 3 **Skeet:** 4 **Five Stand:** 1
See Our Ad, Right

Bay County Conservation
2985 Cadillac Dr.,
Bay City, MI 48706
Val Syring (517) 631-9944
85 mi. NW of Detroit
Type: Public/Member
Hrs: M/W, 4-9; S/Su, 11:30-5
Sporting: 1, 10 stations
Trap: 2 **Skeet:** 4 **HT:** 20 ft.

Big Creek Shooting
PO box 369, Mio, MI 48647
Steven Basl (517) 826-3606
130 mi. NE of Grand Rapids
Type: Public/Member
Hrs: Su-S, Sunup-Sundown
Sporting: 1, 7 stations
Trap: 1 **Skeet:** 1 **HT:** 15 ft.

Blendon Pines
8455 88th Ave., Zeeland, MI 49464
Rog Van Eerden (616) 875-7000
20 mi. W of Grand Rapids
Type: Public
Hrs: W,9-6;Th, 2-6;S, 8-4; Tu & Fr
by app't
Reservs: Recommended
Sporting: 1, 10 stations
Five Stand: 1 **HT:** 30 ft.

Brule
Sporting Clays
397 Brule Mt. Rd.,
Iron River, MI 49935
Steve Polich (800) 362-7853
6 mi. S of Iron River
Type: Public
Hrs: Tues. pm; S/Su, 9-6;
every day by appt.
Reservs: Recommended
Sporting: 3, 45 stations **HT:** 60 ft.
○ Call 1-800-DO BRULE
○ Stay & Shoot Packages
○ $89 Lodging 200 Targets
○ Guns & Ammo Sale & Rent
○ Lodge & Meals

Caledonia Sportsmans Club
Box 162, Caledonia, MI 49316
Mike Fitzsimmons (616) 891-1168
15 mi. SE of Grand Rapids
Type: Public/Member
Hrs: W/Th, 6-10; S, 10-6; Su, 12-6
Sporting: 1, 10 stations
Trap: 2 **Skeet:** 2 **HT:** 30 ft.

Capital Area Sportsman's
7534 Old River Trail,
Lansing, MI 48917
Dave Blankenburg (517) 321-3155
5 mi. from Lansing
Type: Public/Member
Hrs: S, 10am; W, 5-8; Su, 10-2
Sporting: 1, 15 stations
Trap: 1 **Skeet:** 2 **Five Stand:** 1

Cedar
Rod & Gun Club
1811 East Front St.,
Traverse City, MI 49686
Jim Hintz (616) 933-0543
17 mi. NW of Traverse City
Type: Public/Member
Hrs: T, 6:30-10; W, 10-8; F,
6:30-10; S, 10-4
Reservs: Recommended
Sporting: 1, 10 stations
Trap: 2 **Skeet:** 1

Crazy Quail/Sporting
2437 South 4th St.,
Alpena, MI 49707
Jon & Joe Bloomberg
(517) 356-9462 **Hrs:** Mobile Unit

DEER CREEK
HUNT CLUB

Deer Creek Hunt Club
18000 Basswood Rd.,
Three Oaks, MI 49128
George W. Daniels (616) 756-6600
50 mi. SE of Chicago
Type: Public/Member
Hrs: Su-S, 9am-9pm
Reservs: Strongly recommended
Sporting: 1, 16 stations
Skeet: Y **Five Stand:** 1 **HT:** 65 ft.

Detroit Sportsmen's
56670 Jewell,
Shelby Twp., MI 48315
Karen Peterson (810) 739-2210
Type: Public/Member
Sporting: 1, 14 stations
Trap: 5 **Skeet:** 5 **Wobble Trap**

Fenton Lakes Clays
1140 Butcher Rd.,
Fenton, MI 48430
Al Roy (517) 548-4566
50 mi. NW of Detroit
Type: Public
Hrs: W, 3-8:30; Su, 10-5
Reservs: Not required
Sporting: 2, 15 stations
Trap: 1 **Skeet:** 1 **HT:** 25 ft.

Flat River Conservation
332 S. Greenville Rd., PO Box 424,
Greenville, MI 48838
Ed Skinner (616) 754-9855
8 mi. N of Greenville
Type: Public/Member
Hrs: Su, 10-4; Closed 11/15-1/15
Sporting: 2, 24 stations
Trap: 2 **Skeet:** 1 **Five Stand:** 1

Genesee Sportsmans Club
8208 N. Seymour Rd.,
Flushing, MI 48532
Robert Ballard (810) 639-5100
Type: Public/Member
Hrs: W, 5-9; S/Su, 10-4
Sporting: 2 **Trap:** 4 **Skeet:** 4

Grand Blanc Huntsman's
9046 S. Irish Rd.,
Grand Blanc, MI 48439
H.V. Burrow (810) 636-7261
5 mi. SE of Grand Blanc
Type: Public/Member
Hrs: S/Su, 9-5; W, 9-10
Sporting: 1, 13 stations
Trap: 4 **Skeet:** 4

Hunter's Creek Club
675 Sutton Rd.,
Metamora, MI 48455
Charlie Mann (810) 664-4307
30 mi. N of Detroit
Type: Member/Avail
Hrs: Daily, except Monday
Reservs: Strongly recommended
Sporting: 1, 10 stations
Trap: 1 **Skeet:** 1 **HT:** 70 ft.
Wobble Trap
○ Shooting Instruction Available—
See Ad Pg. 213
See Our Ad Pg. 349

Hunter's Ridge Hunt Club
3921 Barber, Oxford, MI 48371
David M. Fischer (810) 628-4868
25 mi. N of Detroit
Type: Public
Hrs: W, 2-4; S, 9-4
Reservs: Strongly recommended
Sporting: 1, 15 stations
Trap: 1 **Skeet:** 1 **HT**
Wobble Trap

The Huntsman Hunt Club
3166 Havens Rd.,
Dryden, MI 48428
Nora M. Tebben (810) 796-3000
40 mi. N of Detroit
Type: Member/Avail
Reservs: Strongly recommended
Sporting: 2, 15 stations
Wobble Trap
See Our Ad Pg. 351

Kent County Conservation
8461 Conservation NE, Box 397,
Ada, MI 49301
Manager (616) 676-1056
8 mi. E of Grand Rapids
Type: Public/Member
Hrs: T/Th, 4-10; S/Su, 10-5
Sporting: 1, 12 stations
Trap: 5 **Skeet:** 5 **Wobble Trap**

Lapeer County Sportsmens
1213 Lake George Rd.,
Attica, MI 48455
Bill Behnke (810) 724-6579
25 mi. E of Flint
Type: Public/Member
Hrs: Su, 10-5; T, 4-10
Sporting: 1, 16 stations
Trap: 5 **Skeet:** 2 **Five Stand:** 1

Lewiston Sportsmen's League
Sheraton Valley Rd.,
Lewiston, MI 49756
Cheryl Scott (517) 786-3104
26 mi. E of Gaylord
Type: Public/Member
Hrs: Tu, 5-dk, Sa/Su, 11-4,
Winter Su only
Reservs: Not required
Sporting: 1, 16 stations

Lost Arrow Hunting Preserve
1749 Bomanville Rd.,
Gladwin, MI 48624
Avery Sterling (517) 345-7774
45 mi. N of Saginaw
Type: Public **Hrs:** **Sporting:** 1

Lucky Feather Game Farm
2040 N. Pittsford Rd.,
Hillsdale, MI 49242
Hal Bennett (517) 523-2050
80 mi. SW of Detroit
Type: Public
Hrs: Su-S, daylight hours; yearly
Sporting: 2 **HT:** 55 ft.

Mid-U.P. Shooters Inc.
PO Box 206, Negaunee, MI 49866
J. E. Frounfelter (906) 475-4957
13 mi. W of Marquette
Type: Public/Member
Hrs: S/Su, 12-6; W, 5-10
Sporting: 1, 10 stations
Trap: 3 **Skeet:** 2

Mid-Upper Peninsula
765 White Ave.,
Ishpeming, MI 49849
Brett W. French (906) 486-4526
Type: Public/Member
Hrs: Varies
Sporting: 1, 10 stations
Trap: 3 **Skeet:** 2

Monterey Sporting Clays
2726 134th Ave.,
Hopkins, MI 49328
James Spray (616) 793-7400
25 mi. SW of Grand Rapids
Type: Public/Member
Hrs: M-Th, 10-Dark; S, 9-6
Sporting: 2, 25 stations
Five Stand: Y **HT:** 30 ft.

North Ottawa Rod & Gun
15596 Pine St.,
Grand Haven, MI 49417
Forrest Palmer (616) 842-9711
Hrs: W, 5-9; S/Su, 9-2
Sporting: None
Trap: 4 **Skeet:** 4 **Five Stand:** 1

Orchard Hill Sporting Clays
PO Box 463, Escanaba, MI 49829
Mike Gierke (906) 466-2887
4 mi. SW of Bark River
Type: Public **Hrs:** T/W/Th, 1-8; S,
9-6; Su, 9-1 **Sporting:** 1, 8
stations **Five Stand:** 1

PGW Haymarsh Hunt Club
9215 Jefferson Rd.,
Lakeview, MI 48850
Bud Gummer (517) 352-6727
50 mi. N of Grand Rapids
Type: Public **Hrs:** Flexible
Sporting: 2, 11 stations
Trap: 1 **Five Stand:** 1

Pere Marquette Sporting
PO Box 3, Chase, MI 49623
Greg Bishop (616) 832-9055
6 mi. W of Reed City
Type: Public
Hrs: F, 4-Dark; S/Su, 9-Dark; Others
by appt. **Sporting:** 1, 5 stations

Pointe Mouillee Shooting
10670 US Turnpike, South
Rockwood, MI 48179
Michael Winter (313) 379-3820
Type: Public/Member
Hrs: W-Su, 10-9
Sporting: None **Trap:** 2 **Skeet:** 5
Five Stand: 1 **Wobble Trap**

Rolling Hills
17025 McKenzie St.,
Marcellus, MI 49067
Curt Johnson (616) 646-9164
60 mi. SW of Grand Rapids
Type: Public
Hrs: Su-S, call for appt.
Sporting: 1, 10 stations

Saginaw Gun Club, Inc.
PO Box 6054, Saginaw, MI 48603
Cindy Baudoux (517) 781-2260
70 mi. NW of Detroit
Type: Public/Member
Hrs: Th, 12-9; S/Su, 12-5
Sporting: 1, 10 stations
Trap: 4 **Skeet:** 4

South Haven Rod & Gun
68611 8th Ave.,
South Haven, MI 49090
Geary Garvison (616) 637-8001
120 mi. W of Detroit
Type: Public/Member
Hrs: S/Su, 10-5 **Sporting:** 1

Southern Mich. Gun Club
34250 Bond Dr.,
Paw Paw, MI 49079
Norm Rushing (616) 388-6581
Hrs: Th, 5-10; Su, 9-2
Sporting: None
Trap: 3 **Skeet:** 4 **Five Stand:** 1

Stoney Point Sporting
12013 Grover Rd.,
Hanover, MI 49241
Mark Nastally (800) 319-6222
14 mi. SW of Jackson
Type: Public
Hrs: S/Su, 9-6; Wkdays by appt.
Sporting: 1, 11 stations

Sugar Springs Sporting
1491 W. Sargeant Rd.,
Gladwin, MI 48624
Lou Dallas (517) 426-2645
Type: Public
Hrs: S/Su, 9-3 by appt.
Sporting: 1 **Five Stand:** 1
Wobble Trap

Thundering Aspens
4421 N. 5 1/2 Rd.,
Mesick, MI 49668
Greg Wright (616) 885-2420
110 mi. N of Grand Rapids
Type: Public/Member
Sporting: 1, 15 stations

Top Gun Hunt Club
1937 68th St., Fennville, MI 49408
George Vuillemot (616) 543-3351
35 mi. SW of Grand Rapids
Type: Public **Hrs:** By appt. only
Sporting: 1

Williams Gun Sight Open
7389 E. Lapeer Rd. (Box 329),
Davidson, MI 48423
Tom Wright (810) 653-2131
50 mi. N of Detroit
Hrs: W/S, 9-6; Su, 10-5
Trap: 1 **Skeet:** 2 **Five Stand:** 1

Willow Lake Sportsmen's
51704 U.S. 131,
Three Rivers, MI 49093
Hal Standish (616) 279-7124
65 mi. S of Grand Rapids
Type: Member/Avail
Hrs: Su-S, 8:30-dark
Sporting: 1, 8 stations HT: 20 ft.

Woodmoor Resort
26 Maxton Rd.,
Drummond Isl., MI 49726
Steve Gilbert (906) 493-1008
40 mi. SE of Sault Ste. Marie
Type: Public
Hrs: May 3-Nov. 14; Open daily
Reservs: Recommended
Sporting: 1, 8 stations HT: 40 ft.

See Our Ad Pg. 353

Wycamp Lake Camp
c/o 5484 Pleasantview Rd., Harbor
Springs, MI 49740
Dirk Shorter (616) 537-4830
16 mi. SW of Macinaw City
Type: Public/Member
Hrs: Apr-Nov, Daily by appt.
Sporting: 2, 32 stations HT: 150'

TRAP & SKEET

Barry County Conservation
PO Box 14, Hastings, MI 49058
Sam Sobey (616) 945-9058
Hrs: S, 1-6 **Trap:** 4

Battle Creek Gun Club
416 Glendale Ave.,
Battle Creek, MI 49017
Robert D. Hall (616) 965-1370
Type: Public/Member
Hrs: Su, 10-3; Th, 4:30-Dusk
Trap: 4 **Skeet:** 3

Berrien Co. Sportsmans
PO Box 325, St. Joseph, MI 49085
George V. Nichols (616) 429-3792
Hrs: Su, 10-2; T, 7-9; S, 1
Trap: 4 **Skeet:** 2

Cass City Gun Club
263 S. Main St., Pigeon, MI 48755
Ronald L. Snider (517) 872-5395
Hrs: W, 5-10; Su, 11-5
Trap: 2 **Skeet:** 1

Elk Rapids Sportsman Club
PO Box 705, Elk Rapids, MI 49629
Pat Fegan (616) 264-5250
Hrs: W, 2-5; Su, 10-5
Trap: 1 **Skeet:** 2

Gun River Skeet & Trap Inc.
620 11th St., PO Box 151,
Plainwell, MI 49080
Dan Doubblestien (616) 685-5280
Hrs: F, 6-9; S, 9-2; Su, 9-12, W, 6-10
Trap: 4 **Skeet:** 4

Iosco Sportsmens Club
1170 Bischuff Rd.,
East Tawas, MI 48730
Neal R. Miller (517) 362-5963
Type: Public/Member
Hrs: M/Th; Eve.; Su, 1pm
Trap: 2

Lost Lake Woods Assn.
4243 Lost Lake Trail,
Lincoln, MI 48742
Stephen Pedersen (517) 736-8197
Hrs: F/S/Su, 10-6 (Apr-Oct)
Trap: 1 **Skeet:** 2

Manistique Rifle & Pistol
Rt. 2, Box 2826,
Mainistique, MI 49854
Jim Creighton (906) 341-2124
Type: Public/Member
Trap: 4 **Skeet:** 2

Michigan Trapshooting Assn.
1534 W. Service Rd.,
Mason, MI 48854
Ben Johnston (517) 676-2295
Trap: 40

Multi-Lakes Conserv. Assn.
8361 Newton Rd.,
Walled Lake, MI 48042
Peter Cesaro (810) 360-2765
40 mi. W of Detroit
Type: Public/Member
Hrs: Th, Noon-6 (Summer); S/Su,
Noon-Dark **Sporting:** 1, 14 sta.
Trap: 2 **Skeet:** 2

Nawakwa Hunt & Gun Club
4957 Bloomfield Ridge,
Bloomfield Hills, MI 48302
Howard Confer (517) 848-2751
Sporting: Y **Trap:** 1 **Skeet:** 2

Northport Pt. Cottage Own.
PO Box 115, Northport, MI 49670
Gerard Jacobson (616) 386-5075
Hrs: 3 Afternoons/wk, 2-5
Trap: 1 Skeet: 1

Oak Hill Gun Club
238 N. Grant, Portland, MI 48875
Dan Pline (517) 647-7303
Hrs: Su, 10; M/W, 6:30-11
Trap: 3 Wobble Trap

Portage Lake Sportsmen
RR1, Box 37, Houghton, MI 49931
Bill Hockings (906) 482-5311
Type: Public/Member
Hrs: W, 6-9 Trap: 2

Reed City Sportsman Club
13877 N. Beech Ave., Reed City,
MI 49677
Linda Sweet (616) 832-4481
Trap: 1 Skeet: 2

Seaway Gun Club
3400 West Bard Rd., Muskegon,
MI 49445
John Hughes (616) 766-3428
Hrs: W, 5-10; Su, 10-3
Trap: 7 Skeet: 4

St. Joseph Co. Conservation
28760 Fawn River Rd.,
Sturgis, MI 49091
Robert Besser (616) 467-7128
Hrs: Su, 9-1; T, 6-9
Sporting:
Trap: 3 Skeet: 1

Wayne County Sportsmans
14115 Burns, Southgate, MI
48195
Ty Cobb (313) 941-9688
Hrs: W, 12-10; S/Su, 10-6
Trap: 3 Skeet: 4

MINNESOTA

SPORTING & 5-STAND

American Heritage
Rt. 2, Box 131,
Eagle Bend, MN 56446
Don/Sue Ellwanger (218)
738-5143
140 mi. NW of Minneapolis
Type: Public/Member
Hrs: Daily, 8am-Dusk by appt.
Sporting: 2, 25 stations
Trap: 1 HT: 35 ft.

Caribou Gun Club
Rt. 1, Box 26, Le Sueur, MN 56058
Randy Voss (612) 665-3796
55 mi. SW of Minneapolis-St. Paul
Type: Public/Member

Hrs: Su-S, daylight-dark
Sporting: 2, 31 stations
Trap: 3 Skeet: 1 HT: 175 ft.

Central Minnesota Gun
3030 12th St., SE, St.
Cloud, MN 56304
Dick Berger (612) 252-5630
Type: Public
Hrs: M/Th, 9-9:30; T/W/F,
12-5:30; S, 9-4, Su
Sporting: 1, 13 stations
Trap: 14 Skeet: 1

Charlie's Hunting Club
RR1, Box 173, Danvers, MN 56231
Jim Langan (612) 567-2276
115 mi. W of Minneapolis
Type: Public Hrs: T-Th, 12-dark
Sporting: 1, 10 stations
Trap: 1 HT: 50 ft. Wobble Trap

Clear Creek Outdoors
2550 Hwy. 23,
Wrenshall, MN 55797
Patrick LaBoone (218) 384-3670
6 mi. SW of Duluth
Type: Public/Member
Reservs: Strongly recommended
Sporting: 1, 14 stations HT: 35 ft
O Shooting Instruction Available—
See Ad Pg. 205

Crookston Gun Club
RR1, Box 259, Crookston, MN 56716
Myron Uttermark (218) 281-5143
70 mi. N of Fargo
Type: Public/Member
Hrs: M/W, 6:30-Dk; Some Wkends
Sporting: 1, 10 stations
Trap: 3 HT: 40 ft. Wobble Trap

Dalton Hunting
RR1, Box 290, Dalton, MN 56324
Dick Henkes (218) 589-8523
60 mi. SE of Fargo
Type: Public Hrs: 12-Dark, 7 days
by appt. Sporting: 1, 20 stations
Trap: 1 Skeet: 1 HT: 40 ft.

Dead Horse Creek
RR 2, Box 103, Frazee, MN 56544
Chris Wacker (218) 334-4868
180 mi. NW of Minneapolis
Type: Public/Member
Sporting: 1, 20 stations

Federal Shooting Sports Ctr.
16128 Varialite St.,
NW, Anoka, MN 55303
Jack McKusick (612) 421-3741
35 mi. NW of Minneapolis
Type: Public
Hrs: Mo-Th, 6-9; Su, 12-5; & by appt.
Sporting: 1, 8 stations
Trap: 9 Skeet: 2 Five Stand: 1

Fischer's Hunt Club
29512 223rd Ave.,
Albany, MN 56307
Pete Fischer (320) 597-2729
85 mi. NW of Minneapolis
Type: Member/Avail
Sporting: 1, 30 stations

Fort Thunder PSC
RR3, Box 30, Perham, MN 56573
Leroy Atkinson (218) 346-6083
170 mi. NW of Minneapolis
Type: Public
Hrs: Su, 1-5; M/W, 5-dusk or by appt.
Sporting: 1, 15 stations
Trap: 5 Skeet: 5 Five Stand: 1

H&R Shooting Preserve
34934 140th Ave., Avon, MN 56310
David J. Raab (612) 356-7427
Sporting: 1

Horse Barn & Hunt Club
RR1, Box 103, Lakefield, MN 56150
Brent Rossow (507) 662-5490
20 mi. NE of Iowa Great Lakes Area
Type: Public/Member
Hrs: W-Su, 1-Sunset or by appt.
Sporting: 1, 13 stations HT: 70 ft.

Johnson Enterprises
Rt. 3, Box 45, Canby, MN 56220
Roger D. Johnson (507) 223-7992
N of Canby Type: Public/Member
Hrs: Fri. & Sat.
Sporting: 1, 13 stations
Trap: 1 HT: 20 ft.

Lac Qui Parle Hunting
RR5, Box 68, Montevideo, MN 56265
Steve Baldwin (612) 269-9769
110 mi. W of Minneapolis
Type: Public/Member
Hrs: S/Su, 9-Dk; Others by appt.
Sporting: 1, 15 stations
Trap: 1 Skeet: 1 HT: 100 ft.

Don Le Blanc
Rt. 5, Box 228, Little Falls, MN 56345
Don/Marge Le Blanc (612)
745-2522
85 mi. NW of Minneapolis
Type: Public/Member
Hrs: Daily, dawn to dusk by appt.
Sporting: 1, 22 stations HT: 60 ft.

LeBlanc Rice Creek
Rt. 5, Box 213, Little Falls, MN 56345
Gregg LeBlanc (612) 745-2451
85 mi. N of Minneapolis
Type: Public Hrs: Su-S
Sporting: 2, 25 stations
Trap: 3 HT: 30 ft.

Little Moran Hunting Club
Rt. 1, Pheasant Valley Rd.,
Staples, MN 56479
Steve Grossman (218) 894-3852
130 mi. NW of Minneapolis

Type: Public **Hrs:** Daily by appt.
Sporting: 3, 30 stations
Five Stand: 1   **HT:** 80 ft.

Lock & Load Hunting Club
Rt. 1, Box 44A,
Middle River, MN 56737
Dan Rantanen (218) 222-3714
210 mi. NW of Duluth
Type: Public/Member
Hrs: Daily by appt.
Sporting: 1, 10 stations **Trap:** 3

Major Ave. Hunt Club
11721 Major Ave.,
Glencoe, MN 55336
Gerald G. Martin (320) 864-6025
Type: Public **Hrs:** Daily, 8am-Dark
Sporting: 2, 22 stations
HT: 50 ft. **Wobble Trap**

Maple Island Hunt Club
425 Hamm Bldg.,
St. Paul, MN 55102
Maurice Grogan (612) 439-2405
Type: Public/Member
Hrs: By reservation
Sporting: 1, 10 stations **Trap:** Y

Metro Gun Club
10601 Naples St., NE,
Blaine, MN 55434
Loren Hentges (612) 786-5880
Hrs: M-Th, 10-9:30; F-Su, 10-5
Sporting: None
Trap: 14 **Skeet:** 6 **Five Stand:** 1

Minneapolis Gun Club
20006 Judicial Rd.,
Prior Lake, MN 55372
Jerry Hazel (612) 469-4386
Type: Public/Member
Hrs: T/W/Th, 12-Dark; F, 12-4;
S/Su, 10-4 **Sporting:** None
Trap: 10 **Skeet:** 8 **Five Stand:** 1
Wobble Trap

MINNESOTA

HORSE & HUNT
CLUB

Minnesota Horse & Hunt Club
2920 220th St.,
Prior Lake, MN 55372
Terry Correll (612) 447-2272
25 mi. SW of Minneapolis-St. Paul
Type: Public/Member
Hrs: T-Su, 9am-Dusk; M, 12-Dusk
Reservs: Recommended
Sporting: 4, 24 stations
Trap: 2 **Skeet:** 2 **HT:** 65 ft.
Wobble Trap

Misty Meadows
HC9, Box 439,
Detroit Lakes, MN 56501
Steve Laine (218) 847-4680
16 mi. E of Detroit Lakes
Type: Public **Hrs:** Su-S, 8-Dark
Sporting: 2, 24 stations **Trap:** 1

North Creek Sporting Clays
RR1, Box 146,
Lakefield, MN 56150
Ted Pehlman (507) 662-6703
70 mi. E of Sioux Falls, SD
Type: Public
Hrs: W, 4-Dk; S/Su, 1-5; & by appt.
Sporting: 1, 9 stations

Northwest Sporting Clays
RR2, Box 247,
Thief River Falls, MN 56701
Tony Dorn, Jr. (218) 681-6857
50 mi. E of Grand Forks, ND
Type: Public/Member
Hrs: By Appt. **Sporting:** 1, 15 sta.
Trap: 3 **HT:** 60 ft.

Oak Point
RR3, Box 44-A,
Wadena, MN 56482
Don Dykhoff (218) 631-4467
Type: Public **Hrs:**
Sporting: 1

Peaceful Acres Sport. Clays
RR2, Slayton, MN 56172
Leroy Kalass (507) 836-6188
20 mi. S of Marshall
Type: Public/Member
Hrs: Open 7 Days a Week
Sporting: 1, 8 stations

Pheasants Plus, Inc.
HCR01, Box 16, Warba, MN 55793
Keith Austin (218) 492-4450
16 mi. SE of Grand Rapids
Type: Public
Hrs: Winter: Sa/Su, 12-dk; Summer
Tu/Th, eves. Su, 12-d
Reservs: Not required
Sporting: 2, 21 stations **HT:** 35 ft.

Pleasant Acres
RR1, Box 129,
Courtland, MN 56021
Lester Zwach (507) 359-5770
70 mi. SW of Minneapolis
Type: Public **Hrs:** T-Su, 9-dark
Sporting: 1, 22 stations
Trap: 1 **Five Stand:** 5 **HT:** 70 ft.

Ringneck Ridge
Rt. 1, Box 319, Motley, MN 56466
John Jacklitch (218) 575-2913
100 mi. N of Minneapolis
Type: Public
Hrs: Everyday, 9-dusk
Sporting: 1, 10 stations **HT:** 27 ft.

Royal Flush Shooting Club
Rt. 5, Box 228,
Little Falls, MN 56345
Bob Schneider (612) 745-2522
85 mi. NW of Minneapolis
Type: Public/Member
Hrs: Daily, by appt. only
Sporting: 1, 12 stations
Trap: 1 **HT:** 60 ft.

Rum River Pheasant Club
30925 CR 5 NW,
Princeton, MN 55371
Rick Johnson (612) 389-2316
45 mi. N of Minneapolis
Type: Public/Member
Hrs: Daily, 3:30-Dark by appt.
Sporting: 2, 13 stations **Trap:** 3

Shoot-Out Sporting Clays
RR2, Box 7, Hwy. 28 West,
Morris, MN 56267
Ed Boettcher (612) 589-1102
150 mi. W of Minneapolis
Type: Public
Hrs: Su, 10-5; Weekday evenings
Sporting: Y

Shooters
Rt. 1, Box 135A, Marshall, MN 56258
Steven Petersen (507) 336-2560
9.5 mi. E of Marshall
Type: Public
Hrs: S/Su, 10-6; & by app't
Sporting: 3, 30 stations
Five Stand: 1

South St. Paul Rod & Gun
600 Gun Club Road,
South St. Paul, MN 55075
Bob Haselberger (612) 455-7249
5 mi. S of St. Paul
Type: Public/Member
Hrs: T/W/Th, 4-dark; Sa/Su, 10-4
Reservs: Recommended
Sporting: 1, 13 stations
Trap: 4 **Skeet:** 3 **HT:** 40 ft.

Ten Mile Creek Preserve
Rt. 1, Box 85, Dunnell, MN 56127
Michael Honnette (507) 695-2544
140 mi. SW of Minneapolis
Sporting: 1, 8 stations

Timber Creek Sport. Clays
9440 95th St. S.E.,
Chatfield, MN 55923
Club Manager (507) 867-4199
40 mi. S of Rochester
Type: Public **Hrs:** T-Su, 9-6
Sporting: 1, 10 stations

Udovich Guide Service
12503 Sethers Rd.,
Gheen, MN 55771

Dennis Udovich (218) 787-2237
225 mi. N of Minneapolis
Type: Public/Member
Hrs: Apr-Sept, W/Su, 12-Dk & by
appt. **Sporting:** 1

Valhalla Hunt Club
RR1, Albert Lea, MN 56007
Gary Pestorious (507) 377-7225
85 mi. S of Minneapolis
Type: Public/Member
Hrs: Daily by appt.
Sporting: 1, 20 stations **HT:** 80 ft.

Vermillion Trail Sport. Clays
6980 Old Vermillion Trail,
Duluth, MN 55803
Bert Schweiger (218) 721-3804
Type: Public
Hrs: T/W/Th, 12-Dark; S/Su, 12-6
Sporting: 1, 10 stations
Skeet: 1 **HT:** 45 ft.

Viking Valley Hunt Club
Rt. 1, Box 198, Ashby, MN 56309
Les Bensch (218) 747-2121
140 mi. NW of Minneapolis
Type: Public/Member
Hrs: 10-7 & by appt.
Sporting: 1, 23 stations **HT:** 80 ft.

Wild Acres Hunting Club
HC83, Box 108,
Pequot Lakes, MN 56472
Mary Ebnet (218) 568-5024
150 mi. N of Minneapolis
Type: Public
Hrs: Daily by appt; 9:30-Dk
Sporting: 1, 8 stations

Wild Marsh Sporting Clays
13767 CR3, Clear Lake, MN 55319
Debbie Mortensen (612) 662-2021
60 mi. NW of Minneapolis
Type: Public/Member
Hrs: S, 11-3; Su, 10-3; W/Th,
4:30-Dark & appt.
Sporting: 1, 40 stations

Wild Wings of Oneka
9491 152nd St., N., Hugo, MN 55038
J. Hughes/G. Schulte
(612) 439-4287
15 mi. NE of Minneapolis-St. Paul
Type: Member/Avail
Hrs: Th/S/Su (Mid-Aug. thru
Mid-April) **Sporting:** 2, 20 stations
Trap: 1 **HT:** 80 ft.

Windsor Fields
6835 Hilda Rd., Tower, MN 55790
Richard Kronmiller (218) 741-5837
75 mi. N of Duluth
Type: Public/Member
Hrs: T-Su, 8-dusk by appt.
Sporting: 2, 30 stations **HT:** 40 ft.

TRAP & SKEET

3M Trap & Skeet Club
280 Hill Top Ct.,
N. St. Paul, MN 55109
Dick Raths (612) 459-8240
Hrs: T-Th, 4-8
Trap: 4 **Skeet:** 2

Albany Sportsmans Club
32496 Ironwood Dr.,
St. Joseph, MN 56374
Jim Moeller (612) 845-4271
Hrs: Su, 1-8 (May-Sept); T/W, 6-Dk
Trap: 4 **Skeet:** 2

Becker Co. Sportsmens
Box 415, Detroit Lakes, MN 56501
Archie Wiedwitsch (218) 847-3743
Hrs: T/Th, 6:30 **Trap:** 5

Bricelyn Sportsmens Club
PO Box 351, Bricelyn, MN 56014
Arden Lium (507) 653-4487
Type: Public/Member
Hrs: Th, 6pm-11pm **Trap:** Y

Fergus Falls Skeet Club
RR4, Box 30,
Ferguson Falls, MN 56537
John Piekarski (218) 736-5073
Skeet: 1

Golden Eagle Gun Club
2612 S. Broadway,
Alexandria, MN 56308
Art Thompson (612) 763-5315
Type: Public/Member
Trap: 5 **Skeet:** 1

Grand Rapids Gun Club
Box 217, Bovey, MN 55709
Dick Sturk (218) 326-3348
Type: Public **Hrs:** T/W/Th, 12-Dk
Trap: 9

Lester Prairie Sportsmens
227 N. Maple St.,
Lester Prairie, MN 55354
Ed Mlynar (612) 395-2258
Hrs: Mid-April-August, Wed. night
& reg. targets **Trap:** 5

Minnetonka Game & Fish
20211 Smith St., NW,
Elk River, MN 55330
S. Vogel (612) 349-9712
Hrs: W, 6:30-10 & Registered
Shoots **Trap:** 2 **Skeet:** 2

MISSISSIPPI

SPORTING & 5-STAND

Bad Rabbit Sporting Clays
Box 677, West Point, MS 39773
Robert Harrell (601) 494-1800
170 mi. SE of Memphis
Type: Public **Hrs:** by app't only
Sporting: 1, 5 stations **HT:** 15 ft.

Capitol Gun Club
PO Box 12973, Jackson, MS 39236
Hugh McInnis, Jr. (601) 957-2212
Hrs: S/Su, 1-Sundown; Th,
3-Sundown **Sporting:** 1, 7 sta.
Trap: 5 **Skeet:** 5

Daybreak Sporting Clays
134 Lilac Dr., Leland, MS 38756
John Ingram (601) 686-9013
14 mi. S of Greenville
Type: Public **Hrs:** By Appt. Only
Sporting: 1, 12 stations
Five Stand: 1 **HT:** 30 ft.

Dunn's Shooting Grounds
Rt. 3, Box 39D4,
Holly Springs, MS 38635
Jim Cassidy (601) 564-1111
35 mi. SE of Memphis
Type: Public
Hrs: S, 9-5; Su, 1-5; Wkdays, resrv.
Reservs: Recommended
Sporting: 1, 10 stations **HT:** 35 ft.
o Factory Ammunition
o On-Site Meals
o Shooting Lodge
o Plantation Style Quail Hunts
   Available
o Shooting School

Get Away Place
PO Box 472, Waynesboro, MS
39367
Dan Young (601) 735-5764
125 mi. SE of Jackson
Type: Public/Member
Hrs: Th, 2-Dark; S, 8-Dark; Su,
2-Dark
Sporting: 1, 14 stations

Make the Best Better
Black's Wing & Clay is the most comprehensive, well organized
and easy-to-use directory available to shotgunning enthusiasts
and the companies that serve them. Help us make it even better. If we've made an error or an omission, let us know. Call:
(908) 224-8700. Thanks.

Kearney Park Shooting
151 Ergon Rd., Flora, MS 39071
Chuck Boyer (601) 879-3249
10 mi. N of Jackson
Type: Public **Hrs:** M-Sa, 8-5
(Apr-Oct/Min. 6 shooters)
Reservs: Strongly recommended
Sporting: 1, 11 stations **HT:** 40 ft.

Levee Break
Sporting Clays
253 Avondale Rd.,
Greenville, MS 38703
Tom Eubank (601) 335-8489
7 mi. N of Greenville
Type: Public
Hrs: T/Th/S, Afternoons
Reservs: Recommended
Sporting: 1, 10 stations **HT:** 20 ft.

Natchez Flyway
338 N. Palestine Rd.,
Natchez, MS 39120
Terry Wagoner (601) 442-0136
80 mi. SW of Jackson
Type: Public **Hrs:** By appt. only
Sporting: 1, 10 stations

Ol' Place Sporting Clays
Rt. 5, Box 360, Lucedale, MS 39452
Joel Fike (601) 947-4726
45 mi. W of Mobile, AL
Type: Public **Hrs:** S/Su, by appt.
Sporting: 1, 20 stations

Plantation Sporting Clays
Box 1082, Picayune, MS 39466
T. Knight (601) 798-6919
50 mi. N of New Orleans
Type: Public/Member
Sporting: 1, 18 stations **HT:** 30 ft.

Rolling Hills Sporting Clays
440 Hickory Grove Rd.,
Dalesville, MS 39326
Derek D. Sevier (601) 681-8459
6 mi. E of Meridian
Type: Public
Hrs: M-F, by appt; S/Su, 12-Dark
Sporting: 1, 10 stations

Tara Wildlife Management
6791 Eagle Lake Shore Rd.,
Vicksburg, MS 39180
Sid Montgomery (601) 279-4261
25 mi. NW of Vicksburg
Type: Public **Hrs:** By Appt. Only
Sporting: 1, 15 stations
Skeet: 1 **HT**

TRAP & SKEET

CBR Skeet Range
209 Canal St., McComb, MS 39648
Milton Burris (601) 684-4781
Skeet: 2

Coast Rifle & Pistol Club
217 Ashley Place,
Ocean Springs, MS 39564
James L. Guernsey (601) 875-3858
Skeet: 2

Columbus Trap & Skeet
149 Alabama Ave.,
Columbus AFB, MS 39701
Steven Barbour (601) 434-5085
Hrs: To be determined
Trap: 1 **Skeet:** 1

Gulfport Skeet & Trap Club
3740 8th Ave., Gulfport, MS 39501
(601) 868-5971
Trap: 2 **Skeet:** 2

Lake Gep Skeet Club
1 Stonesthrow, Laurel, MS 39440
W.M. Deavours (601) 426-3729
Hrs: W, 1-5; S, 9-noon
Skeet: 2

Little Black Creek Gun Club
504 9th Ave., Lumberton, MS 39455
Brent Crider (601) 796-8001
Hrs: S/Su, 12-Dark **Skeet:** 1

Pontotoc Trap & Skeet Club
PO Box 162, Pontotoc, MS 38863
Marty Davis (601) 489-8122
Trap: 1 **Skeet:** 1

Starkville Gun Club
PO Box 383, Starkville, MS 39760
Clark Hartness (601) 320-9774
Type: Member/Avail
Hrs: By Appt. **Trap:** 4 **Skeet:** 4

MISSOURI

SPORTING & 5-STAND

B&C Game Farm
RFD1, St. Catherine, MO 64677
Jeff Sayre (816) 258-2973
110 mi. NE of Kansas City
Type: Public/Member
Sporting: 1, 10 stations **HT**

Baker's Acres Sporting
Ex. 68, Interstate 35,
Pattonsburg, MO
Ken or Sean Baker (816) 387-7915
68 mi. N of Kansas City
Type: Public
Hrs: S, 10-6; Su, 1-5; Wkdys by appt.
Sporting: 1, 15 stations

Big River Hunting Club
PO Box 30, Fletcher, MO 63030
(314) 452-3511
33 mi. SW of St. Louis
Type: Member/Avail
Hrs: M-F, 8-6; S/Su, 8-5
Sporting: 1, 7 stationsHT

Blackhawk Valley Hunting
Rt. 1, Box 118,
Old Monroe, MO 63369
Mickey Palmer (314) 665-5459
40 mi. NW of St. Louis
Type: Public/Member
Hrs: Su-S, 9-5; others by app't
Sporting: 2, 12 stations **HT:** 30 ft.

Boot Hill Sporting Clays
2531 NE JC Penney Dr.,
Hamilton, MO 64644
Ray Evans (816) 583-2275
62 mi. NE of Kansas City
Type: Public
Hrs: S, by appt; Su, 1-6
Sporting: 1, 10 stations

Cedar Creek Rod
and Gun Club
RR#6, Box 96, Columbia, MO 65202
Ralph D. Gates (314) 474-5804
13 mi. NE of Columbia
Type: Public/Member
Hrs: Su, 11-10; Th, 5-10; S, by
resrv.; T, 12noon-10pm
Reservs: Not required
Sporting: 2, 22 stations **Trap:** 6
Skeet: 6 **Five Stand:** 1 **HT:** 45 ft
○ Loaner Guns
○ Factory Ammunition
○ On-Site Meals
○ Formal Instructions
○ Golf Carts

Clear Fork Hunting Preserve
321 SE 671,
Warrensburg, MO 64093
Ruth Dillingham (816) 747-2588
50 mi. SE of Kansas City
Sporting: Y

Devil's Ridge Sporting Clays
209 NW 1771,
Kingsville, MO 64061
Jim Hatch (816) 597-3886
30 mi. SE of Kansas City
Type: Public/Member
Hrs: S/Su, 10-6; other times by
appt. **Sporting:** 1, 14 stations

Geode Hollow
RR2, Box 23A, Revere, MO 63465
Wilbur Himes (816) 754-6347
60 mi. NE of Hannibal
Type: Public
Hrs: Su-S, by reservation
Sporting: 1, 13 stations **HT:** 30 ft.

Kansas City Trapshooters
6420 N.E. 176th St.,
Smithville, MO 64089
Gary Norris (816) 532-4427
30 mi. N of Kansas City
Type: Public/Member
Hrs: W, 5-10; S/Su, 11-5
Sporting: None
Trap: 8 **Skeet:** 2 **Five Stand:** 1
Wobble Trap

Lake of the Ozarks Sporting Clays
Rt. 70, Box 964,
Camdenton, MO 65020
Jason Chappell (314) 873-3566
9 mi. N of Camdenton
Type: Public/Member
Hrs: F/S/Su, 9-5
Reservs: Strongly recommended
Sporting: 1, 10 stations
○ Loaner Guns
○ Factory Ammunition
○ Shooting Lodge

Malinmor Hunt Club
RR4, Box 108, Eolia, MO 63344
Rick Merritt (573) 324-3366
60 mi. N of St. Louis
Type: Member/Avail
Hrs: 7 Days, 8-6; by appt. only
Sporting: 2, 15 stations
Trap: 1 **Skeet:** 1

Midway Farms, Inc.
700 County Road 404,
Fayette, MO 65248
Lee Myers (816) 248-3838
125 mi. E of Kansas City
Type: Public
Hrs: For Corporate Groups &
Individuals by Resrv. Only
Sporting: 2, 10 stations **HT:** 20 ft.

New London Hunting Club & Shooting Preserve
Rt. 1, Box 269a,
New London, MO 63459
Steve & Pam Swon (314) 985-7477
88 mi. N of St. Louis
Type: Public/Member
Hrs: By reservation
Reservs: Strongly recommended
Sporting: 1, 10 stations
Trap: 1 **Five Stand:** Y **HT:** 36 ft.

Newcastle Hunt Club
3100 Broadway, #711, Kansas
City, MO 64111
Larry Carter (816) 931-9551
75 mi. NE of Kansas City
Type: Public **Hrs:** S/Su, Noon-5
Sporting: 1, 9 stations

Ozark Gun Club
Rt. 4, Box 842, Salem, MO 65560
Larry Carty (314) 729-4652
100 mi. SW of St. Louis
Type: Public/Member
Hrs: Th/F, 3-10; S/Su, 10-10
Sporting: 1, 10 stations
Trap: 3 **Skeet:** 3

Ozark Shooters Sports Complex
PO Box 6518, Hwy. 65,
Branson, MO 65616
Peggy M. Siler (417) 443-3093
25 mi. S of Springfield
Type: Public
Hrs: 7 Days, 10am-Dark
Reservs: Not required
Sporting: 3, 30 stations
Trap: 5 **Skeet:** 2 **HT:** 80 ft.
Wobble Trap

Pin Oak Hills
RR1, Chillicothe, MO 64601
Doug Luetticke (816) 646-6069
85 mi. NE of Kansas City
Type: Public
Hrs: M-F, by Res.; S/Su, 10-5
Sporting: 2, 20 stations
Trap: 1 **HT:** 40 ft.

Rockbridge Gun Club
Box 100, Rockbridge, MO 65741
Ray Amix (417) 679-3619
80 mi. S of Springfield
Type: Public **Hrs:** 7 Days, 8-8
Sporting: 1, 10 stations
Trap: 1 **HT:** 30 ft. **Wobble Trap**

Show-Me Safaris
Box 108, Summersville, MO 65571
Mark Hampton (417) 932-4423
30 mi. S of Rolla
Type: Public **Hrs:** Hours by appt.
Sporting: 1, 6 stations

Sorenson's S.C. & Preserve Hunting
1703 Hwy. DD, Defiance, MO 63341
Tom, Kay or T.J. Sorenson
(314) 828-5149
19 mi. W of St. Louis
Type: Public **Hrs:** Su-S, by appt.
Reservs: Strongly recommended
Sporting: 1, 22 stations

Squaw Creek Sporting
RR1, Box 6, Mound City, MO 64470
John Ingram (816) 442-3352
80 mi. N of Kansas City
Type: Public
Hrs: S/Su, 10-5; Weekdays by appt.
Sporting: 1, 18 stations **HT:** 70 ft.

St. Louis Skeet & Trap Club
18854 Franklin Rd.,
Pacific, MO 63026
Patricia Gardner (314) 257-4210
Type: Public/Member
Hrs: T/Th, 3-9; S/Su, 10-4
Sporting: None
Trap: 5 **Skeet:** 7 **Five Stand:** 1

Twin Lakes Sporting Club
Rt. 1, Box 203, Mexico, MO 65265
Wally Feutz (314) 581-1877
110 mi. NW of St. Louis
Type: Public/Member
Hrs: S/Su, 9-dark
Sporting: 1, 18 stations **HT:** 10 ft.

United Sportsmen's Club
4750 Henwick Lane,
Jefferson City, MO 65109
Don Balkenbush (314) 761-4946
2 mi. W of Jefferson City
Type: Public/Member
Hrs: W, 6-9 (Summer); Su, 1-4
Sporting: 1, 22 stations
Trap: 2 **Skeet:** 2 **HT:** 25 ft.

White Oak Ranch
RR1, Box 169, Edina, MO 63537
Bill Ingalls (816) 397-2451
50 mi. NW of Qunicy, IL
Type: Public **Hrs:** By appt.
Sporting: 1, 16 stations

Wildwood Sporting Clays
RR1, Box 143,
Houstonia, MO 65333
Bill Wall (816) 879-4451
100 mi. SE of Kansas City
Type: Public
Hrs: S, 10-Dk; Su, 1-Dk; & by appt.
Sporting: 1, 10 stations **HT:** 60 ft.

Wings - St. Albans
PO Box 49, St. Albans, MO 63073
Gale Braswell (314) 458-6523
35 mi. W of St. Louis
Type: Member/Avail
Hrs: M-Su, 9-6
Sporting: 1, 10 stations
Trap: 1 **Skeet:** 1 **HT:** 32 ft.

Wingtip Game Ranch
Rt. 1, Cainsville, MO 64632
John Rouse (816) 893-5880
85 mi. SE of Kansas City
Type: Public/Member
Hrs: Daily, by appt.
Sporting: 1, 11 stations **HT:** 90 ft.

Zeroed Inn Sporting Clays
Rt. 2, Box 76A, Gallapin, MO 64640
Sam & Jim Boyde (816) 828-4184
60 mi. N of Kansas City
Type: Public/Member
Hrs: S, 9-5; Su, 9-3
Sporting: 1, 10 stations **HT**

TRAP & SKEET

Falcon Skeet Club
524 Oxford Ct., Belton, MO 64012
Jeff Dye (816) 322-0815
Hrs: Th, 3-9; S/Su, 10-5
Trap: 2 **Skeet:** 2

Fallon Gun Club
6307 Sterling, Raytown, MO 64133
Jeff Dye (816) 884-6695
Hrs: Winter: Th, 4-10; S/Su, 10-5
Skeet: Y

Ft. Leonard Gun Club
PO Box 876, Bldg. 498, Ft. Leonard
Wood, MO 65473
Stan Harris (314) 336-3502
Hrs: W-F, 4-8; S/Su, 12-6
Trap: 1 **Skeet:** 2

Joplin Skeet & Trap Club
Rt. 7, Box 559, Joplin, MO 64801
Roger Brown (417) 781-1101
Trap: 1 **Skeet:** 2

KCTA Public Shooting Park
6420 NE 176th St.,
Smithville, MO 64809
Lynn Gipson (816) 532-4427
Type: Public
Hrs: W, 5-10; S/Su, 11-5
Trap: 8 **Skeet:** 2

Missouri Trap Association
Rt. 1, Box 396,
Linn Creek, MO 65052
B.J. Wilson (314) 346-2449
Hrs: T, 1; W-S, 1-5 **Trap:** 40

Settle's Ford Gun Club
PO Box 353, Adrian, MO 64720
Dan Clifton (816) 297-2440
Type: Public/Member
Hrs: T, 7:30
Trap: 1 **Skeet:** 1

Springfield Rod & Gun
2128 W. Elm, Springfield, MO 65803
Robert Hunt (417) 833-2199
Trap: 2 **Skeet:** 4

Wright City Gun Club
57 Quiet Village Dr.,
Foristell, MO 63348
Bob Overstreet (314) 639-5306
Type: Public/Member
Hrs: T/Th, 6-10; S, 12-5
Trap: 5

MONTANA

SPORTING & 5-STAND

Big Sky Sporting Clays at Van Voast's Farms
3100 Irvine Flats,
Polson, MT 59860
Rick Van Voast (406) 883-2000
4 mi. NW of Polson
Type: Public/Member
Hrs: W/Th, 12-5; Fr-Su, 10-5pm
Sporting: 1, 20 stations
Trap: 1 **Skeet:** 1 **Five Stand:** 1
HT: 50 ft.

Billings Rod & Gun Club
2519 Hancock, Billings, MT 59102
Billy D. Williams (406) 259-0006
Hrs: Su, 11-4
Sporting: 1, 10 stations
Trap: 1 **Skeet:** 4 **Five Stand:** 1

Diamond J Guest Ranch
PO Box 577W, Ennis, MT 59729
Felipe Acosta (406) 682-4867
60 mi. SW of Bozeman
Type: Public **Hrs:** By Appt.
Reservs: Strongly recommended
Sporting: 1, 7 stations
Hilly, light coverage
Trap: 1 **Skeet:** 1   **HT:** 40 ft.
See Our Ad Pg. 363

Eagle Nest Lodge
PO Box 470, Hardin, MT 59034
Keith Kelly (406) 665-3711
45 mi. S of Billings
Type: Public **Hrs:** By Appt.
Reservs: Strongly recommended
Sporting: 1, 5 stations
See Our Ad Pg. 365

Fetch Inn Hunting Preserve
Drawer 1429, Hamilton, MT 59840
Tom Fox (406) 363-5111
150 mi. SW of Great Falls
Type: Public
Hrs: Mid April '93 Opening
Sporting: 1, 10 stations **HT**

Gallatin Sporting Clays
PO Box 3483, Bozeman, MT 59772
Sam Robinson (406) 388-1346
W of Bozeman
Type: Public/Member
Hrs: (3/1-9/15), Tu, 5-9; Sa/Su,
12-dusk; by app't
Reservs: Strongly recommended
Sporting: 1, 12 stations **HT:** 80 ft.

Missoula Trap & Skeet Club
PO Box 5365, Missoula, MT 59806
Dale Beelman (406) 549-4815
Type: Public/Member
Hrs: T/Th, 6-9; Su, 1-5
Sporting: None
Trap: 18 **Skeet:** 5 **Five Stand:** 1

Perry Hunts & Adventures
Box 355, Fort Benton, MT 59442
Loran A. Perry
40 mi. NE of Great Falls
Type: Public **Hrs:** Every Day
Sporting: 1, 10 stations **HT:** 30 ft.

Rainwater's Whispering Pines Ranch & Hunt Club
10500 Lost Prairie Rd.,
Marion, MT 59925
Michael Canavan (406) 858-2292
35 mi. W of Kalispel
Type: Public
Hrs: Daily by app't
Sporting: 1, 13 stations

Stillwater Shooting Preserve
1141 Church Dr.,
Kalispell, MT 59901
Brian Tutvedt (406) 755-1959
10 mi. NW of Kalispell
Type: Public **Hrs:** Call for schedule
Sporting: 1, 13 stations

Z Bar Z Sporting Clays
5760 Timber Trail, Helena, MT 59601
Zane Drishinski (406) 278-7713
12 mi. NE of Helena
Type: Public/Member
Hrs: Th-S, Daylight-Dark
Sporting: 1, 10 stations

TRAP & SKEET

Beaverhead Gun Club
436 S. Dakota, Dillon, MT 59725
Henry Greitl (406) 683-4923
Type: Public/Member
Hrs: W, 6-Dark May-Sept.
Trap: 5

Duck Shack Skeet Club
Box 2005, Missoula, MT 59806
Jack Gordon (406) 549-0782
Skeet: 1

Flathead Valley Clay Target
Box 537, Kalispell, MT 59903
(406) 752-4452
Type: Public/Member
Hrs: Sunday days; Wed. evenings
Trap: Y

Great Falls Trap & Skeet
1208 Ave. B NW,
Great Falls, MT 59404
Jerry R. Lane (406) 453-5032
Type: Public/Member
Hrs: W, 4-9; Su, 11-3 Trap: 14

Havre Trap Club
Box 605, Havre, MT 59501
Otto Styber (406) 265-9020
Type: Public/Member
Hrs: W, 6-close; Su, 1-5
Trap: 5

Lewiston Trap & Skeet Club
Box 1141, Lewistown, MT 59457
Rip Noble
Type: Public/Member
Hrs: W, 6-Dark; Su, 1-5
Sporting: 1, 1 station
Trap: 5 Five Stand: 1

Manhattan Wildlife Assn.
9715 Cougar Dr.,
Bozeman, MT 59715
Clay Fracchiolla (406) 586-5705
Hrs: W, 7-10; Su, 1-4 (Winter)
Trap: 5 Skeet: 2

Sun River Skeet Club
Box 1494, Great Falls, MT 59403
Wm. David Manix (406) 761-9035
Hrs: Su, 10-4; T, 6:30-10; Th, league
Skeet: 5

NEBRASKA

SPORTING & 5-STAND

Can-Hunt
RR1, Box 10A, Garland, NE 68360
Todd Halle (402) 588-2448
60 mi. SW of Omaha
Type: Public/Member
Hrs: Daily by appt.
Sporting: 1, 12 stations
Five Stand: 1 HT: 30 ft.

Cedar Hills Range
651 CR 32, Tekamah, NE 68061
Jay Fred Bacon (402) 374-1254
1.5 mi. W of Tekamah on Hwy. 32
Type: Public/Member
Hrs: M-F, Eve. & By Appt; S/Su, 9-6
Sporting: 1, 40 stations
Trap: 1 HT: 70 ft.

Grand Island Sporting
Box 1117, Grand Island, NE 68802
John Hoffman (308) 382-7133
3.5 mi. S of Grand Island
Type: Public/Member
Hrs: Call for hours; Su, 1:30-5:30
Sporting: 1, 10 stations
Skeet: 4   HT: 30 ft.

Honore Hilltop
1605 North E Rd.,
Phillips, NE 68865
Nina/John Honore (402) 886-2215
130 mi. W of Omaha
Type: Public
Hrs: Daily, by app't
Reservs: Strongly recommended
Sporting: 1, 10 stations HT: 55 ft.

Hunt Nebraska
PO Box 317, Arapahoe, NE 68922
J. Hemelstrand (800) 486-8632
180 mi. W of Lincoln
Type: Public
Hrs: S/Su, 8am-Dusk; & by appt.
Sporting: 1, 10 stations

Lincoln County Gun Club
310 E. 4th St., North Platte, NE 69101
Cliff Reed (308) 532-1694
Type: Public/Member
Hrs: Varies Sporting: 1, 5 stations
Trap: 9 Skeet: 5

Nebraska One Box S.C.
Box 394, Broken Bow, NE 68822
Matt Lyne (308) 872-6131
65 mi. NW of Kearney
Type: Public Hrs: Su, 1-6
Sporting: 1, 6 stations HT: 45 ft.

Pheasant Haven Sport. Clays
PO Box 650, Elkhorn, NE 68022
Scott Bruhn (402) 779-2608
15 mi. NW of Omaha
Type: Public/Member
Hrs: W-F, 3-Dusk; S/Su, 10-5
Sporting: 1, 10 stations HT: 50 ft.

Sand Prairie Preserve
Box 94, Alliance, NE 69301
William Lore (308) 762-2735
6 mi. SE of Alliance
Type: Public
Hrs: T-Su, 9-4 (All Year)
Sporting: 1, 15 stations
Five Stand: 1

Seifer Farms Sporting Clays
RR1, Box 90, Sutherland, NE 69165
Ray Seifer (308) 386-2394
23 mi. W of North Platte
Type: Public
Hrs: Th, 5pm-Dusk; 4th Su each
mo., call for appt.
Reservs: Recommended
Sporting: 1, 10 stations
Trap: 1   HT: 50 ft.

Sportsman's Ranch
40212 CR #9, Morrill, NE 69358
Steve Decker (308) 247-3370
1.5 mi. S of Morrill
Type: Public Hrs: By appt. only
Sporting: 1, 10 stations
Skeet: 1

Sumac Sporting Clays
2605 Ridge Rd., Homer, NE 68030
Don Albertson (712) 251-1882
17 mi. SE of Sioux City
Type: Public
Hrs: S/Su, 10-4; W, 4-Dark
Sporting: 1, 18 stations

TRAP & SKEET

Beatrice Gun Club
PO Box 44, Beatrice, NE 68310
Greg Penner (402) 766-4265
Type: Public/Member
Hrs: W, 6-9; Su, 1-4:30
Trap: 4 Skeet: 1

Cozad Gun Club
818 Lake Ave.,
Gothensburg, NE 69138
Nancy Sitorius (308) 784-4159
Type: Public/Member
Hrs: 6 Registered Shoots (Apr-Oct)
Summer League Shoots
Trap: 4

Fremont Izaak Walton
2108 Donald, Fremont, NE 68025
Keith Nieman (402) 721-5874
Type: Public Hrs: Tues., 6-8
Trap: 5

H.A. Koch Trap & Skeet
6802 Harrison, Omaha, NE 68157
Gilbert Johnson (402) 331-1249
Hrs: S/Su, 12-5; W, 4-9; T-F, 4-9
Sporting: 1 Trap: 13 Skeet: 6

Lincoln Trap & Skeet Club
417 Anthony Lane, RR2, Lincoln,
NE 68520
R.L. Klein (402) 467-2153
Type: Public
Hrs: S/Su, 1-5; T/Th, 4-Dusk
Trap: 9 Skeet: 6

NEVADA

SPORTING & 5-STAND

The Capital City Gun Club
Box 1422, Carson City, NV 89702
Ray Smith (702) 882-9904
4 mi. NE of Carson City
Type: Public **Hrs:** W-Su, call for hrs; Mon. Nat'l. Holidays
Sporting: 1, 7 stations
Trap: 8 **Skeet:** 1 **Five Stand:** 1
Wobble Trap

Carson Valley Clays
Box 878, Gardnerville, NV 89410
Steve Stratton (702) 782-3303
15 mi. S of Carson City
Type: Member/Avail
Hrs: Daily
Sporting: 2, 20 stations
Trap: 1 **Skeet:** 1

Circle HH Sporting Clays
HCR#1, Box 512, Nipton, CA 92364
Fred Hymes
78 mi. S of Las Vegas, NV - 100 mi. E of Barstow/20 mi. N I-40
Type: Public/Member
Hrs: F-Su, 8-6; others by appt.
Sporting: 1, 6 stations **Trap:** 1

COTTONWOOD CLAYS GUN CLUB

Cottonwood Clays Gun Club
3444 Peri Ranch Rd., Reno, NV
Duke MacGill (702) 342-0333
6 mi. E of Reno
Type: Public/Member
Hrs: We/Th/Fr, Noon to Dk; S/Su, 10-Dark & by app't
Reservs: Not required
Sporting: 1, 16 stations
Trap: 4 **Skeet:** 1 **Five Stand:** 1
HT: 50 ft.
O Loaner Guns
O Factory Ammunition
O On-Site Pro Shop
O Clubhouse featuring Bar and Snack Bar
O Just 2 miles off of I-80, exit 23

Tell Them You Noticed

It's our advertisers who make it possible to provide Black's Wing & Clay to everyone on our circulation list. Next time you contact one, please say, "I saw you in Black's Wing & Clay."

Nellis Trap & Skeet Club
Box 9745, Nellis AFB, NV 89101
Robert Gilmore (702) 652-1937
10 mi. N of Las Vegas
Type: Public **Hrs:** W/S/Su, 9-4; Th, 6pm-10pm; Call to confirm
Reservs: Not required
Trap: 6 **Skeet:** 12 **Five Stand:** 1

The Oasis Ranch Gun Club
(formerly Peppermill) PO Box 360, Mesquite, NV 89024
Michael Julian (800) 621-0187
77 mi. NE of Las Vegas, NV
Type: Public/Member **Hrs:** Su-S, 8am-Dusk **Reservs:** Not required
Sporting: 2, 12 stations **Trap:** 2
Skeet: 2 **Five Stand:** 1 **HT:** 120'
O Loaner Guns
O Factory Ammunition
O On-Site Pro Shop
O Shooting Lodge
O Formal Instructions
O Golf Carts
See Our Ad Below

Perdiz Sports Shooting
PO Box 735, Eureka, NV 89316
Jerry White (702) 237-7027
112 mi. N of Elko
Type: Public/Member
Hrs: Daily, by appt.; Open weekends
Reservs: Strongly recommended
Sporting: 1, 10 stations
Hilly, trees & brush
Trap: 2 Five Stand: 1

Red Hills Hunting Preserve
Box 493, Gardnerville, NV 89410
Jack DeMars (702) 266-3856
Type: Public/Member
Sporting: 1, 10 stations Trap: 1

Sage Hill Clay Sports
11500 Mira Loma Rd.,
Reno, NV 89511
Rich & Darlene Bullard
(702) 851-1123
12 mi. SE of Reno
Type: Public/Member
Hrs: W/Th, 12-10; F, 12-6; S/Su, 10-6
Reservs: Not required
Sporting: 1, 15 stations Trap: 30
Skeet: 7 Five Stand: 1 HT: 200 ft.

See Our Ad Below

Spring Creek Trap & Skeet
396 North Berry Dr., Elko, NV 89801
Moe Matys (702) 753-6019
12 mi. S of Elko
Type: Public Hrs: W, 5-10; S/Su, 9-4
Sporting: None
Trap: 14 Skeet: 4 Five Stand: 1

TRAP & SKEET

Flying Saucer Trap Club
PO Box 1373, Lovelock, NV 89419
Larry Vonsild (702) 273-2207
Type: Public/Member
Hrs: Sundays Trap: Y

Lander Gun Club
310 Bastian 191 15, Battle
Mountain, NV 89820
Robert Fox (702) 635-2732
Type: Public Hrs: Seasonal
(scheduled on request) Trap: 3

Las Vegas Gun Club
9400 Tule Springs Rd., Las Vegas,
NV 89131
Steve Carmichael (702) 645-5606
Type: Public/Member
Hrs: Th-Su; & Wed. nights
Trap: 30 Skeet: 1

See Our Ad Above, Left

Spring Creek Association
451 E. Spring Crk. Pkwy.,
Elko, NV 89801
Sherri Tervort (702) 753-6295
15 mi. from Elko Type: Public
Hrs: W, 4-9; Su, 9-4 Trap: 16

Winnemucca Trap Club
Box 1413, Winnemucca, NV 89445
Pete Valdon (702) 623-3074
Type: Public Hrs: Su, 10-4
Trap: 5

Attending the SHOT Show?

The 1997 SHOT Show will once again be held in Las Vegas. If you or your colleagues are attending, why not use Wing & Clay to plan a round of sporting clays, trap or skeet? Several clubs are very near or within an easy drivie of the Convention Center. They'd welcome the opportunity to discuss your corporate entertaining needs. Oh! When you call, don't forget to say, "I saw your listing in Wing & Clay!"

NEW HAMPSHIRE

SPORTING & 5-STAND

20th Skeet & Sportsmens
116 Goffstown Rd.,
Hooksett, NH 03106
Mark Sandler (603) 485-5414
8 mi. N of Manchester
Type: Public/Member
Hrs: W/S/Su, 9-5; Others by appt.
Sporting: 1, 20 stations
Trap: 1 **Skeet:** 2 **Five Stand:** 1

Chester Rod & Gun Club
PO Box 337, Chester, NH 03036
Ed Fallon (603) 887-4629
Type: Public **Hrs:** Varies, call for info
Sporting: 1, 10 stations **HT:** 10 ft.

Grafton Cty. Sporting Clays
132 Prospect St.,
Lebanon, NH 03766
Norm Lorrey (603) 448-3506
105 mi. NW of Boston
Type: Public/Member
Hrs: T/S/Su **Sporting:** 1, 80 sta.s
Trap: 2 **Skeet:** 1 **HT:** 65 ft.

Green Mountain Kennels Hunting Preserve
RR1, Box 438F,
Center Ossipee, NH 03814
David Bardzik (603) 539-2106
50 mi. NE of Concord
Type: Public/Member
Hrs: We/Fr/Sa/Su, 8-5; Tu/Th till dk
Reservs: Strongly recommended
Sporting: 1, 10 stations
Five Stand: 1   **HT:** 150 ft.
O Factory Ammunition
O On-Site Pro Shop
O On-Site Meals
O Formal Instructions
O Organized Leagues

See Our Ad, Above

High Point Upland Preserve
Rte. 28 S., Alton, NH 03809
Jonathan Caley (603) 875-3552
75 mi. N of Boston
Type: Public/Member **Hrs:** by app't
Trap: 1 **Five Stand:** 1

Kinnicum Fish & Game
PO Box 191, Candia, NH 03034
Mark Trombley (603) 483-0894
60 mi. N of Boston
Type: Public/Member
Hrs: Su, by appt. only; T, 6-Dark
Sporting: 1, 15 stations **Trap:** 1

Major Waldron Sportsmen's
PO Box 314, Route 9,
Barrington, NH 03825
Lester Waterhouse (603) 742-6866
Type: Public/Member
Hrs: S, 9-3; Su, 9-Noon; T/W, 6-9
Sporting: 2, 14 stations **Trap:** 3
Skeet: 2 **Five Stand:** 2 **HT:** 12 ft.

SKAT
Box 137, New Ipswich, NH 03071
Tony Haigh (603) 878-1257
50 mi. NW of Boston
Type: Public/Member
Reservs: Strongly recommended
Sporting: 5, 70 stations
Trap: 1 **Skeet:** 1 **HT:** 110 ft.
O Loaner Guns
O Factory Ammunition
O On-Site Pro Shop
O On-Site Meals
O Formal Instructions

Smith River Sporting Clays
PO Box 57, Sargent Hill Rd.,
Grafton, NH 03240
Stephen Sudrabin (603) 523-4435
110 mi. N of Boston
Type: Public **Hrs:** W/S/Su, by appt.
Sporting: 1, 12 stations **HT:** 40 ft.

The Timberdoodle Club
One Webster Hwy.,
Temple, NH 03084
Randall Martin (603) 654-9510
55 mi. NW of Boston
Type: Member/Avail
Hrs: By Appointment
Reservs: Strongly recommended
Sporting: 2, 14 stations
Five Stand: 2   **HT**
O On-Site Pro Shop
O Gunsmith Service
O Gun Fitting
O Shooting Instruction Available—
  See Ad Pg. 222

TRAP & SKEET

Cheshire Cty Fish & Game
PO Box 233, Ferry Brook Rd.,
Keene, NH 03431
Richard Clark (603) 358-6829
Type: Public/Member **Hrs:** S,
10-2; W, 4:30-Dark **Trap:** 2

Horseshore Fish & Game
PO Box 147, Nashua, NH 03061
Richard Gath (603) 424-9646
Skeet: 1

Lone Pine Hunter's Club Inc.
11 Groton St., Nashua, NH 03062
John Terrell (603) 888-9969
Hrs: Su, 10-2; T/W, 6-9
Trap: 2 **Skeet:** 2

Pelham Fish and Game
Simpson Mill Rd.,
Pelham, NH 03076
Peter H. Tomaini (603) 472-5624
Type: Public/Member **Hrs:** T/Th,
4-9; S/Su, 10-3 **Trap:** 9 **Skeet:** 2

NEW JERSEY

SPORTING & 5-STAND

Belleplain Farms Sporting Clays
346 Handsmill Rd.,
Belleplain, NJ 08270
Nick Germaino (609) 861-2345
Type: Public **Hrs:** Seasonal
Sporting: 2, 15 stations **HT:** 25 ft.

Big Spring Sporting Clays
RD#3, Box 591, Sussex, NJ 07461
(201) 875-3373
50 mi. NW of New York City
Type: Public **Hrs:** W-Su, 8-4
Sporting: 5, 10 stations **HT:** 40 ft.

Buckshorn Sportsmen Club
507 Friendship Rd., Salem, NJ 08079
Tom Hess (609) 935-4659
40 mi. SW of Philadelphia
Type: Public/Member
Hrs: Su, 9-4
Reservs: Not required
Sporting: 1, 19 stations **HT:** 30 ft.

Buttonwood Game Preserve
810 Harmony Station Rd.,
Phillipsburg, NJ 08865
Gail & Frank Vargo (908) 454-8377
60 mi. W of New York
Type: Public **Hrs:** W/Th/F, 9-5
by app't; Sa, 9-5; Su, 1-5
Reservs: Recommended
Sporting: 1, 13 stations

Cedar Creek Sportsman's
Rahmah Rd., Millville, NJ 08332
Joe Scull, Jr. (609) 383-9619
40 mi. S of Philadelphia
Type: Public/Member
Hrs: S/Su, open at 8:30 am
Sporting: 1, 17 stations **HT:** 30 ft.

Central Jersey Rifle & Pistol
PO Box 710, Jackson, NJ 08527
Frank Pipoli (908) 928-9334
5 mi. W of Toms River
Type: Member/Avail
Hrs: Open daily to membership
Sporting: None
Trap: 5 **Skeet:** 4 **Five Stand:** 1

Country Lakes Gun Club
46 Reeves Rd.,
Brown Mills, NJ 08015
Cliff Leutholt (609) 893-9480
Type: Public/Member
Hrs: 2nd & 4th Sun; Tues eve., 6-10

Sporting: 1, 9 stations
Trap: 6 **Skeet:** 1

Red Wing Sporting Clays
317 Sooys Landing Rd., Port
Republic, NJ 08241
Clem Giberson (609) 652-1939

M&M Hunting Preserve
Hook & Winslow Rds.,
Pennsville, NJ 08070
Anthony Matarese (609) 935-1230
20 mi. SW of Philadelphia
Type: Public
Hrs: T-F, 8-5 (Reservations); Sat &
Sun, 9-4 **Reservs:** Recommended
Sporting: 1, 25 stations **HT**

See Our Ad, Below

Oak Lane Farms
Dutch Mill Rd.,
Piney Hollow, NJ 08344
John Scavelli (609) 697-2196
Type: Public/Member
Sporting: 1

Quinton Sportsman's Club
PO Box 397, Quinton, NJ 08072
Don Ives (609) 935-9843
30 mi. SW of Philadelphia
Type: Public/Member
Hrs: Su, 8-3:30; F, 6-11
Sporting: 1, 12 stations
Trap: 3 **Skeet:** 2 **Five Stand:** 1

Thunder Mountain Trap & Skeet
PO Box 164, Mansion Dr.,
Ringwood, NJ 07456
Rob Landberg (201) 962-6377
35 mi. NW of New York City
Type: Public
Hrs: W/Th/F, 1-10; S/Su, 9-6
Reservs: Not required
Sporting: None
Trap: 4 **Skeet:** 4 **Five Stand:** 1
○ Loaner Guns
○ Factory Ammunition
○ On-Site Pro Shop
○ On-Site Meals
○ Organized Leagues
○ Gunsmith Service

TRAP & SKEET

Englishtown Gun Club
11509 Old Bridge Rd.,
Englishtown, NJ 07726
John Starace (201) 446-9825
Hrs: S/Su, 9-4; M, 1-8; T, 1-4
Trap: 4 **Skeet:** 3

Farmers Sportsman Club
225 Ellis Rd., Milford, NJ 08848
Norbert McGuire, Jr. (908) 996-4862
Hrs: F, 7-10 **Trap:** 3

Farmingdale Gun Club
Box 642, Farmingdale, NJ 07727
Eugene Salomon (908) 938-2189
Trap: 3

Fox Ridge Public Shoot. Ctr.
44 Clove Rd.,
Wantage Twp., NJ 07461
Edwin McGlew, Jr. (201) 875-5791
50 mi. NW of New York City
Type: Public
Hrs: W/F, 1-4 & 6-9; S/Su, 1-4:30
Trap: 3 **Skeet:** 1

Ft. Dix Shooting Range
115 Russel St.,
Woodbridge, NJ 07095
Donn Knowlson (609) 562-4676
Hrs: S/Su, 9:30-4:30; W, 3-9
Trap: 4 **Skeet:** 9

Lenape Park Trap & Skeet
407 Robins St., Roselle, NJ 07203
Mike DePaola (908) 276-0225
Hrs: S/Su, 12-5 **Trap:** 2 **Skeet:** 2

Pine Belt Sportsman's Club
127 Walnut Ave., Marlton
Lakes/ATCO, NJ 08004
Alex Strachan (609) 268-0237
Hrs: W, 11-Dark; Su, 9-Dark
Trap: 16 **Skeet:** 3

Pine Valley Gun Club
18 Ivanhoe Dr., Robbinsville, NJ 08691
Melvina Tindall (609) 767-2661
Hrs: Sat; 2nd, 4th, 5th Sun.
Trap: 8

Square Circle Sportsmen
97 W. Clementon Rd.,
Gibbsboro, NJ 08026
Jim Hudson (609) 435-9722
Type: Member/Avail
Hrs: Su, 12-4 **Trap:** 1 **Skeet:** 1

Union County Trap & Skeet
Kenilworth Blvd., Cranford, NJ 07016
Ronald M. Leonardo (908)
276-0225
Type: Public **Hrs:** S/Su, 12-5
Trap: 2 **Skeet:** 2

Something Missing?
If you know of a clay shooting location that's missing
from this issue of Black's
Wing & Clay, we'd like to
know. Just drop us line of
give us a call: (908) 224-
8700. We'll take care of
the rest!

NEW MEXICO

SPORTING & 5-STAND

Chaparral Sporting Clays
219 South Zinc, Deming, NM 88030
Shaun Reynolds (505) 546-9767
60 mi. W of Las Cruces
Type: Public/Member
Hrs: 1st Sat. of month; 2nd Sun. of
month; & by appt.
Sporting: 1, 15 stations
Trap: 1 **HT:** 30 ft.

Chile County Sporting Clays
PO Box 252, Hatch, NM 87937
Jimmy Lytle (505) 267-4366
37 mi. S of Truth or Consequences
Type: Public
Hrs: Every 3rd weekend of month;
Labor Day **Sporting:** 1, 10 sta.

Holloman Rod & Gun Club
495 SUS/SURO,
Holloman AFB, NM 88330
Recreation Director (505) 475-7398
13.5 mi. W of Alamogordo, NM
Type: Public
Hrs: W, 12-7; S/Su, 9-4
Sporting: 1, 10 stations
Trap: 2 **Skeet:** 2 **Five Stand:** 1

Los Alamos Sportsmen's
1362 Trinity Dr., Suite D-2563, Los
Alamos, NM 87544
Paul Cook (505) 672-3669
35 mi. N of Santa Fe
Type: Public/Member
Hrs: Mon. nights;
Sporting: 1, 10 stations
Trap: 1 **Skeet:** 1

NRA Whittington Center
Box 700, Raton, NM 87740
Mike Ballew (505) 445-3615
Type: Public **Hrs:** M-F, 8am-5pm
Sporting: 1, 12 stations
Trap: 11 **Skeet:** 2

Sandia Skeet Club
2430 Juan Tabo NE, Suite 150,
Albuquerque, NM 87112
Garrett Donovan (505) 846-0196
Hrs: S/Su, 10-4; W, 3-Dark
Sporting: None
Skeet: 4 **Five Stand:** 1

Tinnin Hunt Club
Box 1885, Albuquerque, NM 87103
Tom Tinnin (505) 242-2871
45 mi. S of Albuquerque
Type: Public **Hrs:** Su-S
Sporting: 1, 20 stations
Five Stand: 1 **HT:** 20 ft.
Wobble Trap

Vermejo Park Ranch
PO Drawer E, Raton, NM 87740
Jim Baker (505) 445-3097
170 mi. NE of Santa Fe
Type: Public
Hrs: June 1st thru Mid-December
Sporting: 1, 10 stations
Skeet: 1

TRAP & SKEET

4 Corners Trap Club, Inc.
Box 693, Farmington, NM 87499
Joseph Stotts (505) 334-2143
Type: Public/Member
Hrs: Sun, 2pm **Trap:** 4

Chaparral Skeet Club
HCR31, Box 1318B,
Roswell, NM 88201
Gary Damron (502) 623-9191
Type: Public/Member
Hrs: Su, 1-5; W, 5-7 (Summer)
Skeet: 4

Four Corners Trap Club
Box 693, Farmington, NM 87499
Joe Stotts (503) 334-2143
Hrs: Su, 1pm; W, 5pm **Trap:** 4

Melrose Trap & Skeet Club
PO Box 25, Melrose, NM 88124
Bill Myers (505) 253-4783
Hrs: S/Su, 1-6 **Skeet:** 1

Povery Flats Skeet Club
HC31, Box 1123, Roswell, NM 88201
Charlie Martin (505) 355-7688
Hrs: By Appt. **Skeet:** 1

Roadrunner Trap Club
201 Plainview Dr.,
Alamogordo, NM 88310
Sid Anderson (505) 437-7632
Type: Public/Member
Hrs: Su, 1pm **Trap:** 10

South West Shot Gunners
Box 36086, Fort Bayard, NM 88036
Fred Selders (505) 537-2744
Type: Public/Member
Hrs: Tues. & Sat. **Trap:** 2

Truth or Consequences Trap
PO Drawer 1470, Truth or
Consequences, NM 87901
Jim Stubblefield (505) 743-6860
Trap: 8

WSMR Outdoor Rec. Center
US Army, STEWS-DP-AR-O, White
Sands, NM 88002
Geri Bustos (505) 678-5756
Hrs: M-F, 9-5; S/Su, See Staff
Officer **Trap:** 1 **Skeet:** 2

NEW YORK

SPORTING & 5-STAND

Batavia
Rod & Gun Club
1 Elmwood, Batavia, NY 14020
Paul Levins (716) 343-2656
35 mi. E of Buffalo
Type: Public/Member
Hrs: S/Su, 8-3; Other times by appt.
Reservs: Strongly recommended
Sporting: 1, 22 stations
Hilly, heavily wooded
Trap: 2   **HT:** 70 ft.   **Wobble Trap**

Bath Rod & Gun Club
PO Box 764, Bath, NY 14810
Bob Wagner (607) 522-3712
Type: Public   **Hrs:** Trap/Skeet-Su,
8-1; W, 5; Clays-Su 1pm; M-S, appt.
Sporting: 2, 12 sta.   **Tr:** 2   **Sk:** 3

Bellmore Rod & Gun Club
PO Box 324, Bellmore, NY 11710
Warren Busch 12 mi. NE of Roscoe
Type: Member/Avail
Hrs: By Appt. **Sporting:** 1   **Trap:** 1

Binghamton Gun Club, Inc.
235 Main St.,
Johnson City, NY 13790
Emil Misata (607) 797-3313
5 mi. E of Binghamton
Type: Public/Member
Hrs: Twice a Month
Sporting: 1, 10 stations
Trap: 2   **Skeet:** 4   **Five Stand:** 1

Brookhaven Shoot. Range
Rt. 25, Box 405, Ridge, NY 11961
Paula Lynch (516) 924-5091
Type: Public   **Hrs:** W-Su, 9-5
Sporting: 1, 10 stations
Trap: 5   **Skeet:** 4

Buffalo Shooting Club
563 W. Ferry, Buffalo, NY 14222
James O'Brien (716) 849-2111
Type: Public/Member
Hrs: Sat 11-3,Sun 9-1,We/Th
4:30-9:30
Trap: 9   **Skeet:** 2   **Five Stand:** 1

Catskill Pheasantry
& Sporting Clays
PO Box 42, Long Eddy, NY 12760
Alex Papp (914) 887-4487
100 mi. NW of New York City
Type: Public   **Hrs:** Su-S, 9-5
Reservs: Recommended
Sporting: 1, 12 stations   **Skeet:** 1

Cayuga County
Sportsmen's Assn.
RD2, Rockefeller Rd.,
Auburn, NY 13021
Roger Button (315) 252-2031
25 mi. SW of Syracuse
Type: Public/Member
Hrs: Su, 9-3:30
Reservs: Not required
Sporting: 1, 17 stations
Trap: 1   **Skeet:** 2   **Five Stand:** 1

Cedar Hill
Shooting Preserve
21 Marlin Hill Rd.,
Germantown, NY 12526
Bernie Mortellaro (518) 828-9360
30 mi. S of Albany
Type: Public
Hrs: Every day, 10-dark
Reservs: Strongly recommended
Sporting: 1, 18 stations
HT: 30 ft.   **Wobble Trap**

Chemung Shooting Preserve
115 Lilac Dr., Horseheads, NY 14845
Pat Colligan (607) 739-9238
70 mi. S of Syracuse
Type: Public/Member
Sporting: 1, 10 stations
Trap: 2   **Skeet:** 2

Clinton Fish &
Game Club
PO Box 122, Clinton, NY 13323
Joseph P. Cifarelli (315) 853-8787
from Less than 15 min. So. of
Exit 32, NY State Thruway
Type: Public/Member
Hrs: S/Su, 9-3
Reservs: Not required
Sporting: 1, 15 stations
Skeet: 4   **Five Stand:** 1   **HT:** 36 ft.
O Loaner Guns
O Factory Ammunition
O On-Site Meals

East Mountain
Shooting Preserve
150 McCarthy Rd.,
Dover Plains, NY 12522
Victor D'Avanzo (914) 877-6274
80 mi. N of New York City
Type: Public   **Hrs:**
Reservs: Recommended
Sporting: 1, 10 stations   **HT:** 35 ft.
O Factory Ammunition
O Shooting Lodge
O Formal Instructions

Eldred Preserve
Box 111, Rt. 55, Eldred, NY 12732
Lou Monteleone (914) 557-8316
90 mi. NW of New York City
Hrs: W-M, 11-4
Reservs: Recommended
Sporting: 1
Five Stand: Y
O Factory Ammunition
O Private Motel & Restaurant
O Deer & Turkey Hunting - Trout &
Bass Fishing
O Hunting & Fishing Guide Service
O Family Recreation
O Visa/Mastercard/Discover
Accepted

Friar Tuck Inn Sporting Clays
4858 Rt. 32, Catskill, NY 12414
Mick Howells (800) 832-7600
150 mi. N of New York City
Type: Public/Member
Hrs: S/Su, 10-6
Reservs: Recommended
Sporting: 1, 20 stations
Five Stand: 1
O Annual Columbus Day Weekend
Sporting Clays Tournament
O $25,000 In Cash Prizes (based on
300 entries)
O Call today for dates and
information!
O Shooting Instruction Available—
See Ad Pg. 210

Hamburg Rod & Gun Club
PO Box 187, Hamburg, NY 14075
Mike Gusek (716) 648-2236
16 mi. S of Buffalo
Type: Public/Member
Hrs: W/F, 6pm-9pm; S/Su, 10-3
Sporting: 1, 30 stations
Trap: 5   **Skeet:** 5   **Five Stand:** 1

Hendrick-Hudson F&G Club
252 Palmer Rd., E.
Greenbush, NY 12061
Arthur Milanese (518) 674-5184
13 mi. E of Albany
Type: Public/Member
Hrs: Su, 9-1; W, 5-Dark (May-Sept)
Sporting: 1, 15 stations
Trap: 2   **Skeet:** 4   **HT**

Ilion Fish & Game Club
PO Box 177, Ilion, NY 13357
Ed Freedman (315) 894-2938
12 mi. W of Utica
Type: Public/Member
Hrs: T/W, 4-8 (Apr-Sept); Sat., Clays
Sporting: 1, 10 stations
Trap: 4 **Skeet:** 6 **Five Stand:** 1
O Shooting Instruction Available—
See Remington School Ad Pg. 79

Indian Mountain Lodge
RR1, Box 17, Millerton, NY 12546
Joseph L. Blank (518) 789-6801
100 mi. N of Manhattan
Type: Public/Member
Hrs: Open all week, 8-5
Sporting: 1, 12 stations **Skeet:** 1

Ischua Valley Sporting Clays

Ischua Valley Sporting Clays
9 First Ave., Franklinville, NY 14737
Bill Atwater (716) 676-5230
from 1/4 mi. W. of Franklinville
@ Conservation Club
Type: Public/Member
Hrs: S/Su, 9-4; Th, 5pm-Til?
Reservs: Recommended
Sporting: 1, 22 stations **Trap:** 2

Kayaderros Fish & Game
706 Geyser Rd.,
Ballston Spa, NY 12020
Ken DeLano (518) 399-4481
Type: Public/Member
Hrs: By Resrv. **Sporting:** 1, 15 sta.
Trap: 2 **Skeet:** 1

Mid Hudson Trap & Skeet
411 N. Ohioville Rd.,
New Paltz, NY 12561
Hugh Davis (914) 255-7460
75 mi. N of New York
Type: Public **Hrs:** W-Su, 10-5
Sporting: 1, 15 stations
Trap: 4 **Skeet:** 7 **Five Stand:** 1

Millbrook Shooting School & Preserve Ltd.
RR1, Box 193A, Millbrook, NY 12545
Charles Schneible (914) 677-5756
70 mi. N of New York City
Type: Public **Hrs:** By appointment
Reservs: Strongly recommended
Sporting: 1, 12 stations
Five Stand: 1 **HT:** 75 ft.
O Formal Instructions
O FITASC
O Shooting Instruction Available

Nine Partners Pheasant Farm
RR#3, Box 47, Millbrook, NY 12545
Jonathan L. Wicker (914) 677-3114
80 mi. N of New York City
Type: Public/Member
Hrs: Su-S, 9-4; Reservations only
Sporting: 1, 25 stations
Trap: 1 **Five Stand:** 1
Wobble Trap

North Fork Preserve, Inc.
5330 Sound Ave. (Mail: 349
Pennys Rd.), Riverhead, NY 11901
Brett Jayne or Robert H. Krudop
(516) 369-1728
70 mi. E of New York
Type: Member/Avail
Hrs: Daily, 9-Dark by appt.
Reservs: Strongly recommended
Sporting: 1, 10 stations
Skeet: 1 **HT:** 40 ft. **Wobble Trap**
O Shooting Instruction - Under the
direction of Mark Elliot, formerly
of the West London Shooting
School, with over 20 yrs.
experience teaching and fitting
for Britain's major gunmakers
Exclusive Sportsman's Club on
Eastern Long Island has limited
owner/memberships available.
Facilities include sporting clays,
FITASC, skeet, excellent upland
game and cover, deer, bass
ponds, clubhouse and tennis
courts. Non- member, private
and corporate shoots and
functions may be arranged. Call:
North Fork Preserve: (516)
369-1728 (days); (516) 722-3152
(evenings).

Oneonta Sportsmen's Club
16 Garden St., Oneonta, NY 13820
Daniel Knickerbocker (607)
432-4012
60 mi. SW of Albany
Type: Public/Member
Hrs: W, 5-Dark; Su, 8-Dark
Sporting: 1, 13 stations
Trap: 1 **Skeet:** 3 **HT:** 30 ft.

Orvis Sandanona
PO Box 450, Millbrook, NY 12545
Brian Long (914) 677-9701
60 mi. N of New York City
Type: Member/Avail **Sporting:** Y
O Shooting Instruction Available—
See Ad Pg. 203

Painted Post Field & Stream
PO Box 325, Corning, NY 14830
Lloyd Hurd (607) 936-4912
5 mi. W of Corning
Type: Public/Member
Hrs: 9-Dark, 1st & 3rd Sat.
Sporting: 1, 20 stations **Skeet:** 1

Pathfinder Fish & Game
PO Box 194, Fulton, NY 13069
John LeVea (315) 593-7281

Hrs: S/Su, 10-4; M/W, 5-10 & appt.
Trap: 7 **Skeet:** 7 **Five Stand:** 1

Pawling Mountain Club
PO Box 573, Pawling, NY 12564
Gary Hall (914) 855-3825
80 mi. N of New York City
Type: Member/Avail
Sporting: 1, 15 stations
Five Stand: 1   **HT:** 90 ft.
Wobble Trap
○ Shooting Instruction Available–
  See Ad Pg. 223

Peconic River Sportsmans
RFD 389 River Rd.,
Manorville, NY 11949
Sid Miller (516) 727-5248
Hrs: W/S/Su, 11-5
Sporting: 1, 14 stations
Trap: 5 **Skeet:** 5

Quigg Hollow Hunting Club
3130 Quigg Hollow Rd.,
Andover, NY 14806
Rod Walker (607) 478-8576
90 mi. S of Rochester
Type: Public/Member
Hrs: Daylight-Dark
Sporting: 1, 13 stations

Ramapough Sportsmens
45 Treetop Circle,
Nanuet, NY 10954
Mark L. Dorfman (914) 426-0590
Hrs: W-Su, 10-7
Skeet: 2 **Five Stand:** 1

Richfield Sportsmen's Club
Richfield Springs, NY 13456
Niles Bennett (315) 858-0441
20 mi. SE of Utica
Type: Public   **Hrs:** S/Su, 9-2
Sporting: 1, 10 stations
Trap: 1 **Skeet:** 2

Rochester Brooks Gun Club
Box 289, 926 Honeoye Falls Rd.
#6, Rush, NY 14543
Paul Hawkins (716) 533-9913
15 mi. S of Rochester
Type: Member/Avail
Hrs: We, 9-10; Th/Fr Noon-8;
Sa/Su, 9-5 **Reservs:** Not required
Sporting: 2, 30 stations
Trap: 16 **Skeet:** 14 **Five Stand:** 1
HT: 70 ft.
○ Factory Ammunition
○ Formal Instructions
○ Pistol & Rifle Range
○ Full Service Kitchen and Bar
○ Night-time Shooting
  Under the Lights

Salmon Creek Sportsmen's
781 Gully Rd., Aurora, NY 13026
Gerry Shook (315) 364-8414
15 mi. S of Auburn
Type: Public/Member
Hrs: Su, 9-2 **Sporting:** 1 **Trap:** 1

Serendipity Farms Sporting Clays
12201 Rt. 62, Lawtons, NY 14091
Vince & Barb Lorenz
(716) 337-9828
25 mi. S of Buffalo
Type: Public/Member
Hrs: W/Sa/Su, 9-5; other days by
app't   **Reservs:** Not required
Sporting: 2, 23 stations **HT:** 65 ft.
○ Factory Ammunition
○ Formal Instructions
○ On-Site Clubhouse
○ Brand New 2nd Course in 1995
○ See our listing in NY Wings
  Section

Suffolk Trap & Skeet Range
165 Gerrard Rd., PO Box 181,
Yaphank, NY 11980
Charlie Marino (516) 924-4490
60 mi. E of New York City
Type: Public/Member
Hrs: We/Th/Fr/Sa/Su, 10-6
Reservs: Not required
Sporting: 1, 14 stations **Trap:** 8
Skeet: 5 **Five Stand:** 1 **HT:** 30 ft.

T-M-T Hunting Preserve
RR1, Box 297, School House Rd.,
Staatsburg, NY 12580
Thomas F. Mackin (914) 266-5108
55 mi. N of New York City
Type: Public **Hrs:** By Reservation
Sporting: 1, 10 stations

T.J.PHILIPBAR'S
Taconic Trap Club INC.

Taconic Trap Club
Rt. 82, PO Box 132,
Salt Point, NY 12578
Jeff or Ted Philipbar (914) 266-3788
70 mi. N of New York City
Type: Public/Member
Hrs: Rsrv. only
Reservs: Recommended
Sporting: 1, 12 stations
Mostly Flat, mostly brush
Trap: 9 **Skeet:** 1

See Our Ad Pg. 497

Tamarack Preserve Ltd.
RR#1, Box 111B,
Millbrook, NY 12545
Tim Bontecou (914) 373-7084
85 mi. N of New York
Type: Member/Avail
Hrs: Weekdays by appt., 9-5
Sporting: 1, 18 stations **HT:** 120'

Tioga County Sportsman's
PO Box 598, Owego, NY 13827
Mike Pasquale (607) 687-1418
15 mi. W of Binghamton
Type: Public/Member
Hrs: By Schedule
Sporting: 1, 12 stations
Trap: 4 **Skeet:** 1 **Five Stand:** 1

Tonawanda Sportsman
5657 Killian Rd.,
Tonawanda, NY 14120
Jim Siegmann (716) 692-2161
10 mi. N of Buffalo
Type: Public/Member
Hrs: W, 6-10; S, 12-3; Su, 10-3
Sporting: 1, 18 stations
Trap: 9 **Skeet:** 6

The Trenton Fish & Game
Wood Rd., Box 113, Holland
Patent, NY 13354
William Swarts (315) 337-8516
10 mi. N of Utica
Type: Public/Member
Hrs: Trap: Su, 9am; Clays: 7/22,
8/19, 9/16, 10/21
Sporting: 1, 10 stations **Trap:** 1

West Branch Angler
PO Box 102, Deposit, NY 13057
Jim Serio, (607) 467-5525
Type: Public **Hrs:** **Sporting:** Y

Whispering Pines Hideaway
548 Townline Rd., Lyons, NY 14489
Charlie Buisch (315) 946-6170
30 mi. E of Rochester
Type: Public/Member
Hrs: S/Su, 9-4; & weekdays by
app't. **Sporting:** 1, 23 stations

Wild Woods Sporting Clays
RR8, Box 105A, Oswego, NY 13126
Rhonda Driscoll (315) 343-2349
6 mi. E of Oswego
Type: Public
Hrs: M-F, by rsrv; S/Su, 9-2
Sporting: 2, 10 stations
Trap: 1 **Skeet:** 1

Wilderness Sporting Clays
Old Baker Rd., Box 432,
Arkville, NY 12406
Joe Lombardino (914) 586-2766
45 mi. NW of Kingston
Type: Public/Member
Hrs: Su-S, 9am-Dusk
Sporting: 1, 16 stations **HT:** 30 ft.

TRAP & SKEET

3F Club
532 Pletcher Rd., Lewiston, NY 14092
Richard Falcone (716) 754-2293
Hrs: Th, 6-9; S/Su, 12-4
Trap: 4 Skeet: 14

Addison Fish & Game Club
8482 McCarthy Rd.,
Addison, NY 14801
Bill Lott (607) 359-2542
Hrs: Th, 4-10; Su, 8-1
Trap: 1 Skeet: 3

Bridgeport Rod & Gun
PO Box 117, Bridgeport, NY 13030
(315) 699-3313 Hrs: Su Trap: 12

Burlington Flats Fish & Game
Star Rt. Box 6,
Burlington Flats, NY 13315
David Eckert (607) 965-8700
Skeet: 2

Calverton Shooting Range
395 Nugent Dr.,Calverton, NY 11933
George L. Schmelzer (516) 727-9881
E of Riverhead Type: Public Hrs:
Daily, 8:30-5:30 Trap: 10

Celoron Rod & Gun Club
PO Box 177, Celoron, NY 14720
Bob Bailey (716) 483-6560
Hrs: W, 7-10; S, 1-4; Su, 10-1
Trap: 2 Skeet: 2

Central Square Forest Fish
6736 Lehigh Rd.,
Pulaski, NY 13142
Tom Whitaker (315) 298-6701
Type: Public/Member
Hrs: M/T, Evenings; S/Su, special
events Trap: 6

Clifton Park Fish & Game
Eaglemore Rd., Clifton Pk., NY 12866
Dennis Conrad (518) 371-9869
Type: Public Hrs: T, 6-10
Trap: 3

Conesus Lake Sportsmens
5883 Stonehill Rd.,
Lakeville, NY 14480
Dana Driscoll (716) 346-6527
Type: Member/Avail
Hrs: T/W/Th, Eve; S/Su, 12
Trap: 4 Skeet: 4

Dansville Fish & Game Club
26 Cottage St., Dansville, NY 14437
Fred Blakley (716) 335-5760
Trap: 1 Skeet: 4

DeWitt Fish & Game Club
PO Box 21, DeWitt, NY 13214
Charles Coakley (315) 446-1190
Hrs: S/Su, 10-6; Th, 5-9
Trap: 9 Skeet: 6

East Aurora Fish/Game
11467 Warner Hill,
South Wales, NY 14139
Joe Endres
Trap: 1 Skeet: 2

Eden-North Collins Gun
PO Box 31, Eden, NY 14057
Joseph Zoyhofski (716) 337-0308
Hrs: Th, 7-10; S/Su, 10-3
Trap: 2 Skeet: 2

Five Point Rod & Gun Club
9609 Fargo Rd.,
E. Bethany, NY 14054
John S. Kujawski (716) 584-3107
Hrs: W, Night; S, 12-3; Su, 10-3
Trap: 2 Skeet: 2

Fur, Fin & Feathers
PO Box 323, Elmira, NY 14902
Dennis Wieland (607) 733-3943
Trap: 1 Skeet: 2

Groton Rod & Gun Club
3921 Perris Rd.,
Cortland, NY 13045
Dave Downes (607) 898-4627
Hrs: Su, 8-2
Trap: 1 Skeet: 3

Hudson Falls Fish & Game
Box 332, Hudson Falls, NY 12839
Andrew B. Collins
Hrs: T/Th, 4-9; Su, 8-1
Skeet: 2

Jamestown Skeet/Trap
PO Box 337, Lakewood, NY 14750
Rick Sanders (716) 763-9700
Hrs: Th, 7-10
Trap: Y Skeet: 2

Lost Pond Club
47 Fair St., Norwich, NY 13815
James J. McNeil (607) 336-5678
Trap: 1 Skeet: 4

Medina Conservation Club
PO Box 68, Medina, NY 14103
Howard Robinson (716) 798-0093
Hrs: 9-5
Trap: 1 Skeet: 2

Monroe-Chester Sportsmen
Box 608,
Greenwood Lake, NY 10925
Fred Bramich (914) 469-5553
Hrs: S/Su, 10-4
Trap: 1 Skeet: 2

Mumford Sportsmens Club
3256 Ellen Pl., Caledonia, NY 14423
William P. Taylor (716) 538-2341
Type: Public/Member
Hrs: Varies Trap: 4

New Paltz Rod & Gun Club
PO Box 363, New Paltz, NY 12561

Edward Kara (914) 255-7586
Type: Public/Member Trap: 2

New York Trapshooting
116 Kimry Moor,
Fayatteville, NY 13066
Robert Spence (315) 637-4827
Trap: 24

Newark Rod & Gun Club
140 Dell St., Newark, NY 14513
Dick Sistek (315) 331-0623
Hrs: M/T, 5; W/F, 10-3; Su, 9-1
Trap: 4 Skeet: 4

Olean Rod & Gun Club
1209 Washington St.,
Olean, NY 14760
C.E. "Bud" Johnson (716) 933-6190
Hrs: Su, 9-3; W, 5-10
Trap: 2 Skeet: 2

Ontario Rod & Gun Club
28 Ridge Rd. West,
Rochester, NY 14615
Bill Palermo, Jr. (716) 458-5398
Type: Public/Member
Hrs: T, 4-9 Trap: 4

Outlet Gun Club Inc.
Box 8009, W. Webster, NY 14580
Curtis J. Graham (716) 377-4851
Hrs: S/Su, 9-5 Trap: 4 Skeet: 4

Pine Tree Point Gun Club
Highland Ave.,
Alexandria Bay, NY 13607
W. Gerald Lanterman, Jr.
(315) 482-3911
Type: Public Hrs: W/S, 12-9; Su, 9-9
Trap: 2 Skeet: 4

The Plattsburgh Rod & Gun
Box 616, Plattsburgh, NY 12901
Francis Smith (518) 846-7262
Hrs: Su, 12-Dk (W); W, 5-Dk; S/Su
Trap: 3 Skeet: 3

Portville Conservation Club
PO Box 15, Portville, NY 14770
Jeff Gaylor (716) 592-2700
Hrs: Weekends Trap: 1

Randolph Rod & Gun Club
87 Main St., Randolph, NY 14772
Arnold E. Towers (716) 358-6606
Type: Public Hrs: W, 6; S, 10-5
Trap: 4 Skeet: 2

Red Creek Conservation
PO Box 449, Haminbal, NY 13074
Mark Cole (315) 754-6459
Hrs: Th, 6-9; S/Su, 12-6; By appt.
Trap: 1 Skeet: 2

Saraspa Rod & Gun Club
Box 22, Greenfield Center, NY 12833
Karen Collins (518) 587-5789
Hrs: T/W, 6-9; S/Su, 9-2
Skeet: 1

Sheridan Transit Rod & Gun
551 Ransom Rd.,
Grand Island, NY 14072
J.C. Zimmermann
Trap: 2

Sodus Bay Sportsman Club
Box 106, Sodus Point, NY 14555
Pat O'Neil (315) 483-0051
Hrs: W, Eve; Sun, 10-2
Trap: 2 **Skeet:** 2

St. Joseph Co. Conservation
12284 State Rt. 12,
Boonville, NY 13309
James Terrell
Hrs: Su, 9-1 **Trap:** 4 **Skeet:** 1

Staten Island Sportsmens
Box 45, Staten Island, NY 10314
Vince Ricciardi (718) 448-1155
Hrs: S/Su, 8; W, 6
Trap: 4

Sullivan Trail Rod/Gun
118 John St., Horseheads, NY 14845
Mike Moses (607) 739-1814
Type: Public/Member
Hrs: W, 4:30-Dark; Su, 8:30-1:30
Trap: 2 **Skeet:** 2

Tri-State Rod & Gun Club
N. Orange St., Box 801,
Port Jervis, NY 12771
Eddy Cohen (914) 856-3988
65 mi. NE of New York City
Type: Public/Member
Hrs: Su, 12-4; T, 5-9 (Apr-Oct)
Trap: 2

Victor Rod & Gun Club
PO Box 1323, Fairport, NY 14450
Andy Nolan (716) 924-4427
Type: Public
Hrs: Th, 5-10; Su, 9-12
Trap: 1 **Skeet:** 3

Watervliet Fish & Game
5 David Lane, Burnt Hills, NY 12027
David McDonald (518) 456-9855
Hrs: Su, 9-2; S, 10-2; W, 9-1 &
5:30-8:30
Trap: 1 **Skeet:** 3

Williamson Rod & Gun
PO Box 175, Williamson, NY 14589
Richard Sheffield
Hrs: Su, 9-1; Th, 5
Trap: 1 **Skeet:** 2

Wood & Brook Sportsmens
7 Cambridge Ct.,
Lancaster, NY 14086
Dale Wittig (716) 937-4061
Hrs: Varies **Trap:** 2

NORTH CAROLINA

SPORTING & 5-STAND

Adams Creek Gun Sports
6240 Adams Creek Rd.,
Havelock, NC 28532
Rusty/June Bryan (919) 447-6808
**115 mi. SE of Raleigh near
Morehead City**
Type: Public/Member
Hrs: By appt.
Reservs: Recommended
Sporting: 1, 27 stations
Skeet: 1 **Five Stand:** 1 **HT:** 35 ft.

Apple Wood Sporting Clays
Rt. 2, Box 363,
Hendersonville, NC 28792
John Laughter (704) 697-3757
40 mi. S of Asheville
Type: Public
Hrs: W/F/S, 9-6; Su, 1-6
Sporting: 1, 10 stations

Busick Quail Farms
11933 NC Hwy. 119 South,
Burlington, NC 27217
Roger D. Busick (910) 421-5758
40 mi. NW of Durham or 35 mi. E
of Greensboro
Type: Public/Member
Sporting: 1, 10 stations

Catawba Sporting Clays & Hunting Preserve
345 Hackett St., Salisbury, NC 28144
Drew Arey (704) 642-1710
30 mi. N of Charlotte
Type: Public/Member
Hrs: W-F, 11-Dusk; S, 9-Dusk; Su,
1-Dusk; M/T, by appt.
Reservs: Recommended
Sporting: 1, 20 stations
Five Stand: 1 **HT:** 30 ft.
○ On-Site Pro Shop
○ NSCA Level I Instructor
○ Rental Guns
○ Golf Carts
○ Bird Brain 5-Stand

Central Carolina Sporting
PO Box 1101, Biscoe, NC 27209
Hal Iverson (910) 428-CLAY
60 mi. NE of Charlotte
Type: Public
Hrs: M-F, by appt; W, 12-5; S, 9-5;
Su, 12-5; F, 12-5
Reservs: Recommended
Sporting: 2, 10 stations

Charlotte Rifle & Pistol Club
Box 11183, Charlotte, NC 28220
Jim Bogart (704) 843-2915
15 mi. S of Charlotte
Type: Public/Member
Hrs: Sa/Su, 12-5:30
Sporting: None
Trap: 1 **Skeet:** 2 **Five Stand:** 1

Contentnea Creek
Rt. 1, Box 202,
Hookerton, NC 28530
S.M.Gray/Bob Steed/Gary Tripp
(919) 747-8302
60 mi. SE of Raleigh
Type: Public/Member
Hrs: M-F, 10-Dk; S, 9-Dk; Su, 1-Dk
Sporting: 3, 10 stations
Skeet: 1 **Five Stand:** 2

Deep River Sporting Clays, Inc.
3420 Cletus Hall Rd.,
Sanford, NC 27330
Bill Kempffer (919) 774-7080
28 mi. SW of Raleigh
Type: Public/Member
Hrs: W-S, 10-6; Su, 1-6 & by resrv.
Reservs: Recommended
Sporting: 4, 18 stations **HT:** 35 ft.
○ On-Site Pro Shop
○ Rental Guns
○ Corporate Meeting Facilities
○ Only 35 Minutes South of
   Raleigh/Durham/Chapel Hill
○ Four Certified Instructors on Staff
○ Shooting Instruction Available—
   See Ad Pg. 208

Durham County Wildlife
Rt. 1, Box 213, Hopson Rd.,
Morrisville, NC 27560
Bill Fleeman (919) 544-1306
Type: Public/Member
Hrs: Su, 1-6; S, 11-3
Trap: 6 **Skeet:** 5 **Five Stand:** 1

Honey Hill Shooting Sports
1654 Honey Hill,
Hallsboro, NC 28442
Joe Barefoot (910) 641-1143
52 mi. W of Wilmington
Type: Public **Hrs:** W/F/S, 12-6; Su,
9-6 **Sporting:** 1, 10 stations
Skeet: 1 **Five Stand:** 5

Hunters' Pointe
Sporting Clays, Inc.
506 Decoy Drive,
Washington, NC 27889
Scott/David Downs
(919) 975-2529
20 mi. E of Greenville
Type: Public
Hrs: W/Th/F/Su, 12-dusk; Sa,
9-dusk; M/T, by appt.
Reservs: Not required
Sporting: 2, 45 stations
Mostly Flat, heavily wooded
Five Stand: 1   **HT:** 45 ft.
Wobble Trap
○ On-Site Pro Shop
○ Formal Instructions
○ Rental Guns Available
○ Visa & Mastercard Accepted
○ NSCA 5-Stand with Bird Brain
    Controller
○ Golf Cart Rentals

Pecan Grove Sporting Clays
Rt. 2, Box 154, Ayden, NC 28513
Jerry T. Gibson (919) 746-2527
7 mi. SE of Greenville
Type: Public
Hrs: M-F, appt. only; S, 9-5; Su,
12:30-5 **Sporting:** 2, 30 stations

Pender Co. Gun Club
239 N. Channel Haven Dr.,
Wilmington, NC 28409
Allan Snyder (910) 791-3182
Club Phone: (910) 283-9852
28 mi. NW of Wilmington
Type: Public/Member
Hrs: W/S/Su, 10-Dark
Reservs: Not required
Sporting: 1, 10 stations
Trap: 2 **Skeet:** 2

Powell Farm Sporting Clay
Rt. 2, Box 241-C,
Shawboro, NC 27973
Marsha Powell (919) 232-3092
45 mi. S of Norfolk, VA
Type: Public
Hrs: W/Th/F/Su, 1-Dark; S, 9-Dark
Sporting: 1, 21 stations **HT:** 40 ft.

Rowan County Wildlife
PO Box 612, Salisbury, NC 28145
Joe W. Earley (704) 636-8662

2 mi. SW of Salisbury
Type: Public/Member
Hrs: W, 5-8:30pm; S/Su, 2-8:30pm
Sporting: 1, 13 stations
Trap: 8 **Skeet:** 8

Shane's Sporting Clays
6319 A Hwy. 158, Summerfield,
NC 27358
Shane Naylor (910) 664-0512
12 mi. N of Greensboro
Type: Public/Member
Hrs: S, 8-7; Su, 1-4
Reservs: Strongly recommended
Sporting: 2, 25 stations **HT:** 115'

Shooters Sporting Club
PO Box 93, Turnersburg, NC 28688
Buck Nooe (704) 546-5400
40 mi. N of Charlotte
Type: Public/Member
Hrs: T-S, 10am-Dusk; Su, 1pm-Dusk
Sporting: 1, 13 stations
Skeet: 1 **Five Stand:** 1

Wiccacon Gun Club
Box 385, Harrellsville, NC 27942
R.C. Kennington (919) 356-2912
Hrs: W/S, 1-7 **Skeet:** 2 **Five Stan.** 1

Wintergreen Sporting Clays
Box 981, Bladenboro, NC 28320
Boyce White (910) 648-6171
85 mi. S of Raleigh
Type: Public **Hrs:**
Sporting: 1, 10 stations **HT:** 40 ft.

Yadkin Point
Shooting Preserve
PO Box 313, Advance, NC 27006
Howell W. Woltz (910) 998-9518
10 mi. W of Winston-Salem
Type: Public/Member
Reservs: Recommended
Sporting: 3, 22 stations
Five Stand: 1   **HT:** 30 ft.
Yadkin Point offers 3 sporting
clays courses. Summer hours:
April 1 - Sept. 30; Wed-Fri., 12-7;
Sat., Open all day. Winter hours:
Oct. 1 - Mar. 31; Mon-Sat.,
8:30-6:30. Also:
- Guided quail hunts–wagon style
or on foot
- Bird dog training
- Bird dogs for sale
- Lodging and food available on
grounds
- Bird cleaning available

TRAP & SKEET

Alamance Wildlife Club
211 Travis Lane,
Gibbonsville, NC 27249
John Currin (910) 376-6739
Hrs: Th, 7-10; Su, 2-5
Trap: 2 **Skeet:** 1

Bostic Gun Club
4348 W. Dixon Blvd.,
Shelby, NC 28150
Charles Smith, Jr.
Trap: 3 **Skeet:** 1

Buccaneer Gun Club
322 N. Colony Circle,
Wilmington, NC 28409
Tom Morrison
Hrs: Varies
Trap: 1 **Skeet:** 2

Buncombe Co. Wildlife
PO Box 98, Fletcher, NC 28732
Ray Davis (704) 687-1734
Type: Public/Member
Hrs: W/S/Su, 1-6
Trap: 2 **Skeet:** 2

Carolina Clay Target Club
ox 7372, Greensboro, NC 27417
Kerry B. Ward (910) 294-2569
Hrs: S, 8-Dark; Su, 1-Dark
Trap: 1 **Skeet:** 1

Cleveland Skeet Inc.
131 Appian Way,
Shelby, NC 28150
D. Scott McIntyre (704) 487-7532

Crow Hill Farms Skeet
PO Box 819, Beaufort, NC 28516
Warren J. Davis (919) 728-4080
Hrs: By appt. **Skeet:** 1

Gastonia Skeet & Trap Range
PO Box 174B, Gastonia, NC 28053
Kieffer Gaddis (704) 866-6065
Type: Public **Hrs:** W/F/S/Su, 1-6
Trap: 2 **Skeet:** 2

Horseshoe Neck Gun Club
1102 Horseshoe Neck Rd.,
Lexington, NC 27292
Henry Grubb (704) 858-6138
Skeet: 1

LeJeune Red Shooting Club
6 C Portwest, Swansboro, NC 28584
Jim Hill (910) 451-3889
Hrs: F-M, 9-6
Trap: 2 **Skeet:** 5

Liberty Gun Club
3961 Bunton Swaim Rd.,
Liberty, NC 27298
Tommy Kirkman (910) 622-3197
Skeet: 1

Morganton Skeet Club
3339 Wren Circle, Lenoir, NC 28645
Kevin Story (704) 438-5359
Hrs: W, 4-7; Su, 2-6
Skeet: 2

Ocean Skeet Club
219 Channel Dr., Cape Canteret,
Swansboro, NC 28584
Otis H. Johnston (919) 393-8543
Hrs: Call for appt.
Skeet: 1

Old Hickory Gun Club
Box 7984, Rocky Mount, NC 27804
Louis A. Levy (919) 977-3231
Hrs: W/F/S/Su, Afternoon
Trap: 1 **Skeet:** 5

Piedmont Gun Club
Rt. 5, Box 25,
Rutherfordton, NC 28139
Buddy Lawing (704) 286-4361
Type: Public/Member
Hrs: Sat., by appt. **Trap:** 3

Watauga Gun Club
PO Box 2316, Boone, NC 28607
Randy Jones (704) 264-0843
Type: Member/Avail
Hrs: Open all day **Trap:** 4

NORTH DAKOTA

SPORTING & 5-STAND

Capital City Gun Club
2100 Industrial Park,
Bismark, ND 58502
Darold Asbridge (701) 258-0252
Type: Public
Hrs: T-Th, 6pm-10pm (Apr-Sept)
Sporting: None **Trap:** 14 **Five
Stand:** 1   **Wobble Trap**

Capital City Sporting Clays
214 E. Kavaney Dr.,
Bismarck, ND 58501
Mark S. Sandness (701) 258-4034
4 mi. N of Bismarck
Hrs: T/W/Th, 6:50-Dark; Su, 12-6
Sporting: None **Five Stand:** 1

Dakota Hunting Club
Box 13623, Grand Forks, ND 58208
George Newton (701) 775-2074
12 mi. SW of Grand Forks
Type: Public **Hrs:** 7 days/week
Sporting: 2, 11 stations **HT:** 60 ft.

J.T's Sporting Clays
17425 Highway 11,
Fairmont, ND 58030
Jeff Trom (701) 474-5598
60 mi. S of Fargo
Type: Public
Hrs: S/Su, 9-Dk; Wkdays by appt.
Sporting: None
Trap: 1 **Skeet:** 1 **Five Stand:** 1

Minot Gun Club
608 NW 4th, Minot, ND 58703
John Coffin (701) 838-7472
Hrs: T-Th, 6-10; Su, 1-4
Sporting: 1, 8 stations
Trap: 13 **Skeet:** 2

P.K.'s Sporting Clays
2307 11th St. S., Fargo, ND 58103
Peter Knoff (701) 293-1873
10 mi. E of Fargo
Type: Public **Hrs:** Su-S, 9-Dark
Sporting: 1, 21 stations **HT:** 35 ft.

The Shooting Park, Inc.
4333 167th Ave., SE,
Horace, ND 58047
John/Joyce Nelson (701) 282-3805
Type: Public
Hrs: Su-Th, 2-Dark (Apr-Oct)
Sporting: None **Trap:** 13 **Skeet:**
3 **Five Stand:** 1   **Wobble Trap**

TRAP & SKEET

Buffalo City Gun Club
Box 1052, Jamestown, ND 58402
Jeffrey A. Seher (701) 251-2250
Hrs: Th, 6-10; F, 1x/month
Trap: 4

Minot Rod & Gun Club
1635 2nd St., SE, Minot, ND 58701
Mike Riha (701) 727-4354
Trap: 1 **Skeet:** 2

Northwest Gun Club
1108 2nd Ave.,
E., Williston, ND 58801
R.C. Koch (701) 572-2935
Type: Public/Member
Hrs: T-Th, 7pm (Summer) **Trap:** 4

Tri County Trap & Wildlife
Box 94, Winbledon, ND 58492
Ralph Rudolph (701) 435-2406
Hrs: M, 6-9
Trap: 1 **Skeet:** 1

A&A Shooting & Hunting
12006 Fenstermaker,
Garrettsville, OH 44231
Al or Joe Spolarich (216) 548-8753
40 mi. E of Cleveland
Type: Public/Member
Hrs: W/S/Su, 8-5; also by appt.
Sporting: None
Trap: 2 **Skeet:** 2 **Five Stand:** 1

OHIO

SPORTING & 5-STAND

Anderson's Sporting Clays
237 Cockrell's Run Rd.,
Lucasville, OH 45648
Ed Anderson (614) 259-5211
68.5 mi. S of Columbus
Type: Public/Member
Hrs: Th, 4:30-Dark; S/Su,
8:30-Dark; Others by appt.
Reservs: Recommended
Sporting: 2, 79 stations
Five Stand: 1
O Factory Ammunition
O On-Site Pro Shop
O On-Site Meals
O Shooting Lodge
O Organized Leagues
O Golf Carts
O 30' & 62' High Tower

Avon Sportsman Club
Box 181, Avon, OH 44011
Larry Hocking (216) 937-9006
10 mi. W of Cleveland
Type: Public
Hrs: W, 6-10pm; S/Su, 9-3
Reservs: Not required
Sporting: None
Skeet: 1 **Five Stand:** 1

From Cleveland-Rt. 90 West to
Bradley Road exit, south to
Detroit Rd., west to Lear-Nagle
Rd., south to Swartz Rd., east to
Williams Ct., & south to end of
Williams Ct.

Beaver Creek Club
48430 Cooper Foster Park Rd.,
Amherst, OH 44001
Tim Keller (216) 988-8884
35 mi. W of Cleveland
Type: Member/Avail
Hrs: 7 days a week, 9-5
Sporting: 2, 17 stations **Trap:** 1
Skeet: 1 **Five Stand:** 1   **HT:** 50'

Question or problem?
Give Black's Wing & Clay
a call 9 am - 5 pm E.S.T.
(908) 224-8700.

Brier Oak
Sporting Clays
State Rt. 113, Bellevue, OH 44811
Kevin or Denise Schaeffer
(419) 483-4953
65 mi. SW of Cleveland
Type: Public **Hrs:** S/Su, 8-6;
M/W/Th/F, 8-5, by appt.
Reservs: Recommended
Sporting: 2, 38 stations **HT:** 30 ft.
O Organized Leagues
O Ammunition for Sale
O Formal Instruction by Reservation
O Easy Access between Exts. 6A
   Ohio Tpke. State Rt. 113

Buckeye Valley
Sporting Clays
12360 Shellbeach Rd.,
Thornville, OH 43076
Robert Worrell (614) 467-2868
30 mi. E of Columbus
Type: Public/Member
Hrs: S/Su, 9-6; M-F, By Appt.
Reservs: Not required
Sporting: 2, 10 stations
Rolling, mostly brush
Trap: 1 **HT:** 35 ft.
O Clubhouse
O Lodging Nearby
O On-hand Instructors
O Pro Shop
O Organized Leagues

Cherrybend Pheasant Farm
2326 Cherrybend Rd.,
Wilmington, OH 45177
Mary Hollister (513) 584-4269
40 mi. NE of Cincinnati
Type: Public/Member
Hrs: Wkdays by resrv.; Wkends,
9-Dark
Sporting: 2, 16 stations

Chillicothe Gun Club
4002 Sulfur Lick Rd.,
Chillicothe, OH 45601
Steve Miller (614) 774-4867
55 mi. S of Columbus
Type: Public
Hrs: 7 days/Week, 10-7
Sporting: 2, 12 stations **Trap:** 2
Five Stand: 1 **Wobble Trap**

Conneaut Creek Club
2265 Harcourt Dr.,
Cleveland, OH 44106
H.F. Biggar, III (216) 368-1565
70 mi. NE of Cleveland
Type: Member/Avail
Hrs: Private Club; Reservation only
Sporting: 1, 12 stations

Elkhorn Hunt Club
4146 Klopfenstein Rd.,
Bucyrus, OH 44820
Samuel A. Ballou (419) 562-6131
55 mi. N of Columbus
Type: Public/Member
Hrs: M-F, by Appt; S/Su, 9-6
Sporting: 1, 10 stations
Trap: Y **Skeet:** Y

Evick's Shotgun Sports
70183 Maynard Rd., St.
Clairsville, OH 43950
John Evick (614) 695-6948
10 mi. W of Wheeling, WV
Type: Public
Hrs: Su-S, by appt.
Sporting: 1, 15 stations

Grand Valley
Hunting Ranch
10198 Penniman Rd.,
Orwell, OH 44076
Glenn Rex (216) 437-6440
40 mi. E of Cleveland
Type: Public/Member
Hrs: W/Th/F, by app't; S/Su, 9-4
Reservs: Recommended
Sporting: 2, 23 stations
Mostly Flat, trees & brush
Trap: 2 **Five Stand:** 1 **HT:** 25 ft.

Hidden Haven
Shooting Preserve
9257 Buckeye Rd.,
Sugar Grove, OH 43155
Ronald Blosser (614) 746-8568
50 mi. SE of Columbus
Type: Public/Member
Hrs: Daily, 9am-Dark; Hunting
hours-appt. only
Reservs: Not required
Sporting: 10, 9 stations
Trap: 1 **HT:** 70 ft.
O Loaner Guns
O Factory Ammunition
O On-Site Pro Shop
O On-Site Meals
O Shooting Lodge
O Formal Instructions
O Organized Leagues
O Golf Carts
O 5-Stand Sporting-FITASC

Highfield Shooting Sports
8575 Carson Rd.,
Fultonham, OH 43738
Daniel C. Miller (614) 849-3144
40 mi. E of Columbus
Type: Public
Hrs: S-Su, 9-5; W, 4-dusk
Sporting: 2, 20 stations **HT:** 54 ft

Hill 'N Dale Club
3605 Poe Rd., Medina, OH 44256
Terry L. Eicher (330) 725-2097
50 mi. S of Cleveland
Type: Member/Avail
Hrs: T-S, 8-5; Su, 10-5
Reservs: Strongly recommended
Sporting: 1, 30 stations
Rolling, trees & brush
Skeet: 1 **Five Stand:** 1 **HT:** 45 ft.
○ Factory Ammunition
○ On-Site Pro Shop
○ On-Site Meals
○ Formal Instructions
  NSCA Level I & II

Lone Dove Sporting Clays
8780 Bunker Hill Rd., SW, Port
Washington, OH 43837
Jerry A. Wilson (614) 498-6266
75 mi. NE of Columbus
Type: Public **Hrs:** Su, 9-5; M-S, by
appt. **Sporting:** 2, 10 stations

Lost Bird Sporting Clays
3344 Harrison Rd.,
Fredericksburg, OH 44627
Fred Mowerer (330) 695-3621
15 mi. SE of Wooster
Type: Public
Hrs: M-S, daylight-dark; Su, 10-6
Sporting: 1, 20 stations

Mad River Sportsman's Club
1055 County Rd. 25,
Bellefontaine, OH 43311
Tony Stratton, Mgr.
(513) 593-8245
45 mi. NW of Columbus
Type: Member/Avail
Hrs: T-S, 9-5; Su, 12-5
Reservs: Strongly recommended
Sporting: 1, 16 stations **Trap:** 1
○ Loaner Guns
○ Factory Ammunition
○ On-Site Pro Shop
○ Shooting Lodge
○ Formal Instructions
○ Gunsmith Service
○ Gun Fitting
○ Shooting Instruction Available—
  See Ad Pg. 214
See Our Ad Pg. 503

Marietta Gun Club
RR1, Box 312B, Vincent, OH 45784
Victor A. Rutter, Jr. (614) 678-2631
80 mi. SE of Columbus

Type: Public/Member
Hrs: W, 6-9
Sporting: None **Trap:** 8 **Skeet:** 2
Five Stand: 1 **Wobble Trap**

Medusa Sporting Clays
5515 Centennial Rd.,
Sylvania, OH 43560
Skip Weiss (419) 531-4759
10 mi. W of Toledo
Type: Public/Member
Hrs: Su, 10-5; S, 9-5
Sporting: 1, 14 stations
Trap: 2 **Skeet:** 2

Miami Valley Skeet Club
9292 Cincinnati Columbus Rd.,
Cincinnati, OH 45241
George Quigley (513) 779-7177
4 mi. S of Dayton
Type: Public/Member
Hrs: S/Su, 12-Dark
Sporting: None **Trap:** 1 **Skeet:** 5
Five Stand: 1 **HT:** 40 ft.

Middletown Sportsmen's
6943 Michael Rd.,
Middletown, OH 45042
Darryl Landwehr (513) 422-5112
5 mi. NW of Middletown
Type: Public/Member
Hrs: W/S/Su, 12-7 (Non-Mmbrs);
T/Th, 10-Dark (Mmbrs)
Sporting: 1, 10 stations
Trap: 20 **Skeet:** 2

Milford Gun Club
400 Marietta Ave.,
Terrace Park, OH 45174
Tim Langner (513) 248-0401
15 mi. E of Cincinnati
Type: Public/Member
Hrs: S/Su, 11-5; W, 2-Dark
Sporting: None
Trap: 2 **Skeet:** 2 **Five Stand:** 1

Oak Shade Sport Shooting
16747 County Rd. L,
Wauseon, OH 43567
Ann Lange (419) 337-2529
25 mi. W of Toledo
Type: Public/Member
Hrs: M-F, by appt; S/Su, 9-4
Sporting: 2, 25 stations

Ottawa Sporting Clays
Box 327, Port Clinton, OH 43452
T. Park McRitchie (419) 635-2530
50 mi. W of Cleveland
Type: Public **Hrs:** W/S/Su, 10-4;
Anyday by reserv. of 8
Sporting: 1, 14 stations **HT:** 40 ft.

The Outback Inc.
Box 308, Brinkhaven, OH 43006
Larry Pollard (216) 377-5477
Type: Public/Member
Hrs: W-Su, 10am-7pm
Sporting: 1, 30 stations

Paw Paw Creek
Rt. 2, Box 173C,
Lower Salem, OH 45745
Gary Pontius (614) 585-2214
85 mi. SE of Columbus
Type: Public/Member
Hrs: M-F, by appt; S/Su, 9-Dark
Sporting: 2, 48 stations **HT:** 50 ft.

Pheasant Recreation Inc.
18376 London Rd.,
Circleville, OH 43113
Jack E. Carpenter (614) 477-1587
25 mi. S of Columbus
Type: Public/Member
Hrs: Year Round
Sporting: 1, 10 stations

Portage Sporting Clays
6821 W. Little Portage Rd.,
Oak Harbor, OH 43449
Bill O'Neal (419) 732-3209
5 mi. from Port Clinton
Type: Public
Hrs: S/Su, 9-4; other days by appt.
Sporting: 1, 10 stations
Skeet: 1 **HT:** 25 ft.

Proximre's Outdoor Sports
10140 US 24, Cecil, OH 45821
Brad Proxmire (419) 399-4900
20 mi. W of Ft. Wayne, IN
Type: Public/Member
Sporting: 1, 20 stations **HT:** 25 ft.

Queen City Skeet Club
9292 Cincinnati-Columbus Rd.,
Cincinnati, OH 45241
George Quigley (513) 779-7177
Sporting: 1 **Trap:** 1 **Skeet:** 5

Ringneck Ridge
1818 Cty. Rd. 74,
Gibsonburg, OH 43431
Rick Bowser (419) 637-2332
85 mi. W of Cleveland
Type: Public/Member
Hrs: Su-S, call for reservations
Sporting: 1, 15 stations
Five Stand: 1

Scioto River Hunting Club
17226 St. Rt. 235,
Waynesfield, OH 45896
Mary Zirkle (513) 464-6560
60 mi. NW of Columbus
Type: Public
Hrs: W/Th, 1-Dark; F-Su, 9-Dark
Sporting: 2, 10 stations
Trap: 1 **Skeet:** 1 **HT:** 35 ft.

Shooter's Sporting Clays
11958 Big Bone Rd.,
Union, KY, OH 41091
Jim McHale (606) 643-3411
35 mi. S of Cincinnati
Type: Public/Member

Hrs: S, 9-Dusk; Su, 10-Dusk;
Weekdays by appt. only
Sporting: 2, 20 stations HT: 60 ft.

The Shooting Challenge
PO Box 12, Sullivan, OH 44880
Art & Cheryl Lundquist
(419) 736-2529
10 mi. N of Ashland
Type: Public Hrs: M, 3-9; T, 12-5;
W/Th, 12-9; F, 12-7; S, 8-9
Sporting: 3, 48 stations
Five Stand: 1   HT: 35 ft.

Sportsman's Haven Gun Club
14695 E. Pike Rd.,
Cambridge, OH 43725
Brent Umberger
Type: Member/Avail
Sporting: None
Trap: 1 Skeet: 1 Five Stand: 1

Toledo Trap & Skeet Club
3150 N. Berkey Southern Rd.,
Berkey, OH 43504
Jim Fletcher (419) 829-5101
State Rt. 295 @ Central Ave.
(U.S. 20) Type: Public
Hrs: M-F, 12-10; S/Su, 10-6
Sporting: None
Trap: 4 Skeet: 3 Five Stand: 1

Toronto Rod & Gun Club
PO Box 177, Toronto, OH 43964
Chuck Spencer (614) 544-9948
40 mi. W of Pittsburgh
Type: Public Hrs: W, 5-11 (Trap);
Clays every other Sun.
Sporting: 2, 19 stations Trap: Y

WR Hunt Club
5690 CR237, Clyde, OH 43410
Robert or Betty Wright
(419) 547-8550
50 mi. W of Cleveland
Type: Public/Member
Hrs: T-Su
Reservs: Strongly recommended
Sporting: 1, 20 stations HT

Wrestle Creek Game Club
23605 Fairmont - CR180,
Waynesfield, OH 45896
Jim Hardin (419) 568-2867
12 mi. SE of Lima
Type: Public Hrs: Su-S, 9am-6pm
Sporting: 2, 17 stations
Skeet: 1

TRAP & SKEET

Adams Conservation Club
39 Derbyshire Rd.,
Toledo, OH 43615
Steve Schultz (419) 865-8314
Hrs: S/Su, 12-4
Trap: 4 Skeet: 4

Airport Gun Club
1884 Martinsburg Rd.,
Utica, OH 43080
Frank Lanuzza (614) 653-3712
Type: Public
Hrs: W, 3-10; Th, 12-10; S/Su, 10-5
Trap: 9 Skeet: 1 Wobble Trap

Clinton Co. Sportsmen
682 Pyle Rd., Clarksville, OH 45133
Chuck Muchmore (513) 382-1178
Type: Public/Member
Hrs: Su, 10-5
Trap: 2 Skeet: 2

Coldstream Country Club
400 Asbury Rd.,
Cincinnati, OH 45255
Michael J. Haehnle (513) 231-3900
Hrs: S/Su, 9:30-3
Skeet: 1

Columbiana Co. F&G
20821 #16 School Rd.,
Wellsville, OH 43968
Linda Peterson (330) 532-3253
Type: Public Hrs: W, 6-10:30; F,
7-10; Su, 12-4 Trap: 4

Erie Skeet Club of Ohio
PO Box 608, Norwalk, OH 44857
Gary Kalizewski (419) 668-5710
Hrs: By appt. Skeet: 1

Fairfield Sportsmens Assn.
5696 West Fork Rd.,
Cincinnati, OH 45247
Charles Wentzel (513) 574-8315
Type: Public/Member
Hrs: Su, 12-5; T, 7pm-9:30pm; F,
7pm-11pm; Su,10-2(Skt)
Trap: 6 Skeet: 2

Great Eastern Trap Club
PO Box 55, State Rt. 515,
Walnut Creek, OH 44687
Sue Kaufman (216) 893-2930
Type: Public
Hrs: Sptg. Clays by appt. Trap: 10

Greene Cty. & Game Club
PO Box 64, Xenia, OH 45385
Bob Akers (513) 429-4823
Type: Public/Member
Hrs: Th, 6-11; 1st & 3rd Sun, 12-5
Trap: 4

Greenville Sportsmens Club
906 N. State Line Rd.,
Masury, OH 44438

Dick Cameron (412) 588-9994
Hrs: W/S/Su, 10-5
Trap: 1 Skeet: 3

Hambden Orchard Club
8245 Belle Vernon Dr.,
Novelty, OH 44072
Henry Vavrick (513) 341-2212
Hrs: S, 10-4 Skeet: 1

Hawthorne Valley Skeet
537 Falls Rd.,
Chagrin Falls, OH 44022
John Hazle (216) 425-2500
Hrs: Su, (Sept. 1-June 1)
Skeet: 1

Huber Heights Rod & Gun
4210 N. Hyland Ave.,
Dayton, OH 45424
Bill Colwell (513) 236-6159
Type: Public/Member
Hrs: F, 6-10; Su, 12-5 Trap: 3

Hunting Valley Gun Club
6090 Cochran Rd.,
Solon, OH 44139
John Lennon (216) 246-6515
Hrs: S, 10-4 Skeet: 1

Indian Hill Shooting Club
6053 Sebright Ct.,
Cincinnati, OH 45230
Tom Kanis (513) 831-0994
Hrs: S/Su, 12-5; T/Th, 7-10:30
Trap: 1 Skeet: 1

Inidan Hill Shooting Club
6053 Sebright Court,
Cincinnati, OH 45230
Tom Kanis (513) 831-0994
Hrs: S/Su, 12-5; T/Th, 7-10:30
Sporting: 1, 10 stations HT: 15 ft.

JMS Shooting Center
Rt. 36 West, Marysville Rd.,
Delaware, OH 43015
Richard Turrill (614) 363-7555
3 mi. W of Delaware
Type: Public/Member
Hrs: W/Th, 4-10; S/Su, 10-4
Trap: 5 Skeet: 2 Wobble Trap

Jackson County Trap & Gun
5573 Four Mile Rd.,
Jackson, OH 45640
Steve Riegel (614) 286-3934
Trap: 1

Jaqua Trap Club
900 E. Bigelow Ave.,
Findlay, OH 45840
George Ranzau (419) 422-0912
Hrs: Call for info
Trap: 18

Logan County F&G Club
4494 Co Rd. 43,
Bellefontaine, OH 43311
John Kerr (515) 585-5676
Hrs: Sat. eve.
Trap: 4

Lowellville Rod & Gun Club
2515 South Ave.,
Youngstown, OH 44502
Ronald F. Lysowski (330) 536-8143
Type: Public/Member
Hrs: Th, 6-10pm Trap: 2

Lynchburg Lions Gun Club
9186 Smarthill Ln. Rd.,
Hillsboro, OH 45133
John Condo (513) 764-1314
Hrs: Th, 4:30-10; S, Noon-9
Trap: 2

Mapleton Gun Club
5330 Grandvale St., NE, East
Canton, OH 44730
Dale Wardle (216) 488-0682
Type: Public/Member
Hrs: Th, 7pm; S/Su, per reg.
schedules
Trap: 5

Mentor Harbor Yacht Club
D5330 Coronado Dr.,
Mentor, OH 44124
Jim Misencik (216) 951-0155
Hrs: S/Su, 12-5 (Nov-Apr)
Skeet: 1

Mid State Gun Club
1385 Putnam Rd.,
Clarksburg, OH 43115
Ed Fulton (614) 998-2103
Type: Public/Member
Hrs: S/Su, 10-8; W/F, eve.
Trap: 2 Skeet: 2

Minerva Sportsman Club
9247 Arrow Rd.,
Minerva, OH 44657
Greg Hole (216) 863-1839
Type: Member/Avail
Hrs: S, 5pm-11:30pm (trap shoot
open to public) Trap: 2

Mision Guillermo
PO Box 672, Norwalk, OH 44875
Bill Newcomer (419) 663-3129
Hrs: S/Su, 2-5 Skeet: 1

Newport Sportsmen Club
6377 SR 66, Fort Loramie, OH 45845
Wally Meyer (513) 295-2579
Type: Public/Member
Hrs: Th, 5-11; S/Su, 9-7
Trap: 5

Ohio State Trap Assn.
6010 Opossum Run Rd., Grove
City, OH 43123
Hugh L. McKinley (614) 877-9936
Hrs: 8-6 (during State trap shoot)
Skeet: 52

Sandhill Skeeters
3883 Sandhill Rd.,
Bellevue, OH 44811
Sue Parks (419) 483-2230
Hrs: By appt. Skeet: 1

Sportsmen's Shooting Ctr.
1232 Chelmsford St., NW, North
Canton, OH 44720
J.E. Doebereiner (216) 875-8081
Hrs: T/Th, 6:30-10:30; Su, 1-5
Trap: 4 Skeet: 8

Sylvania-Medusa Gun Club
5747 Talmadge Rd., C-5,
Toledo, OH 43623
Wayne Harvey (419) 885-1790
8 mi. W of Toledo
Type: Public
Hrs: S, 12-4; Su, 10-4; W, 12-10;
Th, 6-10 Trap: 2 Skeet: 2

Urbandale Gun Club
7655 Lakeshore Blvd.,
Madison, OH 44057
Helen Cone (216) 298-3200
Trap: 4

Vienna Fish & Game Club
631 N. Turner Rd.,
Youngstown, OH 44451
C.D. Jones
Type: Public Hrs: W/Su, 1-5
Trap: 4

Williams County Gun Club
214 N. Platt St.,
Montpelier, OH 43543
Rob Heller (419) 485-3176
Type: Public/Member
Hrs: S, 9-2; T, 9-9; F, 6-10
Trap: 3 Skeet: 1

Wright Patterson AFB
PO Box 752, Fairborn, OH 45324
Thomas Lemley (513) 257-3935
Type: Member/Avail
Hrs: S/S/Su, 12-Dark
Trap: 7 Skeet: 9

Youngstown Country Club
201 E. Commerce St.,
Youngstown, OH 44503
Stephen T. Bolton (216) 759-1040
Hrs: S/Su, 11-4
Trap: 1 Skeet: 2

OKLAHOMA

SPORTING & 5-STAND

ADA Skeet & Trap Club
2504 Kirby Dr., Ada, OK 74820
Larry Drennan (405) 332-5286
Type: Public/Member
Hrs: Th/S/Su, afternoons
Sporting: None
Trap: 4 Skeet: 4 Five Stand: 1
Wobble Trap

Bartlesville Sportsmen's
PO Box 391, Bartlesville, OK 74005
L.M. Winkler (918) 333-2583
Type: Public/Member
Hrs: M, 6:30-9; Su; 9-12; T/Th/S,
8:30-12:00
Sporting: 1, 5 stations
Trap: 1 Skeet: 2

Cedar Creek Sporting Clays
Rt. 1, Box 138A, Geary, OK 73040
Robert Rinehart (405) 884-5530
45 mi. W of Oklahoma City
Type: Public
Hrs: W, 4-Dark; S/Su, 12-Dark
(Summer); Others by appt.
Sporting: 1, 12 stations Trap: 1

Melot's Sportsman Club
8900 W. Memorial Rd., Oklahoma
City, OK 73142
Max Melot (405) 721-4394
10 mi. NW of Oklahoma City
Type: Public/Member
Hrs: W/S/Su, 12-7
Sporting: 1, 10 stations

Oklahoma City Sporting Clays
PO Box 91, Arcadia, OK 73007
Jim & Bobbie Jolly (405) 396-2661
10 mi. NE of Oklahoma City
Type: Public/Member
Hrs: W-Su, 10-Dark; All Monday
Holidays Reservs: Recommended
Sporting: 1, 20 stations
Five Stand: 1   HT: 40 ft.
O Pistol & Rifle Range
O 3-D Archery
O R.V. Hookups
O 20 Acre Fishing Lake
O 7 miles east of I-35 then 3 1/2
miles north of Hiwassee

Shawnee Twin Lakes S.C.
704 SW 27th, Moore, OK 73160
Tom Batt (405) 793-9021
10 mi. W of Shawnee
Type: Public/Member
Hrs: Th, 5:30-9; S, 12-5; Scheduled
Sun. Shoots
Sporting: 1, 10 stations Trap: 4

Southern Ranch Hunting
Rt. 2, Box 75, Chandler, OK 74834
Dean Caton (918) 377-4226
45 mi. NE of Oklahoma City
Type: Public/Member
Hrs: W/S/Su, 9-5 (W); Daily, 9-6 (S)
Sporting: 2, 24 stations
Five Stand: 1   **HT:** 50 ft.
Wobble Trap

Wichita Mountains S. C.
Rt. 2, Box 85,
Geronimo, OK 73543
Shelby Kervin (405) 248-1947
Hrs: S, 10-6; Su, Noon-6; Wkdays
by appt. **Sporting:** 1

Woods & Water, inc.
Rt. 1, Box 319, Catoosa, OK 74015
Doug Fuller (918) 266-5551
6.5 mi. E of Tulsa
Type: Public/Member
Hrs: W-Su, 12-Sunset; S, 9-Sunset
Reservs: Not required
Sporting: 1, 13 stations
Five Stand: 1   **HT:** 60 ft.
Wobble Trap
See Our Ad Below

TRAP & SKEET

Altus AFB Rod & Gun Club
Outdoor Rec. Bldg. 343, Altus AFB,
OK 73523
Bob Baker (405) 481-6251
Skeet: 1

Bird Island Gun Club
2042 The Coves, Afton, OK 74331
M. Kinderman (918) 782-2002
Hrs: W/S/Su, 1-4
Trap: 1 **Skeet:** 1

Bullseye
Rt. 3, Box 256A,
Weatherford, OK 73096
Larry William (405) 772-3303
75 mi. W of Oklahoma City
Type: Public
Hrs: By Appt. Weekdays; S/Su,
9am-Dark **Wobble Trap**

Comanche Skeet & Trap
1010 NW 75th, Lawton, OK 73505
Frank Hays (405) 353-2540
Hrs: S/Su, 12-6; W, 4-6:30
Trap: 1 **Skeet:** 5

Enid Elks Gun Club
PO Box 3791, Enid, OK 73702
Darrell Scott (405) 874-2551
Hrs: W, 7-11; Su, 1-6 **Trap:** 4

Hobart Gun Club
1401 W. 11th St., Hobart, OK 73651
Brent Hancock (405) 726-5240
Hrs: Su, 1-6 **Trap:** 1 **Skeet:** 2

Little Clay Target Club
6601 S. Country Club Dr.,
Oklahoma City, OK 73142
Jim Little (405) 682-9296
Hrs: By Invitation Only
Trap: 1 **Skeet:** 1

OTA Shooting Park
5100 E. Evans Rd.,
El Reno, OK 73036
Kenneth Jantzen (405) 422-4111
20 mi. W of Oklahoma City
Type: Public
Hrs: T/Th/F, 5-8; W/S/Su, 12-7
Trap: 18 **Skeet:** 8

Oil Capital Rod & Gun Club
PO Box 52131, Tulsa, OK 74152
H.D. Conklin (918) 835-3379
Type: Public/Member
Hrs: Th/S/Su, 1:30-Evening
Trap: 4 **Skeet:** 5

Oklahoma City Gun Club
609 N. Juniper Ave.,
Midwest City, OK 73130
James Hansen
Hrs: Su, 8:30-1; S, 9-1
Trap: 1 **Skeet:** 2

Sand Springs Sportsman
Box 383, Sand Springs, OK 74063
Rick Wilson (918) 245-8408
Hrs: S/Su, 1-5:30
Trap: 1 **Skeet:** 2

Sooner Skeet Club
10912 Ann Arbor,
Oklahoma City, OK 73162
Chuck Black (405) 278-1451
Hrs: Upon request **Skeet:** 1

Tahlequah Gun Club
Rt. 3, Box 784,
Tahlequah, OK 74464
Hal C. Sammons (918) 456-4749
Hrs: Registered Shoot Dates Only
Trap: 4

Tulsa Gun Club
PO Box 580411, Tulsa, OK 74158
Harold W. Radke, Jr.
(918) 272-0262
Hrs: S/Su/W/F, 1-6
Trap: 5 **Skeet:** 4

OREGON

SPORTING & 5-STAND

B&B Clay Sports
Box 1686, Klamath Falls, OR 97601
David Bleha (503) 883-3373
6 mi. W of Klamath Falls
Hrs: S/Su, 12-Dark
Sporting: 1, 10 stations
Trap: 1 **Skeet:** 2

Bear Creek Shooting Pres.
827519 Crooked River Hwy.,
Prineville, OR 97754
Dan Greenfield (541) 576-2096
26 mi. SE of Primeville
Sporting: Y

Cottage Grove-Eugene
81078 N. Pacific Hwy., Cresswell,
OR 97426
Gary (503) 942-2021
110 mi. S of Portland
Type: Public/Member
Hrs: T, 5-11; Su, 9-5
Sporting: 1, 10 stations
Trap: 13 **Skeet:** 2 **HT:** 35 ft.

Great Expectations Hunting Preserve
HC82, Box 234,
Kimberly, OR 97848
Jerry Russell (503) 934-2117
70 mi. NW of John Day
Type: Public/Member
Hrs: Aug. 1-March 31; till Dark
Reservs: Strongly recommended
Sporting: 1, 12 stations
See Our Ad Pg. 391

Helms Canyon Hunt Club
200 West 9th St., The Dalles, OR
97058
Doug Reid (503) 296-9535
115 mi. E of Portland
Type: Public/Member
Sporting: 1

Hermiston Gun Club
PO Box 202, Hermiston, OR 97838
Patty Carson (541) 567-1855
35 mi. W of Pendleton
Type: Public
Hrs: Su, 10-2; Th, 6:30-10:30
Sporting: 1, 5 stations
Trap: 10 **Skeet:** 2

Hulse Pheasant S. C. Ranch
60277 Tygh Ridge Rd.,
Dufur, OR 97021
Mike & Debbie Hulse
(503) 467-2513
100 mi. E of Portland
Type: Public
Hrs: Daily, Dawn-Dusk
Sporting: 1, 10 stations

JCSA Trap & Skeet Club
7407 Highland Ave.,
Grants Pass, OR 97526
Ron Tripp (503) 476-2040
Sporting: None
Trap: 1 **Skeet:** 4 **Five Stand:** 1

Jefferson State Shooting
2057 Gettle St.,
Klamath Falls, OR 97603
John Juniel (503) 882-0944
235 mi. S of Portland
Type: Public
Hrs: Monthly April-Sept.
Sporting: 1, 10 stations
Five Stand: 1

Josephine County Sporting
7407 Highland Ave. (I-5), Grants
Pass, OR 97526
Ronald Tripp (503) 476-2040

320 mi. S of Portland
Type: Public/Member
Hrs: Su-S, 8-Dark
Sporting: 1, 5 stations
Trap: 1 **Skeet:** 4 **HT:** 25 ft.
Wobble Trap

Muddy Creek Sporting Club
29499 Buchanan Rd.,
Corvallis, OR 97333
Don Hamblin (503) 753-9679
22 mi. N of Eugene
Type: Public/Member
Hrs: By Appointment
Reservs: Strongly recommended
Sporting: 1, 57 stations
Mostly Flat, trees & brush
Five Stand: 1 **HT:** 72 ft.
○ Factory Ammunition
○ Certified Shooting Instructors
○ Corporate Shoots/Catering
  Available
○ Night Shooting
○ 3 High Towers/Innovative Target
  Presentation

Noble Sporting Adventures
Rt. 2, Box 185-X,
Milton-Freewater, OR 97862
Don Noble (541) 558-3675
235 mi. E of Portland
Type: Public **Hrs:** Year Round
Sporting: 1, 10 stations

Pheasant Ridge, Inc.
80420 Ross Rd.,
Tygh Valley, OR 97063
Steve Pierce (541) 544-2183
120 mi. E of Portland
Type: Public/Member
Hrs: M-Su, 9-6, by resv. only
Sporting: 3, 27 stations
Skeet: 1 **HT Wobble Trap**

R&M Game Birds
Hood River, OR
Rodger Ford (509) 365-3245
80 mi. E of Vancouver, WA &
Portland, OR
Type: Public **Hrs:** Year round,
daylight-dark **Sporting:** 1, 15
stations **HT:** 85 ft.

Salem Trap & Skeet Club
6181 Concomly Rd, NE,
Jervais, OR 97026
Bill Lacefield (503) 792-3431
10 mi. N of Salem
Type: Public/Member
Hrs: W/Th, 12-9; F, 12-6; S/Su, 9-6
Sporting: 1, 13 stations
Trap: 22 **Skeet:** 6

Snake River Sportsmen
PO Box 1028, Ontario, OR 97914
Gary McClellan (541) 889-9232

50 mi. NW of Boise on I-84
Type: Public/Member
Hrs: Th, 6-Dark; Su, 1-Dark
Sporting: 1, 15 stations
Trap: 4 **Skeet:** 1   **HT:** 50 ft.
Wobble Trap

TREO Ranches
Rt. 1, Box 3171,
Heppner, OR 97836
Phil Carlson (503) 676-5840
180 mi. E of Portland
Type: Public
Hrs: Daily by appt.
Reservs: Strongly recommended
Sporting: 1, 8 stations
See Our Ad Pg. 393

Tri-County Gun Club
PO Box 99, Sherwood, OR 97140
Phil Morgan (503) 625-7318
18 mi. S of Portland
Type: Public
Hrs: Su, 11-4; T/Th, 6:30-9:30
Sporting: 1, 14 stations
Trap: 4 **Skeet:** 2 **Five Stand:** 1
Wobble Trap

TRAP & SKEET

Baker Trap Club
Baker, OR 97814
Ken Dunleavy (503) 523-6415
Type: Public/Member
Hrs: Th, 7-11pm **Trap:** 4

Hillsboro Trap & Skeet
33295 NW Wren Rd.,
Hillsboro, OR 97123
Linda Lorence (503) 648-2972

Willamette Valley Sports.
2340 Brittany, Eugene, OR 97405
Garay Wilson (503) 752-8491
Hrs: S/Su, 12-5; T/Th, 5:30
Skeet: 3

PENNSYLVANIA

SPORTING & 5-STAND

All Seasons T&S Club
PO Box 787, DuBois, PA 15801
Fred Frantz (814) 590-3777
7 mi. SE of DuBois
Type: Public
Hrs: Su, 9-4; Wed. evenings, 5:30-8
Sporting: 2, 20 stations
Trap: 2 **Skeet:** 2   **HT:** 40 ft.

Angus Conservation & Hunting Farms
RD#1, Box 260, Latrobe, PA 15650
Jay Angus (412) 423-4022

35 mi. E of Pittsburgh
Type: Public/Member
Sporting: 1 **Trap:** Y **Skeet:** Y

Atglen Sportsmen's Club
PO Box 35, Parkesburg, PA 19365
Ed Parker (610) 286-5681
15 mi. E of Lancaster
Type: Public/Member
Hrs: W, 6pm-9pm; Su, 10-4 on the
1st, 3rd & 5th Sun.
Sporting: 1, 24 stations
Five Stand: 1   **HT:** 28 ft.

Big Pine Hunting Club
PO Box 45, Prompton, PA 18456
George Rabtzow (908) 362-9008
20 mi. NE of Scranton
Type: Public/Member
Hrs: Week Ends by Appt.
Sporting: 1

Bradford Gun Club
PO Box 381, Bradford, PA 16701
Mike Schuler (814) 368-6245
6 mi. from Bradford
Hrs: W, 5-8:30; Su, Noon-5
Sporting: 1, 8 stations
Trap: 9 **Skeet:** 3

Mr. Britt's Sporting Clays
PO Box 925, RD2,
Homer City, PA 15748
John A. Boris (412) 479-9813
45 mi. E of Pittsburgh
Type: Public/Member
Hrs: M-S, 9am-Dusk; Su, 10am-Dusk
Sporting: 1, 15 stations **HT:** 40 ft.

The Busted Flush
RD#3, Shreve Rd., Box 57,
Titusville, PA 16354
Jim Berry/Ken Mulford
(814) 827-4030
80 mi. N of Pittsburgh
Type: Public/Member
Hrs: M-F, by appt; S/Su, 9-dark
Reservs: Recommended
Sporting: 1, 18 stations **HT:** 30 ft.
O Loaner Guns
O Factory Ammunition
O On-Site Meals
O Formal Instructions
O Organized Leagues

Cacoosing Gun Club
PO Box 293, Birdsboro, PA 19508
Jack Babb (610) 856-1453
5 mi. SE of Reading
Type: Public/Member
Hrs: W, 9-2; Th, 3-Dark; S, 9-4; Su,
8:30-Dark **Reservs:** Not required
Sporting: 1, 12 stations
Trap: 1 **Skeet:** 2   **HT:** 50 ft.
Wobble Trap

Carlisle Fish & Game Assoc.
Box 157, Rt. 641,
Carlisle, PA 17013
Ben Barrouk (717) 938-2043
10 mi. SW of Harrisburg
Type: Public/Member
Hrs: S, 9-3
Sporting: 1, 25 stations
Trap: 5 **Skeet:** 2

Castlewood Rod & Gun
Box 7411, New Castle, PA 16101
Robert Saunders (412) 924-9010
5 mi. E of New Castle
Type: Public **Hrs:** Su, 9-4
Sporting: 1, 18 stations
Trap: 2   **HT:** 30 ft.

Country Clays
2071 Baus Rd.,
E. Greenville, PA 18041
Joe Andreoli (215) 679-6181
39 mi. NW of Philadelphia
Type: Public **Hrs:** T-Su, 9-Dark
Sporting: 1, 22 stations
Trap: 1 **Skeet:** 1

Critter Path Sporting Clays
3191 Wheelertown Rd.,
Waterford, PA 16441
Mike Wise (814) 796-2658
12 mi. S of Erie
Type: Public
Hrs: S/Su, 9-5; Wkdys by appt
Sporting: 2, 32 stations **HT:** 20 ft.

Dyberry Sporting Clays
RR5, Box 530, Honesdale, PA 18431
Tony Fritz (717) 251-9720
30 mi. W of Stranton
Type: Public
Hrs: S/Su, 9-4, by appt.
Sporting: 1, 17 stations
O Factory Ammunition
O 35 miles from Milford (PA/NJ
border) up Rt. 6

Elstonville Sportsmen
3133 Pinch Rd., Manheim, PA 17545
Brad Deppen (717) 665-6354
20 mi. N of Lancaster
Type: Public/Member
Hrs: W, 4-9; Su, 9-3; Trap, Th, 5-9
Sporting: 1, 12 stations
Trap: 3   **HT:** 20 ft.

Endless Mountains
RD#2, Box 55, Montrose, PA 18801
Jeff Scavazzo (717) 553-2659
18 mi. S of Binghamton
Type: Public/Member
Hrs: M-F, 12-Dark; S/Su, 10-5
Sporting: 1, 12 stations

Factoryville Sportsmen's Club
PO Box 331, Factoryville, PA 18419
Chuck Kasmanski (717) 288-7242
15 mi. NW of Scranton
Type: Public/Member
Hrs: W, 4pm-Dusk (summer); S/Su, 9am-Dusk **Reservs:** Not required
Sporting: 1, 26 stations
Trap: 2 **Five Stand:** 1   **HT:** 30 ft.
○ Factory Ammunition
○ On-Site Meals
○ Organized Leagues
○ Golf Carts
○ Shooting Lodge/Clubhouse
○ Handicap Accessible
○ Clubhouse Phone: (717) 378-2593
○ Call (717) 378-CLUB for Upcoming Events
○ Just 1 hr. from Rt. 80/Delaware Water Gap

Forest Hill Sporting Club
RD#2, Box 389,
Mifflinburg, PA 17844
John B. Punako (717) 966-9419
35 mi. NW of Harrisburg
Type: Public
Hrs: Su-S, by appt.
Sporting: 1, 10 stations
Skeet: 1 **Five Stand:** 1   **HT:** 20 ft. **Wobble Trap**

Greater Pittsburgh Gun Club
RD1, Bulger, PA 15019
Tex Freund (412) 796-9111
18 mi. W of Pittsburgh
Type: Public/Member
Hrs: W/Th, 6-10; S/Su, 10-6 & by Appt. **Reservs:** Recommended
Sporting: 2, 17 stations
Trap: 4 **Skeet:** 3 **Five Stand:** 1

Hill's Sporting Clays
Box 212, Equinunk, PA 18417
Adam Hill (717) 224-4845
45 mi. NE of Scranton
Type: Public/Member
Hrs: 7 days a wk by app't
Sporting: 1, 12 stations **HT:** 70 ft.

Hillside Hunting Preserve & Sporting Clays
PO Box 56, Berlin, PA 15530
James Scurfield (814) 267-5301
60 mi. SE of Pittsburgh
Type: Public/Member
Hrs: Su-S, til dark (closed Mon)
Reservs: Recommended
Sporting: 4, 100 stations
Trap: 1   **HT Wobble Trap**
See Our Ad Below

Hollidaysburg Sportsmen's
RD#2, Box 259, Tyrone, PA 16686
(814) 695-8138
75 mi. E of Pittsburgh
Type: Public
Hrs: Th, evenings; Su
Sporting: 2, 10 stations
Trap: 1 **Skeet:** 6 **Five Stand:** 2 **HT:** 65 ft.

Indian Run Country
Rt. 2, Centerville, PA 16404
Dave Stutzman (814) 967-2635
85 mi. N of Pittsburg
Type: Public/Member
Sporting: 1

JDZ Game Farm
RD#2, Box 75,
Watsontown, PA 17777
John Zaktansky (717) 649-5881
70 mi. SW of Scranton
Type: Public/Member
Hrs: Sept. thru April, no Sundays
Sporting: 1, 5 stations

Langhorne Rod & Gun Club
9247 Annapolis Rd.,
Philadelphia, PA 19114
Vincent Tomes, III (215) 968-9973
Type: Public/Member
Hrs: Th, 6-10; ATA Shoots
Sporting: None **Trap:** 4 **Five Stand:** 1   **Wobble Trap**

Lappawinzo Fish & Game
12 Redwood Dr.,
Northampton, PA 18067
A. J. Hensel, Jr. (610) 262-9904
7 mi. N of Allentown
Type: Public/Member
Hrs: Year Round, 9-Dark; Reserv. for sptg. clays **Sporting:** 1, 12 sta.
Trap: 6 **Skeet:** 2

Laurel Springs Hunt Club
RD#2, Box 162,
Rockwood, PA 15557
"Bob Cat" Weston (814) 352-8803
Sporting: 1, 18 stations
Trap: 1 **Skeet:** 1 **HT:** 75 ft.

Lawrence Co. Sportsmen's
RD3, Harbor Rd.,
New Castle, PA 16105
Scott Rennie (412) 652-9260
Hrs: Su, 12-4; Th eve.
Sporting: 1, 10 stations
Trap: 1 **Skeet:** 3 **Five Stand:** 1

Lehigh Valley Sporting Clays
2750 Limestone St.,
Coplay, PA 18037
Fred Durham, III (610) 261-9616
4 mi. N of Allentown
Type: Public
Hrs: W/Th/F, 10:30-Dk; S/Su, 9-Dk
Reservs: Recommended
Sporting: 1, 15 stations
Five Stand: 1
○ 3 FITASC Parcours–Neil
  Chadwick, Professional

Martz's Gap View
RR#1, Box 85, Dalmatia, PA 17017
Don Martz (800) 326-8442
38 mi. N of Harrisburg
Type: Public **Hrs:** M-S, 8-5
Sporting: 1, 9 stations

McCrea's Sporting Clays
155 Hays Road, Fenelton, PA 16034
Joe McCrea (412) 445-3855
40 mi. N of Pittsburgh
Type: Public
Hrs: S-Su, 9-5; weekdays by app't
Reservs: Strongly recommended
Sporting: 1, 35 stations **HT:** 35 ft.

Oley Valley Fish & Game
114 Old State Rd.,
Reading, PA 19606
Donald Hoffman (610) 779-1317
6 mi. E of Reading
Type: Public/Member
Hrs: Clays–Tues & every 4th Sun;
TR/SK, Wed. eve.
Reservs: Not required
Sporting: 1, 12 stations
Trap: 2 **Skeet:** 1

PAL SPORTING CLAYS

PAL Sporting Clays
524 Main St., #105,
Honesdale, PA 18431
Robert K. Pierce (914) 763-5117
Sporting: Y

Pinewood Hunter Clays
Box 436, RD3, Kutztown, PA 19530
Jack Herbein (610) 683-5232
40 mi. NW of Philadelphia
Type: Public/Member
Hrs: Su-S, by appt. only
Sporting: 3, 45 stations
Five Stand: 1 **HT:** 100 ft.

Potter County Sporting
PO Box 279, Bailey Hill Rd.,
Elysses, PA 16948
Doug Kurtz (814) 848-9958
30 mi. S of Corning, NY
Type: Public **Hrs:** S/Su, 8-Dark;
Weekdays, please call
Sporting: 1, 51 stations

Reading Regulated Hunting & Sporting Clay
RD1, Box 220A, Birdsboro, PA 19508
Buzzy Williams (610) 856-7671
42 mi. NW of Philadelphia
Type: Public **Hrs:** Su-S
Reservs: Strongly recommended
Sporting: 1, 30 stations
Trap: 1 **HT:** 50 ft.
○ Factory Ammunition
○ Shooting Lodge
○ Golf Carts

Rock Ridge Hunting
RD#3, Box 77M,
Pine Grove, PA 17963
Gregory Fedechko (717) 345-8900
50 mi. NE of Harrisburg
Type: Public **Hrs:**
Sporting: 1, 13 stations

Rolfe Beagle Club
134 South St., Ridgway, PA 15853
Paul Rees (814) 772-1487
130 mi. NE of Pittsburgh
Type: Public, Public/Member
Hrs: Su for Sporting Clays only
Sporting: 1, 8 stations
Trap: 1 **Skeet:** 1

Rural Sportsmens Assn.
1090 South Rt. 100,
Trexlertown, PA 18087
Arthur Nevin (215) 536-7835
40 mi. NW of Philadelphia
Type: Public
Hrs: S/Su, 12-5; others by appt.
Reservs: Not required
Sporting: 1, 5 stations
Trap: 5 **Skeet:** 3 **Five Stand:** 1
HT: 20 ft.

Shenecoy Sportsmen
Box 75, McConnelstown, PA 16660
Mark A. Kane (814) 627-4003
4 mi. S of Huntingdon
Type: Public/Member
Hrs: Su, 10-5 (Sk & Tr); Sptg. Clays,
One Sunday/month
Sporting: 1, 10 stations
Trap: 2 **Skeet:** 16 **Five Stand:** 1

Sporting Clays at Pip Inn
HC6, Box 6474, Blooming Grove
Rd., Blooming Grove, PA 18428
Larry Erdman (717) 665-7003
20 mi. W of Milford
Type: Public **Hrs:** F/S/Su, 9-5
Sporting: 1, 20 stations
Five Stand: 1 **HT:** 35 ft.

Spruce Hollow
RD#2, Box 353,
Kunkletown, PA 18058
Junie & Cindy Kuehner
(610) 826-5134
70 mi. NE of Philadelphia
Type: Public
Hrs: 7 days a week by appt.
Sporting: 1, 11 stations

Steelstown Gunning Club
PO Box 601, Palmyra, PA 17078
Jeff Lutz (717) 533-9425
20 mi. NE of Harrisburg
Type: Public/Member
Hrs: S, Feb-Sept, 8:30-1
Sporting: 1, 15 stations **Trap:** 1

Sunset Hill Shooting Range
RD#1, Box 59, Henryville, PA 18332
Anton Bonifacic, Jr. (717) 629-3981
80 mi. N of Philadelphia
Type: Public **Hrs:** All year, 10-5
Sporting: 1 **Trap:** 1

Susquehanna Valley
Box 8, RD2, McClure, PA 17841
S. Kirby Bubb or Todd Musser
(800) 338-7389
20 mi. S of Lewistown
Type: Public
Hrs: M/T/Th, 10-4; S, 9-4
Sporting: 1, 20 stations

TNT Shooting Grounds
Box 236, Waltersburg, PA 15488
Thomas Stewart (412) 677-2609
40 mi. S of Pittsburgh
Type: Public/Member
Hrs: Su-S, 8am-Dark
Sporting: 3, 60 stations

Thundering Pines
RD3, Box 15B, Shelocta, PA 15774
Ron Anthony (412) 726-5140
8 mi. W of Indiana, PA
Type: Public/Member
Hrs: Su-S, 9-5; Reserv. required M-F
Sporting: 2, 40 stations HT: 80 ft.

Twin SS Sporting Clays
9173 Jane's Lane, East Greenville,
PA 18041
Daniel Rufe (215) 679-6633
60 mi. from Philadelphia
Type: Public
Hrs: W/Th/F/S, 9-Sunset; Su,
11-Sunset
Sporting: 1
Five Stand: 1   HT: 85 ft.

The Warrington Club
400 Yeager Rd.,
Wellsville, PA 17365
Reservations (717) 741-7214
15 mi. S of Harrisburg
Type: Member/Avail
Hrs: Daily Except Sunday, 8-Dark -
Year Round
Reservs: Recommended
Sporting: 1, 7 stations
Trap: 1 Skeet: 1
O 100 miles north of Wash., DC
O Alt. Phone: (717) 432-0643 -
   Terry Laird
O Beautiful Grounds - 3 Towers
O Class II Instruction Available
O Complete On-Site Pro Shop
See Our Ad Pg. 511

Western Penn. Sportsmen's
5730 Saltsburg Rd.,
Murrysville, PA 15668
Al Crookston (412) 327-9918
Hrs: Th, 5:30-10; S, 10-2; One ATA
shoot/month
Sporting: 1, 13 stations Trap: 9

TRAP & SKEET

7-H Skeet Club
1840 Glendale Lake Rd.,
Patton, PA 16668
Roy Holtz (814) 674-8241

Hrs: W/F, 7:30-9:30
Trap: 1 Skeet: 4

B&L Skeet Club
RD#3, New Bethlehem, PA 16242
Darl L. Emings (814) 275-1111
Hrs: T, 6 Skeet: 3

Bucks County Fish & Game
Turk Rd., Doylestown, PA
Edward S. Yanchok
(908) 753-2365
Type: Public/Member
Hrs: 3rd & 4th Sunday, 11-5
Trap: 8

Clairton Sportsmen's Club
412 Coal Valley Rd.,
Clairton, PA 15025
Ed Stanton (412) 233-4411
Hrs: W, 6:30-9:30
Trap: 8 Skeet: Y

Cocalico Sportsman Assn.
1000 Thompson Ave.,
Annville, PA 17003
Larry Smith (717) 336-2997
Hrs: W, 5-9; S/Su, 12-4
Trap: 3 Skeet: 2

Delaware Co. Field & Stream
7310 Malvern Ave.,
Philadelphia, PA 19151
Barry Greenberg (610) 872-9728
Hrs: 9-Sunset
Trap: 5 Skeet: 3

Delaware Cty. Sportsmens
168 Fox Rd., Media, PA 19063
Nino Campagna (215) 676-6585
Type: Public
Hrs: 2nd, 4th & 5th Sundays, Wed.
eve., April-Sept. Trap: 5

Erie Skeet Club of PA
1215 E. 31st, Erie, PA 16504
Brad Gregory (814) 838-3601
Hrs: W, 5-10; S, 12-5; Su, 9-2:30
Trap: 1 Skeet: 3

Fayette Gun Club
PO Box 295, Uniontown, PA 15401
Richard Barron (412) 438-9126
Type: Public/Member
Hrs: Su, 1-5; W, 6-9 (Summer)
Trap: 8 Skeet: 1

Flourtown-Sandy Run
Box 84, Southampton, PA 18966
Harry Robinson (215) 343-9872
Hrs: W, 12:30-9; S, 9:30-4; Su, 11-4
Trap: 3 Skeet: 3

Ford City SA
RD2, Box 186, Ford City, PA 16226
John C. Novak (214) 763-3136
Type: Public
Hrs: W, 12-4; F, 6-11 Trap: 2

Greater Jackson Twp.
RD#1, Box 450,
Mineral Point, PA 15942
Terry L. Crouse (814) 749-9773
Type: Public   Hrs: T, 5:30-11
(Apr-Sept); Su, 1-5 (Oct-Mar)
Trap: 4

Greencastle Sportsman's
Box 193, Greencastle, PA 17225
Joe Carbaugh (717) 597-7280
60 mi. SW of Harrisburg
Type: Public/Member
Hrs: F, 6:30-9:30 & scheduled
shoots Trap: 5

Harrisburg Hunters & Angl.
6611 Hunters Run Rd.,
Harrisburg, PA 17111
George Miller (717) 545-6834
Hrs: Sunrise to Sunset
Trap: 2 Skeet: 2

Hegins Trap Club
819 Chestnut St.,
Hegins, PA 17938
Wayne C. Stutzman
(610) 682-9577 Type: Public
Hrs: S, 12-5; 1 Sun. per mo.
Trap: 4

Irem Temple Gun Club
RD5 Country Club Rd.,
Dallas, PA 18612
Alan Mellner (717) 675-1134
Type: Public/Member
Hrs: 2nd & 4th Sun., 12-5
Trap: 2

Keystone Sportsmen Assn.
311 Lyons Ave.,
Williamsport, PA 17701
Roy H. Belcher, III (717) 546-5779
Hrs: Th, 5-10 Trap: 5

Library Sportsmens Assn.
RR1, Box 84B, Finleyville, PA 15332
Arthur Benevento (412) 835-9822
Hrs: 9-1 Trap: 5 Skeet: 2

Lower Providence Gun Club
PO Box 12, Phoenixville, PA 19460
A. Gazzillo (610) 666-9934
Hrs: F, 5-10; 3rd & 5th Sun, 11
Trap: 4

Mahonig Sportsmen Assoc.
Rt. 224, Hillsville, PA 16132
James Gardella (412) 667-7855
Trap: 2

Meadville Sportsman's Club
789 Williamson Rd.,
Meadville, PA 16335
Jeff McNany (814) 336-4240
Hrs: Su, 1-4; W, 6-9
Trap: 2 Skeet: 2

Millvale Sportsmens Club
170 Sunnyhill Rd.,

Wexvord, PA 15090
Karl Borgman (412) 935-9963
Hrs: W, Eve; Su, Afternoons
Trap: 4

New Holland Rod & Gun
59 Blaine Ave., Leola, PA 17540
Franklin D. Bair (717) 354-7814
Type: Public/Member
Hrs: 1st Sat. of month, 11-3
Trap: 5

North End Rod & Gun Club
6401 Schantz Rd.,
Allentown, PA 18104
Freeman Kline, Jr. (610) 395-0140
Type: Public
Hrs: Fri. nights practice; Registered shoots **Trap:** 7

Northside Sportsmans Assn.
Mt. Pleasant Rd.,
Warrendale, PA 15086
Jim Mandera (412) 935-9884
Type: Public/Member
Hrs: W, 6-11pm; Su, 10-3
Trap: Y **Skeet:** Y

Northumberland Point
RD2, Northumberland, PA 17857
Neil Mertz (717) 473-3272
Hrs: W, Eve. **Trap:** 8 **Skeet:** Y

Oxford Gun Club
Box 222, Nottingham, PA 19362
Ted Wallace (610) 932-9213
Type: Public **Hrs:** Th, 5:30pm
Trap: 5

Paradise Shooting Center
Box 188, Rt. 940 East,
Cresco, PA 18236
Joe Harrington (717) 595-3660
Hrs: M-S, 10-5; Su, 12-5
Trap: 2 **Skeet:** 2

Philipsburg Rod & Gun
102 Windsor St.,
Philipsburg, PA 16866
Ned Holdren (814) 342-3225
Type: Public
Hrs: W, 6-10 (Apr-Nov); Su, 1-5
Trap: 5 **Wobble Trap**

Pocono-Slate Belt Shooting
RD1, Box 1420, Bangor, PA 18013
Stanley T. Miller (610) 588-4970
Hrs: Th, 4-8 **Trap:** 6

Richland Shotgun Club
3838 Shepard Rd.,
Gibsonia, PA 15044
Raymond W. Russ (814) 498-2708
Type: Public **Hrs:** S/Su, 9-Dark
Trap: 1

Rosedale Sportsmen's Assn.
Box 14213, Pittsburgh, PA 15239
William D. Straub (412) 337-2403
Hrs: W/Th, 2-10
Trap: 4 **Skeet:** 3

Sandy Lake Sportsmans
118 Cole Rd., Sandy Lake, PA 16145
Carl Johnson (412) 376-3129
Hrs: W, 5-8; Su, 10-1 **Skeet:** 3

Sayre Sportsman's Club
518 Lincoln St., Sayre, PA 18548
Joe Pellicano (717) 888-6084
10 mi. E of Sayre
Type: Public/Member
Hrs: W, 5-9:30; Sun, 10-2
Trap: 1 **Skeet:** 2

Sewickley Heights Gun Club
400 Morgan Center,
Butler, PA 16001
Timothy J. Cowan (412) 741-6160
Hrs: Weekends only
Trap: 1 **Skeet:** 2

South End Gun Club
205 Schweitz Rd.,
Fleetwood, PA 19522
Richard Hamilton (610) 682-6647
Type: Public
Hrs: Every Wed. morn; ATA 2nd & 4th Sun., Mar-Oct
Trap: 12

Union City Sportsmens Club
18520 Hungry Run Rd., Union City, PA 16438
Marsh Klein (814) 438-2768
Trap: 1 **Skeet:** 2

Valley Gun & Country Club
PO Box 327, Elysburg, PA 17824
Andrew C. Long (717) 672-3130
Trap: 48

Victory Hill Gun Club
124 Erivest Ave.,
Monongahela, PA 15063
Frank Hillman (412) 258-9871
Type: Public/Member
Hrs: T, 6-11
Trap: 5 **Wobble Trap**

Washington Sportsman's
15 Wabash Ave., Morgan, PA 15064
F. V. Kosmacki, III (412) 222-0651
Hrs: Th, 6-11 **Trap:** 5 **Skeet:** 2

York/Adams Co. G&F Assn.
PO Box 140, East Berlin, PA 17316
Mike Beard (717) 633-1121
Hrs: S, 12-3; Su, 8-12; T, 4-Dark
Trap: 4 **Skeet:** 2

RHODE ISLAND

SPORTING & 5-STAND

Addieville East Farm
200 Pheasant Dr.,
Mapleville, RI 02839
Geoff Gaebe (401) 568-3185
20 mi. N of Providence
Type: Public/Member
Hrs: Su-S, 7am-Dark
Reservs: Recommended
Sporting: 3, 55 stations **HT:** 105 ft.
O Loaner Guns
O Factory Ammunition
O FAX: (401) 568-3009

Narragansett Gun Club
541 Austin Farm Rd.,
Exeter, RI 02822
G. J. Gazerro, Jr. (401) 397-9182
15 mi. S of Providence
Type: Public/Member
Hrs: S/Su, 9-1; Th, 1-3 & 6-9
Sporting: 1, 5 stations
Trap: 3 **Skeet:** 3

Peace Dale
441 Rose Hill Rd.,
Peace Dale, RI 02879
Richie Frisella (401) 789-3730
20 mi. S of Providence
Type: Public **Hrs:** Su-S, 9-dusk
Sporting: 6, 150 stations **HT:** 40'

Wallum Lake Rod & Gun
200 Brook Rd., Harrisville, RI 02830
Paul Fetschke (401) 568-7171
Type: Public/Member
Hrs: S/Su, Noon 'til dark;
Weekdays by reserv. **Sporting:** 2
Trap: 9 **Skeet:** 2 **Five Stand:** 1

SOUTH CAROLINA

SPORTING & 5-STAND

Back 40 Wing & Clay
4671 Timrod Rd., Bethune, SC 29009
Grady Roscoe (803) 475-4408
53 mi. NE of Columbia
Type: Public/Member
Hrs: M-Su, 8-Sundown
Reservs: Recommended
Sporting: 2, 20 stations
Wobble Trap
O One of the Best Courses in the Southeast!
O Special Weekend Camping/Shooting/Fishing Packages
O Just 49 miles east of I-77
O 25 miles from I-20
O Major Credit Cards Accepted

Back Woods Quail Club
Rt. 3, Box 253F,
Georgetown, SC 29440
Dave Lemmen (803) 546-1466
20 mi. W of Georgetown/Myrtle Beach
Type: Public/Member
Hrs: Open 7 days/week; 7am-dark
Reservs: Recommended
Sporting: 1, 15 stations
Trap: 2 **Skeet:** 2 **Five Stand:** 1
O Loaner Guns
O Factory Ammunition
O On-Site Pro Shop
O Shooting Lodge
O Organized Leagues
O Lighted trap, skeet & 5-stand fields

Bostick Plantation
PO Box 728, Estill, SC 29918
Joe Bostick (803) 625-4512
50 mi. N of Savannah, GA
Type: Public **Hrs:**
Sporting: 1

Boykin Mill Sporting Clays
73 Boykin Mill Rd., Boykin, SC 29128
Whit Boykin (803) 424-4731
6 mi. S of Camden
Type: Public/Member
Hrs: Su, 2-6; other days by appt.
Sporting: 1, 14 stations

Brays Island Plantation
PO Box 30, Sheldon, SC 29941
Owner Services (803) 846-3100
50 mi. SW of Charleston
Type: Member/Avail
Hrs: Su, 12-6; M-S, 8-6
Sporting: 4, 37 stations
HT: 62 ft. **Wobble Trap**

Broxton Bridge Plantation
Box 97, Hwy. 601,
Ehrhardt, SC 29081
Jerry Varn, Jr. (800) 437-4868
60 mi. W of Charleston
Type: Public
Hrs: Anytime by appt.
Reservs: Strongly recommended
Sporting: 2, 47 stations
HT: 65 ft. **Wobble Trap**
O Loaner Guns
O Factory Ammunition
O On-Site Pro Shop
O On-Site Meals
O Shooting Lodge
O Formal Instructions
O Organized Leagues
O Golf Carts
See Our Ad Pg. 401

Carolina Breeze Sporting
7963 Van Wyck Rd., PO Box 186,
Van Wyck, SC 29744
Michael Hobbs (803) 286-6610
Sporting: Y

Carolina Sporting Clays
NW Stroud Rd., Nichols, SC 29581
Eric Haselden (803) 392-1401
105 mi. E of Columbia
Type: Public
Hrs: M-F, by appt; S, 9:30-Dusk; Su, 12:30 **Sporting:** 1, 10 sta..
Trap: 1 **Skeet:** 1 **Wobble Trap**

Greenville Gun Club
111 Shaftsbury Rd.,
Clemson, SC 29631
Ed Prater (864) 277-6154
8 mi. S of Greenville
Type: Member/Avail
Hrs: W, 4-Dusk; S/Su, 1-Dusk
Sporting: 1, 11 stations
Trap: 3 **Skeet:** 4 **Five Stand:** 1
HT: 35 ft.

Harris Springs Sporting Clays
PO Box 278, Cross Hill, SC 29332
Jake Rasor (864) 677-3448
45 mi. SE of Greenville
Type: Public/Member
Hrs: Th/F/S, 9-Dark; W/Su, 1-Dark; other days by appt.
Sporting: 1, 14 stations
Five Stand: 1

Hermitage Farm Shooting Sports
PO Box 1258, Camden, SC 29020
Joe B. Cantey, III (803) 432-0210
25 mi. E of Columbia
Type: Public/Member
Hrs: T-S, 10-8; Su, 1-8
Reservs: Recommended
Sporting: 2, 17 stations
Skeet: 1 **Five Stand:** 1
O Loaner Guns
O Factory Ammunition
O On-Site Pro Shop
O Shooting Lodge
O Formal Instructions
O Rifle & Pistol Range
O FITASC-2 Parcourses

Little River Plantation Sporting Clays
PO Box 1129, Abbeville, SC 29620
Jim & John Edens (864) 391-2300
80 mi. NW of Columbia
Type: Public/Member
Hrs: M-S, 8-Dark; Su, 1-Dark
Reservs: Recommended
Sporting: 1, 14 stations
Five Stand: Y **HT:** 35 ft.
O Loaner Guns
O Factory Ammunition
O On-Site Pro Shop
O Formal Instructions
O Custom Ear Plugs
O 14 Stations

Live Oaks Inc.
PO Box 1277, Swansea, SC 29160
Billy Mitchum (803) 568-5104
1.5 mi. E of Swansea
Type: Public/Member
Hrs: W-S, 10:30-7; Su, 1:30-7:30; M/T, by appt.
Sporting: 1, 10 stations
Trap: 1 **Skeet:** 1 **Five Stand:** 1

Mill Creek Sporting Clays, Inc.
PO Box 6613 (957 Longwood Rd.),
Columbia, SC 29260
Bob Murphy (803) 695-0637
2.5 mi. SE of Columbia
Type: Public/Member
Hrs: Th/F/Su, 1-Dk; S, 10-Dk
Reservs: Not required
Sporting: 1, 15 stations
Mostly Flat, heavily wooded
Skeet: 1 **Five Stand:** 1 **HT:** 22 ft.

Moore's Sporting Clays
2290 Martin Rd.,
Hickory Grove, SC 29717

Doug Moore (803) 925-2064
45 mi. SW of Charlotte, NC
Type: Public **Hrs:** M/T, by appt;
W-S, 10-Dk; Su, 1:30-Dk
Sporting: 2, 26 stations

Myrtle Beach Shooting
3432 Hwy. 501 W
Myrtle Beach, SC 29577
Ted Gragg (803) 236-4344
14 mi. NW of Myrtle Beach
Type: Public
Hrs: T/W/S, 9-6; M/Th/F, by appt.
Sporting: 2, 16 stations **HT:** 30 ft.

Oak Ridge Hunting
1002 Hatchaway Bridge Rd.,
Aiken, SC 29803
Clarence Chapman (803) 648-3489
25 mi. E of Augusta
Sporting: Y

**River Bend
Sportsman's Resort**
PO Box 279, Fingerville, SC 29338
Ralph N. Brendle (864) 592-1348
15 mi. NW of Spartanburg
Type: Public/Member
Hrs: W/F, 1-8; S, 8:30-8; Su, 2-6
Reservs: Strongly recommended
Sporting: 1, 10 stations
Skeet: 1 **Five Stand:** 1 **HT:** 40 ft.
O Loaner Guns
O Factory Ammunition
O On-Site Pro Shop
O On-Site Meals
O Shooting Lodge
O Formal Instructions

Singletree
Rt. 1, Box 564, Clinton, SC 29325
C.C. May (803) 833-2618
55 mi. NW of Columbia
Type: Public
Hrs: Call for reservations
Sporting: 1, 6 stations **Skeet:** 1

So. Carolina Outdoor Shoot.
371 Cedar Branch Rd.,
Windsor, SC 29856
Richard Sherman (803) 648-5132
17 mi. E of Augusta, GA
Type: Public/Member
Sporting: 2, 32 stations
Trap: 6 **Skeet:** 4 **Five Stand:** Y

South Carolina Waterfowl
PO Box 450, Pinewood, SC 29125
David Watson (803) 551-4610
Sporting: 1 **Five Stand:** 1

Spartanburg Gun Club
Box 779, Whitestone, SC 29386
Eddie Glance (864) 474-2628
Type: Public/Member
Hrs: T-Su, 11-Dark
Sporting: 1, 13 stations

Trap: 9 **Skeet:** 4 **Wobble Trap**

Teddy's Sporting Clays
3432 Hwy. 501, Box 25,
Myrtle Beach, SC 29577
Ted L. Gragg (800) 844-5795
18 mi. NW of Myrtle Beach
Type: Public
Hrs: T/W/F/S, 9-Dark
Sporting: 3, 24 stations

Tinker Creek Sporting Clays
Rt. 2, Box 76, Williston, SC 29853
(803) 266-4840
40 mi. E of Augusta, GA
Type: Public/Member
Hrs: S/W, 9-Dark; Other days by
reserv. **Sporting:** 6, 45 stations

Triangle Gun Club
15 Clarendon Rd.,
Newberry, SC 29108
Allen Morrison (803) 276-8679
35 mi. NW of Columbia
Hrs: W/S/Su, 1-6 **Sporting:** None
Trap: 1 **Skeet:** 4 **Five Stand:** 1

Wagon Trail
P.O. Box 141, Gable, SC 29051
Thomas Durant (803) 495-2529
50 mi. E of Columbia (5 mi. east of
Sumter on U.S. Rt. 378)
Type: Public/Member
Hrs: Sa, 9-6; weekdays by app't
Sporting: 1, 15 stations

TRAP & SKEET

Beaufort Skeet Club
2910 4th St., Beaufort, SC 29902
Wayne Anderson (803) 522-7783
Hrs: Su, 9-5:30 **Skeet:** 1

Charleston AFB Sk. & Tr.
210 Lipman St.,
Summerville, SC 29483
Bobby Barrett (803) 566-5271
Hrs: M-F, 9-5; S/Su, 12-5
Trap: 1 **Skeet:** 2

Mid-Carolina Gun Club
Box 237, Orangeburg, SC 29115
Jack Rash (803) 534-4437
Trap: 1 **Skeet:** 5

Pageland Wildlife Action
515 Griggs St., Pageland, SC 29728
Richard Pigg
Type: Public/Member
Trap: 2 **Skeet:** 2

Polk County Gun Club
107 Hotel Hill Dr.,
Landrum, SC 29356
Randall Arthur (704) 863-4445
Type: Public/Member
Hrs: Su-S, 10-6
Trap: 2 **Skeet:** 1

School House Skeet & Trap
PO Box 363, Pamplico, SC 29583
Jimmy Ard (803) 493-3028
Hrs: 4-10
Trap: 1 **Skeet:** 1

Shaw Rod & Gun Club
2275 Drexel Ct., Dalzell, SC 29040
Robert Thompson (803) 668-2492
Hrs: S/Su, 1-7; W, 7-10; T/Th, 11-1
Trap: 1 **Skeet:** 3

SOUTH DAKOTA

SPORTING & 5-STAND

Aberdeen Gun Club
721 S. State, Aberdeen, SD 57401
Jerry Brick (605) 225-6383
Type: Public/Member
Hrs: T/Th, 1-9; S/Su, 1-5 (May-Sept)
Sporting: 1, 13 stations
Trap: 9 **Wobble Trap**

Dakota Ridge
RR2, Box 67, Altamont, SD 57226
Charles Shomaker (605) 874-2813
95 mi. N of Sioux Falls
Type: Public **Hrs:** Su-S,
10:30-sunset; Sept-March
Sporting: 1

Dakota Sporting Clays
PO Box 369, Jefferson, SD 57038
Jim Langstraat (605) 966-5399
15 mi. NW of Sioux City, IA
Type: Public/Member
Hrs: T/Th, 5-dusk; Su, 9-4
Sporting: 1, 16 stations

Funkrest Dakota Skat
RR3, Box 167, Madison, SD 57042
Don Funk (605) 256-3636
50 mi. NW of Sioux Falls
Type: Public/Member
Hrs: Su-S, 9-dk; Others by appt.
Sporting: 1, 10 stations **HT:** 40 ft.

Ghost Town Sporting Clays
45778 278th St., Parker, SD 57053
Steve Naatjes (605) 647-5691
24 mi. SW of Sioux Falls
Type: Public/Member
Hrs: By Appt. Only
Sporting: 1, 12 stations
Five Stand: 1 **HT:** 30 ft.

**Hunters Pointe
Shooting Club**
45743 260th St.,
Humboldt, SD 57035
Tony Bour (605) 363-6489
22 mi. W of Sioux Falls

Type: Public/Member
Hrs: T-W-T, 1-8; S-Su 9-5
Reservs: Strongly recommended
Sporting: 6, 60 stations
HT: 60 ft. **Wobble Trap**

James Valley Sporting Clays
43765 298 St., Utica, SD 57067
Harold Klimisch (605) 364-7468
55 mi. SW of Sioux Falls
Type: Public **Hrs:** Year round
Sporting: 1, 10 stations

Paul Nelson Farm
119 Hilltop Dr., PO Box 183,
Gettysburg, SD 57442
Paul Nelson (605) 765-2469
65 mi. NE of Pierre
Type: Public **Hrs:**
Sporting: 1
See Our Ad Pg. 409

Pearson's Hunting
HC74, 256, Forestburg, SD 57314
Marvin R. Pearson (612) 935-2514
16 mi. SE of Huron
Type: Public **Hrs:** By appt. only
Sporting: 1, 5 stations **HT:** 60 ft.

Stukel's Birds & Bucks
Rt. 1, Box 112, Gregory, SD 57533
Frank Stukel (605) 835-8941
90 mi. SE of Pierre
Type: Public
Hrs: 6/1-12/30, daylight hours
Reservs: Strongly recommended
Sporting: 1, 7 stations

Valley West
Shooting Complex
809 W. 10th St.,
Sioux Falls, SD 57104
Francis Phillips (800) 424-2047
5 mi. W of Empire Mall/Sioux Falls
Type: Public/Member
Hrs: Year Round-7 days/wk
Reservs: Recommended
Sporting: 2, 14 stations **Trap:** 2
Skeet: 2 **Five Stand:** 1 **HT:** 80 ft.

Willow Creek
20628 Willow Creek Rd.,
Ft. Pierre, SD 57532
Steve Stoeser (605) 223-3154
12 mi. W of Pierre
Type: Public

Hrs: M-F, Sun-up - Sunset; S/Su,
Noon-Sunset
Sporting: 2, 15 stations **HT**

TRAP & SKEET

Crooks Gun Club
Box 427, Sioux Falls, SD 57101
Bob Felber (605) 543-5481
Type: Public/Member
Hrs: T-F, 1-5; W/Th, Nights; Su, 1-5
Trap: 13 **Skeet:** 2 **Wobble Trap**

Devel County Ikes
512 5th St. West, Box 143, Clear
Lake, SD 57226
Lewis J. Shelsta (605) 874-2384
Type: Public/Member
Hrs: S/Su, by appt; T, 5:30
Trap: 2 **Skeet:** 1

Mitchell Gun Club
421 W. 4th Ave., Mitchell, SD 57301
Jerry Opbroek
Type: Public **Hrs:** **Trap:** 9

Rapid City Trap Club
9206 S. Hwy. 79,
Rapid City, SD 57702
Jim White (605) 341-4412
Type: Public/Member
Hrs: T/Th, 5-10pm; Su, open shooting
Trap: 9

Sioux Falls Gun Club
PO Box 944, Sioux Falls, SD 57005
Jerry Vander Esch (605) 332-9558
Hrs: T, 6-9 **Trap:** 8

TENNESSEE

SPORTING & 5-STAND

Arrowhead
Hunt Club
PO Box 598, Whiteville, TN 38075
Elmer Kahl (901) 231-8684
45 mi. E of Memphis
Type: Public
Hrs: S, 8:30-Dark; Su, 12:30-Dark;
Weekdays by appt.
Reservs: Recommended
Sporting: 1, 9 stations
○ Shoot American ZZ, Sporting
  Clays and Crazy Trap
○ Hunt Dove, Deer, Quail,
  Pheasant and Woodcock
○ Fish Bass, Bream, Crappie and
  more
○ Educational Programs:
  Wilderness Camping, Shooting,
  Fishing & Hunting Schools
Come spend a day or a week at
Arrowhead. We have the
facilities to make your outdoors

experience a memory that will
last a lifetime.

The Barn Gun Club
PO Box 664, Brentwood, TN 37024
Al Menefee, Jr. (615) 293-2141
Sporting: 1, 10 stations
Trap: 2 **Skeet:** 2

Crockett Hunting Preserve
1213 Woodgate,
Humboldt, TN 38343
Van Holyfield (901) 784-5368
13 mi. NW of Humboldt
Type: Public **Hrs:** T/W/Th/S/Su
Sporting: 1, 15 stations
Trap: 1 **Skeet:** 1 **Five Stand:** 1

Eagle Skeet Club
1656 Adswood Rd.,
Clarksville, TN 37042
Frank Clark (502) 798-9958
Hrs: Th, 2-6; S/Su, 11-5
Sporting: None
Trap: 1 **Skeet:** 3 **Five Stand:** 1

Estanaula Hunt Club
PO Box 26, Brownsville, TN 38012
Harbert Mulherin (901) 772-9780
50 mi. NE of Memphis
Type: Public **Hrs:** 10/15-3/15
Sporting: 1

Falls Creek Hunt Club
HC69, Box 234, Spencer, TN 38585
Frank Hanwright (615) 946-2095
85 mi. SE of Nashville
Type: Public/Member
Hrs: Daily by appt.
Sporting: 1, 8 stations **HT:** 20 ft.

Great Guns
20492 Raceway Rd., Harrisburg,
AR 72432
Steve Skillern (501) 578-9700
60 mi. NW of Memphis, TN
Hrs: M-S, by app't; Su, 10-dk.
Reservs: Recommended
Sporting: 1, 13 stations
Five Stand: 1

Grinders Switch Club
1608 Chickering Rd.,
Nashville, TN 37215
Barry Claud (615) 729-9732
35 mi. SW of Nashville
Type: Public/Member
Hrs: W-S, 8-5
Sporting: 5, 40 stations
HT: 80 ft. **Wobble Trap**

Happy Springs Sport. Clays
4350 Happy Springs Rd., Red
Boiling Springs, TN 37150
Gary McCarter (615) 699-3414
80 mi. NE of Nashville
Type: Public/Member

Hrs: S, 8-Dark; Su, 1-Dark
Sporting: 1, 10 stations HT: 25 ft.

The Hunting Lodge
Box 381, Manchester, TN 37355
Harry L. Taylor (615) 728-7260
75 mi. SE of Nashville
Type: Public Hrs: By appt. only
Sporting: 1, 25 stations

Lakeway Sporting Clays
4925 County Home Rd.,
Paris, TN 38242
Mike McDaniel (901) 642-7293
75 mi. W of Nashville
Type: Public
Hrs: S, 9-Dark; Su, 1-Dark
Sporting: None
Five Stand: 1

Memphis Sport Shooting
PO Box 97, Brunswick, TN 38119
Jim Norris (901) 867-8277
10 mi. N of Memphis
Type: Member/Avail
Hrs: W-Su, 12-Dark
Sporting: 1, 8 stations
Trap: 5 Skeet: 5 HT: 41 ft.

Montlake Public Shooting
2009 Mowbray Pike,
Soddy Daisy, TN 37379
Carl N. Poston (423) 332-1195
Type: Public Hrs:
Sporting: 1, 25 stations
Trap: 4 Skeet: 5

Nashville Gun Club
2323 Mt. Juliet Rd.,
Mt. Juliet, TN 37122
Sam Jennings (615) 742-1101
W of Nashville
Type: Public/Member
Hrs: W-F, 10-6; S/Su, 9-6
Sporting: 1, 10 stations
Trap: 6 Skeet: 5 Five Stand: 1

Nashville Gun Club
Box 90131, Nashville, TN 37209
Jeff Carrigan (615) 742-5297
3 mi. W of Nashville
Type: Public/Member
Hrs: W-F, 11-6; S/Su, 10-6
Sporting: 2, 20 stations
Trap: 4 Skeet: 4 Five Stand: 1

Shaw Creek
2055 Burnett Rd.,
Williston, TN 38076
Randy Reeves (901) 854-0121
29 mi. E of Memphis
Type: Public Hrs:
Sporting: 1, 13 stations

Short Creek Sporting Clays
191 County Rd. 50,
Athens, TN 37303
Carey Bishop (423) 334-5034
55 mi. N of Chattanooga

Type: Public Hrs: M/W/S
Sporting: 1, 30 stations
Five Stand: 1 HT: 30 ft.
Wobble Trap

SMOKY MOUNTAIN
SPORTS CLUB, Inc.

Smoky Mountain Sports Club
4286 Miser Station Rd.,
Lousiville, TN 37777
Jeff Smith (615) 995-9291
20 mi. S of Knoxville
Type: Public/Member
Hrs: M/T, by appt; W-F, 12-Dusk;
S, 11-Dusk; Su, 1-Dusk
Reservs: Not required
Sporting: 1, 10 stations
Trap: 2 Skeet: 2 Five Stand: 1
HT: 30 ft.

Southgate Public Shooting Center & Gun Shop
Rt. 1, Box 211B, Lavinia, TN 38348
E.V. Hillard (901) 783-3845
N of Jackson Type: Public/Member
Hrs: Su-S, Noon-Dark
Sporting: 1, 24 stations
Trap: 5 Skeet: 5

Upper Cumberland Sports
R#3, Box 195-C,
Crossville, TN 38555
Roy South (615) 484-1624
60 mi. W of Knoxville
Type: Public
Hrs: S, 9-Dusk; Su, 12-Dusk
Sporting: 2, 40 stations HT: 30 ft.

TRAP & SKEET

Bend of the River Trap Club
2880 Standing Stone Hwy.,
Cookeville, TN 38501
Charles Pardue (615) 526-1136
Type: Public/Member
Hrs: S, 9-6
Trap: 1 Skeet: 1

Big Springs Sporting Club
8890 Big Springs Rd.,
Christiana, TN 37037
Tommy Jackson (615) 890-6360
39 mi. E of Nashville
Type: Public
Hrs: W-S, 10-7; Su, 12-7
Trap: 2 Skeet: 2

Brownsville Skeet Range
899 Breckenridge,
Brownsville, TN 38012

Chuck Overton (901) 476-5255
Hrs: T/Th, 6-10; Su, 1-6
Skeet: 3

Cedar City Gun Club
5940 New Hope Ct.,
Hermitage, TN 37076
Gene Provost (615) 444-0104
Type: Public/Member
Hrs: S/Su, 12-6
Trap: 1 Skeet: 2

Chilhowee Rod & Gun Club
PO Box 345, Athens, TN 37371
Carey Bishop (423) 334-5034
Hrs: Su-S
Trap: 1 Skeet: 2

Cleveland Skeet Club
PO Box 685, Cleveland, TN 37364
Todd Korn (423) 479-7426
Skeet: 1

Dyersburg Gun Club
PO Box 40, Newbern, TN 38059
John Uitendaal (901) 627-3398
Type: Public
Hrs: Wed. afternoons (Apr-Aug)
Trap: 1 Skeet: 2

Gatlinburg Sportsman's
Box 1666, Gatlinburg, TN 37738
Don Walling (615) 436-0271
Hrs: Th/S/Su, 12-8
Trap: 2 Skeet: 1

Henry Horton Skeet League
637 Scenic Dr., Lewisburg, TN 37091
Charles W. Rogers (615) 364-2093
Hrs: W-Su, 12-Dark
Trap: 9 Skeet: 5

Highland Rim Shooters Club
2209 E. Lincoln St.,
Tullahoma, TN 37388
Joe P. Hill (615) 455-0509
Hrs: Th, 4-Dark; Su, 12-Dark
Trap: 1 Skeet: 3

Hog Heaven Gun Club
560 Hwy. 113, White Pine, TN 37890
Wade Frazier (423) 674-2282
30 mi. from Gatlinburg
Type: Public/Member
Hrs: S/Su, 1-Dark Trap: 6

Maury County Gun Club
1514 Galloway St.,
Columbia, TN 38401
Claude Mays (615) 381-3006
Skeet: 5

Mill Road Gun Club
90 Blackjack Pike,
Manchester, TN 37355
B.J. Yates (615) 728-3585
Hrs: Su, 1-Dark
Trap: 1 Skeet: 3

Morristown Trap Club
302 Fleming Dr.,
Morristown, TN 37814
Tommy Cope (423) 581-3444
Hrs: M, 5-10; S, 1-10
Trap: 4

Oak Ridge Sportsmens Assn.
732 Kempton Rd.,
Knoxville, TN 37909
Bobbie Dearden (423) 693-4937
Hrs: S/Su, 1-5
Trap: 1 **Skeet:** 3

Orion Gun Club
615 McLaughlin Dr.,
Munford, TN 38058
Howard Terry (901) 873-5665
Hrs: W, 4-6; S, 12-6; Su, 1-6
Trap: 1 **Skeet:** 1

Tenn. State Trapshooting
3912 Hillshire Dr.,
Antioch, TN 37013
Joseph Nevins (615) 361-7785
Hrs: W-Su **Trap:** 8

TEXAS

SPORTING & 5-STAND

Abilene Gun Club
PO Box 1213, Abilene, TX 79604
Harold Powell (915) 692-9002
Hrs: T-Th, 4-Dark; S/Su, 1-Dark
Sporting: None
Trap: 4 **Skeet:** 4 **Five Stand:** 1

Alpine Sporting Clays
5482 Shelby Rd.,
Ft. Worth, TX 76140
Jack Johnson (817) 478-6613
12 mi. SE of Ft. Worth
Type: Public **Hrs:** Daily, 8-Dark
Reservs: Not required
Sporting: 1, 14 stations **Trap:** 2
Skeet: 3 **Five Stand:** 1 **HT:** 25 ft.
○ Loaner Guns
○ Factory Ammunition
○ On-Site Pro Shop
○ Formal Instructions
○ Golf Carts
○ Gunsmith Service
○ Gun Fitting

Amarillo Gun Club
PO Box 30064, Amarillo, TX 79120
C. Moss/D. Rhoads (806) 372-0678
Type: Public/Member
Hrs: W/Th/F, 3-Dark; S/Su, 12-Dark
Sporting: 1, 5 stations
Trap: 14 **Skeet:** 5 **Five Stand:** 1

American Shooting Centers
16500 Westheimer Pkwy.,
Houston, TX 77082
Bill Bacon (713) 556-1597
17 mi. W of Houston
Type: Public/Member
Hrs: W/Th/F, 12-7; S/Su, 9-7
Reservs: Not required
Sporting: 2, 15 stations **Trap:** 1
Skeet: 7 **Five Stand:** 2 **HT:** 120'

Arlington Sportsman Club
3021 Pecan Circle, Bedford, TX 76021
Bryan Cullen (817) 473-0581
15 mi. S of Dallas/Ft. Worth
Type: Member/Avail
Sporting: 1, 10 stations
Trap: 1 **Skeet:** 5 **HT**

Backwoods T.R.A.P.S.
26828 US Hwy. 380,
Little Elm, TX 75068
Ron Dupler (214) 346-2823
Sporting: 1 **Trap:** Y **Skeet:** Y

Bayou Rifles, Inc.
1905 Johanna #B-2,
Houston, TX 77055
Skip Jobe (713) 894-2448
10 mi. W of Houston
Type: Public/Member
Hrs: 2nd & 4th Sun/month; Special
events by appt.
Sporting: 1, 5 stations
Skeet: 1 **Five Stand:** 1

HUNTING PRESERVE

Black Creek Ranch
26081 Bulverde Rd.,
San Antonio, TX 78261
Lee McClintick (210) 438-4188
58 mi. S of San Antonio
Type: Public **Hrs:** Daily by appt.
Reservs: Strongly recommended
Sporting: 1, 20 stations **HT:** 66 ft.
See Our Ad Pg. 417

Blue Goose
PO Box M, Altair, TX 77412
John R. Fields (409) 234-3597
50 mi. SW of Houston
Type: Public **Hrs:** By Reservation
Sporting: 1, 10 stations **HT:** 60 ft.

Brown Dog Sporting Clays
Box 157, Elysian Fields, TX 75642
Ronnie Mericle (903) 633-2334
17 mi. SE of Marshall
Type: Public **Hrs:** M-F, by appt; S,
10-Dk; Su, 1-Dk
Sporting: 1, 16 stations **HT:** 35 ft.

Brushy Creek Sporting Clays
Rt. 1, Box 203 A4,
Scroggins, TX 75480
Forrest Baker (903) 860-3800
10 mi. E of Winnsboro
Type: Public **Hrs:** M-Th, 12-Dark;
F/S, 12-9; Su, 1-9
Sporting: 2, 23 stations **HT:** 18 ft.

Caney Creek Sporting Clays
1702 Garrett Court,
Wharton, TX 77488
W.S. Sherrill (409) 532-1789
45 mi. SW of Houston
Type: Public **Hrs:** By Appt.
Sporting: 1, 8 stations

Capitol City Trap/Skeet Club
PO Box 141277, Austin, TX 78714
Mike Peebles (512) 272-4707
8 mi. E of Austin
Type: Public/Member
Hrs: W-Su, Noon-Dark
Reservs: Recommended
Sporting: 1, 10 stations **Trap:** 3
Skeet: 4 **Five Stand:** 1 **HT:** 45 ft

Carter's Country Shooting
6231 Treaschwig Rd.,
Spring, TX 77373
Billy Carter, Jr. (713) 443-8393
10 mi. N of Houston
Type: Public **Hrs:** Open 7 Days a Wk
Sporting: None
Trap: 1 **Skeet:** 1 **Five Stand:** 1

Clear Creek Gun Range
306 Crystal, League City, TX 77573
Ernest Randall (713) 337-1722
20 mi. S of Houston
Type: Public **Hrs:** T/W/Th, 1-8;
S/Su, 9-8 **Sporting:** 2, 11 stations
Trap: 3 **Skeet:** 5 **Five Stand:** 1

Competitive Edge Shooting Schools
Box 293913, Lewisville, TX 75029
Scott Robertson (214) 914-8496
Sporting: 1
○ Shooting Instruction Available—
See Ad Pg. 209

CYPRESS VALLEY PRESERVE

Cypress Valley Preserve
PO Box 162525, Austin, TX 78716
Philip C. Walker (817) 793-3341
25 mi. N of Austin
Type: Member/Avail
Hrs: W-F, 12-Dark; S/Su, 9-Dark
Reservs: Strongly recommended
Sporting: 1, 18 stations
Five Stand: 1 **HT:** 100 ft.
Wobble Trap

Dallas Gun Club
3601 IH-35 South, PO Box 292848,
Lewisville, TX 75067
Bill Scott (214) 462-0043
15 mi. N of Dallas/Ft. Worth
Type: Member/Avail
Hrs: W-F, 12-10; S/Su, 10-10
Sporting: 1, 10 stations
Trap: 5 **Skeet:** 8 **Five Stand:** Y

Dos Vaqueros
PO Box 1035, Refugio, TX 78377
Joan Rooke (512) 543-4905
45 mi. N of Corpus Christi
Type: Public, Member/Avail
Hrs: Year round, except July/Aug.
Reservs: Strongly recommended
Sporting: 1, 5 stations

Double R Ranch
2035 Victoria Garden Drive,
Richmond, TX 77469
Roland Reichardt (713) 342-9361
Type: Public/Member
Hrs: 7 Days/Week
Sporting: 1, 6 stations
Trap: 3 **Skeet:** 2

El Canelo Ranch
Box 487, Raymondville, TX 78580
Ray Burdette (210) 689-5042
75 mi. S of Corpus Christi
Type: Public
Hrs: S, 8-12 & by resrv.
Reservs: Strongly recommended
Sporting: 1, 10 stations
Mostly Flat, mostly brush
Trap: 1 **HT:** 30 ft.
See Our Ad Pg. 419

Elm Fork Shooting Park
10751 Luna Rd., Dallas, TX 75220
Dennis Reed (214) 556-0103
Type: Public
Hrs: (Sum) T-F, 12-7; S/Su, 9-7;
(Win) T/S/Su
Sporting: None
Trap: 4 **Skeet:** 6 **Five Stand:** 1

Fort Bliss Rod & Gun Club
PO Box 6118, Fort Bliss, TX 79916
Thomas J. Piasecki (915) 568-2983
Near El Paso
Hrs: Closed Mondays
Sporting: 1, 5 stations
Trap: 3 **Skeet:** 2

Greater Houston Gun Club
Box 97, Missouri City, TX 77459
Curt Sporull (713) 437-6025
10 mi. S of Houston
Type: Public/Member
Hrs: W-Su, 9-Dark
Sporting: None
Trap: 10 **Skeet:** 8 **Five Stand:** 1
HT: 20 ft.

 Greystone Castle Sporting Club

Greystone Castle Sporting Club
PO Box 158, Mingus, TX 76463
Dan VanSchaik (817) 672-5927
70 mi. W of Ft. Worth
Type: Public
Hrs: 9-4pm; Closed Mondays
Reservs: Strongly recommended
Sporting: 2, 18 stations **Skeet:** 1

Hawkeye Hunting Club
PO Box 27, Center, TX 75935
(409) 598-2424
55 mi. SW of Shreveport, LA
Type: Member/Avail
Hrs: By Appt.
Sporting: 1, 10 stations **Trap:** 1

Herradura Ranch Inc.
PO Drawer 698, Cotulla, TX 78014
David Schuster (210) 373-4492
95 mi. W of Corpus Christi
Type: Public **Hrs:**
Sporting: 1, 7 stations
Trap: 1 **Skeet:** 1

Hilltop Fish & Game Ranch
HCR67, Box 58C,
Pleasanton, TX 78064
Steve Hill (210) 569-HILL
35 mi. S of San Antonio
Type: Public **Hrs:** Daily
Sporting: 3, 11 stations

Hwy. 44 Shooting Range
RR3, Box 484,
Corpus Christi, TX 78415
Max Heatherington (512) 265-0258
Type: Public **Hrs:** S/Su, 4-Dk by Appt.
Sporting: 1, 9 stations

Pat Johnson's Wild Goose
2718 West Creek,
El Campo, TX 77437
Pat Johnson (409) 543-7553
70 mi. SW of Houston
Type: Public **Hrs:**
Sporting: 1, 10 stations

Joshua Creek Ranch
PO Box 1946, Boerne, TX 78006
Ann Kercheville (210) 537-5090
25 mi. NW of San Antonio
Type: Public/Member
Hrs: T-Su, 9am-7pm
Reservs: Strongly recommended
Sporting: 1, 30 stations
Wobble Trap
o Loaner Guns
o Factory Ammunition
o On-Site Pro Shop
o On-Site Meals
o Shooting Lodge
o Formal Instructions
o Organized Leagues
See Our Ad Pg. 423-25

Kat Creek Sporting Clays
PO Box 987, Henderson, TX 75653
Chester Martin (903) 854-2232
135 mi. SE of Dallas/Ft. Worth
Type: Public/Member
Hrs: Su, 1-Dk; S, 10-Dk; & by Appt.
Sporting: 1, 12 stations
Five Stand: Y **HT:** 65 ft.
Wobble Trap

Kleberg County T&S
823 South 24th St.,
Kingsville, TX 78363
Ronald Lewis (512) 595-8505
Type: Public **Hrs:** W, 6-10; F,
6-11; Su, 1-8
Trap: 2 **Skeet:** 2 **Five Stand:** 1
Wobble Trap

Krooked River Ranch
PO Box 85, Haskell, TX 79521
Steve Packer (915) 773-2457
200 mi. W of Dallas/Ft. Worth
Type: Member/Avail
Hrs: By Appt.
Sporting: 1, 6 stations
Trap: 1 **Skeet:** 1

La Media Sportsman's
PO Box 319, Linn, TX 78563
Jerry Pippen (800) 437-3903
110 mi. S of Corpus Christi
Type: Public **Hrs:**
Sporting: 1 **Trap:** Y **Skeet:** Y

LaPaloma Sporting Club
Box 160516, San Antonio, TX 78280
Henry Burns (210) 980-4424
Type: Public/Member
Hrs: W-Su, 9am-dark
Sporting: 2, 20 stations
Skeet: 1 **Five Stand:** 1 **HT:** 55 ft.

Le'Z Acres Shooting Range
Rt. 3, Box 256,
Pottsboro, TX 75076
Ray Zipper (903) 786-3254
4.5 mi. N of Pottsboro
Type: Public/Member
Hrs: W-Su, Noon-Dark; (winter)
10-Dark **Sporting:** 1, 13 stations

Loma Blanca Ranch
1300 S. University Dr., #410, Fort
Worth, TX 76107
Greg Williamson (817) 396-4570
15 mi. SW of Ft. Worth
Type: Member/Avail
Hrs: Reservation only
Sporting: 1, 12 stations **HT:** 50 ft.

Lone Star Sporting Clays
Rt. 1, Box 241A,
Glen Rose, TX 76043
Mike K. Lewellen (817) 897-2918
60 mi. SW of Ft. Worth
Type: Public/Member
Hrs: W, 3-Dark; S/Su, 11-Dusk;
other days by appt.
Sporting: 1, 15 stations

Los Cuernos Ranch
PO Box 200105,
San Antonio, TX 78220
Pat Moore (210) 676-3317
132 mi. SW of San Antonio
Type: Public/Member
Hrs: W-Su, 8-Dark; Call for resrv.
Reservs: Strongly recommended
Sporting: 1, 10 stations
O Loaner Guns
O Factory Ammunition
O On-Site Pro Shop
O On-Site Meals
O Shooting Lodge
O Formal Instructions
O 5,000 Ft. Runway Lighted

McGuire Lodge
PO Box 42, Seminole, TX 79360
Terry Cox (915) 758-3640
160 mi. S of Amarillo
Type: Public **Hrs:** Su-S
Trap: 1 **Five Stand:** 1

NSCA - National Gun Club
5931 Roft Rd.,
San Antonio, TX 78253
Mike Hampton (210) 688-3371
20 mi. NW of San Antonio
Type: Public
Hrs: Special Events Only
Sporting: 3, 36 stations
Trap: 16 **Skeet:** 38 **Five Stand:** 2
HT Wobble Trap

N.W. Texas Field & Stream
Box 4280, Wichita Falls, TX 76308
Cliff Wurster (817) 322-4845
130 mi. W of Dallas
Type: Public/Member
Hrs: W, 5-9; S, 8-Close; Su, 1-6
Sporting: 1, 10 stations
Trap: 2 **Skeet:** 2 **HT:** 20 ft.

One in One Hundred
1228 FM 421, Lumberton, TX 77657
John Stockwell (409) 755-9903
10 mi. N of Beaumont
Type: Member/Avail
Hrs: W-F, 1-dark; S/Su, 8-dark
Sporting: 1, 10 stations
Trap: 2 **Skeet:** 3 Wobble Trap

P.S.C. Shooting Club
2027 Sieber, Houston, TX 77017
Matt Fleming (713) 585-0068
25 mi. S of Houston
Type: Member/Avail
Hrs: S/Su, (Winter); S/Su/T/Th,
(Summer) **Sporting:** None
Trap: 1 **Skeet:** 1 **Five Stand:** 1

Paris Skeet & Trap Club
PO Box 164, Paris, TX 75460
Bill Gossman (903) 785-2155
Type: Public/Member
Hrs: S/Su, 12-Dark
Sporting: 1, 6 stations
Trap: 1 **Skeet:** 3

Pines Shotgun Club
318 S. First St., Lufkin, TX 75901
Don Byrd, Sec. (409) 824-2574
2 mi. SE of Lufkin
Type: Member/Avail
Hrs: By app't only
Sporting: 1, 12 stations
Trap: 2 **Skeet:** 3 **Five Stand:** 1

Possum Walk Ranch
Rt. 2, Box 174, Huntsville, TX 77340
Buddy Smith (409) 291-1891
70 mi. N of Houston
Type: Public/Member
Hrs: Oct-Mar, daily by appt;
Apr-Sep, wkends by appt.
Sporting: 1, 11 stations
Trap: 1 **Skeet:** 1 **HT:** 90 ft.

Prairie Creek Sporting Clays
Rt. 5 - 112 Allen Dr.,
Kilgore, TX 75662
Steve Brown (903) 845-6431
94 mi. W of Dallas
Type: Public
Hrs: Th/F, 1:30-Dark; S/Su,
8:30-Dark; M/T/W, by appt.
Reservs: Recommended
Sporting: 1, 10 sta. **Five Stand:** 1
HT: 30 ft. Wobble Trap
O Loaner Guns
O Factory Ammunition
O On-Site Pro Shop
O On-Site Meals
O Formal Instructions

Riverside Farms
Rt. 3, Box 217-R, Hamilton, TX 76531
Jill Bishop(817) 386-8921

Rustic Range Sporting Clays
Rt. 2, Box 182, Slaton, TX 79364
Dub Dillard (806) 828-4820
11 mi. E of Lubbock
Type: Public
Hrs: S, 11-Sunset; Su, 1-Sunset
Sporting: 1, 10 stations **HT:** 22 ft.

San Antonio Gun Club
928 E. Contour,
San Antonio, TX 78212
Mike Valerio (512) 828-9860
Type: Public/Member
Sporting: None
Trap: 5 **Skeet:** 8 **Five Stand:** 1

Silver Lake Gun Club
3300 Euless South Main,
Euless, TX 76040
Cliff Mycoskie (817) 355-1311
4 mi. SW of DFW Airport
Type: Public/Member
Hrs: W/F, 12-Dk; Sa, 9-Dk; Su, 9-6,
Other days by appt.
Reservs: Recommended
Sporting: 1, 15 stations
Trap: 1 **Skeet:** 2 **Five Stand:** 1
Wobble Trap
O On-Site Pro Shop
O Formal Instructions
O Centrally located to Dallas/Ft.
Worth
O Corporate Outings
O Lighted Skeet Field
O Friendly Staff

Spanish Dagger
PO Box 1325, Uvalde, TX 78802
George Cooper (210) 278-2998
70 mi. W of San Antonio
Type: Public

Hrs: T/W, Eve; Others by appt.
Sporting: 1, 6 stations
HT: 35 ft. **Wobble Trap**

Sporting Clays International of Dallas
Rt. 1, Box 118, Allen, TX 75002
John Holiski/Lynn Carley
(214) 727-1998
15 mi. NE of Dallas/Ft. Worth
Type: Public/Member
Hrs: W-F 11 - dark; Sat/Sun 9 - dark
Reservs: Not required
Sporting: 2, 18 stations
Trap: 1 Five Stand: 1

Shoot pheasant like the British, red-legged partridge like the Spaniards, grouse like the Vermonters and many, many more. Our sporting clays can simulate the thrill of hunting these favorites. Hone your hunting skills as you walk with us along the beautiful and serene Rowlett Creek. Come for the "Ultimate Shooting Experience": Wed/Thurs/Fri, 11am; Sat/Su, 9am. We have CORPORATE OUTINGS available, call for information and reservations, (214) 727-1998; FAX: (214) 727-6420.

TargetMaster
1717 S. Jupiter Rd.,
Garland, TX 75042
Thomas Mannewitz (214) 442-4565
15 mi. NE of Dallas/Ft. Worth
Type: Member/Avail
Hrs: T-Su   Sporting: 1, 14 stations
Five Stand: 1   HT: 45 ft.

Texas Waterfowl Outfitters
22413 Katy Frwy., Katy, TX 77450
Tony Hurst (800) 899-2650
20 mi. W of Houston
Type: Public/Member
Sporting: Y Skeet: Y

Texoma Trap Club
506 Oxford Dr., Sherman, TX 75090
Bob Overturf (903) 892-1992
55 mi. S of Dallas
Type: Public/Member
Hrs: W/Th, 1-6; Su, 8-6
Sporting: 1, 13 stations Trap: 9

Three Amigos Sport. Clays
Rt. 4, Box 64, El Campo, TX 77437
Jay Harris (409) 543-9475
60 mi. SW of Houston
Type: Public Hrs: Daily by appt.
Sporting: 1, 10 stations HT: 40 ft.

Top Flight
Rt. 1, Box 233, Beasley, TX 77417
Leon Randermann (409) 387-2284
30 mi. W of Houston
Type: Public/Member
Hrs: Oct.-March, by appt.
Sporting: 1, 8 stations

Tyler Gun Club
PO Box 6945, Tyler, TX 75711
Steve Fry (903) 597-3345
80 mi. SE of Dallas/Ft. Worth
Type: Public/Member
Hrs: W/S/Su, 2:30-Dark
Sporting: 1, 5 stations
Trap: 5 Skeet: 4 Five Stand: 1

Upland Bird Country
PO Box 730, Corsicana, TX 75151
Steve Stroube (903) 872-5663
55 mi. SE of Dallas
Type: Public Hrs: Tues., after 5 or Sat., by resrv. Sporting: 1, 10 stations
Skeet: 1   HT: 60 ft.

Waco Skeet & Trap Club
7209 Airport Rd., Waco, TX 76708
Stan Nesmith (817) 753-2651
1 mi. NW of Waco
Type: Public/Member
Hrs: W-Su, 1:30-Dark
Sporting: None Trap: 6 Skeet: 17 Five Stand: 1   HT: 30 ft.

West Texas Sportsman's
PO Box 14214, Odessa, TX 79768
Pete Wrenn (915) 561-9379
10 mi. E of Midland
Type: Public/Member
Hrs: T-Su, 10-Dusk
Sporting: 1, 12 stations Trap: 2
Skeet: 1 Five Stand: 1 HT: 45 ft.

Westside Shooting Grounds
1627 N. Hearthside,
Richmond, TX 77469
Jay Herbert (713) 371-2582
20 mi. W of Houston
Type: Member/Avail
Hrs: W-Su, 9-Dark
Sporting: 1, 14 stations Skeet: 1

Windwalker Farm
4202 Dawn Circle, Midland, TX 79707
Ralph Cramer (915) 694-2311
17 mi. NE of Midland
Type: Public/Member
Hrs: T-F, 1-Dark; S/Su, 10-Dark
Sporting: 1, 10 stations
HT: 90 ft. **Wobble Trap**

TRAP & SKEET

Arrowhead Gun Club
Rt. 1, Box 134,
College Station, TX 77845
Jim E. Broome (409) 690-0276
Hrs: T-Su, 10-Sunset
Trap: 2 Skeet: 3

Austin Skeet Range
5700 Avenue F, Austin, TX 78752
Stanley S. Castano (512) 272-8437
Hrs: 9-Dark Trap: 1 Skeet: 2

Bandera Gun Club
Rt. 1, Box 506, Bandera, TX 78003
J.M. Clements (512) 796-4610
Hrs: W-F, 3-Dk; S/Su, 1-Dk
Trap: 1 Skeet: 1

Briley Gun Club
1230 Lumpkin, Houston, TX 77043
Terry Hetrick (713) 932-6995
Hrs: By appt. only Skeet: 1

Buckyland Gun Club
1600 N. I-35, #106,
Carrollton, TX 75006
Barbara Coleman (214) 245-3030
Skeet: 1

Callahan 4-H Shoot. Sports
Rt. 2, Box 204, Clyde, TX 79510
Terry Ellis (915) 529-3652
Hrs: S/Su, 1-6 Skeet: 1

Corpus Christi Pistol/Range
Box 7117, Corpus Christi, TX 78467
Ken Crawford (512) 852-1212
Hrs: W/F, 3-Dk; Th, 3-12; S/Su, 9-Dk Trap: 4 Skeet: 5

Creekwood Gun Club
PO Box 327, Groveton, TX 75845
Tommy Walton (409) 642-1775
Hrs: Th, 2-6; S/Su, 9-8
Trap: 1 Skeet: 3

Cuero Gun Club
PO Box 604, Cuero, TX 77954
Mark Henneke (512) 275-9044
28 mi. W of Victoria
Type: Member/Avail
Hrs: Su-S, 8-7 Trap: 1 Skeet: 1

Desoto Gun Club
1117 Joshua Tree Dr.,
Plano, TX 75023
Clifford Hicks (214) 576-3338
10 mi. S of Dallas
Hrs: W, 6-9; S/Su, 12-Dark
Trap: 3 Skeet: 6

El Paso Trap Club
9817 Alameda Ave.,
El Paso, TX 79927
Earl Scripture (915) 859-7325
Hrs: W, 2-5; S/Su, 10-5
Trap: 6

Fort Worth
Trap & Skeet Club
Rt. 17, Box 283B,
Ft. Worth, TX 76126
Stan Peterson (817) 244-9878
Type: Public/Member
Hrs: W/Th/Su, 1-7; S, 10-7
Reservs: Recommended
Trap: 10 Skeet: 6 Five Stand: 1

Ft. Hood Skeet & Trap Club
810 Cagle Lane,
Harker Heights, TX 76548
Winters Hope (817) 532-2422
Hrs: S/Su, 10-Dark (Win), 10-6 (Sum)
Trap: 2 Skeet: 3

Graham Gun Club
Drawer 270, Graham, TX 76450
Kevin Stephens (817) 549-4758
Hrs: Various Wkends
Trap: 1

Grand Prairie Gun Club
Box 530274, Grand Prairie, TX 75053
Mike Vestal (214) 641-9940
Hrs: W/S/Su, afternoons
Trap: 2 Skeet: 3

Hill Country Gun Club
3009 Fawn Ridge,
Fredericksburg, TX 78624
Don E. Landers (210) 997-6745
Hrs: Su/W, 1-Dark
Trap: 1 Skeet: 1

Hot Wells Skeet Range
PO Box 8, Cypress, TX 77429
Dallas Lamar (713) 373-0232
Skeet: 4

Iowa Park Gun Club
PO Box 368, Iowa Park, TX 76367
(817) 592-9557
Hrs: 4th Wkend of Month (Feb-Nov)
Trap: 4

LaBota Skeet & Trap Club
14426 Mines Rd., Laredo, TX 78041
Lester W. Early (512) 723-6328
Hrs: W, 5-12; S/Su, 1-12
Skeet: 2

Lackland Rod & Gun Club
37 MWRSS/MWBR, 5325 Military
Dr., Lackland AFB, TX 78236
Wayne Allen (512) 674-7831
Hrs: M-Th, 4-9; S, 9-1; Su, 1-6
Trap: 1 Skeet: 2

Loma Alta Skeet & Trap Inc.
66665 E. 14th St.,
Brownsville, TX 78521
Richard Harding (210) 831-3445
Hrs: W/Su, 4
Trap: 1 Skeet: 2

The Metro Gun Club
4601 Kelvin St., Houston, TX 77005
Louis Poutous (713) 524-9074
10 mi. S of Houston
Type: Public Hrs: S/Su, all day
Trap: 2

Midland Shooters Assn.
PO Box 7444, Midland, TX 79708
Bill Smith (915) 563-5116
Hrs: W/Th/S/Su, 10-Dark
Trap: 16 Skeet: 6

Nacogdoches Skeet Club
3734 Tudor,
Nacogdoches, TX 75961
Robert Akins (409) 564-5455
Hrs: T/Th/S/Su
Skeet: 1

Orange Gun Club Inc.
PO Box 986, Orange, TX 77631
Buddy Bourque (409) 883-5622
Hrs: Daylight Trap: 1 Skeet: 1

Quail Creek Range
PO Box 1006, Argyle, TX 76226
James Collvins (817) 648-3356
20 mi. N of Ft. Worth
Type: Public Hrs: T-Su, 10-6
Skeet: 1

Randolph Skeet & Trap
PO Box 188, Randolph, TX 78148
Paul Guitierrez (210) 652-2064
Hrs: S/Su, 10-2; W, 5-8
Trap: 1 Skeet: 2

Rockdale Gun Club
Box 506, Rockdale, TX 76567
W.P. Hogan (512) 446-6669
Hrs: 10am, except Wed.; also
night shooting
Trap: 1 Skeet: 1

Rockwall Gun Club
1404 Fernwood Dr.,
Mesquite, TX 75149
Rodonna Wolfe (214) 288-5676
Type: Member/Avail
Hrs: S/Su, 1-Dark; W, 5-Dark
Trap: 2 Skeet: 3

Sands Skeet Club
Box 181228,
Corpus Christi, TX 78480
Cliff Sellers (512) 992-6532
Hrs: Private Club
Trap: 1 Skeet: 3

Stonehill Shooting Ranch
PO Box 21, Marble Falls, TX 78654
Cindi Darragh (512) 693-5296

Hrs: T/F, 10-Dark; S/Su, 9-Dark
Trap: 1 Skeet: 2

Tejas Gun Club
1214 Old Tyler Rd.,
Nacogdoches, TX 75961
Linda M. Pronge (409) 560-2774
Type: Public/Member
Hrs: F, 4-9; Su, 12-9
Trap: 3 Skeet: 1

Uvalde Gun Club
PO Box 5291, Uvalde, TX 78802
Carl Dee Castellaw (210) 278-5454
Trap: 1 Skeet: 1

Victoria Gun Club
PO Box 4116, Victoria, TX 77903
Cliff Denton (512) 575-8285
Hrs: 9-10 Trap: 1 Skeet: 1

UTAH

SPORTING & 5-STAND

Cache Valley Hunter Ed Ctr.
780 E. 350 So., Hyrum, UT 84319
Lloyd Johnson (801) 245-4000
Hrs: W/Th, 6-9:30; S/Su, 10:30-3
Sporting: None
Trap: 4 Skeet: 2 Five Stand: 1

Castle Country Sportsmen's
3679 S. 180 W., Price, UT 84501
Robert Migliori, Sr. (801) 637-7841
35 mi. S of Price
Type: Public/Member
Hrs: 7 Days/Wk; AM-Dusk
Sporting: 1, 12 stations Trap: 1

Goshen Dam Sport. Clays
11609 W. Hwy. 6,
Goshen, UT 84633
Kris Morgan (801) 667-3574
60 mi. S of Salt Lake City
Type: Public Hrs: Seasonal
Sporting: 3, 25 stations
Trap: 1

Goshute Sporting Clays
PO Box 187, Goshen, UT 84633
Ron Christensen (801) 667-3390
60 mi. S of Salt Lake City
Type: Public Hrs: S/Su, 9:30-5
Sporting: 1, 8 stations

Hatt's Ranch
Box 275, Green River, UT 84525
Rey Lloyd Hatt (801) 564-3224
16 mi. SW of Green River
Type: Public/Member
Hrs: T-Su, 9-5pm
Sporting: 1, 5 stations

Holladay Gun Club
PO Box 17304, Holladay, UT 84117
(801) 942-9802

10 mi. SE of Salt Lake City
Type: Public
Hrs: S/Su/Holidays; Wkdys by Appt.
Sporting: 1, 14 stations
Trap: 5 **Skeet:** 4   **HT:** 60 ft.

Pheasant Valley
16840 W. 12800 N.,
Howell, UT 84316
Carlos Christensen (801) 471-2245
75 mi. N of Salt Lake City
Type: Public/Member
Hrs: Daily by reservation
Sporting: 2

TRAP & SKEET

Bonneville Trap & Skeet
2100 S. 6000 West,
Salt Lake City, UT 84120
Fred Kuhn (801) 972-9853
Hrs: W, 7pm; S/Su, 10am
Trap: 16

Cedar City Trap Club
844 W. Mt. View Dr.,
Cedar City, UT 84720
Jack Matheson (801) 586-8921
Type: Public/Member
Hrs: S, 11am (Win); W, 6pm (Sum)
Trap: 4

Golden Spike Trap Club
Box 771, Brigham City, UT 84302
Earl Kerkove (801) 723-3427
Hrs: Th, 7pm; Su, Noon
Trap: 4

Heber Valley Gun Club
215 Little Sweden Rd.,
Heber City, UT 84032
Lynn Luke (801) 654-1356
Hrs: W, 7pm; Su, Noon
Trap: 6

Helper Gun Club
Rt. 1, Box 121, Helper, UT 84526
Bill Curtice (801) 637-1086
Hrs: S/Su, 10 **Trap:** 6

Hill Rod & Gun Club
Box 187, Clearfield, UT 84015
Robert D. Walker (801) 777-6767
Hrs: Su, 11-4; T, 4-7; Th, 3-6; S,
10-2 **Trap:** 3 **Skeet:** 4

Magna Gun Club
2964 Continental Cr.,
Salt Lake City, UT 84118
Jim Hardy (801) 250-9818
Hrs: S/Su, 10am **Trap:** 6

Ogden Gun Club
1577 Burton Ct., Ogden, UT 84403
Ralph McEntire (801) 782-3556
Hrs: W, 6pm; Su, 10am
Trap: 4

The Salt Lake Gun Club
208 S. Redwood Rd., North Salt
Lake City, UT 84054
Larry Mitchell (801) 298-7516
5 mi. N of Salt Lake City
Type: Public/Member
Hrs: S/Su, 8-Dk; Others by appt.
Trap: 18 **Skeet:** Y **Wobble Trap**

Spanish Fork Gun Club
PO Box 305, Springville, UT 84663
Jerry Batley (801) 489-8283
Type: Public/Member
Hrs: Th, 5:30pm **Trap:** 13

Vernal Rod & Gun Club
PO Box 35, Vernal, UT 84078
Gail Herrmann (801) 789-2727
Hrs: S/Su, 10am **Trap:** 10

VERMONT

SPORTING & 5-STAND

Bull's-Eye Sporting Center
RR2, Box 4140, Barre, VT 05641
David Brooks (802) 479-2534
7 mi. W of Barre
Type: Public **Hrs:** Su-S
Sporting: 1, 30 stations **HT:** 30 ft.

Hermitage Inn
Coldbrook Rd.,
Wilmington, VT 05363
Jim McGovern (802) 464-3511
25 mi. E of Bennington
Type: Public **Hrs:** Daily, 10-3
Reservs: Recommended
Sporting: 1, 15 stations
Wobble Trap

North Country Sportsmen's
Box 5598, Essex Junction, VT 05452
Keith Turman (802) 878-0330
6 mi. E of Burlington
Type: Public/Member
Hrs: Su, 9-4 year round; W, 5-Dark
summer only **Sporting:** None
Trap: 2 **Five Stand:** 1

Tinmouth Hunting Preserve
Box 556, Wallingford, VT 05773
Rick Fallar (802) 446-2337
70 mi. NE of Albany
Type: Public/Member **Hrs:** Daily
Year Round by Appt., 10am & 1pm
Sporting: 1, 16 stations **HT:** 75 ft.

Upper Valley Fish & Game
PO Box 5, East Thetford, VT 05043
Chuck Frazier (802) 785-4254
14 mi. N of White River Jct.
Type: Public **Hrs:** By Appt. Only
Sporting: None **Five Stand:** 1

TRAP & SKEET

Barre Fish & Game Club
PO Box 130, Barre, VT 05651
Byrond Moyer (802) 479-1266
Hrs: 8-Dusk
Skeet: 2

Underhill Rod & Gun Club
37 Barnum St. Ext., Milton, VT 05468
Dean King (802) 893-4584
Hrs: T/Th, 3-8; Su, 9-5
Trap: 2 **Skeet:** 3

VIRGINIA

SPORTING & 5-STAND

Bull Run Shooting Center
7700 Bull Run Dr.,
Centreville, VA 22020
Gene Hutsky (703) 830-2344
30 mi. S of Washington, DC
Type: Public **Hrs:** S/Su, 9-6;
Weekdays, 4-9:30
Sporting: 1, 12 stations
Trap: 3 **Skeet:** 5 **Five Stand:** 1
HT: 40 ft.

Cavalier Sporting Clays
1601 Melissie Ct.,
Richmond, VA 23233
Henry Baskerville (804) 740-5263
30 mi. W of Richmond
Type: Public **Hrs:** Th/Su, 1-Dark;
Others by appt. **Reservs:** Not
required **Sporting:** 4, 40 stations
Five Stand: 6 **HT:** 80 ft.
Wobble Trap

Charles City Sporting Clays
501 Shirley Plantation Rd.,
Charles City, VA 23030
(804) 829-6270
19 mi. SE of Richmond
Type: Public **Hrs:** W/Th, 2-6;
S/Su, 9-5; Call for seasonal times
Sporting: 2, 45 stations **HT:** 35 ft.

Cumberland State Forest
Rt. 1, Box 250,
Cumberland, VA 23040
Lewis Martin (804) 492-9526
40 mi. W of Richmond
Type: Public
Hrs: W-S, 8:30-5:30; Su, 1-5:30
Sporting: 1, 10 stations

Eastern Shore Safaris
6276 Sturgis House Rd.,
Jamesville, VA 23398
Tom Webb (757) 442-6035
40 mi. E of VA Beach
Type: Public
Hrs: M-Su, by appt.
Sporting: 1, 60 stations **HT:** 50 ft.

Fairfax Rod & Gun Club
7039 Signal Hill Rd.,
Manassas, VA 22111
Phil Spector (703) 368-6333
25 mi. E of Washington, DC
Type: Member/Avail
Hrs: Su-S, 12-7:30; Private Club
Sporting: 1, 7 stations
Trap: 8 **Skeet:** 8 **Five Stand:** 1

Falkland Farms
PO Box 1297, Halifax, VA 24558
Tom Rowland (804) 575-1400
85 mi. SW of Richmond
Type: Public
Hrs: Year Round by Reservation
Sporting: 1, 13 stations

Flying Rabbit
PO Box 1234, 1015 Greystone St.,
Harrisonburg, VA 22801
Gregory Weaver (540) 432-3969
95 mi. SW of Washington, DC
Type: Public
Hrs: T-F, 5-Dk; S, 8-Dk; Su, 1-Dk
Sporting: 1, 11 stations
Five Stand: 1

Forest Green Shooting
Forest Green Ln., PO Box 361,
Spotsylvania, VA 22553
Thad Sutter (540) 582-2566
60 mi. S of Washington, DC
Type: Public/Member
Hrs: S, 9-Dusk; Su, 1-Dusk;
Weekdays by appt.
Sporting: 1, 10 stations
Five Stand: 1

Franklin Co. Gun Club
Rt. 5, Box 582,
Rocky Mount, VA 24151
Jim Rucker (540) 483-5608
5 mi. S of Rocky Mount
Type: Public/Member
Hrs: W/Su, Afternoons
Sporting: 1, 13 stations
Trap: 2 **Skeet:** 5

Franklin Skeet & Trap Club
108 Tanyard Rd.,
Rocky Mount, VA 24151
Dan Heckman (540) 483-5608
7 mi. S of Rocky Mount
Type: Member/Avail
Hrs: W, 4-Dark; Su, 1-Dark
Sporting: 1, 13 stations
Trap: 2 **Skeet:** 5 **Wobble Trap**

Ft. Lee Skeet & Trap Ranges
15014 5th St., Ft. Lee, VA 23801
Jayne Thacker (804) 765-2210
Hrs: W-Su, 12-Dark
Sporting: None
Trap: 4 **Skeet:** 3 **Five Stand:** 1

The Homestead
Box 2000, Hot Springs, VA 24445
David C. Judah, Club Mgr.
(540) 839-7787
75 mi. N of Roanoke
Type: Public/Member
Hrs: Year round: Apr-Nov, 10-5:30;
Nov-Apr, 10-5
Reservs: Recommended
Sporting: 2, 24 stations
Trap: 2 **Skeet:** 4 **Five Stand:** 1
○ Shooting Instruction Available—
See Ad Pg. 220
See Our Ad Pg. 281

Oceana Skeet & Trap
Bldg. SR-6, NAS Oceana,
Virginia Beach, VA 23460
Reb Nantz (804) 433-2875
Type: Public **Hrs:** T/Th/F, 3-8; W,
11-10; S/Su, 10-7 **Sporting:** None
Trap: 4 **Skeet:** 5 **Five Stand:** 1

Old Forge Sporting Clays
7945 Long Reach Rd., PO Box 428,
Providence Forge, VA 23140
John Yakshe, Mgr. (804) 966-2955
15 mi. W of Williamsburg
Type: Public
Hrs: M/T, by appt; W/F, 9-Dark;
S/Su, 9-Dark or appt.
Reservs: Not required
Sporting: 2, 50 stations
Five Stand: 1 **HT:** 40 ft.
○ Loaner Guns
○ Factory Ammunition
○ Formal Instructions
○ Corporate & Fundraisers &
   Leagues
○ Golf Carts Available
   Upon Request
○ Shooting Lodge Coming in '96

Primland
Rt. 1, Box 265-C,
Claudville, VA 24076
Johnny Lambert (540) 251-8012
60 mi. N of Greensboro
Type: Public **Hrs:** W-S, 8-5
Reservs: Recommended
Sporting: 1, 15 stations
See Our Ad Pg. 433

Quail Ridge Sporting Clays
Rt. 3, Box 116A,
Lexington, VA 24450
R. Chris Salb (540) 463-1800
45 mi. N of Roanoke
Type: Public
Hrs: Th-S, 9am-Dusk; Su, 12-Dusk;
Closed M/T/W
Reservs: Strongly recommended
Sporting: 1, 17 stations
○ On-Site Pro Shop
○ NSCA & NRA Certified Instructor
   Available
○ 5 mi. S of Junctions Interstates
   I-81 & I-64W in Lexington
   off Rt. 251
○ Corporate & Fundraising Shoots
○ Beretta Loaner Guns Available

Sandy Point Recreational Park
3551 Hunsucker Lane,
Charles City, VA 23030
Rick Hunsucker (804) 966-2421
30 mi. NE of Richmond
Type: Public/Member
Hrs: W-S, 9-4
Reservs: Recommended
Sporting: 1, 30 stations
Skeet: 1 **HT:** 40 ft.
○ 3-D Archery Course/20 Target
   Practice Range

Virginia Is for Outdoor Adventure

In addition to the excellent fee hunting areas in Virginia, 29 state owned Wildlife Management areas and more than 1.7 million acres of National Forest land are accessible for public hunting.

For additional information on state and national lands, contact the Virginia Department of Game & Inland Fisheries at (804)367-9369 or the George Washington and Jefferson National Forests at (540)265-5100. For contact information of locations listed on the map turn to the Virginia listings in this book.

For Virginia outdoor adventure information call 1-(800)-827-3325, or visit our web site at http://www.VIRGINIA.org.

VIRGINIA IS FOR LOVERS™

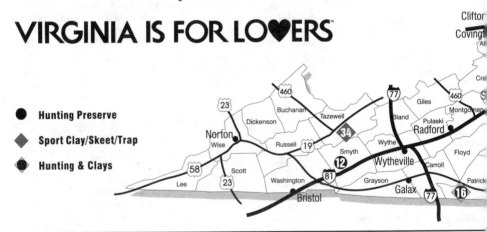

● Hunting Preserve

◆ Sport Clay/Skeet/Trap

◆● Hunting & Clays

Hunting Preserve
1   Buffalo Creek Sporting Club
2   Charles City Hunting Preserve
3   Christmas Hill Game Preserve
4   Eastern Shore Safaris
5   Falkland Farms
6   Feathers-Fur & Fin Kennels
7   Forest Green Shooting Preserve
8   Jonakin Creek Hunt Club
9   King Kennels & Shooting Preserve
10 Magnolia Shooting Preserve
11 Merrimac Farm Hunting Preserve
12 Mountain Empire Quail Ranch
13 Old Coppermine Hunting Preserve
14 Orapax Plantation
15 Plain Dealing Hunting Preserve

16 Primland
17 Red Oak Ranch-Virginia Upland Outfit
18 Sandy Point Recreational Park
19 Shady Grove Kennel & Hunting Preserve
20 Sundance Hunting Preserve, Inc.
21 Sussex Shooting Sports
22 Walnut Run Shooting Preserve
23 Windwood Farm

Sport Clay
1   Buffalo Creek Sporting Club
24 Bull Run Shooting Center
25 Cavalier Sporting Clays
2   Charles City Sporting Clays & Hunting
26 Cumberland State Forest
4   Eastern Shore Safaris

overs

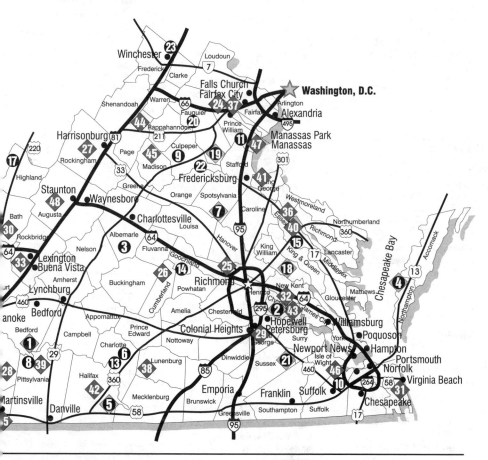

5 Falkland Farms	**Skeet/Trap**
27 Flying Rabbit	37 Arlington Fairfax Izaak Walton
7 Forest Green Shooting	38 Arrowhead Gun Club
28 Franklin Skeet & Trap Club	39 Brushy Mountain Club, Inc.
29 Ft. Lee Skeet & Trap Ranges	40 Dunbrooke Hunt Gun Club
30 The Homestead	41 Fredericksburg Rod & Gun Club
31 Oceana Skeet & Trap	42 Halifax County Gun Club
32 Old Forge Sporting Clays	43 Izaak Walton S&T Club
16 Primland	44 Page Valley Sportsmens Club
18 Sandy Point Recreational Park	45 Piedmont Sportsman Club
19 Shady Grove Kennel & Hunting Preserve	46 Portsmouth-Norfolk Co. Izaak
33 Quail Ridge Sporting Clays	47 Quantico Shooting Club
21 Sussex Shooting Sports	48 Shenandale Gun Club
34 Thompson Valley	
35 Virginia-Carolina Shooting	
36 Walnut Hill Shooting Center	

Shady Grove Kennel
And
Hunting Preserve
And
Sporting Clays

Shady Grove Sporting Clays
11986 Lucky Hill Rd.,
Remington, VA 22734
Neil Selby (540) 439-2683
45 mi. SW of Washington, DC
Type: Public/Member
Hrs: Everyday, 8-dark
Reservs: Recommended
Sporting: 2, 30 stations **Trap:** 1
Skeet: 1 **Five Stand:** 1 **HT:** 30 ft.

Sussex Shooting Sports
Box 624 (Rt. 460),
Waverly, VA 23890
Bob Hall (804) 834-3200
35 mi. SE of Richmond
Type: Public/Member
Hrs: T-F, 1-Dk; S/Su 9-Dk, & by resrv.
Sporting: 2, 20 stations
HT: 35 ft. **Wobble Trap**

Thompson Valley
PO Box 429, Tazewell, VA 24641
J.E. Cooper (540) 988-5770
100 mi. W of Roanoke
Type: Public/Member
Hrs: W-Su, By appt.
Sporting: 2, 14 stations **HT:** 30 ft.

Virginia-Carolina Shooting
Rt. #4, Box 379,
Ridgeway, VA 24148
W. Prillaman, Jr.
(540) 956-4778
38 mi. N of Greensboro, NC
Type: Public
Hrs: By Appointment
Sporting: 1, 12 stations

Walnut Hill Shooting Ctr.
PO Box 177, Caret, VA 22436
Ruther Allen (804) 443-9229
7 mi. N of Tappahannock
Type: Public
Hrs: F, 10-7; S/Su, 9-7; M-Th, by
appt. **Sporting:** 1, 12 stations

Something Missing?
If you know of a clay shooting location that's missing
from this issue of Black's
Wing & Clay, we'd like to
know. Just drop us line or
give us a call: (908) 224-
8700. We'll take care of
the rest!

TRAP & SKEET

Arlington Fairfax Iz. Walton
4082 Creels Lane,
The Plains, VA 22171
Steve Janoschka (703) 631-4497
Hrs: S, 10-5; Su, 12-5; W, 2-6
Trap: 4 **Skeet:** 3

Arrowhead Gun Club
734 Huston St.,
Chase City, VA 23924
Milton H. Mills (804) 372-4581
Hrs: Su, 1-Dark **Trap:** 1 **Skeet:** 10

Brushy Mountain Club, Inc.
Rt. 4, Box 304, Gretna, VA 24557
Oscar Shelton **Hrs:** Su, 1-Dark
Skeet: 5

Dublin Skeet Club
701 Hanks Ave., Dublin, VA 24084
David Skewes (703) 674-6072
Hrs: W/Su, 1-6 **Skeet:** 2

Dunbrooke Hunt Gun Club
Rt. 1, Box 597,
Tappahannock, VA 22560
M.E. Courtney (804) 443-3221
Hrs: W, 6-9 & Reg. Shoots **Trap:** 2

Fredericksburg Rod & Gun
Box 418, Fredericksburg, VA 22404
Cyrus Hutchings (540) 898-9595
Hrs: 7-10 **Trap:** 1 **Skeet:** 10

Halifax County Gun Club
605 Main St., Danville, VA 24541
Bill Garrett (804) 792-7731
Hrs: S/Su, 2-6 **Skeet:** 4

Izaak Walton S&T Club
5100 Charles City Rd.,
Charles City, VA 23030
Jim Wallace (804) 966-7313
Trap: 5 **Skeet:** 12 **Five Stand:** 1

Page Valley Sportsmens Club
Rt. 2, Box 214, Luray, VA 22835
James Mozisek (540) 778-1757
Hrs: Anytime to members; most
Sun. afternoons **Trap:** 1 **Skeet:** 2

Piedmont Sportsman Club
HC6, Box 106, Banco, VA 22711
Kathy Moscoe (702) 832-5266
Hrs: Su, afternoon; Th, evening
Trap: 2 **Skeet:** 3

Quantico Shooting Club
PO Box 212, Quantico, VA 22134
Sgt. Hank Jones/Sgt. Tony
Spellings (703) 640-6336
Hrs: Weekends **Skeet:** 2

Shenandale Gun Club
PO Box 901, Staunton, VA 24401
B. W. Erskine, Jr. (540) 337-7800
Trap: 2 **Skeet:** 2

WASHINGTON

SPORTING & 5-STAND

Boeing Employees Gun Club
22656 24th Ave., S.,
Des Moines, WA 98042
Bill Hardrath (206) 872-9960
Hrs: T, 4-8; Su, 10-2
Trap: 4 **Skeet:** 3 **Five Stand:** 1

Bremerton Trap & Skeet
4956 State Hwy. 3 SW, Port
Orchard, WA 98366
Gordon Campbell (360) 674-2438
16 mi. W of Seattle
Type: Public/Member
Hrs: W, 7-10; Su, 11-4
Sporting: 1, 17 stations **Trap:** 5
Skeet: 6 **Five Stand:** 1

Evergreen Sportsmen Club
12736 Marksman Rd., SW,
Olympia, WA 98512
Peter Strobl (360) 357-9080
25 mi. S of Olympia
Type: Public/Member
Hrs: S, 10-4; Th, 6-10; other days
by appt. **Sporting:** 1, 10 stations
Trap: 36 **Skeet:** 1 **HT:** 20 ft.

Fort Lewis Army Post
NW Adventure Ctr., Main Fort,
Bldg. 3969, Ft. Lewis, WA 98433
Norman Neubert (206) 967-7056
Type: Public
Hrs: W, 11-1; S/Su, 10:30-3:30
Sporting: 1, 10 stations
Trap: 2 **Skeet:** 4 **Wobble Trap**

Kenmore Range
1031 228th SW,
Bothell, WA 98021
(206) 481-8685
10 mi. N of Seattle
Type: Public/Member
Hrs: Daily **Sporting:** 1, 10 stations
Trap: 4 **Five Stand:** 1 **HT:** 60 ft.

Landt Farms Sporting Clays
W. 16308 Four Mound Rd., Nine
Mile Falls, WA 99026
Ellwood Landt (509) 466-4036
10 mi. NW of Spokane
Type: Public/Member
Hrs: Su-S, by appt.
Sporting: 1, 14 stations
HT: 50 ft. **Wobble Trap**

Northwest Adventure Ctr
Box 33156, Fort Lewis, WA 98433
Norman Neubert (206) 967-7056
8 mi. S of Tacoma
Type: Public **Hrs:** Special Events
Only; W, 11-1; Su/Su, 10:30-3:30
Sporting: 1, 10 stations
Trap: 2 **Skeet:** 4 **Five Stand:** 2

Pheasant Valley Sport. Clays
PO Box 201, LaCrosse, WA 99143
Jerry Townsend (509) 549-3912
75 mi. SW of Spokane
Type: Public/Member
Hrs: Daylight to Dark, Year Round
Sporting: 1, 40 stations

Pomeroy Gun Club
PO Box 532, Pomeroy, WA 99347
Elton Brown (509) 843-1460
100 mi. S of Spokane
Type: Public Sporting: 1, 10 sta.
Trap: 2

R&M Game Birds
495 Fisher Hill Rd., Lyle, WA 98635
Rodger Ford (509) 365-3245
80 mi. E of Vancouver, WA &
Portland, OR
Type: Public
Hrs: Year round, daylight-dark
Reservs: Strongly recommended
Sporting: 1, 15 stations HT: 85 ft.

Rimrock Sporting Clays
Rt. 1, Box 10B,
Uniontown, WA 99179
John Moehrle (509) 229-3287
20 mi. N of Lewiston
Type: Public
Hrs: S-Su, by appt.
Sporting: 1, 30 stations

Spokane Gun Club
19615 E. Sprague Ave.,
Greenacres, WA 99016
Philip Kimere (509) 926-6505
10 mi. E of Spokane
Type: Public/Member
Hrs: W, 1-9; S/Su, 11-4 & by appt.
Sporting: 1, 5 stations
Trap: 18 Skeet: 8 Five Stand: 1

Sumner Sportsman Assoc.
15711 96th St. East,
Puyallup, WA 98372
Jim Peterson (206) 848-9519
20 mi. N of Tacoma
Type: Public/Member
Hrs: SC; 2nd Sat, 10-til; TR/Sk, Su,
10-4; T, 7-10
Sporting: 1, 6 stations
Trap: 6 Skeet: 1 Five Stand: 1

Sun Valley Shooting Park
1452 Suntargets Rd.,
Moxee, WA 98936
Rangemaster (509) 576-0866
14 mi. E of Yakima
Type: Public
Hrs: W-Su, 8am-Dusk
Sporting: 1, 10 stations
Trap: 1 Skeet: 1 Five Stand: 1

Sunnydell Shooting
292 Dryke Rd., Sequim, WA 98382
Chuck Dryke (206) 683-5631
60 mi. W of Seattle
Type: Public
Hrs: Daily, 10-Dark
Sporting: 1, 22 stations
Trap: 2 Skeet: 2 HT: 100 ft.

Tacoma Sportsmen's Club
16409 Canyon Rd.,
E., Puyallup, WA 98373
Bob Hutton (206) 537-6151
Hrs: T/Th, 6-10; Su, 10-4; W, 10-4
(Smr), 10-2 (Wtr)
Sporting: 1, 10 stations Trap: 4
Skeet: 2 Five Stand: 1   HT

Turkey Ridge
1565 Evans Cutoff Rd.,
Evans, WA 99126
Deryl Ruston (509) 684-2735
88 mi. N of Spokane
Type: Public
Hrs: By Reservation Only, 9-5:30
Sporting: 1, 10 stations

Upper Nisqually
PO Box 831, Eatonville, WA 98328
Todd Franzen (360) 832-8727
25 mi. S of Tacoma
Type: Public
Hrs: 4th Sunday of month @ 9:00
Sporting: 1, 10 stations
Five Stand: 1   Wobble Trap

Winter Hawk
6362 Hwy. 291,
Nine Mile Falls, WA 99026
Gary Scheinost (509) 276-5150
14 mi. NW of Spokane
Type: Public/Member
Hrs: Su-S, by appt.
Sporting: 1, 25 stations

TRAP & SKEET

NAS Whidbey Island Trap
1038 Midway Blvd.,
Oak Harbor, WA 98277
Steve Drusby (206) 257-5539
Hrs: W, 4-7; S/Su, 12-4 (Sum),
11-2 (Win)
Trap: 3 Skeet: 3

Sportsmens Club Inc.
Box 4056, McChord AFB, WA 98438
Larry Clark (206) 984-2706
Hrs: W/S/Su, 11:30-Dark
Trap: 5 Skeet: 2

Wenatchee Gun Club
Box 416, Chelan, WA 98816
John Snyder (509) 884-6490
Hrs: Su, 10-4
Trap: 5 Skeet: 2

WEST VIRGINIA

SPORTING & 5-STAND

Prospect Hall
Rt. 1, Box 370,
Kearneysville, WV 25430
Christine Martin (304) 728-8213
60 mi. NW of Washington, DC
Type: Member/Avail
Hrs: 7 days a week, by appt.
Sporting: 1, 24 stations
Trap: 1 Skeet: 1   HT: 80 ft.

Warrior Trail Sporting Clays
Rt. 2, Box 167B,
Terra Alta, WV 26764
Andrew P. Serdich (304) 789-2422
15 mi. W of Deep Creek Lake, MD
Type: Public/Member
Hrs: Su-S, all daylight hours
Reservs: Strongly recommended
Sporting: 1, 26 stations HT: 50 ft.

Westlance Arms, Inc.
1610 Jones Spring East Rd.,
Hedgesville, WV 25427
Mark T. Ewing (304) 754-7100
21 mi. S of Hagerstown
Type: Public Hrs: 7 days, by appt.
Sporting: 1, 10 stations Trap: 1

White Oak Mountain
PO Box 859, Beaver, WV 25813
Mike Estes (304) 763-5266
10 mi. SE of Beckley
Type: Public
Hrs: W/F, 12-6; S/Su, 10-6; and by
appt. anytime
Sporting: 1, 21 stations
Five Stand: 1

TRAP & SKEET

Brooke County S&FA
1715 Main St., Wellsburg, WV 26070
Eugene Elcesser (304) 737-2243
Hrs: W, 6pm; Su, 1pm   Trap: 8

The Greenbrier Gun Club
300 West Main St., White Sulpher
Springs, WV 24986
Tom Buskirk (800) 624-6070
80 mi. W of Roanoke, VA
Type: Public
Hrs: M-S, 9:30-5:30; Su, 2-5:30
Trap: 4 Skeet: 2

High & Low Skeet Club
Rt. 12, Box 187,
Morgantown, WV 26505
James Bowers (304) 983-8146
Hrs: Call First Skeet: 1

Piney Ridge Skeet & Trap
Rt. 1, Box 305, Weston, WV 26452
Bobby Cayton (304) 269-4227
Hrs: T/Th, 6-9; Su, 1-6
Trap: 1 Skeet: 2

Sportsman's Gun Club
2 Charlotte Lane,
Scott Depot, WV 25560
David M. McClave (304) 757-9738
Hrs: S/Su, 1-5; W, 6-9
Trap: 4 Skeet: 2

Sportsmens & Farmers Assn.
1141 Pennsylvania Ave.,
Weirton, WV 26062
Tom Weaver (304) 479-TRAP
Hrs: W, 5:30; Su, 1 Trap: 10

WISCONSIN

SPORTING & 5-STAND

Acres for Recreation
6999 Retreat Rd., PO Box 24,
Shawano, WI 54166
Barry Fredrich (715) 526-6055
35 mi. NW of Green Bay
Type: Public/Member
Hrs: Mar-Sep, 12-Dk; & by appt.
Sporting: 1, 10 stations
Trap: 4 HT: 32 ft.

Big Rock Hunting Preserve
W15664 Chuck Rd.,
Gilman, WI 54433
Chuck Birkenholz (715) 668-5557
60 mi. NE of Eau Claire
Type: Public/Member
Hrs: Su-S, 8-5 by appt.
Sporting: 2, 20 stations

Cadens Kennels & Hunt Club
W2738 Scenic Dr.,
Campbellsport, WI 53010
Dennis Brath (414) 533-8579
40 mi. NW of Milwaukee
Type: Public/Member
Hrs: M-S, 8-5
Sporting: 1, 13 stations

Cassville Conservation Club
201 W. Dewey, Cassville, WI 53806
Robert Bohringer (608) 725-5293
Type: Public Hrs: T, 5pm
Sporting: None
Trap: 3 Five Stand: 1

Cur-San's Clays
RR1, Box 87, Hancock, WI 54943
Curt Dollar (715) 228-5151
60 mi. N of Madison
Type: Public
Hrs: S/Su, 10-5; other by appt.
Sporting: 1, 11 stations Trap: 1

F&R Sporting Clays
6431 Pleasant Hill Dr.,
West Bend, WI 53095
Brett Richson (414) 675-6196
15 mi. S of Plymouth
Type: Public Hrs: S/Su, call for hrs.
Sporting: 1, 13 stations

Fox Ridge Game Farm
8585 Valley Line Rd.,
Oconto Falls, WI 54154
Bill or Kathy (414) 846-2508
135 mi. N of Milwaukee
Type: Public/Member
Hrs: By appt. Sporting: 1, 9 sta.

Game Unlimited
871 Ct. Rd. E., Hudson, WI 54016
Patrick Melloy (715) 246-2350
20 mi. E of Minneapolis
Type: Public Hrs: M/W, S/Su, 9-6
Sporting: 3, 18 stations Trap: Y

Gateway Gun Club
Box 596, Land O'Lakes, WI 54540
John Muir (715) 547-3321
Type: Public/Member
Hrs: M-Su, by appt.
Sporting: 1, 20 stations Trap: 4

**Geneva National
Hunt Club**
555 Hunt Club Ct.,
Lake Geneva, WI 53147
Mark Hanna (414) 245-7205
40 mi. N of Milwaukee
Type: Public Hrs: W-Su, 10-5
Reservs: Strongly recommended
Sporting: 1, 10 stations HT: 52 ft.

**Highland
Shooting Grounds**
N3041W Cty A, Cascade, WI 53011
Mike or Joann Sommers
(414) 528-8848
50 mi. N of Milwaukee
Type: Public/Member
Hrs: May 1-Sep 30, We-Fr, 1-7;
Sa/Su, 10-5
Reservs: Strongly recommended
Sporting: 1, 18 stations HT: 60 ft.
O Loaner Guns
O On-Site Pro Shop
O Formal Instructions
O Clays Course Features 3 Ability
   Levels: Beginner, Intermediate &
   Competition
O Flurry Shooting
O Group Meeting Facilities Available

J&H Game Farm
RR1, Box 221, Shiocton, WI 54170
James or Joanne Johnson
(715) 758-8134
27 mi. W of Green Bay
Type: Public/Member
Hrs: T-Th, 8-Dark; F-Su, 8-5; by appt.
Reservs: Strongly recommended
Sporting: 4, 40 stations HT: 35 ft.
O Loaner Guns
O Factory Ammunition
O On-Site Pro Shop
O On-Site Meals
O Shooting Lodge
O Formal Instructions
O Organized Leagues
O Home of the 1996 NSCA Zone
   Shoot
O Host to '95 Field & Stream Jeep
   Classic

Lake Mills Conservation Club
PO Box 222, Lake Mills, WI 53551
Lee Braatz (414) 648-5758
25 mi. E of Madison
Type: Public/Member
Sporting: 1, 12 sta.Trap: 3

Little Creek Lodge
4408 Sampson Rd.,
Little Suamico, WI 54141
Jerry Boomsma (414) 826-7382
18 mi. N of Green Bay
Type: Public Hrs: T-Su, 8-Dk; by
Appt. Sporting: 2, 20 stations

Longshot Sportsman's Club
N8995 Townline Rd.,
Van Dyne, WI 54979
John Eiden (414) 688-2314
Type: Public Hrs: W, 3-7; S/Su,
10-2 (Summer); Su, 10-2 (Winter)
Sporting: 1, 10 stations

Mayville Gun Club
PO Box 31, Mayville, WI 53050
Phil Nogalski (414) 387-9996
Type: Public/Member
Hrs: Call for current schedule
Sporting: 1, 10 stations Trap: 5

McMiller
Sports Center
S. 103 W. 38754 Hwy. NN,
Eagle, WI 53119
Bob Christiansen, Mgr.
(414) 594-5900
40 mi. W of Milwaukee
Type: Public
Hrs: Sun, 9-5; Th, 4-dusk
Reservs: Not required
Sporting: 1, 10 stations
O Extensive Rifle and Pistol Target
   Facilities

North Shore Winchester
3109 Hwy. 41, Franksville, WI 53126
Thomas V. Joerndt (414) 835-1112
Type: Public Hrs:
Sporting: 1, 9 stations
Trap: 6 Skeet: 4

Ozaukee Co. Fish & Game
PO Box 12, Newburg, WI 53060
Roger Perlewitz (414) 692-9923
3.5 mi. N of Newburg on Hwy. Y
Sporting: 1, 10 stations Trap: 5

Pheasant City Hunt Club
R#1, Box 272, Markesan, WI 53946
Bill Scallon (414) 324-5813
65 mi. NW of Milwaukee
Type: Public Hrs: Su, 10-5; M/Th,
5-Dark Sporting: 2, 16 stations

Quail Haven Hunt Club
Rt. 4, Box 821,
Clintonville, WI 54929
Michael K. Duffey (715) 823-6123
35 mi. W of Green Bay
Type: Public Hrs: By Appt.
Sporting: 1, 10 stations

R&R Ranch
8923 Richfield Dr.,
Marshfield, WI 54449
Steve Strong (715) 676-3365
6 mi. from Marshfield
Type: Public/Member
Hrs: Su-S, with reservations
Sporting: 1, 16 stations HT: 30 ft.

Ripon Clays
Box 543, County Hwy. FF,
Ripon, WI 54971
(414) 748-3453
70 mi. NW of Milwaukee
Type: Public/Member
Hrs: W; 5:30-Dark; 1st Su of
Month, May-Sep, 10-4
Sporting: 1, 8 stations
Trap: 2   HT: 30 ft. Wobble Trap

River Wildlife
Kohler, WI 53044
Max Grube (414) 457-0134
55 mi. N of Milwaukee
Type: Member/Avail
Sporting: 1, 5 stations
Trap: Y Five Stand: Y

Rivers Edge Sporting Clays
R2, Box 181,
Chippewa Falls, WI 54729
Robert D. Buss (715) 723-5865
10 mi. N of Eau Claire
Type: Public Hrs: By appt. only
Sporting: 1, 12 stations HT: 25 ft.

Rush Creek Hunt Club
400 Springs Dr.,
Spring Green, WI 53588
Lee Bilke (608) 588-2219
40 mi. W of Madison

Type: Public/Member
Hrs: By reservation only
Reservs: Strongly recommended
Sporting: 1, 13 stations HT: 50 ft.

Shooters Sporting Club
RR2, Box 2344,
Soldiers Grove, WI 54655
John Generalski (608) 538-3200
60 mi. NW of Madison
Type: Public
Hrs: Su-S, by appt.
Sporting: 1, 10 stations

Smoky Lake Reserve
1 Lake St., PO Box 100,
Phelps, WI 54554
Miriam Saucke (715) 545-2333
45 mi. NE of Rhinelander
Type: Member/Avail
Hrs: As requested
Sporting: 1, 10 stations
Trap: 1 Skeet: 1

Summit Lake Game Farm
PO Box 810, Hayward, WI 54843
John Treslley (715) 354-7241
75 mi. SE of Superior
Type: Public/Member
Hrs: Th, 12-8; S/Su, 10-6; Closed
M/W/F
Reservs: Strongly recommended
Sporting: 1, 15 stations
Rolling, trees & brush
Trap: 1 HT: 55 ft. Wobble Trap

Thunderbird Game Farm Sporting Clays
W23119 Thunderbird Rd.,
Chilton, WI 53014
Todd Doughty (414) 853-3030
30 mi. S of Green Bay
Type: Public/Member
Hrs: Apr.-Sept.: Sa/Su, 9-2; wk
days 6pm-dk, by app't
Reservs: Recommended
Sporting: 1, 10 stations
O Loaner Guns
O Factory Ammunition
O Shooting Lodge
O Formal Instructions
O Golf Carts

Trout & Grouse
11110 110th St.,
Kenosha, WI 53142
Andrew Burrows (414) 857-7232
60 mi. N of Chicago
Type: Public
Hrs: T-S, 10-5:30; Su, 12-5; Closed
June-Aug.
Sporting: 1, 35 stations HT: 30 ft.

Wausau Skeet & Trap Club
PO Box 2154, Wausau, WI 54402
Roger Retzinger (715) 875-7227
Type: Public/Member
Hrs: Th, 5-9 (May-Aug)
Sporting: 1, 10 stations
Trap: 3 Skeet: 3 Five Stand: 1

Wern Valley Sportsmen's Club
S36 W29657 Wern Way,
Waukesha, WI 53188
Steve Williams (414) 968-2400
20 mi. W of Milwaukee
Type: Public/Member
Hrs: Sat., 9-3; W, 4:30-Sunset
(May-Sept)
Reservs: Not required
Sporting: 1, 15 stations HT: 60 ft.

Whispering Emerald Ridge
N3952 640th St.,
Menomonie, WI 54751
Mike Kettner (715) 235-1720
60 mi. E of Minneapolis-St. Paul
Type: Public Hrs: by appt.
Sporting: 1, 13 stations HT: 45 ft.

Woodhollow Sporting Clays
517 Copeland Ave.,
La Crosse, WI 54603
Roger Wendling (608) 784-0482
11 mi. N of LaCrosse
Type: Public/Member Hrs:
Sunday only (May-Sept) or by appt.
Sporting: 3, 20 stations
Skeet: 1 Five Stand: 1 HT: 120 ft.

Woods & Meadows
Rt. 1, Warrens, WI 54666
Scott Goetzka (608) 378-4223
100 mi. NW of Madison
Type: Public
Hrs: S, w/o appt; Su-F, appt. only
Sporting: 2, 22 stations HT: 30 ft.

TRAP & SKEET

Ashley Shooting Club
1022 W. 4th St., Mosinee, WI 54455
Hi-D Giese (715) 693-2949
Hrs: Su-T, 6-9 (Apr-Nov)
Trap: 4 Skeet: 6

Beaver Dam Conservationists
206 Hamilton St.,
Beaver Dam, WI 53916
Mike Connaughty (414) 887-1575
Type: Public/Member
Hrs: W, 7-10 Trap: 9

Daniel Boone Conservation
W 158 N 8315 Steven Mac Dr.,
Menomonee Falls, WI 53051
Bob Ehrgott (414) 628-1328
Hrs: W-Th, 5-9 Trap: 5 Skeet: 1

Brown County Sportsmens
Box 12085, Green Bay, WI 54307
Don Jared (414) 434-9930
Hrs: S, afternoons; Su, mornings
Trap: 6 Skeet: 6

Cudahy Sportsmen's Club
Box 243, Cudahy, WI 53110
Ron Applebee (414) 747-9284
Type: Public/Member
Hrs: T/W, 6:30pm-10pm
Trap: 8

Darien Sporting Goods
N2669 Hwy. 14, Darien, WI 53114
David E. Ennis (414) 724-3433
Type: Public Hrs: T-Su, 9-6
Trap: 4

Delavan Sportsmens Club
PO Box 453, Delavan, WI 53115
W. Kosrock, Jr. (414) 728-9550
Type: Public/Member
Hrs: T, 4-10; S/Su, 9-4
Trap: 5 Skeet: 1

Eau Claire Rod & Gun Club
PO Box 1572, Eau Claire, WI 54702
Robert Webber (715) 832-4391
Type: Public
Hrs: Nights, 6-9:30; Su, 12-4
Trap: 7 Skeet: 1

Faskells Gun Club
E. 6136 Hwy. 54 W., New London,
WI 54961
Peter Ziebell (414) 596-2100
Hrs: Weekdays by appt.
Trap: 8 Skeet: 6

Fox Valley Huntsmen Club
PO Box 2983, Oshkosh, WI 54903
Rick Sebora (414) 685-6335
Type: Public/Member
Hrs: S, 10-3 (all year); M/Th, 5-9
(April-Aug) Trap: 6

Hodag Sports Club
4340 Aberdean Rd., Rhinelander,
WI 54501
Don Minder (715) 362-2784
Type: Public/Member
Hrs: W/Th, 5-9; S, 12-5
Trap: 5 Five Stand: 2

Hudson Rod, Gun & Club
PO Box 83, Hudson, WI 54016
(715) 386-9955
Hrs: T/Th, Noon-8 (Summer); Su,
10-4 Trap: 8 Skeet: 2

Janesville Conserv. Club
4370 Milton Ave.,
Janesville, WI 53546
Ron Morse (608) 756-4647
Type: Public/Member
Hrs: S, 10-4 (Jan-Apr); W, 10-2; 5-9
(Apr-Oct) Trap: 8

Lafarge Trapshooting Assn.
109 E. Main St., PO Box 67,
Lafarge, WI 54639
La Verne Campbell (608) 625-2180
Type: Public Hrs: Th, 7pm-11pm
Trap: 4

Lakeview Trap & Sport
S80 W. 14401 Schultz Lane,
Muskego, WI 53150
Loreen L. Klauser (414) 422-9025
Type: Public Hrs: T/Th, 6-9:30; W,
3-9:30; F, 3-7:30; S/Su, 11-3:30
Trap: 4

Manitowoc Gun Club
Box 201, Manitowoc, WI 54221
David Kuehnl (414) 758-2727
Hrs: T/W/F/S, 10-5; Th, 10-10; Su,
10-2 Trap: 5 Skeet: 2

Middleton Sportsmen's Club
7910 Airport Rd.,
Middleton, WI 53562
Roger Pasch (608) 836-1118
Hrs: Su, 1-4; Th, 7-9:30
Trap: 2 Skeet: 1

Mosinee Sportsmans Alliance
977 Rocky Ridge Rd.,
Mosinee, WI 54455
Douglas K. Davis, (715) 693-6587
1 mi. NW of Mosinee
Hrs: Th, 5:30-8:30pm (Apr-Sep)
Trap: 4

Muscoda Sportsmens League
430 Beech St., Muscoda, WI 53573
Virgil Bomkamp (608) 739-3634
Type: Public/Member
Hrs: W, 6-10; S/Su, 10-4
Trap: 6

Oshkosh Gun Club
PO Box 425, Oshkosh, WI 54901
Mike Kobussen (414) 231-0682
Hrs: 9-Dark, year round
Trap: 2 Skeet: 2

Pete's Skeet
Rt. 1, Box 190, Berlin, WI 54923
E.C. Leach, Jr. (414) 361-1880
Skeet: 1

Racine Co. Line Rifle Club
PO Box 71, Oak Creek, WI 53154
John Chojnacki (414) 762-7774
Hrs: Private
Trap: 1 Skeet: 2

Sauk Prairie Trap & Skeet
E. 11102 Sauk Prairie Rd., Prairie
Du Sac, WI 53578
Bill Skinner (608) 643-4844
30 mi. N of Madison
Type: Public
Hrs: W, 6-10; S, 12-5
Trap: 6 Skeet: 6

Saukville Rifle & Pistol
933 7th Ave., Grafton, WI 53024
David Schinker
Trap: 4 Skeet: 1

Sheboygan Falls Conserv.
914 Linden St., Cleveland, WI 53015
Thomas Steinbeck (414) 467-2970
Hrs: Su, 11-4
Trap: 4 Skeet: 2

Van Dyne Sportsmens Club
PO Box 8, Van Dyne, WI 54979
Dick Baier (414) 688-2433
Hrs: Su, 1-4; T, 6-10; Th, 9-12 &
6-10 Trap: 4 Skeet: 1

Waukesha Gun Club
Box 1509, Waukesha, WI 53187
Gary Schaetzel (414) 547-9785
Hrs: T/Th, 4-9; W, 10-10; S,
12-3:30; Su, 9-1
Trap: 29 Skeet: 5

Westgate Sportsman Club
4909 Sportsman Dr.,
Eau Claire, WI 54701
Dennis Freid (715) 832-4548
5 mi. W of Eau Claire
Type: Public/Member Trap: 2

WYOMING

SPORTING & 5-STAND

Canyon Ranch Gun Club
PO Box 629, Big Horn, WY 82833
Jim Roach (307) 674-9097
15 mi. S of Sheridan
Type: Public Hrs: By appt.
Sporting: 3, 15 stations

Clear Creek Sporting Clays
3004 Hwy. 14-16 East,
Clearmont, WY 82835
Doug Kauffman (307) 737-2217
140 mi. N of Casper
Type: Public/Member
Hrs: Su-S, daylight-dark
Sporting: 1, 10 stations Skeet: 1
HT: 100 ft. Wobble Trap

Cody Shooting Complex
1385 Sherdian Ave.,
Cody, WY 82414
John J. Gibbons (307) 587-9556
180 mi. NW of Casper
Type: Public
Hrs: Su, 10am; W, 5-Dark
(May-Sept); Su, 10am (Sep-Apr)
Sporting: 5, 50 stations
Trap: 5 Skeet: 3   HT: 20 ft.

HF Bar Ranch
1301 Rock Creek Rd.,
Saddlestring, WY 82840
Richard Platt/Jason Smith
(307) 684-2487
180 mi. N of Casper
Type: Public
Hrs: Daily by Appt.
Reservs: Recommended
Sporting: 5, 40 stations **HT:** 100'

Pinedale Sporting Clays
PO Box 1191, Pinedale, WY 82941
Steve Griggs (307) 367-2893
Sporting: 1

Sheridan County
44 Fort Rd., Sheridan, WY 82801
Robert L. Prill (307) 672-6450
Type: Public/Member
Hrs: Su, 10-3; W/Th, 5-9 (Summer)
Sporting: 1, 5 stations
Trap: 14 **Skeet:** 1 **Wobble Trap**

TRAP & SKEET

Buffalo Trap & Skeet
647 N. Desmet, Buffalo, WY 82834
Terry Barnhart (307) 684-9287
Type: Public/Member
Hrs: 5/15-9/1; Summer, T/Th
Evenings **Trap:** 3 **Skeet:** 1

Casper Skeet Club
3532 E. 23rd St., Casper, WY 82609
Roland Kessler (307) 234-6958
Hrs: T, 5-7; Su, 12-4
Trap: 1 **Skeet:** 3

Cheyenne Municipal T&S
Box 1065, Cheyenne, WY 82003
Wade Dumont (307) 634-2504
Hrs: W, 5-9; Su, 9-3
Trap: 9 **Skeet:** 2

Heart Mountain Gun Club
211 Grand, Powell, WY 82435
Bob Hammond (307) 754-5577
Hrs: Varies **Trap:** 2 **Skeet:** 1

Jackson Hole Trap Club
PO Box V, Jackson, WY 83001
Dean K. Bark (307) 733-5067
Hrs: W, 6pm; Su, 1:30pm **Trap:** 8

Laramie Trap Club
PO Box 669, Laramie, WY 82070
Tony Classi (307) 742-3068
Type: Public/Member
Hrs: W, 5:30-9:30; Su, 11-2; Call
for other times **Trap:** 14

Niobrara Sportsmens Club
PO Box 1344, Lusk, WY 82225
Club Manager (307) 334-3318
Type: Public/Member
Hrs: Th, 5pm **Trap:** 5

Rocky Mt. Gun Club
13940 Grady, Casper, WY 82601
Joy Trim (307) 265-6403
Type: Public/Member
Hrs: W, 5-8; Su, 1-5 **Trap:** 14

Sweetwater Trap Club
421 I St., Rock Springs, WY 82901
Robert Bettolo (307) 362-5245
Type: Public/Member
Hrs: W, 6pm; March-Aug.
Trap: 9

White Mountain Trap Club
505 P St., Rock Springs, WY 82901
Rick Carrillo (307) 362-2619
Type: Public/Member
Hrs: Th, 6-Dark; April-Aug.
Trap: 2

DOMINICAN REPUBLIC

Casa de Campo Shooting Center
PO Box 140, LaRomana,
Dominican Republic
Hermogenes Guerrero
(809) 523-3333
3 mi. W of La Romana
Type: Public/Member
Hrs: Su-S, 8-5
Sporting: 7, 110 stations
Trap: 1 **Skeet:** 1 **Five Stand:** 3
HT: 110 ft.

Going on a sporting adventure?

That't great! But to get the most out of your trip, you'll want to go fully outfitted. A new travel gun case might be called for. New clothes? Boots? Perhaps, a brand new shotgun. If it's a trip that will include sporting clays, you may want to get a new set of chokes, or perhaps have that gunfitting you've put off for a while. Fortunately, you're in the right place. Turn to the following sections to begin. And enjoy your trip!

WING & CLAY 1998
EQUIPMENT · INSTRUCTION
FREE LISTING REQUEST FORM

Are shotgunners your target? If so, your company may qualify for a FREE listing in the Equipment or Instruction section of the 1998 edition of Wing & Clay. To see if you qualify, just complete and return the form below. Questions? Call: (908) 224-8700.

1 COMPANY INFORMATION

Name:

Address:

City:

State: Zip:

Phone:

FAX:

Year Established: No. of Employees:

Contact Name:

2 LISTING SECTION *Please indicate the Product or Service section of the Shotgunner's Source in which your company's listing should appear:*

- ☐ Accessories/ Hunting & Shooting
- ☐ Apparel Manufacturers
- ☐ Associations/Conservation Groups
- ☐ Booksellers
- ☐ Carts
- ☐ Chokes/Choke Accessories & Tube Sets
- ☐ Course Designers
- ☐ Ear Protection
- ☐ Eye Protections
- ☐ Gamebird Breeders
- ☐ Gun Case Manufacturers
- ☐ Gunsmiths
- ☐ Gunstocks
- ☐ Insurance
- ☐ Mail Order Catalogs

- ☐ Publications
- ☐ Real Estate
- ☐ Recoil Reduction Products
- ☐ Reloading Equipment & Accessories
- ☐ Safes
- ☐ Shooting Schools
- ☐ Shotgun Care
- ☐ Shotgun Manufact. & Importers
- ☐ Shotgun Shells
- ☐ Targets
- ☐ Trap Manufacturers & Importers
- ☐ Trap Accessories
- ☐ Trap Distributors
- ☐ Travel Agents
- ☐ Trophies, Awards & Promotions
- ☐ Vests

3 PRODUCT or SERVICE DESCRIPTION *Please briefly describe your primary product, product line, or service in the space provided below. (Please limit description to 30 words.)*

4 SALES INFORMATION
How do you market your products or services? (Check all that apply)
☐ Direct to consumer   ☐ Through retailers

PLEASE RETURN FORM TO: WING & CLAY, P.O. BOX 2029, RED BANK, NJ 07701
TELEPHONE: (908) 224-8700   FAX: (908) 741-2827

WING & CLAY 1998 GUARANTEED DISTRIBUTION 50,000 COPIES

Double-Barrel Distribution Targeted to Meet the Advertising Needs of the Shotgun Industry.

At WING & CLAY your needs as an advertiser come first. That's why, unlike magazines and other periodicals, WING & CLAY offers you a chance to reach an audience of 50,000 prospects with a one-time buying decision that works for you for a full 12 months!

Double-Barrel Distribution

WING & CLAY's distribution provides advertisers with maximum impact at minimum cost.

How? By delivering a selective audience of avid sportsmen and blanket coverage of shotgun trade and industry groups. This unique, "double-barrel" distribution system works this way:

SPORTSMEN - 30,000 COPIES

☐ **Wingshooters** - WING & CLAY delivers thousands of copies to avid sportsmen whose names are gathered from top-flight hunting publications and catalogs. Other wingshooters receive copies at hunting/wildlife conservation group dinners and celebrity hunts; or purchase them at retail locations through direct response ads in leading shotgunning publications.

☐ **Sporting Clays Enthusiasts** - A copy of WING & CLAY is sent to every member of the major sporting clays associations—NSCA, SCA, and NESCA. WING & CLAY also works with numerous organizations, including the state-wide sporting clays associations, the Women's Shooting Sports Foundation, and sponsors of charitable shoots to reach new and experienced shooters who rely heavily on WING & CLAY when they are buying shotgun related equipment.

SHOTGUN TRADE & INDUSTRY GROUPS - 20,000 COPIES

☐ **Club & Range Operators** - 5,127 Copies are sent to the operators of all hunting preserves, sporting clays courses, trap and skeet locations, and shooting schools in WING & CLAY's comprehensive private and published databases.

☐ **Retail Gun Dealers** - No one has more influence on an individual sportsman's buying decision than the gun counter sales person. That's why thousands of highly-targeted, storefront gun dealers nationwide receive a special *Gun Counter* edition of WING & CLAY— drilled through the corner so that it can be secured for easy reference.

☐ **Professional Sporting Goods Buyers** Over 2,400 copies of WING & CLAY are distributed to these professionals who are responsible for buying millions of dollars worth of guns, ammo and shooting supplies annually.

☐ **Sporting Goods Wholesalers & Sales Representatives** - This relatively small but influential group—serving the needs of both manufacturers and retailers— receives copies of WING & CLAY.

☐ **Shotgun Industry Executives** - Individual copies are sent to executives culled from WING & CLAY's own SHOTGUNNER'S SOURCE database. Avid sportsmen in their own right, this key group of executives are a "must hit" target for the advertiser trying to build product awareness and sway industry opinion.

☐ **Outdoor Writers & Editors** - The sporting press plays an important role in influencing the buying and shooting habits of America's sportsmen. Consequently, copies of WING & CLAY are sent to all members of the Outdoor Writers Association of America and to hundreds of independent journalists at hunting and shooting publications.

SHOTGUNNER'S
SOURCE INDEX

Name	Category	Listing Pg.	Ad Pg.
A A & E Leathercraft	Accessories/Slings	90	
A.D.S. Vest	Vests	96	
ACTIV Industries, Inc.	Shotgun Shells	54	
ATS-SONIC	**Training**	**129**	**130**
ATS-SONIC	Computer	115	
Joe Abbott Tours	Travel Agents	268	
AccurateScot Powders	Reloading Comp.	199	
Action Ear-Bionic Ear	Ear Protection	134	
Addieville East Farm	Gamebird	143	
Addieville East Farm	Schools	204	
Addieville East Farm	Dog Trainers	122	
Addieville Adventures	Travel Agents	268	
Ainley Kennels & Fabrication	Kennels	127	
All Purpose Ammo	Shotgun Shells	54	
All Star Lead Shot	Reloading Comp.	199	
Allem's Gun Craft	Gunsmiths	163	
Bob Allen Companies	**Bags & Cases**	**84**	**84**
Bob Allen Companies	**Clothing**	**90**	**84**
Bob Allen Companies	**Vests**	**96**	**84**
New River Energetics	**Reloading Comp.**	**199**	**9**
Aluma Sport by Dee Zee	Gun Case	151	
Aluma Sport by Dee Zee	Kennels	127	
Alwerdt's Pheasant Farm	Gamebird	143	
Amateur Trap. Assn (ATA)	Shooting Org.	103	
America Outdoors Web Site	**Computer**	**115**	**117**
American Arms, Inc.	**Shotgun Man.**	**26**	**27**
Amer.Custom Gun. Guild	Trade Assn.	105	
American Field	Publications	184	
American Firearms Industry	Publications	184	
American Forests Assn.	Conserv. Groups	98	
Amer. Friends Game Conserv.	Conserv. Groups	98	
American Hunter	Publications	184	

Name	Category	Listing Pg.	Ad Pg.
American Kennel Club	Dog Clubs	103	
Amer.Shoot. Sports Co. (ASSC)	Gun Rights	103	
AmericanZZ, Inc.	Targets	227	
AmericanZZ, Inc.	**Trap Manf.**	**236**	**236**
Americase	**Gun Case**	**151**	**151**
Angell Pedigree Service	Miscellaneous	130	
Angle Porting	Chokes	111	
Angle Porting	Gunsmiths	163	
Angle-Ease	Recoil Reduct.	173	
Angler's & Shooter's	Booksellers	108	
Argentina Estancias	**Travel Agents**	**268**	**269**
Argentina Wings	**Travel Agents**	**268**	**270**
Armes de Chasse	**Shotgun Man.**	**26**	**26**
Armes de Chasse	Shotguns/Dealers	46	
Armsport, Inc.	Shotgun Man.	26	
Custom Shooting Sports	**Schools**	**204**	**206**
Arrieta, S.L.	Shotgun Man.	26	
Art's Gun & Sport, Inc.	Gunsmiths	163	
Asprey Gun Room	Shotgun Man.	26	
Atlantic British Ltd.	Mail Order	179	
Auto-Counter	Trap Access.	258	
Auto Pilot	Trap Access.	258	
Auto-Arm Rabbit	Trap Manf.	236	
Auto-Sporter	**Trap Manf.**	**237**	**237**
Auto-Sporter USA	Trap Dist.	260	
Auto-Sporter Vertical/Teal	Trap Manf.	237	
AutoClay TrapsAcorn Systems	Trap Manf.	237	
B&B Trap Services	Trap Dist.	260	
B&D Game Farm	Gamebird	143	
B-SQUARE	**Accessories/Gun**	**88**	**86**
B-SQUARE	**Choke Access.**	**114**	**114**
B-SQUARE	**Gunsmith-Tools**	**170**	**170**
B-SQUARE	**Shotgun Care**	**147**	**114**
B.A.T. Products, Inc.	Accessories/Gun	88	
B.E.C. Productions	Lead Shot Issues	157	

Name	Category	Listing Pg.	Ad Pg.
Whiteside's Mfg.	Trap Manf.	257	257
Whitetails Unlimited	Conserv. Groups	100	
Wilderness Adventures	Travel Agents	276	
Wilderness Adventures	Booksellers	109	
Wilderness Expeditions	Travel Agents	276	
Wilderness Pursuits	Travel Agents	276	
Wilderness Society	Conserv. Groups	100	
Wildfowl	Publications	192	
Wildlife Den	Trophies	266	
Wildlife Habitat Council	Conserv. Groups	100	
Wildlife Harvest	Publications	192	
Wildlife Harvest	Manage. Services	160	
Wildlife Legislative Fund	Gun Rights	103	
Wildlife Management	Conserv. Groups	100	
Wildlife Society	Conserv. Groups	100	
Wilkinson, Tom	Gunsmiths	169	
Willis & Geiger	Mail Order	182	
Wills, Dr. Jack O.D.	Opticians	142	
Winchester Ammunition	Computer	116	
Winchester Ammunition	Reloading Comp.	201	
Winchester Ammunition	Shotgun Shells	62	63
Windy Rock Kennels	Dog Trainers	126	
Wing & Clay	Publications	192	
Wing & Shot	Publications	192	
Wing Shooting Advent.	Travel Agents	277	
Wing Supply	Mail Order	182	
Wings & Clays Shooting	Schools	226	226
Wings & Clays, Inc.	Mail Order	182	42
Wings, Inc.	Travel Agents	277	277
Wingset	Mail Order	182	
Wingshooting Dealer	Publications	192	187
Wise Wingshooting	Schools	226	
Women & Guns	Publications	142	
Women's Shoot. Sp. (WSSF)	Shooting Org.	105	104
Woodcock Hill	Gunsmiths	169	
Woodcock Hill	Schools	226	
Woodland Advert.	Marketing Services	160	
Woods and Water	Shotguns/Dealers	47	
Woods and Water	Schools	226	
Woodward Long	Insurance	179	
Woolrich, Inc.	Clothing	94	
World Hunts, Inc.	Travel Agents	277	
Worldwide Hunting	Travel Agents	277	
Wright's	Chokes	113	
Wright's	Gunsmiths	169	169
Yellow Rose Kennels	Kennels	128	
Zanika Sportswear	Clothing	94	
Robert W. Zeller	Trap Dist.	261	
Zero Halliburton	Gun Case	157	
Ziegel Engineering	Gun Case	157	
Von Zinshof Kennel	Dog Trainers	126	
Antonio Zoli	Shotgun Man.	44	